REMAINS OF INNOCENCE

&

THE OLD BLUE LINE

A JOANNA BRADY NOVELLA

ALSO BY J. A. JANCE

J. P. Beaumont Mysteries
Until Proven Guilty
Injustice for All
Trial by Fury
Taking the Fifth
Improbable Cause
A More Perfect Union
Dismissed with Prejudice
Minor in Possession
Payment in Kind
Without Due Process
Failure to Appear
Lying in Wait
Name Withheld
Breach of Duty
Birds of Prey
Partner in Crime
Long Time Gone
Justice Denied
Fire and Ice
Betrayal of Trust
Ring in the Dead: J. P. Beaumont Novella
Second Watch

Joanna Brady Mysteries

Desert Heat

Tombstone Courage

Shoot/Don't Shoot

Dead to Rights

Skeleton Canyon

Rattlesnake Crossing

Outlaw Mountain

Devil's Claw

Paradise Lost

Partner in Crime

Exit Wounds

Dead Wrong

Damage Control

Fire and Ice

Judgment Call

Other Novels

Hour of the Hunter

Kiss of the Bees

Day of the Dead

Queen of the Night

Edge of Evil

Web of Evil

Hand of Evil

Cruel Intent

Trial by Fire

Fatal Error

Left for Dead

Deadly Stakes

Moving Target

Poetry

After the Fire

REMAINS OF INNOCENCE

&

THE OLD BLUE LINE

A JOANNA BRADY NOVELLA

J. A. JANCE

WILLIAM MORROW

An Imprint of HarperCollinsPublishers

DOUBLEDAY LARGE PRINT HOME LIBRARY EDITION

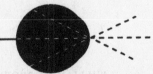

**This Large Print Book carries the
Seal of Approval of N.A.V.H.**

In honor of the Hotshots,
twenty good men and true,
and to Marty Gossenauer,
because I felt like it

REMAINS OF INNOCENCE

PROLOGUE

Liza Machett's heart was filled with equal parts dread and fury as she pulled her beater Nissan into the rutted driveway of her mother's place, stopped, and then stepped out to stare at the weedy wasteland surrounding the crumbling farmhouse. In the eleven years since Liza had left home, the place that had once been regarded as messy or junky had become a scene of utter desolation.

Spring had come early to western Massachusetts and to the small plot of land outside Great Barrington that had been in her father's family for generations. Liza had heard that in a much earlier time, while her great-grandparents had lived there, both the house and the yard had been immaculate. People said Great-Grandma Machett herself had tended the garden full of prize-winning roses that had surrounded the front porch. Shunning help from anyone, she had donned an old-fashioned homemade bonnet and spent hours toiling in the yard, mowing the grass with a push-powered mower.

Great-Grandma Machett had been gone for decades now, and so was all trace of her hard work and industry. Thickets of brambles and weeds had overrun the grass and choked out the roses. Long ago a swing had graced the front porch. Swinging on that with her much older brother, Guy, was one of Liza's few happy childhood memories. The swing was gone. All that remained of it were two rusty chains that dangled uselessly from eye-bolts still screwed into the ceiling boards. As for the porch itself? It sagged in the middle, and the three wooden steps leading up to the front door were completely missing, making the door inaccessible.

As a consequence, Liza walked around the side of the house toward the back. On the way, she tried peering into the house through one of the grimy storm windows that had been left in place for years, but the interior view was obstructed by old-fashioned wooden window blinds that had been lowered to windowsill level and closed tight against the outside world. A shiver of understanding shot through Liza's body, even though the afternoon sun was warm on her skin. The blinds existed for two reasons: to keep prying eyes outside and to keep her mother's darkness inside. Liza was tempted to turn back, but she squared her shoulders and kept on walking.

In the backyard, the freestanding wood-framed one-car garage, set away from the house, had collapsed in on itself long ago, taking Selma's ancient Oldsmobile with it. That was the car Liza remembered riding in as a child—a late-1970s, two-toned cream-and-burgundy Cutlass that had once been her father's. Somewhere along the way, her mother had parked the Cutlass in the garage and told her children that the car quit working. Liza thought she had been in the third grade when her mother had announced that they no longer needed a car. From then on, Liza and Guy had been responsible for their own transportation needs—they could catch the bus, ride their bikes, or, worst case, walk. Now the vehicle was a rusted-out hulk with only a corner of the back bumper still visible through pieces of the splintered garage door. Looking at the wreckage, Liza wondered if her life would have been different had the car kept running. After all, that was about the same time her mother had turned into a recluse and stopped leaving the house.

The only outbuilding that seemed to be in any kind of reasonable repair was the outhouse. The well-trod footpath to it led through an otherwise impenetrable jungle of weeds and brambles. Liza had hated the outhouse growing up. The smell had been vile; the spiders that lurked in the corners and would swing down on cobwebs in front of her eyes had terrified her. The presence of the path told her that the anachronistic outhouse, probably one of the last ones in the county, was still in daily use. That made sense. The social worker had told her that Selma's electricity had been turned off months ago due to lack of payment. Without electricity to run the pump at the well, the house would no longer have any indoor plumbing, either.

Liza's father had left when she was a baby. She didn't remember ever having met him, but she had heard stories about how, decades earlier, he and his father, working together, had remodeled the place for his widowed grandmother, bringing the miracle of running water and indoor toilets into the house. Legend had it Great-Grandma Machett had stubbornly insisted on using the outhouse and on keeping the hand pump at the kitchen sink that drew water from a cistern near the house. If that hand pump was, through some miracle, still in operation, it was probably the only running water Liza's mother had.

"Stubborn old bat," Liza muttered under her breath.

She had never admitted to the kids at school that they used an outhouse at home. Guy hadn't told anyone about that, either. Once Great-Grandma Machett passed on, they had moved into her place, and after Liza's father left, the only bathroom in the house had become Selma's private domain. No one else was allowed to use it because, she had insisted, running all that water through the faucets and down the toilet was a waste of electricity and a waste of money.

"We're too poor to send money down the drain like that," her mother had insisted. "I'm not going to waste the pittance your no-good father left me on that."

That meant that the whole time Liza and Guy were in grade school, they had been forced to do their sponge-bath bathing at the kitchen sink. That was where they had hand-washed their clothing as well. All that had been doable until the hot water heater had given out, sometime during Liza's last year of elementary school. After that it had been cold water only, because heating water on top of the stove for baths or for washing clothes had been deemed another extravagant waste of electricity and money.

Liza remembered all too well the jeering boys on the grade-school playground who had bullied her, calling her "stinky" and "dirty." The stigma stayed with her. It was why, even now, she showered twice a day every day—once in the morning when she first got up, and again in the evening after she got home from work.

Gathering herself, Liza turned to face the back door of the house she hadn't stepped inside for more than a decade, even though the place where she lived now was, as the crow flies, less than five miles away. Looking up, she noticed that, in places, the moss-covered roof was completely devoid of shingles. Just last year, Olivia Dexter, her landlady in town, had replaced the roof over Liza's upstairs apartment in Great Barrington. That roof hadn't been nearly as bad as this one was, but Liza had seen firsthand the damage a leaky roof could do to ceilings and walls and insulation. How, she wondered, had her mother made it through the harsh New England winter weather with no electricity and barely any roof?

Liza's mission today was in her mother's kitchen, and that was where she would go. The disaster that inevitably awaited her in the rest of the house would have to be dealt with at a later time. She remembered all too well the narrow paths between towering stacks of newspapers and magazines that had filled the living room back when she was a girl. Maybe all those layers of paper had provided a modicum of insulation during the winters. Even so, Liza wasn't ready to deal with any of that now, not yet.

Liza made her way up the stairs and then stood for a moment with her hand on the doorknob, willing herself to find the courage to open it. She knew how bad the place had been eleven years earlier, on that distant morning when she had finally had enough and fled the house. Rather than facing it, she paused, unable to imagine how much worse it would be now and allowing a kaleidoscope of unwelcome recollections to flash in and out of focus.

The memory of leaving home that day was still vivid in her mind and heart, even all these years later. Her mother had stood on the front porch screaming taunts and insults at Liza as she had walked away, carrying all her worldly possessions in a single paper grocery bag. She had walked down the half-mile-long driveway with her eyes straight ahead and her back ramrod straight. There were still times, when she awakened in the middle of the night, that she could hear echoes of her mother's venomous shouts—**worthless slut, no-good liar, thief**. The ugly words had rained down steadily as she walked away until finally fading out of earshot.

Liza Machett had heard the old child-hood rhyme often enough:

Sticks and stones may break my bones
But names will never hurt me.

That was a lie. Being called names did hurt, and the wounds left behind never really healed over. Liza's heart still bore the scars to prove it. She had learned through bitter experience that silence was the best way to deal with her mother's periodic outbursts. The problem was, silence went only so far in guaranteeing her safety. There were times when even maintaining a discreet silence hadn't been enough to protect Liza from her mother's seething anger.

Liza understood that, on that fateful day, a pummeling from her mother's fists would have come next had she not simply taken herself out of the equation. Their final confrontation had occurred just after sunrise on a warm day in May. It was the morning after Liza's high school graduation, an event that had gone totally unacknowledged as far as Selma Machett was concerned. Liza's mother, trapped in a debilitating web of ailments both real and imagined, hadn't bestirred herself to attend. When Liza had returned home late that night, dropped off by one of her classmates after attending a graduation party, Selma had been waiting up and had been beyond enraged when Liza came in a little after three. Selma had claimed that Liza had never told her about the party and that she'd been up all night frantic with worry and convinced that Liza had really been out "sleeping around."

For Liza, a girl who had never been out

on a single date all through high school, that last insult had been the final straw. A few hours later, shortly after sunrise, Liza had quietly packed her bag to leave and had tiptoed to the door, hoping that her mother was still asleep. Unfortunately, Selma had been wide awake and still furious. She had hurled invectives after her departing daughter as Liza walked across the front porch and down the steps. The porch had still had steps back then.

Liza walked briskly away with her head unbowed beneath Selma's barrage of insults. At the time, Liza's only consolation was that there were no neighbors nearby to witness her mother's final tirade. Walking away from the house, Liza had realized that she was literally following in her older brother's footsteps and doing the same thing Guy had done five years earlier. He had walked away, taking only what he could carry, and he hadn't looked back.

Liza had been thirteen years old and in eighth grade on the day Guy left home for college. A friend had stopped by shortly after he graduated and given him a lift and a life. During the summer he had waited tables in the Poconos. Then, armed with a full-ride scholarship, he had enrolled at Harvard, which was only a little over a hundred miles away. As far as Liza was concerned, however, Harvard could just as well have been on another planet. Guy had never come back—not over Christmas that first year nor for any of the Christmases that followed, and not for summer vacations, either. From Harvard he had gone on to Maryland for medical school at Johns Hopkins. Unlike Guy, all Liza had to show for enduring years of her mother's torment was a high school diploma and a severe case of low self-esteem.

Did Liza resent her brother's seemingly charmed existence? You bet! It was perfectly understandable that he had turned his back on their mother. Who wouldn't? Liza remembered all too well the blazing battles between the two of them in the months and weeks before Guy left home. She also recalled her brother's departing words, flung over his shoulder as he walked out the door.

"You're not my real mother."

Those words had been true for him, and that was his out—Selma was Guy's stepmother. Unfortunately, she was Liza's "real" mother. Half brother or not, however, Guy had always been Liza's big brother. In walking away from Selma, he had also walked away from Liza. He had left her alone to cope with a mentally damaged, self-centered woman who was incapable of loving or caring for anyone, including herself.

All the while Liza had been growing up, there had been no accounting for Selma's many difficulties, both mental and physical, real and imagined. There had been wild mood swings that most likely indicated Selma was bipolar—not that she'd ever gone to a doctor or a counselor to be given an official diagnosis. There had been episodes of paranoia in which Selma had spent days convinced that people from the government were spying on her. There was the time she had taken a pair of pliers to her own mouth and removed all the filled teeth because she was convinced the fillings were poisoning her. It wasn't until long after Liza left home that there was a name for the most visible of Selma's mental difficulties. She was a hoarder. Liza found it disquieting that hoarding was now something that could be spoken of aloud in polite company and that, in fact, there was even a reality television show devoted to the problem.

Liza had watched the show occasionally, with a weird combination of horror and relief, but she had never found a way to say to any of the people who knew her now, "That was my life when I was growing up." Instead, like a voyeur driving past a terrible car wreck, she watched the various dysfunctional families on the small screen struggling with issues she knew intimately, from the inside out. In the well-ordered neatness of her own living room, she could compare what she remembered of her mother's house with the messes and horrors in other people's lives, all the while imagining what Selma's place must be like now after another decade of unchecked decline.

Sometimes what she saw on one of the shows moved her to tears. Occasionally the televised efforts of loved ones and therapists seemed to pay off and damaged people seemed to find ways to begin confronting what was wrong with their lives and perhaps make some necessary changes. With others, however, it was hopeless, and all the painful efforts came to naught. The people trying to help would throw things in the trash—broken toys, wrecked furniture, nonworking appliances—only to have the hoarder drag the garbage back into the house because it was too precious to be tossed out.

For her part, Liza suspected that Selma was one of the ones who wouldn't be helped or fixed. She doubted her mother would ever change, and Liza knew for a fact that she had neither the strength nor the will to force the issue. If Guy had offered to come home and help her? Maybe. But all on her own? No way.

As a teenager, Liza had dealt with the shame of how they lived—the grinding poverty and the utter filth of their existence—as best she could. She had put up with her mother's ever-declining health and occassional screaming rages. Liza's smallest efforts to clean anything up or throw away one of her mother's broken treasures had been met with increasingly violent outbursts on her mother's part. Liza understood now that she most likely wouldn't have survived high school had it not been for the timely intervention of first one and subsequently several of her teachers.

It had been at the end of phys ed during the first week of her freshman year. After class, some of the girls had been taunting Liza about being dirty when Miss Rose had come into the locker room unannounced and heard what they were saying. She had told Liza's tormentors to knock it off and had sent them packing. Ashamed to show her face, Liza had lingered behind, but when she came out of the locker room, Miss Rose had been waiting for her in the gym.

"How would you like a job?" she had asked.

"What do you mean, a job?" Liza had stammered.

"I need someone to come in after school each afternoon to wash and fold the towels," Miss Rose said. "I couldn't pay you much, say ten bucks a week or so, but you'd be able to shower by yourself and wash your own clothes along with the towels."

That was all Miss Rose ever said about it. Liza didn't know how Miss Rose had known so much about her situation. Maybe she had grown up in the same kind of squalor or with the same kind of mother. Not long after that, some of the coaches of the boys' sports teams had asked Liza to handle their team laundry needs as well. Eventually she had been given her own key to both the gym and the laundry. She spent cold winter afternoons and hot spring days in the comforting damp warmth of the gym's laundry room, doing her homework, turning jumbles of dirty towels and uniforms into neat stacks and washing her own clothing at the same time. As for the money she earned? The collective fifty dollars a week she got for her efforts from various teachers and coaches, all of it paid in cash, was money that Liza's mother never knew about, and it made all the difference. It meant that Liza was able to eat breakfast and lunch in the school cafeteria rather than having to go hungry.

In the end, Liza had done the same thing her brother did—she left. But she didn't go nearly as far as her brother's hundred miles. Guy had been brilliant. Liza was not. Her mediocre grades weren't good enough for the kind of scholarship help that would have made college possible, but her work record with the coaches and teachers had counted as enough of a reference that she'd been able to land a job in Candy's, a local diner, the first week she was on her own. She had started out washing dishes and had worked her way up to waitress, hostess, and finally— for the last year—assistant manager. Candy had taught her enough about food handling that, in a pinch, she could serve as a passable short-order cook.

She didn't earn a lot of money, but it was enough to make her self-supporting.

Liza's car was a ten-year-old rusted-out wreck of a Nissan, but it was paid for and it still ran. That was all she needed. Her home was a tiny upstairs apartment in an old house off Main Street in Great Barrington. It could be freezing cold in the winter and unbearably hot in the summer, as it was right now in this unseasonably late April heat wave, but the apartment was Liza's and Liza's alone, and she kept it immaculately clean.

She never left home in the morning without first washing and drying the dishes. Her bed was made as soon as she climbed out of it. Her dirty clothes went in a hamper, and when she came back from the Laundromat, her clean clothes went in dresser drawers or on hangers. Her floors were clean. Her trash always went out on time. There was never even so much as a hint of mouse droppings in the freshly laundered towels she took out of her tiny linen closet and held up to her face.

Driving out to her mother's place from

the hospital that morning, Liza had measured the distance on the odometer. She had been surprised to realize that the hospital was a mere four miles and her apartment only another mile beyond that from her mother's squalid farmhouse. Somehow, in all the intervening years, she had imagined the distance to be much greater. She had always told herself that she would never go back, no matter what, and she hadn't—not until today. Not until a social worker had tracked her down at work and given her the bad news.

Selma had evidently fallen. Unable to get up, she hadn't been found for a number of days. A postman had finally notified someone that her mail was piling up in the mailbox at the end of the driveway, and a uniformed deputy had been dispatched to do a welfare check. Selma had been found unconscious on the floor of a room that bore no resemblance to a living room. Revived at the scene, she had been forcibly removed from her house and taken by ambulance to the hospital. Selma was currently in the ICU where doctors were doing their best to rehydrate her with IV fluids and nourishment. Liza had been told that Selma was in stable condition, but the social worker had made it plain that the outlook wasn't good. Despite her relatively young age—Selma was only fifty-seven—her emphysema was much worse, and her next stop would most likely be a bed in the hospice care unit of the Sunset Nursing Home. The end might come in as little as a few days or a few weeks at the most.

Hearing the news, Liza tried to feel sorry for her mother, but she could not. The woman had brought it on through years of chain-smoking and neglecting her health. Liza had always told herself that as far as her mother was concerned, she was done; that if Selma ever needed help, Liza wouldn't go—wouldn't cross the street or lift a finger to help her mother, but when push came to shove, Liza had caved.

The social worker had come by the diner to let Liza know. Before the social worker had finished telling her what had happened, Liza had her phone in hand and was dialing her boss's home number to let Candy know that she was going to need someone else to cover her shifts for the next few days. Within forty-five minutes, she had turned up at the ICU, as dutiful as any loving daughter. She rushed down the polished corridor to Selma's room as though there hadn't been a lifetime's worth of bad history and eleven years of total estrangement between them.

And what had Liza expected for her trouble? Maybe she hoped the long-delayed reunion with her mother would turn into one of those schmaltzy Hallmark moments, with Selma reaching out to embrace her daughter and saying how precious Liza was; how much she had missed her; how glad she was to see her; how sorry she was for all the awful things she had said those many years ago. Of course, that wasn't what happened—not at all.

Selma Machett's eyes had popped open when Liza warily approached her mother's bedside.

"Where've you been?" Selma demanded. "What took you so long? I told them not to do it, but those stupid jerks in the ambulance brought me here anyway. And when I told them I needed my cookbook, they couldn't be bothered. You know the one I mean—my old **Joy of Cooking**. I need it right now. I want you to go to the house and get it—you and nobody else."

No, not a Hallmark moment by any means. Liza understood full well that her mother simply issued orders rather than making requests. **Please** and **Thank you** weren't part of Selma's vocabulary. Liza also knew that her mother had a vast collection of cookbooks, moldering in her filthy kitchen. Not that she'd ever used any of them. In fact, Liza couldn't remember her mother ever cooking a single meal. All the while Liza was growing up, they'd survived on take-out food, burgers and pizza that her mother had somehow managed to pay for. Afterward, the wrappers and boxes, sometimes with stray pieces of pizza still inside, were left to rot where they fell.

Even though Liza knew it to be a futile exercise, she attempted to reason with her mother. "Look, Mom," she said placatingly. "They have a very good kitchen here at the hospital. You don't need a cookbook. When it's time for you to eat, they'll bring your food on a tray."

"I don't care about that," Selma snapped. "I want my cookbook, and I want it now. The key's still where it's always been, under the mat on the back porch. Go now. Be quick about it."

Which is exactly how Liza came to be here. When she lifted the mat, it disintegrated in her hands, falling in a brittle heap of disconnected rubbery links on the top step. After inserting the key and turning it in the lock, Liza stood on the far side of the door for the better part of five minutes, trying to summon the courage to venture inside.

Knowing that the power was off and that the inside of the house would be beyond filthy, Liza had done what she could to come prepared. She had stowed a small jar of Vicks in her purse. She had stopped at the drugstore and bought a package of face masks and a box of surgical gloves. Finally, after dabbing the eye-watering salve under her nostrils and donning both a mask and a pair of gloves, she opened the door.

No amount of advance warning could have prepared her. The stench was unimaginable. Covering her face with her hand, Liza fell backward and fought, unsuccessfully, to push down the bile that rose in her throat. Giving up, she clung to the crooked porch rail and heaved the hamburger she had eaten for lunch into a waist-high mound of moldering trash that had accumulated next to the steps.

At last, wiping her mouth on the tail of her blouse and steeling herself for another assault on her senses, Liza edged the door open again. To begin with, that was all she could do—crack it open. A heaping wall of rotting garbage, this one stacked almost ceiling high, kept the door from swinging open completely. As Liza sidled into the room, finger-sized roaches and fist-sized spiders scurried for cover.

Selma had always been a chain-smoker. Underlying everything else was the stench of decades' worth of unfiltered Camels, but that was only in the background. In the foreground were the unmistakable odors of rotting garbage and of death. Liza chalked up the latter to some dead varmint—a rat or mouse perhaps—or maybe a whole crew of them whose decaying corpses were buried somewhere under the mounds of trash.

Leaving the back door open, Liza stepped gingerly into the room, sticking to a narrow path that meandered through the almost unrecognizable kitchen between unstable cliffs of what looked to her like nothing but refuse. The mountains of garbage were tall enough that they obscured the windows, leaving the room in a hazy gloom. Although Liza knew this to be the kitchen, there was no longer any sign of either a stove or a sink. If her great-grandmother's hand pump still existed, it was invisible, completely buried under masses of debris. The refrigerator was hidden behind another evil-smelling mound. Standing on tiptoe, Liza saw that the door to the freezer compartment was propped open, revealing a collection of long-abandoned contents, their labels indecipherable behind a thick layer of mold. Next to the fridge was the tall stand-alone bookcase that held her mother's cookbooks. She could see the books, their titles completely obscured behind a thick curtain of undisturbed spiderwebs.

There were few things in life that Liza hated more than spiders and their sticky webs. These were clotted with the desiccated corpses of countless insects who had mistakenly ventured into the forest of silky threads and died for their trouble. Liza knew that hidden behind the layer of webs was the book she was charged with retrieving. If she squinted, she could almost make out the bright red letters of the title through the scrim of fibers.

Gritting her teeth, Liza pushed the webs aside far enough to reach the book. She had the cover in her hand when a spider glided down a web and landed on her arm. Screaming and leaping backward, Liza dropped the book and, with a desperate whack from the back of her hand, sent the startled spider sailing across the room. When Liza looked down, she saw that the book had landed spine up on the floor, sitting like a little tent pitched on the dirty floor among an accumulation of mouse turds. And scattered across the filthy floor around the half-opened book were what appeared to be five one-hundred-dollar bills.

For a moment, Liza could barely believe what she was seeing. Squatting down, she picked them up one at a time. The unaccustomed gloves on her hands made for clumsy fingers, and it didn't help that her hands were shaking. She examined the bills. They looked real enough, but where had they come from, and what were they doing in Selma's copy of **Joy of Cooking**?

Stuffing the bills in the pocket of her jeans, Liza picked up the book itself. Holding it by the spine, she flapped the pages in the air. As she did so, two more bills fluttered out from between the pages and drifted to the floor.

Liza was amazed. Seven hundred dollars had been hidden in one of her mother's cookbooks! Where had the money come from? How long had it been there? Had her mother kept the bills squirreled away the whole time Liza had been growing up—the whole time she was struggling to fit in at school while wearing thrift shop clothing and buying her school lunches with money she had earned by doing sports teams' laundry? Had there been money hiding in her mother's cookbook even then? And if there were seven hundred dollars in this one book, what about the others? Was money concealed in those as well?

Using the book in her hand, Liza swept away the remaining spiderwebs and reached for another book. The two mammoth volumes next to the empty spot left behind by the absent **Joy** turned out to be Julia Child's **Mastering the Art of French Cooking,** Volumes 1 and 2. A quick shuffle through the 652 pages of

Volume 1 was good for five hundred bucks. Ditto for Volume 2. With close to two thousand dollars now crammed in her pocket, Liza reached for the next book on the shelf: **Betty Crocker's Quick and Easy.** A thorough examination of that one surfaced only three hundred dollars, but by the time Liza had worked her way through the entire collection, she had amassed close to thirty thousand dollars. It was more money in one place than Liza had ever seen in her life, more money than she had ever thought her mother had to her name.

At last the bookshelf was cleared. The cookbooks, plucked clean of their hidden treasure, lay in a careless heap on the floor. During the search, Liza had gone from first being surprised and amazed to being beyond furious. The more money she found, the more she wondered if the small fortune in hidden bills had been in Selma's possession the whole time. If so, why had Selma always pretended to be poor? Why had she denied her children and herself simple creature comforts like running water and hot baths that some of that money might have afforded all of them?

As a teenager, Liza had never thought to question the fact that they were poor. Their poverty was an all too demonstrable reality. She had listened in silence while her mother bewailed their fate, complaining about their lot and blaming the fact that Liza's father had run off—presumably with another woman—leaving them with barely a roof over their heads and not much else. Liza knew from something her brother had said that before Anson Machett bailed, he'd at least had the decency to quitclaim the family home—the farm and the run-down house that had belonged to his great-grandparents—to his soon-to-be-abandoned wife. Before Guy left home, Selma had told the kids that their father was dead, having died in a car wreck somewhere in California. Selma had offered no details about a memorial service or a funeral. First their father was gone and then he was dead.

Now, at age twenty-nine and standing

in the desolation of Selma's filthy kitchen, Liza Machett found herself asking for the very first time if anything her mother had told them was true. If Selma had lied to them about being poor, maybe she had lied about everything else, too.

After gathering the last of the money from the books, Liza stayed in the kitchen for a long time, too stunned to know what to do next. Should she go to the hospital and confront her mother about all this? Should she demand to be told the truth, once and for all?

Ultimately Liza realized that a direct confrontation would never work. Instead, she reached down, pawed through the pile of books, and retrieved the one at the bottom of the heap—the **Joy of Cooking.** Pulling the thick wad of bills from her pocket, she extracted seven of them and placed them in various spots throughout the book. If Selma remembered the exact pages where she had stuck the money, then Liza was screwed. Otherwise, Liza could hand the book over to Selma and act as though she hadn't a clue that there was money hidden inside.

She hoped the trick would work. If Selma didn't realize Liza had discovered her secret, it would buy Liza time—time to look for answers on her own and to sift through the rest of the debris in the house. Liza knew that once she reached the living room, she would find stacks of back issues of **National Geographic, Life,** and **Reader's Digest** as well. What if those had all been seeded with money in the same way the cookbooks had? There was only one way to find out for sure, and Liza was determined to do so—she intended to search through every single one.

Back outside with the cookbook in hand, Liza stripped off her mask and gloves and drew in a deep breath of clean fresh air. Her Nissan, parked at the end of the driveway, sat unlocked and with the windows wide open. Leaving the windows open kept the interior from getting too hot. That was important especially during hot weather since the Nissan's AC had stopped working long ago.

Liza dropped the book on the passenger

seat before going around to the other side to climb in. When she turned to fasten her seat belt, the tail end of her ponytail swished in front of her face. That's when she smelled it—the same pungent combination of foul odors that had plagued her as a girl and that had been the cause of so much painful bullying from the other kids. The odor of decay in her mother's home had somehow permeated Liza's hair and clothing. She could barely tolerate sitting in the car knowing that she was probably leaving the same stinky residue on the car seats and carpeting.

Hating the very idea, Liza headed for her apartment rather than for the hospital. She would go see her mother and deliver the book, but only after she had showered and washed her hair. Looking at the book, she realized it probably smelled the same way. Once she hit Great Barrington, she pulled in to the drive-in window of the local Dunkin' Donuts and ordered a bag of their Breakfast Blend coffee beans. She had heard that coffee beans helped get rid of bad smells. It seemed worth a try.

At home, Liza located a gallon-sized Ziploc bag. She placed the book inside that along with all the bills she had stuffed in her pockets. Then, having added the whole beans, she zipped the bag shut before going into the bathroom to shower.

She stood under the stream of hot water for the next fifteen minutes, trying to wash away the dirt and grit from her mother's house. With her eyes closed, she hoped she was washing off something else as well—the soul-destroying contamination of her mother's many betrayals.

She needed to send Selma Machett's perfidy circling down the drain every bit as much as she needed to rid herself of the odor of mouse droppings and rotting food that, despite all her scrubbing, still seemed to cling to her skin.

CHAPTER 1

The sun was just coming up over the distant Chiricahua Mountains to the east of High Lonesome Ranch when a rooster crowed at ten past five in the morning. At that hour of the day, it might have been one of the ranch's live resident roosters announcing the arrival of a new day, but it wasn't. This was the obnoxiously distinctive crowing of Sheriff Joanna Brady's cell phone.

Groping for the device in its charging stand on the bedside table, Joanna silenced the racket and glanced across the bed. Her husband, Butch, slept undisturbed with a pillow pulled over his head. Taking the phone in hand, Joanna scrambled out of bed. Now that Lady, her rescued Australian shepherd, had decamped to a spot next to Joanna's son's bed, she no longer had to deal with tripping over a dead-to-the-world dog when it came to late-night callouts, which usually meant there was serious trouble somewhere in Cochise County.

Hurrying into the bathroom and closing the door behind her, Joanna answered, "Sheriff Brady."

"Chief Bernard here," a male voice rumbled in her ear. "Sorry to wake you at this ungodly hour, but I could sure use your K-9 unit if you can spare them."

Alvin Bernard was the police chief in Bisbee, Arizona. Once known as a major copper-producing town, Bisbee's current claim to fame was its reputation as an arts colony. It was also the county seat. Alvin Bernard's departmental jurisdiction ended at Bisbee's city limits, the line where Joanna's countywide jurisdiction began.

Years earlier, Joanna had been elected to the office of sheriff in the aftermath of her first husband's death. Andy Brady had been running for the office when he died in a hail of bullets from a drug cartel's hit man. When Joanna was elected sheriff in her late husband's stead, members of the local law enforcement old boys' network had sneered at the outcome, regarding her election as a straight-up sympathy vote, and had expected Joanna to be sheriff in name only. She had surprised the naysayers by transforming herself into a professional police officer. As she developed a reputation for being a good cop, that initial distrust had melted away. She now had a cordial working relationship with most of her fellow police administrators, including Bisbee's Chief Bernard.

"What's up?"

"Junior Dowdle's gone missing from his folks' house up the canyon. He left his room sometime overnight by climbing out through a bedroom window. His bed hasn't been slept in. Daisy's frantic. She and Moe have been up and down the canyon several times looking for him. So far there's no trace."

Junior, Moe and Daisy Maxwell's developmentally disabled foster son, had been found abandoned by his paid caregiver at a local arts fair several years earlier. Once his blood relatives were located, they had declined to take him back. That was when the Maxwells had stepped in. They had gone to court and been appointed his legal guardians. Since then they had cared for Junior as their own, giving him purpose in life by teaching him to work as a combination busboy and greeter in the local diner that bore Daisy's name.

In recent months, though, Junior's behavior had become increasingly erratic, both at home and in the restaurant. Only a few weeks earlier the family had been given the dreaded but not-so-surprising diagnosis—not so surprising because the doctor had warned the Maxwells a year earlier about the possibility. Now in his early sixties, Junior was suffering from a form of dementia, most likely Alzheimer's, an affliction that often preyed on the developmentally disabled. Under most circumstances, a missing person report of an adult wouldn't have merited an immediate all-out response. Because Junior was considered to be at risk, however, all bets were off.

"He's on foot then?" Joanna asked.

"Unless some Good Samaritan picked him up and gave him a ride," Alvin answered.

"Okay," Joanna said. "I'll give Terry a call and see what, if anything, he and Spike can do about this."

Terry Gregovich was the human half of Joanna's departmental K-9 unit. Spike, a seven-year-old German shepherd, was Terry's aging canine partner.

"You're sure Junior left through a window?"

"Daisy told me they've been concerned about Junior maybe wandering off, so they've gotten into the habit of keeping both the front and back doors to the house dead-bolted. It was warm overnight, so Daisy left the window cracked open when Junior went to bed. Had Daisy Maxwell ever raised a teenage son, she would have known she needed to lock the window as well."

"That's how he got out?"

"Yup, it looks like Junior raised the

window the rest of the way, pushed open the screen, and climbed out."

"Do you want me to see if I have any additional patrol officers in the neighborhood who could assist with the search?"

"That would be a huge favor," Alvin said. "We'll be using the parking lot of St. Dominick's as a center of operations. Once the neighbors hear about this, there will be plenty of folks willing to help out. From my point of view, the more boots we have on the ground, the better. It'll make our lives easier if Terry and Spike can point the search crews in the right direction."

"I'll have Dispatch get back to you and let you know if anyone else is available."

She called Terry first, dragging him out of bed, then she called Dispatch to let Tica Romero, her overnight dispatcher, know what was going on. The City of Bisbee and Cochise County had a standing mutual aid agreement in place, but it was better to have everything officially documented in case something went haywire. Mutual aid in the course of a hot pursuit was one matter. For any-thing else, Joanna had to be sure all the necessary chain-of-command **t**'s were crossed and **i**'s were dotted.

Butch came and went through the bathroom while Joanna was in the shower. Once dried off, she got dressed, donning a neatly pressed everyday khaki uniform and a lightweight pair of lace-up hiking boots. Early on in her career as sheriff, she had worn business-style clothing, most of which couldn't accommodate the Kevlar vest she wore each day right along with her other officers. Then there was the matter of footwear. After going through countless pairs of pantyhose and wrecked pairs of high heels, she had finally conceded defeat, putting practi-cality ahead of fashion.

Minutes later, with her bright red hair blown dry and her minimally applied makeup in place, she hurried out to the kitchen, where she found Butch brewing coffee and unloading the dishwasher.

"What's up?" he asked.

"I'm on my way to St. Dominick's," she

explained. "Junior Dowdle took off sometime overnight. Alvin Bernard is using the
parking lot at St. Dom's as a center of
operations, and he's asked for help from
my K-9 unit."

Joanna knew that her husband maintained a personal interest in Junior's life
and welfare. She and Butch hadn't been
married when Junior first came to Bisbee
after being abandoned at the Arts and
Crafts Fair in Saint David. Bringing him to
Bisbee in her patrol car, Joanna had been
stumped about where to take him. Her
own home was out. The poor man wasn't
a criminal and he wasn't ill. That meant
that neither the jail nor the hospital were
possibilities, either. In the end, she had
taken him to Butch's house in Bisbee's
Saginaw neighborhood, where Junior
had stayed for several weeks. A restaurant Butch had owned previously, the
Roundhouse in Peoria, Arizona, had once
fielded a Special Olympics team, and
Butch had been one of the team
coaches. He had taken charge of Junior
with practiced grace and had kept him

until more suitable permanent arrangements could be made with the Maxwells.

"You're going to join the search?" Butch asked, handing Joanna a cup of coffee.

She nodded.

"All right," he said. "If they haven't found Junior by the time I drop the kids off at school, I'll stop by and help, too. Do you want breakfast before you head out? It won't take more than a couple of minutes to fry eggs and make toast."

That was one of the advantages of marrying a man who had started out in life as a short-order cook. Joanna didn't have to think long before making up her mind. Depending on how her day went, the next opportunity to eat might be hours away. Besides, this was Alvin's case. She and her people were there as backup only. In addition, Butch's over-easy eggs were always perfection itself.

"Sounds good," she said. "Do you want any help?"

"I'm a man on a mission," Butch told her with a grin. "Sit down, drink your coffee, and stay out of the way."

Doing as she'd been told, Joanna slipped into the breakfast nook. She'd taken only a single sip of coffee when Dennis, their early-bird three-year-old, wandered into the kitchen dragging along both his favorite blankie and his favorite book—**The Cat in the Hat**. There wasn't a person in the household who didn't know the story by heart, but Joanna pulled him into a cuddle and started reading aloud, letting him turn the pages.

They were halfway through the story when two dogs scrambled into the kitchen—Jenny's stone-deaf black lab, Lucky, and a relatively new addition to their family, a fourteen-week-old golden retriever puppy named Desi. The puppy carried the tattered remains of one of Jenny's tennis shoes in his mouth. Both dogs dove for cover under the table of the breakfast nook as an exasperated Jenny, wearing a bathrobe and with her wet hair wrapped in a towel, appeared in the doorway.

"I was only in the shower for five minutes," she fumed. "That's all it took for Desi to wreck my shoe."

"Wait until you have kids of your own," Butch warned her. "Desi will be over it a lot faster than a baby will. Besides, it could have been worse. It's only a tennis shoe. When Lucky was a pup, he always grabbed one of your boots."

Leveling a sour look in Butch's direction, Jenny knelt down by the table. Rather than verbally scolding the miscreant puppy, she glowered at him and gave him two thumbs-down—her improvised sign language equivalent of "bad dog." Next she motioned toward her body with one hand, which meant "come." Finally she held out one cupped hand and patted the cupped one with her other hand, the hand signal for "give it to me."

There was a momentary pause under the table before Desi squirmed out from under his temporary shelter and handed over the mangled shoe. In response, Jenny gave him a single thumb-up for "good dog." Two thumbs would have meant "very good dog," and currently, no matter what he did right, Desi didn't qualify. Once the puppy had been somewhat forgiven, Lucky dared venture out, too. He was rewarded with the two-thumb treatment before Jenny took her damaged shoe in hand and left the room with both dogs on her heels.

Joanna couldn't help but marvel at how the hand signals Jenny had devised to communicate with Lucky were now making it possible for her to train a service dog as part of a 4-H project. There was the expectation that, at some time in the future, Desi would make a difference in some person's life by serving as a hearing assistance dog.

"Your breakfast is on the table in five," Butch called after Jenny as she left the room. "Two eggs scrambled, whole wheat toast. Don't be late."

"I'm afraid training that dog is more work than Jenny anticipated," Joanna commented. "After losing Tigger the way we did, I'm worried about her ability to let Desi go when it's time for him to move on." Tigger, their previous dog, a half golden retriever, half pit bull mix, had

succumbed within weeks of being diagnosed with Valley Fever, a fungal disorder
commonly found in the desert Southwest
that often proved fatal to dogs.

"Jenny and I have already discussed
that," Butch said, "but you're right. Talking
about letting go of a dog is one thing.
Handing the leash over to someone else
is another."

Joanna nodded in agreement. "We all
know that when it comes to horses and
dogs, Jennifer Ann Brady has a very soft
heart."

"Better horses and dogs than boys,"
Butch observed with a grin. "Way better."

That was a point on which Joanna
and Butch were in complete agreement.

"Speaking of horses, did she already
feed them?"

For years the horse population on
High Lonesome Ranch had been limited
to one—Kiddo, Jenny's sorrel gelding,
who was also her barrel-racing partner.
Recently they had added a second horse
to the mix, an aging, blind Appaloosa
mare that had been found, starving and

dehydrated, in the corral of a recently foreclosed ranchette near Arizona Sunsites. The previous owners had simply packed up and left town, abandoning the horse to fend for herself. When a neighbor reported the situation, Joanna had dispatched one of her Animal Control officers to retrieve the animal.

After a round of veterinary treatment at county expense, Butch and Jenny had trailered the mare home to High Lonesome, where she seemed to have settled into what were supposedly temporary digs in the barn and corral, taking cues on her new surroundings from Kiddo while she gained weight and recovered. Dennis, after taking one look at the horse, had promptly dubbed her Spot.

In Joanna's opinion, Spot was a far better name for a dog than it was for a horse, but Spot she was, and Spot she remained. Currently inquiries were being made to find Spot a permanent home, but Joanna suspected that she had already found one. When Butch teased Joanna by saying she had turned High Lonesome Ranch into an

unofficial extension of Cochise County
Animal Control, it was more true than not.
Most of the dogs that had come through
their lives had been rescues, along
with any number of cast-off Easter bunnies
and Easter chicks. Now, having taken in
a hearing impaired dog and a visually
impaired horse, they were evidently a
haven for stray animals with disabilities as
well.

"The horses are fed," Butch answered.
"Jenny and the dogs went out to do that
while I was starting the coffee and you
were in the shower."

By the time Jenny and the now more
subdued dogs returned to the kitchen,
Joanna was ready to head out. After
delivering quick good-bye kisses all
around, she went to the laundry room to
retrieve and don her weapons. For
Mother's Day a few weeks earlier, Butch
had installed a thumb recognition gun
safe just inside the door. Located below a
light switch, it was within easy reach for
Joanna's vertically challenged five-foot-
four frame. With her two Glocks safely

stowed—one in a holster on her belt and the other, her backup weapon, in a bra-style holster—Sheriff Joanna Brady was ready to face her day.

It generally took the better part of ten minutes for Joanna to drive her county-owned Yukon the three miles of combination dirt and paved roads between High Lonesome Ranch at the base of the Mule Mountains and her office at the Cochise County Justice Center. In this instance she drove straight past her office on Highway 80 and headed into Bisbee proper. St. Dominick's Church, up the canyon in Old Bisbee, was another four miles beyond that.

The time Joanna spent in her car each day gave her a buffer between her job and her busy home life. On this late-spring day, she spent some of the trip gazing off across the wide expanse of the Sulphur Springs Valley, taking in the scenery—the alternating squares of cultivated fields and tracts of wild desert terrain punctuated with mesquite trees—that stretched from the nearby Mule

Mountains to the Chiricahua Mountains in the distance, some thirty miles away. She loved the varying shades of green that springtime brought to the desert, and she loved the very real purple majesty of the mountains rising up in the distance to meet an azure sky. As much as she thought of this corner of the Arizona desert as being hers, it was always humbling to remember, as her history-loving father had loved pointing out to her, that much less than two hundred years ago everything she could see had been the undisputed domain of the Chiricahua Apaches.

Today, however, she didn't bother admiring the landscape. Her thoughts were focused on Junior Dowdle—a troubled individual with the body of a grown man, the ailments of an old one, and the heart and mind of a child. Knowing that Junior was out in the world somewhere—lost, alone, and unprotected—was heartbreaking, and she uttered a quiet prayer as she drove. "Please help us find him," she pleaded. "Please let him be okay."

Driving through the central business

district of Old Bisbee on Tombstone Canyon Road, Joanna kept her eyes peeled, watching for anything out of the ordinary on side streets or on the steep scrub-oak-dotted hillsides that loomed above the town. If Junior had wandered outside in the dark, it wouldn't have taken him long to cross that narrow strip of civilization and find himself lost in a desert wilderness with neither food nor water.

Joanna had just passed Tombstone Canyon Methodist Church when her radio crackled to life.

"Alvin Bernard just called. Terry and Spike have arrived at the Maxwells' house. They're working on finding a scent. Everyone else is at St. Dom's."

"Okay," Joanna told Tica. "I'm almost there, too."

When Joanna arrived at the parking lot for St. Dominick's Catholic Church, she found Father Matthew Rowan, one of St. Dom's two resident priests, standing at the gate directing traffic. He pointed Joanna toward a clutch of official-looking vehicles. Tucked in among the collection of patrol cars sat a 1960s-era VW. The chaplain sticker on the VW Bug's back bumper explained its odd presence among the other official vehicles. The vintage VW belonged to Joanna's friend and pastor, the Reverend Marianne Maculyea, who in the past month had been certified as a chaplain for the local police and fire departments. It was no surprise to Joanna that, if first responders were on the scene, Marianne would be, too.

Pulling into the open spot next to the VW, Joanna stayed in the car for a moment, taking in the scene. The hustle and bustle might have been part of something as innocuous as a church bazaar. Cars came and went. The center of activity seemed to be a hastily erected eight-by-ten-foot canvas canopy. Some enterprising soul had used several matching sawhorses and a piece of plywood to create a massive makeshift table on which a six-foot-long paper map of the city had been tacked down. Surrounded by teams of officers and volunteers, Chief Bernard was bent over the map, assigning people to the streets and neighborhoods they were expected to search.

Twenty yards away from Chief Bernard's command center, a clutch of ladies from several nearby churches were setting up a refreshment buffet complete with a coffee urn, stacks of Styrofoam cups, and a surprising selection of store-bought and homemade baked goods and cookies. A blond teenage boy, someone Joanna didn't recognize, sprinted past her. Carrying a thermal coffee carafe in one hand, he waved in Joanna's direction with the other. Looking at her rather than at traffic, he came close to stepping into the path of another arriving vehicle.

"Look out!" Joanna called out, and he jumped back just in time.

Another stranger, a woman Joanna had never seen before, shouted after him, too. "For Pete's sake, Lucas! Watch what you're doing! Pay attention."

Joanna turned to the woman, a harried-looking thirty-something. Her long dirty-blond hair was pulled back in a scraggly ponytail. "He's yours?" Joanna asked.

When the woman nodded apologet-
ically, a faint whiff of booze and an even
stronger scent of cigarette smoke floated
in Joanna's direction.

"My son," she answered, "fourteen
years old and full of piss and vinegar.
Once the coffee was ready, he wanted to
be the one to take it to Chief Bernard."
Then, glimpsing the badge and name tag
on Joanna's uniform, the woman's eyes
widened in recognition."You're Sheriff
Brady?"

Joanna nodded.

"I'm Rebecca Nolan. Lucas is my son.
My daughter, Ruth, Lucas's twin sister, is
over there."

The woman nodded toward the refreshment table. Following Rebecca's gaze,
Joanna caught sight of a teenage girl who,
with her mouth pursed in concentration,
was laying out straight lines of treats in a
carefully designed fashion. Rebecca had
said the girl was Lucas's twin. True, they
were about the same size—fair skinned
and blue eyed—with features that were
almost mirror images. They were also

dressed in matching bright blue track suits. When it came to hair, though, the two kids weren't on the same page. Lucas's dark blond hair resembled his mother's. Ruth's, on the other hand, was mostly dyed deep purple, with a few natural blond strands showing through here and there. A glance at the girl's purple locks was enough to make Joanna grateful that her own daughter's hair didn't look like it came from a box of crayons.

"I hope you don't mind the kids being here," Rebecca added quickly. "I'm homeschooling them, and we've been doing a unit on community service. When I heard what happened, I told the kids to get their butts out of bed because we were coming down to help. I don't know Moe and Daisy well, but we live just up the street from them. It seemed like the right thing to do."

Marianne stepped into the conversation and handed Joanna a cup of coffee. "Good morning, Rebecca," she said cordially. "So glad you and the kids could make it."

Rebecca nodded. "I'd better go help," she said, backing away.

"You know her?" Joanna asked as Rebecca melted into the refreshment crowd.

"I met them at Safeway shortly after they arrived in town," Marianne said. "They've only been here a few months. Rebecca is divorced. Moved here from someplace in New Mexico with a boyfriend who disappeared almost as soon as they got to town."

"What does she do for a living?" Joanna asked.

Marianne shrugged. "I'm not sure, but she's homeschooling the two kids, which strikes me as a full-time job all its own. I know for a fact that I wouldn't be any good at homeschooling, and neither would Jeff." Jeff Daniels was Marianne's husband.

Joanna nodded. "The same goes for me," she agreed. "I've never been teacher material."

They stood for a moment, sipping their respective cups of coffee in the early morning cool and appreciating the quiet comfort of an enduring friendship that had started in junior high. Bisbee may not have boasted an official Welcome Wagon organization, but Reverend Maculyea filled the bill anyway. When it came to newcomers in town, you could count on Marianne to have a handle on them— where they came from, what they were about, and whether or not they needed any kind of assistance. Other people lived their lives by drawing circles in the sand designed to keep people out. Marianne's whole purpose in life was to draw circles that pulled people in.

"You got here fast," Joanna observed as another pair of cars nosed into the lot and parked where Father Rowan indicated. "I'm the sheriff. How come you got the call before I did?"

To anyone else, it might have sounded like a dig, but Marianne didn't take offense. "I wasn't called," she explained. "I heard it from Jeff. He went out for an early morning run up the canyon and came across Moe Maxwell, who was already out looking for

Junior on his own. Jeff convinced Moe that he needed to call the cops, then came straight home and told me."

"You're the one who summoned all the ladies?" Joanna asked, nodding toward the gathering of women who were bustling around setting out tables and folding chairs.

Marianne grinned. "I didn't have to summon all of them," she replied. "All I had to do was call the first two people on my list. Each of those called two more. It's the first time we've used CCT," she added. "It worked like a charm."

For months, Marianne had been spearheading a team of local pastors and parishioners who had established something they called Christ's Crisis Tree, a phone tree organization that used a combination of text messages and landline calls to mobilize members of various churches to respond quickly to community emergencies, where they provided refreshments to all those involved, first responders and volunteers alike.

Marianne's grin faded as quickly as it

had come. Joanna turned in time to see Daisy Maxwell, disheveled and distraught, coming toward them. Marianne hurried forward to embrace the woman.

"So sorry," Marianne said. "I'm sure they'll find him soon."

Daisy nodded numbly. "I hope so," she agreed. Then she turned to Joanna. "That guy from your department was up at the house, the one with the dog."

"Terry Gregovich," Joanna told her.

"Before I left, I gave him some of Junior's clothing so the dog would have his scent. I hope and pray it works. That's why Chief Bernard had everyone else, including these wonderful volunteers, meet here at the church instead of at our place. He didn't want people disrupting the scent and interfering with the dog."

"Spike's good at his job," Joanna said reassuringly. "Would you like some coffee, Daisy? Something to eat?"

That was what people did in difficult times—they offered food and drink. Daisy rejected both with a firm shake of her head, all the while gazing in wonder at the bustling parking lot.

"Where did all these people come from and how did they get here so fast?" she asked. "It's only a little past six. How did they even know what had happened?"

"They care about you," Marianne said, "and they care about Junior, too. Let's go sit down for a while."

Taking Daisy by the arm, Marianne led her to a nearby table. Meanwhile, Detective Matt Keller, a Bisbee police officer and Alvin Bernard's lead investigator, wandered over to the refreshment area and collected a cup of coffee before joining Joanna.

"Making any progress?" she asked.

Matt shook his head. "Not much. I've talked to all the people who live on O'Hara, the Maxwells' street," he said. "Because it was so warm last night almost all the neighbors had their windows open, but nobody seems to have heard or seen anything out of line, including Jack and Lois Radner, who live right next door. I talked to both of them and to their son, Jason, whose bedroom faces Junior's. So far I've got nothing that would help with timing, not even so much as a barking dog."

Joanna looked away from the detective in time to see two sheriff's department patrol vehicles nose into the parking lot. As she walked over to confer with her deputies, her phone rang and Terry Gregovich's name appeared in her caller ID.

"I could use some help up here," he said.

"Where are you? Did you find a scent?"

"We found one, all right. The trail from the house led up to the highway above town at milepost 337," he said. "We're there now. Spike may be able to follow the trail on the pavement or across the pavement, whichever it turns out to be, but we won't be able to do either one until we have someone up here to direct traffic."

"Two patrol deputies just arrived," Joanna told him. "I'll send them right up. You said milepost 337?"

"That's right," Terry confirmed.

"If somebody up on the highway gave Junior a ride, he could be miles away by now."

"I know," Terry said. "If the trail ends in the middle of the pavement, we'll know that's probably what happened."

Joanna hustled over to the two cars just as Deputies Ruiz and Stock stepped out of their vehicles. Deputy Stock's usual patrol area was on Highway 80 between Tombstone and Benson, while Deputy Ruiz spent most of his time on the stretch of Highway 92, west of Don Luis and out as far as the base of the Huachuca Mountains.

Joanna turned to Deputy Stock. "Did you see anyone walking on the highway as you came over the Divide?" she asked.

Jeremy shook his head. "Not a soul," he said. "Do we have any idea how long Junior's been gone?"

"Less than ten hours," Joanna said. "He took off sometime during the night. Right now, I need both of you up on the highway at milepost 337 to assist the K-9 unit. Spike picked up Junior's scent and followed it there. Before they can venture onto the pavement, they need someone directing traffic."

"On our way," Jeremy said. He turned to head out, but Joanna stopped him.

"No lights or sirens until you get there," she cautioned. "I don't want a hundred civilians milling around on the highway. One of them might get killed."

As the deputies hurried to do her bidding, Joanna went in search of Alvin Bernard. She wanted to tell him she had just heard from Terry Gregovich. To do so, she had to get in line behind one of her least favorite people, Marliss Shackleford, the **Bisbee Bee**'s intrepid reporter. Marliss may have been Joanna's mother's closest chum, but she was also a gossipy busybody and the bane of Joanna's existence. Knowing that Marliss dished out the same kind of torment to Alvin Bernard made it only slightly less irksome to Joanna.

As soon as the reporter caught sight of Joanna, she registered her surprise. "How come you and your people are here, Sheriff Brady?" Marliss demanded abruptly. "My understanding is that Junior disappeared from the Maxwells' place on O'Hara. That's well inside the city limits and outside your jurisdiction. Isn't this whole circus a bit of an overreaction to someone simply wandering off?" She waved dismissively at the crowd of people milling in and out of the parking lot.

"Most of these folks are volunteers," Joanna told her. "My people are here because Chief Bernard requested my department's assistance, and we're happy to oblige. As for its being an over-reaction? I doubt that's how Daisy Maxwell would characterize it. In fact, Daisy is right over there chatting with Marianne. Why don't you ask her?"

Marliss scurried off in search of Daisy Maxwell. "Thanks for getting rid of her," Alvin Bernard muttered once the reporter was safely out of earshot. "I was afraid she was going to be on my case all morning long."

Quickly Joanna briefed him on the situation with Terry and Spike.

"Should I call off the street search, then?" Chief Bernard asked.

"Not yet," Joanna replied. "Just because Junior wandered up to the highway doesn't mean he didn't come back down into town somewhere else. I sent a pair of uniformed deputies up there to direct traffic. What we don't need on the scene is a mob of civilians."

"You're right about that," Bernard agreed.

"Why don't I go see if I can assist my guys?" Joanna told him. "I'll call you directly if we find any sign of Junior."

When their conversation was interrupted by questions from someone else, Joanna took the opportunity to slip away. Once in her Yukon, she exited the parking lot, drove back down to Tombstone Canyon, and then headed north to the junction with Highway 80. Merging into the south-bound lane, she turned on her light bar and flashers and drove slowly down the highway, scanning the shoulders on both sides of the road as she went. When she reached mileage marker 337, she pulled over to the side of the road and tucked in behind Deputy Stock's Ford Explorer.

"Where's Terry?" she asked.

"Up there," he said, pointing up the

steep hillside above the highway. "He and Spike took off up that gully."

Years earlier, when the new highway bypass was built, the roadway had been carved out of the series of undulating limestone cliffs that covered the hillside. The mounds of cliffs were separated by steep gullies. During rainstorms those washes turned into cascades of fast-running water. Bone dry at the moment, they offered a natural but rough stairway leading up through otherwise impassable terrain. Pulling a pair of binoculars off her belt, Joanna scanned the mountainside.

When Anglos had first arrived in what was now southeastern Arizona, the Mule Mountains had been covered by a forest of scrub oak. The trees had been cut down to provide firewood for home use as well as for smelting the copper being mined underground. As a girl, Joanna had hiked these hills with her father. Back then most of the scrub oak had been little more than overgrown bushes. Decades later those same slow-growing shrubs had matured into genuine trees, growing here and there in dense clusters.

Joanna was still scouring the hillside with her binoculars when Spike and Terry popped out from behind the cover of one of those groves of trees. They remained visible for only a matter of moments before resuming their climb and disappearing into another clump of scrub oak a few yards farther on. Even from this distance Joanna could see that Terry was struggling to keep up with his agile dog. Spike, nose to the ground and intent on his quarry, lunged forward with his brushy tail plumed out behind him.

Joanna knew that Terry Gregovich prided himself on being in top physical condition. If this was proving to be a tough climb for him, how had Junior managed it? The missing man was in his early sixties. He was naturally clumsy and anything but a natural athlete. Joanna was hard-pressed to imagine Junior making the same climb, especially alone and in the dark. Still, she also understood that the trail didn't lie. Junior's scent had to be there because that's what Spike was following.

"Did there happen to be a full moon last night?" Joanna asked.

"Yes, ma'am, there was," Deputy Stock answered. "Out between here and Tombstone it was almost as bright as day."

Just then Joanna heard the dog. Spike's excited, purposeful barks alerted everyone within earshot that he had located his target. Almost a minute later, Terry reappeared, popping out of the second grove of trees. As Deputy Gregovich came into view, Joanna's phone rang.

"I found him," Terry said urgently.

"Where?" Joanna asked. "Is he all right?"

"I can't tell if he's all right or not," Terry replied. "I can see him, but I can't reach him. I called to him, but he didn't respond. He doesn't appear to be breathing."

"Where is he?"

"At the bottom of a glory hole inside a cave of some kind. I always heard rumors about a series of limestone caverns under the mountain, but I never really believed it. The narrow opening that leads into it is hidden in the trees directly behind me."

Joanna knew that the Mule Mountains were riddled with natural caverns and man-made glory holes—small test holes that had been drilled into the earth by prospectors and left abandoned when no ore was found.

"Which is it?" Joanna asked, "a glory hole or a cave?"

"A little of both," Terry replied. "The cave itself is natural, but there's a small glory hole inside it that someone must have worked for a while. The tailings outside the entrance are hidden under the trees. If I'd been on my own, I would have missed the opening completely. Fortunately, Spike didn't. Someone put an iron grate across the entrance to keep people out. Junior evidently crawled under it. So did Spike and I. The glory hole is a few feet inside the cave, and it's a big drop-off. I can see Junior facedown at the bottom of that, lying on top of a layer of loose rock and boulders where it looks like the side of the hole collapsed. There's a cat or kitten stuck down there, too. It's on an outcropping halfway between where I was and where Junior is. I can't see it, but I can hear it crying. I'll bet that's what happened. Junior was following the kitten, and they both fell."

"Can you get to him?" Joanna asked.

"Not me, not without ropes and a winch."

"Okay," Joanna said. "I'm on it. Calling for help right now."

CHAPTER 2

Within seconds of Joanna's 911 call, Rescue numbers 5 and 6, along with an ambulance, were on their way. She warned the operator that the firefighters needed to arrive with whatever equipment was required to cut through the metal grate that blocked the way into the cavern. Junior, Terry, and Spike may all have been able to slither under the barricade to gain entrance, but if Junior was inside and injured, they'd need an opening wide enough for rescuers to carry him back out.

Joanna's second call, a terse one, was to Chief Bernard. "I think Terry and Spike found him," she said.

"Dead or alive?"

"Can't tell," Joanna said. "He's taken a bad fall in a cave up above the highway.

Terry says that so far he's not responding. Until an EMT can reach him and
check him out, we won't know if he's just
unconscious or if it's something worse.
The fire department is dispatching trucks,
equipment, and an ambulance. Let's give
them a chance to do their thing before you
mention any of this to Moe and Daisy.
There's no point in upsetting them any
more than they already are until we know
the real score. Besides, the fewer people
we have to work around up here, the
better."

"What about traffic?" Chief Bernard
asked.

"I sent Jeremy Stock and Armando Ruiz
out to shut down highway traffic in both
directions and divert it through town.
That's the only way to make it safe for
emergency personnel to operate. You
know as well as I do that there's no room
to park on the shoulder without having
vehicles obstruct the traffic lanes."

"Makes sense," Chief Bernard said
gruffly. "Keep me informed."

By the time Joanna was off the phone,

she heard the wail of approaching sirens echoing off the canyon walls. She waited for the crew to scramble out of their vehicles and begin assembling loads of equipment to pack up the mountain. The incident commander, a Bisbee Fire Department lieutenant named Adam Wilson, approached Joanna.

"Morning, Sheriff Brady," he said. "Where's the problem?"

She pointed up the gully through the limestone cliffs toward the spot where Terry and Spike had disappeared into the dense grove of trees. "In a cave up there," she said. "I'll take you."

"Any word on the victim?"

"Unresponsive as far as I know," she said. "To get him out, you'll have to cut through a metal grate."

"Right," Wilson said. "Will do." He turned back to his crew. "I'll go up top with Sheriff Brady and bring the K12 saw with me. You guys bring the come-along, ropes, rappelling harnesses, chains, the Stokes basket, blankets, and medical supplies. Oh, and box lights, too. Move it."

It was a steep climb. Shimmying over rocks and dragging herself up the steep grade hand over hand, Joanna was grateful for the tough khaki of her pants as well as her sturdy hiking boots. There were spots where she worried that her scrabbling along would send a shower of loose rocks and boulders raining back down on Lieutenant Wilson, who was behind and beneath her.

When they finally reached the trees, Joanna was out of breath and panting with exertion. Beads of perspiration rolled down her face, stinging her eyes. It provoked her to realize that Lieutenant Wilson, despite carrying the thirty-pound gas-powered saw on his back, had barely broken a sweat. Then she remembered that he had won the Bisbee Hill Climb the previous two years. With that in mind, she decided she wasn't doing too badly after all.

"Where to now?" Wilson asked, looking around as he came into the shady gloom beneath the canopy of trees. The ground around them was littered with a layer of loose rock that she recognized as tailings from the glory hole. For a time Joanna had no answer, but then she caught sight of Terry and Spike as they came into view, slithering, one at a time, under a rusty iron grate that was virtually invisible in the muted sunlight.

She stepped up to the metal barrier made from iron rods that had been drilled into the limestone cliff face and then welded together to form what should have been an impenetrable barrier. Determined digging by some four-footed creature had created a cleft under the grate that granted entrance. No doubt that was how Junior had gotten inside as well.

"Still no response from Junior?" Joanna's question came out in a breathless gasp.

Standing up, Terry made a futile attempt to brush the coating of gray dust off his uniform and off the dog's burnished black-and-brown coat.

"Not so far," he replied. "At least not from him, but that poor cat is raising all kinds of hell. It must be hurt pretty bad."

He looked at Joanna. "Are you going in?"

She nodded.

"If you've got some Vicks on you," Terry cautioned, "you'd better plan on using it."

A dot of Vicks VapoRub under the nostrils was a time-honored way for cops to deal with the foul odors often associated with homicide scenes. Considering Junior had been missing for only a matter of hours, Joanna was surprised that the smell could already be that bad, but she didn't argue. Instead, she reached into the pocket of her uniform and pulled out the tiny can marked Burt's Bees Lemon Butter Cuticle Cream.

For Christmas, Maggie Dixon, Joanna's clueless mother-in-law, had sent her a zipped plastic container full of Burt's Bees products. Maggie's presents were always a little off. The previous year she had sent a gift package of makeup that had clearly come with the purchase of some cosmetic or perfume item at an upscale shopping emporium. The pastel hues in the collection had clearly not been chosen to complement Joanna's complexion or her red hair and green eyes. She had donated the unopened package to the church rummage sale and forgotten about it.

This year's present, a Burt's Bees assortment of salves and ointments, was most likely a regifted item Maggie had picked up somewhere along the trail as she and Butch's father motored their hulking RV from one campground to the next. Maggie was prickly enough that Joanna and Butch spent as little time as possible in her company. Even with limited contact, however, Maggie had made it clear that she disapproved of Joanna's minimalist approach to cosmetics, which included short fingernails that were seldom, if ever, professionally manicured and polished.

Upon seeing this year's gift, Joanna had regarded it as yet another snide commentary on what Maggie considered to be Joanna's hopelessly inadequate beauty regime. Joanna's first instinct had been to toss the whole thing in the trash without even bothering to open it, but then she spied that small metal container of cuticle cream.

For a long time, Joanna had kept standard-sized jars of Vicks VapoRub in the glove compartments of her various vehicles, leaving the jars in the car because they were too bulky to carry on her person. The cuticle cream container was flat and no larger than a silver dollar. Once she got rid of the cream, she had refilled the tiny slender container with Vicks and carried it with her everywhere, slipped invisibly into the shirt pockets of her various uniforms.

"Step back now," Lieutenant Wilson warned as Joanna daubed some Vicks under her nostrils.

A moment later, the metal-slicing K12 saw howled to life. With a shower of sparks, it bit through the iron rods, slicing them as easily as if they had been made of butter. By the time the opening was large enough to allow upright passage in and out of the cavern, the remainder of the crew had arrived, bringing along the rest of their equipment.

Wilson shut off the saw and turned to Joanna. "Are you in or out?" he asked.

"In," she replied, passing him the Vicks. "Want some? Terry says we're going to need it."

"Thanks," he replied. Wilson applied some of the gel and then addressed his crew. "Okay, guys. Somebody give Sheriff Brady here a helmet. She'll need a head-lamp, too."

The guy who handed over his helmet was another six-foot bruiser. Once on Joanna's head, the thing was so big that it covered her eyes completely. While Joanna adjusted the helmet straps for a better fit, Wilson buckled on his rappelling harness and then helped her into one as well, giving both harnesses a final snap to be sure they were properly secured.

"You'll need these," he said, handing her a pair of leather rappelling gloves. Predictably, the gloves were too big, too.

"This way," Wilson explained. "If what Terry says is true and the rocks inside are unstable, the harnesses guarantee that we won't fall to the bottom the same way

Junior did. Ready?"

Nodding in reply, Joanna followed Wilson through the opening and into the cavern. Despite the sharp odor of menthol under her nose, her unwilling nostrils filled with the ugly smell of death that was thick in the air. As a rule Joanna wasn't claustrophobic, but as the darkness closed round, she more than half expected that their sudden intrusion might send a colony of bats bursting into flight. The only sound that greeted her straining ears, however, was the plaintive yowling of what sounded like a badly injured kitten.

The LED lights on their helmets helped lighten the gloom. Even so, it took several moments for their eyes to adjust to the darkness. Once Joanna could see, she realized that she and Lieutenant Wilson were standing in a low earthen entryway that led back into what was probably a much larger cavern. The ceiling in the first room was tall enough that Joanna, at five foot four, was able to stand upright. Adam Wilson, who was well over six feet, had to stoop over in order to walk. In one corner of the room just inside the doorway, a slight depression in the earthen part of the floor and a scatter of small bones indicated that an animal of some kind— a coyote or maybe even a bobcat— occasionally used the place as a den.

Lieutenant Wilson moved forward a foot or two and then stopped abruptly. "Watch your step," he warned. "There's a long drop-off here."

Even with the sturdy harness, Joanna approached the edge warily and peered down into the hole some hopeful prospector had carved out of the earth probably more than a century earlier. About ten feet down, stranded on a narrow ledge, was the marooned kitten. Another twenty feet below that, Junior Dowdle lay, facedown and unmoving, on a boulder-littered floor.

"Looks like there's been at least one rockfall in here and maybe more," Wilson observed, "but there's no way to tell when the last one happened. Maybe that's what caused Junior to fall. You stay here. I'll rappel down and check things out."

Joanna had attended a mountain rescue workshop. Rappelling wasn't something she was good at, but she had done well enough to pass the course. If the situation called for rappelling, her technique wouldn't be pretty, but it would get the job done.

Wilson spoke into the radio on his shoulder. "Okay, guys," he said. "Bring in a crew to handle my rope. The cat's down about ten feet. At my signal, haul me back up. Once the cat's safely out of the way, I'll rappel down and assess the victim."

On his command, the rope-handling team edged into the cave, filling the cramped space and forcing Joanna up against the rough wall. Standing there, looking out across the void, she caught sight of a crystal winking back at her in the reflected lights of any number of headlamps. Her father, D. H. Lathrop, had once shown her a broken chunk of geode, its interior alive with lavender crystals. He claimed that someone had carried it out of another limestone cavern, a much larger one townspeople had always dubbed the Glory Hole, before the entrance to that had been walled off with tons of debris from construction of the Highway 80 bypass.

Joanna turned her attention back to the scene just as Lieutenant Wilson went over the edge and dropped out of sight. The crew manning his rope let it out slowly. Moments later, two sharp tugs on the rope indicated he was ready to return to the surface. When he reappeared, he was holding a bloody, struggling kitten by the nape of its neck.

Joanna edged her way over to the lieutenant to take charge of the injured animal. Once she had it in hand, she very nearly dropped it. Clearly terrified, the traumatized kitten fought for its freedom, biting and scratching anything that got near it. Needle-sharp claws penetrated Joanna's shirt, slicing through any skin not covered by either the leather gloves or her Kevlar vest.

Careful not to disrupt the crew, Joanna edged back out through the entrance. In the blinding sunlight her first real glimpse of the wounded animal sickened her. It was a gaunt and gangly tabby, a female, probably not more than three or four months old. Her face was a bloody mess. The ears had been sliced through over and over, most likely with a tool like a razor, leaving behind wreckage that was little more than an ear-shaped fringe. The kitten's entire body was covered with tiny round scabs where someone had burned her with lit cigarettes.

Absolute fury surged through Joanna's body like a bolt of electricity, and it took a moment for her to regain control. "I need water over here," she barked. "Now."

One of the firefighters, a guy whose name tag identified him as Corporal Arturo Fisher, sprang forward with a bottle of electrolyte-infused water in hand. Seeing the injured kitten, Arturo's face contorted in anger, but he immediately understood what was needed. Opening the bottle, he poured water into his cupped hand and offered it to the injured animal, who lapped up every drop. When the kitten finally had her fill, she looked up into the man's eyes as if to say thank you.

"If the bastard who did this isn't dead, he sure as hell should be," Fisher muttered.

Joanna found herself nodding in agreement. She was accustomed to dealing with the terrible things people did to other people. The damage that had been inflicted on this helpless animal made her blood boil.

The kitten heaved a plaintive sigh. As if aware that she had arrived in a safe haven, she closed her eyes and subsided limply against Joanna's chest, resting and relaxed this time rather than squirming and fighting. Just then another member of the fire crew walked up behind Joanna and tapped her on the shoulder.

"Excuse me," he said. "Lieutenant Wilson's calling for you. He says the victim is dead. He wants to know if you want to go down and do a survey."

At that point in the investigation, Joanna had no homicide detectives on the scene. Of all the people in her department, she was by far the smallest physically. If the firefighters were going to have to be raising and lowering people up and down with ropes, she was a better candidate than anyone else. She had some training in crime scene investigation. Armed with the camera on her phone, she knew she'd be able to record what was down there as well as any of her CSI folks could. Besides, before Joanna delivered the bad news from the scene to anyone else, including Moe and Daisy Maxwell, she wanted to verify that the dead man really was Junior.

"Okay," she said, nodding. "I'm ready, but what do I do with this?" she asked, glancing at the sleeping kitten.

"I'll take care of her," Corporal Fisher volunteered, stepping forward. "Give her to me while you go check things out. If the dead guy did this, the bastard got what he deserved."

CHAPTER 3

As the guys in the cave adjusted the rigging on her harness, Joanna looked down into the darkness and pondered what Corporal Fisher had just said. She had known for some time that Daisy and Moe had been having issues with Junior—that he'd been acting out and behaving in ways he never had before. Still, was it possible that he could have done something so appallingly evil to a defenseless kitten? In Joanna's previous dealings with him, the man had almost always been unfailingly kind—sweet, even. Up until only a matter of weeks ago, he had been at Daisy's every day, where he spent his shifts greeting customers with stacks of menus and a beaming smile.

Whenever Joanna had seen Junior around animals, he had been gentle and respectful. Only a week ago, when Jenny had taken Desi into the restaurant on a service dog training exercise, not only had Junior been there, he had also been absolutely delighted with the pup. Joanna couldn't make a connection between the Junior she recalled laughing at Desi's antics and the cold-blooded person who had mutilated a helpless animal. Was it possible that Alzheimer's could cause those kinds of personality changes and result in episodes where people would behave in ways that were entirely foreign to their previous natures? Try as she might, Joanna couldn't wrap her mind around the idea that Junior would do such a thing. She doubted Moe and Daisy would be able to, either.

As the team of rope handlers lowered Joanna into the hole, she was grateful for the light on her helmet and for Lieutenant Wilson's steadying hands on her shoulders as he caught her on the way down and guided her to a smooth landing. The rough surface at the bottom of the hole meant that every shifting rock underfoot was an invitation to a twisted ankle or a broken leg.

"This is a crime scene," she admonished. "Did you touch anything?"

Wilson shook his head. "All I did was check for a pulse; there wasn't one."

Joanna pulled out her iPhone and turned on the camera application. As she began snapping pictures, she used pages torn from a pocket notebook, folded and numbered, as makeshift evidence markers. Each time the flash went off, the contrast of the brilliant light followed by overwhelming darkness left Joanna momentarily blinded, but as near as she could tell, there were no footprints or marks of any kind visible on the rock-strewn surface that would indicate anyone other than the dead man had been here.

"Do you think he fell?" Joanna asked, pausing her photo shoot.

"I'm not so sure about his falling," Wilson waffled. "Maybe he jumped, or he could have been pushed. Come take a look at his face. I doubt a simple fall from that distance would have caused that much damage."

With Lieutenant Wilson's hand leading her forward, Joanna made her way closer to the fallen victim. The first thing she noticed about the man was that he was wearing a pair of blue-and-white-striped short-sleeved pajamas. One house slipper, a slip-on Romeo, was still on his right foot. Its mate lay ten feet or so away, toe up against the side of the rock wall.

As soon as Joanna got a clear look at the victim's face, she recognized Junior, despite the fact that only half his face was still intact. The other half, pancaked on top of a boulder, had crumpled in on itself like a squashed jack-o'-lantern. She didn't need a medical examiner to tell her that much of what she was seeing on the floor around the victim was the mixed splatter of gray matter and blood. Only a tiny amount of blood had dribbled out of the corner of the mouth of the disfigured face. That told her that Junior had most likely died instantly. For a moment she was struck by the unfairness of that. The kitten had suffered; he hadn't.

Steeling herself for the task at hand, Joanna resumed taking pictures. She stayed at it long enough to create a comprehensive photo and evidence marker log that contained fifty or more shots.

"What now?" Wilson asked as she finished and pocketed her phone.

"My next call is to the M.E.," she said. "In situations like this, do you bring the remains out or does the M.E.?"

"We do, although Dr. Machett sometimes has his own ideas about how things should be done," Wilson said. "I'm not sure his new helper, Ralph, is physically capable of coming down here, and I doubt Dr. Machett will want to do so, either. Might dirty one of the fancy suits he's always wearing. He strikes me as one of your basic prima donnas."

Dr. Guy Machett wasn't high on Joanna's list, either. The still relatively new M.E., who never let anyone forget that his medical degree came from Johns Hopkins University, had been hired to take over as Cochise County medical examiner when Dr. George Winfield had retired. Doc

Winfield, who happened to be Joanna's stepfather, had been a well-loved and much-respected colleague. The same could not be said of his successor.

Machett's whole way of doing business— including his high-handedness and lack of empathy—had put him at odds with many of the folks in law enforcement circles. It came as no surprise to Joanna that he had developed a less-than-stellar working relationship with local fire-fighting teams as well. Joanna didn't add chapter and verse to Lieutenant Wilson's derogatory comment. A simple nod of her head was agreement enough.

"Okay," she said. "I'll go back up and make some calls. Are you coming?"

"Not yet," Wilson said, shaking his head. "I'll stay with the remains until someone decides what's to be done. It's a matter of respect."

Joanna tugged on her rope. Moments later she rose through the cool dark air. As she neared the surface, her vision improved enough so she could just make out the legs of the rope handlers through the murky darkness on the surface. Moments later hands reached out to deposit her on firm ground.

"Thanks, guys," she said.

One of them laughed. "Better you than Ernie Carpenter," he told her. "If he'd been the one down there, we'd have needed another four guys just to handle the rope."

Outside the cave, Joanna found Corporal Fisher sitting in the shade, tucked up against the trunk of a scrub oak, tenderly cradling the sleeping kitten. She nestled comfortably against his chest as though she belonged there. One front leg draped down casually over the arm of the firefighter's protective gear.

"Mind if I share your tree trunk?" Joanna asked.

"Help yourself." Fisher paused and then added, "What's going to happen to this poor little thing?"

"First we'll get her some veterinary care," Joanna answered. "Then we'll try to find her owner."

When Joanna pulled her telephone out of her pocket, she was surprised to discover it was nearly eight o'clock. Close to two hours had passed since she had first arrived in the parking lot at St. Dominick's. With the victim found and identified, Joanna's first call was to Chief Bernard.

"I've seen him," she said. "It's Junior, all right."

"He's dead then?" Bernard asked.

"Yes."

"Figured as much," Bernard said. "Someone from the fire crew just called for Reverend Maculyea and she took off in a hell of a hurry. My guess is she's on her way to you right now." He paused then asked, "How did it happen?"

"He either fell or was pushed," Joanna answered. "In any case, I'd say he died on impact. That's not official, but it's what I saw."

"Have you called Dr. Machett?" Chief Bernard asked. "If the body's on the far side of the highway, it's not inside the city limits—your jurisdiction instead of mine."

"I haven't called him yet," Joanna answered, "but I will."

"Best of luck with that," the chief said. "So what's the deal? Are we dealing with an accident, a suicide, or a homicide?"

Joanna remembered what Lieutenant Wilson had said about the possibility that Junior might have jumped or been pushed. "Too soon to tell," she answered.

"He died on impact?"

"That's how it looks."

"Knowing he didn't suffer will be a comfort to Moe and Daisy."

Joanna thought about the horribly damaged kitten. Hearing about that wouldn't provide the Maxwells any comfort at all.

"There are some troubling details at the scene that will need to be investigated and could be difficult for Moe and Daisy to handle," she told him. "Whatever you do, don't let them come here. For one thing, it's rough terrain. I doubt either one of them is in any condition to make the climb." She paused for a moment. "The Maxwells belong to St. Dom's, don't they?"

"That's my understanding," Chief Bernard said.

"Before you call off your search teams,

have Father Rowan take Moe and Daisy into his office. Ask him to have them wait with him there until Marianne and I arrive."

"Does that mean you'll be doing the next-of-kin notification?" Chief Bernard asked. "What about Dr. Machett? Shouldn't he be there, too?"

"As I said, he's one of my next calls."

"Okay," Chief Bernard said with a sigh. "Better you than me on both counts—doing the notification and dealing with the M.E."

Joanna's first call was to Dispatch. Tica Romero was now off shift. Joanna's lead dispatcher, Larry Kendrick, had come on duty.

"I need a homicide detective and the CSI unit at a crime scene above the highway west of Old Bisbee," she told him. "I don't know which detective is up right now. I'm hoping for Deb Howell. I don't think Ernie Carpenter can handle the climb. Whichever it turns out to be, tell him or her to drive as far as milepost 337. We're straight up the gully from where the emergency vehicles are parked. If they come that way, they'll walk right into the crime scene. Have them call my cell when they're close, and I'll direct them the rest of the way up the hill."

"Got it," Larry said. "Anything else?"

"Yes, I need to call the M.E. next, and after that Jeannine Phillips at Animal Control. I'll make those calls while you're summoning everybody else."

When Joanna dialed the M.E.'s office, the phone was answered by Machett's gravelly voiced receptionist and secretary, Madge Livingston. Madge had adored Guy Machett's predecessor and made no bones about despising her current boss. She was a pushy sixty-something who could have retired years earlier. Rumor had it that she was staying on now for no other purpose than to make Guy Machett's life miserable.

"Good morning," Joanna said when she answered. "Sheriff Brady here. Could you put me through to Dr. Machett?"

According to Guy Machett's playbook, the M.E. expected to be addressed as Dr. Machett no matter what. None of this informal Doc stuff for him. "Doc," he had informed Joanna snippily early on when she had erred in that regard, "is one of the seven dwarfs. Do I look short to you?"

You look like a jerk, she had thought, but she hadn't said so.

"Does this have anything to do with you guys having the highway shut down? What happened? Did a couple of drug dealers off each other?" Madge demanded. "Good riddance. Maybe it'll spare the taxpayers some expense."

"It's not a couple of drug dealers," Joanna said patiently. "Now could you please put me through to Dr. Machett?"

"I can't. He's on his way out of town and won't be back for two days. He just left."

"Call him back," Joanna said. "We need him."

"It'll be better for me if you call him," Madge said.

Joanna found the situation almost laughable. Chief Bernard didn't want to call Guy Machett and neither did the M.E.'s own secretary. No doubt Madge was right. Whoever had the misfortune of interrupting whatever was penciled into Dr. Guy Machett's day-planner was going to get an earful.

"Do you have his cell-phone number?" Madge asked.

It was Joanna's turn to sigh. "Yes," she said, scrolling through her contacts. "I've got it."

She punched in the number. "Sheriff Brady here," she said when Dr. Machett answered. "We've got a body for you."

"Crap," he grumbled. "Just what I wanted on a bright spring morning. Who and where?"

"It's a male named Junior Dowdle who took a bad fall."

"You've already identified him?"

"Junior is someone I know," Joanna explained. She wasn't surprised that the M.E. didn't recognize the name. Daisy's Café was far beneath Guy Machett's level of sophistication. "Junior was found at the bottom of a glory hole inside one of the limestone caves above Highway 80 in Old Bisbee. Outside Old Bisbee, actually," she corrected. "My jurisdiction rather than Alvin's."

"Did you say he's in a cave?" Machett asked.

"That's right. He went off a thirty-foot drop into an old mine shaft. The guys from the fire department can probably raise and lower you in and out on a rope."

"Me on a rope?" Machett said with a short laugh. "Are you kidding? Couldn't I just swing in on a vine?"

Cochise County—Joanna's jurisdiction as well as Dr. Machett's—included huge tracts of empty, mesquite-covered desert. Dr. Machett always seemed offended that the people who lived and died there often did their dying in inconvenient, out-of-the-way places.

"I've never been in a cave," Machett declared, "and I've never wanted to be, either. Just because some brain-dead spelunker decides to die in a hole in the ground doesn't mean I'm going to go up and down a rope ladder to examine the guy in situ. No way. They don't pay me enough money to go crawling around in snake-infested caves."

Joanna remembered what Adam Wilson had said about the M.E. not wanting to dirty one of his precious suits, which, Joanna had noticed, were almost always of the expensive Italian-made variety. Cochise County obviously paid him enough to make Dr. Machett's expensive wardrobe possible. As for snakes? Joanna had seen no sign of one of those anywhere inside the cave.

"Are you saying you want me to have the guys from the fire department retrieve the remains before you take a look at them?"

"By all means. Tell 'em to have at it!"

Joanna heard the genuine relief in Machett's voice. It occurred to her that maybe his reluctance wasn't just about the suit. Maybe the M.E. was actually afraid of cold dark places and of snakes, too.

"Once they get the dead guy out, have them call my new diener, Ralph Whetson, to come pick up the body."

The first time Machett had dropped the five-dollar word "diener" into casual conversation, Joanna had gone to the trouble of looking it up. She knew it was highbrow, in-crowd jargon that meant nothing more or less than "morgue assistant." She might have liked Dr. Machett more if he hadn't insisted on using it at every possible opportunity. She also noted that where the rescue crew on the mountain had spoken with unfailing respect about "the remains," Guy Machett felt free to refer to "the dead guy" with something verging on contempt.

"Any idea when you'll be able to do the autopsy?" Joanna asked.

"Not until Saturday sometime. I'm out of town today and tomorrow, getting back late in the evening, so probably not first thing in the morning, either. Maybe in the afternoon. I'll have to let you know. Do you want Ralph Whetson's number?"

"I can get it," Joanna said. "Thanks."

Ending the call, she went over to the group of men gathered near the entrance of the cave. "Dr. Machett isn't available. He says you should bring the remains up now," she told them. "I'll call Ralph

Whetson and have him wait down on the highway for you to bring Junior there."

As the crew went into body-retrieval mode, Corporal Fisher stood up and handed the kitten to her. "Duty calls," he said.

Tucking the sleeping feline inside her shirt, Joanna dialed Animal Control. The woman in charge, Jeannine Phillips, was a longtime Cochise County Animal Control officer. Years earlier, when the unit had been moved over to the sheriff's department, supposedly on a temporary basis, Jeannine had been none too happy about the new chain of command. There had been a period of bad blood between her and Joanna. Then, just when their relationship was finally smoothing out, Jeannine had been severely wounded in an altercation with people running a dogfighting ring at the far north end of the county. When her injuries left Jeannine incapable of returning to active duty, Jeannine had accepted a desk job. With her in charge, Joanna's Animal Control unit had a reputation for being one of the best in the region.

"Sheriff Brady here. I'm up above Old Bisbee. Where's your closest ACO?" Joanna asked. "I need one."

"Natalie Wilson is somewhere out around Double Adobe," Jeannine answered. "She's coming to the shelter with a load of north county strays. Why? What's up?"

"I've got a badly injured kitten who needs some immediate attention from Dr. Ross."

Millicent Ross was the only vet in town these days. She was also Jenny's boss and Jeannine Phillips's longtime domestic partner.

"What happened?" Jeannine asked.

"She took a bad fall among other things," Joanna answered. "There may be some internal injuries, but she's also been severely traumatized. Somebody shredded her ears, most likely with a razor blade. They also covered her body with burns from lit cigarettes."

Joanna heard a sharp intake of breath over the phone.

"Okay," Jeannine said. "I'll put the phone

on voice mail and come there myself. The last thing that poor kitten needs is to be stuck riding around in a truck full of barking dogs. Where are you?"

"A little north of the old Glory Hole," Joanna said. "Milepost 337. We're up the mountain right now. A dead man was found in a cave along with the kitten. The fire department is in the process of recovering the remains. When they bring him down to Dr. Machett's minivan, I'll bring the kitten down, too."

After calling Madge back and asking her to dispatch Ralph Whetson, Joanna stood up gingerly so as not to disturb the kitten. She walked over to the entrance of the cave in time to see a group of sweat-soaked men emerge, carrying Junior's blanket-swathed body in a basket.

Once outside, they paused long enough to remove their helmets and stand at attention, waiting. Terry Gregovich and Spike joined them. Corporal Fisher did not. He was the only one of Wilson's crew who moved determinedly away from the quiet gathering, his helmet still firmly atop his head.

Lieutenant Wilson was the last to emerge. When he saw Fisher walking away and still wearing his helmet, the lieutenant called after him. "Get back here, Fisher," he ordered. "Helmet off. Show some respect."

"Respect?" Fisher repeated. He stopped moving but he didn't turn around, and he didn't remove the helmet, either. "Are you kidding me? Did you see what that monster did to that poor cat? He doesn't deserve any respect. If you think I'm going to be part of this..."

"If you want to have a job when this incident is over," Wilson growled, "then you will be part of it because I'm ordering you to be part of it. I don't care what you think Junior Dowdle did or didn't do. Now get back here and stand at attention with everybody else."

"But—" Fisher began.

"No buts," Wilson warned him.

Sighing, Corporal Fisher complied. He returned to the crew, removed his helmet, and came to attention. Once he was in place, Wilson assumed the same stance and bowed his head.

"Let us pray," he said quietly.

One by one the men clustered around the blanket-shrouded body bowed their heads, too, including Deputy Terry Greg-ovich and Sheriff Joanna Brady.

"Into thy hands, O Lord, we commend his spirit," Wilson intoned. "Amen."

"Amen," the others agreed.

"Amen," Joanna added.

It was a quiet moment—a simple moment. It was also, Joanna feared, the last vestige of real respect that would ever be paid to Junior Dowdle. If it turned out he was responsible for torturing the kitten, the good things the man had done before would soon be forgotten. She was sorry to have been there for the solemn ceremony and glad to have been there— sorry Junior was dead and glad to have witnessed the quiet decency of the group of hardworking men who were taking his remains back home to the people who would grieve over Junior's death no matter what he had done.

Some of the men made as if to gather up their equipment. Lieutenant Wilson forestalled that with a shake of his head. "Leave it for now," he said. "We'll get it later. Right now let's walk him down the hill."

One by one the other members of the crew fell into step behind the four guys charged with carrying Junior's body. The ungainly procession made its way back down the rugged pathway to the highway in complete silence. Joanna, bringing up the rear, occasionally had to scoot along on her butt in order to keep from falling and jarring the sleeping kitten tucked inside her shirt.

Her descent was the exact opposite of dignified. When she finally reached the bottom, she scrambled to her feet and brushed off the coating of gray dust that covered her clothing. Looking around, she was grateful to find Marliss Shackleford had not yet arrived on the scene. The last thing the sheriff of Cochise County needed right then was to have her photo plastered on the front page of the next day's **Bisbee Bee** with a demeaning caption saying something to the effect of SHERIFF JOANNA BRADY FALLS ON BUTT WHILE RESCUING INJURED KITTEN.

With Moe's and Daisy's broken hearts hanging in the balance, Joanna thought the less said about that poor kitten, the better.

CHAPTER 4

By the time Joanna reached the highway, the basket laden with Junior Dowdle's earthly remains had already been loaded into the Dodge Caravan known around town as the M.E.'s "meat wagon." As the van pulled away, Lieutenant Wilson sidled up to Joanna. "A word, please?"

"Of course," Joanna said. "What's up?"

In answer, Wilson removed an iPhone from his pocket. After turning it on and locating a file, he handed it to Joanna. Squinting at the screen in the bright sunlight, all she could see was what looked like a pile of brown and white rags, lying on the rubble-strewn floor.

"What is it?" she asked.

"This mess was under Junior's body," Wilson said tersely. "I can't tell for certain, because they were all pretty well smashed together, but I think it's a bunny, a puppy, and at least one other kitten. They weren't visible until we moved the body."

Joanna swallowed hard. That was why the whole cavern had reeked of death. Junior Dowdle wasn't the only victim who had died there; so had several others.

"I guess I'll need to send one of my techs back down to take more photos and gather more evidence," Joanna said after collecting herself.

"I thought you would," Wilson agreed. "That's why I told the guys to leave our equipment in place."

Marianne's VW appeared on the scene. In her role as chaplain, she was there to offer support for the first responders as well as to comfort the other people affected by the incident. Joanna had finished briefing her when the folks from her department began showing up.

Jeannine Phillips had something of a reputation as a speed demon. This time, fueled by a case of severe moral outrage, she was the first of Joanna's officers to arrive. Jeannine came equipped with a tiny receiving-blanket-lined pet crate. When Joanna removed the sleeping animal from inside her shirt and placed her in the crate, the exhausted kitten didn't so much as stir.

"Poor little thing," Jeannine murmured, peering at the animal's visible injuries. "Who would do such a thing?"

"At first glance," Joanna replied, "it looks like the bad guy could be Junior Dowdle."

"Daisy Maxwell's Junior?" Jeannine asked in disbelief. "The guy who always hands out the menus?"

Joanna nodded.

"No way!" Jeannine exclaimed.

"As I said, that's how it looks," Joanna replied. "Junior was found dead on the floor of an old glory hole. We found the kitten in the glory hole too, and she's not the only animal victim. I've just been told the bodies of three other dead animals were found under Junior's body—another kitten, a rabbit, and a puppy, too."

"I can't believe Junior would be capable of a stunt like this," Jeannine declared. "I would have sworn the man didn't have a mean bone in his body."

"That's my thought, too," Joanna agreed. "My initial assumption was that he was responsible, but as I came down the moun-tain, I arrived at a different conclusion, and I believe the crime scene photos bear that out. Let's take a look."

Removing her iPhone from her pocket, Joanna turned it on, found the camera roll, and then scrolled through the set of photos she'd taken inside the cave. After studying several of them closely, she handed the phone over to Jeannine. "Here," she said. "Take a look at this one and the three that follow."

Frowning, Jeannine stared at the screen. "What am I looking for? What am I supposed to see?"

"I want you to notice what you're not seeing," Joanna said. "Junior is wearing short sleeves. Do you see any bite marks or scratches on either of his hands or forearms?"

Jeannine peered at the screen again. "Not really," she said with a frown.

"May I look, too?" Marianne asked.

Joanna nodded and Jeannine passed the phone to Marianne, who also stared at the photos for several long seconds.

"We know Junior died last night. It's safe to say the cat ended up in the glory hole about the same time. Believe me, when Lieutenant Wilson handed that kitten over to me a little while ago, she scratched the daylights out of me. If Junior was responsible for her injuries, she would have fought him, too, but there's not a single scratch or bite mark anywhere on his arms or hands."

"He might have had her in some kind of restraints," Jeannine suggested.

"True," Joanna agreed, "but I didn't see any evidence of that on the cat, either. If he'd used duct tape, for example, there'd still be adhesive clinging to her coat."

"You're saying that someone else besides Junior might be involved?" Marianne asked.

Knowing that anything said at the scene would be subject to Marianne's chaplaincy vow of silence, Joanna wasn't concerned about answering.

"We'll get Dave to use the photos to recreate some 3-D images. Lieutenant Wilson thought the spot where Junior landed was farther away from the side of the hole than a simple fall would suggest."

"Like maybe he was pushed?"

"Maybe," Joanna agreed. "And it's possible whoever tortured that kitten might have had something to do with it." Joanna turned to Jeannine. "Have there been any reported cases of missing kittens recently?"

The head of Animal Control nodded. " A couple," she answered. "And now that you mention it, we had a missing Easter bunny, too. In fact, the rabbit and at least one lost puppy were from houses up in the canyon, here. Most of the time when pets go missing like that, we chalk it up to coyotes."

"In this case, the coyotes may be getting a bum rap," Joanna observed, "and perhaps Junior Dowdle is, too."

"What do you want me to do?" Jeannine asked.

"Take the kitten to Dr. Ross. Tell her that

there's a slim chance that a killer may have left trace evidence on the kitten's fur. We'll need her to take swabs of every speck of blood she finds, in case there's been some DNA transfer."

"Will do," Jeannine said.

"In the meantime," Joanna continued, "I'll dispatch a detective to Dr. Ross's clinic to stand by while the animal is being treated and the samples collected. If human DNA is present, we'll need to maintain the chain of evidence, the same way we do when Dr. Machett performs an autopsy."

Nodding, Jeannine strode off, cradling the injured kitten's crate in her arms as tenderly as if she were carrying a baby. She was driving away when a sheriff's department unmarked patrol car pulled up. Detective Deb Howell, one of Joanna's three homicide detectives, stepped out.

"What's going on?" she asked. "Dispatch told me somebody was dead. When I asked homicide, suicide, or accident, they had nothing to tell me."

Joanna responded to Deb's question with one of her own. "Who's back at the office, Ernie Carpenter or Jaime Carbajal?"

"Both," Deb answered. "They were there doing paperwork when I left. Why?"

"I have an assignment for one of them," Joanna said. "Whoever draws that short straw isn't going to thank me."

Over the years Joanna and her entire investigation team had stood in on their share of autopsies. Still, it was one thing to be in the morgue while an M.E. dissected a dead body. It was quite another to be in a treatment room with a veterinarian working on a living, breathing kitten. Joanna wasn't sure if she'd be able to handle a situation like that, and she wasn't sure how either one of the Double C's would respond, either. When her call was put through to the bullpen, Ernie Carpenter answered.

"We've got a chain-of-evidence problem," Joanna told him. "I need someone to go to Dr. Ross's office and stand by while she works on a badly injured kitten."

"As in a kitten that's still alive?" Ernie asked.

"Junior Dowdle was found dead, and the injured kitten was found nearby,"

Joanna explained. "There may be blood evidence on the kitten that will help us determine what happened to Junior."

"Sorry," Ernie said. "It sounds like Jaime's your man. I fainted dead away in the delivery room when my son was born. I caused such a fuss that Rose wouldn't let me anywhere near her when our daughter was born two years later. So, no. I can deal with autopsies on dead guys until hell freezes over, but I'm squeamish as all hell when it comes to living creatures."

Ernie Carpenter had a reputation for being tough as nails, but Joanna didn't even rib him about his admission.

"All right, then," Joanna replied. "Send Jaime to Dr. Ross's office. Since Deb's going to be making like a mountain goat and heading back to the crime scene, I'd like you to meet me at St. Dominick's. I want you there when it's time for me to give Moe and Daisy Maxwell the bad news."

"They don't know he's dead?" Ernie asked.

"Not yet," Joanna said. "At least I don't

think they know."

"All right," Ernie said. "I'm on my way. I'll find out everything else there is to know when I get there."

By the time Joanna ended the call, her lead CSI tech, Dave Hollicker, had arrived and was awaiting orders. "What's the deal?" he asked.

"Junior Dowdle ran away from home last night," she explained. "He was found dead inside an old mine shaft halfway up the mountain. A crew from the Bisbee Fire Department was called in to retrieve the body and bring it back down here."

"I saw Ralph Whetson leaving in the minivan," Deb said, "but where's Dr. Machett? Shouldn't the M.E. be here in person? Isn't that his job?"

"Not today," Joanna replied. "The M.E. is currently out of town and out of the picture."

"What about the autopsy, then?" Deb asked. "When is it and who'll do it?"

"Dr. Machett will do it when he gets back," Joanna answered. "We don't have a firm schedule on that. Most likely it won't happen before Saturday afternoon at the earliest."

"Where's the crime scene?" Dave asked.

Joanna pointed. "Up there. The shaft is a glory hole inside a limestone cavern. The entrance to that is hidden inside that second big grove of scrub oak halfway up the hill. If it hadn't been for Terry and Spike, we never would have found him. The scene's been pretty well disturbed because of all the comings and goings of the recovery crew. Some additional evidence was found once Junior's body was moved. Once you retrieve that, I want you to measure the distance from the rim of the glory hole to the point of impact so we can do a computerized simulation. We need to know if he simply fell, took a running jump, or was pushed."

"Did you take photos?" Dave asked.

"Some, but I want you to take a whole lot more." She paused and gave Dave a searching look. "How are you in caves?"

"Don't worry about me," he said with a grin. "I'm an old spelunker from way back."

"Good; go talk to Adam Wilson. Bisbee

F.D. still has equipment up there to help you in and out. Once you're back on solid ground, I'd like you and Deb to cover the whole area, starting from the entrance to the cave and working your way down the trail Junior followed. From there go all the way back to his house. Terry and Spike can show you the route. Collect whatever you find along the way."

"Are we looking for anything in particular?" Dave asked.

"Anything that doesn't belong," Joanna said. "Somewhere between point A and point B, I'm hoping you'll find a mess of cigarette butts or chewing gum and maybe even some helpful DNA. I also want you to be on the lookout for any kind of blood spatter. Whatever you find, bag it, tag it, and bring it back."

"What about you?" Deb asked.

"Reverend Maculyea and I are going to meet up with Ernie Carpenter down at St. Dominick's, where the three of us will have the dubious honor of breaking a few hearts."

CHAPTER 5

As Joanna headed back down to St. Dominick's, twenty-five hundred miles away on a hillside outside Great Barrington, Massachusetts, Selma Machett's small, sad funeral was just getting under way.

Liza Machett had heard about Haven's Rest Cemetery from one of her customers at Candy's, and she was surprised to learn that was also the cemetery in which Selma herself had chosen and partially paid for a plot well in advance of her final illness. From its website Liza learned Haven's Rest offered a low-cost, all-inclusive service that came complete with a memorial service on the grounds, cremation, and burial in a two-foot-by-two-foot plot that was much smaller in both size and cost than a standard burial plot.

Each grave came with a flat granite

marker that would cover half of the plot itself. The old cemetery in town featured a motley collection of moss-covered head-stones in all sizes and shapes. Some had fallen over completely. Others stood canted at crazy angles. The carved inscriptions there, some of them barely visible, dated back for most of three centuries. Haven's Rest was different. One of the reasons it was so "affordable" was due to the fact that the uniformly flat headstones meant the whole thing could be mowed by one guy—the funeral director's brother-in-law—who could cover the entire cemetery on a riding mower in twenty minutes from beginning to end.

Even though Guy had been out of their lives for years, once Selma had gone into hospice, Liza had swallowed her pride and tracked her brother down at his new office somewhere in the wilds of Arizona. He had immediately made it clear that he had written Selma off years ago and that, for him, showing up at the funeral would be nothing short of hypocritical.

"So that's it, then?" Liza had demanded, her voice rising. "That's what you do, isn't it? You wash your hands of everything. You go off to live your perfect life and leave me stuck cleaning up the mess!"

Guy had hung up on her then, and that was the last time they spoke. When Selma died, Liza didn't bother calling. There was no point. That was why, on this rainy Thursday morning, there was only one folding chair reserved for grieving family members under the blue canvas canopy next to Selma Machett's tiny grave.

As Craig Masters, the funeral director, intoned his comforting words, Liza was struck by the fact that her mother had had no friends of her own. The people who had come today were Liza's friends, and most of those were people from work—her fellow employees at the diner and the customers from there as well, all of whom seemed like family but were far less trouble.

Studying those gathered there, Liza sorted the familiar faces in her customary fashion, by order rather than by name: two eggs over easy, hold the hash browns, with English muffin on the side; French toast, no cinnamon, crisp bacon; two eggs scrambled with sausage patty, cottage cheese instead of hash browns; short stack with scrambled eggs, sugar-free maple syrup. These were Candy's stock-in-trade—guys who worked hard, drove hefty pickup trucks, and brought their big appetites to the diner for breakfast almost every day. When the city had come through and tried to restripe the parking lot to make more spaces for compact cars, Clifford "Candy" Small had gone ballistic.

"These guys all work for a living," he had told the clipboard-wielding and very much cowed emissary from the City Planning Department. "They need someplace to eat where they can park their trucks without having to worry about scratching somebody's precious Prius. Now get the hell out of here and leave me alone."

The guy with the clipboard left. The faded parking lot striping big enough for pickups stayed put, at least for now, and so did the guys who drove them. Many of those same guys had come to the funeral today, along with the restaurant's full contingent of worker bees. Candy, Liza's boss, was there, as were her fellow waitresses—Sue Ellen, Honey, Jeanette, Frieda, and Lois. The funeral's attendees included all the busboys and dish-washers—Ricky, Salvatore, Xavier, and Tommy—and the other two cooks, Alfredo and Cosmo, had shown up as well. Liza was touched that they had all come to the funeral to show their support, and she was equally sure they'd all be coming back to the diner later where some of them would have to work. Candy's had been closed to the public for the day both so employees could attend the funeral itself, and also because it was the site of the postfuneral reception.

In the twenty-six years Candy had owned the place, he had shuttered his doors only twice before. Once he had been forced to close because the power had gone off for twelve hours and all the food in the coolers went bad. The second time had been in honor of his own mother's funeral. This was number three.

Someone pushed a button, and the earthenware urn began its slow descent into the ground as Liza, dry-eyed and stone-faced, watched it disappear. The top had just slipped out of sight when a beefy hand dropped heavily onto Liza's shoulder.

"Sorry," Candy Small muttered under his breath. "So sorry. Take as much time off as you need. Whenever you're ready to come back to work, you'll still have a job."

Liza looked up at him gratefully because she knew that that single word from him, "sorry," was meant to cover it all—not only for the fact that Selma Machett was dead, but also for everything that had gone before. He understood more than anyone else the tangled relationship she'd had with her mother because Candy was the only person in town to whom Liza had confided the gory details. Candy was her boss, her friend, and the closest thing to a father Liza Machett ever had.

When it came to stature, Candy Small

didn't match his name—he wasn't in the least bit small. He had been born with the name of Clifford, although hardly anyone in town remembered his given name. As a child he had never gone anywhere without at least two jawbreakers in his possession—one tucked into his cheek and another held in reserve in the pocket of his jeans. By the time he graduated from eighth grade, the other kids and most of the teachers, too, had started calling him Candy. In high school a few of the older kids had tried making fun of him for having a girlish-sounding name. Back then, Candy had yet to grow to his full height of six foot four. Even so, once he had cleaned the clocks of all his would-be tormentors, no one ever made fun of his name again, at least not to his face.

Occasionally a new traveling salesman, making a cold call, would stop by Candy's Diner with the preconceived notion that the owner of the place would turn out to be some blue-haired lady in her sixties or seventies. That would have been true if Candy's widowed mother, Wanda, had still been at the helm. Instead, she had retired to Florida several years before her death, passing the family diner, previously named Wanda's, along to her oversize son. Employees always got a kick out of seeing the startled expressions on the hapless newcomers' faces when Candy, all three hundred pounds of him, emerged from the kitchen, wiping his huge hands on his apron and demanding to know what they wanted.

The newbies quickly learned that when it came to business, Candy Small drove a hard bargain. When it came to people, however, the man was a pushover. If a kids' sports team in town needed a sponsor, he was there. If the high school band was looking to raise money for new uniforms or a trip to the Rose Bowl, he was happy to oblige. And if someone was down on his or her luck, Candy would help out by having a load of groceries delivered to the home of a struggling single mother or sending one of his busboys out to shovel the sidewalks of elderly people who could no longer handle that task themselves. Candy's innate kindness was how he had come into Liza Machett's life in the first place.

He had heard about her situation from one of Liza's teachers at school. When she had fled home that morning with a high school diploma, no money, and no prospects, he had taken a chance on her. First he gave her a job in his restaurant and then he helped her find a place to live, advancing her enough money to cover the first and last month's rent on an apartment. Liza wasn't the first employee he had helped, and she wasn't the last, either, which partially explained the diner's stable of long-term and very loyal employees.

As Craig Masters closed out Selma's brief ceremony, he announced that everyone was welcome to come to the reception. Liza knew that she'd be given a ride to the restaurant in the funeral home limo, so she stayed where she was as the small crowd dispersed. Only when the others were gone did the single stranger in attendance—a stoop-shouldered, balding old man wearing a rain slicker and leaning on a cane—make his approach. When he arrived at Liza's chair, he spoke to her in a quiet voice as if concerned about being overheard.

"I knew your father," he said. "Back when he still drove a bread truck, back before he took off. I've been out of the game for a long time now, but I still hear things on occasion. I'd be careful if I was you, Miss Machett. Those guys don't never forgive, they don't forget, and they don't play around, neither."

Having delivered what sounded very much like a warning, he turned abruptly and limped away, threading a path between the granite markers and leaving behind a trail of footsteps in the damp grass. Watching him go, Liza was left with a hundred unasked questions. She wanted to chase after him and say, "You knew my father? Who are you? What bread truck? What can you tell me?" But she did not. Could not. It was almost as if she were bolted to that flimsy folding chair.

She was still watching him walk away when Mr. Masters appeared at her elbow, holding out a hand to assist her to her feet. "Ready?" he asked.

"That man," she said, pointing toward the figure disappearing in the distance. "Do you know who he is or where he's from?"

"Name's Jonathan Thurgard," Mr. Masters answered. "I believe he lives in Stockbridge, and he's a Korean War vet. At least, that's what I've heard, but I don't know it for sure because when he signs the guest book he never lists an address. He has a reputation for showing up at funerals all over western Massachusetts, usually when the deceased served as a member of the military. He stands on the sidelines and then plants a tiny American flag next to the flowers before he leaves. He didn't leave a flag, but was your mother a veteran by any chance?"

"Not that I know of," Liza said.

"Well then, perhaps he was one of your mother's friends."

Liza shook her head. She knew better than anyone that Selma Machett didn't have any friends. "He said he knew my father."

"There you go then," Mr. Masters said with a dismissive shrug that indicated the topic had been adequately covered. He held out his arm. "Shall we go?"

Taking Craig Masters's arm, Liza allowed herself to be led across the field of markers and deposited in the idling limo that had been waiting patiently on the shoulder of one of the many paved lanes that wandered through the cemetery. Liza knew Craig's brother-in-law, Lester Woundy, from the restaurant—three eggs, scrambled hard, a side of ham along with biscuits and gravy. When he came into Candy's for breakfast, he was usually dressed in his lawn-mowing/grave-digging overalls. Today, though, tapped as the on-call limo driver, he was dressed in a dark suit and a white shirt, with his bulging neck confined inside to a too-tight collar and a blue-and-gray-striped tie.

Once Liza was inside the limo, Craig leaned over and spoke to Les. "Drop her at Candy's," he directed. "You won't need to wait. Someone else will take her home after the reception."

"Nice turnout," Les said to Liza as he put the Town Car in gear and in motion.

While standing at the cash wrap either as hostess or cashier, Liza was often a party to the conversations of people sitting at the counter. She remembered hearing Les say once that he liked small funerals best because there weren't as many chairs to fold up and put away afterward. From those overheard conversations, she also knew what Les's game plan would be.

Once he dropped her off, he'd return to the cemetery and change out of his limo-driving duds and into work clothes. Then he'd retrieve the backhoe that was always kept discreetly out of sight in a garage during funerals. Armed with the backhoe, he'd push all the bouquets of flowers into the grave before adding in the dirt he'd dug up earlier and stored twenty yards or so away from the grave, decorously covered with a green tarp during the proceedings. Once any remaining flowers and the excavated dirt had been dumped back into the hole on top of the urn, Les would unroll and replace the turf he had carefully cut out earlier that morning. After that it would be time to return the backhoe to the garage and go out for a beer. Or two. Or maybe even three.

"Yes," Liza agreed. "It was a nice turnout."

Leaning back against the headrest, Liza allowed her eyes to close. She was exhausted. For the past month, she had worked harder than she had ever worked in her life, and that superhuman effort had exacted a terrible toll—physically, mentally, and emotionally. She had worked most of her shifts at the diner, she'd visited her mother at least once a day, and she'd used every other remaining moment to oversee the workmen rehabbing Selma's house.

It had taken almost as long for Selma to die as it had to fix the house. In the end, and with the help of Ted Jackson, the local We've Got Junk franchisee—pecan waffle, crisp bacon, iced tea—she'd had thirteen Dumpster loads of stuff hauled away from her mother's house. Liza had realized early on that she would have to tackle the enterprise in a systematic fashion.

When the rehab project started, there was no electricity in Selma's house and no sign of any kerosene lanterns, either. Selma Machett had evidently learned to live like the birds, rising with the sun and bedding down at sunset. Because Liza needed to work on the house around her shifts at the diner, there were times when she had to be at the house far into the night. That meant one of her first tasks was to bring her mother's utility bill situation up-to-date and get the power turned back on. She had also begun the process of reinstating her mother's home owner's insurance.

Once the power was back on, Al of Al's EZ Plumbing—whole wheat BLT with no T, french fries, and a Pepsi—came in and got the sewer pipe cleared and the septic system pumped. Although it was most likely not an entirely environmentally approved activity, Al had pumped out the outhouse as well, after which the hole had been filled, the outhouse demolished, and a sweet little some-assembly-required potting shed straight from Home Depot was erected where the outhouse had once stood.

"If you're trying to sell the place and some nosy home inspector comes looking for an outhouse," Al instructed her, "you look at him all innocent like and say, 'Outhouse? What outhouse? That's my mother's gardening shed.'"

Supplied with power and water, Liza went to work on the books and on the magazines, too, that had been stacked, row upon row, in Selma's house. It wasn't just the cookbooks that had money squirreled away inside them. Liza had to look through everything—through hundreds of dog-eared paperback mysteries and romance novels; through every single volume of the **Encyclopaedia Britannica** with corners of pages turned down where Selma had researched the symptoms of her many various and untreated maladies; through stacks and stacks of crumbling **National Geographic** and **Life** and **People** magazines to say nothing of countless **Reader's Digest**s. Early on, Liza managed to unearth the dining room table. That way she could sit under an overhead light and with a fan blowing cool air in her direction during the endless hours while she paged through book after book after book and magazine after magazine.

It was like a nightmare Easter egg hunt. Not every volume held a cache of cash, but enough did that it was worth Liza's while to do a complete job of it. By the time she finished, $147,000 had been filtered through her coffee bean decontamination process. She had also found a flock of canning jars filled with coins. Those amounted to around five hundred dollars and didn't stink the way the bills did.

Every hundred-dollar bill that surfaced added another brick to the wall of resentment Liza was building toward her mother. Had Selma had all this money in her possession the whole time Liza had been growing up? If so, why the hell had she pretended to be poor? Why had she forced her daughter to live as though they didn't have two pennies to rub together? Why?

For the first Dumpster load, Liza had hauled the crap out through the kitchen door, down the crooked back steps, and then up into the Dumpster. After that, Ted convinced her to let him install a chute from the dining room window down to the next waiting Dumpster. She got to the point that she could toss a book from across the room and hit the Dumpster chute window almost every time.

Liza handled the books and magazines herself. For the kitchen, she hired two of the busboys from the restaurant, brothers Salvatore and Xavier Macias. Hardworking immigrants from Ecuador who sent money to their family back home each week, Salvatore and Xavier were more than happy to tackle that ungodly mess during their off-hours. Once they started, Ted rigged up a second Dumpster chute from the kitchen to make their lives easier as well. When the kitchen had been cleared of garbage and dead appliances, Liza looked around and had them remove the kitchen cabinets and the ancient linoleum along with the damaged wallboard. Then they moved on to the bathroom and bedrooms and did the same, stripping everything down to the studs.

In Selma's bedroom and bathroom, Liza was appalled at how much of the trash was stuff that had been purchased and never even opened, much less used. Unfortunately, mouse droppings rendered the excess paper products as well as the new and used clothing, some with price tags still attached, unusable and unsalvageable. When they finally got down to the bare bones of furniture, Salvatore and Xavier were happy to take the chests of drawers and the tables and the plain wooden chairs. The putrid odor clinging to the cloth meant that all upholstered pieces went to the Dumpster.

By this time, the army of pickup-driving guys from Candy's was on full alert, and they were all more than happy to work for cash on the barrel. As long as the money was good, none of them asked where it came from, and because it was all in the Candy's Diner family, as it were, not one of them cut any corners when it came to his part of the job.

John, of Great Barrington Electric—two eggs over easy; bacon crisp; hash browns crisp; coffee, cream and sugar; and a coffee, cream and sugar, to go—redid the electrical service, bringing it into the twenty-first century. Ralph Boreson of Boreson Home Remodeling—OJ; oatmeal with raisins, brown sugar, and cream; whole wheat toast—handled all the permits in a timely fashion since his sister-in-law worked in the building department and was able to move things along. Ralph also managed to find the low-end cabinets and fixtures, which had been installed the previous week. This week he'd had a full crew on-site, installing and taping wallboard, painting walls, installing new flooring, and replacing single-pane windows with double panes.

"It's not all top of the line," Ralph told Liza, "but the house will look good enough that no one will be able to rip you off by claiming it's nothing but a teardown."

Seeing the results, Liza had to agree. The place looked clean and smelled clean.

In fact, it was downright livable again, not that she ever intended to live there. Now, though, she'd be able to list it and sell it. In fact, she had made an appointment for early next week with Rose Kelly—egg salad sandwich, hold the bread, tomato slices on the side, and green tea. Rose was a local real estate agent whose bright red Kia was often the only small car tucked in among all those hulking pickups. Rose was eager to do the listing and already had a potential buyer in mind.

"Excuse me, miss," Les Woundy was saying. "We're here."

Liza roused herself out of her stupor and looked around. The limo had pulled up in front of Candy's, where a handwritten sign on the door said, SORRY! CLOSED FOR A PRIVATE FUNCTION.

After allowing Les to help her out of the limo, Liza shook off her lethargy and went inside. The counter by the cash wrap had been turned into a bar, with Honey Baxter pouring generous drinks into red paper cups. Honey was an energetic seventy-something with bright blue eye shadow and a beehive hairdo that was decades out-of-date. She still worked full-time and cared for an ailing husband even though she was almost twenty years older than Selma Machett had been when she died.

Honey looked up as Liza came in the door, and there was a tiny lull in the general conversation.

"Well, there she is!" Honey announced. "You come right on over here, sweetheart, and let me give you something that'll be good for what ails you. I make a mean sloe gin fizz."

"How about a glass of white wine?" Liza suggested. "I have a feeling one of your sloe gins would put me on my lips."

In a matter of seconds, conversations in the room resumed and the noise level amped up. The restaurant was full of people juggling loaded plates, napkins, silverware, and drinks. The long counter had been turned into a makeshift buffet, which meant that there was far less seating than people were used to, especially considering that customers who usually drifted in and out over the space of several hours had all arrived at once. Since none of these people knew Selma personally, the after-funeral gathering was a far more lighthearted party than one would have anticipated.

Candy sidled up beside her. "How are you holding up?" he asked.

"Okay," Liza said. "Better than expected. Thanks for doing this," she added.

"Least I could do," Candy replied. "The guys tell me that work on the house is pretty much finished."

Liza nodded. "Everybody really pitched in. They've done an amazing amount of work in an astonishingly short time."

"You have me to thank for that," Candy said with a self-satisfied grin. "I told some of those lazy bastards to get with the program, otherwise they'd have to deal with me!"

When someone came by to ask Candy a question, Liza wandered off through the crowd—mingling, talking to people, thanking them for coming, and thanking them for whatever role they had played in the home-rehab miracle. She had taken only a sip or two of wine and a single bite of an egg salad sandwich when a vehicle with flashing blue lights pulled up outside the restaurant's front door.

Moments later a beefy deputy—Leon Bufford—ham and cheese omelet, side of bacon, double hash browns, double white toast, coffee, and a large milk—barged into the room.

The crowd fell silent. Deputy Bufford stood in the door briefly, scanning the room. At last his eyes found their target. "Hey, Liza," he said. "You'd better come with me. Quick."

"Why?" she asked. "What's wrong?"

"Looks like somebody burned down that house of yours—all the way to the ground."

CHAPTER 6

By the time Joanna returned to the parking lot at St. Dominick's, the place was deserted because Alvin had dismissed his entire crew of volunteers. The church ladies, along with their accompanying refreshment tables, chairs, and any remaining goodies, had also disappeared.

As Joanna and Marianne stepped out of the midmorning sunlight and into the cool interior of the church, Joanna felt a sudden chill that had nothing to do with the building's stone-clad exterior and everything to do with the emotional burden of her job.

While serving as Cochise County sheriff, Joanna attended not one but two fallen officer memorials inside the hallowed halls of St. Dominick's Catholic Church. The first had been for a departmental jail matron, Yolanda Ortiz Cañedo, who had succumbed to cervical cancer. The second had been for Deputy Dan Sloan, who had been gunned down by a fleeing homicide suspect. In fact, Joanna's first dealings with Father Rowan had been on the night Deputy Sloan had died, when she and the newly arrived Catholic priest had joined forces to do a next-of-kin notification to Deputy Sloan's widow. Sunny Sloan had been pregnant at the time. Now a single mother, she worked part-time as a clerk in the sheriff department's public office.

This time, as Joanna entered the church, she was carrying the burden of knowing she was the bearer of heartbreaking news. Turning to Marianne, she asked the question that was in her heart. "When bad things happen, why do we always end up at St. Dominick's?"

Marianne simply shook her head. It wasn't necessary for her to say anything aloud. She understood. Unspoken communication was one of the blessings of their longtime friendship.

They walked down the center aisle together. At the front of the church, they turned left into what they knew to be the study—a book-lined office Father Rowan shared with the parish's other priest, Father Patrick Morris, who was currently away on an extended sick leave. The room was dimly lit. In the artificial gloom, Father Rowan sat at a polished wood desk facing Moe and Daisy Maxwell. A few feet away, Ernie Carpenter stood at ease in front of a towering bookcase. As Joanna and Marianne entered, everyone in the room turned toward them expectantly. From the anguished look on Daisy's tear-streaked face, Joanna knew the woman already understood the new arrivals wouldn't be bringing good news.

"You found him?" Daisy asked in a hushed voice.

Joanna nodded. "I'm sorry," she said.

"He's dead then?"

Joanna nodded again.

"Where?" Daisy asked. "What happened to him?"

"He fell at least thirty feet into an old

mine shaft inside a cave up above the highway."

"Junior in a cave?" Daisy asked. "That makes no sense. He was afraid of the dark. Terrified. That's why we always had to leave a lamp on in his room—in case he woke up at night."

"But that's where he was found," Joanna continued, "in a cave. I saw him myself. The M.E. has yet to confirm this, but I believe he died on impact. As I said, he fell about thirty feet. Is there a chance Junior would have taken his own life?"

"No," Daisy insisted at once. "That's simply not possible. Absolutely not. Suicide is a mortal sin. It must have been an accident."

"You said you thought he died on impact," Moe interjected softly. "Does that mean he didn't suffer?"

"I don't believe he did," Joanna replied, "but again, that's just my opinion. The real answer to that will have to come from the medical examiner."

"I'm glad he didn't suffer," Moe said resignedly, reaching out to take Daisy's hand. "As sick as he was and the way things were going, it's probably just as well."

Joanna understood the reasons behind Moe's quiet statement. Junior had been developmentally disabled. He suffered from a horribly debilitating illness that eventually would have left him lost and helpless. Had he somehow managed to outlive his foster parents, who would have cared for him? What would have become of him? Those may have been the tough realities behind Moe's comment, but Daisy definitely wasn't on the same page.

She snatched her hand away from her husband's in sudden fury. "It is **not** just as well!" Daisy hissed at him. "There's nothing about this that's 'just as well'! For one thing, we never got to say good-bye to him. Besides, what would Junior be doing outside by himself in the middle of the night? And why would he go near a cave? Remember what happened when we tried to take him to Kartchner Caverns? Once Junior realized we'd be going into a cave and that it would be dark, he absolutely refused to set foot inside, even though we'd already paid for the tickets."

"But the people were very nice about it," Moe reminded her. "They refunded the tickets, remember?"

Without acknowledging his comment, Daisy turned beseechingly to Joanna as if looking for answers. Unfortunately, all Sheriff Brady had to offer Junior's grieving foster parents were more questions, tougher ones at that.

"Did Junior have any pets?" she asked.

"Pets?" Daisy repeated. "You mean like a dog or a cat? We had a parakeet named Budgie once, back when Junior first came to live with us, but he died."

Joanna felt her heart rate quicken. "How did he die?" she asked.

Daisy shrugged. "Budgie? Who knows how come birds die? I came out to the living room one morning, uncovered his cage, and there was Budgie, lying dead on the floor of the cage with his feet sticking straight up in the air."

"Had he been harmed in any way?"

"Harmed?" Daisy asked. "How would I

know? It's not like somebody did an autopsy. Budgie was a parakeet, for Pete's sake, and he died. We put him in a matchbox and buried it in the backyard. Why on earth are you asking me about Budgie? What does he have to do with what happened to Junior?"

"Did you ever observe Junior doing anything harmful to animals?"

Daisy's fury, once focused on Moe, was now fully trained on Joanna. "Never!" she exclaimed. "Not one single time. Junior loved animals, and he was as gentle as can be with them. You saw how he was when Jenny brought that new puppy of hers into the restaurant. He absolutely loved it. But you still haven't told me why you're asking these idiotic questions."

"Because Junior's body wasn't the only thing we found in the mine shaft," Joanna explained. "There were several animals in there with him. Three of them were dead. The fourth, a kitten, is severely injured but still alive."

Daisy seemed mystified "What kind of animals?"

"Pets, most likely," Joanna answered. "A small dog or else a puppy, a rabbit, and two cats. The one that's still alive shows signs of having been tortured. She's at Dr. Ross's office being treated."

"You're saying you think Junior had something to do with what happened to all those animals—the dead ones as well as a tortured kitten?" Daisy asked in disbelief. "Are you crazy?"

She stood up and made as if to leave. Until now Ernie had stood still and silent in the background. Now he stepped forward, notebook in hand, and blocked Daisy's way. "Excuse me, Ms. Maxwell," he said. "If you don't mind, we still have a few more questions."

Moe took Daisy by the hand. "Wait," he urged. "We have to answer their questions. It's the only thing we can do to help. Please."

Reluctantly Daisy allowed herself to be guided back to her chair. Once there, she sat bolt upright, as if prepared to flee at a moment's notice.

"When's the last time you saw Junior?"

Ernie asked.

Daisy closed her eyes before she answered. "About eight thirty, when we all went to bed. We have to get up early to open the restaurant. We're usually in bed before nine."

"Had you noticed anything out of the ordinary with Junior in the past few days?" Ernie asked. "Had he been out of sorts or upset about anything?"

Daisy leveled an icy glare in Ernie's direction. "What do you know about Alzheimer's patients?" she demanded.

Ernie shook his head. "Nothing," he admitted.

"Trust me, anything and everything can upset them," Daisy answered. "Even though Junior could no longer work, I took him to the restaurant with me anyway. He liked having a regular schedule. That way, even if I was in the kitchen and he was out front, I could keep an eye on him. His mood swings came and went, but they weren't any worse than usual."

"Was he aware of his condition?" Ernie asked. "Of his prognosis?"

"You mean since he already wasn't quite right in the head, was he aware he was losing even more of his marbles?" Daisy replied sarcastically. "No, Detective Carpenter, one of the few blessings of his being developmentally disabled meant that those kinds of abstract concepts were beyond him. Moe and I knew, of course. Even though we told him to begin with, I doubt Junior ever understood what was happening. I wanted him to have as much time as he could, and I wanted it to be as good as we could make it. The idea of taking his own life would never have occurred to him."

With that, Daisy lapsed into uncontrollable sobs. Moe absently patted her shoulder, but the woman was beyond comforting. Eventually Moe turned to Joanna. "What happens next?"

"There will have to be an autopsy, of course."

"When?"

"Not until Saturday. Dr. Machett is out of town."

"When will we be able to schedule the

funeral mass?"

"Not until Dr. Machett releases the body. You can go ahead and talk to the people at the funeral home and do some tentative planning—maybe for sometime early next week—but you won't be able to finalize those plans until the M.E.'s office gives you the word."

Moe nodded.

"Did Junior have any particular friends?" Ernie asked. This time he addressed his question to Moe rather than Daisy.

"He knew lots of people in town from the restaurant. He sometimes played checkers and dominoes with the kid from next door, Jason Radner. Jason was always great with Junior. He never teased him or made fun of him, and he didn't let the other kids pick on him either."

"Detective Keller from Bisbee PD already talked with the Radners," Joanna told Ernie. "I believe he interviewed both parents early this morning and maybe Jason, too."

After jotting this down, Ernie turned again to Moe. "Is there anything you can add to what your wife already told us about Junior's situation in the days and weeks before this happened? She didn't notice anything out of the ordinary. Did you?"

"Not really," Moe said. "For months now we've been dealing with a new normal, which means everything was out of the ordinary. Junior would wake up in the morning talking about people being in his room during the night—people we never saw or heard. We often heard him pacing back and forth in his room overnight, awake and restless. That's why we had to start locking the doors with the dead bolt—to keep him inside. It never crossed my mind that he might crawl out a window. What was I supposed to do, put bars on it? Turn him into a prisoner in his own home?" With that, Moe Maxwell, too, dissolved into uncontrollable sobs.

In the interim, Daisy's tears had subsided. This time she was the one who reached out and offered a comforting hand to her husband. Joanna took heart from that small gesture. As waves of sorrow and blame ebbed and flowed around the couple, she hoped that Daisy and Moe would manage to form a united front in the face of their mutual tragedy—that Junior's death wouldn't become an insurmountable wedge that would drive them apart. Unfortunately Joanna knew that all too often the death of a loved one, especially the death of a child, could doom the marriage of the parents.

"Those people he talked about," Daisy offered, taking up where Moe had left off. "The nighttime visitors weren't real, you understand; they were more like hallucinations. Junior would tell us that his family had come to see him. He didn't have any birth sisters, but I understand there were girls in one of the foster families where he lived when he was younger.

"Not one of those people have ever visited here, at least not in real life, but that's what happens with Alzheimer's patients. Their minds slip back to some long-ago time in a way that turns the past into the present. And what Moe said is right. Junior wasn't upset about anything.

Yes, he'd had occasional angry outbursts recently, but the last one of those was several weeks ago when he dropped a dish at the restaurant and it broke."

"Nothing since then?"

"No," Daisy said.

"Aside from Junior's mental deficiencies," Ernie continued, "did he have any physical ailments? Was he in pain, by any chance?"

"He was getting older," Daisy conceded. "He had some joint pain in his lower extremities and some difficulties walking. His doctor suggested we use over-the-counter medications. We were limited in what we could give him because the wrong combinations of drugs might have added to his confusion and made his Alzheimer's symptoms worse."

"Was he ever violent?" Joanna asked. She had seen Junior in full meltdown mode at the restaurant once. Daisy had ultimately been able to calm him down, but at the time Joanna had been startled by how angry he had been and how seemingly out of control.

"Do you mean, was he violent with us?"

Daisy asked.

Joanna nodded.

"No," Daisy said firmly, shaking her head. "Not ever."

"How was he with other people?"

"He threw the checkers board at Jason once," Moe admitted. "Junior didn't like to lose."

Ernie made another notation in his notebook.

"He may have thrown the checkers, but he didn't hurt Jason," Daisy offered quickly as if attempting to minimize Moe's last comment. "Junior never hurt anybody, not ever."

Joanna's phone rang just then. Glancing at the caller ID and seeing Casey Ledford's name on the screen, Joanna walked out of Father Rowan's study to take the call.

For years the war on drugs had been the gift that kept on giving as far as high-tech budgetary items at the Cochise County Sheriff's Department were concerned. Before the well went dry, Joanna's department had been given a latent fingerprint setup that had lain fallow for months because she had no one trained to run it. Then Casey Ledford had come back home to Bisbee as a single mother with a relatively useless fine arts degree that offered few opportunities for supporting her daughter, Felicity. Joanna had been smart enough to hire her on the spot. In the years since, Casey's skill at drawing had made her a whiz at enhancing partial prints and uploading them into AFIS, the national Automated Fingerprint Identification System. Together Casey and Dave Hollicker made up Joanna's CSI unit.

"Hi," Casey said when Joanna came on the phone. "I just talked to Larry Kendrick and heard about Junior. I'll bet Moe and Daisy are wrecks."

That was one of the disadvantages about small-town law enforcement—everyone knew everyone else.

"They're taking it pretty hard," Joanna agreed.

"Sorry to be late to the party," Casey continued. "My dad had surgery at the VA hospital in Tucson early this morning, and I wanted to be there with my mom.

Dad came through the surgery with flying colors, and I'm just now coming back into town. Is there anything you need?"

Joanna thought about that and about what she had heard from Moe and Daisy.

"Do you happen to have your equipment with you?"

"Yup," Casey said. "You know what they say—never leave home without it. I've got everything I need in the trunk of my car. Why?"

"Moe and Daisy are still at St. Dom's with Father Rowan right now," Joanna answered. "Junior evidently left the house in the middle of the night by climbing out a window. That's where Terry and Spike picked up his trail. Do you know where their house is?"

"Sure," Casey answered. "The Maxwells live just up the hill from my folks."

"There's an element of animal abuse in all of this, something that seems out of character for Junior," Joanna said. "Daisy says that since he was scared of the dark, his leaving the house on his own to take a hike in the middle of the night seems off.

I'd like you to call Terry Gregovich and get a fix on which window Junior used to exit the house. Then I'd like you to go to the Maxwells' place and dust the windowsill, the screen, and whatever else you deem appropriate. I'm wondering if anyone else was involved in Junior's going AWOL."

"Got it," Casey said. "I'm on the far side of the Divide, but I'll get right on it."

As Joanna ended the call, Moe and Daisy emerged from the study with Marianne right behind them. Lost in their own world of hurt, the grieving couple walked past Joanna without even noticing her. Marianne stopped.

"They're on their way to the mortuary," she explained. "Father Rowan and I both offered to come along as backup, but they said they'd manage on their own. How are you doing?"

Joanna's phone rang again. This time Jenny's number appeared in the caller ID screen.

"It's not true, is it?" Jenny asked when her mother answered. She sounded close to tears.

"What's not true?"

"I just heard about Junior," Jenny said, "and I heard about that poor kitten, too. Someone said Junior is the one who hurt it, but I can't believe that, Mom. Junior wouldn't do something like that, would he?"

"How do you even know about all this?" Joanna asked. "Has word of what happened already spread to the school?"

"I'm not at school," Jenny corrected. "The teachers have an in-service meeting today. We got out early—at noon. Dad picked me up and took me to work so I could get in a few extra hours because we'll be gone this weekend. When I got here, Detective Carbajal's patrol car was parked outside, and Amy, the receptionist, told me what was going on."

One of the ways Joanna maintained her sanity was by trying to keep her work life and her home life completely separate. When she was at work, Butch kept the home fires burning. That meant he routinely handled most of the afterschool travel arrangements, including ferrying

Jenny to and from her part-time job at Dr. Ross's office.

At the time Joanna had sent the injured kitten there and dispatched Detective Carbajal to keep watch, it never occurred to her that Jenny would be there, too. And Jenny's remark about the weekend was a reminder that Joanna had somehow forgotten that the whole family was scheduled to trek over to Silver City, New Mexico, that weekend, leaving on Friday. The three-day excursion to a rodeo would include Jenny and Kiddo's participation in a barrel-racing competition.

"Well?" Jenny asked impatiently. "Would he?"

Brought back to the present, Joanna answered. "I don't know for sure one way or the other. Maybe he did; maybe he didn't. That's what we're looking into right now."

"Junior never seemed like that kind of person," Jenny objected. "Anybody who would do horrible stuff like that to a helpless animal has to be really sick."

"Yes," Joanna agreed. "Whoever did it

was sick, all right. The problem is, sometimes people you know—even people you think you know well—don't show their true colors in public. They present one face to the world while, underneath, they're somebody else entirely."

There was a brief silence after that. Finally Jenny said, "I still don't think Junior did it."

In that case, Joanna thought, **you and Daisy Maxwell are of one mind.**

CHAPTER 7

Liza Machett stood on the shoulder of the road, leaning against Candy Small's comforting bulk and staring at the clot of emergency vehicles blocking her mother's driveway. Beyond the vehicles was the still-smoldering heap of wreckage that had once been her mother's house. Liza's weeks of intensive labor, to say nothing of the thousands of dollars she had spent on cleanup and repair bills, had literally gone up in smoke. Firefighters were still on the scene, putting out hot spots, but Liza already knew the place was a total loss. Even the garage had caught fire and burned. All that remained standing was the newly installed garden shed.

While Liza watched, one of the vehicles in the drive, a bright red SUV, detached itself from the others, executed a U-turn, and then sped in their direction. It stopped next to where Liza and Candy stood. When the driver's door opened, Great Barrington's fire chief, Roland Blakely—ham and cheese omelet, cottage cheese, tomato slices, hold the toast—stepped out, doffing his hat to Liza.

"Someone told me you were here," he said. "Sorry about all this. It's a tough break. I know you've invested a whole lot of time and effort in this over the last few weeks. Unfortunately, both the house and garage were completely engulfed before the first units arrived on the scene. I knew you were at the funeral. Nobody else was in the house, were they? None of your coworkers?"

Liza shook her head. "They were all at the funeral," she answered. "Why do you ask?"

"Was anyone working here with equipment that might have caused a short or a spark or something like that? When you're dealing with a fire at a construction site, that's what we often find—that one of the workers screws up and does a faulty

installation or some new piece of equipment suffers a case of infant mortality."

"No," Liza replied. "As far as I know, no
one was working today, and I wasn't here,
either. I went straight from my apartment
to the funeral."

Chief Blakely nodded. "Let's say for
argument's sake that it turns out the fire
wasn't accidental."

"You're saying it might be arson?"

Blakely nodded. "Since both structures
burned, that's a possibility. Do you know
of anyone who bears a grudge against
either you or your mother? Maybe there
was a property dispute of some kind with
one of the neighbors?"

Liza shook her head. "No," she said,
"nothing like that, and I can't think of
anybody who would wish us ill."

That wasn't true, of course. Even as she
said the words, Liza was thinking about
the warning she'd been given just that
afternoon when Jonathan Thurgard had
spoken to her in the cemetery. Was this
what he had meant? Did the fire have
something to do with the people he had

mentioned, the ones her father had dealt with, the ones who didn't forgive or forget? Or—and this seemed far more likely—was it something to do with the money Selma had kept hidden away in the house? Liza had already suspected there had to be something wrong with the money. Otherwise, why would Selma have kept it hidden? Now whatever that was had come back to bite her in the butt—starting with burning down the house.

"Do you have home owner's insurance?" Blakely asked.

Liza nodded. She had renewed the policy only two weeks earlier. She'd had to wait until the cleanup was done and the remodel far enough along before an insurance underwriter could come through and assess the situation. He had checked on all the permits and had carefully inspected the new plumbing and electrical work.

"You'll need to call, report the loss, and get a claims adjuster out here," Chief Blakely said. "If you call my office in the morning, we can give you our file number as well as the one for the police report."

Since the policy had been reinstated so recently, Liza couldn't help but worry. What if the fire did turn out to be arson? Would the insurance company assume that Liza herself was behind it? Would they accuse her of burning down her own home in order to collect on the insurance? In that case, the insurance company might balk and refuse to pay the claim altogether.

Putting her roiling thoughts aside, Liza realized Chief Blakely was still talking. "Right now, the fire's still too hot and the structure too unstable for us to send anyone inside to look for the cause. I'm sure the sheriff's department will want to talk to you about this, and one of our fire inspectors will be reaching out to you as well. How should they get in touch?"

Liza reeled off her phone numbers—her cell and home numbers as well as the number at work.

"All right then," Blakely said when she finished. "Again, sorry about this, and sorry about your mother, too."

Liza nodded. "Thank you," she murmured.

Having been dismissed, Candy took hold of her arm and led her back to the car. "Come on," he said. "Let's get you home, unless you'd rather come back to the restaurant. I'm sure there are still people there."

Between the funeral and the fire, Liza was beyond crushed. Going back to the diner and having to break the bad news about the house to all the people who had invested so much time and effort in it was more than she could handle.

"Home would be better," she said. "What am I supposed to say to all the guys who helped me? How can I face them?"

"I'll tell them for you," Candy said grimly. "After all, you're not the one who burned the place down."

"Let's hope the insurance company believes that," Liza added.

Twilight was ending as Candy turned the corner onto Liza's tree-lined street. The neighborhood contained any number of older, larger homes, some of which had been converted into buildings with multiple-unit rentals. Liza was lucky in that her landlady, Olivia Dexter, a spinster who had inherited the family home, still occupied the two lower floors along with her two kitties and her extensive collection of hardback books. Olivia still had access to Liza's apartment from inside the house, but she had converted what had once been a fire escape into a separate entrance that allowed Liza to come and go from her attic apartment with as little disruption of Olivia's life as possible.

"You'll be all right, then?" Candy asked as he parked his Impala across the street from the house. "You don't want me to come up and stay with you for a while?"

"No," Liza said. "I'll be fine. Thanks for taking me out there. It would have been tough to do alone."

"You're welcome," he said.

She got out of the car and watched as he drove away. It was only after the car had turned the corner and disappeared from sight that she looked up at her apartment and noticed that the lights were on. That was odd. It had been almost noon when she left to go to the funeral home. Because she didn't have a separate meter on her apartment and because she knew Olivia was always struggling to make ends meet, Liza was conscientious about turning off the lights when she left for the day. As Selma Machett's daughter, she was incapable of doing anything else.

If the lights were on in her apartment and if someone had been inside, there was probably a simple explanation. Maybe there had been a problem at the house that day—a leak in the new flashing on the roof during the afternoon rainstorm or maybe a blocked pipe—that had resulted in Olivia's calling in a repairman of some kind. However, Liza was able to entertain that idea for only as long as it took her to walk up the driveway.

When she was even with the passenger door of her Nissan, she saw that the window had been broken. Even though the aging Nissan was unlocked, a brick had been thrown through the passenger-seat window. A layer of shattered glass covered the front seats. The paperwork from the glove box—her registration and insurance papers—was strewn on the floor. The mat on the floorboard, under which she kept a spare key to her apartment, had been lifted and pushed out of place. The spot where the key should have been was empty.

Shocked, Liza backed away from the car door without touching it while a wave of fear spread through her body. Someone had burned down her mother's house during the funeral. Now it looked as though someone had let themselves into Liza's apartment. For all she knew, they might have forced their way inside.

Liza studied the windows on the ground floor. Lights blazed throughout Olivia's portion of the house, too, but that didn't mean anything. Olivia spent most of her waking hours in a sitting room at the back of the house, reading or watching television. With her television set blaring, it was unlikely that she would have noticed the sound of breaking glass when the car window was smashed in the driveway out front.

Liza felt violated, so her first inclination was to charge up the stairs and order whoever had invaded her space to leave at once. After a moment, however, good sense prevailed. How many times had the unsuspecting heroine in a movie gone to the basement to check on something that wasn't quite right even though everyone in the audience was yelling, "Don't go in the basement"?

The women in the movies might not be smart enough to take the hint, but Liza was. She didn't climb the stairs, and she didn't step up on the front porch and ring Olivia's doorbell, either. Instead, on shaking knees, she backed all the way across the street and then sank down onto the curb with her silhouette hidden behind the shielding bulk of an out-of-control laurel hedge.

Her hands shook violently as she dug in her purse for her cell phone. Once she had the phone in hand, her trembling fingers were so clumsy that it was almost impossible to dial. Eventually, on the third try, she connected with the emergency operator.

"Nine one one. What are you reporting?"

"I just got home from a funeral," she said, whispering urgently into the phone. "Somebody broke into my car, and there are lights on in my apartment—lights I didn't leave on. There's a chance whoever did it may still be inside."

"What's your name, and what's the address?"

Struggling to speak normally, Liza gave the operator the required information.

"Where are you right now?" the operator asked.

"I'm across the street and out of sight. A friend just dropped me off."

"Stay right there," the operator cautioned. "I'm summoning units right now. If you see someone coming out of the house, do not engage them in any way. If they drive off in a vehicle, try to get the make, model, and license plate number, but that's it. Do not attempt to detain them, and do not try to follow them. Understand?"

"I understand," Liza repeated.

She didn't require much convincing.

First her mother's house had been torched, and now this. Liza was petrified—beyond petrified, especially with James Thurgard's stern warning still ringing in her ears, the warning about the people who never forgot and never forgave. Apparently, they were now after her.

The operator came back on the line. "Are you still there, Liza?"

"Yes, I'm here."

"Any sign of movement inside the house?"

Liza had been keeping an eye on the windows in her apartment. "None," she said. "I haven't seen anybody."

"Stay put," the operator advised. "Officers are on their way."

Even as she spoke, Liza heard the sound of an approaching siren. Only after the patrol car stopped in front of the driveway and an officer stepped out did Liza emerge from her hiding place and hurry to meet him.

"Hi, Liza," Bruce Schindler said at once. "How's it going? You think someone's broken into your place? Which one is it?"

Liza recognized Officer Schindler, too—corned beef hash, two poached eggs, whole wheat toast, coffee, tomato juice.

"Up there," she said pointing. "When I left there this morning, none of those lights were on."

"That's Mrs. Dexter's house, right?" he said. "I grew up in this neighborhood. Have you talked to her?"

"I was afraid to ring the bell. If whoever did it is still upstairs, I didn't want to let them know that I was home."

A second patrol car pulled up and stopped, and an officer named Michael Lundgren stepped out. He was someone who came into the restaurant occasionally. Liza recognized his face, but he wasn't enough of a regular that she could recite his standard order.

"Okay," Officer Schindler said. "You stay right here, Liza. Mikey and I will go check things out. Where's the entrance?"

Liza pointed. "There's an outside entrance on the far side of the house."

As she said the words, Liza realized that if someone had come sneaking down the stairs and gone out the back way, she might not have seen them, even though she had been sitting right there. The house itself would have shielded them from view.

"Any other doors in or out?"

"There's another stairway inside the house, just to the right of the front door. The door at the top of that, the one that leads into my apartment, is usually left unlocked so Olivia or workmen can get inside as needed."

"All right then," Officer Lundgren said. "Let's go catch ourselves some bad guys. I'll go up the outside stairs; Bruce, you keep an eye on that front door."

The two of them set out at a trot while Liza melted back into the darkness to watch. Officer Lundgren made for the outside stairway. Bruce Schindler stationed himself just outside the front door in a spot where he'd be able to see into the vestibule through the sidelights. Behind her Liza heard doors opening and closing as curious neighbors up and down the street came out on their porches to see what was going on.

Eventually a shadow darted across one of the lit windows in her apartment. Sometime after that, Olivia's front door opened and Lundgren stepped out onto the porch. For several long moments the two cops conferred, then they both disappeared into the house. Again they were gone for some time before reappearing on the front porch. As they came down the walkway toward her, Liza stepped back into view.

"Did you find anyone?" she asked.

Bruce Schindler nodded grimly. "Someone had been there, all right, but by the time we arrived he was long gone. When's the last time you saw Olivia Dexter?" he asked.

"This morning," Liza said. "She was working out in her garden when I was waiting for the mortuary limo to show up. She came over and apologized to me for not coming to the funeral. She has a phobia about funerals."

"She won't have to worry about that anymore," Officer Lundgren observed.

"Why?" Liza asked. "What do you mean?"

"Because she's dead," he said. "Strangled, most likely. I found her at the top of the inside stairway leading to your apartment. She was right outside the door. She may have heard someone moving around up there and gone to investigate."

"She's dead?" Liza repeated numbly. "You're sure? I can't believe it. Someone murdered Olivia?"

As the world spun around her, Liza stumbled forward and leaned against the front fender of the nearest patrol car. Her legs gave way. If Bruce hadn't moved quickly enough to catch her, she would have fallen. He opened the door and eased her into the backseat of the patrol car, where Liza sat with her teeth chattering and with her breath coming in short hard gasps.

"Mike's calling for the homicide unit," Bruce said. "Are you going to be all right? Should I call an ambulance?"

"No," Liza managed at last. "Just let me sit here for a few minutes. I'll be okay."

CHAPTER 8

It was three o'clock in the afternoon before Joanna finally made it back to the Cochise County Justice Center. As she pulled into the parking lot, the presence of several media vans gave notice that her chief deputy, Tom Hadlock, was holding a press briefing.

Tom had once served as Joanna's jail commander. When her former chief deputy, Frank Montoya, had been hired away to become chief of police in Sierra Vista, Joanna had tapped Tom to be her new chief deputy. What she hadn't understood at the time was that although Tom was fine in one-on-one interactions, he was painfully shy when it came to any kind of public speaking. Since Joanna's chief deputy also functioned as her media relations officer, that had been a problem.

However, a year's worth of Toastmasters training meant Tom was now in far better shape to field any and all media questions concerning Junior Dowdle's death.

Joanna herself was happy to avoid the press by driving around back, parking in her reserved shaded spot, and ducking into the building through the private door that led directly into her office.

Kristin Gregovich, Joanna's secretary, had placed the day's worth of correspondence in several neat stacks on Joanna's desk, organized in order of relative importance and urgency, with the topmost layer being the most critical. Joanna had spent most of the day riding herd on the Dowdle investigation. Now she had only a couple of hours in which to handle that day's mundane paperwork so she could leave things in good shape for Tom over the weekend. She felt guilty about leaving him with such a full plate. When she and Butch had made plans to be out of town for three days, it hadn't occurred to her that Tom would be in charge of an active investigation that might or might not turn out to be a homicide.

Joanna had barely started when Kristin poked her head in the door. "I thought I heard you come in," she said. "Detective Howell is on the phone."

Joanna picked up the handset. "Hey, Deb," she said. "Any luck?"

"We had some luck, all right," Deb Howell said, "all of it bad. Terry and Spike led Dave Hollicker and me all the way back to the Maxwells' place, following the same trail Junior took. We found nothing at all along the way—no blood, no cigarette butts, and no footprints, either. At the last minute when we were almost back at the house, Dave slipped on some loose gravel and took a tumble. He's either broken his ankle or sprained it. He's on his way to the hospital to have it x-rayed. Terry's driving. I've arranged for someone to come collect Dave's car and take it back down to the motor pool."

"Good thinking," Joanna said, trying not to sound as exasperated as she felt. It was bad enough that she was going out of town and leaving Tom Hadlock in charge of the Dowdle investigation. Now, with one member of her two-person CSI unit on the disabled list, he would be working with one hand tied behind his back. As for Dave's injured ankle? That meant her department was looking at a workman's comp claim that would most likely generate mountains of paperwork.

"What about Casey?" Joanna asked. "Did she have a chance to dust for prints?"

"She did, and she found some, both inside and outside Junior's room. When Dr. Machett finishes with the autopsy, we'll have Junior's prints. Casey will need to get elimination prints from both Daisy and Moe."

"Be sure she collects a set of prints from Jason Radner, too," Joanna suggested. "According to Moe, he sometimes palled around with Junior."

"Will do. That should be easy enough since all three Radners are due at the department any minute."

"They're coming here?" Joanna asked.

"For all I know, they're already there,"

Deb replied. "I believe Ernie is. Matt Keller told Ernie that when he was interviewing the Maxwells' neighbors first thing this morning, he got the feeling there was something slightly off about Jason, as though he knew more than he was saying. At the time Matt talked to him, it was early in the day, and he didn't know Junior was dead. Ernie went ahead and scheduled an additional interview. I'm coming, too, and I'm only minutes away."

"Are the Radners coming armed with an attorney?" Joanna asked.

"I can't speak to that," Deb replied, "but I wouldn't be surprised if they do. If a cop working a homicide invited my son to drop by for a little heart-to-heart, I'd see to it that an attorney was present, just to be on the safe side."

Joanna thought about Jenny. "I would, too."

"One more thing," Deb said. "What's going on with the autopsy?"

"Dr. Machett has a conflict," Joanna answered. "He's out of town today and tomorrow, too. He says the autopsy can't be done until sometime Saturday, but he didn't specify an exact time."

"We're pulling out all the stops to work this case," Deb muttered. "Wouldn't it be nice if Guy Machett had the same sense of urgency?"

"Yes," Joanna said. "It would indeed."

Once she was off the phone, Joanna headed for the interview room. The OCCUPIED sign had already been turned over. Rather than going inside and interrupting the process, Joanna went into an adjacent room and turned on the audio/video feed. Jack and Lois Radner sat perched nervously on two of the molded plastic chairs that surrounded a small Formica table while their son slumped dispiritedly in the far corner. Next to him and on full alert was Burton Kimball, Bisbee's leading criminal defense attorney. Ernie Carpenter, notebook open in front of him, sat diagonally across the table from Jason.

"You'd say that you and Junior were friends?" he asked.

"Sure," Jason answered. "We played

checkers and sometimes dominoes."

"When's the last time you saw him?" Ernie asked.

"Yesterday," Jason replied with a shrug. "Yeah, last night when I took our garbage can out to the street. He was sitting on his porch."

"Did you say anything to him? Exchange words?"

"Just, 'Hey,' I guess. We didn't really talk. It was time for dinner. I had to get back inside."

"Have you noticed any changes in Junior's behavior recently?" Ernie asked.

"Look," Jason replied. "I knew he was sick, with that old-timer's disease."

"You mean Alzheimer's?"

"Yeah, that's the one. So he had been a little different lately, but nothing really bad. Sometimes he would get sort of upset."

"Like when he threw the checkers at you?" Ernie asked.

Jason shot a quick look in the detective's direction, as though surprised that Ernie already knew about the thrown checkerboard.

"Yeah," he said. "Like that."

"Did Junior have any other friends besides you?" Ernie asked.

"I don't know," Jason said. "Maybe. I mean he knew people from his mom's restaurant. They're all sort of friends of his, right?"

"But no other close friends?"

"No," Jason said, "not that I know of."

That was the moment when Joanna saw what Matt Keller had seen. Jason Radner was lying about something. Ernie must have seen it, too.

The door to the viewing room opened behind Joanna. Deb Howell stepped inside and sat down. "How's it going?" she asked.

Joanna put her finger to her lips.

"You never saw him hanging out with anyone else from the neighborhood?" Ernie continued. "It sounds like you were his only friend."

"I guess," Jason conceded.

"Were you ever inside Junior's room?" Ernie asked.

"Sure," Jason said, "lots of times. We

went there to play with his Xbox."

"In that case, before you go home, we'll need a set of prints from you."

Jason's father, Jack, rose to his feet. "Fingerprints!" he roared. "You want to fingerprint my boy? Are you accusing him of murdering Junior? You told me we were coming in here for a routine interview, and now you want to take his prints?"

Burton Kimball held up a calming hand, and Jack Radner subsided back into his chair. "Is that really necessary, Detective Carpenter?"

"Yes, it is," Ernie answered. "Casey Ledford, our latent fingerprint tech, just finished dusting Junior's room. That means we'll need elimination prints from anyone who has been inside his room. That's the only way we'll be able to sort known visitors from unknown ones. We'll be taking Moe's and Daisy's prints as well."

"Asking for elimination prints isn't the same as making an accusation, Jack," Kimball assured Jason's parents. "It's standard procedure."

"Let's go back to last night for a moment," Ernie continued, turning back to Jason. "I understand your bedroom is directly opposite Junior's on the far side of a narrow passageway that runs between your house and his. Is that correct?"

Jason nodded.

"Is your bedroom window usually open or closed?"

"It was open last night," Jason volunteered. "It was hot. The window was open and the fan was on, so I wouldn't have heard anyone talking."

"Are you saying there were people talking?" Ernie asked.

"No," Jason said a bit too forcefully. "I said if there had been people talking, I wouldn't have been able to hear them."

"Look at his face," Deb observed. "He's lying about that or he's lying about something else. Maybe there were people outside, and he heard them. That might mean we have a witness who doesn't want to talk."

Joanna nodded. "Sounds like a possibility," she said.

"What time did you go to sleep?" Ernie asked.

Jason shrugged. "I don't know exactly. Sometime after Mom and Dad went to bed."

"We usually go to bed once the news is over," Lois Radner said, speaking for the first time. "So right around ten thirty or so."

"I'm assuming you and Mr. Radner didn't hear anything, either?" Ernie inquired.

"No, we didn't. Jason has a fan in his room, and we have one in ours. They're noisy, but they work. We have an AC unit up on the roof, but it's so expensive to operate that we don't use it unless we absolutely have to."

"You didn't participate in the search this morning?" Ernie asked.

"No, we commute together to Fort Huachuca," Jack said. "We both work on post and have to leave the house by seven."

"What happened to Junior?" Jason asked.

In Joanna's experience, guilty parties didn't have to ask about what happened to a homicide victim because they already knew. Jason Radner was lying about something, but the fact that he'd asked the question was a mark in his favor. On the other hand, there was a chance that Jason might be smarter than they thought.

"He fell," Ernie answered. "Fell far enough and hard enough that he died."

Jason swallowed hard and blinked as though trying to stem some tears. "I'm sorry," he mumbled. "I mean, I'm sorry for him and for Mr. and Mrs. Maxwell, too."

If Ernie read anything into Jason's sudden apology, he didn't let on. "Let me ask you this," Ernie said. "What was Junior like when it came to animals?"

"What do you mean?"

"I mean, did you ever see him doing anything inappropriate as far as animals are concerned?"

"You mean like messing with them or hurting them or something?"

"Exactly," Ernie said.

Jason shook his head, but he looked decidedly uncomfortable.

"See there?" Deb whispered excitedly.

"He does know something."

That was Joanna's take, too.

"So you never saw him mistreating animals?"

"No," Jason said quickly. "I never saw anything like that."

The defense attorney suddenly seemed to have seen and heard enough. Burton Kimball held up his hand. "I think that's about it, Detective Carpenter. If you have no intention of holding my client, I believe we'll be on our way."

"Of course," Ernie said agreeably. "But do remember to stop by the front desk on your way out. I still need those prints."

The Radners rose to leave. Ernie waited until they left the room before shutting off the recorder and joining Joanna and Detective Howell in the adjacent room.

"The kid is hiding something," Ernie said. "And we need to figure out a way to get him to tell us what it is."

When Joanna returned to her office, Detective Jaime Carbajal was in the lobby just outside her door. Seated on a chair near Kristin's desk, he was leaning back with his eyes closed and his head resting against the wall. He wasn't asleep, however, because he got to his feet as soon as Joanna walked by and followed her into his office.

"Sometimes I hate people," he said quietly.

"The vet's office was that bad?" she asked.

"It was bad."

"Is the kitten going to make it?"

"Dr. Ross thinks so. She has a couple of broken ribs along with everything else. The doc used Super Glue to try to put the poor thing's ears back together. If it doesn't take, the ears may have to be amputated. By the way, did you know that's why they invented Super Glue—to use in surgical procedures?"

"I had no idea," Joanna said, "but here's what I want to know—did Dr. Ross find anything we can use?"

"Maybe," Jaime said. "There were blood-stains all over the poor thing, but some of them look more promising than others because they don't appear to be connected to any of the existing wounds. Dr. Ross collected dozens of samples. I already handed the samples over to the evidence clerk and asked him to put them in the fridge. You want me to take them to the crime lab in Tucson in the morning?"

"Yes, please."

"You don't think Junior is responsible for what happened to the cat, do you?" Jaime asked.

"No, I don't," Joanna said, "and I'm beginning to think he didn't kill himself, either, accidentally or otherwise." She paused and then asked, "What kind of people start their journey to the dark side by torturing animals?"

"Serial killers," Jaime answered at once.

"Right."

"So maybe Junior was a serial-killer wannabe?"

"No," Joanna said. "I don't think so. For one thing, that kitten is tough. She didn't go down without a fight. I took the crime scene photos. There weren't any bite marks or scratches on Junior's arms and hands. In addition, Moe and Daisy claim

Junior was scared of the dark, and he was especially scared of caves. I believe someone enticed him out of the house and into the cave. Think about it. What if the killer convinced Junior that the kitten was in trouble and needed his help? He would have gone there in an instant, middle of the night or not, no questions asked."

Even as she said the words, Joanna knew she was right, as a lightbulb switched on inside her brain. The injured kitten may not have been Junior's victim, but she could still be the reason he was dead.

"DNA testing on that much material is going to cost money," Jaime observed.

Joanna looked at him and nodded. "Yes, it is," she said, "and we're going to pay the piper, whatever the price may turn out to be. I believe we've got a budding serial killer on our hands, and I'm hoping Junior Dowdle was the first victim. We'll do whatever it takes to keep from having a second."

Jaime walked as far as the doorway, then he stopped and turned back. "By the way," he said. "I almost forgot. Dr. Ross makes sure that every animal that comes into her office gets chipped, whether the owners can afford it or not."

"Does our kitten have a chip?"

Jaime nodded. "Sure does. Her name's Star. She belonged to a family named Jalisco. They live in one of the apartment buildings up by the old high school."

"Belonged?" Joanna asked. "As in past tense?"

"Dr. Ross's secretary called to let them know Star had been injured and was undergoing treatment. The mother, Rose-anne, is a clerk out at Safeway. She's also newly divorced. She said she already told her daughter that Star ran away and probably got run over. Roseanne says that at the time the kitten disappeared, she was wearing a pink ribbon and no tag. She also said that whatever the vet bill is, she can't afford it. Her suggestion was that Dr. Ross go ahead and put Star down."

"That's not going to happen," Joanna declared.

"No, it's not," Jaime agreed. "I told Dr. Ross that if nobody else will take Star, Delcia and I will, and that whatever the bill is, we're good for that, too."

"You don't have to do that," Joanna said. "That cat is evidence. The department will pay for her care."

"All right then," Jaime said, "but there's one more thing I should mention."

"What's that?"

"The next time you have a case like this, it's Ernie's turn to go to the vet's office."

"Fair enough," Joanna replied. "Are you going to interview Roseanne Jalisco directly?"

Jaime nodded. "Her kids are out of school this afternoon and tomorrow, too. I thought I'd track her down at work tomorrow, rather than questioning her at home in front of the little ones. She told Dr. Ross's receptionist that Star has been missing for about three days. Dr. Ross estimates that's how old some of the wounds are."

"Whoever did it is going to jail," Joanna declared forcefully.

"I know," Jaime replied with a grim nod. "That's what I told Star, too."

With that, Detective Carbajal walked out of Joanna's office. Watching him go, Sheriff Joanna Brady couldn't help but smile. On the surface Jaime was a big, tough guy. What Joanna had learned about him was that under that gruff, scary exterior lurked a real softie. Joanna liked him all the better for knowing that.

It was almost nine o'clock that night before she finished doing what needed to be done. She had written up an official report about the crime scene and printed out the collection of photos she had taken down in the mine shaft. She had pulled Tom Hadlock in and briefed him on everything that was going on. She had spoken to Dave Hollicker and confirmed that his ankle was badly sprained, but that he'd be in to work on crutches as long as someone would agree to drive him. She also had managed to reach Guy Machett, had a firm schedule for the Dowdle autopsy, and had notified Deb, the lead detective, of same. Joanna ended her long day by knocking off the remainder of her paperwork. Only when her desk was clear did she gather up her purse, turn off the lights, and head out the door.

Dennis was in bed and Jenny incommunicado in her room by the time Joanna got home. She reheated the plate of green chili casserole Butch had left for her in the fridge, slathered on some sour cream, and then went looking for him, taking her plate of food along with her. She found her husband in his office, hunched over his computer, working on his third book. He looked up at her when she came in and then glanced at his watch. "Another fifteen-hour day," he observed. "How are you doing?"

"Better than Moe and Daisy Maxwell," she said.

"Do you want to talk about it?" Butch asked.

Joanna had touched base with Butch earlier in the evening and briefed him on some of it, but after living the case all day, she was done. "Not really," she said. "What time do we need to leave in the morning?"

Butch seemed genuinely surprised. "You still want to go?"

A couple of years earlier, Joanna might have used the Dowdle investigation as an excuse for canceling the Silver City excursion, but she was older now, and, she hoped, a little wiser, too. Life had taught her a few lessons. For one, she now understood that her father wasn't nearly as perfect as she'd always thought him to be. Sheriff D. H. Lathrop had often used involvement in the job as a way to dodge his responsibilities as a husband and father. Joanna was determined that she wouldn't make the same mistake.

"Homicide investigation or no," she said, "I promised Jenny I was going, and I will. What time do we leave?"

Butch grinned at her. "Wonders will never cease," he said. "Let's say wheels up at ten. It's a four-hour drive, hauling that trailer, and I'd like to be there before everybody else gets off work. We can caravan over. Jenny and I will be in the truck pulling the horses; you and Denny can follow in my car. Jenny, Desi, and the horses will stay at Katy Beltran's place outside of town. There's a dance tomorrow night and Jenny and Katy plan on going to that together. You, Denny, and I have hotel reservations in town. The three of us will go someplace nice for dinner both nights."

Katy was someone Jenny had met on the rodeo circuit. The girls had become friends as well as friendly competitors. If the horses had been boarded at the rodeo grounds, Jenny would have had to stay there, too, sleeping in the camper shell on the truck. As far as Joanna was concerned, having everybody stay at the Beltrans' ranch was far preferable, as was having Jenny go to an out-of-town rodeo dance with a girlfriend rather than alone.

"You've got it all planned out, don't you," Joanna said.

Butch nodded and grinned. "I do my best," he said.

CHAPTER 9

Liza Machett stole a glance at her watch and rubbed her eyes. It was after midnight. She was alone in an interview room at the Great Barrington Police Department, where she had spent the better part of the last five hours. Some of the time she had been left alone, waiting, but most of the time Detective Amos Franklin, a homicide cop, had been with her, asking questions.

He had assured her that this was just a routine interview and that he was trying to get a handle on everything that had happened, but Liza wasn't convinced. He hadn't read her her rights, so she assumed that meant that she hadn't been declared a suspect, at least not so far. She also hadn't asked for an attorney, although she was beginning to wonder if she should have.

The door opened. Franklin came back into the room, carrying a cup of foul-smelling coffee—brackish, ugly stuff that had been at the bottom of a coffeepot and should have been thrown out hours ago.

Liza didn't want coffee. She wanted to go to bed, but she didn't know where. Her apartment was an active crime scene. Her landlady's home was an active crime scene. And whatever was left of her mother's house, the one she had labored so hard to make livable, was also an active crime scene. She didn't want to answer any more questions; she wanted to quit for the night—to tell the detective that she'd come back and tackle all this tomorrow. The problem was, she worried how Detective Franklin might interpret that. Would her pleading to be let out of the interview room cause him to assume she was a guilty party rather than an innocent one?

"Okay," Franklin said, resuming the chair opposite her that he had abandoned fifteen minutes earlier. "I know this has been a terribly difficult day for you, Ms. Machett, and I won't keep you much longer. Let's just go over a couple of things again to make sure I have it all down."

He made a show of opening a notebook and spreading it out in front of him. Then he took out a pen and sat with it poised over a perfectly clean page. Liza knew that was all for appearance's sake. She had already spotted the video camera in the far corner of the room, up near the ceiling. Each time the interview was interrupted or resumed, Detective Franklin made a production of turning his high-tech equipment off and on.

"What things?" Liza asked.

"We've already verified your alibi any number of times. You were at the funeral with at least forty people when the fire broke out at your mother's place. We don't have an official time of death on Ms. Dexter just yet, but unofficially it looks like you were either still at the reception or else at the arson scene when her homicide took place. The location of her body would suggest that she overheard something happening in your apartment and was murdered when she went to investigate. Although she was the homicide victim, her part of the house hadn't been disturbed in any way. Your apartment, on the other hand, was ransacked. Your car was broken into. That leads me to think that you're the real target here, and yet you sit here claiming to have no enemies and no idea why someone might have it in for you?"

"That's right," Liza said. "I don't."

"What about your brother—your half brother?"

"Guy? What about him? What does he have to do with this?"

"I was just on the phone to the attorney who's handling your mother's estate. He tells me that, according to the terms of Selma Machett's will, her home—or whatever is left of it—goes to you and you alone. Even though the property was originally owned by your father's family—Guy's father's family—your brother isn't named as a beneficiary under your mother's will."

That wasn't exactly news to Liza. Selma and Guy had been estranged for years. Liza said nothing.

"As to your mother's house—the house you've spent a small fortune on rehabbing during the last few weeks—it's been burned to the ground," Franklin continued. "Maybe your brother took exception to the will. It wouldn't be the first time a disgruntled heir who was written out of a will decided to go after the person who made out like a bandit."

"My brother wouldn't do this," Liza said. "Guy has his own life. He wrote us off a long time ago."

"He didn't come to the funeral?"

"He didn't have to. He was my mother's stepson."

"Where does he live these days?"

"In Bisbee, Arizona. I understand he's the M.E. there."

"Anyone else that you're aware of who might have a murderous grudge against you or your mother or Olivia Dexter? When stuff like this happens, there's usually a reason. I'd like to know if you have any idea about that—not only who but why."

Sitting alone in the little interview room while Franklin went to get his evil-smelling cup of coffee, Liza had concluded that this had to be about the money. Maybe the money belonged to the people Jonathan Thurgard had warned her about. Somehow they had determined that Liza had the cash, and now they wanted it back. That must have been what they were searching for in her apartment, and they had murdered Olivia when she interrupted them, all of which made Liza glad that she'd been smart enough not to store the money in her apartment.

The sensible thing would have been for Liza to come clean right then and tell Detective Franklin the whole story, but she didn't. She had grown up under Selma Machett's thumb and lived by her rules for too many years. Some of Selma's paranoid rants about the world being full of crooked cops had rubbed off on her daughter.

Liza had worked in the diner for almost a third of her life. When a jerk of a customer came in and hassled the waitresses, they always served him the worst possible coffee and then made fun of him behind his back when he wasn't smart enough to send the bad coffee back. As Detective Franklin sat there, drinking his cup of swill, Liza Machett made up her mind. Anyone so dim as to drink that appalling excuse for coffee didn't deserve to be trusted, not with Liza's money and certainly not with her life. As a consequence, the answer she gave him now was the same one she had given him hours earlier.

"I have no idea," she said.

"If you'll pardon my saying so, you're a very attractive young woman," he said, favoring her with a sly look. "Is it possible you have a disappointed boyfriend lurking in the background?"

Liza's difficult childhood and worse adolescence had left her in a social vacuum. She could handle the easy banter that was tossed back and forth in the restaurant, but she had trust deficits that made romantic entanglements pro-hibitive. At twenty-nine, she didn't like to think of herself as an old maid, but she suspected she was well on her way to that outcome.

"No boyfriends of any kind," she said.

"Girlfriends then?" Franklin persisted. She caught the small smirk at the corners of his lips and understood what it meant. If Liza didn't have boyfriends, he automatically assumed she was a lesbian.

"None of those, either," she told him.

"If you can't say who or why, how about what?" Franklin said. "They went through both your car and apartment in a way that indicates they were looking for something specific. Maybe they found it; maybe they didn't. We won't know for sure until you can get back inside to take an inventory of what's missing. What occurs to me is that often when we encounter these kinds of unexplained break-ins, there may be some other agenda involved, like illicit drugs, for example, or the presence of drug-making paraphernalia. Is that a possibility here, Ms. Machett? Are you involved in the drug trade, or is it possible someone mistakenly believes you to be?"

Liza's hackles came up. "I'm not involved with drugs. I don't use them; I don't sell them; I don't manufacture them. I'm a law-abiding citizen without so much as a speeding ticket on my record. I didn't burn down my house. I didn't murder Olivia Dexter. I didn't ransack my own apartment, so I'd like you to start treating me like a victim instead of a criminal. Now, if you're not going to arrest me, I'm going to leave."

She stood up, expecting Franklin to object and order her back in her chair. Instead, he didn't move. "Where exactly are you going?" he asked. "You won't be able to go home, at least not tonight, and probably not tomorrow, either."

"I'll figure it out."

"Would you like me to give you a lift?"

"No, thank you," she said. "Wherever I'm going, I'll get there on my own."

A telephone hung on the wall. Franklin reached over, lifted the receiver, and pressed in a code. After a moment, the lock on the door buzzed and the door itself swung open. Without another word, Liza stepped out into the hallway.

"Stay in touch," Detective Franklin called after her.

She walked away from him without looking back. Halfway down the hall, she realized she'd made a mistake. She was still dressed in the clothing she'd worn to the funeral, including a pair of heels— low heels, but heels nonetheless. It was the middle of the night, she had no idea where she was going, she had no car, and her feet were killing her.

Out in the lobby, she was astonished to see the familiar figure of Candy Small, slumped and dozing in a chair next to the door.

"What are you doing here?" she asked.

"Bruce Schindler called and told me what had happened. I came right down. Are you all right?" He glanced as his watch. "What the hell have you been doing in there all this time?"

"Being interviewed by Detective Franklin. I'm supposedly the victim here, but if you ask me, he's treating me more like a suspect."

Candy shook his head. "Amos Franklin

was a jerk when we were in fifth grade. Nothing has changed. Come on."

"Where are we going?"

"Since your place is tagged as a crime scene, I guess you're coming home with me," Candy answered.

"I could always stay at the Holiday Inn," Liza suggested. It was only a halfhearted objection because she was too exhausted to make more of a fuss.

"No," Candy said. "You're staying in my spare room. You'll need some different clothing and shoes and whatever else, but we can get those later today after the stores open up. Right now I'm taking you home. No arguments."

His car was parked right outside in what, during the day, was a loading zone. Candy's collection of waitresses swore he was the model for the Norwegian bachelor farmers that peopled Lake Wobegon on NPR's **Prairie Home Companion**. Liza understood at once that he wasn't making a pass at her; this was an offer of a safe place to spend the night, no strings attached.

"Thank you," she murmured as he helped her into his car, a two-year-old Impala.

"You're welcome."

Candy climbed into the driver's seat and started the engine. "Is this about the money?" he asked. "Is that what the bad guys were looking for in your apartment?"

She had told Candy about finding the money. He was, in fact, the only person she had told. It had come up in conversation when she had been trying to figure out how to organize repairing her mother's house. At Candy's suggestion, she had used one of the empty employee lockers off the restaurant's kitchen to store the bulk of her cash. Since the place was open round the clock, that had seemed like a wise idea. Now she hoped that whoever had broken into her apartment hadn't done the same thing at the restaurant.

"I think so," she said.

"Did you tell Amos about the money?"

"No, I was afraid he'd figure out some way to confiscate whatever I have left.

He's already as good as accused me of committing fraud, suggesting that I burned down my own place just to collect the insurance money. Since I was at the funeral and couldn't possibly have started the fire, he must think I hired someone to do it."

"Why would you fix up the house and then burn it down?" Candy asked. "That makes no sense."

"Not to me, either," Liza said miserably.

They turned into the driveway of Candy's 1950s-era bungalow and pulled inside a surprisingly spacious two-car garage, with a door that closed behind them. The house was only a few blocks from the restaurant. When the weather was decent, Candy often walked back and forth to work. When the door finished closing, he came around to help Liza out of the passenger seat.

"Somebody I didn't know came to the funeral today," Liza said as they headed into the house. "His name is Jonathan Thurgard. He claimed that he knew my dad and he said something about watching out for people who never forgive and never forget. It sounded like he was trying to warn me about something or somebody."

"What did he say exactly?" Candy asked.

"That he had known my dad back in the old days when they both drove bread trucks."

Candy stopped in his tracks just inside the kitchen. "Your dad drove a bread truck?" he echoed.

"Evidently," Liza said.

"Holy crap! Why didn't I know about this before?" Candy demanded. "Why didn't you tell me?"

He sounded either surprisingly angry or surprisingly scared; Liza couldn't tell which.

"How could I tell you something I didn't know myself until this afternoon?"

"Come on," he said. "We've gotta go." Grabbing Liza's upper arm in a surprisingly painful grip, he spun her around and propelled her back into the garage and toward the car.

"Ouch," she whimpered. "That hurt. Let

go of me."

"I meant it to hurt," he said.

"Why?" she demanded, more angry now than scared. "What do you think you're doing?"

"I gave you a set of bruises because you're going to need them. They're your ticket to ride."

"What on earth are you talking about?"

When they reached the car, instead of opening the front passenger door, he opened the rear one and shoved Liza inside.

"Lie down on the seat so no one can see you," he ordered, "and don't move."

"I'm not lying down until you tell me what's going on and where we're going."

"Don't you watch the news?" Candy demanded. "Haven't you been following that big racketeering trial going on in Boston?"

"Hello," Liza said. "Are you kidding? In case you haven't noticed, my mother just died. Between her being in the hospital and me rehabbing her house, I haven't exactly been sitting around eating bonbons and watching the evening news. I know there's been a big trial—some kind of old mobster guy—but I haven't been paying attention."

"It's not just some old mobster," Candy replied. "The mobster happens to be Johnny 'Half-Moon' Miller. His older brother, James, aka 'Big Jim' Miller was a stone-cold killer if ever there was one. Ditto for Half-Moon."

"But what does any of this have to do with me?"

"It has everything to do with you, because if the Millers are after you, sweetheart, you are in deep trouble."

"You're scaring me."

"And it's a good thing, too. Now give me your cell phone."

"Why? Don't you have yours?"

He stood there with his hand out-stretched, not taking no for an answer. Finally, she dug her phone out of her purse and handed it over. He immediately turned it off and removed the battery.

"Hey," she objected. "What are you doing? I need that."

In response, he stuffed the now-dead phone into his shirt pocket. "No, you don't," he replied. "Now, are you going to lie down or not?"

"Do I have a choice?"

"Not if you want to live," he said grimly. "If somebody's watching my house, it's close enough to time for me to go to work that they won't think twice about my leaving for the restaurant at this hour."

"What about me?"

"As far as they're concerned, they'll t hink you're still here, which is exactly what we want."

With no further objections, Liza did as she was told and lay down in the backseat. Slamming the back door, Candy hustled around to the front seat. Once in the driver's seat, he opened the garage door, turned the key in the ignition, and then shifted into reverse. After waiting long enough for the garage door to close again, he tore out of his driveway and rocketed forward with the tires screeching on the pavement.

"So that's where we're going?" Liza

asked. "The restaurant?"

"That's right. First we're going to collect your money, then we're going to see a friend of mine and figure out a way to get you the hell out of town."

"How come? What's wrong?"

"The Millers spent decades ruling the roost as far as the Massachusetts drug trade was concerned. In the seventies and eighties they were able to operate practically out in the open, because they paid off everybody who needed to be paid off."

"I still don't understand."

"That's because you're not paying attention," Candy said irritably. "How do you suppose the Millers transported their drugs out to their various suppliers and brought the money back to Boston? How did they deliver the bribes that made it possible for them to stay in business? I'll tell you how. They bought themselves a bakery, a working bakery, but the guys who drove bread trucks for them delivered a hell of a lot more than bread, and once Big Jim was gone, Half-

Moon ran the business on his own."

"You're saying my dad was mixed up in all that?"

"Don't be naive," Candy admonished. "Of course he was mixed up in it. He took off, didn't he?"

"Yes, he did," Liza conceded, "when I was just a baby. He ran off with another woman—a blonde."

"I'm willing to bet that your father didn't take off with any blonde," Candy declared. "More likely, he took off with some of Big Jim's money, and now some of Half-Moon's associates are coming after you to get it back."

"You think they're watching us right now?" Liza asked.

"They'd be stupid not to. They'll have someone watching the house and someone watching me."

He pulled into what Liza guessed was his customary parking place behind the restaurant. Instead of getting out, however, he picked up Liza's cell phone. Without turning it on, he held it to his ear, pretending to be talking on it when he was really talking to Liza. Realizing Candy was that sure they had been followed from his house, Liza felt a shiver of real fear pass through her body.

"What happens next?"

"They used bread trucks, so we'll use a bread truck, too," Candy said. "I'll pull up next to the loading dock. Andrew McConnell should be here with the bread delivery in forty-five minutes. I'll get your money out of the locker. Once Andrew shows up, I'll give it to him. Then I'll create a diversion. When that happens, get out of the car, climb into the back of Andrew's truck, and stay there. He'll know where to drop you off. All you have to do is follow instructions. Got it?"

"It sounds like you and Andrew have done this before," Liza observed quietly.

"Yup," Candy said. "Many times. You ever hear of the Underground Railroad?"

"Sure," Liza said, "but that was back in the old days, during the Civil War, when they were smuggling slaves out of the South."

"That was Underground Railroad 1.0,"

Candy replied with a chuckle. "Welcome aboard 2.0. From now on, this is the story: you're on the run from your bad-guy husband—the one who put those ugly bruises on your arm. I'm putting you in the care of some good folks who would be a lot less likely to help if they knew that the people who are after you are some of Half-Moon Miller's old pals."

"That's how this works? I claim to be a victim of domestic violence?"

"That's right. Make up a good story and stick to it like glue. Whatever you do, don't get back in touch with me. Since you were with me earlier tonight, they'll probably be watching me, too, same as they are right now. Got it?"

"Got it," Liza replied, "but where do I go?"

"You must have someone. What about your brother? Where's he?"

"In Arizona."

"Go there, then," Candy advised. "As I recall, your brother was always a real smart guy. Have Guy help you figure out how to deal with this mess. Good luck, and for Pete's sake, keep your head down."

Pocketing her phone, Candy got out of the car and slammed the door behind him. For the next hour Liza stayed where she was, not daring to move and hardly daring to breathe. She heard the bread truck pull up beside her and then she waited some more, wondering what the diversion would be.

When it came, there was no mistaking it. Sirens sounded and lights flashed as a fire truck pulled up behind the Impala. Doors slammed open and shut as another emergency vehicle arrived on the scene. With amber and red lights pulsing behind her, Liza cautiously pushed open the door and scrambled outside. The bread truck was parked right next to her, and the driver's door was wide open. Holding her breath, she clambered into the vehicle, made her way into the back, and sank down onto the floor.

For a long time after that, nothing happened. Much later she heard the grumble of engines as the emergency vehicles departed. Soon after that, Andrew

McConnell—two eggs over hard, whole wheat toast, hot cocoa—came out of the restaurant and loaded a dolly into the back of the truck. Next to the dolly he set Liza's roll-aboard suitcase, the one that held the money.

"Just settle in and stay put," Andrew warned her. "You don't get dropped off until close to the end of my route."

CHAPTER 10

On Saturday morning, when the parade of girls on horseback charged through the gate and surged into the dusty rodeo arena at a full gallop, Denny squealed with excitement. "There she is," he said, pointing. "There's Jenny."

Joanna saw at once that he was right—there was Jenny, bent low over Kiddo's back, holding aloft a huge American flag that streamed out behind both horse and rider. The troop of girls circled the arena at a gallop several times before coming to a stop before the judge's stand, where they stood stock-still while a recorded version of the "Star-Spangled Banner" blared over the loudspeakers.

Butch and Dennis immediately doffed their Stetsons. Standing next to them with her hand over her heart, Joanna felt her eyes fill with tears of motherly pride. She knew that only the best riders were tapped for flag duty. Jenny's proficiency on horseback was a skill she had acquired all on her own. Jenny and Kiddo had won countless barrel-racing competitions, but the trophies and buckles they had accumulated had everything to do with Jenny's own pursuit of excellence and very little to do with parental guidance or insistence. Yes, Butch and Joanna made sure horse and rider made it to the various far-flung rodeo venues, but Jenny and Kiddo were the ones who put in the hours of practice, day after day and month after month.

An hour later, when Jenny and Kiddo placed second in the barrel-racing competition, there was no hiding Butch's disappointment. They cleared the three barrels flawlessly but had come up short in the speed department, well behind Katy Beltran on her dapple gray mare, LaLa.

"Kiddo's a great horse," Butch said, "but if Jenny's going to participate at collegiate levels of competition, she needs a mount that's younger and faster."

Joanna gazed at her husband in astonishment. "You're kidding, right?"

"Not at all," Butch replied. "If Jenny wanted to be a concert pianist, we'd be in the market for the best possible piano. This is the same thing. We should be in the market for the best possible horse. Kiddo will be fine when comes time for Denny to learn to ride, but for right now I think the horse has earned the right to retire from competition. He can hang out at home with Spot instead of being dragged all over God's creation to rodeos."

"Do you understand how much good quarter horses go for?" Joanna asked.

"I've got a pretty good idea," Butch said with a cagey grin. "More than we paid for the pickup truck and trailer we bought to haul Jenny and all her gear from place to place."

"You've been looking into this, haven't you?" Joanna surmised, finally tumbling to the fact that she was late to this particular party. Evidently the Kiddo retirement conversation had been taking place for some time without Joanna's being privy to it.

Butch nodded, a little sheepishly.

"Have you already found a suitable candidate?"

"Katy's dad raises quarter horses. Yesterday when we got here, Jenny and I took a look at the horses he currently has available. None of them really grabbed her. She has her heart set on one that's about to go on the market north of Phoenix—a five-year-old mare that Dr. Ross heard about. She belongs to friends of a vet Dr. Ross knows up in Payson. They're willing to make us a good deal."

"It sounds like this is already a fait accompli."

"Pretty much," Butch admitted, "but remember, Joey, we're lucky. This is all about horses, not boys." He smiled at her, then said to their son, "Come on, Denny. Let's go get us some hot dogs."

Butch and Denny left Joanna sitting alone and stewing about having been left odd man out of the new horse discussion. Still, she had to acknowledge that Butch's final argument was a winning one. At Jenny's age, an abiding interest in horses was far preferable to an abiding interest in boys, especially considering the fact that at seventeen, the same age Jenny was now, Joanna was already pregnant without being married. Her wedding to Andy Brady had been somewhat tardy.

A few minutes later, when Butch and Dennis returned with hot dogs for everyone, Joanna stifled an urge to gripe about the mustard and ketchup smeared all over Denny's face and on his relatively clean clothes. This was a time to have fun, she reminded herself, not a time to be the mean mommy. Jenny showed up a few minutes later with Desi on a lead at her side. The dog, excited by all the commotion around him, was being a handful, not at all unlike an unruly toddler. As Jenny struggled to get him to behave, Joanna once again acknowledged the wisdom in Butch's approach—better horses and dogs than an unwed pregnancy and a baby.

"Sorry you didn't take first," Joanna said, handing over the hot dog Butch had brought for Jenny. If it had been up to Joanna, there would have been two hot dogs—a fully loaded one for Jenny and a plain one for Desi—but sharing people food wasn't an approved activity in the service dog training manual.

"We should have done better," Jenny said glumly, "but at least it was Katy and LaLa we lost to rather than Sonja from El Paso. I would have hated to lose to her. She's such a snob."

"Yes, you should have done better," Butch agreed. "Tough break, but there's always the next round."

"Maybe," Jenny agreed. "I hope so."

Having seen the error of her ways and been outvoted besides, Joanna decided now was as good a time as any to concede defeat. "I expect that your future barrel-racing events will be just fine," she said, "especially if the rumors I'm hearing are true."

"What rumors?" Jenny asked.

"That we're getting a new horse."

Jenny turned to her mother with her face suddenly alight. "Really? You mean it?"

she asked. "We can do it?"

"Yes," Joanna said.

"Her name's Maggie," Jenny continued. "She's a palomino."

Joanna could see that since the new horse already had a name, she was indeed late to the party. On the other hand, she couldn't deny that the prospect of having a horse that shared the same name as her troublesome mother-in-law had a certain perverse appeal.

"I can hardly wait to meet her," Joanna said.

They sat in the grandstand with the late-spring afternoon sun beating down on their backs and with gritty rodeo action unfolding in front of them. Denny loved every bit of it. The first bronco-riding competitor landed facedown in the dirt. Standing up and brushing himself off, he exited the arena accompanied by the rodeo announcer's familiar but unwelcome words, "Nice try, but no time."

That was the moment Joanna's phone rang. When she went to answer, Deb Howell's number showed on the screen.

"I went to the morgue for Junior Dowdle's autopsy," Deb announced. "Dr. Machett didn't show. I've been here waiting for more than an hour. Ralph Whetson is here, too. He's tried calling the M.E.'s home as well as his cell. No answer. Rather than putting Chief Deputy Hadlock in Guy Machett's crosshairs, I thought I'd check with you first and get your read on the situation."

Over time Joanna had encountered plenty of difficulties in dealing with Guy Machett, but missing a scheduled autopsy had never been one of them. Scheduling was sometimes tough, but once something was on the calendar, the M.E. had always been reliable and punctual. He also demanded punctuality from any detectives who were supposed to be in attendance.

"Have you checked with Madge Livingston?" Joanna asked.

"Tried," Deb answered. "With her boss out of town, Madge and some of her fellow Harley riders are off on a weekend road trip to Lake Havasu. She isn't picking up, either."

"Maybe Dr. Machett had car trouble and is stranded somewhere," Joanna sug-gested. "Even so, just to be sure, you should probably do a welfare check at his house. You know where he lives, don't you?"

"Of course I know where he lives," Deb replied. "On the Vista. Where else?"

The Vista, in Bisbee's Warren neigh-borhood, was composed of two parallel streets that ran on opposite sides of a now mostly barren park. The Vista had long been home to members of Bisbee's upper crust, all the way back to the town's early mining days.

"Keep me posted," Joanna said as she rang off.

To derogatory hoots and hollers from the grandstand, another bronco-riding hopeful had just bitten the dust half a leap after his horse, War Paint, a comical-looking black-and-white paint, had cleared the chute.

"What's up?" Butch asked over Denny's head.

"Dr. Machett was due at an autopsy at

two, but he's currently MIA," she said.

"It's the weekend," Butch said. "He's a bachelor. Maybe he got lucky."

The bull-riding event was just getting under way when Deb called back. "I hate to bother you again, Sheriff Brady, but I think you need to come home."

"Why?" Joanna asked. "What's wrong?"

"Dr. Machett is dead," Deb said.

The words took a while to sink in.

"Dead?" Joanna repeated. "How? What happened?"

"At first glance I'd say he was subjected to several different kinds of torture," Deb responded, sounding shaken. "It's bad— as bad as anything I've seen."

"Have you contacted Chief Bernard?" Joanna asked.

"Yes, ma'am. That was my first call," Deb said. "Detective Keller is on his way, but Chief Bernard said I should call you and see if you have any suggestions about what to do. He's asking that we make this a joint operation, but without an M.E. available, what the hell are we supposed to do about the crime scene?"

"Give me a few minutes," Joanna said. "Let me see what I can do."

Butch had heard enough of Joanna's side of the conversation to know something was terribly amiss. He reached into his pocket, pulled out his wallet, and handed a five to Jenny. "Why don't you take Dennis down to the snow cone booth?"

"What's up?" he asked once the kids were out of earshot.

"Guy Machett is dead," Joanna said. "Murdered. Deb just found his body. She's called Chief Bernard. He's asked for our help, but with no M.E. to do the preliminary crime scene analysis..."

Butch didn't let her finish the sentence. "Of course you have to go," he said. "Just put Denny's car seat in the truck. He can ride home with Jenny and me tomorrow."

"You're sure?"

"Of course I'm sure," Butch said. "We'll be fine. You go do your job."

Joanna left the grandstand at a run. Out in the parking lot, she jumped into Butch's Subaru. Once inside that, she drove through the part of the lot that was reserved for participants' horses and trailers. When she found their rig, Kiddo and Spot were tethered together near the back of the trailer, munching away on a pile of hay. Jenny had been unwilling to leave Spot to fend for herself alone in a relatively new corral over the weekend, so the blind horse had come along for the ride.

The two horses looked up with interest as Joanna raced past to put Dennis's car seat in the back of the truck. Headed back to the Subaru, she paused long enough to give both horses a quick scratch on their respective noses.

Then, leaving the horses to their hay, Joanna hurried back to the car, connecting her Bluetooth as she went. Before she got into the car, she pulled a set of bubble lights out of the glove box, attached them to the top of the Subaru, and turned them on. Heading out of town, she couldn't help noticing how much the landscape around Silver City and Tyrone, complete with miles of flat-topped rust-colored mine tailings dumps, reminded her of Bisbee.

Only when she was well under way did Joanna place her first phone call. That one was to Claire Newmark, a member on the Cochise County Board of Supervisors and one with whom Joanna had developed a reasonably cordial relationship. Claire answered on the third ring.

"Sheriff Brady here," Joanna said urgently. "Sorry to interrupt your Saturday afternoon, but we've got a problem."

"Sounds bad," Claire returned.

"It is," Joanna answered. "Someone has murdered Guy Machett."

"Our M.E.?" Claire was clearly shocked. "Are you serious?"

"Very. I've got an active homicide crime scene with investigators there or else en route, but until there's a medical examiner to perform a preliminary analysis, there's no way to process anything."

"A while ago, when Dr. Winfield was unavailable, didn't we bring in an M.E. from Pima County on a contract basis?" Claire asked.

"You're right. We did. The problem is, they would only send someone to us if there wasn't something urgent in their own jurisdiction. Even if their workload is clear, any sub they could send out instantly is still more than two hours away. And we're not just dealing with the Machett case, either," she added. "We discovered his homicide only after he failed to show up to perform a previously scheduled autopsy."

"The one on Junior Dowdle?" Claire inquired.

"Yes," Joanna agreed. "Junior's."

"Okay, we're talking two cases rather than one," Claire confirmed. "What are you suggesting?"

"My mother will probably give me all kinds of hell for this, especially since she and George are about to head out for their summer cabin in Minnesota. Even so, I might be able to talk them into delaying their departure long enough for George to help us out. He's familiar. We know him, and we know his work. If we offered to take him on a contract basis with the same kind of pay we'd have to fork over for a sub from Pima County,

George might be willing to help out for a time. The problem is, I don't want to raise the issue with George without first having some sort of go-ahead from the board. Before I broach the subject, I need to be able to say with some confidence that he'll be adequately paid for his trouble."

Claire thought about that for a moment. "Even if we offered him the same hourly rate, we'd still be getting a bargain because we wouldn't be having to pay travel time, too. Right?"

"That's how it looks to me. Assuming he agrees and is currently available, we could have someone at the crime scene at least two hours before anyone else could get there. Time counts in cases like this, Claire," Joanna added. "The sooner we process the crime scene, the sooner we can get to the bottom of whatever happened."

"Where are you right now?"

"I just left the rodeo grounds in Silver City. The GPS says I should be back in Bisbee in a little under three hours. With my blue lights flashing, I'll be able to shave some time off that. If you can get me some kind of quasi-official go-ahead, I'll call Doc Winfield and see if I can negotiate a peace treaty with him."

"With him or with your mother?" Claire asked.

That was one of the reasons Joanna and Claire got along so well. Claire's prickly relationship with her own mother was surprisingly similar to Joanna's relationship with Eleanor Lathrop Winfield. Claire may have been the person elected to the board of supervisors, but her mother, Winifred Holland, considered herself to be an ex officio member of that same body, complete with all the rights and responsibilities thereof.

"A little of both," Joanna agreed with a slight laugh. She was not looking forward to tackling Eleanor on the subject, but if it had to be done, she was the one to do it. Joanna doubted George Winfield would mind stepping up to the plate if the county needed him, but she knew her mother would be less than thrilled.

"Drive safely," Claire advised. "I'll be

back in touch."

Joanna's phone rang before she had time to call anyone else. "Chief Bernard here," Alvin said. "You know what's happened?"

"Yes," Joanna answered. "Deb brought me up to speed."

"Is it okay with you for me to declare this a joint operation?"

"Whatever you need."

"Where are you now?" Chief Bernard asked.

"Coming back from Silver City as fast as I can," Joanna told him. "What's happening on your end?"

"For right now, we've got the crime scene secured. No one's to go back inside until we've got search warrants in place. Detective Keller is on his way to see Judge Moore with warrant requests for Guy Machett's home, his office, his Internet accounts and telephone lines, as well as his banking information."

"Sounds like a plan," Joanna said.

"Since no one's allowed at the crime scene right now, I'd like to draft Deb Howell to help my officers canvass the neighborhood."

"Done," Joanna said. "I'll call Dispatch to summon my troops and put them at your disposal."

"What about the M.E. situation?" Chief Bernard asked.

"I've got a phone call in to Claire Newmark on the board of supervisors. I'm waiting for a call back."

"How do we handle the crime scene?" Alvin asked. "When it comes to investigating homicides, Fred, my poor little CSI guy, is completely out of his depth."

Joanna knew that to be true. After the Bisbee Police Department's longtime evidence tech, Charles Reppe, had retired a year earlier, budgetary constraints had sent the city personnel department looking for the cheapest possible replacement. Joanna was familiar with the old saying "There's cheap, fast, and good. Pick any two." In that regard, Fred Harding was in a class by himself. With a diploma in crime scene investigation from a none-too-up-and-coming online school, he was cheap, all right, but he was also neither quick nor good.

"I know Dave Hollicker got hurt yesterday," Alvin continued, "but if your people could help us out here, I'd really appreciate it."

"Since Dave is on crutches, he won't be much use at a crime scene, but he's not bad when it comes to computers and data-mining searches. Let's use him to see if he can uncover what's behind this. I don't want to jump to conclusions here, but we both know that it's a good bet that Guy Machett was killed by someone he knew, or, rather, by someone who knew him."

"You're suggesting that we put Dave to work doing a background check on the victim?"

"Yes," Joanna answered.

"Good," Alvin Bernard said. "I'll direct that all the telecommunications info gleaned from the warrants should go to him."

"As for the crime scene itself," Joanna suggested, "Deb Howell may be a relatively new homicide detective, but she's also taken every crime scene investigation course the Arizona Department of Public Safety offers. Working together, Deb and Casey Ledford should be able to get the job done."

"Thank you." Alvin sounded relieved. "I owe you one. Maybe even two."

Joanna sped along for the next hour or so, alternately making and receiving phone calls. She summoned her folks to the crime scene, outlined what was expected of them, and let them know that until the M.E. situation had been clarified, there might be precious little for them to do.

As she traveled the almost empty highways, cruising around whatever traffic was out there, she had time to think. The murder of a medical examiner was bound to be big news. That meant there would be a media storm surrounding this case. In the process, whatever had happened to Junior Dowdle was likely to be pushed to a back burner no matter how determined Joanna was to prevent it. She had a limited number of assets at her disposal. With two homicides to solve in as many days, she would find her investigative resources stretched to the breaking point.

Deb's brief description of the scene made it sound as though Guy Machett's murder was anything but a random event. He'd been targeted by someone, but why? Was the cause to be found in his work life or in his personal life? Guy had always struck Joanna as an arrogant twit with a very high opinion of himself and his accomplishments and little regard for others. Joanna realized now that she had no idea who his friends or relations were. Was he married? Had he ever been married? He never failed to mention going to Harvard and getting his medical training at Johns Hopkins, but he'd made almost no mention of where he had grown up. In order to understand why the man was dead in the here and now, Joanna and her investigators would need an encyclopedic understanding of Guy Machett's past and present.

As Joanna approached the first Willcox

exit, the Subaru's fuel gauge showed she had less than a quarter of a tank left. She pulled off and stopped at the first gas station. She was reaching for the hose when her phone rang again. This time Claire Newmark's name and number appeared on the screen.

"We won't be able to make this official until next week's meeting," Claire said, "but for right now, if you can talk Doc Winfield into coming back on a contract basis, you're authorized to do so."

"All right," Joanna said. "Thank you so much. George will be fine, but wish me luck with my mother."

"Always," Claire said with a laugh.

She was about to hang up when Joanna had a sudden stroke of inspiration. "Wait," she said. "There's one more thing."

"What?" Claire asked. The shortness of that clipped one-word question indicated that Claire Newmark felt she had already done more than her share of Cochise County business for a weekend afternoon.

"When the board of supervisors hired Guy Machett to be the new M.E., did you run a background check on the man?"

"Of course we did," Claire answered. "We wouldn't have been doing our due diligence if we hadn't."

"Do you still have it?"

"We must. In fact, I might even have a copy of it on my laptop. Why do you ask?"

"I've asked Dave Hollicker, one of my CSIs, to look into whatever there is to be found about Guy Machett. Having access to that background check would give us a huge leg up."

"But that was a confidential report," Claire said, hesitating. "I'm not sure I can release it to just anyone."

"This is a homicide investigation," Joanna reminded her. "Machett is dead, and I'm not asking you to release that report to just anyone. I want you to send it to Dave Hollicker, the criminalist I've assigned to look into Machett's past. Using that report as a jumping-off point will save huge amounts of wasted time and effort. If you're concerned about liability issues, check with the county attorney. Arlee Jones should be able to advise you on that."

"Okay," Claire agreed. "I was looking through my files. It turns out I do have it. I'll check with Arlee and then get back to you."

That was exactly how Joanna wanted it to work. In the complicated world of Cochise County bureaucracy, a request that came to Arlee Jones top down from a member of the board of supervisors was more likely to receive favorable treatment than one that came from Joanna. She was coming up on the end of her second term in office, and she had learned it was better to dodge certain obstacles than butt up against them.

Having put that request out into the universe, Joanna finished filling the tank and got back into the car before taking a deep breath and punching in the number for her mother's landline.

"Good afternoon," George Winfield boomed. "How are things in the world of barrel racing?"

Grateful to hear her stepfather's voice on the phone and not Eleanor's, Joanna knew she was in the clear, but only temporarily.

"We've got a homicide, George," she said. "Alvin Bernard and I need you."

"Excuse me," George said with a chuckle. "I believe you must have perfected the art of time travel. I'm not the medical examiner anymore. Guy Machett is."

"The problem is, Guy Machett is the victim," Joanna explained. "I'm calling on behalf of the board of supervisors to ask if you'd consider coming back on a contract basis for however long it takes to work out some other more viable plan."

When George spoke again, he was no longer joking. "Where and when did he die?" George asked seriously. "And where and when do you need me?"

"When is your call. As to where? The body was found at Machett's house on the Vista over an hour ago after he failed to show up for a scheduled autopsy. I took the time to check with the board of supervisors before I called you. Claire Newmark just now got back to me with the okay. They'll pay you the same rate they paid Pima County when they subbed for you a couple of years ago."

"How sure are you this is a murder?"

"Deb Howell says that's how it looks to her. I'm prepared to believe her, but I haven't arrived at the scene yet. I'm coming from Silver City. I'm on I-10 west of Willcox, but I'll be turning down 191 in a couple of minutes. Traffic is light. I'm making good progress."

For the longest time, there was dead silence on the phone. Joanna held her breath. If George turned her down, she was in trouble. She'd have to go crawling to Pima County. After already wasting an hour, she knew there was no telling how much longer it would take to get another medical examiner to the scene.

Finally George spoke again. "Ellie is not going to like this. You do know that we're supposed to leave for Minnesota next week?"

"I do," Joanna conceded, "and I didn't suggest this to make your life miserable. I'm asking because I'm desperate, because I've got two deaths that both need investigating."

"Junior's and this one?" George asked.

"Right."

"I've got no equipment."

Joanna had sold insurance long enough to understand this as a pro forma objection. George had already said yes. Now he was merely haggling over the details. She went for the assumed close.

"I'll have Ralph Whetson, Guy's assistant, meet you at the crime scene. He'll bring along everything you need. Do you want me to talk to Mom about this?"

"I'll tell her myself," George said, "but I expect you'll be hearing from her soon."

Joanna barely had time to give Ralph Whetson the lowdown before Eleanor's call came through.

"My husband is supposed to be retired." Eleanor launched into her tirade without bothering with the telephone nicety of saying hello. "You can't just disrupt our lives willy-nilly. I have some say in the matter, you know, and I won't stand still for this kind of treatment."

"We need him, Mom," Joanna said as

soothingly as she could manage. "Desperately. Did he tell you what's happened?"

"He said Guy Machett is dead."

"That's true," Joanna agreed. "Who knows how long it will take the board of supervisors to find a permanent replacement? In the meantime, without an M.E. available, my people can't process the scene."

"Well, I guess you've got him," Eleanor returned ruefully. The speed of her concession was one for the record books. "He took off like he'd been shot out of a damned cannon. He hasn't moved that fast since last fall when he was chased by that swarm of yellow jackets, the ones that had taken up residence in his outdoor grill." Eleanor paused. "You said two cases?"

"Yes, Guy Machett's case and Junior Dowdle's."

"Well, then," Eleanor said with a sniff, "if that's the case, I suppose you really do need him, but I won't have him taken advantage of, either. You promised to pay him a fair wage, right?"

"Yes," Joanna said. "I've already verified that with the board of supervisors."

"I guess that means he won't be home for dinner."

"I don't suppose he will," Joanna agreed.

Joanna hung up the phone with the sad realization that she wouldn't be home for dinner, either.

CHAPTER 11

Liza lay in the upstairs bunk over the cab of a rumbling Peterbilt and watched as the ribbon of asphalt that was westbound I-90 unspooled in front of her. She had lain there, awake and watchful, for hours as the gigantic rig lumbered through the late afternoon and on into the night.

It turned out Candy Small's underground railroad wasn't a railroad at all. It was trucks, first the bread truck that was really nothing more than a delivery van and now this long-haul rig heading west. It had been a long day of riding and waiting. After exiting Candy's Impala, Liza had spent several uncomfortable hours being bounced around in the back of Andrew McConnell's van. He had finished his route in the early afternoon and immediately hustled Liza into his own car, a rusted-out

Jeep.

"Where to now?" she asked.

"Next stop is Albany, New York," he told her. "We work with a women's shelter there. They're the ones who put together the rest of the transportation package."

"You've done this before?"

Andrew nodded. "More than once. Candy says most of the time cops can't do much to help in domestic violence situations. When the best thing for someone to do is get out of Dodge, that's when we step in."

Liza stole a self-conscious glance at the bruises Candy had deliberately planted on her upper arm. She could see now that his was an ingenious plan. Those telltale marks gave Liza a visible and perfectly understandable reason to be an anonymous woman fleeing for parts unknown. Those injuries apparently had also served to mobilize an invisible cadre of committed people who were willing to help domestic violence victims escape their tormentors and who would therefore respect Liza's need for secrecy. She would leave behind no trail of plane, rail, or bus reservations or even gas station receipts that would reveal where she had gone.

As far as her pursuers were concerned, it would seem she'd simply vanished into thin air. She couldn't help but wonder, though. What would happen if some of Half-Moon Miller's stray mobsters or even the cops caught wind of Andrew's involvement? How much would it take for him to blurt out everything he knew?

Andrew's Jeep was noisy and came with a nonexistent suspension system. Even so, riding in the passenger seat of that was far more comfortable than bouncing around on the floor of the delivery van. It was comfortable enough that Liza actually dozed off. When she awakened nearly an hour later, they were pulling into the underground parking garage of a low-rise mixed-use building.

"Take the elevator up to the first floor," Andrew directed. "You're looking for Aimee's House of Beauty. Ask for Doreen. They're expecting you."

"I thought you said you were taking me

to a shelter," Liza objected. "You're dropping me off at a beauty shop?"

"Trust me," Andrew said. "If you want to disappear, this is the place to do it. Good luck."

Walking in the front door of the salon and dragging her precious roll-aboard behind her, Liza discovered that Aimee's looked like any other beauty shop on the planet. A row of shampoo basins lined the back wall. Along the other walls were six separate operator chairs, five of which were occupied with customers. Liza stopped at the front desk and asked for Doreen. That transaction caused an immediate but subtle shift in the atmosphere of the room as everyone—beauticians and customers alike—glanced in her direction, while the young woman at the reception desk came to attention.

"Of course," she said. "Right this way. Doreen's expecting you."

The receptionist hustled Liza past the other stations, through a curtained doorway, and into a back room, one that contained little else but another station complete with a chair and a shampoo bowl. A woman stepped forward to greet her, hand outstretched. "I'm Aimee," she said.

"What about Doreen?" Liza asked.

Aimee gave her a wink accompanied by a conspiratorial smile. "There is no Doreen," she explained. "It's a code. I take it you're Candy Small's friend?"

Liza nodded mutely.

Aimee gave Liza a critical up-and-down appraisal. "Did you bring along any other clothes?" she asked, nodding in the direction of the roll-aboard. "Maybe something a little more comfortable?"

Liza glanced down at the rumpled outfit she had worn to her mother's funeral. More than twenty-four hours later, it was much the worse for wear. Then she looked guiltily at the suitcase. She suspected that most women fleeing abusive spouses did so with a suitcase full of spare clothing rather than one full of money.

"Sorry," she said quickly, making up the story as it tumbled off her lips. "My mother just died. My husband forbade me to go to the funeral. One of Mother's friends brought some of her things to the funeral for me—photo albums and stuff. When I decided I was leaving, I couldn't just abandon it. It's all that's left of my mother's life."

It was a lie, of course, but it was also close enough to the truth to ring true.

"Don't worry," Aimee said soothingly. "You'd be surprised how many women in your situation show up with nothing but the clothes on their backs. Believe me, we're fully equipped. We've got a room down in the basement that's full of donated clothing and toiletries. You'll be able to find whatever you need there, including something suitable to wear and a bag to carry it in, too. Right now, let's work on your hair. You left home today as an abused wife. Right now you're a brunette with a long ponytail. I could probably turn you into a blonde, but there's another option I've found to be faster and more effective."

"What's that?"

"We'll turn you into a cancer patient."

"What do you mean?"

"People don't stare at cancer patients," Aimee said. "It's not polite. If we shave your head and give you a scarf to wear, I promise people will do their best not to look at you. That includes anyone who is actually looking for you. Of course, if you don't want to do something that drastic..."

Liza thought about Olivia lying dead on the stairway. The people who had murdered her landlady were also looking for her. In other words, drastic was exactly what was called for. "Shave away," she said.

Liza's transformation took less than an hour. Once her head was completely bald, Aimee spent the next twenty minutes demonstrating how to properly wrap her bare skull in a bright blue silk scarf. Looking at her unfamiliar reflection in the mirror, Liza was stunned by the difference.

"Amazing," she murmured.

"Wardrobe is next," Aimee announced. "Come on."

Liza followed her guide out into the corridor and down in the elevator to an underground storage area that had been cordoned off from the parking level. Inside was a room that looked like a department store's bargain basement. Racks of clothing filled the center of the space. Glass-topped counters along the sides of the room were stocked with everything from toothbrushes and dental floss to compacts and multiple shades of lipstick. Aimee stopped just inside the door and handed Liza an athletic bag she took down from a nearby shelf.

"You'll be able to carry this on top of your roll-aboard," she explained. "Fill it with what you need, but be sparing. In your situation, traveling light is better than being bogged down with too much luggage. As I said, don't take too much and don't take too long," she added, glancing at her watch. "This is a well-oiled machine. We're due to meet up with your ride at four o'clock. Do you have somewhere to go?"

"I have a brother in Arizona," Liza said.

"Okay, tell your drivers your general direction," Aimee advised. "Don't give them too many details. In fact, it might be better to say you're going to California. That way, if your ex does come looking for you, it'll be harder for him to pick up your trail. You'll start out on I-90. Go west on that until you want to turn south. This is a tag-team operation. The drivers of one truck will hook you up with the next one."

Liza was no stranger to thrift shop shopping. The process took her straight back to her childhood. She had spent most of her school years buying her clothing from other people's castoffs at the thrift stores both before and after Selma became a hermit. The differences between those trips and this one weren't lost on Liza. Then she had been resentful and angry. This time she was supremely grateful.

Liza spent the better part of an hour on her "shopping" spree. The racks and furnishings in the place looked as though they'd been liberated from a shut-down JCPenney store. Deep drawers that had once stocked lingerie for sale now stocked the same items for free. The selection of bras and panties came in a variety of sizes and, although donated, they were clearly new, most of them with price tags still attached. Liza had no problem finding some that fit. For clothing she settled on two pairs of worn jeans and several different T-shirts.

The far end of the room featured several racks of shoes. Liza looked through the section marked size eight and happily traded in her worse-for-wear heels for a pair of leather sandals. At the purse counter she emptied the contents of her own purse—a bargain basement last year's model from Marshall's—for a slightly used but still serviceable Coach bag. She had always longed for a Coach bag but had never imagined coming into possession of one, especially not under these circumstances, as someone on the run.

On their way out of the dressing room, Aimee handed Liza two more silk scarves—one red and the other bright yellow. "Variety's the spice of life, you know," she said with a smile as Liza tucked the silk pieces into the top of her now bulging athletic bag.

As a last order of business, Aimee opened a file drawer, took out a black, no-frills cell phone, and handed it over.

"It's what they call a burner," she explained. "The minutes on it are already paid for, but it's recommended for emergency use only. If you call people you know, even people you think you can trust, they might inadvertently put your abuser on your trail. Understand?"

Nodding, Liza slipped the phone into the pocket of her jeans. There was no cash register at the door and clearly no expectation that she should pay for any of the goods.

At four o'clock that afternoon, dressed in brand-new used clothing, minus her ponytail, wearing the blue scarf, and armed with the roll-aboard, the bulging athletic bag, and a slightly used Coach purse containing a sack lunch, Liza arrived at Blackie's Truck Terminal in Albany in the passenger seat of Aimee's bright red Prius. After parking the car among a collection of towering semis, Aimee led Liza over to an orange-and-black moving

van and introduced her to the two-man
team of drivers lounging outside—Sam
and Joe.

"This is Linda," Aimee said as the three
of them shook hands. "She's on her way
to L.A."

A few minutes later she handed Liza's
luggage and purse first into the cab and
then up into the overhead sleeping compartment. "Sam and Joe are only going
as far as Chicago," she explained.
"Because they'll take turns driving through
the night, you can ride up here. You should
be somewhere close to Chicago by seven
or so tomorrow morning."

"What then?"

"Don't worry. They'll hook you up with
your next ride before they drop you off.
They won't leave you stranded."

"You're sure?" Liza asked uncertainly.

"I'm sure. These are good guys."

"What do I owe you for all this?" Liza
asked.

"Not a single thing," Aimee said. "Someone helped me years ago, and now I'm
helping you. Maybe someday, when you're

in a better place, you can do the same."

"I hope so," Liza said.

The hours rolled by as the truck lumbered westward through the night. Liza could hear Joe and Sam chatting down in the cab, sometimes with each other and sometimes with other truckers over their CB radio. Above them there was nothing but silence and worry. It made Liza's heart ache to think that she was somehow responsible for Olivia Dexter's death. Her landlady was dead for no other reason than that—she had been Liza's landlady. If Detective Franklin really did suspect Liza of being involved in Olivia's death, what did that make Liza now—a wanted fugitive? Then there was her brother. What about Guy? How would her brother react when she showed up unannounced on his doorstep after all these years? The problem was, Liza had nowhere else to go. Guy was it.

Hungry, Liza scrounged through the sack lunch Aimee had stuffed in her purse. Bologna had never been her first choice for sandwich makings, but in this case hunger was the best sauce. She devoured the sandwich, the chips, and the accompanying apple with a relish she wouldn't have thought possible. Somewhere along the way, several hours later, the truck pulled into a truck stop. While Sam and Joe stayed at the fuel island, Liza hurried inside to use the facilities.

She was still awake when Sam and Joe stopped for coffee and yet another pit stop. Again, Liza availed herself of the facilities but turned down the coffee. Going in and out of those places made her nervous. Security cameras seemed to be everywhere. She hurried past them, doing her best to avert her face, all the while praying that her scarf would stay where it belonged.

Back in the truck and back on the road for the second time, she pulled the scarf off, carefully folded it, and laid it aside. Then with the steady motion of the truck rocking her, she pulled a loose blanket over her body and finally fell asleep.

CHAPTER 12

The last thirty minutes of Joanna's two-and-a-half-hour drive were done in relative silence. She'd summoned everyone who needed summoning. Now she appreciated having some peace and quiet as well as time to think. Why was Guy Machett dead? Most of the time the basis for murder was either love or money. Which was this?

Had he been involved in some kind of illegal activity—drug dealing, maybe, or possibly money laundering? Or was his death related to his personal life? Was he involved in some kind of love triangle? Now that Joanna thought about it, she realized that she knew nothing about Guy Machett's love life. Did he have a steady girl stowed somewhere who would be devastated by his loss?

The one thing that raised any red flags

was the fact that when the M.E. wasn't at work, he spent most of his time out of town. Maybe he had some kind of secret life going on. She thought about Dr. Machett's well-groomed appearance— his expensive taste in clothing, his perfectly coifed hair.

"What if he was gay?" Joanna said aloud, speaking only to herself. What if he spent time out of town in order to keep his love life away from the prying eyes of Bisbee's gossipmongers? If so, evidence of that kind of relationship was bound to surface in his phone or Internet records.

Joanna's phone rang again as she turned off Highway 80 and onto the Douglas Cutoff. A glance at the telephone screen revealed Madge Livingston's name.

"Deb Howell called me a while ago," Madge said in her gravelly voice. "She claims Dr. Machett is dead—that some-one murdered him—but I'm having a hard time believing it. Is it true?"

"I'm not at the crime scene yet," Joanna answered, "but that's my understanding."

"What the hell happened?"

"Someone killed him. I don't know any of the details."

"It's a good thing I was out of town, otherwise I'd be at the top of your suspect list," Madge said. "I've been ready to throttle the man for months now."

The fact that Madge had despised Guy Machett was hardly news. Madge was a prickly, opinionated woman who had spent her entire career working in various departments of Cochise County government. Shipping her off to the M.E.'s office had effectively moved her out of the courthouse proper and out of everybody else's hair, as well. Over the years she had found all her bosses wanting. To hear Madge tell it, George Winfield had been the only exception to that rule, although Joanna seemed to remember there had been a few bumps in the road there, too.

"Do you know of anyone who wished him harm?"

"You should be asking if I know anyone who didn't wish him harm," Madge countered. "Guy Machett was a most unlikable young man."

"As far as you know, though, there've been no problems at the office? No threats of any kind?"

"None," Madge said. "At least none that I know of, but Dr. Machett wasn't the sort who took people into his confidence."

"He wasn't what you would call forth-coming?"

"No, he was not." Madge paused for a moment and then continued, "Deb asked me about his computer and phone. I told her if they weren't at the house, he might have left them in the office. I believe she's sending someone uptown to check."

"Good," Joanna said.

"Do you know how he died?"

"No," Joanna answered. "As I said, I'm not there yet. By now Doc Winfield may have established an approximate time of death, but I'm not aware—"

"Wait," Madge interrupted. "Is Doc Winfield coming back?"

"Just temporarily," Joanna began. "We needed an M.E. on the scene and—"

Madge didn't wait for Joanna to finish.

"You tell Doc Winfield that I'm leaving Lake Havasu within the hour. I'll be home to help out just as soon as I can get there."

The phone call with Madge ended as Joanna turned right onto Cole Avenue. A few blocks later, she paused at the top of the Vista. The cluster of flashing lights breaching the twilight told her that the crime scene was a few blocks south and to the left, across from the tennis courts.

Due to the crush of vehicles, emergency and otherwise, Joanna was forced to park a block and a half from the crime scene and walk the rest of the way. She had shaved half an hour off the expected travel time from Silver City to Bisbee. Even so, the time lag had given media types from all over southern Arizona time to gather at the scene. As predicted, the murder of the medical examiner was big news.

Joanna was still dressed in what she'd worn to the rodeo—jeans, a western shirt, and a pair of outgrown cowboy boots she had inherited from her daughter. Out of uniform and without her badge, she found it easy to slip unnoticed through the crowd of mostly out-of-town reporters. An old-fashioned wrought-iron fence surrounded Guy Machett's front yard. Joanna was almost to the gate when her luck ran out. Marliss Shackleford spotted her.

"Yoo-hoo," she called. "Sheriff Brady, have you got a minute?"

Marliss trotted forward with a young purple-haired girl following at her elbow. Joanna recognized the young woman at once, but it took a moment to remember her name. Ruth. She and her brother had been among the volunteers who had gathered in the parking lot at St. Dominick's during Thursday's early morning search for Junior Dowdle.

Joanna stopped short. "Sorry, Marliss. I don't have a minute," she said. "And in case you haven't noticed, this is a crime scene. It's no place for children."

"I'm not a child," Ruth objected. "I'm fourteen years old, and I'm a blogger. Ms. Shackleford is letting me shadow her for the day. I was hoping I could interview you."

Joanna favored Marliss with what she hoped was a sufficiently withering glare before turning back to Ruth."If you want to interview me, you'll need to make arrangements by contacting my office, not by showing up at a crime scene. Right now I have a job to do. I'm surprised Ms. Shackleford didn't inform you of that."

The girl looked disappointed. Marliss Shackleford simply shrugged off Joanna's implied criticism.

"Still," Marliss insisted, "as long as you're here, if you could just shed a little light..."

"As you can see, I've only just arrived," Joanna answered brusquely. "That means I don't know anything, and I can't tell you anything, either. Now, if you'll excuse me. I need to get inside."

"But—"

A bright light went on and Joanna realized that Ruth was using a cell-phone camera to record everything that was being said. As a result, some of the other media types started paying attention.

"Turn that thing off," Joanna ordered.

"Sorry," Ruth replied, quickly stowing the offending machine.

It occurred to Joanna that she was dealing with a kid and perhaps her response had been more forceful than necessary. The truth was, Marliss Shackleford had an unerring ability to bring out the very worst in her.

"Call my office next week sometime," Joanna told the girl. "We'll set up a time for an interview."

With that, Joanna donned a pair of gloves, shoved open the gate, and made for Guy Machett's low porch, where the front door stood wide open. Through that Joanna glimpsed lights and movement inside the house, but no glimmer of light showed through any of the windows. Once she was on the porch, Joanna saw that the blinds on all the windows were closed and most likely covered with an inside layer of pulled drapes or curtains as well.

A uniformed Bisbee police officer stood next to the door. "Evening, Sheriff Brady," he said as she paused long enough to slip on a pair of paper crime scene booties.

"Is Chief Bernard here?" she asked.

"No, he and Detective Keller just left to join Detective Carbajal at the second crime scene."

"What second crime scene?"

"Up the canyon, at the morgue," the cop said. "Dr. Machett's office up there has been ransacked, too."

"When did that happen?"

"Probably sometime last night, the same as everything else. But they just found out about the problem uptown a little while ago when Jaime went up to Old Bisbee to check out the office."

Attempting to step inside, Joanna almost collided with George Winfield. Their momentary do-si-do might have been comical but neither of them was in any mood for joking around.

"You're done already?"

"With as much as I can do here," George replied with a nod toward the back of the house. "Ralph Whetson will be back to pick up the body once Detective Howell finishes taking the crime scene photos. I told him that when he comes back to the morgue, he should bring a detective with him so we can go ahead and do the Dowdle autopsy."

"Tonight?" Joanna asked. "How can you? I was just told that the morgue is under investigation as a possible crime scene."

"That's right," George answered. "As a matter of fact I just finished having a telephone conversation with Alvin Bernard on that very topic. He's still up at the morgue with Matt Keller and Jaime Carbajal. According to the chief, damage at the morgue is limited to Dr. Machett's private office. There's no sign that anyone entered or disturbed the lab area. Chief Bernard said he's designating the office area as off-limits, but we're free to work in the lab. Junior's autopsy has already been postponed for two days. I'm sure Moe and Daisy are anxious to move forward with funeral arrangements. This will allow them to do so. As for my performing an autopsy tonight? Your mother's already mad enough to spit nails, so there's not much point in my hurrying home. I could just as well get as much done as possible while the getting is good."

Joanna had plenty of firsthand experience with her mother's moodiness, but she doubted that she would prefer performing or observing an autopsy to doing battle with Eleanor Lathrop Winfield.

"Anything you can tell me on a preliminary basis?"

"Not much. Tentative time of death is overnight sometime, probably in the early morning hours. I'll know more about that later. There was a struggle. Guy's watch got broken and stopped at 11:46 P.M., but I'm estimating that the time of death is several hours later than that. From the number of visible cuts and contusions, he put up a hell of a fight. He had burns on his chest and groin that would be consistent with being repeatedly hit by a stun gun."

"Any idea about cause of death?"

George shrugged. "Unofficially, I'd say this was a case of waterboarding gone bad. Some of the bruising on his chest would be consistent with a failed attempt to revive him. What that says to me is that the assailants were trying to get him to tell them something, but he died before they got it out of him."

"He drowned?"

"I suppose it could have been something else," George said. "We'll have to wait and see. More on that later—probably tomorrow sometime."

With that, George continued on his way. Once Joanna was inside, her immediate impression was that the living room resembled a war zone. The remains of a shattered coffee table lay in front of a sofa. A plasma TV had been knocked from its supports over the mantel of the fireplace, and the hearth and a good part of the living room carpet were covered with a debris field of splintered glass from the broken screen. Off to one side of the room, an easy chair that matched the sofa lay tipped on its side. A scatter of mail covered the floor. Looking at it, Joanna imagined Guy coming into the house with an armload of mail only to be attacked from behind with so much force that the mail had been propelled into the air and across the room.

The plush beige carpet was dotted with spatters of blood and a dusting of micro-dots from a deployed Taser cartridge. A long archway marked the line of demarcation between the living room and the dining room. Several antique dining room chairs lay in broken heaps of wood next to a matching table, the polished top of which was marred by spatters of blood. Each piece of debris and blood spatter was accompanied by a numbered crime scene marker. The thin layer of black dust that covered every available surface indicated that Casey Ledford had already been here checking for prints.

"Deb?" Joanna called.

"Come on through," Detective Howell replied. "I'm in the kitchen bagging up the victim's clothes. Casey's working in his home office. Welcome to the party."

"Some party," Joanna said, pausing in the doorway of the kitchen.

The room was a scene out of a 1950s horror flick. The familiar gray Formica table and matching chairs were the same ones Joanna's former in-laws still used, but the chair sitting in the middle of the room also sat in the middle of a spray of blood spatter that covered the floor. Deb stood in front of the kitchen sink carefully removing an item of discarded clothing from a heap on the floor and preparing to slip it into an evidence bag. Joanna thought she recognized the item in Deb's gloved hand. It looked very much like the jacket to one of Guy Machett's expensive Italian suits.

Joanna knew that in the aftermath of serious assaults, perpetrators shed DNA along with their victims. She also understood that in some situations it was possible to retrieve DNA and even fingerprints from items made of cloth. The hope of finding usable evidence accounted for Detective Howell's careful handling of the clothing, and it was something Joanna applauded. She waited quietly until Deb finished.

"Can you tell how this went down?" Joanna asked. "From the looks of the living room, I'd say it started in there."

"Yup," Deb agreed. "No obvious broken windows, so no breaking and entering. I'd say someone picked the lock on the back door. They let themselves in and then sat around and waited for Machett to show up."

"No alarm?"

"He has one," Deb said. "It may have been turned on, too, but with the access code posted on the wall right next to the keypad, it didn't do a whole lot of good."

"Why put the access code there?"

"For a cleaning lady maybe, so she could let herself in and out without triggering the alarm?" Deb suggested. "Machett wouldn't have needed to write it down for his own use because the code was nothing but his birthday—month, date, and year. He probably used the same code for the alarm at his office, which means that once the bad guys had one code, they had them all. It also explains how they were able to access his office at the morgue without triggering an alarm there, either."

"If Guy Machett was that lax about security," Joanna mused, "he must not have thought he was in any danger. What about his neighbors? Did anyone see or hear anything out of the ordinary?"

"Nope," Deb said, "not a peep, but that's mostly because no one was home. Mr. Roland, the guy next door, moved into an assisted-living facility a month ago. Mrs. Holland, the neighbor on the other side, is off on a two-week cruise down the Danube."

"Excuse me," Ralph Whetson said, coming in through the back door, pushing a gurney loaded with a body bag in front of him. "Are you ready for me?"

"Not quite yet," Joanna said. "Let me finish taking a look around first." She turned back to Deb. "Walk me through it."

"From what I can see, I'm assuming the initial attack occurred in the living room and that there was more than one assailant. The scene suggests they tasered him there. Casey's already swept up enough of the microdots that she'll be able to ID the weapon," Deb said, gesturing in that direction. "He must have come around sooner than they expected and then he put up a hell of a fight. When they finally subdued him, they dragged him into the kitchen. You can see the marks the heels of his shoes left on the hardwood floor."

Joanna went back to the dining room and studied the floor where two matching heel marks were clearly visible.

"After that, they spent a considerable length of time here in the kitchen," Deb said.

"They took off his clothes?"

"All of them," Deb agreed, nodding at the stack of evidence bags that now contained the pile of clothing. "They duct-taped him buck naked to this chair. Look at this." She pointed to the single chair that had been placed in the middle of the room. "There's duct tape residue on the front legs of the chair and on the back uprights, too. They must have taped both his arms and legs to the chair and then ripped off the tape when they moved him into the bathroom. There's hair stuck to both the chair legs and the uprights."

In order for Joanna to see the residue, she would have had to step into the spatter of dried blood. She chose not to. "For right now, I'll take your word about that," Joanna said. "Doc Winfield was on his way out when I came in. He mentioned something about a stun gun. Is this where they used that?"

"That's my guess," Deb answered. "Once the initial Taser had been deployed, they could still use the weapon's stun-gun capabilities. That part of the program most likely happened here, and they used it over and over. When the Taser ran out of gas, they moved the operation into the bathroom."

"You keep saying 'they,'" Joanna observed. "Are you sure there was more than one perpetrator?"

Deb nodded. "Machett was a fit kind of guy who was into tae kwon do. The level of destruction present tells us that he fought back. If you look at the shoe prints here in the kitchen, you'll notice there are two different sets. One looks to be a size twelve or thirteen. The other one is smaller, maybe a size ten. So, yes, definitely more than one person involved in the attack."

The bit about Machett's martial arts proficiency surprised Joanna. It was something Deb knew about Guy Machett that Joanna Brady didn't. "How do you know he was into tae kwon do?" she asked.

"Trophies," Deb answered dismissively. "He must have had at least five or six trophies on the shelf in his office and a collection of belts hanging on the wall behind his desk. Haven't you ever noticed them?"

"Not really," Joanna said. The truth was, since Guy Machett came to town, she had never once set foot inside his office. She had been to the morgue on occasion, of course, but not into his private office. As far as she was concerned, that spot still had George Winfield's name on it. In her dealings with Guy Machett, avoiding his office had been Joanna's one small protest rite, and a secret one at that.

Leaving Deb in the kitchen, Joanna

made her way down the hall and into the bathroom on her own. Like the rest of the house, it had escaped any kind of updating. The room was nowhere near what would nowadays be considered a suitable "master bath." The stains on the black-and-white tile indicated that the original toilet had probably been replaced at some point in the past, but everything else—the tile, the washbasin with its two separate spigots, and the oversize claw-foot tub—were most likely as-built equipment.

Guy Machett lay faceup on the tile. His naked body took up most of the available floor space in the small room. The cuts and bruises George had mentioned were readily apparent on his arms, legs, and face. Bare strips on his arms and legs indicated where duct tape had been brutally yanked away, taking a layer of skin and hair with it. The used duct tape had been left behind in a ball that had rolled under the sink. Machett's chest and groin were covered with the distinctive tracks left behind by the stun gun. Those burns were all too visible on the pale dead flesh, and so was everything else. Joanna was tempted to drop a discreet washcloth over the part of Guy Machett that should have been covered, but she didn't. This was a crime scene, after all.

Turning around, Joanna found both Deb and Casey standing behind her in the narrow hallway.

"Any idea what the attackers were looking for?"

"None," Deb said, shaking her head. "His phone and laptop are both missing. When we couldn't find any trace of them here at the house, Detective Keller and Jaime Carbajal took a search warrant and went to check out Guy's office. That's when they discovered that someone had broken in there as well."

"But nothing else is missing?"

"Not that we can tell, but there's a lot that isn't missing. Some high-end sound equipment, a second plasma TV, and several reasonably expensive pieces of jewelry—including a Patek Philippe watch—are all still here."

Joanna chewed on that for a moment. If Guy could afford that kind of watch, why hadn't he bothered to update the house?

"So this definitely wasn't a robbery," Joanna concluded. She turned to Casey, who was nodding her agreement. "What about the print situation? Find anything?"

"There are two distinct sets of prints that you see throughout the house. I'm pretty sure one set belongs to Guy Machett. Since the other set also shows up on the handle of the vacuum cleaner and on a broom handle and a mop, too, the second set probably belongs to a cleaning lady. In other words, unless the cleaning lady is also the bad guy, I'm saying the perpetrators wore gloves."

"Do we have any idea who the cleaning lady might be?"

"Not so far," Casey said.

"Hey," Ralph Weston called from the far end of the hall. "I'm still here. Are you ready for me now?"

"Sure," Joanna said. "Will you need a hand?"

"Nah," Ralph said. "I can manage it

myself."

His use of that particular pronoun—it—really struck Joanna. The dead man who had always insisted on being "Dr. Machett" suddenly had been demoted to the lowly status of "it." As far as Ralph was concerned, his former boss was now nothing more or less than a job to be done and a body to be handled. Joanna couldn't help but remember how, just two days earlier, Guy Machett's whole manner of dealing with Junior Dowdle's death had been somewhat less than respectful.

Now his former helper was treating him in exactly the same way.

Just deserts, Joanna thought to herself. **What goes around comes around.**

CHAPTER 13

Joanna, Detective Howell, and Casey were standing in the living room when Joanna's phone rang. Dave Hollicker's name and number appeared on the screen. "Hey," she said. "Are you making any progress on that background check?"

"Not really," Dave admitted. "Claire Newmark just sent me something that's going to help with that, but I'm caught up in something else at the moment. I'm about to send it to you."

In Joanna's opinion, the background check on Guy Machett should have been Dave's top priority, but she stopped herself from delivering a reprimand. "What?" she asked.

"Detective Carbajal called me from Dr. Machett's office," Dave said. "He asked me to come out to the department and check out last night's security tape feeds. I thought that was more important, so that's what I'm doing. I just sent it to you, and I'm copying Chief Bernard."

"Good," Joanna found herself saying, despite her earlier misgivings. "Excellent!"

Joanna felt a sudden stirring of excitement. In recent years, Cochise County had, at great expense, installed top-of-the-line security cameras at the entrances to all county facilities. The base station was located inside the sheriff's department. That way, if an alarm was triggered at one of the sites, Dispatch could check on the situation before sending officers to the scene. Since the bad guys had evidently used Guy Machett's access code to let themselves into the M.E.'s office, no alarms had sounded, and no one had been alerted. Even so, there was now a good chance Guy Machett's killers had been caught on tape.

Moments later, Joanna's phone dinged an alarm announcing the arrival of new mail. When she opened the message from Dave, it was empty except for a single attachment that took its own sweet time to load.

"Tell me," she urged. "Does it show anything or not?"

"It shows something, all right," Dave told her, "but it's not going to help much."

At last the document opened. After another long wait, it began to play. The video came with a time stamp that read 3:26:42 AM. For a long time, nothing showed but a view of the tiny empty parking lot behind the morgue, then two figures appeared. When they came close enough, Joanna saw Dave's assessment was correct. The film established when the bad guys had entered Guy Machett's office, but that was all. Both of their faces were completely obscured by ski masks, and both were wearing gloves.

"Crap," she said. "You're right, Dave. It gives us a time and that's about it."

"Not quite," Dave said. "I think it tells us something more. I suspect we're dealing with some genuine bad guys. They're no doubt in the system; hence the gloves. That means someone took their fingerprints somewhere along the way, and they'll turn up in AFIS. They're also wearing masks. That means their mug shots are on somebody's facial recognition program as well. Now that we know that, I'll go back to working on the background check and see if it'll tell me where Guy Machett's life intersected with these thugs."

"You do that."

As Joanna ended the call, another one came in. Chief Bernard's name showed on the caller-ID screen. "Jaime and Dave made a hell of a catch on that video feed," he said. "You can tell them I said so."

"I will," Joanna said.

"What about that pack of reporters? Are they still milling around outside?"

Joanna walked as far as the front door and peered outside. "Affirmative," she said. "They're all lying in wait and most likely won't leave until somebody talks to them. Are you coming back?"

Alvin sighed. "I guess I'd better come face the music. Doing a press conference with no next-of-kin information isn't my idea of a picnic. Any progress on that?"

"Dave didn't mention it, so I guess the answer is no. He'll be in a better position to tell us about Guy's friends and relations once he can lay his hands on Guy's phone and social media records. In the meantime, that's what we should turn our people loose on, too—finding out who his pals are. We also need to know the name of his housecleaner."

"Why's that?"

"The killers most likely wore gloves," Joanna explained, "but Casey Ledford says she found two sets of fingerprints all over the house. The location of some of them suggests they belong to a cleaning lady, most likely. Once we find her, she might be able to tell us if anything important is missing from the house."

"Okay," he agreed. "I'm on my way back. I'll be there soon."

For the next fifteen minutes or so, Joanna waited while Deb and Casey finished gathering their equipment and packing up. When Joanna led them out onto the porch, she found that the collection of media vans had expanded.

Upon seeing them, the crowd of reporters fell silent. Then, as if on cue, Marliss shouted, "Sheriff Brady, are you going to give us a briefing now?"

"No," Chief Bernard said, striding into view. "This crime scene is in my jurisdiction, and I'll be doing the briefing. The sheriff's department is working this case jointly, however, and Sheriff Brady is welcome to join me."

For the next interminable half hour Joanna stood next to Alvin Bernard on Guy Machett's front porch while the reporters lobbed one question after another in their direction. Despite the lights from the various cameras, Joanna was able to see some of the folks assembled outside the fence. She was disappointed but not surprised that Ruth Nolan was among them. Joanna had hoped that Marliss would have had enough sense to take the girl home. Naturally she had not.

Things were starting to wind down when Joanna's phone rang in her shirt pocket. Excusing herself, she hurried inside.

"Okay," Dave Hollicker said. "The background check Claire Newmark sent has been a great help. I have the names of Guy Machett's next of kin. His mother, Selma, and sister, Liza, both live in Great Barrington, Massachusetts. I can't find a phone listing for the mother, but I'm texting you one for the sister along with the nonemergency phone number for the Great Barrington Police Department."

"Thanks, Dave," Joanna said. "That's a huge help. I'll give the information to Chief Bernard as soon as he finishes the briefing."

"What information?" Chief Bernard asked, following Joanna into the house.

Joanna opened the text application and handed him the phone. He looked at his phone and then at his watch. "It's midnight on the East Coast," he said. "Since it's a joint operation and I just did the briefing, how about if you handle next of kin?"

Which is how, a few minutes later, Joanna found herself speaking to the clerk who answered the phone at the Great Barrington Police Department. Once she explained that she needed someone to do a next-of-kin notification to either Selma Machett or her daughter, Liza, Joanna wasn't the least bit surprised to be put on hold. She also wasn't surprised by the extended delay before someone else picked up the phone, but she was surprised by the way he answered the phone.

"Homicide, Detective Franklin."

"I'm sorry," Joanna said quickly, switching the phone to speaker. "I'm afraid there's been a slight misunderstanding. I'm Sheriff Joanna Brady, calling from Bisbee, Arizona. I didn't want to speak to a homicide detective. The homicide is here on my end. I'm looking for someone to do a next-of-kin notification."

"They said you were looking for Selma Machett," Detective Franklin said. "You missed her. She's deceased. Her funeral was Thursday. You're saying someone else is dead?"

"Her son, Guy Machett," Joanna answered. "He was found murdered in his home here in Bisbee, Arizona, earlier today. Perhaps you could put me in touch with his sister, then. I believe her name is Liza."

"No can do," Detective Franklin said.

"Why not?"

"Her boss reported her as a missing person when she didn't show up for work yesterday. That's bogus, of course. There's a big difference between going missing and being on the lam. As far as Liza Machett is concerned, I'm pretty sure it's the latter."

"What do you mean?"

"Miss Machett's mother's house burned down Thursday afternoon either during or after the funeral. Miss Machett's land-lady, Olivia Dexter, was found murdered later that same evening. I brought Liza in for questioning because I think there's a good chance she was responsible for both—for the landlady's murder and for the house fire as well, which, by the way, we know for sure was arson. I knew Liza was lying when I talked to her, but I had no way to prove it. I had to let her go. However, when a person of interest in a homicide investigation goes missing the moment she's let loose, it doesn't take a Philadelphia lawyer to figure out what's really going on."

"Do you have any idea where she went?" Joanna asked.

"None at all," Franklin answered, "and believe me, we've been looking. She's not driving. She left her car behind. We've checked car rental agencies, airports, train stations, and bus terminals. I'm guessing she's holed up here in town somewhere."

"Is there a chance she might be responsible for her mother's death as well?"

Detective Franklin laughed heartily. "I like the way you think, Sheriff Brady. Since Liza was Selma's sole beneficiary, I wondered the same thing. I went so far as to check with Selma's doc. He told me Selma had been in hospice for two weeks before she passed and that she definitely died of natural causes. Anything else I can do for you?"

The conversation had taken such a turn that for a moment Joanna had no idea what to say next.

"Are there any other relatives, then?" she asked at last. "Anyone else we should know about?"

"Not around here, certainly," Detective Franklin answered. "I've been asking questions, of course. It turns out Liza's father took off years ago, when she was little. My understanding is that he ran off with another woman. As far as I know, no one's heard a word from him since, but he could still be alive. Do you have a cause of death on your victim?"

"We're not sure at this point. He may have drowned, but he was tortured extensively before he died. Was there any evidence of something like that in the landlady's death?"

"Nope, that was a straight-out strangulation. She was found on the stairway leading to Liza's upstairs apartment. She may have stuck her nose into something Liza was trying to keep quiet and, as a consequence, poor Olivia had to go. That's one theory anyway. We're still referring to Liza as a person of interest in the Dexter homicide, but between you and me, I think she's a lot more than that."

"Is there a chance that Liza's involved in what happened here?" Joanna asked.

"When did your guy die?" Franklin asked.

"Sometime Friday night or early Saturday morning. He was supposed to perform an autopsy on Saturday afternoon. When he didn't show up for that, someone went looking for him and found his body."

"Much as I'd like to say otherwise, I don't see how it's possible for Liza to be involved in what happened on your end. I'd be willing to bet dollars to doughnuts that she's still somewhere right here in Great Barrington. The last time I saw her was early Friday morning. I suppose she could have flown out in time to get to your side of the country and off her brother that night, but like I told you, we've been checking with all the airlines. I can tell you for sure that no one using her ID flew on any commercial flight on Friday. I suppose she could have used fake ID or else have flown private, but that's highly unlikely for someone who earned her living as a waitress in a diner."

When the call ended, Joanna turned to Alvin Bernard.

"That was unexpected," she said.

He nodded. "Sounds like that next-of-kin notification is going to be a problem."

"I'll say," Joanna agreed. "In more ways than one."

CHAPTER 14

"Up and at 'em, Linda," Sam called into the berth above the Peterbilt's cab. "This is the end of the road for you as far as we're concerned, because we've found you another ride. Want me to give you a hand with your stuff?"

It took a moment for Liza to realize first where she was, who she was, and that the truck was no longer moving. Sitting up and throwing off the blanket, she wondered how long she'd slept.

"Coming," she called. It took several long fumbling minutes before she managed to get the scarf on right. Finally finished, she passed down her luggage and purse.

"Sorry I took so long," she said, stepping out of the truck and into what turned out to be haze-covered early morning sunlight. "Where are we?"

"Welcome to Truck City in beautiful Gary, Indiana," Sam told her. "We were planning on taking you all the way into Chicago, but the guy we were supposed to hand you off to there had trouble with his rig on the far side of Detroit. Overnight we hooked you up with a buddy of ours, Howard Prince. Everybody calls him Bruiser. Aimee said you were headed for L.A., and Bruiser is going to Kansas City by way of Des Moines. That'll put you on Interstate 80. The good thing about ol' Bruiser is that he drives weekends. A lot of the guys don't, but Bruiser says he makes better time on Saturday and Sunday than he does during the week."

"Is he here?" Liza asked.

"Nope," Sam answered, picking up Liza's luggage and heading into the building. "He's still about an hour out."

Joe, who had already been inside, hurried out to meet them. "I talked to Bertha, and we're good," he said.

"Who's Bertha?" Liza asked.

"As far as Truck City is concerned"

—Joe grinned—"you should call her Your Royal Highness. She's the old broad who owns the place. She says you're welcome to come on into the truckers' lounge. You can freshen up there and take a shower if you want. There are phones if you need one and some computers, too. You do whatever you need to do. When you finish, go out into the restaurant to wait. Bruiser's gonna have to gas up, but he'll come looking for you when he's ready to rumble."

Sam and Joe escorted Liza into a lounge area that came complete with worn but comfortable leather lounge chairs, several television sets, and a pair of what turned out to be pristinely clean restrooms. Sam set her luggage down outside a door marked HERS.

"You take care now," he said, reaching out and pulling her into a strong-armed hug. "You're doing the right thing getting away from a scumbag like that. A man who would hurt his woman when she's busy fighting cancer..." He stopped and shook his head. "There's words for low-down curs like that, but I can't say none of 'em in front of a lady. Best of luck to you."

When Sam let Liza loose, Joe gave her a hug and an encouraging pat on the shoulder. "If anybody gives you any guff about being here, just tell 'em to talk to Bertha."

Liza nodded. She was worried about being passed off from one set of strangers to another, and some of that discomfort must have showed.

"Don't you worry none about Bruiser," Sam added consolingly. "He talks way too much, which is one of the reasons he drives solo, but the man's a gentleman from the top of his head to the tips of his shoes."

"Boots," Joe interjected. "Bruiser wears boots, not shoes."

"Thank you," Liza said. "Thank you both for everything."

A few minutes after they left, Liza stood in a steaming shower with a powerful stream of water raining down on her naked body. It was odd to feel the water pounding directly on her tender bare scalp and even odder to shower without needing to use shampoo or conditioner.

After the shower she dried off and changed into clean underwear. She still had the small makeup kit that she had kept in her old purse. Once she had fixed her face and rewound the scarf she was ready to face the world again. Or at least the truck stop.

Out in the lounge, she tentatively approached the table where two aging desktop PCs sat side by side. One was taken by a beefy guy who was so completely engrossed in what he was watching that he didn't bother glancing in Liza's direction as she slid onto the chair beside him. What showed on his screen was something a very long way on the wrong side of R-rated, and it made the note taped to the bottom of the PC monitor self-explanatory: CLEAR YOUR HISTORY WHEN YOU LEAVE. WE DON'T WANT TO SEE WHAT YOU'VE BEEN WATCHING.

Using Safari, Liza typed in the words: **Great Barrington Herald**. The **Herald** was the local newspaper, print copies of which were often left behind by customers who breakfasted at Candy's. Until the site came up on the screen, Liza wasn't even sure there was an online edition. What she saw took her breath away. Staring back at her was her own image—a copy of her senior photo taken from Great Barrington High's yearbook, the **Crusader**. According to the caption, Liza Elaine Machett was being sought as a person of interest in the Thursday-night homicide of longtime Great Barrington resident Olivia Octavia Dexter.

With her heart hammering in her chest, Liza quickly closed the page and shut down the search engine. She sidled a glance toward the man beside her. He was too engrossed in the naked images on his screen to pay the slightest attention to hers. She didn't need the reminder from the hand-printed sign to erase her search history before she grabbed her luggage and purse and fled the lounge.

Inside the restaurant, a large woman with a bright red bouffant hairdo and a beaming smile stood at the hostess counter. "I'm Bertha," she announced as she led Liza to a booth near the window. "Hope you enjoyed your shower."

"I did, thank you," Liza said.

"Have yourself some breakfast now," Bertha added kindly, handing over a menu. "Order whatever you want. It's on the house. Someone in your condition needs to keep up her strength. I didn't have cancer at the time, but I had me a husband just like yours once. He's dead and gone now and good riddance. I know, it hurts like hell to leave, but sometimes it's the only thing to do. When Bruiser gets here, I'll let him know where you are."

With that Bertha flounced back to the hostess station, leaving Liza flushed with a combination of embarrassment and guilt. Between them, Candy and Aimee had provided Liza Machett with the perfect disguise. Everybody felt sorry for battered women and for cancer patients, too, and they all wanted to help. It filled Liza with shame to realize she was misleading these wonderful strangers by playing on their pity and their generosity.

How was it possible that she was here, fleeing everything familiar and throwing herself on the mercy of people she didn't even know rather than staying put and taking her chances with Amos Franklin? After all, he wouldn't be able to find any proof that she had done anything wrong because she hadn't. The detective scared her, but what scared her even more was whoever had burned down the house and murdered Olivia. Those people were after her, and they were deadly. Liza had no faith whatsoever that Amos Franklin and the Great Barrington Police Department would be able to offer her enough protection. In fact, given Amos's surly attitude, he was more likely to throw her to the wolves.

"Excuse me, would you be Miss Linda?" someone asked in a distinctly southern drawl.

Finished with her breakfast, Liza had been staring off into space and thinking about her photo on the **Herald** website. Startled out of her reverie, Liza found a tall man standing next to her booth. He was dressed in jeans, a faded flannel shirt, worn black cowboy boots, and an equally worn Stetson. He looked to be somewhere north of sixty. He had piercing blue eyes, and a network of smile lines crisscrossed his weathered cheeks.

Caught unawares, Liza almost blurted out her real name. Instead she managed to stifle the urge and simply nodded her reply.

"I'm Howard," he said. "Are you ready?"

When Liza started to rise, he offered an arm to help her up out of the booth. "My friends all call me Bruiser, my lady. Your coach awaits."

He led her out to the parking area. The coach in question was a sleek red Kenworth hauling a silver trailer. Black letters on the end of the trailer and penciled onto the doors on the cab read PRINCE AND SON TRANSPORT SERVICES, LEXINGTON, KENTUCKY.

"Prince would be my stepdaddy, and I'm the son," Bruiser explained as he stowed Liza's two pieces of luggage in an outside compartment. "He's eighty-seven and doesn't drive anymore, but I'm too damned cheap to change the name. I'd have to paint the whole truck. Besides, I sorta like it. You can ride up above if you want, or down here with me, whichever you prefer."

After spending most of the previous night lying down, Liza was ready to sit up for a while. She almost changed her mind when she climbed into the passenger seat and caught sight of the half-smoked cigar resting in the ashtray. Bruiser bounded into the driver's seat and caught her looking at the cigar. "Hope you don't mind," he said. "The little woman won't let me smoke at home, so I do it on the road."

"I don't mind," Liza said, thinking to herself, **Beggars can't be choosers**.

Sam was right. Bruiser talked. Steadily. He explained that the trip to KC, as he called it, would take eight hours, give or take.

"Assuming the guy's there at the warehouse with his forklift the way he's supposed to be, it'll take us forty-five or so to drop off the load in Des Moines. That'll put us into KC about six o'clock or so. Where you headed next?"

"West," Liza said. "L.A. eventually."

"Let me see what I can do, then. Lots of folks drive back and forth on I-80. I'll see if I can't fix you up with one of them. Not as many on weekends as during the week, but I'm sure we'll find you someone."

Liza settled back in the seat and simply let him talk. And smoke. He spent more than an hour talking into his Bluetooth before he had what he told her was a satisfactory set of drivers for the next leg.

"They'll be great. Kimi Sue and Oxman are a husband and wife team with a cute little dog name Major. They drive for Yellow Freight. We can meet up with them at Turk's in KC and they'll have you in Denver by morning. They'll be going on west from there, to Salt Lake and then south to their home base. They're willing to take you on as far as Salt Lake or else send you south to Albuquerque. It's up to you."

Liza closed her eyes and tried to visualize a map of the United States. She had been as far as New York City a couple of times, and her senior class had taken a trip to D.C. She'd already traveled farther into the interior of the country than she had ever expected to venture. Where was Albuquerque in relation to Bisbee? She was pretty sure Arizona and New Mexico were next door to each other. In Albuquerque maybe she'd only be an hour or so from where Guy lived.

"I'm not sure."

Bruiser laughed. "Well," he said. "You've got yourself plenty of time to think about it, little lady. You just settle back and relax."

With that, he punched in the lighter and pulled out another cigar.

CHAPTER 15

It was almost midnight when Joanna finally pulled into the garage at High Lonesome Ranch. She stopped long enough to key in the alarm code and lock her weapons away in the laundry room safe.

It was strange to come into a house that was dead quiet and empty. No Butch; no Jenny; no Dennis; no dogs running over one another as they raced to greet her. She couldn't remember when that had happened any time in recent history. Lucky and Lady were spending the weekend at Carol's house just up the road, and Desi, as part of his service dog training experience, was in Silver City with Jenny attending his first-ever rodeo.

Having spent a very long day in a pair of unfamiliar boots, Joanna's feet were killing her. The first thing she did upon entering

the kitchen was drop into the breakfast
nook and strip off the offending footwear.
Then, in her stocking feet, she went
looking for food. That was something
else about being home alone. No Butch
meant foraging for herself.

She had made a peanut butter and
jelly sandwich and was about to take the
first bite when the landline phone rang.

"You're home," Butch said, sounding
relieved.

"Just got in," she replied.

"I know. I've been calling every fifteen
minutes."

"Why didn't you call my cell?"

"Because I knew you were dealing with
a homicide," Butch said. "I figured you
had your hands full and thought it
would be better if I talked to you after you
got home. You were gone a long time.
How are things?"

Joanna had taken a bite out of her
sandwich and had to finish chewing and
swallowing before she could answer. She
gave him a shorthand version of Guy
Machett's death, ending with the water-

boarding followed by the failed attempt at resuscitation.

"In other words, he didn't tell them what they wanted to hear or give them what they came to get," Butch replied.

Joanna had come to rely on bouncing ideas off Butch. Now was no exception.

After pouring herself a glass of milk, she told him about the problem with Guy's next-of-kin notification.

"Calling her a person of interest is bogus," Butch observed. "You know as well as I do that's just a way of splitting legal hairs to keep Franklin from having to give her the Miranda warning the moment he lays eyes on her. And if Guy's sister has gone underground, how do you handle the press when you can't do a next-of-kin notification?"

"That's one of the things Alvin and I were huddling about. Everyone who lives on the Vista already knows who died. We can't very well hold up releasing Machett's name until Liza Machett is found. According to the people in Great Barrington, she's Guy's only living relative.

We talked to Madge Livingston. She says she remembers the sister calling some- time in the last month. She said it wasn't a terribly long conversation and that it ended with Guy raising his voice. Madge claims that after that one call, Guy told her that if Liza ever phoned again, she should take a message rather than putting the call through."

"Sounds like there's some bad blood there," Butch suggested. "Is there any chance the sister is responsible for what happened to Guy?"

"That's what we're trying to figure out. If she is, she would have had to hire local talent for the hit. That's not easy to do when you're on one end of the country and your target is on the other."

"Maybe she's in Arizona, too."

"Detective Franklin says not. He claims to have had people checking to see if she purchased an airline ticket. So far no luck on that score. He thinks she's holed up somewhere right there in town with someone helping her stay out of sight."

"There are plenty of airports to choose

from back east," Butch said. "I can't see how Franklin could have checked all of them. How's your mother taking to the idea that you pulled George back into your orbit?" he added, changing the subject.

"How do you think?" Joanna replied. "With two cases pending, we needed an M.E., and we needed one fast. Mother was on the phone to ream me out about it before George made it to the stop sign on Arizona Street. Since he was already in trouble tonight, he went ahead and did Junior's autopsy."

"And?"

"Junior Dowdle died of blunt force trauma from hitting his head on a rock when he fell. He also broke his neck. Either injury would have been fatal, so take your pick. George also found bruising on the small of Junior's back that could be consistent with his being pushed."

"So that's a homicide, too?"

"Looks like," Joanna agreed. "Now that the autopsy's done, George was able to release the body to the mortuary. Junior's funeral is scheduled for late Tuesday morning. That's all the news on my end. How about yours?"

"I called Dr. Ross and told her it's a go on buying Maggie," Butch answered. "I'm hoping Jenny and I can drive up to Payson next weekend to pick her up. Jenny is over the moon. Dennis is pissed. He wants to know when he's getting a horse."

Joanna laughed. "I think he's still a little young."

"That's what I told him." Butch chuckled. "He's a stubborn little guy. Takes after his mom on that score. He was still giving me the cold shoulder when I put him to bed."

"About Maggie," Joanna began. "Don't you think we should try to convince Jenny to change Maggie's name? I mean, what's going to happen when your mother finds out that she shares her name with our new horse?"

"She'll be fit to be tied," Butch said, laughing aloud. "I hope I'm there to see it."

"Yes," Joanna said, "and you know who she'll blame. It won't be her precious son!"

"I'm not worried at all," Butch replied. "If

anyone knows how to handle my mother, you do. Now go to bed and go to sleep. I'm glad you're home safe."

Joanna went to bed, but she didn't go to sleep, not for a long time. For one thing, her conscience was bothering her. She hadn't liked Guy Machett. In fact, she had been less than kind to him on occasion, but she certainly hadn't wished him ill. And no one, arrogant asshole or not, deserved the kind of treatment that had been visited on him. The level of violence involved in Guy's death indicated the existence of some kind of secret life. The search warrant requests for phone, Internet, and bank records were being processed, but Dave Hollicker said it was unlikely that he'll have any results to work with on that score before Monday.

Then there was Junior. Poor Junior had been anything but arrogant. In fact, he appeared to be innocence personified, but he was dead, too. Was he also involved in some kind of secret life that Moe and Daisy Maxwell knew nothing about? Now that George Winfield had found the bruising and declared Junior's death a homicide, it was time to take a closer look at that crime scene. Someone must have been in the cave with Junior when he died, someone who had gone in and out of the cave by slithering under the grate the same way Junior had.

Joanna remembered that after Adam Wilson had used his saw to cut through the grating, he had wrenched it open wide enough for people to pass through, but the metal bars themselves were still sitting there, cemented into the limestone. Joanna sat up in bed and used her iPhone to write herself a note: **Find out if Casey dusted the grating for prints.**

Feeling she had finally done something constructive, Joanna put down the phone and tried to sleep. Then, just as she was about to drift off, she remembered little purple-haired Ruth Nolan trotting along at Marliss Shackleford's side. Ruth had used her self-proclaimed status as a blogger to justify her presence at the Machett crime scene. If she was pals with Marliss Shackleford, the girl probably also viewed herself as something of an intrepid reporter.

The thing that made Joanna's eyes pop back open was the realization that Ruth's family lived just up the street from Moe and Daisy's house. Ernie had questioned the next-door neighbors, the Radners and their son, Jason. They had claimed no knowledge about what had happened. Now Joanna found herself wondering if anyone had bothered to interview Ruth or Lucas Nolan. They were kids who lived on the same street. They were also kids who didn't seem to have the same kind of parental supervision as some of the other kids in town. If the mother had a reputation for staying out until all hours, maybe the kids came and went at odd hours, too.

Back at the Machett crime scene Ruth Nolan had asked Joanna for an interview. That was a request Joanna was now prepared to grant at the first possible opportunity. Before she did so, though, Joanna planned to take a look at Ruth's blog and see what kind of stuff was posted there.

With that much resolved in her head, Joanna was finally able to fall asleep.

CHAPTER 16

Bruiser handed Liza off to Kimi Sue and Jonathan "Oxman" Warner in the coffee shop at All Truck Travel outside of Kansas City. Based on size alone, it was clear why Howard Prince had earned the moniker Bruiser. It wasn't at all clear how Jonathan had become Oxman, but no one bothered explaining the origin of the nickname to Liza, and she didn't ask. Once turned loose, however, her new drivers told her everything else.

Kimi Sue and Oxman were a cheerful couple in their late forties. Onetime banking executives from Columbus, Ohio, they had been forced out of their former careers by a series of bank consolidations that had occurred in the late nineties. Lucky enough to come away with generous severance packages, they had pooled their resources, bought a truck, gotten their CDLs, and taken their show on the road. Fifteen years later they were still traveling together, and, to all appearances, enjoying it immensely. They now owned a home in Barstow, California, the home base of the trucking firm they worked for, but they generally spent very little time there. Instead, they traveled the country eighteen-wheeler style with Major, their tiny goateed Yorkie, along for the ride. Kimi Sue estimated that they listened to at least two hundred books a year as their truck rolled back and forth across the country.

Even though Bruiser had long since taken his leave, Kimi Sue and Oxman were content to hang around the truck stop, chewing the fat with friends, until well after dark. "Driving directly into the sun is a killer," Kimi Sue explained. "We usually take an afternoon break until after the sun goes down and then we drive through the night. At least that's what we do when we're heading west."

While the driving team was taking a

break, Liza took one, too. Leaving Kimi Sue and Oxman in the truckers' lounge, she went into the restaurant and took a seat at the counter, where it felt odd to be on the customer side of things. Ready for a hot meal, she ordered the daily special —fried pork chops, mashed potatoes, and green beans. The pork chops were fine, the mash was instant. The green beans were canned and would never have made the cut at Candy's. At the end of her meal, when the waitress brought Liza a final coffee refill, she told Liza about her mother who had just been diagnosed with breast cancer and who would be having a lumpectomy the following week.

That was something Liza had learned. The scarf that worked so effectively as a disguise was also a license for strangers to strike up unwelcome conversations about their own or their friends' or relatives' battles or near misses with cancer. When the waitress walked away, the man seated next to Liza picked up the cancer thread and ran with it.

"A lot of people from around here head

down to MD Anderson for cancer treatment," he said. "They're supposed to be good."

Liza had noticed the man when he came in. Wearing a sports jacket, white shirt, and tie, he was better dressed than most of the people in the restaurant. She had him pegged as a salesman of some kind. His next words threw her.

"So what part of Massachusetts are you from?" he asked.

Liza almost choked on her coffee. How did he know that's where she was from? Was he one of the people following her? If so, how could they possibly know she was here? What were his intentions? Would he try to snag her outside in the parking lot and keep her from making it back to the truck?

Feeling as though she had been stripped of all her supposedly effective disguises, Liza looked around desperately for help. The waitress, coffeepot in hand, was at the far end of the counter. Kimi Sue and Oxman had come into the restaurant, but they were seated in the section reserved for professional drivers.

The man next to her glanced in her direction, as if waiting for an answer. Had he seen her picture in the news and was he mentally comparing that high school photograph from the **Herald** with the features of the woman next to him?

"Boston," she murmured. It was the best she could do and as far away from Great Barrington as she could manage.

"Thought so," he said with a grin. "I can tell a Boston accent a mile away."

So that was it—her accent! On the one hand, she was relieved. On the other hand, it was a blow to her confidence. What good were disguises if someone could suss out where she was from the moment she opened her mouth? The less she spoke to anyone, the better.

"Is that where you're headed?" he asked.

"My aunt lives in Dallas," she said. "I'm going to visit her."

When Kimi Sue stood up to leave, Liza happily followed suit. "Nice talking to you," she said to the man, whose dinner order had just arrived. After paying her tab, she headed for her eighteen-wheeled moving refuge. Crossing the parking lot, she had to force herself to walk rather than run.

Once at the rig, Kimi Sue gave Liza the option of riding up front with whoever was doing the driving at the time or using the sleeping compartment upstairs, which she would most likely have to share with its usual occupant, Major.

Having spent ten of the previous twelve hours with Bruiser, a regular fire hose of conversation, Liza didn't have a problem making the choice. "I'll take the bunk," she said. "But are you sure you don't mind? If one of you needs to sleep, I'll be glad to come back down."

"Don't you worry about us, honey," Kimi Sue said. "It's Oxman's turn to drive. After all these years, I can sleep damned near anywhere. I'll grab some shut-eye between now and the next fuel stop. If his back is bothering him by then, he might want to go upstairs. If not, we'll leave you be. And don't mind Major. His bark is worse than his bite."

Clearly, Major was not fond of having strangers invade his space. When Liza first came up into the bunk, he barked nonstop for the next half hour. By then Liza was seriously questioning her decision. At last, though, with one final grumbling bark, Major turned tail and retreated to the far end of the bunk, where he curled up on one of the two pillows, daring Liza to even try appropriating one of those. For a long time, she simply sat on the edge of the bed, safe in her traveling cocoon, sensing the passage of miles and marveling at how much bigger this long swath of country was— bigger than she had ever imagined. When it finally came time to sleep, she curled up across the foot of the bed, careful to keep from coming into too close contact with the dog's declared territory.

They stopped for fuel at a place called Hank's, a truck stop on the far side of Topeka, a place so deep in the middle of nowhere that no other lights were visible in any direction. During Bruiser's interminable conversation, he had explained how some male truck drivers used empty milk or juice jars to relieve themselves along the road without having to make numerous stops. The bottle routine evidently didn't work for Kimi Sue, and Liza knew it wouldn't work for her, either.

While waiting for Kimi Sue to exit the restroom, Liza stood in front of the cashier staring up at a huge framed map of the United States that served as a wall decoration. The map depicted the country's system of interstates with references to major cities rather than small ones.

Studying it, Liza retraced her travels, remembering how long it had taken to get from place to place. Now, staring at New Mexico and the distance from Albuquerque to where she knew Bisbee must be, she realized that she had been sadly mistaken about how long it would take her to get from one to the other. Still, going south from Denver seemed like a good bet.

"Planning your route?" Kimi Sue asked.

Liza nodded.

"Where do you want to end up?"

"L.A."

"You could stick with us," Kimi Sue suggested. "We'll be back in Barstow by the end of next week. But you'll get there faster if you head down to I-10. Lots of long-haul guys there. Someone in the UR will find a good one for you."

"The UR?" Liza asked.

"The Underground Railroad. I thought you knew," Kimi Sue said. "That's what we call it. With me it was growing up with a father who beat my mother. With Oxman it was the other way around—his mother was the violent one. But we both grew up living that nightmare. It's one of the reasons we never had kids. We didn't want to put anyone else through that kind of living hell."

When Liza climbed back up into the upper berth, Major glowered at her, but he was now resigned enough to her presence that he didn't bother barking this time. She remembered what Bertha had said to her in the restaurant where Joe and Sam had dropped her off—that she'd once had a husband she'd had to put in her rearview mirror. Sam had hinted about some kind of violence in his past, and so had Bruiser. His truck driving company partnership had been in conjunction with a stepfather rather than a father.

And what did that say about Candy Small? When he had put those telltale bruises on her arm, he had known exactly what he was doing. Was it something he had seen as a kid with his father taking his frustrations out on his mother? Or perhaps it was the other way around. Maybe Candy was a confirmed bachelor for the same reason Kimi Sue and Oxman didn't have kids—because he didn't trust himself to be any better at marriage than his parents had been. And what about Aimee and the women who worked in that salon that was really a front for a mostly invisible women's shelter? Were they all victims, too? If so, Liza realized, the numbers were staggering. She had grown up trapped in her own particular brand of misery. She had always known that her own life was bad, but it had somehow escaped her understanding that other people's lives might have been just as bad if not worse.

Now, here she was benefiting from all those other people's experiences and from their misery as well. The UR, as Kimi Sue called it, was a loose-knit but effective army dedicated to rescuing domestic violence victims, one battered spouse at a time. It occurred to Liza then that perhaps she did belong here. The obvious bruises Candy had placed on her arm were phony, but the physical abuse she had suffered as a child at her mother's hands had been real enough. It turned out her mother's violence was the price of admission for this journey and for what she had originally considered to be undeserved assistance from this cadre of kind and motivated folks.

Traveling through the night, Liza no longer felt undeserving. With that thought in mind, she took off her scarf and folded the long strip of material into a small silk square. Holding it close to her breast, she closed her eyes and fell asleep.

CHAPTER 17

In the dream Joanna was running desperately after Dennis, who flew down High Lonesome Road, riding bareback on Spot. The horse was racing at a full gallop. Joanna chased after them, barefoot, screaming at Dennis that he needed to stop—that the horse couldn't see where she was going. All he did was turn back, look at her, laugh, wave, and keep right on going.

It was a relief when her rooster-crowing telephone awakened her out of the nightmare. "Good morning," George Winfield said. "Just like old times. I'm on my way to do the Machett autopsy. When I came through Bakerville, Daisy's was open, so I decided to stop in for breakfast. Care to join me?"

"I'm surprised they're open," Joanna

said.

"So am I," George agreed, "but since they are, I wanted to give them my business—as a show of solidarity if nothing else."

"Where's Mom?" Joanna asked.

"Ellie was asleep when I got home last night, or at least she pretended to be, and she was still asleep just now when I left. If I can finish the autopsy in time to make it to church, I might start to worm my way back into her good graces. She has dinner plans scheduled for this evening. If I know what's good for me, I won't be late or absent."

"I'll come to breakfast," Joanna agreed, "but I have to shower and dress first."

"Take your time," George said. "I'll sit here, look at the paper, and drink coffee. Matt Keller is meeting me at the morgue at nine, so there's no rush."

"Since this is a joint case, do you want one of my people there?" Joanna asked.

"Up to you," George said. "It's Sunday. With two separate cases to solve, you've got to be chewing up overtime like crazy."

That was true. When Joanna had handed out work assignments for today, she had hoped that Guy Machett's autopsy wouldn't happen until Monday. Doing it on Sunday would increase the cost if she had to pay for one of her detectives to be on hand to witness the procedure. With Matt there, it wasn't as vital to have one of her people present, but stil...

"You could do it," George pointed out, interrupting her thought process. "You're on salary. You get paid the same no matter how many hours you work. As you said, it's a joint operation. I know things are all hunky-dory with Alvin Bernard right now, but if that goes south, you're going to want your department to have its own record of what went on during the autopsy."

"I've witnessed some autopsies," Joanna cautioned, "but not that many."

"Neither has Matt Keller," George advised. "That's one of the reasons I think you should be there."

Joanna liked the fact that George was a straight shooter. When he passed out unsolicited advice, she tended to pay attention.

"Fair enough," she said. "I'm on my way."

With no kids to juggle, no animals to feed, no pets to dodge, and no breakfast to eat, Joanna was showered, dressed, and in the car in record time. She paused at the stop sign on High Lonesome Road long enough to send a text to Casey asking if she had dusted the metal grate for fingerprints.

Inside Daisy's, Joanna was surprised to find Moe Maxwell stationed at the front door with a stack of menus in hand. She was dismayed not only at finding Moe filling in at Junior's usual station but at his being there at all. Her thoughts must have been written on her features because Moe's face darkened.

"I told Daisy we had to open," he explained. "All we were doing was sitting at home, crying, and driving each other nuts. Besides, you can't leave a restaurant inventory of food sitting around forever—use it or lose it."

George waved to her from the far corner of the room. "Don't bother with a menu,"

Joanna told Moe. "I know what I want, and you don't need to lead me to the table, either. I can find my way."

"Coffee?" Moe asked.

"Please."

While he went off to fetch it, George looked at her over the top of his reading glasses as well as over the top of the print edition of the **Arizona Daily Sun**. "Hope you didn't make the mistake of suggesting that it was too early for Moe and Daisy to be back at work. I did, and he nearly bit my head off."

Moe arrived at their booth with coffeepot in hand. He filled Joanna's mug. Then, without a word, he slopped enough coffee into George's mug to top it off before stomping away.

"Fortunately I was smart enough to keep my mouth shut," Joanna said. Then, after pausing long enough to take a sip of coffee, she added, "I'm glad to have you back."

George frowned. "That's the same thing Madge said last night when she called— that she was glad I'm back. I'm not, really.

I told you I'd help you with these two cases, but that's it. Your mother and I have plans to leave town next week, and we're going. In the unlikely event that you make a quick arrest and the case goes to trial before we get back in October, then I'll have to fly in to testify if need be, but this isn't a permanent arrangement."

Moe came over to take their order. The retired letter carrier wasn't especially good when it came to taking orders or waiting tables, so it took some time. Once Moe walked away, George apologized to Joanna. "I didn't mean to growl at you, but I spent too many of the years with my first wife working too hard and not paying attention to the relationship. I'm not making the same mistake with Ellie. I said as much to Claire Newmark, too."

"Got it," Joanna said. "I won't ask again. Now, what else can you tell me about Junior's autopsy?"

"He died sometime around midnight," George answered. "The bruising on his back would be consistent with his being shoved from behind and propelled forward with considerable force, most likely by a blunt object of some kind—a round blunt object, the business end of a baseball bat perhaps. I was surprised by the amount of animal hair I found on his clothing—make that on the front of his clothing. Do Moe and Daisy have a number of pets?"

"The animals didn't belong to Moe and Daisy," Joanna answered grimly. "They were victims, too. They were dropped off the ledge alive and left to die. There were four animals in all. Three of them were already dead when Junior landed on top of them. The fourth, a kitten, is still alive—mutilated and badly injured but still alive. Millicent Ross is working to save it. We've also sent evidence from both the living kitten and the dead animals to the State Patrol crime lab in Tucson in hopes of locating human DNA."

George sipped his coffee reflectively. "It sounds to me as though you're dealing with a serial killer's starter kit and a starter victim, too."

"That thought crossed my mind," Joanna agreed. "Is there any chance

Guy's murder and Junior's are related?"

George shook his head. "I don't think so. The two incidents are very different. What happened to Junior is consistent with an unprovoked attack. His back was turned. No defensive wounds at all. I'd say he was taken completely by surprise."

"Do you think his killer might have been someone he knew?" Joanna asked.

"Possibly," George agreed. "Guy Machett, on the other hand, tried to fight off his attackers. He had a number of visible defensive wounds, and I should be able to get scrapings from under his fingernails."

"What about the burns?" Joanna asked. "If we locate the weapon, do you think you'll be able to match his wounds to that?"

"Possibly," George said, "although I'm not sure. If you locate the weapon, however, there may be DNA evidence on it as well as on the duct tape that was used to secure him to the chair. Did you find any rolls of tape at the scene?"

"Only remnants," Joanna answered. "There weren't any rolls in Guy's garage, either. I don't think Dr. Machett was a DIY kind of person."

"So we're operating on the assumption that the killers came prepared with both the tape and the stun gun."

Joanna nodded. "We're also hoping that some of the perpetrators' DNA will show up on the tape, too. After all, that's what duct tape does—it sticks to things."

"Since Guy is mentioned by name in the article in the **Sun,** I assume that means you've located his next of kin?"

"No such luck." Joanna went on to explain everything Amos Franklin had told her about Guy's family and about the sister who had mysteriously disappeared.

"In other words, after the autopsy, I won't be releasing the body to a mortuary?"

"Not for the time being," Joanna said. "Not until we find some kind of family connection."

Their food came. Moe had mixed up the orders. Joanna waited until his back was turned before she traded her platter of over-easy eggs for George's over-hard. Considering what was coming, Joanna surprised herself by falling on her food as though she was starving—because she was. The paltry nourishment from last night's peanut butter sandwich had long since disappeared. When the bill came, George grabbed it first and insisted on paying. Ten minutes later, they pulled their respective vehicles into the parking lot at the M.E.'s office. They found Detective Keller, already green around the gills, pacing nervously back and forth in front of the office door.

"You took long enough," he grumbled.

Matt made it through the cataloguing of the visible wounds and the fingernail scraping, but once the first major incision was made, the detective bailed. "I told you he was a newbie," George said under his breath over the sound of Matt's retching from the lab's restroom. Gritting her teeth to choke back her own nausea, Joanna nodded and held her ground.

Sometime later George finally nodded more to himself than to anyone else. "Just as I suspected. Guy Machett drowned. The bruising on the back of his neck suggests that he drowned because someone bodily held his head under water."

By then Matt had eased his way back into the room and stood warily on the perimeter. "It's homicide, then?" he asked.

"Yes," George told him, snapping off his gloves. "Definitely a homicide."

Joanna let herself out the back door. She stood next to her Yukon in the parking lot behind the morgue, grateful for the blue sky arching overhead and for the heat of the late morning sun shining down on her body.

"Sorry about that," Matt Keller said, coming out to join her. His color was somewhat better, but she could tell he was embarrassed by his squeamishness. "Chief Bernard asked me to come give him a verbal briefing on the autopsy before we meet up with you and your people at one. I'd better get going, unless there's something else you want me to do here."

Down the canyon and just visible on the flank of the hill, Joanna caught a glimpse of St. Dominick's where Mass had most likely just ended. Moe and Daisy's place was just up the hill from the church. Beyond that was the house Ruth and Lucas Nolan shared with their mother. Joanna had meant to ask either Marliss or Ruth for the name of Ruth's blog so she could glance at it before the interview. Now, though, on the off chance that the budding reporter might be able to shed some light on Junior Dowdle's killer, Joanna wanted that interview to happen sooner than later. Reading the blog entries could wait.

"Go brief your chief," Joanna said, "but just out of curiosity, did you do in-depth interviews with either Lucas or Ruth Nolan?" Joanna asked.

"Since they live just up the street from Moe and Daisy, I talked to both of them," Matt said. "Didn't get much."

"Ruth showed up at the crime scene with Marliss last night and asked to do an interview with me. I gave her the bum's rush, but maybe doing the interview would be a good idea. It might give me a chance to ask her some questions as well."

Once Matt left, Joanna did the same. Driving past St. Dom's, she noticed that the parking lot was empty. Rebecca Nolan's house on O'Hara, a small wooden rental with a tin roof, was perched on the hillside ten steps down from street level. When Joanna knocked on the wobbly screen door, Rebecca herself, barefoot and wearing a bathrobe, came to the door.

"Sheriff Brady," she exclaimed in surprise, peering around the door inside the screen. "What are you doing here?"

"I was hoping to talk to Ruth," Joanna said.

"What about?"

"She requested an interview last night," Joanna said, "for her blog. I was too busy then, but I have some time this morning. Is she available?"

"Oh, my," Rebecca said with a harsh laugh that sent a fog of boozy breath out through the screen. "Not that blog nonsense again. I'm afraid I've unleashed a monster on the world. It was an English writing assignment I gave her and Lucas several months ago. Now she's gone nuts. I keep telling her that the world isn't ready for a fourteen-year-old blogger."

"Who is it, Mom?" Ruth asked from somewhere behind her mother.

Rebecca spun around. "It's Sheriff Brady," she grumbled. "I keep telling you that you shouldn't be bothering important people with requests for interviews."

"It's no bother," Joanna replied, making sure that her voice carried through the open doorway to the ears of the purple-haired girl, standing listening but invisible behind her mother's back. "I was in the neighborhood and thought, if Ruth was home, perhaps we could do it now."

"I have time," Ruth interjected quickly. "Please, Mom. It's a chance to interview a real sheriff."

"Oh, I suppose it's all right," Rebecca conceded, "but don't make a pest of yourself. You're just a kid. There's no reason Sheriff Brady should bother giving you the time of day."

With that, Rebecca Nolan disappeared into the house. As soon as she was out of the way, Ruth's eager face appeared around the edge of the door. Unlike her mother, Ruth was fully dressed in a T-shirt and a pair of shorts.

"Let me go get my phone," she said. "I'll be right back."

Joanna waited for a few moments on the tiny landing that constituted the house's front porch. Glancing up at the mountain from where she stood, she could barely see the sharp edges in the rocks that marked the old Glory Hole. When Ruth reappeared, she had put on a pair of flip-flops and was carrying an old-style flip-top cell phone. An orange stripe had been added to her otherwise mostly purple hair, which was pulled back in a multicolored ponytail.

"You really don't mind?" Ruth asked eagerly.

"No, I don't," Joanna said. "Where would you like to do the interview? There's really no place to sit here. My car is up on the street. Is that all right?"

"The car is fine," Ruth said.

Joanna led the way back to the Yukon.

When she opened the rear passenger door, the girl stopped and stared. The SUV had been rigged out as a patrol vehicle, complete with a protective screen between the front and back seats and again between the backseat and the luggage compartment. That way prisoners and suspects could be transported safely in the backseat without endangering whoever was at the wheel. The vehicle came complete with a full complement of radio transmission gear and an onboard computer. On the passenger side of the drive shaft sat Joanna's holstered shotgun.

"Can you really shoot that thing?" Ruth asked, pointing at the weapon.

"Can and do," Joanna replied. "I also have one of these." She patted the holstered Glock on her hip. "I can shoot this as well. I'm expected to maintain the same kind of shooting proficiency as the rest of my officers."

"I have to sit in the back, like a prisoner or something?" Ruth asked.

"That's right," Joanna replied with a smile. "As long as the shotgun is up front, you have to be in the back."

"And there really aren't any door handles back here?"

"That's right," Joanna said. "Nobody in back gets out until I let them out." Closing the door, she walked around to the driver's door and climbed in. "Now tell me, what did you want to ask?"

When she looked back at Ruth, the girl had her phone out and was using her thumbs to type in a message at what, to Joanna, appeared to be lightning speed. Joanna's texting skills weren't up to recording an entire interview.

"Did you always want to be sheriff?" Ruth asked.

"Not really," Joanna answered. "My husband wanted to be sheriff. He died in a line-of-duty shooting and the people elected me in his place. In other words, my becoming sheriff was more or less an accident. That was seven years ago now, though, and it turns out I love it."

"What's the worst thing about being sheriff?"

"Having to tell someone their loved one

is dead."

"Like Mr. and Mrs. Maxwell with Junior?"

"That's right."

"What's the best thing?"

"Locking up a serious criminal and knowing that society is protected from additional harm from that individual for a very long time."

"Like lock them up and throw away the key?"

Joanna laughed. "Exactly."

"Were you an only child?"

The unexpected question wasn't an easy one to answer. Joanna's older brother had been born before her parents married and had been given up for adoption. She hadn't met him until long after her father was dead and she herself was an adult.

"Yes," she said after a moment's pause. "I was raised as an only child."

"I wish I was," Ruth said pensively. "Lucas is the perfect one. I'm not. He's way smarter than I am, especially at math. I'm better at English, though, and I read more than he does."

"We can't all be good at all things,"

Joanna said. "For instance, I'm not nearly as good at texting as you are."

Ruth shrugged. "Maybe I just practice more." She paused for a moment as if thinking about the next question. "Do you think you'll be able to find out what happened to Junior?"

"You need to understand that even the sheriff isn't allowed to comment on an active investigation. I guess I have to say, 'No comment' to that one."

Ruth's face broke into a grin. "I heard you say that to Marliss last night, but I've never had anyone say it to me before. It almost feels like I'm a real reporter or something."

"Aren't you?" Joanna asked.

"I guess."

"But you asked about Junior like you knew him. Did you?"

"I felt sorry for him," Ruth said. "When we first moved here, I'd see him out walking sometimes, but then his parents started locking him in at night. I think they were afraid that he'd get lost or something. At night, when the windows were open, I could hear him crying sometimes. A couple of times, when it was really bad, I went over and sang to him to help settle him down."

Joanna was stunned. "You sang to him?"

Ruth nodded. "I sang some of the songs we learned in Sunday school before Mom made us stop going. You know the ones I mean, 'Jesus Loves Me' and 'This Little Light of Mine.' He really liked those."

Joanna felt a shock of recognition. She remembered Moe and Daisy saying something about Junior claiming he'd sometimes had nighttime visitors. Daisy had insisted the phantom visitors were hallucinations, but now Joanna knew that wasn't true. Junior had had at least one nocturnal visitor. Joanna wondered if there were others.

"Did you go there often?" Joanna asked. "To sing to him, I mean."

"Not often," Ruth answered, "just a couple of times."

"Did you ever see Junior hanging out with anyone?" Joanna asked.

"Jason," Ruth said at once. "Jason Radner."

Noticing movement at the corner of her eye, Joanna saw a towheaded boy, Ruth's brother, Lucas, bound up the stairs. He came over to the Yukon and pressed his face against the rear passenger window.

"Mom says you should come inside," he said to Ruth. "Now," he added. "She says you should stop wasting the sheriff's time."

Joanna climbed out of the Yukon, came around the vehicle, and opened the back door so Ruth could exit.

"Thank you," Ruth said. "Should I send you what I write about you?"

"Please," Joanna answered, "or you could just send me the link to your blog. You can find my work e-mail address on the sheriff's department website."

Ruth nodded. "Okay," she said. "I'll do that."

By then Lucas had already disappeared down the stairs with Ruth trailing behind. Joanna remembered how she had trotted up the stairs, eager to be out of the house. She didn't seem nearly as happy to be going back inside.

Watching her go, Joanna felt a certain sadness. She hoped that neither Jenny nor Dennis would ever feel that way about her—that one of them was wanted and the other was not.

It was clear to her that Ruth Nolan was at war with her mother. Joanna had considerable experience in that kind of intergenerational conflict. In Ruth's case, dyeing her hair purple and singing "Jesus Loves Me" were both acts of rebellion, ones that most likely carried about the same weight in terms of motherly disapproval.

Shaking her head, Joanna put the Yukon in gear and headed out. It was almost time for the meeting she had called, and she didn't want to be late.

CHAPTER 18

It was just after sunrise when Kimi Sue and Oxman's rig pulled into the Trux-Travel truck stop outside Denver. Overnight the immense flatness of the Great Plains had been replaced by the soaring Rockies. When Liza climbed down from her overhead berth into the mountainous chill, she felt stiff and sore as her body protested the long hours of confinement. Kimi Sue had shown Liza how to exercise her ankles to keep them from swelling, and that seemed to be working.

"You might want to bring your stuff inside," Kimi Sue suggested. "William is your next ride, but he won't be here for another hour and a half. Grab a shower and some breakfast. William drives a tanker truck. We told him he should look for the lady with the bright blue head scarf."

After bidding Kimi Sue good-bye, Liza immediately took a shower. Because she didn't have to shampoo or rinse her hair, showering was a surprisingly fast process. Dressed in a change of clothing, she ventured out into the truckers' lounge. Once again, there was a bank of computers—three of them this time—situated along one wall. Since most of the truckers seemed to be focused on their own laptops, iPads, or iPhones, the idle PCs sat there in lonely, unused splendor.

Availing herself of one of those, Liza did a preliminary search for used car dealerships in Albuquerque. Kimi Sue had told her that the next driver would be going all the way to I-10, but Liza had already decided that she'd cut herself loose from the Underground Railway in Albuquerque and find her own transportation from there to Bisbee.

After locating several possible dealerships and jotting down the addresses, she gave herself permission to check out the news from Great Barrington. The headline on the **Herald**'s website took Liza's breath away: BELOVED RESTAURATEUR, CLIFFORD SMALL, DEAD AT AGE 53.

Local restaurant icon, Clifford (Candy) Small, age 53, was found dead in the burned-out ruins of his house just after 7 AM today. The Great Barrington Fire Department has labeled the fire suspicious. The incident is being investigated by both local fire and police departments.

This is breaking news. No further details are available at this time.

Astonished and horrified, Liza read through the brief piece again. Then, before anyone could read the story over her shoulder, she closed the website, erased her history, and fled the room. Outside, she paced back and forth in the chill air. Candy was dead, too? Why, because he had helped her? What other reason could there be? That made his death Liza's fault, too. Awash in guilt, she realized that if she was a person of interest in Olivia's case, she would most likely be one in this case as well. That meant the authorities would ramp up their search for her, and so would whoever else was after her. Liza had no doubt that those people were behind this new fire, the one in which Candy had perished.

Then another thought crossed her mind. What if the people who were chasing Liza had somehow forced Candy to divulge where she was, how she was traveling, and who was helping her? Did that mean that now all those Underground Railroad people were also in danger—Aimee, Sam and Joe, and Bruiser as well as Kimi Sue and Oxman? Standing shivering and with her teeth chattering, she stared back at the building—at the people coming and going, at the trucks and cars pulling in and out. Her pursuers could be any of those passing people. By now, despite all the Underground Railroad's careful precautions, the bad guys might already know exactly where she was.

It took all of Liza's willpower to stay where she was and not go racing for the nearest hiding place, wherever that might be.

She had no idea how long she stood there, shivering in the frigid wind blowing down from the snowcapped peaks. At last the cold forced her inside. She slunk into the truck stop's restaurant and collapsed in the booth farthest from the front door that still offered a clear view of the entrance. Not that seeing the people coming and going would do her any good. Liza didn't know the faces of the people who were chasing her; she wouldn't have recognized them if they showed up at the same booth and sat down directly across the table from her.

A waitress arrived to take Liza's order. She wore her hair in an old-fashioned beehive that reminded Liza of Honey's back home. Thinking about Honey reminded her of Candy, and thinking about Candy caused unbidden tears to spring to her eyes before she could blurt out her order.

"Sweetie pie," the waitress said consolingly, "you just sit here and take a deep breath. Things may be bad right now, but they're bound to get better. What you need is something to eat. How about some bacon and eggs?"

Liza nodded. "Over easy, please, and some coffee, too," she managed. "Black coffee."

The coffee came. Liza dried her tears with some of the extra napkins the waitress had thoughtfully delivered along with the coffee. She sat with her hands wrapped around the cheap china mug hoping that the heat from the cup would leach into her chilled body.

When breakfast came, Liza tried to eat it. She downed one of the slices of bacon and nibbled at the toast, but that was all. She understood that what should she do now was walk as far as the nearest police station and turn herself in. If she didn't, other people might die, and if she did? That left the very real possibility that **she** might die, too. Just because she was in a jail somewhere wouldn't necessarily mean she was safe. The people who were after her were obviously ruthless and would stop at nothing.

No, she decided, turning herself in wasn't the answer, at least not yet. She'd go to Bisbee, talk with Guy, see if he had any ideas about what this was about— about who was after her and why. She'd ask his advice. After all, he was her big brother. With Candy gone, Guy was the only one left to ask. If he said Liza should turn herself in, she would.

She looked at her luggage. The roll-aboard, still full of the money, was stowed on the bench seat next to her. If whoever was trying to kill her had simply asked her to return the money, she would have done so, no questions asked. After all, it wasn't really hers in the first place. Whatever was left of it—a little under a hundred grand— was blood money now. People had died because of it—her friends had died because of it. Liza didn't know if she'd ever be able to bring herself to touch one of those bills again, much less spend it.

"Excuse me, ma'am," a deep voice asked. "Would you happen to be Linda?"

Liza looked up. The man standing in

front of her was tall and muscular, with
biceps the size of tree trunks. He was also
a walking gallery of tattoos. The tops of
some of the designs peeked out past the
open collar of his denim shirt. Every inch
of bare skin on his arms—from the bottom
of his shirtsleeves to his wrists—was
covered with an uninterrupted layer of
colorful inks, everything from birds to but-
terflies, American flags to golden eagles.
His nose had been broken, most likely
more than once. He was completely
bald—almost as bald as Liza herself.
Clutched in one hand was a John Deere
baseball cap.

Liza's first instinct was to blow him off
and pretend she wasn't his intended
passenger, but at last she managed a
brief nod.

"I'm William, ma'am," he said, grinning
and clapping the cap back on his head.
The grin revealed several missing front
teeth. "William Gray. I'm fueled up and
ready to go anytime you are."

If anyone should have been called
Bruiser or Oxman, this guy was him. The

somewhat dignified name of William didn't
suit him at all. He was fierce-looking. Liza
should have been terrified of him. She
should have stayed where she was and
hitched a ride with someone else. The
problem was, she was even more terrified
of the people who were looking for her—
the people who had killed Candy. No
matter how scary this guy might appear,
he couldn't possibly be that bad.

Liza reached for her bags. "I'm ready,"
she said. "As soon as I pay the bill, we can
be on our way."

Outside William led her to a semi with
two shiny tankers hooked on behind it.
He didn't volunteer what was in the
tanks, and Liza didn't ask. For the first
time there was no overhead berth. That
meant Liza rode in the cab with William,
who chatted away in an amiable fashion.
Liza was so upset over the news of
Candy's death that she had a hard time
listening or responding.

Before, she had ridden along in the
series of rumbling trucks with some confidence that she was doing so under

everyone's radar—that the people who were after her would never be able to pick up her trail. All that had changed. She had told Candy she was going to Arizona. What if he had told someone else?

Thinking about Candy led Liza to thinking about the restaurant. What would happen to the business? With Candy gone, who would take over and run it? And what about all the people who worked there? They would most likely be thrown out of work as well, all because of Liza.

As the tanker truck sped down the road, rather than watching the pavement ahead, Liza kept her eyes glued to the rearview mirror, keeping track of each vehicle that came speeding up behind them. Each time one came a little too close or stayed too long, Liza found herself holding her breath and letting it out only when the worrisome car or truck merged into the other lane and surged past.

"You can stop worrying," William said at last, penetrating her cloud of silence. "There's nobody out there, you know. I've been watching, too, and I ain't seen anybody suspicious."

"Sorry," she said. "I guess I'm just paranoid."

"From the looks of that arm, I'd say you've got good reason. What kind of cancer?" he added. Now that he had her attention, he seemed determined to engage her in conversation, choosing the most obvious option—cancer.

"Breast," she said, "lumpectomy and chemo." The lie came all too easily, without her even having to think about it.

William nodded. "My mom had that," he said. "Seven years ago. They caught it early. Now she does that Susan Komen race thing every year. What's amazing is that she was never a great one for exercising before she got sick. Now she's doing cancer walks and cancer bicycle rides all over the country, which, considering her age, is pretty impressive."

"How old is she?" Liza asked, more courtesy than due to any real interest.

"Seventy-one," William answered. "Other than having that one bout with cancer, the woman's ornery as all get-out and has never been sick a day in her life."

William's cheery answer sent Liza's mind down yet another dark channel. Candy Small hadn't made it to seventy-one, and right that minute, it seemed unlikely that Liza would make it that far, either.

Back in the truck stop in Denver, Liza had already decided that she'd only stick with the next ride as far as Albuquerque, but she didn't mention that to William Gray. As far as he was concerned, she was going all the way to Las Cruces. It wasn't until two in the afternoon when they pulled into the Albuquerque Truck Terminal that she told him she was bailing.

"You're sure?" William asked with a frown. "I've already lined up someone who can meet us in Las Cruces and take you as far as Phoenix."

She didn't want to admit that she was opting out of the Underground Railroad because she was afraid it had been compromised.

"No, thank you," she responded quickly. "I appreciate all your help and concern, but

I'm sure. I have friends in here in Albuquerque," she added, hoping the lie didn't show. "I'll spend a few days with them."

"Give me the address," William said. "I can drop you off."

"No," she insisted. "I already called them. They'll come pick me up."

William wasn't thrilled with the arrangement, but he went along with it. Liza sat in the restaurant and pretended to be texting her friends on the burner phone while she waited for him to refuel and leave. Sitting with the phone in her hand, she wished she could call Guy. She'd had his number once, of course, but that had been in her own phone, the one Candy had taken away from her. The only way to reach Guy now would be to get the number from information, and she didn't want to do that. Instead, she'd wait until she got to Bisbee. She'd go to his office and talk to him face-to-face. Together they'd figure out what to do.

Once William's tanker eased back out onto the roadway, Liza found a pay phone and called a cab. Before it arrived, she went into the restroom with her luggage. Inside the stall, far away from prying eyes, she opened the roll-aboard and let the all-pervading scent of coffee beans overwhelm the restroom's industrial-grade room deodorizer. When this was over, Liza wondered if she'd ever feel the same way about coffee beans.

One by one she counted out fifty of her remaining and still astonishingly fragrant one-hundred-dollar bills and stashed them in the side pocket of her worn Coach purse. Five thousand was the top dollar she was prepared to pay for a vehicle. If she couldn't find a ride for less than that, she was either taking the bus or walking.

CHAPTER 19

Joanna was still in Old Bisbee and on her way to the Justice Center when Butch called. "Jenny's just now loading the horses," he said, "then we'll be heading out."

"You're not staying for the afternoon events?" Joanna asked.

"Jenny's call," Butch said. "For some reason she's ready to go home now. Surprised me, too. It's never happened before. She usually wants to stay until the bitter end. Not today, though, and it's just as well. I'm tired of eating dust, and Denny is cranky, too. He misses his mommy, and I miss my wife. What's happening on your end?"

"I started my day by witnessing Guy Machett's autopsy."

"Great," Butch groaned. "How did he

die?"

"Just what I told you last night—he drowned. I've had people out combing the streets all morning, trying to see if anyone on the Vista saw or heard anything unusual. Dave Hollicker should be off work with a sprained ankle but came in anyway. He's at the department sorting through the information that's coming in from the search warrants. In the meantime, Casey Ledford has driven another load of crime scene evidence up to the Department of Public Safety crime lab in Tucson."

Call waiting buzzed with a blocked number on the screen. With as much as she had going on, Joanna decided she'd better take it. "Another call," she told Butch. "Sorry." She switched over to the incoming call.

"Sheriff Brady?"

The voice was familiar, but Joanna couldn't place it instantly. "Yes."

"Detective Amos Franklin here. Sorry to interrupt your Sunday. I called your department looking for you, and whoever answered the phone there gave me this number. I hope you don't mind. I never let anyone give out my home number."

"It's my cell," Joanna said impatiently, "and no, I don't mind. What's up?"

"We've got a new wrinkle on our end. A man by the name of Clifford Small was found dead in the burned-out wreckage of his home here in Great Barrington early this morning. I waited until our M.E. did the autopsy before I ran up the flag to you. He was Liza Machett's boss."

"Her boss?" Joanna repeated. "Wasn't he the guy who gave Liza Machett a ride home the other night after you interviewed her?"

"A ride to **his** home," Franklin corrected.

"Were he and Liza in a relationship of some kind?"

"Not that I know of," Franklin replied. "Liza Machett worked for him for years —ever since she graduated high school —but everyone I've talked to says it was strictly that—an employee/employer relationship, nothing more."

"No friends with benefits?"

"If it was, nobody's saying," Franklin

replied, "but we're beginning to get a better idea of what we've got here. The autopsy clearly shows that Candy was tortured before he was stabbed, and he was dead before the fire started. The M.E. found no sign of smoke inhalation."

"Candy?" Joanna asked. "I thought you just said his name was Clifford. And you're saying he was tortured?"

"Candy's what everyone in town called him, ever since we were kids, and yes, he was tortured—badly."

"Are you thinking Liza is responsible for what happened to him?"

"I can't see how that's possible unless she had plenty of help. Candy weighed a good three hundred pounds. Liza couldn't be more than a third of that. Besides, call me sexist if you want, but I can't see a woman involved in something where torture is such a big part of it."

"What kind of torture?"

"His fingers and toes were systematically whacked off over a period of time, probably several hours. When the fun and games were over, he was killed with a single stab wound to the heart. That took some physical strength. Again, I don't think a woman could or would have done it."

Joanna thought about the footprints in the blood around the chair in Guy Machett's kitchen, a larger set and a smaller one. A man and a woman together? It was a possibility, and just because the search hadn't shown anyone traveling with Liza Machett's ID didn't rule out the idea of her traveling with fake ID of some kind. Joanna knew there were plenty of places where fake IDs were bought and sold on the open market, even in her small-town corner of the world.

"After Liza disappeared," Detective Franklin continued, "I started looking into a few things, because there were some rumors floating around. Several people suggested that Liza must have come into a substantial sum of money fairly recently. Before the house burned down last week, she'd spent a small fortune cleaning out and redoing her mother's place.

"Once I started asking questions, I

learned that she'd been paying her workers mostly in cash. On a hunch, I called Craig Masters, the guy who runs the local funeral home. Sure enough, part of Selma Machett's final expenses had been paid in advance by Selma herself, but the remainder was paid in cash— thirty one-hundred-dollar bills that Liza handed over the morning of the funeral. According to Craig, that wad of money stunk to high heavens of coffee.

"Then I called another old friend of mine, Nancy Haller, who manages First National Bank and Trust here in Great Barrington. She says that she and her staff have been seeing an influx of what they call 'coffee money' for some time now, for at least the past month or so.

"She says it usually comes into the bank in hundred-dollar denominations. When the first batch showed up, one of the tellers brought it to Nancy's attention. The serial numbers on the bills were so old that most of their contemporaries have been taken out of circulation. It turns out that, other than the smell, these bills were in good shape. Since then Nancy's had her people keep track of the serial numbers, but she also put in a call to someone at the Treasury Department early on because she was afraid they might be dealing with some kind of counterfeit. Treasury sent out an investigator who determined that the bills were real enough. He said not to worry—that it was probably money someone, Selma Machett most likely, had been hoarding for a very long time—the old money-in-the-mattress kind of savings account."

By then, Joanna had pulled the Yukon into the private parking place behind her office at the Justice Center. "How old are these bills exactly?" she asked.

"Most of them date back to the late seventies. Some are a little earlier."

"The money may be what this is all about, then, or it could be something else," Joanna commented. "Whatever the killers are looking for, they're prepared to do whatever's necessary to lay hands on it. Do we have any idea how much money is involved?"

"Not exactly," Detective Franklin replied. "I've spent the morning tracking down everybody who did rehab work on Selma Machett's house. Nobody's willing to give me a straight answer. They're all claiming that it was a volunteer project organized by Candy Small. That's probably because they were paid in cash, and nobody's bothered to declare it as income. When I struck out with them, I checked with several local building supply places and lumberyards.

"It turns out Liza had recently become a very steady customer at more than one of those. Since she paid cash there, too, the stores don't have exact records of what she purchased, but they acknowledge her having ponied up money for a substantial amount of building material—plumbing fixtures, new kitchen appliances, flooring. Based on what I can verify and estimating the rest, I'd say she must have spent at least forty grand just on fixing up the house."

"The same house that burned down the other night," Joanna concluded.

"Correct," Franklin agreed, "all of which leads me to believe that we're talking about a fairly large sum of money since there's still enough of it out there to make it worthwhile to commit three separate murders."

"You've got the drop on us by a few days in all of this," Joanna observed. "We have yet to get responses on our requests for phone and e-mail information. Have you been able to uncover any kind of pattern of communication between Liza and her brother? Are there any records of phone calls or e-mails back and forth between them?"

"Everyone here is saying the same thing—that she and Guy were estranged. We did find a single call placed from Liza Machett's cell phone to a number in Bisbee that we've just now verified as the number for Guy Machett's office. That call was placed after Selma Machett was moved to hospice care and before she died. There's no sign that Liza made any effort to contact him by phone after Selma's death, at least not from her home or cell-phone numbers and not from any of the numbers associated with the restaurant where she worked, including the pay phone there."

"If she has a cell phone, have you tried locating her with that?"

"Yes, we did and came up empty. The last ping from her cell came through the cell tower closest to Candy's house. That was early Friday morning. Since then it's gone dead silent."

"What about e-mail?" Joanna asked.

"If Liza had a computer at home, we didn't find it," Detective Franklin answered. "It could be that it was taken during the break-in at her apartment. Without the computer, we don't know her search engine history, but she did have an e-mail account that we've been able to access. There's a lot of spam on it, mostly shopping sites, but most of her online correspondence was chatting back and forth with friends and some of the other waitresses at work. In other words, Liza Machett wasn't much of a social butterfly."

"No mention of the money or where it

came from?"

"Not a peep. Not a single mention to anyone."

"Given all this," Joanna said, "what's your best guess about what's going on?"

There was a small pause before Franklin answered. "As I said before, one way or another, Liza came into a sizable sum of money, most likely money her mother had in her possession for some time. Other people may have become aware of that money, especially her contractors. It occurred to me that maybe one of them got greedy and thought Liza would be an easy target. I was in the process of looking into the whereabouts of all those guys last night when you called to tell me Liza's brother had been murdered. By the way, so far all the workers are present and accounted for."

"What happened the other night when you brought Liza in for questioning?" Joanna asked.

"I asked all the usual questions. Did she know who might have a grudge against her mother or her or her landlady? She claimed she had no idea, which, I'm now sure, was a straight-out lie. By then she must have figured out that whoever broke into her apartment was really after the money. If she'd had a brain, she would have come clean and given me a chance to help her. Instead, she chose to go into hiding. Given what happened to Olivia Dexter and now Candy Small, whoever is sheltering her isn't likely to come forward."

"You think she's still there?"

"That's what I think," he said.

"But this sounds as though you no longer consider her a suspect."

Amos Franklin sighed. "Unfortunately not. I thought for sure that she was behind the first fire, the one at her mother's house. She couldn't have set it herself, but she could have hired it out and walked away with the insurance proceeds. The fire investigators tell me that both of these fires—the one at Selma Machett's house and the one at Candy Small's place—were set by the same arsonist. I can't find any reason why Liza would have turned against Candy, so now I'm forced to admit that Liza has most likely been targeted, too, the same as her brother was. In fact, there's another possibility. Maybe Liza isn't in hiding at all. Maybe she's already dead, and we just haven't located her body."

"As far as we know, then, what your banker friend calls 'coffee money' is still the only motivating factor," Joanna theorized. "Will she let you know if any more of it surfaces?"

"Yes, and so will any of the other bank branches in town," Franklin replied. "I'm in the process of alerting all of them, but I wish I knew more about what the deal was between Guy Machett and his sister. Obviously something was out of kilter. Knowing what it was might help us. Did he ever confide anything to you about his family background?"

"Guy Machett and I worked together, but we were hardly pals," Joanna responded. "Our relationship never developed to the point of sharing confidences. He kept his distance. The people who worked most closely with him are Madge

Livingston, the woman who was his secretary, and Ralph Whetson, his assistant up at the morgue. My people have already spoken to both those individuals. In the light of what you've just told me, we'll talk to them again. If you'd like to speak to them directly, I'll be happy to send along their contact information."

"Please," Detective Franklin said.

"I'm outside my office right now and late going into a meeting," Joanna said. "Either I'll e-mail you what you need once the meeting is over, or one of my people will be in touch."

"Fair enough," Franklin said.

Feeling that news about Candy Small's murder signaled a sea change in the investigation, Joanna hurried inside, where she found her investigations people assembled in the conference room along with Alvin Bernard and his detective, Matt Keller. Chief Deputy Hadlock was there as well, taking copious notes and preparing for the next journalistic assault. Having seen the collection of media vans in the parking lot as she passed, Joanna suspected that he had called another press conference, which was due to happen soon.

"Sorry I'm late," she apologized as she hurried to the empty chair at the head of the conference table next to Chief Bernard's.

"We figured you'd turn up sooner or later," Alvin observed with a grin. "You look like someone with something important to say. Care to share?"

Joanna nodded. "I just got off the phone with Detective Franklin back in Great Barrington. Clifford Small, also known as Candy—the guy who used to be Liza Machett's boss and the one who took her into his home early Friday morning after she was questioned by the police— was found dead this morning in the burned-out wreckage of his house. He had been tortured and murdered."

"Liza's mother's house was burned down," Deb Howell said. "This is a second case of arson?"

Joanna nodded. "According to Detective Franklin, both fires were likely set by the same arsonist. Presumably whoever set the fire also murdered Mr. Small. According to the autopsy, the victim was dead before the fire started."

"What about the torture?" Ernie Carpenter asked. "Same M.O. as what we've got here?"

"No," Joanna answered. "For one thing, no stun gun was involved. Instead, the victim's fingers and toes were cut off over an extended period of time. Whether or not the bad guys got what they wanted, when it was over, they stabbed the victim to death and then burned down his house with his body inside. So we've got two questions for you to consider: Did Mr. Small tell them what they wanted to know? If so, what was it?

"According to Detective Franklin, Liza Machett has been handing out loads of cash for the past month or so in amounts that don't seem to jibe with her hand-to-mouth waitress existence. A local banker became suspicious about the money because the serial numbers were so old."

"How old?"

"Most of it came from the late seventies; some earlier. Oh, and it all smells of coffee."

"Coffee?" Ernie asked, as if not quite trusting his ears.

"Coffee," Joanna verified.

"How much money?" Jaime Carbajal asked.

"No way to tell," Joanna said, "but it's enough to cause a three-time killer to come calling." Turning her attention to Dave Hollicker, she continued. "Detective Franklin says Liza and Guy were estranged. Has your background check given you any clues about the Machett family dynamics?"

Dave opened his computer and stared at the screen. "As far as I can tell, he was an outstanding citizen. The only thing on his record was a speeding citation when he was eighteen. He owned his own home and carried very little debt. His car was paid for. In contrast, his sister works for minimum wage and just barely makes ends meet."

"In other words, you've been doing background checks on both of them."

"Pretty much," Dave agreed. "Guy's mother died when he was young. His father, Anson, remarried a few years later. Selma, Liza's mother, was Anson Machett's second wife. From what I've been able to learn, Anson deserted the family when Liza was a baby. Guy was your basic overachiever—smart, voted most likely to succeed, class valedictorian. He attended Harvard on a full-ride scholarship. On his college applications, he listed his father as deceased, but so far I'm unable find any verification that Anson Machett is dead.

"It looks like Liza never measured up to her older brother scholastically. She made it through school with only average grades and went to work in Clifford Small's restaurant shortly after high school graduation. There's no indication of any schooling beyond high school."

"It sounds like we have a golden boy on the one hand and an overshadowed sibling on the other," Joanna observed. "That could make for a dicey family dynamic."

"Yeah," Dave continued. "I don't think they're especially close. Guy's phone records came in this morning, a day earlier than I expected them. I found only one call from Massachusetts to him in the six months preceding his death. That one was placed to his office and came from what I've determined to be Liza's cell phone. That call was made about the middle of last month."

"According to Detective Franklin, that's also about the time Selma was moved into hospice care," Joanna supplied. "But that's all? No other telephone backing and forthing between them?"

Dave shook his head. "None, and that seems odd. When someone's dying, that's usually when the relatives—even feuding relatives who hate each other's guts—bury the hatchet temporarily, rally round, and burn up the phone lines. I suppose there could have been e-mail correspondence between them, but so far I haven't been able to get information from Doc Machett's Internet provider. That should come tomorrow."

Joanna noticed that without Guy being there to object, he had been summarily demoted from Dr. Machett to Doc Machett by Dave, and most likely by everyone else in the room as well. He would not have been pleased.

"Anything else interesting?" Joanna asked. "Since Liza came into some money, did he come into a windfall as well?"

Dave clicked over to still another screen. "Not that I can see. His bank records showed up last night. I've been going over them, but there's no sign of any irregular deposits. We did learn a few interesting things, however. For example, we were able to establish the names of both his former cleaning lady, Carmelita Ortiz, and his new one, Carmelita's granddaughter, Josie. Carmelita is having some health issues. Doc Machett left a check for Josie on the kitchen table, which she cashed on Saturday morning. This was only Josie's first week, and she came on Friday. Jaime's going to talk to both Carmelita and Josie later today."

"A new cleaning lady would help explain

why the alarm access code was there on the wall," Deb offered. "It was posted so Josie could let herself in."

"The bank records do reveal that our upstanding Doc Machett did have one dirty little secret," Dave added with a mischievous grin.

"Enough of a secret to get him killed?" Alvin Bernard asked.

"I doubt that," Dave said. "Turns out the M.E. was a nudist who visited nudist colonies all over the Southwest. His favorite is one called the Whetstone Mountain Retreat. According to his credit card records, he spent a lot of his spare time and a good deal of his money there."

"A nudist colony in the Whetstones?" Alvin Bernard repeated. "Are you kidding? I didn't know we had any of those around here."

The Whetstone Mountains, one of the smaller mountain ranges in the area, lay between Sierra Vista and Tucson. Joanna didn't know the Whetstones boasted a nudist colony, either.

"Turns out there's more than just one

nudist facility," Dave continued, "and Doc Machett seems to have visited them all. There's one on the outskirts of Tucson, up near Saddlebrooke, and another near the Boulders north of Phoenix, but the one on the Whetstones, north of Huachuca City, is where he evidently spent the bulk of his time."

Despite the seriousness of the situation, the people seated around the table couldn't quite contain their mirth or their grins. The idea of Guy Machett strutting around in the great outdoors and doing whatever nudists do without benefit of his upscale suits seemed to have tickled everyone's funny bones. Joanna felt obliged to bring her people up short.

"What is said inside this room is entirely confidential," she warned them. "If I hear of any leaks about the victim's having visited nudist colonies, there will be serious consequences. Understood?"

The grins disappeared. Everyone nodded in turn. "Yes, ma'am," Dave said, "and that's about all I have."

"All right," Joanna said. "After the

meeting, I want you to get back to Detective
Franklin in Great Barrington. Give him
whatever he needs."

"Will do," Dave said.

Joanna glanced around the table.
"Anyone else?"

Deb Howell raised her hand. "Doc
Machett had a girlfriend. Her name's
Amber Sutcliff, and she called me earlier.
She told me the two of them were together
at the Whetstone Mountain Retreat on
Thursday and Friday. When she said that,
I had no idea it was a nudist colony, but
she's probably a nudist, too. She said
she'd been trying to reach Doc Machett
all day yesterday by phone and by texts.
She was worried when he didn't respond,
but she had no idea what had happened
until she saw the story on the news this
morning. She called in immediately, and
Dispatch put her through to me. I asked
her to come down here to do a formal
interview. She's due any minute. I also told
her we'd need a DNA sample. She said
that would be no problem."

"How did she strike you on the phone?"

Joanna asked.

"Very upset but also very cooperative."

"Was Guy out of sorts or worried about anything the last time she saw him?"

"She said he had mentioned earlier this month that his stepmother was sick and most likely dying, but he also said they were estranged and that showing up for her funeral would be hypocritical."

"Did Amber have any knowledge of Machett's family situation?"

"She mentioned there was a dying stepmother and a half sister named Liza. That's about all she knew—the half sister's name and the fact that Doc Machett and the sister weren't close."

Joanna turned her attention to Casey. "Other than driving two hundred miles this morning, what do you have to say for yourself?"

"When I showed up this morning with another load of evidence, the people at the crime lab in Tucson weren't exactly happy to see me. They asked if I had to pick one case over another, which one should take priority, I said this one. I hope that's all right." Casey looked at Joanna questioningly.

As far as Joanna was concerned, it wasn't all right. She didn't want Junior's case to get lost in the shuffle, but she also didn't want to contradict Casey with the whole investigation crew gathered in the conference room. "That's fine," Joanna said.

"I also heard back from Taser International," Casey continued. "The microdots I swept up in Doc Machett's living room lead back to a Taser that was reported stolen in a residential burglary in Tucson two months ago. I have a call in to the detectives on that case. So far I haven't heard back from them."

Joanna said, "At this point we believe we have three linked homicides—two in Massachusetts and one here. Since time and distance make it unlikely that one person is responsible, we're apparently dealing with two separate killers or teams of killers. That also means there's probably one individual behind all of it. He's the one standing offscreen and pulling the strings.

The Taser connection may be our best lead to whatever local talent was used in the homicide here. Jaime, how about if you follow up on that? Property crimes don't get a lot of attention, but we might get lucky. Maybe we'll stumble into evidence that will lead us back to a known criminal operating in this area."

"I keep wondering about the money situation," Alvin Bernard said thoughtfully. "Shouldn't we be checking with banks around here for more of that coffee money?"

"I'll do that," Dave Hollicker volunteered. "I'm not much good right now when it comes to limping around talking to witnesses, but I can work on the phone and on the computer."

"Fair enough," Detective Keller said. "And I'll keep after Machett's neighbors. This is a small town. Someone must have seen something."

Deb's phone rang. She listened, hung up, and turned to Joanna. "Amber Sutcliff is here," she said. "Are we done?"

"As far as I'm concerned."

Deb stood up and then tapped Casey on the shoulder. "Could you come do the swab?"

Casey Ledford and Deb Howell left the room together.

Jaime stood up, too. "On my way to see Carmelita and Josie," he said and sauntered out of the room.

As the meeting disbanded and people filed out, Joanna counted them off in her head. Seven of the people in attendance, including Chief Deputy Hadlock, were totally preoccupied with Guy Machett's homicide. That left Joanna alone focused on Junior Dowdle, and she knew she needed help. Ernie Carpenter, who had paused long enough to hold the door while Dave maneuvered through it on his crutches, was the last to leave.

"Wait, please, Ernie," Joanna called after him. "I wanted to talk to you about your interview with Jason Radner."

Ernie came back into the room. "It's in the report," he said. "I didn't make much progress. The kid was lying about something, but Burton Kimball stepped in just when I was starting to get somewhere."

"I know," Joanna said. "I was watching, and that was my impression, too—that the kid was lying. Do you think he's responsible for what happened?"

"Are you asking if I think Jason killed Junior?" Ernie said. "No, I don't, but I do believe he knows something that he hasn't seen fit to tell us."

"So he's not a suspect?"

"No," Ernie said. "Not as far as I'm concerned."

"Then why don't we go see him?" Joanna suggested. "Just the two of us, you and I."

"Right now?" Ernie glanced at his watch and grimaced.

"Why not?" Joanna asked.

"Because today is Tina's birthday," Ernie said. "Rose is having a party for her, and I told her I'd be home by three. I could call her, but..."

Christina Aguilar was Ernie's grand-daughter and the apple of his eye. She was also about to turn five. With two homicides on the table, Joanna needed all hands on deck. Still, a grandchild's fifth birthday party was something that happened only once in a lifetime. As Joanna struggled to balance work and family in her own life, she wanted her people to achieve the same thing.

"Don't worry about it," she said. "Go to the party. We can talk to Jason later."

"What about his parents?" Ernie asked. "After what happened the other evening, I don't think the Radners will let us anywhere near their son. What if it turns out we're both wrong about his being involved? Supposing we talk to him without having an attorney present. If he breaks down and admits to killing Junior, we'll never be able to use his confession in court because anything we take away from that interview won't be admissible."

Joanna considered Ernie's on-point objections for a moment before she replied. She had observed the changing expressions on Jason's face. He had been genuinely grief-stricken about Junior's death, but, like Ernie, she remained convinced that the boy had been lying about something. There was some bit of knowledge Jason wasn't willing to share. Whatever that was might well be the key to what had happened.

"I guess," Joanna said finally, "the possibility of not being able to use a confession in court is a risk I'm willing to take."

CHAPTER 20

On the ride from Denver to Albuquerque, Liza had rethought her original idea of going to a car dealership in search of transportation. Buying a car privately was probably her best option. She had friends who had bought cars and furniture and plenty of other things through Craigslist and eBay and even from newspaper want ads. To do any of those things, however, she needed to be online. Once she exited the cab, she strolled into the Alvarado Transportation Center and deposited her luggage in a locker. After getting directions to the main library, she set out walking.

It was windy and cold. A surprisingly strong gust whipped off her scarf and sent it skittering down the sidewalk. Shocked by how cold the wind felt on her bare head,

Liza raced after the scarf for the better part of a block before she finally managed to snag it. She paused at the entrance of the library and used her reflection in the plateglass doors to tug the scarf back into place. A man who was exiting waited patiently inside the lobby until she finished adjusting her head covering, then he pulled the door open and held it for her.

"Good luck," he told her, smiling as she passed.

Knowing he was referring to her phantom cancer diagnosis, Liza blushed furiously as she walked away, but she also understood that she needed the stranger's good luck wishes far more than he could possibly know.

Once William had finally given up on talking and had turned on whatever audiobook he was listening to as he drove, Liza had spent several hours mulling over her situation. Gradually the shock of learning about Candy's death had worn off. What hadn't worn off was her sense of culpability. She remembered Candy's reaction when she had told him about her father and the bread truck—the tiny snippet of information that had been passed along to her by Jonathan Thurgard. That was what had pushed Candy over the edge and caused him to launch Liza off on this cross-country trek. With Candy dead, Liza wanted to know—needed to know—what else Jonathan could tell her. She was convinced he was the key to all this.

Intent on finding a car, she made her way to the rows of computer terminals. Since all the computers were currently occupied, she wandered over to the periodicals section and searched out the Sunday edition of the **Albuquerque News.** After locating the want ads, she combed through the autos-for-sale section. Sitting in the library on the far side of the country from where Aimee had given her the cell phone, Liza finally dared use it for the first time and for several times after that as well. She went down the list of ads one at a time and hit pay dirt on her fifth try.

"I'm calling about your ad in the paper," Liza said tentatively, because all the vehicles in the previous listings had already been sold by the time she dialed the numbers. "Is the car still available?"

The woman who answered the phone sighed. "Yes, it is," she said. "It belongs to my mother. I had to take away her car keys this week when I checked her into an assisted-living facility. She just can't see well enough to drive. As a consequence, I'm afraid her Camry has more than a few bumps and bruises on it. It's fifteen years old, but it's very low mileage—only about sixty thousand miles—and it's in good shape mechanically. She's had it in for all the scheduled maintenance, and there's a book in the glove compartment to prove it."

"How much do you want for it?" Liza asked.

"I'd like to get about thirty-five hundred," the woman answered. "I was asking four thousand, but I'm willing to lower the price because I'm almost through cleaning out her house. We had the garage sale yesterday, and the junk people are coming to pick up everything else tomorrow morning. I've been using the car while I was here, but I'd really like to have it out of my hair before I fly home later this week."

Liza felt a jolt of empathy. She understood what this woman was going through. She had been through a similar nightmare with her own mother.

"Where are you? Can I come look at it this afternoon?" Liza asked.

"Of course," the woman said. "If you want to buy it, though, we'll probably have to finalize the deal tomorrow. I couldn't let you take it without my having a cashier's check."

"We'll sort it out," Liza said. "The car sounds like just what I'm looking for—old but reliable—and I may be able to lay hands on that much cash."

"Good," the woman said. As she reeled off an address, Liza heard the relief in the woman's voice. "When do you think you'll be here?"

"As soon as I can," Liza said.

Twenty minutes later a second cab deposited Liza outside a small apartment building on Mesa Street SE on the far side of I-25. The car, complete with a hand-painted FOR SALE sign on it, was parked on the street outside a small, run-down apartment building. Calling the damage to the car "bumps and bruises" was understating the case. Liza remembered hearing that Camrys were the most stolen vehicle in the country. Obviously this one—dented or scraped on almost every panel and with one primer-covered door that didn't match the rest of the color scheme—was considered beneath contempt by even the least ambitious of car thieves. It also explained why no one had taken it off the seller's hands at the optimistic asking price of four thousand dollars.

Liza was prepared to bargain beneath the thirty-five-hundred-dollar mark. What she wasn't prepared for was the woman's very understandable questions about why Liza so desperately needed a car and why she was walking around with a purse full of cash. Liza was forced to spin a series of lies about being ditched by an abusive boyfriend and having to drive back home rather than fly because the boyfriend had stolen her ID. As she told that series of whoppers, Liza was embarrassed by how lame they sounded although the woman appeared to accept them without question.

Forty-five minutes later, after getting the paperwork done and listening to another daughter's woes about having to clean up her mother's messes, Liza drove away in the scuzzy Camry for thirty-two hundred cash on the barrel. She went back down the hill, parking as close as she could to the bus depot, where she retrieved her two bags. With them safely stowed in the trunk, she headed for the freeway. Knowing that William was headed south on I-25, she went back north to the junction with westbound I-40. She didn't need a map to look at to know that I-40 would carry her west and into Arizona.

Despite its ratty appearance, the Camry seemed to be in good working order. After adjusting the seat, the first thing Liza noticed was that the gas gauge was riding on empty. In the past few days, she had come to value the pleasant anonymity of truck stops. At Candy's, everyone had known everyone else. At truck stops, people came and went. Regulars were sometimes recognized and acknowledged, but no one tried to remember their individual orders the way the waitresses at Candy's had remembered their cadre of customers. At Candy's, the appearance of a hundred-dollar bill to pay a fifteen-dollar breakfast tab was a rarity and would have caused a stir. Liza had noticed that at truck stops, no one batted an eyelash when she dragged out one of her fragrant hundreds and handed it over to the cashier at a dining room cash wrap or at a travel shop counter, either. She guessed the same would be true at truck stop gas pumps.

She pulled into the next advertised truck stop, Poncho's. After filling the tank, she bought a pair of maps, one for Arizona and another for New Mexico, then she settled into a booth in the restaurant, ordered lunch, and studied the maps, planning her route. She could see that taking I-25 to I-10 would have been a more direct route to Bisbee, but she was still concerned about possibly running into William along the way or else into someone who knew William and who might have heard about the scarf-wearing cancer patient passenger who had bolted from his truck in Albuquerque. No, even though this might be the long way around, she marked off a route that led her through Flagstaff and then south on I-17 through Phoenix and eventually to Tucson, from which she'd head southeast to Bisbee.

Her food came—surprisingly good meatloaf with an equally tasty side of mac and cheese. While she ate, she thought about Jonathan Thurgard and wondered how much more he knew about her father and how much he would tell her. All she had to do was pick up the phone and ask. Finally, that's what she did. Still using her burner, Liza dialed information and asked for Stockbridge, Massachusetts. She had a pen ready so that when the operator gave her the number, she was able to write it down.

Moments later a distant phone rang in her ear. "Hello."

Liza had expected a man to pick up the phone. Having a woman answer took Liza by surprise. "Is Jonathan there?" she mumbled.

"Who's this?" the woman asked.

"A friend of his," Liza managed feebly.

"What friend?" the woman demanded. "What's your name?"

Not wanting to reveal her name, Liza made up one on the spot. "Mary," she said. "Mary Frost. Could I please speak to Jonathan?"

"You can't talk to him," the woman responded brusquely, "and I'm guessing you must not be much of a friend. If you were, you'd already know he's dead."

"Dead?" Liza echoed faintly, not having to fake her dismay. "When? How?"

"Last Thursday night," the woman answered. "Hit-and-run. Funeral's tomorrow. The obituary is available online. I have to go now. There's another call. The phone keeps ringing off the hook."

The woman hung up, leaving Liza to

stare in disbelief at the disconnected cell phone in her hand. Jonathan Thurgard was dead, too, along with Candy Small and Olivia Dexter? Who else? Liza wondered. And for the first time ever, she wondered about her mother's death. The doctor claimed that Selma had died of natural causes. She had been in hospice, after all, and under a doctor's care. When she had turned up dead, how carefully had anyone checked? There had been no autopsy. The body had been released to the funeral home immediately, and the remains had been cremated well in advance of the funeral. If Selma had been murdered, it was unlikely anyone would ever be held accountable.

Scarcely daring to look around, Liza left enough money on the table to cover her check and a generous tip. Then, gathering her purse and phone, she fled the restaurant. The people responsible for all those deaths were the ones who were looking for her. Liza was convinced that Jonathan Thurgard's death wasn't a random hit-and-run. It was a "hit" in the worst sense of the word. Just by speaking to Liza for those few seconds at Selma's funeral, Jonathan Thurgard had signed his own death warrant. Clearly, anyone connected to Liza or who attempted to help her was in mortal danger.

As Liza sped westward on the freeway, her head was a jumble of questions. Why was all this happening? Was it just about the money? How could it be? After all, there was far less money in the roll-aboard now than there had been when she first began finding the squirreled-away bills in her mother's moldering house, and yet people were still dying. Liza's friends and acquaintances were still dying.

She glanced at the phone lying on the passenger seat beside her. She desperately wanted to talk to her brother. Maybe Guy would be able to answer some of her questions. Liza had put off calling him. She had wanted to show up unannounced so she could ask her questions without him having any advance warning that she was coming. Guy was five years older than she was. If he knew something about their father and those damned bread trucks, Liza Machett was determined that he was going to share that knowledge with her.

CHAPTER 21

Leaving the conference room, Joanna stopped in the break room long enough to collect a cup of coffee before going to her office. By now Butch and the kids would be well on their way home from Silver City. She felt a little guilty about that, but she couldn't be in more than one place at a time.

She was in her office and still puzzling over what to do about Jason Radner when there was a timid knock on the door. "Come in."

When Joanna looked up, she was surprised to see Sunny Sloan step through the door. Sunny had been working in the sheriff's department's public office for the better part of six months. Even so, each time Joanna encountered Dan Sloan's widow, there was that awful instant of remembrance that took Joanna back to the night she and Father Rowan had come calling at Sunny's door, waking the poor woman with the appalling news that her husband was dead. Looking up from her desk, Joanna wondered if the reverse wasn't also true for Sunny—if seeing Joanna always took Sunny back to that terrible night as well.

"Someone's out in the lobby asking to see you," Sunny said.

"If it's a reporter, send them to Chief Deputy Hadlock," Joanna said.

"He claims he isn't a reporter," Sunny replied. "I already asked. His name's Lyle Morton, and you're the only one he's willing to talk to."

"Okay," Joanna said. "Bring him back."

Sunny nodded and disappeared. When she returned a few minutes later, she was followed by an elderly man riding a scooter. His craggy face, tanned and weathered, was topped by a headful of thinning white hair. The twisted knuckles on his hands went a long way to explain why he might have resorted to using a scooter.

Joanna stood and walked around to the front of her desk to greet him. "I'm Sheriff Joanna Brady, Mr. Morton," she said. "I understand you want to speak to me?"

"I'm Lyle," he said. "Nobody calls me Mr. Morton."

"What can I do for you?"

"I own the Whetstone Mountain Retreat," he said. "Guy Machett was a friend of mine."

"I'm so sorry for your loss," Joanna said at once, but in the momentary pause that followed, Joanna was dismayed to find herself imagining this angular old man riding a scooter in the nude.

Although she tried to suppress her consternation, Lyle seemingly read her mind and called her on it. He grinned at her. "I guess you know what kind of a retreat it is."

She nodded.

"When people come to the retreat the first time, my scooter makes a bit of a stir, but they adjust. There aren't many wheelchair-accessible nudist facilities on the planet, but ours is." He gave the handle of his scooter a fond pat. "Living in the nude may seem a bit far-fetched to begin with," he continued, "and being old and living in the nude even more so, but after a while what's odd is having to put on clothes and come into town like I've done today."

Joanna said nothing. Blushing, she simply nodded.

"I knew your dad, by the way," Lyle added, surprising Joanna for a second time.

"You did?"

"Yup. When I first got here, the property was caught up in a family feud, and I was able to get it for a bargain basement price. Everything was hunky-dory until I started pulling permits to go from running a ranch to running a retreat. Some of my cattle-raising neighbors took exception to that idea. There were several instances of fences being cut and livestock being allowed to roam onto my land and cause trouble. There was even one occasion when the pump on one of my wells was damaged. Your dad was sheriff back then.

I called him, and he took care of it. He came by in person and gave the miscreants—a couple of teenagers at the time—a lesson in the realities of owning private property. Nobody went to jail, but D. H. Lathrop put the issue to bed once and for all.

"I'm still not best of friends with those neighbors," Lyle continued, "but we've learned to get along—live and let live. Last year, when we were all looking down the barrel at a forest fire, those same guys—all grown up now—came over to my place and helped build the fire line. The firefighters were there, dolled up in all their gear. The cowboys were there in their jeans and boots and hats, and my people were there in boots and hats and nothing else. You should have seen it. It was quite a sight!"

Lyle laughed heartily. Picturing the scene, Joanna chuckled, too.

"Please sit," Lyle added. "Makes me uncomfortable when folks end up standing when I can't do the same."

Instead of returning to the far side of the

desk, Joanna sank down on one of the captain's chairs in front of it. "What can I do for you, Lyle?"

In a sudden transformation, all trace of laughter left the man's face. "Like I said, Guy Machett was a friend of mine—a friend as well as a client. The report on the news said he was killed sometime Friday evening. Since he left the retreat late Friday afternoon, I may have been one of the last people to see him alive. I came to see if I could be of any assistance."

Joanna sobered, too. "The homicide happened inside the city limits, but both the Bisbee PD and the sheriff's department are involved in the case. The lead investigators are Bisbee's Detective Matt Keller and one of my homicide detectives, Deb Howell. Detective Keller left a few minutes ago. Detective Howell is here, and she'll be glad to take your statement, but she's currently interviewing someone else, a woman named Amber Sutcliff."

"I know Amber," Lyle said. "Not well, but I've met her. She was Guy's girlfriend—a relatively new girlfriend. She's only been at the Whetstone a few times. They met at another colony closer to Phoenix. Guy enjoyed mixing it up now and then. He didn't just come to my place. He went to others, too."

Joanna recalled being shocked at seeing Guy Machett's naked body lying supine on the floor. The idea of his willingly trotting around wearing shoes and socks while otherwise in the buff was something she couldn't quite grasp. She preferred picturing the man properly attired in his expensive and carefully pressed suits. As for being in the nude with other people, to say nothing of with someone he was just starting to date? That didn't work for her either.

"How did he appear to you when you saw him last?" Joanna asked. "Was he upset or worried about anything?"

"Upset, yes," Lyle said. "Inconvenienced more than worried. He and Amber had planned to stay at the retreat for the entire weekend, but he had to cancel part of it—something about having to work on Saturday."

Junior Dowdle's autopsy, Joanna thought, **but how did the killers know about that?**

"Do you know anything about Dr. Machett's family situation?" Joanna asked.

Lyle frowned. "His father's evidently been out of the picture for a long time. I know his stepmother had been very ill. His half sister called to let Guy know that she was moving the mother . . ."

"Selma," Joanna said, supplying the name.

"The sister said she was moving Selma into hospice care. I asked Guy if he planned on going home for the funeral. He told me he had no intention of doing so. He and his stepmother had been estranged for some time—a number of years—and he felt there was no reason for him to make the trip."

Joanna's phone rang. Matt Keller's name appeared in the caller window. Excusing herself, Joanna went out into the reception area and sat down at Kristin's desk to take the call.

"Hey, Matt," she said. "What's up?"

"I just got off the phone with Sandy Henning," Detective Keller said.

Through a process of mergers and attrition, there was only a single bank left in town—a single bank with several branches. Sandy Henning was the manager in charge of the whole shebang.

"I know Sandy," Joanna said.

"Me, too," Matt said. "We were sort of an item back in the day, and we're still friends. Rather than wait until tomorrow to ask her to be on the lookout for that coffee money, I gave her a call at home just now. Turns out she's already been notified about that. She was told to have her people watch their transactions for any hundred-dollar bills reeking of coffee, especially ones with out-of-date serial numbers."

"Who notified her?" Joanna asked. "And how did they contact her?"

"The notice came through by e-mail on Friday afternoon. I'll forward a copy of it to you."

"Okay," Joanna said. "I'll get back to you."

She waited long enough for the e-mail to arrive and then read it through. The sender was listed as Cesar Flores, Special Agent, U.S. Treasury.

U.S. TREASURY ALERT

You are advised to be on the lookout for currency, specifically one-hundred-dollar bills, containing out-of-date serial numbers. Some or all of the bills may be readily recognizable due to the distinct odor of coffee. If any of the bills in question arrive in your banking establishment, please call the following number immediately.

The alert looked genuine enough; what bothered Joanna about it was the timing. According to Detective Franklin, the banker in Great Barrington had raised the coffee money issue weeks earlier. At the time, the banker had been told that the bills, although old, were still good. If he'd had some kind of reservations about them, why hadn't a notice been sent out then? Instead, this one had appeared weeks later, on the day before Guy Machett had been murdered and before Liza had been reported missing. Maybe Guy wasn't the only target. Maybe his sister was, too. If Liza was on the lam and using her so-called coffee money to cover expenses, maybe someone was using the power of the Treasury Department—most likely someone inside the Treasury Department—to cast a net wide enough to track her down.

Making up her mind and leaving Lyle cooling his heels in her office a while longer, Joanna called Matt back. "I need Sandy's number," Joanna said. "I'd like to talk to her."

A moment later, Sandy Henning was on the line. "Sheriff Brady here," Joanna told her. "I'm calling about that coffee money alert. Do you have a minute?"

"Sure," Sandy said. "What do you need?"

"Do you get alerts like this often?"

"Sure, they come in all the time, usually when there have been incidences of counterfeiting in the area. They send out lists of bogus serial numbers. I print up copies and pass them along to my tellers. That's what I did with this one. I sent e-mail copies to everyone on Saturday morning."

"Is there anything off about this one?" Joanna asked.

"What do you mean, off?"

"Out of the ordinary," Joanna answered. "For instance, who usually sends out these kinds of notices?"

"A guy in D.C., a Treasury agent named Cesar Flores. I doubt he sends them out personally. Cesar's department is the one in charge of communications with banks, so I'm sure they have a massive database. Still, his name is always the one on the send line. What's this all about, Sheriff Brady?"

"The currency we're all calling 'coffee money' has now been linked to three separate homicides," Joanna answered, "and the timing on this seems strange. Would you mind taking another look at it?"

"I just sent it to Matt. Give me a minute, and I'll look at the e-mail."

"You're right," Sandy said when she came back on the line. "I never noticed it until you asked, but the phone number is wrong. It's not a D.C. area code. I thought maybe Treasury had parceled weekend responses to a call center operating somewhere else, but I just tried calling it. After three rings, it came up as a disconnect. That's weird. Why would they send out an alert and then cancel the number before people have a chance to call in a report? It doesn't make sense."

It would if whoever sent the message already figured out what they need to know, Joanna thought.

"Is there anything else?"

"Yes," Joanna said. "If you happen to have it handy, I'd like Agent Flores's number."

"Of course," Sandy said. "I'm sure it's in my contact list." She found the number and read it off.

"Thanks," Joanna said after jotting the number down.

Joanna was about to hang up, but Sandy stopped her. "Matt hinted that this might have something to do with Guy Machett's homicide," Sandy said. "Is that true?"

"I can't answer that directly," Joanna said, "but I will say this. If anyone shows up in one of your branches this week and passes along any coffee money, have your tellers dial 911, because their lives may be in danger. Is that clear enough?"

"Absolutely," Sandra Henning breathed.

Joanna ended the call and then dialed Cesar's number. An answering machine clicked on after only one ring. "Special Agent Cesar Flores," a deep voice said. "I am currently out of the office. If this is a banking emergency, please wait for the tone and then press one to be connected directly to my cell phone."

In other words, Cesar Flores was important enough to be on call 24/7. Joanna waited for the tone and then pressed one.

"Agent Flores speaking."

"My name is Sheriff Joanna Brady," she said. "I'm calling about the alert you sent out on Friday warning banks to be on the lookout for certain kinds of currency."

"What alert? I wasn't even in the office on Friday. I was in New York City at a meeting. Notices like that don't go out without my personal stamp of approval. Who is this again?"

"Sorry," Joanna said quickly. "I'm sure there's been some kind of mistake."

There's a mistake here, all right, she thought, hanging up, **and the killers just made it.**

With the phone still in her hand, she consulted her contact list, settling at last on the name Frank Montoya. For years Frank had been her chief deputy and right-hand man, until he had been lured away from her department by a lucrative offer to take over as chief of police in the neighboring city of Sierra Vista. Joanna and Frank were still friends and colleagues, but she sorely missed having Frank's technical savvy at her disposal.

Cueing up the e-mail that Cesar Flores had categorically denied sending, Joanna turned it into a forward. She typed in both

Frank's and Alvin Bernard's e-mail addresses along with the following message:

> Alvin and I are working the Machett homicide, and we could use your help. Cesar Flores denies having sent this notice. Either he is lying about not sending it or the person who sent it was pretending to be him. Is it possible to verify that one way or the other?
>
> Also could you see about tracking down the contact telephone number listed at the end of the notice? It's now been disconnected, but I need to know who owned it and where it was located.
>
> Thanks, and boy, do I miss you.
> J.B.

After that she scrolled through her incoming calls. Once she located the one from Detective Franklin in Great Barrington, she hit the call button.

"Franklin here," he said.

"This is Sheriff Brady. Did your M.E. list a time of death for Clifford Small?"

A distant sound of papers being shuffled preceded Detective Franklin's answer. "Between one and two this morning. Why?"

"When was the fire first reported?"

"The 911 call came in shortly after three AM. The fire was extinguished about half an hour later. The body was found around five, but why all the questions?" Amos asked.

"I'm looking for a pattern here," Joanna said. "If something comes of it, I'll get back to you."

Joanna was about to go back into her office when Deb Howell came past Kristin's desk. "I just finished interviewing the girlfriend and sent her on her way."

"Do any good?"

"Not much, but I'll go write it up."

"Before you do that, there's one more interviewee waiting in my office," Joanna told her. "His name's Lyle Morton. He's the owner of the Whetstone Mountain Retreat. He claims to be a friend of Guy's and says he last saw Guy on Friday afternoon when he and Amber left the retreat. It sounds like Lyle and Amber may have been the last people to see Guy alive."

"Is Mr. Morton dressed?" Deb asked.

Joanna smiled. "Yes."

"I'd better go talk to him then."

"A word of caution," Joanna said. "Lyle seems to know quite a bit about Guy's family background. I'd like to know what he knows without telling him everything we know, so please hold back the information that Guy's mother is dead and that his younger sister, his half sister, has gone missing. The last Lyle knew, Liza Machett was in Great Barrington and Selma was in hospice."

Deb nodded. "You've got it," she said. "My lips are sealed."

Detective Howell detoured into Joanna's office, collected Lyle Morton, and headed back to the interview room. Lyle trailed behind with the rubber tires of his cart whispering on the hallway's polished concrete floor.

Joanna sat for a while longer, lost in thought, after Deb and Lyle Morton disappeared. She was still sitting there when her new e-mail alert sounded. She wasn't surprised to see it was from Frank:

> **Looks interesting. I'll see what I can do.**
> **F.**

Relieved as she was to have Frank onboard with the problem, she still felt like a Ping-Pong ball being batted back and forth between the two opposing cases. Once again all her assets seemed to be focused on Guy Machett's murder while no one was working Junior's. Maybe it was time to change that dynamic. The other night, Ernie Carpenter had been the only officer in the interview room when Jason Radner's parents had put a stop to the questioning. She had been outside the room rather than in it. Matt Keller had been absent as well, and right now she was counting on his having been too busy to view the tape. She would leave Ernie to

enjoy Tina's birthday party and use Matt
Keller to do her dirty work.

She picked up the phone and dialed
Matt. "Bringing Sandy Henning into the
picture was definitely the right move," she
told him. "Good work."

"Thanks," he said.

Joanna felt a momentary qualm of
conscience. For days now, Matt Keller had
been working his heart out. He didn't
deserve to be thrown under the bus.
Approaching Jason Radner behind his
parents' backs wasn't fair to Jason, either,
but right at that moment Joanna couldn't
afford the luxury of being fair, especially
since she knew the answer to her next
question before she even asked it.

"You don't happen to know Jason
Radner, do you?"

"Sure," Matt said. "He was on the JV
football team last year when I was a
volunteer coach. He and Curt, my son,
hang out together occasionally. Why?"

"Jason's parents brought him in for an
interview with Ernie Carpenter the evening
we found Junior Dowdle's body. There are

a couple more things that I'd like him to clarify, but I don't want to put his parents into a state of panic. Is there any way you could spirit him away from the house so I could ask him a few questions?"

"Jason's a good kid," Matt declared. "In fact, I'd say he's a great kid. I hope you're not thinking he had something to do with what happened to Junior. He wouldn't!"

"I agree completely," Joanna responded truthfully. "I don't think he's in any way responsible for Junior's death, but I do believe he knows more than he's letting on. He was in an interview room with a homicide cop asking him questions. He was probably scared to death. If we approach him again with more questions, we run the risk of making it look like he's ratting someone out even if he doesn't say another word. That's why I want to keep this informal and off the record. If we need what he says to be on the record later, we'll cross that bridge when we come to it."

"What if he says something self-incriminating?" Matt asked.

"Then I won't be able to use it."

There was a long pause after that while Matt Keller struggled with his own conscience. "Okay," he said finally. "What do you need?"

"See if you can spirit him out of the house long enough for me to have a private word with him."

"I'll see what I can do," Matt said.

Hanging up, Joanna left Kristin's desk behind, returned to her own office, and pulled four sheets of paper out of the printer behind her desk. Using a pencil she labeled them with the names of the four victims—Olivia Dexter, Guy Machett, Clifford Small, and Junior Dowdle. Since Junior was the first, she wrote down as much as she knew—time and manner of death, animal torture, interviews conducted, questions remaining, and finally a personal to-do list: talk to Jason; move the crime lab forward on the DNA issue; check on the injured kitten.

Setting Junior's sheet aside, she went to work on the Great Barrington cases, jotting down everything she could recall on each of those from her conversations with Detective Franklin. Olivia had been murdered on Thursday. Clifford Small had died in the wee hours of Sunday morning. The same arsonist who burned down Clifford's house on Sunday had burned down Liza Machett's mother's house on Thursday afternoon. In the meantime, Liza had disappeared into thin air. Joanna pulled out another piece of paper and labeled that one with Liza's name. She had to be the heart of the matter. After all, she had connections to the two victims in Massachusetts and to Guy as well. Unfortunately, she was the one about whom Joanna knew the least.

As she drew out the diagrams, an ominous pattern began to emerge. With crimes and crime scenes washing back and forth across the country, Joanna could see they were dealing with a collection of perpetrators: at least two in Bisbee and maybe more than one in Great Barrington as well.

Guy's killers had made mistakes. They had failed to contain Guy when they first encountered him. The damage from the fight in the living room testified to that. Then there was the bruising that suggested a futile attempt to revive their victim when the waterboarding went too far. It was easy to mark these guys off as less-than-adequate guns for hire, but it was inarguable that they had come to their mission in possession of first-rate intel.

They must have known in advance that Guy would be out of town, since they had used his absence to conceal themselves inside their victim's house. They must also have known when he was expected to return. That probably meant they had kept Guy under some kind of surveillance. Since it was unlikely that a pair of murderous thugs would risk turning up and showing their faces at a nudist colony, Joanna discounted the possibility that there had been any physical surveillance. It was more likely that they had somehow hacked into his phone or Internet communications.

Pushing Guy's paper to one side, she laid the one for Clifford Small next to it. Clifford "Candy" Small had been tortured, too, but in a way that differed from what had been done to Guy. Besides, bouncing back and forth across the country to commit three murders a day or so apart made no sense. So what had Clifford's tormentors wanted from him? If Liza Machett was the real target, maybe they suspected him of helping her and wanted him to tell them where she was. Had he capitulated? Had he given up Liza's whereabouts? There was no way to tell.

Gradually, though, pieces began to shift into focus, and you didn't have to be a conspiracy nut to see it. There were the bad guys who had been hired to do the actual work, but Joanna remained more interested in the guy behind the scenes—the one issuing the orders while staying safely out of sight. It had to be someone with money, power, and, without a doubt, connections to banking and/or the U.S. Treasury Department. As for Cesar Flores himself? Possibly. He had denied any knowledge of the coffee money alert, but he could have been lying.

Joanna's phone rang, startling her. Frank Montoya's name and number showed up on the screen.

"I found your phone," he said when she answered. "It's a burner, bought at a drugstore in Boston, Massachusetts, on Friday afternoon and activated that same day within ten minutes of the time stamp on the Treasury Department alert. One incoming call was placed to it. That number leads back to a bank in Gary, Indiana. At the time of the incoming call, the phone pinged off a cell tower in a town called Stockbridge, Massachusetts. Does that have anything to do with your case?"

"Not that I know of," Joanna answered.

"What about Great Barrington?" Frank asked.

Joanna felt her heart speed up. "What about Great Barrington?" she asked.

"That's the last place it pinged before it went dark. Cell tower 672. Downtown Great Barrington."

"What time was that last ping?"

"Two thirty-five this morning," Frank said. "It went off then and hasn't come back on since. Someone probably pulled the battery."

Joanna looked at the Clifford Small sheet. That was just after Clifford's time of death and just before the 911 call came in, reporting the fire. As far as she could tell there were two possibilities: (1) the killers got what they wanted from Clifford and wouldn't need to use the coffee money trail in their pursuit of Liza or (2) they had dropped the phone accidentally and the remains would be found in the ashes of Clifford Small's burned-out house.

"Thanks, Frank," she said. "Thank you more than you know. Send Dave Hollicker everything you can on that burner—where it was purchased, when, all of it. I'll have Dave forward the information along to Amos Franklin, the homicide cop in Great Barrington. What about the e-mail?"

"That's a little harder, but it's also more interesting. I can tell you that it didn't come from where it says it did, because the last IP address it bounced from is located somewhere in Poland."

CHAPTER 22

As Joanna made her way down the corridor, intent on seeing Dave Hollicker, Deb and Lyle Morton exited the interview room in front of her and turned in the opposite direction to return to the lobby. Lyle was busy regaling Detective Howell with a story about how people never believed him when he told them his tan line started at the tops of his boots.

"There were rattlesnakes all over the place when I bought the Whetstone twenty-five years ago, and they haven't exactly moved on. So we always tell first-time arriving guests, they don't have to go completely nude if they're not comfortable that way, but everybody wears boots, no exceptions."

That odd snippet of conversation gave Joanna pause. It sounded like a well-practiced comedy routine, and not something a grieving friend would say to a homicide cop investigating a good pal's murder. Curious, Joanna went into the viewing room and reviewed the digital recording. She listened through the first several minutes of the tape that featured the usual kinds of questions: How long had Lyle known Guy? Lyle estimated that Guy had been visiting the Whetstone Mountain Retreat for eleven or twelve years. Joanna found that bit of information surprising. It meant that Guy had been coming to Cochise County since long before he came here to work as the M.E.

The whole time Joanna had known the man, Guy had complained about being stuck in the wilds of Arizona. She had assumed that meant he had arrived in Bisbee as a newcomer to the desert. Now she knew he wasn't, and she wondered if Bisbee's proximity to the Whetstone Retreat was one of the reasons he had accepted the M.E. job in the first place.

Doing some math in her head, she realized that he would have started visiting the nudist colony while he was still in medical school. She remembered that Dave had told her Guy had gone to school on a scholarship, so how could a poor scholarship student afford to take vacations at a pricey nudist colony on the far side of the country? Up to now, this whole thing seemed to be about money that had mysteriously turned up in the hands of Liza Machett. Now it occurred to Joanna that perhaps a similar sum of money had found its way into Guy's hands as well.

Clearing the computer screen, Joanna went to the lab space at the far end of the corridor where her CSI unit held sway. With his crutches leaning against his desk, Dave Hollicker, alone in the office, was hunched over a desktop computer. He looked up at Joanna as she entered.

"Thanks for coming in when you could be out on the injured list," she said. "How's it going?"

"Plugging away," Dave said. "Much to my surprise Guy's e-mail records just came in. So far nothing jumps out at me.

Can I help you with something?"

"Several somethings. Didn't you tell me Guy went to both Harvard and medical school on full-ride scholarships?"

"He did his first year," Dave said. "Strangely enough, I never saw a record of any additional scholarships being awarded to him, but I checked his credit report. Unlike most people, he graduated from Harvard and later from Johns Hopkins without a dime's worth of tuition debt. The money must have come from somewhere."

"Do me a favor and google Whetstone Mountain Retreat. I want to know how much it costs to stay there."

She waited while Dave tapped away at the computer keys and then read through whatever material appeared on his screen. He had to scan several pages before he found what he wanted.

"Here it is. Depending on the season, packages range from one to two grand a week. Off-season daily rate is a hundred thirty-five bucks. So it's not too pricey. Others are a lot more expensive. Here all meals are included. Horseback riding is extra."

"Naked horseback riding?" Joanna asked. "Not a pretty picture, and also staying there isn't cheap."

"Hardly," Dave agreed, "but then I could have told you that from just looking at Guy's credit card receipts."

"When did Guy finish up at Johns Hopkins?"

"He graduated from there five years ago and finished his residency a little over two years ago."

"So shortly before he came here?"

Dave nodded. "According to the background check."

"Lyle Morton, the owner of the Whetstone Retreat, claims Guy Machett has been a regular guest there for the past eleven or twelve years."

Dave nodded. "I can see where you're going with this. How could he afford to go there while he was still in school?"

"Maybe he had a benefactor," Joanna suggested, "an unknown benefactor."

"Maybe even the same one who gave Liza Machett her so-called coffee money?"

Dave asked. Joanna liked the fact that Dave had immediately drawn the same conclusion she had.

Joanna nodded. "You mentioned that their father is supposedly deceased. What do we know about him?"

Dave clicked through several files. "Not much, but here it is. First name is Anson— Anson Jerome Machett. Born in Great Barrington, Massachusetts."

"Find out everything you can about him."

"Will do."

"Any minute now you should be getting an e-mail from Frank Montoya with some information on the phone number that was listed on the coffee money alert."

"Since when is Frank Montoya working this case?"

"Since I asked him," Joanna replied. "The phone's a burner. I want you to pass everything Frank sends along to Detective Franklin so it goes to him from us, rather than from Frank. Frank can tell us where the phone was bought and when. Detective Franklin will need to go for surveillance tapes. Frank is also sending along the ID number of a cell-phone tower where the phone last pinged. We need to know its proximity to Clifford Small's house."

Dave was still scribbling notes when Joanna's cell-phone rooster crowed at her. Matt Keller's name appeared in the caller window. "Let me know what you find," Joanna said to Dave as she walked away.

"I'm feeling a little underhanded about all this," Matt said, "but we've got a window of opportunity that gives us a clear shot at Jason. His folks have an event of some kind out on post this afternoon, so Curt and I invited him to come down to the park and shoot some hoops. We should be there in about fifteen. Does that work for you?"

"Perfectly," Joanna said. "I'll come by ostensibly to talk to you and then just happen to have a word with Jason. It'll be my Columbo moment."

For some strange reason, Butch and Jenny had both taken a shine to Peter Falk's television depiction of the bumbling detective. Compliments of Netflix, the two of them were gradually working their way through the Columbo canon. Joanna wasn't nearly as charmed as they were, but she had come to appreciate Columbo's seemingly throwaway comments upon which the solutions often hinged.

"Right," Matt said. "Copy that."

On her return trip down the corridor, Joanna again stopped off in the viewing room. This time she cued up Ernie's interview with Jason. She watched it again, paying particular attention to the questions that had elicited the boy's most visible responses. He had reacted strongly to the mention of Junior's hearing people talking through his open window and again to questions about Junior's involvement in any kind of animal abuse.

Armed with that much knowledge, Joanna headed out. Butch called as she pulled out of the Justice Center parking lot. "We just got home," he said. "We stopped for a late lunch in Willcox, so I'm serving notice that the cook is taking the evening off. Either grab something before you come home or plan on raiding the fridge after you get here. What's up with you?"

"I'm working," she said. "On my way uptown to talk to a potential witness."

Butch was using the speakerphone, and Joanna didn't want to advertise her intentions to her daughter. After all, Curt Keller and Jason Radner were younger than Jenny, but they all attended the same school.

"Okay," Butch said. "Do what you have to. Be safe."

It was midafternoon by the time Joanna reached the park that had once served as the playground for a now repurposed school building. The play area was at the far end of Tombstone Canyon, and Joanna parked on the street near the entrance. When she stepped out of the Yukon, she noticed at once that although it might be late spring down at the Justice Center, up here, where the sun had already disappeared behind the canyon walls, it was far cooler. She strode across the park and made her way to the basketball court where Jason Radner and Curt Keller were playing a fast-paced game of one-on-one with Matt watching from the sidelines.

Approaching Matt, Joanna made a show of carrying on an urgent discussion. "Hey, Curt," Matt called to his son when she finished, "come on. I need to run by the office for a minute. Sheriff Brady says she'll be glad to give Jason a ride back home."

Curt caught the ball and then looked questioningly at Jason. "Is that okay?"

Jason shrugged. "I guess," he said.

"How are you doing?" Joanna asked the boy as Matt collected his son and their gear and walked with Curt toward his car.

"Okay," Jason mumbled with a shrug.

It was important to establish some common ground. "Losing a friend like that is tough," Joanna said, walking Jason over to a bench in the far corner of the park. Taking a seat, she patted the spot next to her, inviting him to sit. With a reluctant sigh, Jason joined her.

"Will you be going to Junior's funeral?" she asked.

"I dunno," Jason answered. "It depends on if my mom can get off work. She doesn't want me to go alone."

"I don't blame her. That's what parents do when they see that their kids are in over their heads or having to deal with something difficult," Joanna explained. "They want to protect them."

"I don't need protecting," Jason insisted. "Why should I? I didn't do anything wrong."

"Maybe not," Joanna said, edging into the heart of the matter. "But you know something, don't you?"

She tossed the words into the air and then waited in silence to see what he would do. For a time the only sounds in the empty park came from birds chattering up and down the canyon and from the occasional vehicle driving past on the street. Eventually Jason spoke.

"I saw a dead cat," he said finally, speaking so quietly that Joanna had to strain to hear him.

A dead cat? The hair rose on the back of Joanna's neck. She had called that shot. Jason did indeed know something.

"Where did you see it?" she asked. "When?"

"At the end of the walkway between our house and Junior's. It was really messed up." Jason shuddered at the memory. "I remembered it as soon as Mr. Carpenter asked me about Junior messing with animals."

"Why didn't you mention it then?"

"Because I couldn't believe Junior would do such a thing."

"I don't think he did, either," Joanna said quietly.

Jason looked at her questioningly. "You don't? Really?"

Wanting him to feel free to talk to her, Joanna primed the pump with a little more information.

"No, I don't," she said. "There were dead and injured animals in the hole where we found Junior's body. One of those, a kitten, was still alive, but it had been horribly mutilated."

"Were the ears cut up?" Jason asked.

Joanna nodded.

"The cat I saw was like that, too," Jason

said.

"I was one of the people who went down into the hole where Junior was found," Joanna continued. "I saw his arms and hands. He was wearing short-sleeved pajamas. If he had done something like that to a cat, he would have had scratches and bite marks showing, but he didn't have any—not a single one."

Another long silence followed. When Jason said nothing, Joanna spoke instead. "How long ago did this happen, Jason, and what did you do with the cat you found?"

"It was a month or so ago," Jason answered. "And I buried it."

"Where?"

"In the vacant lot between our house and the road. I can show you if you want me to. Are you going to dig it up?"

"We may need to," Joanna told him. "If we do, I'll have someone from my office be in touch with you. You're sure you'll be able to find it again?"

Jason nodded. "I put up a marker. I made a little cross out of sticks and twine."

"Did you tell your parents about this?" Jason shook his head.

"What made you think Junior did it?"

"The walkway is between our house and the Maxwells'. Junior is the only other person I ever saw hanging out there."

"Did you tell Junior's parents about it at the time?"

"No," Jason said. "Not mine either, and I still haven't. I figured the Maxwells knew. They must have. It was right after that when they started locking Junior in at night. He hated that. I could hear him in his room sometimes, crying and begging them to let him out. Other times he spent the whole night pacing back and forth. I could see him through the window."

"Did you tell anyone else about the cat or about your suspicions about Junior?"

"Only Ruth."

"Ruth Nolan?" Joanna asked.

Jason nodded. "We're friends. Not boyfriend and girlfriend or anything, just friends. The Nolans live up the street. I told Ruth about the cat, and I told her about Junior, too—about what I suspected he had done to the cat and about his parents keeping him locked in his room. She felt sorry for him, too. She said that even if he did it, someone like that couldn't be held responsible for his actions. She came over to keep him company sometimes. She'd talk to him through the window; sing to him even."

Joanna already knew about the singing. Ruth had told her about that, but she had made no mention of the mutilated cat.

"This singing would happen when, in the middle of the night?"

"Yes."

"What did Ruth's mother think about her doing that?"

Jason shrugged. "She probably didn't even know," Jason said. "Ruth and Lucas aren't like other kids. They don't have a curfew. Their mother stays out until all hours, and they do, too. I heard my parents talking about Mrs. Nolan once. Mom said she should spend more time looking after her kids and less time hanging out at Grady's."

Grady's Irish Pub, a full-service bar, had

once been one of several watering holes located in Bisbee's notorious Brewery Gulch. The bar's owner, Timothy Grady, had proven to be such a troublesome neighbor that other nearby clubs and eateries had finally prevailed on his landlord not to renew the bar's lease. Timothy had taken his bad attitude and equally bad clientele and moved a mile or so up the canyon to the site of a long-abandoned fast-food restaurant.

"You're saying their mother drinks?" Joanna asked. "And leaves her kids alone while she's out partying?"

Jason nodded. "Ruth says her mom goes to Grady's because it's close enough to walk. Mrs. Nolan got a DUI once. They took away her license, so she can't drive anymore; at least she's not supposed to, although I think she still does sometimes."

Having caught a couple of whiffs of Rebecca Nolan's early morning beer breath, Joanna had already decided that the woman wasn't a likely candidate for mother of the year, and it seemed as though Jason's parents shared that opinion. Ruth and Lucas as recent arrivals and homeschooled kids were already considered to be outsiders in town. Having a mother with a reputation as a barfly would make their social standing even less tenable. The tidbits Jason had provided made Joanna wonder if the situation was worse than she had originally thought. If Rebecca was a neglectful mother, how was she at homeschooling? The woman was probably a neglectful teacher as well. If so, her kids were being shortchanged in every way imaginable.

"How much do you know about Ruth's family?" Joanna asked.

"Not a lot," Jason answered with a shrug. "Her parents are divorced. They moved here from somewhere in New Mexico. Her father is a missionary or something on an Indian reservation."

"Where in New Mexico?" Joanna asked.

Jason frowned. "Some little town. I think it has something to do with cowboys."

For a moment, Joanna was stumped— Indians, cowboys, horses. Then it came to her. "Gallup, maybe?"

"Right," Jason said. "That's it—Gallup."

It didn't surprise Joanna to hear that Lucas and Ruth came from a fractured family, but it did surprise her to learn that they were left to their own devices much of the time while their mother was hanging out in bars. They lived just up the street from Moe and Daisy Maxwell. Was there a chance one of them had been out and about the night Junior died? If so, they might have spotted something out of the ordinary.

Eager to ask the Nolan twins about that very thing, Joanna stood up. "Thanks so much for your help, Jason. How about I take you home?"

Jason shook his head. "Thanks," he said, "but I'd rather walk. There's a shortcut from here. I go that way all the time."

He jerked his head in the direction of a series of steep stairs that zigzagged between houses perched on the side of the canyon. Joanna didn't envy Jason the climb. She also understood the real reason he was refusing her offer of a ride. He didn't want to run the risk of having friends and neighbors seeing him climb out of a vehicle with a Sheriff's Department logo on the side. After thinking about it for a moment, Joanna concluded that maybe he was right. With a possible wannabe serial killer loose in the neighborhood, being branded as a potential snitch was a bad idea. It might, in fact, be downright dangerous.

"Sure thing," Joanna said, stepping away from the bench. "Suit yourself."

"Sheriff Brady?" Jason called after her.

Joanna turned to look back at him. "What?"

"Thank you for telling me that you don't think Junior hurt that cat. When I thought he had done it, I was almost glad he was dead. Now I can be sorry. He's still dead, but it makes me feel better somehow."

"I understand," Joanna said, and she did. Jason was still sitting alone on the bench, staring at the ground and wrestling with a storm of conflicting emotions as Joanna drove away.

Half a mile down Tombstone Canyon she turned right past St. Dominick's and

drove up the hill to Rebecca Nolan's place.
Joanna wanted a chance to talk to Ruth
again and to speak to Lucas as well, but
when she knocked on the door of the little
tin-roofed house, no one answered.
Joanna stood on the small porch for
several minutes in hopes someone would
come back home. When they didn't, she
got back into the car, drove straight to
Grady's, and parked in a lot crammed with
close to a dozen motorcycles.

For the better part of forty years the
worn clapboard building had functioned
as a hamburger joint that catered mostly
to generations of teenagers dancing to a
blaring jukebox. Now the hamburgers,
fries, and milk shakes were long gone.
Even though it was broad daylight, a red
neon cocktail glass complete with a green
neon olive glowed brightly in the window
facing the street. Beyond the sign hung a
blackout curtain designed to keep any
outside light from entering the building.

Joanna was a small-town sheriff—a
female small-town sheriff at that. Even in
the twenty-first century, her walking into a

bar alone during daytime hours would be sufficient to set local tongues wagging. As she entered the artificially darkened room, Joanna more than half expected to find her nemesis, Marliss Shackleford, lurking at the bar.

Once Joanna's eyes adjusted to the light, she was relieved to see that Marliss wasn't there, but Rebecca Nolan was, slouched on a wooden-backed barstool with a mostly empty pitcher of beer parked on the counter in front of her. Next to the pitcher sat an ashtray with a half-smoked cigarette resting in one of the slots. Bright red lipstick that resembled the faded shade on Rebecca's lips had left a stain on the cigarette's filter. Joanna guessed that Rebecca had most likely gone outside to smoke and then returned to the bar with the remainder of the half-smoked cigarette on hold for later.

Timothy Grady himself stood behind a grungy homemade counter, one that still hinted at its humble fast-food origins. The wooden surface was scarred with hundreds of carved initials. As Joanna entered the joint, both Timothy and Rebecca were staring up at a major-league baseball game playing silently on a flat-screen TV fastened to the faded wooden paneling on the wall above the bar. Joanna noticed that the other customers, most of them clad in leather motorcycle riding gear, were seated in booths around the perimeter of the room. Rebecca was the only person seated at the bar itself.

Timothy Grady initially glanced at Joanna with a welcoming grin as she slid onto the stool next to Rebecca's. Then, recognizing her or perhaps registering the significance of her uniform, his grin faded abruptly.

"Great," he muttered. "To what do we owe the honor of a visit from one of our local gendarmes? I assume you've dropped by to hassle me for some phony reason or other?"

"If you don't mind, I came here to talk to Mrs. Nolan," Joanna said pleasantly. "I'll have a cup of coffee if you have it, a Coke if you don't."

Hunching closer to the glass and staring into her beer, Rebecca sat with her arms resting on the edge of the bar. "Never did like cops much," she muttered under her breath.

The woman's mumbled delivery told Joanna that Rebecca Nolan was probably already over the limit. If she tried driving back home rather than walking, she would be ripe for adding another DUI to her collection, not to mention driving without a license. Joanna knew better than most that drunk drivers didn't lose their driver's licenses over one measly DUI conviction.

"You were a lot more friendly up in the parking lot the other morning when we were searching for Junior Dowdle," Joanna observed.

"Why wouldn't I be?" Rebecca shot back. "I was out there with my kids doing our civic duty. This is me on my free time. What I do on my free time is no business of yours."

"Speaking of your kids," Joanna said, "where are they?"

"At home most likely," Rebecca

answered glumly. "Why do you want to know?"

"They're at home alone?"

"That's where I left them," Rebecca replied. "Hey, they're fourteen. That's a little too old to need a babysitter, especially in broad daylight. Come to think of it, why were you there talking to Ruthie this morning? What's that all about? I didn't think cops could talk to minors without their parents present?"

"Usually," Joanna agreed. "As for talking to Ruth earlier? Our getting together was her idea. As I told you earlier, she wanted to interview me for her blog. She said it was a homework assignment."

"Was a homework assignment," Rebecca muttered. "I already told you, that was months ago. She wrote that one essay and then that geeky Radner kid—what's his name?"

"Jason."

"Yeah, right. That's the one. He told her that if she wanted him to, he could put it up on the Internet for her and turn it into a blog. So, yes, the first one was a homework assignment, but it sort of got out of hand. To begin with, she wrote the entries and Jason posted them. Now Ruth has learned to post them herself. She calls it 'Roxie's Place,'" Rebecca added, drawing a pair of sarcastic airborne quotation marks around the last two words. "God, how I hated that yappy little mutt!"

Timothy came back and slammed a mug of coffee on the bar in front of Joanna, slopping some of the coffee in the process.

"That'll be five bucks," he announced. Joanna suspected he had doubled the usual price on her account. That's how much lattes went for downtown. He stood there staring at her belligerently. Joanna couldn't tell if he expected her to argue about the price or if he was simply waiting for his money. Either way, he made no move to offer her a coaster or a napkin. Reaching into her purse, Joanna pulled out five one-dollar bills. She carefully counted them out and then slapped them onto the bar in the middle of the puddle of spilled coffee.

Coffee money, Joanna thought, half

smiling to herself and wondering if any of Sandy Henning's bank tellers would notice and sound an alarm.

Glowering at her, Timothy picked up the sodden bills. "What about the tip?" he demanded.

"What tip?" she replied. "You spilled a third of my coffee."

He stalked off, and Joanna turned back to Rebecca. "Who's Roxie?" she asked.

"You mean, who **was** Roxie," Rebecca replied. "I never wanted a dog to begin with, but my ex dragged that nasty little dog home from the pound. She peed and crapped all over the place. One day she disappeared. Slipped out of the house somehow. Lots of coyotes where we used to live. One of them probably got her. Good riddance. That's all I've got to say about that. Ruth acted like losing that damn dog broke her heart. It sure as hell didn't break mine."

A shiver went up and down Joanna's spine. A pet goes missing for some unexplained reason, a loss that pushes a troubled young girl closer to the edge.

Was it possible that months later, that same girl might turn Sunday school ongs into a siren call and lure a mentally impaired man to his death? And what were the chances that the same girl would find a way to insert herself into the framework of the investigation into a murder she herself had committed?

How many times had Joanna heard of instances of serial killers insinuating themselves into criminal investigations? They did it to find out whether the cops were onto them, true, but there was often another reason as well—they truly believed they were better than everybody else and that no one would ever be smart enough to figure it out.

Ruth Nolan had come to Joanna, in all her blue-eyed, purple-haired innocence, asking to do an interview. She hadn't mentioned the Junior Dowdle situation in the beginning, but the interview had certainly led there. The possibility that Junior's killer had been right under Joanna's nose shocked her to the core, and it galled her to think that Ruth might have played her for a sucker.

Joanna took a tiny sip of Timothy's bitter, hours-old coffee while she assessed the situation. Rebecca was already drunk—enough so that not only was her speech slurred but her tongue was loosened as well. It was in Joanna's best interests and in Junior Dowdle's, too, that Joanna keep the woman talking as long as possible.

"Sounds tough," she said, feigning a sympathy she didn't feel. "When did all this happen?"

"When did Roxie disappear?" Rebecca's reply included a careless shrug. "Long time ago, before the divorce. When we came here, I put my foot down. I told Ruth that we were not getting another dog. Period!"

"Perfectly understandable. Losing a pet is hard on everybody, especially kids. Speaking of kids," Joanna added. "Did any of the detectives ever get around to talking to Ruth or Lucas?"

"About Junior Dowdle, you mean? Maybe they did or maybe they didn't. I'm not sure. Why would they?"

"For one thing, you live just up the street. Ruth and Lucas strike me as smart kids. They might have been outside the evening Junior died. Perhaps they noticed something unusual. Maybe they saw a stranger of some kind hanging around the neighborhood."

"I don't think so," Rebecca said. "They were home all day and for most of that they were inside. Lucas was on the computer working on an online algebra program. Algebra's beyond me. I can do arithmetic out the yin-yang, but since algebra is way over my head, I signed him up for an online tutorial. As for Ruth? She was out of it completely—never left her room all day except to go to the bathroom a couple of times."

"What do you mean, 'out of it'?"

Rebecca poured more beer, emptying the remains of the pitcher into her glass. "She got her period. Had the cramps. She was crying and bellyaching and wanting me to take her to the doctor. My ex still has the kids on his health insurance, but it only covers major medical. Doesn't cover doctor's visits or prescriptions, so I gave her one of my muscle relaxers. Put her out like a light. No more complaining."

Rebecca's casual admission of having given her daughter an illegal dose of prescription medication was enough to take Joanna's breath away. There was nothing warm and fuzzy about this woman; nothing maternal or loving, either. Here was a textbook case of a dysfunctional family breeding a dysfunctional child. How many defense attorneys had used that as an excuse to ask for leniency for their clients' murderous actions? If Ruth ended up on trial for Junior's murder, would Burton Kimball point at Rebecca Nolan and attempt to use the same defense in Ruth's favor?

Suddenly Joanna's focus narrowed. She stared hard at Rebecca's ashtray and the lipstick-stained cigarette hanging off it. What she had just learned about Ruth Nolan put Rebecca's DNA-drenched cigarette filter in a whole new light. After a moment of consideration, Joanna picked her purse up off the back of her stool.

Standing up, she swung the purse in a seemingly careless fashion, managing to crash it into Rebecca's still half-full glass of beer and into the empty pitcher as well. Spilled beer poured off the counter and onto Rebecca while the pitcher crashed to the floor on the far side of the bar, shattering into a thousand pieces.

"You stupid broad!" Timothy roared as he raced toward the mess. "What the hell do you think you're doing?"

While Rebecca gazed down in despair at her suddenly sodden tank top, Joanna plucked the cigarette out of the ashtray. Avoiding touching the filter, she slipped the cigarette into her purse. Pulling a twenty out of her purse, she slapped it down on the bar.

"Sorry about that pitcher," she said. "I'm pretty sure this will cover the damage."

With that she turned on her heel and walked away in an exit that was, in its own way, worthy of Columbo.

CHAPTER 23

Driving west on I-40 at 75 mph through the wide open landscape of northern New Mexico, Liza Machett found herself speeding around the semis lumbering along at much lower speeds and sticking mostly to the right-hand lane of the freeway. Alone and vulnerable in her little Camry, she was the hare to their slow-moving tortoise. She had felt safe and protected tucked away in the upper berths of those immense long-haul vehicles. Now, out in the open, she couldn't help wondering what secrets the trucks she passed were carrying along with their stated and advertised loads.

Her want-ad Camry had a radio. At least there was a device with knobs and buttons on it occupying that part of the cracked and sun-faded dash that was designated for a sound system. Unfortunately no sounds came out of it, so Liza traveled along in silence with nothing to divert her or keep her mind from straying back to the people who had already died because of her.

Other than the drivers' lounges in the various truck stops along the way where flat-screen TVs ran nonstop programming from Fox News, her traveling cocoon had been almost completely devoid of news coverage. Had it not been for the computers reserved for truckers to use, she wouldn't have known about Candy's death. When she made a pit stop just outside Gallup, she looked longingly at the lounge reserved for professional drivers, wishing she could go inside and glean more details about what progress, if any, was being made in the murders back home in Great Barrington and the one in Stockbridge, too. It sickened her to think that three people were dead for no other reason than having known and/or tried to help her. This was all her fault. Their blood was on her hands as surely as if she herself had murdered them.

Tonight was Sunday. By the time she stopped for the night, the public libraries would all be closed. She had heard that some of the more upscale hotels had business centers where she might be able to go online. If she could manage that, maybe she'd be able to learn more. If that proved impossible, however, she would show up in Bisbee on Monday morning without any more details than she already had. Guy was enough older than she was that Liza hoped he'd be able to supply some of the missing threads about their father's involvement with the mysterious bread trucks. That's where this all led—back to those damnable bread trucks.

Whatever the outcome of her conversation with Guy, however, Liza was determined that once it was over, she would go to law enforcement. She would go to the cops with him or without him. She was the one person who could tie together the two homicide cases back home in Massachusetts. She alone had the power to put the cops on the right trail and bring the murderer or murderers to justice. If she had to relinquish what money remained in her roll-aboard to make that happen, then so be it. The money had never been hers to begin with.

When she crossed the border into Arizona, she was surprised and disappointed that there were no saguaros anywhere in sight. Where had they gone? After all, didn't Arizona and saguaros go together like bread and butter or peanut butter and jelly? Instead, the long straight road rose gradually through a vast wasteland toward a line of blue-tinged mountains that had suddenly appeared on the far horizon. By the time she neared Flagstaff, she was amazed to realize that she had gone from empty desert into a forest of stately pines. Arizona was supposed to be a desert. Why were there so many trees?

Liza had expected to find some place to stay the night in Flagstaff, but as she drove through town, she realized it was too early to stop. Flagstaff was still a long way from Bisbee. Liza wanted to show up at Guy's office bright and early in the morning. Besides, if her pursuers had somehow stumbled on her connection with Candy's Underground Railroad, Liza wanted to put as much distance as possible between her present location and that of William, her most recent driver. She kept right on driving.

Heading south on I-17, she was amazed to see signs warning her of elk crossing the freeway. Elk? On a long downhill grade, she drove past the exit to Sedona. It was a place Liza had always wanted to visit. She remembered seeing photos of Sedona while she was still in school. The red cliffs had been hauntingly beautiful, but just now she felt no temptation to turn off and go exploring. Focused on her mission, she refused to be sidetracked.

After crossing a long, grassy plateau, she hit another steep downhill grade and there, unexpectedly, were the saguaros she had been missing earlier. They stood in tall ungainly poses, casting long shadows in the setting sun. As darkness fell, a huge metropolis of lights fanned out across the valley in front of her.

Phoenix was immense—too immense. Instead of turning off at one of the Phoenix-area exits, Liza kept right on going on I-17 until it intersected with I-10. Some two hours later she finally pulled off onto a frontage road in Tucson. It was after nine before she found a seedy enough hotel where the desk clerk accepted cash without requiring her to show any ID, which she claimed had been stolen. Naturally, the hotel in question wasn't upscale enough to include a business center.

Once in her room, Liza ate the hamburger she had picked up at a fast-food joint across the parking lot from the hotel. Her room boasted a bed with a dingy flowered spread, an equally forlorn sofa, and worst of all, a grimy carpet. Liza didn't care. Stripping out of her clothing, she showered. The tub was cracked and smelled faintly of mold. The torn shower curtain drooped because several of the hooks were either broken or missing. The tiny sliver of soap melted away just as the water went from hot to tepid. After drying herself with a threadbare towel, she fell into bed wearing only the oversize Trux-Travel T-shirt she'd bought in Denver.

The mattress was lumpy. The sheets felt like paper. The pillows were rock hard. The feeble air-conditioning unit under the window barely cooled the room, but none of that mattered. Oblivious to the freeway traffic roaring past outside her window and grateful to be stretched out on a bed that wasn't moving, Liza Machett closed her eyes. Thinking about finally seeing her brother again after all these years, she fell fast asleep.

CHAPTER 24

Once outside Grady's, Joanna used a pair of latex gloves to retrieve Rebecca's half-smoked cigarette from her purse. After dropping it into an evidence bag and labeling same, she called Dispatch.

"I need a deputy up in Old Bisbee on the double," she told Tica Romero. "I've got something that needs to go to the crime lab in Tucson ASAP."

"Deputy Stock is closest," Tica answered. "He just hauled in a DUI and is getting him booked."

"Good," Joanna said. "Send him along. I'm up the canyon in the parking lot at Grady's."

"Grady's Irish Pub?" Joanna heard the surprise in Tica's voice.

"Don't ask," Joanna said. "Just tell him to get here on the double. Is Detective

Howell still there?"

"She went home."

"Too bad," Joanna said. "Have her come meet me, too. Same place. Tell her to wear her vest. We might be paying a visit to a homicide suspect."

Off the phone, Joanna scrolled through her contacts list until she found the crime lab number in Tucson. Her CSIs—Casey Ledford and Dave Hollicker—as well as her detectives were the people from Joanna's department who usually interacted with the DPS crime lab folks. Without specific contacts, all Joanna could do was call the main number. Early on a Sunday evening, it took time to get someone to pick up the phone and even more time to be put through to someone working DNA issues. The guy who finally took her call was a criminalist named Calvin Lee.

"Sheriff Brady," she told him. "From Cochise County."

"Oh, right," he said. "You're the lady who has us working overtime this weekend due to your having two homicides in as many days. If you've got somebody running Murder Incorporated down there, shouldn't you have your own designated crime lab?"

"Sorry about that," Joanna said.

"Don't be," Lee assured her with a chuckle. "Turns out I can use the extra hours. Besides, my wife's an animal lover. If I can help lock up whoever tortured that poor cat, I'll earn big points with her. What's up now?"

"Are you making any progress?"

"Some," he answered. "We've determined that some of the hair samples from your injured kitty contain both human and animal blood, feline presumably. That's easy enough. Despite what you see on TV, getting a DNA profile is not something we can wave a magic wand and have sorted before the ten o'clock news comes on. Once we have a profile, we'll still need something to compare it to. I was also told that you want us to check the clothing of your other homicide victim, and we will. We've had some success doing touch DNA, but that process takes longer than your basic cheek swab."

"This is about the case with the injured cat," Joanna said, "and that's what I have for you now—a possible comparison sample," Joanna told him. "Deputy Jeremy Stock is just now leaving my office east of Bisbee. He'll be bringing along a cigarette with lipstick on the filter."

"You want me to collect DNA from a cigarette filter?" Calvin asked disparagingly. "Couldn't you give me a straight-up cheek swab for a change?"

"The woman who smoked the cigarette isn't my suspect," Joanna explained. "Her fourteen-year-old daughter is a potential serial killer who may have murdered one person and might also be responsible for torturing the cat. At least that's my thinking at this time."

Calvin Lee took that in. "Only fourteen?" he asked. "That sucks. Okay, I can see how getting a cheek swab under those circumstances might be problematic. When's your deputy gonna get here?"

"An hour and a half to two hours," Joanna said. "I'll tell him to put the pedal to the metal."

"Did you say Deputy Stock?" Lee asked. "That's what his name is?"

"Yes," Joanna confirmed. "Jeremy."

"Okay, I'll send his name down to reception so they'll know he's coming and send him right up. I'm going to go on my dinner break before he gets here, because I probably won't have time to eat later. On the off chance that we're able to make this happen in a timely fashion, do you want it to go through regular channels?"

"No," Joanna said. "This is urgent. Call me directly."

She had just finished giving Calvin the number and hung up when Deputy Stock pulled into the lot behind her with his red lights flashing. "You have something for me?" he asked, leaning down to speak to Joanna as she opened her window.

Wordlessly Joanna handed him the see-through bag holding the half-smoked cigarette.

"That's it?" he asked, holding it up to the light. "All this fuss over a damned cigarette?"

"If it does what I think it will, it may help us take down a killer."

"All right, then," Jeremy said, slipping the bag into his shirt pocket and heading back to his Explorer. He had barely driven away when Deb Howell pulled up behind Joanna's Yukon. She came around to the side and slipped into the passenger seat.

"Tica said you may have found a killer. Which one?"

"Junior's," Joanna answered.

"Who is it?"

"I think it may be Ruth Nolan."

"You're kidding—that skinny little girl with the purple hair?"

"That's the one. I'd give you more details, but right now Ruth's mother is planted inside that bar. I want to have a chat with Ruth before we have to actively declare her a suspect, and I don't want to go see her alone."

"I don't blame you," Deb said. "I'll follow you there."

After parking Joanna's Yukon and Deb's Explorer on O'Hara Street, Joanna led the way to the Nolans' front door. As soon as she stepped onto the porch, she heard the unmistakable sounds of a video game shootout coming from inside. Joanna rang the bell. The front door had been left ajar. She heard the doorbell buzzing inside, but no one responded. Next she rapped sharply on the frame of the screen door. Still no answer. Finally she opened the screen door and let herself into the house with Deb on her heels. Inside the room, the noise from the video game was overpowering. Lucas Nolan sat on a shabby couch, totally engrossed in whatever was happening on his computer screen.

"Hey," Joanna shouted, trying to be heard over the racket. "Anybody home?"

Startled, the boy looked up and then immediately closed his computer. From the guilty expression on his face, Joanna suspected that playing computer games wasn't one of the things on his mother's list of approved activities.

"Sheriff Brady," he said. "Sorry, I didn't hear you. My mom's not here."

"I know," Joanna said. "I just saw her. I

was hoping to talk to you or your sister."

"Ruth's not here, either," he said. "She went out early this afternoon, right after you left, and she still isn't back."

"Did she say where she was going?"

"Are you kidding?" Lucas asked with a grimace. "I'm her brother. Why would she bother telling me anything?"

"So then I guess we'll have to settle for talking with you," Joanna said. Not waiting for an invitation, she moved the computer aside and sat down on the couch. Deb chose a nearby chair. "Did any of the detectives interview you or Ruth about what happened last week?"

"About what happened to Junior, you mean?" Lucas asked.

Joanna nodded.

"Detective Keller asked us a few questions," Lucas replied. "At least he asked me a few questions. I talked to him that morning in the parking lot at St. Dominick's. I don't know if he talked to Ruth at the same time, but most likely he did."

"We've been too busy to get all the

reports passed back and forth," Joanna said. "I'm sorry to have to go back over the same questions, but can you tell us what you told Detective Keller?"

"He asked about what happened the day before and did I see anything. I told him I was here at home, working on the computer."

"All day?" Joanna asked.

Lucas nodded.

"What about that night?"

"Same thing."

"What about your sister?"

"She was here, too. We both were. She was sick that day. I don't think she even got dressed."

Joanna wondered if Lucas had any idea that Ruth had slept through the day because her mother had slipped her a high-powered pill. "What about your mom?" Joanna asked. "Was she here?"

"She was here most of the day."

"What about that night?"

A cloud passed over Lucas's face. He didn't answer immediately.

"I take that to mean that she wasn't

here," Joanna suggested. "I understand your mother spends a good deal of time at Grady's up the canyon. Is that that where she was that night?"

Lucas bit his lip and nodded. "Probably," he said.

"Did you go outside at all that night?" Joanna asked.

"No, I already told you. I was here the whole night. Most of that time I was here in the living room."

"What about Ruth?"

"She was here, too."

"Could she have slipped out without your knowing she was gone?"

"Maybe," he allowed. "The only time I get to play my games is when Mom isn't here. She's always complaining that I play them too loud and that they're going to damage my ears. Ruth might have left and I didn't notice, but I doubt it."

"Had there been anything out of line in the neighborhood that day or in the preceding days—strangers or vehicles that you didn't recognize or ones that shouldn't have been there?"

"Not that I remember," Lucas answered. "I went to bed before Mom got home. The next thing I knew it was morning. Mom was shaking me awake and telling me that Junior had gone missing. She said everyone in the neighborhood was going down to the church to help look for him, and we needed to go, too."

"You knew Junior?"

Lucas nodded. "He was a little weird. You know, different. He was like a grown man and a little kid, all at the same time. Ruth felt sorry for him, but she's like that about everything. She once found a grasshopper with a broken leg, and she wanted to take it to the vet."

"What happened to it?" Joanna asked.

"To the grasshopper? Mom stepped on it."

Joanna's opinion of Rebecca Nolan's mothering skills dropped several more notches.

"What about Roxie?" Joanna asked. "What happened to her?"

"You mean Ruth's dog?"

Joanna nodded.

Lucas shrugged. "She ran off, I guess. She got out of the house and disappeared. We looked everywhere for her for days, but we never found her. She was tiny. I think maybe an eagle got her or else a coyote."

With serial killers, there was often some traumatic event or a series of events in their past that set them off. From what little Joanna knew of Ruth's life, there seemed to be plenty of possible triggers: she had lost her dog; her parents had divorced; she had moved to a new town where she was a perpetual outsider due to being homeschooled. Added together, Joanna could see how all those separate events could take a serious emotional toll. Maybe it was unfair to focus so completely on Ruth, but right now that purple-haired girl was Joanna's primary target.

"Do you miss your old home?" Joanna asked, turning her attention back to Lucas.

"Are you kidding?" he asked derisively. "How could anybody ever miss Gallup? I hated it. I liked where we lived before— that was back in Missouri while Dad was going to seminary. When he graduated, we got shipped off to Gallup. That's what they do—they ship the new guys off to the worst places."

"What about Ruth?" Joanna asked. "Did she hate Gallup, too?"

"She didn't mind it as much as Mom and I did," Lucas said. "Especially after Dad gave her that dog. He got the dog for both of us, really—for our birthday. People do that with twins. They think one birthday present is enough for two people. Dad said we were supposed to share, but Roxie was Ruth's dog. She didn't want to have anything to do with me."

"Do you like being homeschooled?" Deb asked. "It must be tough to meet other kids."

"Not really," Lucas said with a shrug. "I go down to the Boys and Girls Club. And there's a new gym in town where some of my friends and I go to lift weights. Then there's a different bunch of us who play video games and keep score in a chat room."

"What about Ruth? Does she have any

friends?"

Lucas sniffed. "Not many. She mostly hangs out with Jason Radner, and sometimes Junior."

Joanna was under the impression that Ruth's interactions with Junior were limited to midnight serenades. "She hung out with Junior Dowdle?" Joanna asked.

"Sure, he lived just down the street. Everybody knew him. Mom says Ruth thinks it's her job to fix every broken bird. She and Jason spent time with Junior. I didn't."

"Did Ruth ever say anything to you about finding a cat?" Joanna asked. "A dead cat?"

Lucas frowned and then nodded.

"When did that happen?"

"I don't know. A while ago. Jason found it and then told Ruth about it."

"Did Ruth ever say anything to you about how the cat died?"

Lucas shrugged. "Not to me."

Joanna was running out of questions. Worried that Rebecca might come home and find them there, Joanna decided it was time to leave. The last thing she needed was to end up in a confrontation with a pissed-off drunk.

She stood up, and so did Deb. "We'd better be going and let you get back to your game. Are you winning?"

"I was a little while ago," Lucas said. "Before I closed the computer." He added, "I'm real good at games, though. I'll be able to catch up."

Joanna pulled a business card out of her pocket. "My numbers are all there," she said. "When Ruth comes home, tell her I'd like to talk to her. Have her give me a call."

"Will do," Lucas said.

Back outside, it was full dark with only a few sparse streetlights to illuminate the way as Deb's and Joanna's shoes crunched on the gravel. Between the sides of the narrow canyon a tiny sliver of moon was rising on the far horizon.

"If Ruth really is our doer," Deb said, "where is she? It's past suppertime. Shouldn't she be home by now?"

"I don't think Rebecca Nolan is big on

family dinners," Joanna said, "and that means I have no idea where Ruth might be."

As Joanna said the words, an eerie chill washed over her, one she couldn't shake. The neighborhood seemed peaceful enough, but she had a feeling that something evil was out there, prowling the darkening streets and hunting for another victim.

CHAPTER 25

Joanna was in the Yukon and slipping the key into the ignition when her phone rang. "Where are you?" Dave Hollicker demanded.

She heard the excitement and urgency in his voice. "Up in Old Bisbee and on my way home. Why?"

"I've found something interesting, and I want to show it to you."

"What is it? Can't you just tell me?"

"No, that would be like trying to give someone a haircut over the phone. Maybe I'm wrong. I want you and Deb to see it together so I can tell if the two of you have the same reaction I did."

Obviously, as far as Dave was concerned, his discovery couldn't wait until morning. "Okay," Joanna agreed reluctantly. "I'm coming, and I'll call Deb next."

After letting Deb know, Joanna drove through Bisbee's quiet streets. On Fridays and Saturdays the town filled up with out-of-town tourists. The motorcycle riders partying in Grady's were typical weekend visitors, but by Sunday evening, most of the out-of-towners went back home, leaving Bisbee's winding thoroughfares and steep streets to the locals.

As Joanna drove, she worried. If Ruth Nolan wasn't home, where was she? Would Joanna awaken tomorrow morning to discover that someone else had been murdered overnight? Should she call Alvin Bernard and Matt Keller and put them into the picture, or should she sit on her suspicions for the time being? Because that's all she had right now—suspicions. Tomorrow she'd contact Rebecca Nolan and ask her to bring Ruth into the department so they could take a set of elimination prints to match against the prints Casey Ledford had lifted from the window surround outside Junior's bedroom or maybe from the grate at the glory hole.

She wouldn't mention to Rebecca that the prints might not be exculpatory at all. It was more likely they'd be evidence of guilt. The problem was, Joanna knew from both Jason and Lucas that Ruth had been one of the nighttime visitors outside Junior's room. So even if her prints were found there, a good defense attorney would be able to convince a jury to discount them. There would have to be evidence over and above the prints. The best thing they had going for them might turn out to be the human DNA from the injured kitten. It would be ironic if evidence from the cat was what ended up bringing Junior's killer to justice.

Joanna and Deb caravanned back to the Justice Center together and parked side by side at the back of the building, Joanna in her reserved spot and Deb claiming squatters' rights to Chief Deputy Hadlock's currently unoccupied space.

"What's Dave up to?" Deb asked as Joanna punched the door code on the private entrance into her office.

"No idea," Joanna said, "but it better be

good."

She switched on the overhead light. The moment it came on, the door into Kristin's office opened. Dave limped through it on his crutches. Held between his teeth was a single piece of copy paper. He had evidently overheard at least part of their conversation.

He stopped, removed the paper from his mouth, and laid it on Joanna's desk. "It is good," he said. "Take a look."

Together, Joanna and Deb peered down at the paper. It was a photograph of an old man and a towheaded boy, both of them grinning proudly. They were standing side by side on what looked like a wharf of some kind. The boy was holding a fish that was a foot or so long. The caption under the photo said, "This year's Fourth of July Fishing Derby winner is ten-year-old Guy Machett, pictured here with his grandfather, Jerome Machett." The photo's credit line read "Photo courtesy of the **Great Barrington Herald.**"

The photo was old and blurry—made with some old-fashioned technology that resulted in visible dots of ink on paper. Wanting a closer look, Joanna picked up the photo to study it. When she realized what she was seeing and recognized the craggy face and thinning white hair, her jaw dropped.

"That's Lyle Morton!" she exclaimed. "He was here just this afternoon."

Joanna passed the picture to Deb Howell. After studying it for a moment, Deb nodded in agreement. "It's got to be him," she said.

"But it isn't," Dave said triumphantly. "That's Jerome Machett—Guy's grandfather. I was out in the hallway when Deb was taking Lyle Morton into the interview room. The resemblance is so striking that I'm sure Lyle must be Guy's father and Jerome's son."

Contemplating that turn of events, Joanna went around the desk and sank down in her chair. "Sit," she ordered. Deb and Dave sat. Joanna turned on Dave. "How did you ever manage to sort this out?"

"The **Great Barrington Herald** was established in 1860 and has been continuously in print ever since," Dave replied. "The town has a very active historical society. A number of years ago, they began digitizing back issues of the local paper. Their website is amazing. You asked me to see what I could find out about Guy Machett. I went to their website and typed in his name and hit a gold mine.

"There were articles about Guy being valedictorian of his class, leading the debate team that took a statewide title, winning a scholarship to Harvard, and graduating from med school. This photo was the next-to-last item I found. When I looked at it, I thought the old man looked familiar, but it took me a while to make the connection. As soon as I did, first I checked out Deb's interview with Lyle Morton, and then I returned to checking my databases. I found Jerome's date of death with no difficulty, but there's no sign at all of Anson's. I did notice, however, that shortly after he disappeared into the ether, a guy named Lyle Morton turned up owning a ranch in southern Arizona."

Dave paused long enough to give them

a grin along with a dramatic wave of his hand. "Ladies," he announced, feigning a bow, "I believe that we have stumbled upon an early and rather successful member of the witness protection program."

For a time the room was quiet. "When I was interviewing Lyle, he never gave anything away," Deb said at last. "He acted like Guy was a friend and a client, nothing more."

"**Acting** is the operant word," Dave said. "The man's been doing nothing but acting for a very long time."

"Wait," Joanna said. "Think about this. All this time we've been thinking Guy's killers were after the coffee money, and maybe they are, but what if they were also looking for his father? What if Lyle is the real target? Do we know anything about what Anson did for a living?"

"No idea," Dave said, "but I'll try to find out."

"People don't go into witness protection for no reason. Once they do, they're supposed to cut all ties to the past. We know from the Morton interview that Guy had been visiting the Whetstone Retreat for years—starting while he was still in med school. That means Lyle broke with the WITSEC protocol early on, at least as far as his son was concerned. Guy was tortured before he died. The attempts to revive him suggest that he didn't give the killers what they wanted."

"You mean they were really looking for Lyle?" Dave asked.

Joanna nodded. "But that doesn't mean someone else wouldn't give up Lyle Morton's ID and location."

Joanna turned to Deb. "Did you tell him about Liza's going missing?"

Deb shook her head. "You asked me not to, so I didn't."

Joanna stood up hard enough to send her desk chair thumping into the wall behind her. She reached for her purse. "Let's go," she said. "Deb, you're with me. Dave, you're to get in touch with the U.S. Marshals Service and let them know that Lyle Morton's cover has been blown and that we suspect there may be people after him who are willing to commit wholesale murder in order to find him."

"Where are we going?" Deb asked.

"We're going to drive out to the Whetstone Retreat and give Lyle Morton the news that if bad guys are after him, they've not only murdered his son, but they may also have kidnapped his daughter. If we have to, we'll take the man into protective custody."

"We can't go there," Deb objected. "The Whetstone is a nudist colony."

"When the retreat had a forest fire emergency last year, I have it on good authority that the firefighters got to wear their firefighting gear. We're claiming the same first responder privilege."

Grabbing his crutches, Dave headed back to his lab. Once Joanna and Deb stepped outside, Joanna stopped on the sidewalk and stared at the two vehicles parked side by side. As the department's newest detective, Deb Howell's ride was a much-used Explorer. Joanna's, on the other hand, was an almost new Yukon.

"Get your weapons out of your car," Joanna directed. "We'll take my vehicle.

It's in better shape—more power and way better springs. And here," she added, tossing her car keys in Deb's direction. "You're driving. You'll be Captain Kirk to my Lieutenant Uhura. I've got at least a dozen phone calls to make, starting with one to my long-suffering husband."

"Do you want me to light 'em up?" Deb asked after she clambered into the driver's seat and was buckling her belt.

"No," Joanna said after a moment's consideration. "No lights and stick to the speed limit. The less attention we call to this operation, the better. Do we even know for sure that Lyle was heading back home when he left the department after the interview?"

"That's what he said," Deb replied.

"It turns out Lyle Morton said a lot of things," Joanna said grimly, "and most of them weren't true. We'll go to the retreat first. If he's somewhere else, we'll have to figure out how to find him."

One at a time, Joanna punched her way through the necessary calls. She let Butch know what was up; ditto for Deb's sister, who was babysitting Deb's son. Next up was Alvin Bernard. These were joint cases and joint operations, Joanna decided, and keeping what she now suspected about Ruth Nolan or the Lyle Morton revelations to herself would not qualify as playing well with others.

The call to Alvin lasted almost half an hour. Joanna told him about what Frank had discovered and passed along the information that had been forwarded to Detective Franklin back in Great Barrington. She told him about the Lyle Morton/ Anson Machett situation. Finally she got around to her suspicions and concerns about Ruth Nolan. After a long time spent talking back and forth about that thorny problem, Alvin and Joanna together decided that with everything going on with the Guy Machett case, they should focus on that and leave the Ruth Nolan situation alone for the time being. Joanna was relieved to have that decision be a joint one. If Ruth was out on the hunt tonight—if one night's delay in taking the girl into custody meant that someone else died—at least the responsibility wouldn't be Joanna's alone. At the end of the conversation, they agreed to a nine o'clock briefing at the Justice Center the next morning for all personnel involved in either or both investigations.

By the time that call was over, Joanna's iPhone was hot enough to burn her ear. Reluctant to use the police radio in case someone was following their movements on a scanner, Joanna called Tica Romero and asked her to station deputies on either side of the Whetstone Retreat on Highway 90, one patrol car north of Huachuca City and the other at the junction of Highway 90 and I-10. That way, if all hell did break loose at the retreat, they'd still have some chance of netting the bad guys.

The call after that was to Amos Franklin in Great Barrington. "Hey," he said, sounding downright cordial despite the lateness of the hour. "You and your people have done some great work out there, Sheriff Brady. Guess what? Cell tower 672 is less than one hundred yards from Candy Small's house. Arson investigators will be combing through the wreckage tomorrow. I've told them to be on the lookout for a cell phone, and I've got a ten o'clock appointment at the drugstore to come by and pick up their surveillance tape."

"No court order necessary?"

"Surprised me, too. Who woulda thought we'd find a drugstore owner who's willing to cooperate with the cops without having a gun held to his head?"

"Who would?" Joanna agreed.

"And I got back to Nancy, my friend from the bank. She went through her e-mails and located her correspondence about the coffee money. She found the response from Agent Flores at Treasury and forwarded it to me. Do you want me to send you a copy?"

"My phone's almost out of power. Can you text it to Detective Howell's phone?"

"Sure."

By the time Joanna finished relaying the phone number, they had just passed through the border check station on Highway 90. Lyle had told Deb in the interview that the turnoff to the retreat was the first left north of that. Deb had slowed and was looking for the intersection when call waiting buzzed in Joanna's ear. Holding the phone away from her ear, she saw "Blocked Call" on the screen.

"Sorry, Detective Franklin," she said. "I have to take this."

"Sheriff Brady?" a clipped male voice asked. This one wasn't nearly as cordial.

"Yes."

"I'm Roger Stephens with the U.S. Marshals Service. You are not to approach Mr. Morton in any way. He is to be left alone! That's an order."

"Excuse me, Mr. Stephens," Joanna returned mildly. "This is my jurisdiction, and you're not authorized to give me orders. We're investigating a homicide that occurred on my turf, and Mr. Morton is a critical witness."

"I'm aware of your homicide," Stephens replied. His exasperated tone reminded Joanna of Butch on those rare occasions when Denny's litany of why questions went one "Why?" too far.

"However," Stephens continued, "Mr.

Morton's safety is our problem, and we will handle it our way."

Deb swung the steering wheel to the left onto a dirt road, and the SUV bounced noisily over the rails of a metal cattle guard.

Stephens was still talking when Joanna covered the phone's microphone with her hand. "How far?" she asked.

"Google says it's five miles to the next turnoff," Deb answered. "Two more miles after that."

Wishing she knew the man's rank, Joanna uncovered the phone. "Sorry," she said, "you were breaking up. I'm afraid I didn't get all that."

"I said," Stephens said, raising his voice considerably, "any effort on your part to approach Lyle will put him in grave danger."

"In case you haven't figured this out," Joanna said, "Mr. Morton is already in grave danger. So is Anson Machett, by the way. His son, Guy, has been murdered. His daughter, Liza, is missing. The daughter's boss was murdered and so was her landlady. If your job is to protect Anson Machett and his family, Mr.

Stephens, allow me to say that you're doing a piss-poor job of it."

Joanna heard the man's sharp intake of breath. The long period of silence that followed indicated Stephens wasn't accustomed to being addressed in that fashion. Joanna suspected he was usually the one dishing out criticism and issuing orders rather than being on the receiving end of either.

"Where are you right now?" Joanna asked.

"At my office in Washington, D.C." he answered. "I came here to deal with this situation. I've put in a call to my agent in charge in Phoenix. He should be able to have someone at Mr. Morton's location shortly."

"How shortly?" Joanna asked.

"I'm not sure exactly, but probably within an hour or two."

"Not a good answer," Joanna said. "Too little too late. I have an armed response team on its way to his residence right now. The GPS gives us an ETA of a little over twenty minutes."

"An armed response team? You need to tell them to stand down."

"That's not going to happen."

"What exactly are your intentions, Sheriff Brady?"

"I intend to keep the man safe!" Joanna replied. "I believe some people—seriously dangerous people—are trying to kill him. I suspect you already know who those people are, or at least who's behind them. If you were any kind of a team player, you'd tell us what you know so we'd have some idea of what we're up against."

"I can't possibly divulge the nature of Mr. Morton's situation."

"Of course you can't," she said, "so I'm hanging up now."

"But—"

"No buts. You can stick your cover-your-ass excuses where the sun don't shine, Mr. Stephens. Feel free to have your agent in charge contact me at his convenience tomorrow. In the meantime, don't bother calling me back. I'm busy, and my phone's battery is at seven percent."

Joanna ended the call. Then, holding

the power button down, she switched it off completely.

"Whoa," Deb said. "Why didn't you tell him how you really felt?"

They both broke into a fit of giggles. It was a natural enough reaction, just as Joanna's angry outburst had been. They were preparing to go into battle. They had no idea what would await them at the next turn in the road.

"I'll need to use your phone," Joanna said to Deb, holding out her hand. "That bastard won't have your number."

Without a word, Deb Howell pulled the phone out of her pocket and handed it over.

CHAPTER 26

What they encountered at the end of the road was the entrance to Whetstone Mountain Retreat and a formidable iron gate complete with a guard shack. An armed guard stepped up to the driver window when Deb stopped the SUV. The retreat may have been a nudist colony, but the guard was fully clothed. His khaki uniform, the businesslike semiautomatic pistol on his hip, and his Kevlar vest indicated that Lyle Morton was serious about security.

"We're closed," he said when Deb buzzed down the window. "Check-in is from ten AM to six PM daily. No exceptions. You'll have to come back tomorrow."

"We're not here to check in," Deb told him, flashing her ID. "We're here to see Mr. Morton."

"Names?" he asked, peering in the window.

"Detective Deb Howell and Sheriff Joanna Brady."

"One moment."

He returned to the guard shack and picked up the receiver on an old-fashioned telephone handset. After speaking into it briefly, he returned to the Yukon. There, using a cell phone, he snapped a photo of each of them and e-mailed them to someone else. Returning to the guard shack again, he picked up the telephone receiver. After a minute or so of waiting, the gate swung open. Before they could pass, he motioned for Deb to roll down the window again. "Do you know where you're going?"

"No idea," Deb told him.

"The first building, the one on your right, is the changing facility. You can put your clothes in an empty locker and take the key with you. Then follow the road all the way to the big house at the end. You'll go past several casitas, the dining hall, and the recreation building."

"This is official business," Deb said. "We won't be changing."

The guard shrugged. "Suit yourself, and watch out for golf carts," he added. "They have the right of way."

The dirt road ended just inside the gate. From there on, it was paved. They saw a building marked Changing Facility and drove straight past it. The guard's warning about golf carts having the right of way proved to be correct. They met three of them on the way and had to pull over on the shoulder to let them pass. Each cart carried two passengers. As they drove past, illuminated in the Yukon's headlights, it was clear that all the passengers were stark naked—except for the boots.

"Yikes," Deb said. "When they say nude, I guess they mean it."

The road wound past any number of casitas, small stucco-covered cabins that looked like they might have wandered over the state line from New Mexico. Some of the casitas had lights on inside. Others were dark and unoccupied. There was no mistaking the big house at the end of the road. Long and low and constructed of river rocks, it had probably started out as an ordinary ranch house built from whatever materials came most easily to hand. Lights glowed from every window. As they approached, a massive front door swung open. Lyle Morton, naked except for his pair of boots, rolled out onto the porch in his cart and then sat there waiting for them, backlit in the doorway.

Deb gaped at him for a moment and then turned uncertainly to Joanna. "Are you sure about this, boss?" she asked.

"I'm sure," Joanna said. "Let's do it."

When they stepped out of the vehicle, Joanna led the way.

"Good evening, officers," their host said cordially as they made their way up the winding wheelchair ramp that led to the porch. "It's rather late. What seems to be the problem?"

"We're here about your son, Mr. Machett," Joanna said.

Momentary shock registered on his face followed by resignation. "I see," he said.

"Come in. I was just having a sip of cognac. Care to join me?"

"No, thank you," Joanna said. "We're on duty."

He rolled his cart into the house and then waited by the door until they both walked past. After closing it and turning the dead bolt, he directed them into a large living room, where several well-worn leather chairs were grouped around a coffee table in front of a river rock fireplace. On this late-spring evening it was laid with an unlit fire.

The coffee table was made from a single slice of polished wood that must have been cut from an ancient tree trunk. From the way the chairs were arranged, it was clear that one spot at the table—the one closest to the fireplace—had no chair. Lyle rolled past them and stopped his cart in the empty space, where a bottle of Courvoisier and a single snifter with a layer of amber liquid awaited his attentions. Beside the snifter sat a marble ashtray. An empty pipe lay inside the ashtray with a packet of tobacco and a book of matches positioned nearby.

"I'm afraid I wasn't entirely honest with you when I came to see you this afternoon," he admitted.

"We noticed," Joanna said. "It turns out we weren't entirely honest, either. That's why we're here."

Lyle picked up the pipe and proceeded to load and light it. Watching him, Joanna was struck by how thin he was. Dressed in clothing in her office he had seemed much larger. Now she saw him for what he was—a painfully thin, scrawny old man.

With the pipe successfully lit, he picked up the snifter and leaned back in the cart. "All right," he said, "who goes first?"

"Let's start with why you came to see us today," Joanna said.

"That's easy—because I wanted to find out as much as I could about what happened to Guy," he said. "There are some bad people in my past that I need to avoid. I wanted to know if they were behind what happened. You and Detective Howell here were very coy and didn't give anything away. I didn't learn a thing."

"It's an active investigation," Joanna said. "We're not supposed to discuss it."

"Fair enough," Lyle said. "Your turn."

Joanna decided to go for the gold. "We're prepared to discuss it now," she said. "We changed our minds because we believe you to be in danger. We know, for instance, that you're in the witness protection program. It seems likely that Guy's death has something to do with that."

Lyle nodded. "Can you tell me exactly how my son died?" During his visit to the Justice Center he had managed to make them believe his interest in Guy was that of a friend or acquaintance. That was no longer true. The grief on Lyle's face was as naked as the rest of him.

Joanna took a deep breath. "Guy was tortured before he was murdered. Someone used a stun gun on him over and over. When that didn't give them what they wanted, they tried waterboarding and apparently went too far. The M.E. found bruises on his body that suggest they tried to revive him at some point.

Which also suggests that, even with the waterboarding, they didn't find what they were looking for."

A pained expression crossed Lyle's face. "You're saying Guy didn't give me up?"

"We don't believe he did."

Now Lyle's face contorted in anguish. There was a basket on the front of the cart with a small leather packet in it. When he regained his composure, he opened the packet, pulled out a hankie, and blew his nose. When he finished, he shook his head.

"I've been in witness protection for close to thirty years," he said, "living here most of that time. In all those years, nobody's called me Mr. Machett until just now when you showed up. How did you figure it out? Guy and I went to great pains to cover our tracks."

"Not great enough," Joanna observed. "One of my investigators happened across a photo of both your father and your son. At the time Guy was a boy and your father must have been about the age you are now. The resemblance between you and your father is remarkable. But what really set everyone looking for you is your daughter," Joanna said quietly.

Lyle's face fell. "My daughter?" he repeated. "I've done everything in my power to keep Selma and Liza out of it."

"Are you aware that Liza's mother is dead?"

"Was she murdered, too?"

"As far as I know she died of natural causes."

"Guy told me Selma was in hospice. I'm surprised he didn't let me know she was gone."

"He may not have known," Joanna said. "The phone records we've found show only a single call between Liza and Guy. That call was placed to him at his office several weeks ago. By that time, someone may have been monitoring Liza's phone calls."

"Monitoring her phone calls? Spying on her? After all these years, why would they do that now?"

"We believe it's about the money," Joanna said.

"What money?"

"In the past month or so, a large number of very old one-hundred-dollar bills were put back into circulation in and around Great Barrington. The bills were far enough out-of-date that a local banker asked the Treasury Department about them. Eventually those bills were traced back to your daughter."

"Crap!" Lyle exclaimed. "I gave Selma that money to help her take care of the kids. It wasn't meant to put anyone in danger."

"I take it you know about the money?"

Lyle ran a hand over his eyes as if trying to block out a memory. "Of course I do. It's money I stole from people I worked for years ago—mob-related people. They were moving drugs and money up and down the East Coast. They bought a bakery to use as a front for their business and used the bread trucks for cover. I drove one of those trucks. The amount of money involved was astonishing. Since there was so much going back and forth, I decided no one would be the wiser if some of it disappeared."

"You stole from the mob?" Deb asked.

Lyle nodded. "It didn't seem like a big deal at the time. I'd skim only one or two bills out of packages full of hundreds. Most of the people on both ends of the deals weren't that bright. They were generally also greedy and in a hurry, which meant they'd end up counting the packages but not the bills."

"How long did this go on?"

"A long time, and I wasn't the only one doing it, either. The drivers were the chumps running all the risks. We were the ones out on the highways with loads of illegal drugs and money, and we thought we deserved a little extra compensation. That worked fine until one of the drivers got too greedy. Once they figured out he was skimming, the guy was history."

"They murdered him?"

Lyle nodded. "No one ever found his body, but they located the car. It was full of bullet holes and spattered with blood. That sent a message to everybody involved. Since I had been in on the ground floor of the skimming, I had amassed a fair amount of cash. Instead of waiting around for the hit men to come after me, I went to the feds with what I knew on one particular crook and asked for a deal. They offered me witness protection."

"You, but not your family?"

Lyle bit his lip. "I had a girlfriend," he said. "I could take one but not both."

"In other words, you chose the girlfriend?"

Lyle sighed and nodded. "I had to. Trying to take the kids along would have been too complicated, although I hated leaving Guy behind."

"You hated to leave Guy," Joanna said, "but what about Liza?"

"Hell, she wasn't even mine. Selma put the screws to me. She was pregnant and claimed I was the father. I shaped up and married her, but as soon as I saw the baby—eight pounds two ounces and supposedly two months premature—I knew she had lied to me. I wasn't about to go off into my new life dragging along a wife who was a liar and a kid who wasn't even mine. I told Selma I had a girlfriend and I was leaving her, but it's not like I left them penniless. I deeded over the house so they'd have a place to live, and then I gave Selma a crapload of money. I told her I was paying my child support in advance."

A hard lump of anger formed in Joanna's gut. She disapproved of fathers who abandoned their families.

"Did Selma even know about the witness protection program?"

Lyle shot Joanna an appraising look before he answered. "No," he said finally. "She did not."

"What happened to the guy you testified against?"

"I never did—testify, that is. The guy died, supposedly of natural causes, before the case ever came to trial. I never had to go to court, but by then a couple of the other drivers had bitten the dust, too. I didn't dare go back."

"Probably a good decision," Joanna observed drily.

Lyle seemed to sense her change in

attitude. "I didn't leave her broke," he said as if that should exonerate him. "Selma was supposed to use the money. I never expected she'd just hang on to it. Do you have any idea how much was left?"

"It must have been a fair amount. The detective I talked to from Great Barrington estimates Liza spent at least forty thousand in cash fixing up Selma's house. We initially thought the people targeting Liza and her friends were looking for the money. After talking to you, I'm convinced that's wrong. When the money started surfacing, whoever is behind all this must have thought you were the source of it. I believe you're the one they're really after, and they're killing people along the way, including Liza's landlady, her boss, and your son—all in hopes of finding you. For all we know, Liza may be dead by now, too, or she may just be on the move. She vanished the day after Selma's funeral and hasn't been seen since, but the last time some of her coffee money was reported, it surfaced in Gary, Indiana."

"Coffee money?" Lyle asked. "What's

that?"

"The bills may have gotten moldy at some point. Coffee beans are what paper restorers use to get rid of the smell of mold. As recently as Friday, alerts purportedly from the Treasury Department went out to banks all over the country asking them to report the appearance of either old and/or coffee-smelling bills."

"Purportedly?"

"We've learned that Friday's alert didn't come from anyone in D.C.; it was routed through a server in Poland."

"So the alert was bogus?"

Joanna nodded. "Even though it didn't come from the Treasury, that doesn't mean we can rule out Treasury Department involvement. When the questionable bills first surfaced in Great Barrington, a concerned banker reported them to a Treasury agent named Cesar Flores. I asked Amos Franklin, the detective back there, to get me a copy of the banker's correspondence on the topic. He just sent it to me. I'd like you to take a look."

Joanna pulled out Deb's phone and

turned it on. After locating Amos Franklin's text, she passed the phone to Lyle. He squinted at it and had to enlarge the image several times before resorting to a pair of reading glasses. Joanna watched the movement of his eyes as he scrolled through the document. When his eyes stopped moving, she noticed an unmistakable twitch in his jawline.

"Did you recognize someone there?" she asked.

"No," he said too quickly. "Not at all."

Joanna had learned to play poker at an early age. Her father, D. H. Lathrop, had taught her the ropes. He had also tutored her in the art of recognizing a tell, and this was clearly one of those. Three people were dead, including Lyle's own son. The young woman who considered herself to be his daughter was, if not already dead, then certainly in danger. Yet, instead of helping them, Lyle Morton sat there, looked Joanna in the eye, and lied about it.

Joanna took the phone back and reread the message herself, paying close attention to the names listed on the cc lines at the bottom. Finally she pocketed the phone.

"You referred to the people you worked for as 'bad people.' We need names, Lyle. I tried asking the guy from the Marshals Service about them, but his lips are sealed."

Lyle didn't answer immediately. Joanna waited him out.

"I'm not supposed to talk about them," Lyle said at last. "There were two brothers—the Millers. The older one—the one I worked for—was called Big Jim. His much younger brother had a birthmark shaped like a moon on his face. His name was Johnny, but everybody called him Half-Moon."

Deb, who had been busily taking notes, came to attention. "You mean Half-Moon Miller, the mobster guy who's currently on trial in Boston?"

Lyle nodded. "That's the one."

"Have you been asked to testify against him?"

"No, I've been out of the loop for too long. I wouldn't have anything useful to add."

"Maybe they were worried that you might," Deb suggested. "The appearance of that money right around the time the trial was starting might have sent ripples in every direction. It could have been reason enough for someone to want to take you off the board."

"Are you sure none of the names in that letter rang a bell?" Joanna asked.

"No," Lyle insisted, shaking his head. "There was no one there I knew."

"Have it your way, Mr. Morton," Joanna said abruptly, then she stood up. "Come on, Detective Howell. Since Lyle here isn't going to help us, we're done. No need to show us to the door," she added when Lyle made as if to accompany then. "We know the way."

Deb didn't speak until they were back outside "What just happened? I thought we were going to take him into protective custody."

"Screw protective custody," Joanna muttered. "Lyle Morton may be in witness protection, but he's also a lying piece of crap."

"He lied?" Deb asked. "About what?"

"About recognizing one of the names on that correspondence," Joanna said. "If we can figure out which one, we'll be a whole lot closer to figuring out what's going on."

"How do you propose to do that?"

"I'm going to call the U.S. Marshals and locate Mr. Stephens. He may not have a line on everything there is to know about the Miller operation, but he's on the right side of the country and has better sources than we do. One of the names in that banker's letter hit Lyle Morton where he lives, and we need to know which one it is."

CHAPTER 27

Back in the Yukon, Joanna used Deb's phone to work her way through the U.S. Marshals Service until she finally found a duty officer who knew the score. Once Joanna explained the situation, he put the call through to Agent Stephens.

"I thought you said your phone was dead."

"It is. This one belongs to someone else. Now, do you want to continue to argue or are you interested in knowing why I called?"

"Why did you? I've already sent agents to look in on Mr. Morton."

"Is this a cell phone or a landline?" Joanna asked.

"Cell."

"Give me the number. I need to text you something. Once you read it, you can call me back."

"Okay," Stephens said grudgingly when he called back a few minutes later. "I've seen the letter. What about it?"

"I showed it to Lyle Morton," Joanna explained. "One of the names on the cc list got his attention, but when I asked him if he recognized anyone, he lied about it."

"So?" Stephens said. "Lots of people lie. Is that any reason to wake me up in the middle of the night?"

"It is when the guy who's lying happens to be in your witness protection program. It is when people are dying because your precious Lyle Morton poses a threat to someone. My first choice is an unknown someone who is hooked in with Big Jim and Half-Moon Miller, the guys Anson Machett used to work for back in the day. My best guess is that it's also someone who went under everybody's radar back then and is still under the radar now. I need to know who that person is, and so do you."

Knowing he was making up his mind, Joanna waited through the long silence that followed. "Okay," Stephens conceded finally. "I'll look into it. Should I call you back at this number?"

"No," Joanna said, "use mine. This phone belongs to one of my detectives. I'll be home in about an hour and I'll be able to charge mine then."

Joanna handed Deb her phone. "Thanks," she said. "I believe I'm over my temper tantrum now."

Almost two hours after leaving the Whetstone Retreat, Joanna was back home at High Lonesome Ranch. After locking away her weapons and plugging in her discharged phone, Joanna made herself a peanut butter and jelly sandwich, poured a glass of milk, and settled down in the breakfast nook for a solitary late-night meal that certainly didn't qualify as dinner. With Jenny's dogs locked in her room, only Lady padded into the kitchen from Denny's room to keep her company.

Half an hour later, when Joanna tiptoed into the bedroom, she transferred the phone over to her bedside charger. Sunday was supposedly a day of rest, but it hadn't worked out that way. Once undressed and in bed, she was still too wound up to sleep. Unable to the switch off her brain, she tossed and turned as her thoughts bounced back and forth from case to case and problem to problem.

She couldn't quite wrap her mind around the idea that her hometown might also be an incubator for a fourteen-year-old wannabe serial killer. And how was it that a Boston mob case that had been making nationwide news for months had now inserted itself into Joanna's relatively mob-free Cochise County? Bringing someone like Roger Stephens into the equation was a gamble, but if someone in the upper echelons of the Treasury Department was involved in Guy Machett's horrific murder, Joanna's small-town police agency would be at a distinct disadvantage in dealing with them. She understood that people sometimes used fire to fight fire, so didn't it make sense to use feds to fight feds?

The last time Joanna looked at the clock it was twenty minutes to one. Her cell phone crowed her awake four and a half hours later at ten past five. Bleary-eyed and still half asleep, she was surprised when Alvin Bernard's name appeared on the screen.

"What's up?" she asked, heading for the bathroom with the phone and quietly closing the door behind her.

"We've got another situation up here in Old Bisbee," Alvin told her. "Ruth Nolan has gone missing."

Ruth? Joanna was instantly on full alert.

"On the surface it looks like an instant replay of the Junior Dowdle case," Alvin continued. "Her bed hasn't been slept in. The window is wide open; the window screen is unlatched and open. No sign of a struggle. Looks like she let herself out the window and walked away. She's a teenager; she's got purple hair. Maybe it's just what it looks like—a runaway and nothing more."

"When did this happen?"

"We're not sure. Ruth's mother was evidently out for most of the evening. She came home about an hour or so ago and went to the kids' rooms to check on them. Lucas was in bed fast asleep. Ruth was nowhere to be found.

"The mother's a mess," Alvin went on, "drunk and hysterical rather than drunk and disorderly. I was afraid for a while we were going to have to cuff her and lock her in a patrol car to cool off. She's raising hell and expecting the same kind of all-out response we did for Junior. I tried to explain that Junior's situation was different, but Mrs. Nolan told me that if we don't work just as hard to find her Ruth, she intends to file suit. She's right, of course. We do need to find the girl. My biggest concern is that she's dead, too."

"How can I help?" Joanna asked. "Do you need my K-9 unit?"

"Yes," Alvin answered without hesitation. "Absolutely, and any officers you can spare. If you could come uptown in the next little while, I'd appreciate your having a word with Mrs. Nolan while I'm organizing the search. You might have better luck reasoning with her than I did."

"I doubt that," Joanna said, "but I'll try.

See you soon."

Once the call with Alvin was over, Joanna dialed Dispatch and told Larry Kendrick what was needed. Then, putting the phone down on the bathroom counter, she turned on the shower. By the time she stepped out from under the water, she could smell coffee brewing. Once she was dressed, she could tell that Butch was frying bacon and eggs.

"A peanut butter and jelly sandwich in the middle of the night does not constitute good nutrition," Butch scolded as he handed over a freshly poured mug of coffee.

Joanna gave him a quick good-morning peck on the cheek. "You sound like my mother," she said. "That's what she always said when Dad came in late and had a PB&J for dinner."

"It's one of those times when your mother was right," Butch said. "By the way, I tried calling you after I put Denny to bed. Your phone went straight to voice mail."

"The battery ran down," Joanna said. "I

had to turn it off."

There were times she couldn't tell Butch everything, and this was one of them. She didn't mention that she had turned off her phone in order to dodge calls from Mr. Stephens of the U.S. Marshals Service. Had she told Butch about that, she would have had to tell him about Lyle Morton being Guy Machett's father and about Anson Machett being in the witness protection program. Since she couldn't talk about any of that, she couldn't mention Mr. Stephens, either.

"I gave you a new car charger for Christmas," Butch commented. "What happened to that?"

"When I came back from Silver City, I must have left it in your car."

"Figures," he grumbled, shaking his head. "I guess we need spare chargers in every car." Without another word, he brought a plate of bacon and eggs from the stove to the table and set the food down in front of her. "Eat," he ordered. "And while you're at it, tell me who called and woke us up bright and early this morning, and what's the current emergency?"

Between bites, Joanna filled Butch in on the situation with the Nolan family—the partying mother; the disaffected kids; the girl with the purple hair; Roxie, the dog that had gone missing.

"Sounds like things are tough for them all the way around," Butch commented. "If Ruth already interviewed you for her blog, have you looked at what she wrote?"

"Not yet. I've been a little busy."

"What's her website called again?"

"Roxie's Place. Before the interview, I meant to scan some of the entries, but I ran out of time."

"If you'd like, I can try taking a look at the blog a little later," Butch offered. "In the meantime, what do you think happened to her?"

Joanna thought about that for a moment before she answered. "My first choice would be that Ruth ran away. In that case, we find her and bring her home. My second choice would be, she ran into the same unknown bad guy who killed Junior

Dowdle and who has now killed her, too. If that's what happened, we need to find her body."

When Joanna didn't continue, Butch looked at her questioningly over his raised coffee cup. "Is there a third choice?"

"Unfortunately," Joanna replied, "that's the worst one of the bunch. It would mean that Ruth Nolan turns out to be the person who killed Junior. If she left the house because she had personal issues that were escalating out of control, then it's likely we'll end up finding another body."

"I believe I'll stick with number one," Butch said gravely.

Joanna nodded. "My sentiments exactly."

It was ten past six when Joanna pulled into the parking lot at St. Dominick's. Father Rowan was there prepared to direct traffic. So far that didn't appear to be necessary.

"Not quite as big a turnout as for Junior," the priest observed. "The thing is, everybody in town knows the Maxwells. The Nolans are relative newcomers."

Father Rowan wasn't the only one to

note the diminished response. As Joanna parked her car, an angry Rebecca Nolan turned up with Lucas in tow.

"So where is everybody?" she demanded when Joanna rolled down her window. "Last week the whole town went nuts when that dim-witted Junior went missing. Now that it's my little girl who's gone, where are all those goody-goody church ladies with their coffee urns and trays of cookies?"

Rebecca still wore the same grungy tank top she had been wearing in the bar the day before. She reeked of beer and cigarette smoke. Joanna noticed that Lucas, too, was still in the same blue track suit she'd seen him in on several previous occasions. Whatever the family income was, apparently not much of their budget was spent on wardrobe purchases.

Joanna was tempted to point out that it wasn't exactly in anyone's best interest, most especially Ruth's, for Rebecca to spout off about Junior Dowdle's diminished mental capacity. Considering the woman's current state, Joanna didn't bother. "Tell me what happened," she said.

"What do you think happened?" Rebecca shot back. "Ruth wasn't home when I got there! Aren't you a cop? I should think someone might have mentioned that to you by now."

Joanna ignored the barb. "What time did you get home?" she asked.

"I don't remember exactly," Rebecca said. "Sometime after the bars closed, I guess. Maybe two o'clock or so. When Ruth wasn't there, I woke Lucas up and asked him where she'd gone. He said she'd been out most of the afternoon. After that, I walked around the neighborhood looking for her. Finally I called 911."

By then it was also four o'clock in the morning, Joanna thought.

She turned to Lucas. "Did she ever come home after I talked to you?"

Lucas shook his head.

Rebecca rounded on Joanna. "Wait just a minute. You talked to Lucas? When? I never gave you permission to talk to him!"

"Please, Mrs. Nolan, could we just focus

here? What's important is finding Ruth. What time did Ruth leave the house?"

Lucas looked first at his mother and then back to Joanna before he answered. "Right after Mom did," he said with a shrug. "One o'clock maybe?"

"They both left about the same time then?" Joanna asked Lucas.

"I think so," he said.

"Did she seem upset about anything?"

"No, everything was fine."

"Did she make any mention of where she was going?"

"Nope, she just left."

"When she still wasn't back when it was time to go to bed, weren't you worried about her? Shouldn't you have called your mother?"

"It's not my job to look after my sister," Lucas said indignantly. "We're the same age. I'm not her babysitter."

"Does Ruth have any good friends?"

"Only Jason Radner."

"I already talked to the Radners," Rebecca put in. "I did that first thing. I don't care for Jason much. He used to pal around with Junior."

Joanna's phone rang. She excused herself and walked away to take the call. "Hey, boss," Terry Gregovich said. "Spike and I are coming up empty here. The window screen is pushed open, all right, but if Ruth Nolan went out through that, she flew away without ever hitting the ground. Spike alerted a couple of times, but those trails led out to the street. I'm thinking maybe she got into a vehicle of some kind and rode away. Casey says to tell you that there are no visible prints of any kind on the window or frame. What do you want us to do now?"

"Keep going around the neighborhood in ever-widening circles," Joanna said.

"Will do," Terry replied.

Joanna ended the call as Marianne Maculyea drove into the lot. Her aging seafoam VW Bug was followed by a caravan of several vehicles bearing what Rebecca had jeeringly referred to as the "goody-goody church ladies." Joanna hoped the arrival of the refreshments and most especially Marianne would do something to improve Rebecca's agitated state of mind.

A few minutes later, Ernie Carpenter and Jaime Carbajal showed up as well. Knowing how late she and Deb had been out the night before, Joanna had directed Larry Kendrick to leave Detective Howell off the list for the early morning callout. Joanna pointed Ernie and Jaime in Chief Bernard's direction, telling them that, for now, the chief's orders and her orders were one and the same.

Joanna followed Ernie and Jaime over to the command post. Once the dectectives were given their separate assignments and had left, Joanna took a moment to notify Chief Bernard that the K-9 search had yielded zero results.

"Not zero exactly," Alvin replied. "If Ruth left in a vehicle, either under her own power or under duress, we have a whole other problem. In that scenario, a street-by-street search on foot is probably useless. I'm issuing an Amber Alert. I've already gathered what's needed to post it, but I've been holding back, thinking she'd turn up."

"Send it," Joanna advised. Minutes later the Amber Alert sounded on her phone.

Joanna spent the next half hour greeting deputies arriving from far-flung corners of the county and helping map out search areas. She also let people know that, under the circumstances, the 9:00 AM joint briefing had been postponed until further notice.

When Joanna's phone rang at ten to eight, the words "Guy Machett, office," appeared on her screen. She hoped that meant the call was from George Winfield, but when she answered, Madge Livingston was on the line.

"A woman just showed up here at the office," Madge said in her distinctively low-throated voice. "Says her name is Liza Machett, and she's looking for her brother. Doc Winfield isn't here yet, and I don't want to be the one who has to tell her what's happened."

"Don't," Joanna said. "I'll handle it. I'll be right there."

CHAPTER 28

It took less than five minutes for Joanna to arrive at the former mortuary that had been repurposed and turned into the medical examiner's office and morgue. When Joanna entered the reception area, Madge Livingston's desk was deserted. The room's only occupant, seated in a visitor's chair, was a young woman wearing jeans, a tank top, and a bright blue scarf wrapped around a recently shaven head.

"Ms. Machett?" Joanna asked.

The woman looked up uncertainly. "Yes," she said. "I'm Liza Machett. Who are you?"

There was no way to sugarcoat what was coming. "I'm Sheriff Joanna Brady, and I'm afraid I have some very bad news for you. Your brother is dead."

"Dead?" Liza repeated.

"Murdered," Joanna answered. "He was killed in his home on Friday night—tortured and murdered by at least two assailants. We've been doing our best to locate you and let you know."

Liza's face paled, but she didn't cry. Maybe she was too shocked for tears. "This is my fault, isn't it? Whoever did it is looking for the money I found in my mother's house. I thought it was hers, I swear, and I was using it to fix up her place so we could sell it. If I had known the money belonged to someone else, I would have returned it. Now the people who are after the money are chasing me, and they've killed everyone who has tried to help me—Candy, my landlady, Jonathan Thurgard, Guy, and maybe even some of the people from the Underground Railroad."

"The what?" Joanna asked.

"It doesn't matter."

It did matter, but Joanna let the remark slide because she had focused in on something else in Liza's previous statement.

"We know about Candy Small and Olivia Dexter," Joanna said, "but who's Jonathan Thurgard—a friend of yours?"

"Not a friend, not even an acquaintance," Liza answered. "He worked with my father, years ago. I had never seen him or even met him until last week when he showed up at my mother's funeral. He told me I needed to be careful because the guys my dad used to work for when he drove a bread truck were the kind of people who never forgot and never forgave. It must have been true. Somebody's been after me ever since, killing everyone who gets near me."

"Tell me about Jonathan Thurgard," Joanna insisted. "Is he from Great Barrington?"

"No, he's from Stockbridge, a town a few miles north of there."

"When did he die, and how do you know about it?"

"I don't know exactly when. I only know about it because someone told me—the woman who answered the phone at his house. I was looking online for information about the Olivia Dexter investigation and stumbled across what had happened to Candy.

"Jonathan Thurgard was the first person who told me about the bread trucks, but Candy knew about them, too. Candy was the one who said I was in danger and insisted that I leave town. With Candy dead, I thought maybe Mr. Thurgard could clue me in on what was going on, but when I called, I learned he was dead, too—supposedly the victim of a hit-and-run. I don't believe it. The same people who murdered Candy must have murdered Jonathan. Now Guy is dead, too, and it's all my fault."

At last the tears came. For obvious reasons the reception area at the M.E.'s office was fully stocked with boxes of tissues. Joanna passed one of those to the sobbing woman and then excused herself. Ducking outside, she pulled out her phone and dialed Deb Howell's number.

"Where are you?" Joanna asked when the detective answered.

"Still at home, getting ready to go in for the briefing. Why?"

"The briefing's been canceled because Ruth Nolan has gone missing. Where I really need you is here at the M.E.'s office. Liza Machett just showed up, looking for her brother. She's a wreck right now, and I want you to take charge of her."

"Will do," Deb said. "I'm on my way."

"Wait, before you come here, I need something else. When you interviewed Lyle Morton yesterday, did he happen to give you his phone numbers?"

"I'm pretty sure he did. They're probably in the report. Why?"

"I need them," Joanna said. "If they're in the report, Tom Hadlock can locate them for me. He's been holding down the fort at the Justice Center while I've been all over hell and gone."

While Joanna waited for her chief deputy to locate the necessary information, she struggled with her conscience. Lyle Morton was still a protected witness, but he was also a lying protected witness who wasn't even willing to share information when it might help track down the people who had murdered his own son.

And then there was Liza Machett, a woman who had been told that her presumed father was dead and who had crossed most of the continent to see the man she believed to be her brother. Joanna's heart went out to Liza. Her family had betrayed her; her friends had been murdered; she herself had been targeted. In this web of evil, didn't Lyle Morton owe his daughter the truth?

When Lyle answered the phone a few minutes later, he sounded testy. "I've already had an early morning visit by a U.S. marshal. Now, to what do I owe the pleasure?"

"This isn't a social call," Joanna said brusquely. "Consider it an official notification. Liza Machett just turned up at Guy's office looking for her brother. I have every intention of telling her exactly what's happened and why. If you want to give her your side of the story, I suggest you put some clothes on and come straight to the Justice Center. She won't be there, but we'll know where she is."

"No," Lyle said. "You can't tell her. You can't!"

"I can, and I will," Joanna said determinedly. "Just watch me. You have been duly notified, but tell me one thing. Does the name Jonathan Thurgard mean anything to you?"

"He worked for the Millers," Lyle said after a pause. "Drove a bread truck just like I did. Why?"

"Mr. Thurgard reached out to Liza at her mother's funeral. Now he's dead, too, supposedly as a result of a hit-and-run. I haven't had a chance to check this out— Liza just told me about it—but considering the timing, she's probably right. The people who killed Thurgard are most likely the same ones who are after you. Isn't it about time you came clean?"

"I'm coming to Bisbee," he said.

"Do that," Joanna said, "but once I tell Liza what I know about you, I wouldn't expect a very cordial reception. By the way, there's one more thing I should warn you about."

"What?"

"I believe the woman who thinks she's your daughter is dealing with some kind of cancer. Her head has been shaved fairly recently. She wears a scarf. When you talk to her, you might want to take that into consideration."

Joanna hung up without waiting to see if Lyle had anything more to say. She started to go back inside the M.E.'s office but changed her mind and dialed Amos Franklin's number instead. Her call went straight to his answering machine, so she left a curt message. "Sheriff Brady here. Liza Machett just turned up here in Bisbee. She's safe. She came looking for her brother and had no idea he was dead until we told her. She thinks there may be another victim who's tied into all this—a guy named Jonathan Thurgard. He's from somewhere near you, a town called Stockbridge. Thurgard came to Selma's funeral claiming to be a friend of Liza's father. While there, he warned Liza to be careful of some of her father's former associates. You may want to check this out."

Hanging up, Joanna walked back into the building only to discover that George Winfield had arrived in her absence. Liza's storm of tears had abated. George was sitting next to the distraught woman, quietly conversing with her. Madge, acting with uncharacteristic kindness, was in the process of delivering a cup of coffee. All three of them looked at Joanna expectantly when she came back inside.

Joanna went straight to Liza. "I've just been speaking on the phone with a man named Lyle Morton who may or may not be your father."

"My father is dead," Liza said at once.

"No, he's not," Joanna insisted. "He lives near here. I believe the people who murdered your brother and your friends—the same ones who targeted you—are really after your father. They must have thought you could lead them to him."

"How could I?" Liza asked in dismay. "As far as I knew, he ran off with another woman when I was a baby. My mother told me he died years ago."

"Anson Machett did leave with another

woman, but he's definitely not dead," Joanna told her. "I'm not sure what happened to the girlfriend, but your father has spent most of the last three decades hidden from view in the witness protection program."

"Witness protection?" Liza echoed faintly.

"Your father worked for the mob back in Boston and stole money from them. The sudden appearance of your mother's money must have caused them to see him as a renewed threat, because they've been moving heaven and earth to find him ever since."

"This is unbelievable," Liza declared. "Why didn't anybody ever tell me the truth about him?"

"I'm not sure anybody, including your mother, knew the truth. Financial records show that your father and Guy probably reconnected while Guy was in medical school, maybe even while he was in college. The two of them have been in contact ever since. Your father seems to be fairly well off. He may have given Guy some financial help in getting through school."

"If he helped Guy, why didn't he help me?"

Joanna hesitated. Liza's mother and brother were both dead. She had lost her home, her job, and her friends. Now Joanna was about to take away the one thing the poor woman had left—the man she had always thought to be her father. Having suffered all those losses, Joanna believed Liza deserved the truth. What was it the scripture said? "The truth shall set you free."

"Anson didn't take you with him because he didn't believe you were his child," Joanna said carefully. "He claimed your mother had slept with someone else and had pretended you were his in order to trick him into marrying her."

Joanna said the words and left them there. When Deb Howell opened the door and walked into the reception room, the lingering silence was deafening.

"This is Detective Howell," Joanna added, leading Deb forward. "Do you have your own vehicle?"

Liza nodded numbly.

"You've had a series of terrible shocks. If you think you're up to driving, you can follow Detective Howell. If you'd rather she drove, that's fine. I'd like you to go out to the Justice Center for an official interview. And since Detective Howell was in attendance when I spoke to Mr. Morton last night, she'll be able to fill you in on the details. Is that okay?"

Liza nodded again. She and Deb were gathering up to leave when Joanna's phone rang. Once again she went outside to answer. "Sheriff Brady."

"Calvin Lee from the crime lab. I pulled one of those all-nighters," he said, "and I'm happy to tell you, we've got a match. The DNA on the cigarette belongs to the mother of whoever left the human DNA on your injured kitty. I'm confused, though. I could have sworn you said your suspect was a fourteen-year-old girl. The DNA definitely belongs to a boy. We haven't gotten around to checking out the clothing for either victim. The clothing problem has been assigned to another criminalist. I can tell you that someone is working on it, but it's not yet completed."

Joanna drew a sharp breath. He had given her what she needed, but with one unexpected twist—their suspect was the cigarette smoker's son? Lucas? Unbelievable!

"Great," Joanna said. "Thank you."

"One more thing, about that cat. What's her name again?"

Joanna had to think for a minute. "Star."

"How's she doing?"

Joanna wanted nothing more than to get off the phone, but Calvin had gone to the mat for her. "Okay, I think," Joanna answered.

"Well, my wife said to tell you that if she ends up needing a new home, you know who to call."

"I will," Joanna said quickly. "Thank you so much, but right now I've gotta go."

Fumbling her phone back into her pocket, she sprinted to her SUV. Then, with lights flashing and siren blaring, she raced back down the canyon's narrow twisting main drag.

She didn't dare send out a radio message. The last time she had seen Lucas, he had been in the parking lot at St. Dominick's with his mother, supposedly involved in the search for his sister along with everyone else. If he was anywhere near one of the patrol cars, he might possibly overhear the transmission. Joanna didn't want to give him any advance warning that she was coming.

That didn't leave much else for her to do but drive, hope, and pray.

CHAPTER 29

Turning into the parking lot of St. Dominick's, Joanna stopped next to Father Rowan and rolled down the window. "Have you seen Lucas Nolan?"

The priest frowned. "I think I saw him heading up the hill just a few minutes ago, probably going back to the house. I can ask his mother if you like."

If there was going to be a confrontation with Lucas, the last thing Joanna needed was to have Rebecca in the middle of it.

"No," Joanna said quickly. "Don't bother. I'll find him."

Lucas was only fourteen but, Joanna suspected, an exceptionally dangerous fourteen. Since he was also a self-proclaimed weight lifter, Joanna wasn't prepared to take him on without backup. She glanced around the lot and caught sight of Detective Keller walking away from the command post.

"Hey, Matt," she called. "Can I borrow you for a minute?"

"Sure," he said, striding toward her. "What's up?"

"Lots," she said. "Get in."

He was barely inside with the door closed when Joanna slammed the gearshift into reverse and backed out of the lot onto the street. "What's the hurry?" he asked. "Where are we going?"

"To Rebecca Nolan's place. The crime lab just called me from Tucson," she said grimly. "They got a match from the human DNA left on our injured cat. It belongs to Lucas Nolan."

"Lucas? Holy crap!"

"That's what I say. Father Rowan told me that he saw Lucas going back up the hill a few minutes ago. Presumably he's headed for the house. We're going to go pick him up."

Since Lucas had left the parking lot, there was no further need to maintain radio silence. Joanna thumbed her radio.

"Locate Detective Carbajal," she told Larry Kendrick. "Tell him we've got a DNA match from Star, the cat. Lucas Nolan is a suspect as far as the cat is concerned. He's currently a person of interest in the Dowdle homicide. Matt Keller and I are on our way to his mother's house right now. Since we believe Ruth to be in danger, we won't need a warrant to go inside at the moment, but we'll need one for later. Tell him I want one ASAP."

"How do you want to do this?" Matt asked once she finished.

"Is there a back door to their house?" Joanna asked.

"Yes," Matt said. "It leads out to the garage, which is behind the house. The entrance to the garage is from Curve Street, the next street over."

"Okay," Joanna said, pulling to a stop half a block away in front of Moe and Daisy Maxwell's house. "We'll walk from here. You go to the front door. I'll cover the back."

"What's your take?" Matt asked. "Is this kid going to be armed and dangerous?"

"I'm not sure about the armed part," she answered, "but he's sure as hell dangerous."

They had gotten out of the Yukon and were approaching the Nolans' place on foot when a vehicle, an older-model orange Mazda, charged out the driveway behind the house. It screeched to a skidding stop, then reversed direction and barreled directly toward them, spraying gravel in its wake. As Matt leaped out of the way, he grabbed Joanna by the arm and dragged her with him. Matt's viselike grip on her arm was the only thing that saved her from being run over. Had they been walking with weapons drawn, one or the other of them might well have been shot.

"Hey, that was him," Matt gasped, looking at the fast-receding vehicle. It took a few seconds for him and Joanna to untangle themselves and struggle to their feet. "Are you hurt?"

"No," Joanna said, brushing herself off. "I'm fine."

"Lucas is only fourteen. What's he doing

driving?"

Joanna was already heading for the Yukon. "He must not have gotten the memo that he's too young to drive," she answered over her shoulder. "Come on. Let's stop him before he kills somebody."

Matt was a good foot taller than Joanna, and most of his height was in his very long legs. He sprinted past her. By the time she climbed into the Yukon, Matt was on the radio, alerting Dispatch to the situation and asking for roadblocks at either end of Tombstone Canyon. It was a good call. Both Joanna and Matt understood that if Lucas made it to the highway intersections at either end of town, he would be that much harder to catch.

Joanna fastened her seat belt, rammed the Yukon into drive, and then pulled a dazzling U-turn in a space barely large enough for the maneuver. By the time they made it down to the intersection with Tombstone Canyon Road, the Mazda was out of sight.

"Which way?" Matt asked. "Right or left?"

"Fleeing felons always turn right," Joanna answered, so she did too, racing downhill toward the town's main area of commerce, which, by this time on a Monday morning, would be fully stocked with innocent shoppers and pedestrians—people totally unaware that mortal danger was hurtling toward them.

"That's how come Terry and Spike couldn't pick up Ruth's trail," Joanna observed. "She didn't leave on foot. Lucas must have carried her out of the house and then driven away in the car."

Matt nodded. "Probably in the trunk."

With lights and siren fully engaged, they careened down Tombstone Canyon. Joanna slowed considerably as they rounded Castle Rock, a huge stack of jagged limestone cliffs that rose up abruptly from the canyon floor. And there, in a cloud of dust, they found where Lucas's Mazda had come to grief.

An inexperienced driver, he had tried to take the turn too fast and lost control. From the skid marks on the pavement, they saw where he had zigzagged out of his lane and into oncoming traffic. After bouncing off the sidewalk on the far side of the street, Lucas had overcorrected, recrossed the roadway, smashed through the barrier on the far side, and finally crashed nose down into a cement-lined drainage ditch that had once been a natural stream through the canyon. Most of the year the ditch was bone dry, but occasionally, after heavy rains, it carried flash-flood runoff and debris away from houses and businesses and down through the canyon.

Joanna slammed on the brakes and screeched to a halt. She and Matt leaped out of the Yukon. With weapons drawn they raced to where the Mazda had crashed through a flimsy barrier—a guardrail made of two-inch pipe—that had never been intended to hold back a speeding vehicle. Already a crowd of twenty or so curious onlookers had emerged from the hotel on the far side of the ditch. They stood on the building's Victorian-era verandah, watching the action.

"Lucas," Joanna shouted. "We know you're in there. Come out with your hands up."

Other than clouds of steam billowing up from the shattered radiator, there was no sign of movement inside the vehicle. Matt used one of the supports on the barrier to lower himself into the ditch, dropping to a crouched landing the last three or four feet. Joanna watched anxiously as he approached the wrecked vehicle. After peering inside, he stood up and shook his head. "Nothing here but an exploded airbag," he told her.

Joanna turned to the audience of curiosity seekers. "Did anyone see where the driver went?"

The people on the porch shook their heads in unison.

"What now?" Matt called.

Joanna thought quickly. It's easier to run downhill than up, and that's the way Lucas was going originally—downhill. The kid was far shorter than Matt Keller, and Joanna knew that even Matt wouldn't be able to exit the ditch without assistance.

She had no idea how many tributaries might lead into the concrete-sided ditch or if they would be accessible or not as the waterway went underground beneath the businesses on Main Street. It seemed likely that the only spot where Lucas would be able to scramble up and out would be just beyond the main downtown area. There a steeply graded opening, locally known as "the subway," allowed access into the underground passage. It also allowed runoff from Brewery Gulch to enter the buried storm drain.

"You follow him downstream," Joanna directed. "I'll come upstream from the subway. With any luck, we'll meet up in the middle and cut him off."

"I'll need a flashlight," Matt shouted, "and so will you. Do you have an extra?"

One of the men on the verandah, a guy Joanna recognized as the hotel manager, must have overheard the question. "Hold on," he shouted. "There's one in the office. I'll be right back."

They listened to the sounds of a dozen sirens echoing off the canyon walls as emergency vehicles converged on the scene. While Matt waited for a flashlight, Joanna jumped into the Yukon and headed down the street, grabbing the radio as she went. "Where's Jaime?" she barked.

Detective Carbajal had grown up in Old Bisbee and had spent his childhood exploring the neighborhood's every nook and cranny.

"He's on his way uptown to meet with the judge. There's a daylong conference of some kind at the Copper Queen Hotel." Larry said after a moment. "What do you need?"

"Our suspect just bailed out of his wrecked car and fled down the drainage ditch where it goes underground above Main Street. Matt's following him downstream. I'm going in through the subway so I can come upstream. We're going to try to catch him in a squeeze play. Have Jaime meet me at the subway."

"Got it," Larry said.

In Bisbee, the subway was a concrete-lined, truck-sized access hole, located at the far end of Main Street in the middle of a small plaza with lanes of traffic moving on either side. A chain fastened to several posts provided the only barrier. A chain-link fence might have been a more effective deterrent for keeping people out, but it would also have caused a dangerous backup when floodwater debris from up above roared down Brewery Gulch.

Turning on her flashers, Joanna parked next to the fence and looked around. Jaime wasn't there yet, but she couldn't afford to wait. Bailing out of the Yukon, she sat down at the top of the steep incline and slid into the ditch. Only a few steps from where she landed, the pavement closed over her head. Instinctively, her hand sought her holstered Glock, but after a moment's consideration, she didn't draw it. With sheer rock walls on either side, she didn't want to risk being injured by a ricocheting bullet.

Only a yard or two from the entrance she needed help from her flashlight to pick her way through the jungle of trash and fallen boulders that littered the surface. Rusty metal hulks—the remains of discarded stoves and dishwashers and refrigerators—had ridden some long-ago flood this far downstream and no farther. As Joanna eased past each piece of wreckage, she was painfully aware of how much cover those items offered her quarry and how little protection they gave her.

It was difficult to judge distances, but she suspected she had gone barely a hundred yards when she heard noisy footsteps pounding behind her. "Wait up, boss," Jaime shouted. "I'm coming."

She huddled behind a piece of something that turned out to be an old car engine of some kind and waited as a pinprick of light gradually blossomed into the welcome company of a handheld flashlight.

"Any sign of him?" Jaime gasped when he caught up with her.

Putting her finger to her lips, Joanna shook her head. Then, gesturing, she motioned for Jaime to take the far side of the tunnel while she took the near one. They moved forward in cautious tandem with their muffled flashlights aimed at the floor. Now and then they paused to listen for the sounds of footsteps approaching from the opposite direction.

Joanna estimated the tunnel's length to be half a mile or so. If Lucas was coming at a dead run, it wouldn't take long for him to cover the distance—longer if he hadn't had the foresight to bring along his own flashlight. A minute or so later, they heard him, blundering toward them in the dark. Without any discussion, Jaime and Joanna doused their lights completely and sought shelter. Joanna hid behind a rocky outcropping in the tunnel while Jaime ducked behind the unidentifiable remains of a rusted-out car that had come to rest several yards behind where Joanna was hiding.

She stood in the impenetrable darkness with her heart pounding in her chest. Lucas would pass her position first. That would mean she would have the first opportunity to tackle him. He was young and had not yet reached his full growth, but with a history of weight lifting, he might be far stronger than he looked. Based on that, Joanna knew she needed to take him by surprise and come after him with overwhelming force.

From the way he was scrabbling along, occasionally crying out in pain and cursing as he slammed into some unexpected obstacle, Joanna realized they were in luck. Lucas really was running blind. He had been in the dark far longer than she and Jaime had, especially since they had just extinguished their flashlights. That meant his eyes would be better adjusted and his vision would be marginally better than theirs would be. But if Lucas was more comfortable in the dark, that gave Joanna a chance to turn light into a weapon.

With that in mind, she tightened her grip on the business end of the new Mag-Tac LED flashlight Butch had given her for Christmas. Fingering the device in the dark, she located the switch that would activate the strobe light function. For someone who had grown accustomed to moving in utter darkness, she hoped the flashing strobe would be both blinding and disorienting. The problem was, it might disorient her as well. She hoped that Jaime, farther away from the light, would be somewhat less affected. He was Joanna's second line of defense.

Lucas was much closer now, running headlong in her direction. She heard his breath coming in ragged gulps. She waited until she was sure he was almost on her. Even then, she counted to three before she pushed the switch on the strobe and stepped away from the sheltering rock wall. He came bearing down on her, dancing in awkward jerks like some devil made incarnate before stumbling to a sudden stop. That was the moment when Joanna switched on the full beam of the powerful flashlight, shining it directly into his eyes. Blinded, he took a single swing at her, but he didn't come close to connecting.

That one missed blow provided all the incentive Joanna needed. Brandishing the heavy flashlight like a club, she swung it through the air and grunted in satisfaction as her very first well-aimed blow connected with Lucas in a dull, bone-breaking thud. He tumbled to the ground like a crumpled rag doll.

"Great work, boss!" Jaime exclaimed, coming out of hiding and aiming his own flashlight at their fallen quarry. "You nailed him."

"Keep an eye on him," Joanna ordered. "I need to check something."

When Joanna knelt down beside Lucas, she shined the light on his face at the stream of blood flowing from the cut her flashlight had left on his cheekbone. He was still wearing the same blue track suit that she had seen him wearing on several earlier occasions. It was far worse for wear now—torn, tattered, and stained with a layer of reddish dust. Reaching for the sleeve, she pulled it up, baring Lucas's forearm. The web-scape of scratches marring the pale skin were exactly what she had expected to find. The wounds appeared to come in several layers with the older ones scabbed over while some of the newer ones were still draining.

When Joanna pulled up the second sleeve, the damage on that arm mirrored what she had seen on the first.

She shoved him hard in the ribs. The blow wasn't hard enough to do any damage, but it was enough to rouse him. Lucas groaned. His eyes blinked open.

"Where is she, you worthless punk?" Joanna demanded, shouting the words into his face. "Where's Ruth? What have you done to your sister?"

By then two flashlights were trained full on his face. Lucas squinted up at Joanna through the moving beams of light. "I'm not talking to anybody," he said with a sneer. "I don't have to."

Joanna realized then that it hadn't been just an illusion cast by the flickering strobe light that had made Lucas Nolan look like a devil. He really was.

Afraid she might be tempted to hit him again, harder this time, Joanna stepped away. "Cuff him, Jaime," she ordered.

From far up the tunnel, they heard the pounding sound of another set of approaching footsteps. "It's okay, Matt,"

Joanna called into the darkness. "We've got him in custody."

By the time Matt arrived, Jaime had Lucas in restraints and on his feet. The look of pure hatred Lucas aimed in Joanna's direction was meant to make her squirm with fear. It served only to make her mad as hell.

"Let's read this piece of garbage his rights and get him out of here. Then we need to figure out what the hell he's done to his sister."

CHAPTER 30

By the time they made it back to the subway, a crowd had gathered on the plaza. As officers and medics converged on the scene, so did everyone else. Sliding down the concrete bank to get into the ditch had been easy. Getting back up and out was not. A fire department crew equipped with ropes appeared on the scene.

Using a rope and pulling herself hand over hand, Joanna was the first to emerge. Then two firefighters along with Matt Keller and Jaime Carbajal formed a human fire brigade and passed Lucas up to the surface. As soon as he appeared, handcuffed and with blood streaming down his cheek and onto his filthy track suit, his mother managed to slip through the perimeter of officers.

"What have you done to him?" Rebecca screeched, her voice echoing off the canyon walls. "What have you done to my boy?"

Joanna planted herself in Rebecca's path and barred the way. "Your son is under arrest," she announced. "At the moment we'll be charging him with two counts of assault with a deadly weapon, driving without a license, and reckless driving. I expect additional charges will be forthcoming."

"He's only a boy. You can't do this to him," Rebecca objected. "You can't!"

"This is a police matter," Joanna insisted. "Please step back."

As Matt and Jaime came up out of the hole, Rebecca made one further attempt to push past Joanna and reach her son. Joanna stiff-armed her.

"I told you to move back, Mrs. Nolan," Joanna warned. "If you don't, you'll be placed under arrest right along with Lucas and charged with interfering with a police officer."

Matt placed a firm hand on Rebecca's

shoulder and steered the still-protesting woman away from the action. Meanwhile Alvin Bernard turned to Joanna. "What assault?" he asked.

"Matt and I were approaching Lucas's house when he tried to run us down with a vehicle. If Matt hadn't jumped for his life and pulled me along with him, we'd both be dead meat by now. We'll hold him on those charges for now, but what you really need to know is there are scratches all over his arms. I sent the crime lab a sample of Rebecca's DNA. Her profile came back as the mother of the male human whose DNA was found on our wounded cat."

Alvin's jaw dropped. "I thought we were looking at Ruth for all this," he said.

"Believe me," Joanna said. "So did I."

"So is Ruth in on it or is she another victim?"

"Good question. It could be she's an accomplice, but I doubt it. It's more likely that she's another victim, too, and we need to find her. I asked Lucas what he had done with his sister. He refused to answer."

Joanna paused before continuing. "What's happening to the wrecked Mazda?"

"I believe a tow truck is on the scene. Why?"

"Have Fred Harding go over that wrecked car with a fine-tooth comb. I have a feeling that's how Lucas smuggled Ruth out of the house—in his mother's car. Jaime was on his way to get a search warrant on the house before I pulled him into the tunnel. Judge Moore is involved in some kind of meeting at the Copper Queen. I'll have Ernie take charge of the search warrant paperwork and handle that. Once Judge Moore signs off, Ernie and Matt can execute the warrant. I'd like to have Casey Ledford in on that as well. She's great for fingerprints, but she's also good at crime scene investigation."

"I take it you think Lucas attacked his sister in their house?"

"I'd bet money on it," Joanna said.

It took time to sort out the logistics. The medics examined Lucas's bleeding jawline and pronounced that, although he would most likely have "a helluva headache," a trip to the ER wasn't necessary. Instead, the boy was hustled into a Bisbee PD patrol car and driven off to police headquarters, accompanied by Jaime Carbajal. Since Matt's vehicle was still parked outside Rebecca Nolan's house up the canyon, Ernie took Matt with him while Joanna summoned Casey.

Vehicles and people dispersed. At last Joanna's car was the only one still there, parked haphazardly next to the subway with the flashers on the light bar still blinking. She was about to leave when Moe Maxwell approached. She hadn't noticed him in the crowd, but when she saw him, she was saddened to see how haggard and lost he looked.

"Someone said you arrested Lucas Nolan. Did he do it?" Moe asked. "Is he the one who murdered Junior?"

This was still an active investigation. Moe was a grieving relative. Even so, Joanna had to be circumspect in her response. "Maybe," she said. "Matt and

Ernie are on their way to Lucas's house to execute a search warrant."

"Tell them to look for a rabbit's foot," Moe said.

"What rabbit's foot?"

"Doc Winfield returned Junior's personal effects to us last night, and that's the only thing that's missing—Junior's lucky rabbit's foot. He had it in his pocket when he first came to live with us. He always carried it in his pants pocket during the day and in his pajama pocket at night."

"Thank you for that, Moe," Joanna said, climbing into the Yukon. "If anything comes of this, we'll let you know."

As she turned the key in the ignition she found herself uttering an unlikely prayer. "Please, God, let Lucas Nolan be stupid enough to keep trophies."

She was driving around Lavender Pit when Butch called. Not wanting to mention that someone had deliberately tried to run her down, Joanna tried to put him off. "I'm pretty busy right now," she said.

"I'm sure you are," he agreed, "but I thought I should let you know that I've just skimmed through some of the later stuff in Ruth Nolan's blog. It's unusual in that the earliest stuff is what shows on the welcome page and right after. The first entries are all sweetness and light, but along the way, it morphs into something much darker. You need to read from the back to find the most recent stuff, and that's downright ugly. She refers to the newer material as a collection of 'short stories.' Reading between the lines, you can tell it's coming from someone raised in a totally dysfunctional family. Plenty of physical violence. The father is depicted as a religious lout. The mother sleeps around. And the brother is drawn as a sweet-faced kid who would as soon knife you in the back as look at you. There are plenty of hints that both the kids may have been subjected to sexual abuse."

Joanna was aghast. "That's all in the blog?" she asked.

"That and more," Butch answered grimly. "This is Dear Diary with a really ugly twist. The difference between the first posts and the most recent ones is glaring. I think there must have been some kind of adult oversight when the posting first started. The later entries have little or no adult editorial input, and no adult savvy, either. As I said, the newer, darker posts take some navigating to find. Even so, they garner a lot of attention—four thousand or so readers per entry. From the names on the comments, I'd say there are a lot of kids out there paying attention to Roxie's Place."

Joanna knew the statistics. Most of the kids who run afoul of law enforcement had some sort of sexual abuse lurking in their backgrounds. As Joanna pulled into the lot and parked in a visitors' slot next to Chief Bernard's aging sedan, she asked, "Was there anything in the most recent posts about what's been going on with her this past week?"

"Nothing that jumped out at me. Why?"

"We believe Lucas Nolan may be responsible for his sister's disappearance. We've just taken him into custody. I'm on my way to talk to him right now. Is there anything in the posts that refers to problems between the brother and the sister?"

"Not that I noticed," Butch said, "but if you like, I can go back through the entries again. If I see something, I'll call."

"Thanks."

Inside the reception area at Bisbee PD, a clerk buzzed Joanna through a locked door and into the back of the building. She made her way to the booking area, where a solidly built matron was processing Lucas. Already clothed in an orange jumpsuit, he deposited his other clothing on the counter. When the matron reached for it, Joanna intervened.

"Please use gloves for that," she insisted. "It's possible that shirt contains important DNA evidence. I want all of Mr. Nolan's clothing placed in evidence bags, and I want the scratches and bite marks on his arms—all of them—swabbed for possible evidence as well—one swab and one bag per scratch."

The matron glanced at the complex road map of scrapes and scratches covering Lucas's forearms, then she gave

Joanna a scathing look. "Are you kidding? All of these? Do you have any idea how long that will take?"

Joanna shrugged. "I don't care how long it takes," she replied. "I've got all day, and so does he."

"You're not going to find anything," Lucas boasted.

"I'm a cop," she cautioned. "Are you sure you want to talk to me?"

"It doesn't matter," Lucas said. "I'm a kid. What are you going to do to me? Send me to jail? Big deal. At least there they'll give me three meals a day and I won't have to cook them myself."

"Look," Joanna said. "The prosecutor will be here before long. He's the one who decides what the charges will be. If you tell me where to find your sister, I might be able to persuade him to give you a better deal."

"Screw you," Lucas jeered at her as the matron lined him up for his mug shot. "If you're so interested in Ruth, find her your own damned self."

Alvin emerged from his office and

beckoned to Joanna. He led her inside and closed the door before he spoke. "I just spoke to Fred, my CSI. He got to the scene of the accident in time to take a look at Rebecca's sedan before the tow truck pulled it out of the ditch. He found a single strand of purple hair in the trunk of the vehicle and something else, too. A patch of something that appears to be vomit. He cut that part of the rug out. Our lab is a joke. I told him to take the hair and the piece of contaminated carpeting out to your CSI people at the Justice Center."

Joanna nodded.

"Of course, you understand that you, Jaime, and Matt will all need to be interviewed about what went on in the tunnel."

"Yes, I do," Joanna said determinedly, "but not right now, not until after we find Ruth Nolan."

Turning her back on Alvin, she left him standing in his office and went back to booking, where the matron was taking Lucas's prints. As Joanna entered the room, she took her phone from her pocket, switched it to record, and set it down on the counter. Lucas was staring at Joanna. The presence of her phone didn't seem to faze him.

"Be sure to collect a DNA swab from his cheek, too," Joanna reminded the matron as she returned Lucas's hard-edged gaze.

"Your sister told me about you," she added, lying through her teeth. "She told me that you like to torture animals in your spare time. You know, burn them, cut them, shred their ears—that sort of thing. Is that true, or is she making things up?"

"My sister's a liar," Lucas said venomously.

"In her blog, she claims she's been molested."

"I already told you. Ruth's always been a liar."

"You're saying she hasn't been molested?"

"I didn't know she put it in her blog. She pretended our dad molested her so we could leave Gallup with our mom. She hated it there."

"I thought you told me yesterday that she was fine with Gallup—that you were the one who hated it there."

"I guess I was mistaken."

"Either that or you were lying. Or are you lying now?"

Lucas pursed his lips and didn't answer. The matron had swabbed his cheek and was starting to work on his arms.

"You don't like your sister very much, do you?"

Again there was no reply.

"So here's the deal," Joanna said. "You're sitting here charged with a couple of felonies. Right now there's a chance you'll be tried as a juvenile and get off with being locked up until you turn eighteen. I understand that you despise your sister. I get that, but I doubt you'd want to hurt her. Help us out here, Lucas. Tell us where she is."

"What happens if I don't?"

"If your sister dies, all bets are off. Chances are you'll get tried as an adult and be sentenced to twenty years or so. Tell me about Junior Dowdle."

The sudden change of direction seemed to catch Lucas off guard. "What about him?"

"Did he like your sister too much, maybe?" Joanna asked. "Did he have a crush on her? Were you jealous of him?"

"Junior was stupid," Lucas said. "Dumb. Why would I be jealous of him? You think that's what happened? I killed him because I was jealous of him? That's the funniest thing I've ever heard."

Lucas started to laugh then, a laughter that was utterly devoid of humor. When the hollow cackle ended, he glared at Joanna in sneering insolence.

"You've got nothing," he declared. "Nothing at all. I'm not telling you a thing."

Joanna knew that she had pushed him as far as she could. He had already been read his rights. This wasn't an official interrogation, but if he called for a lawyer, it would all be over, and she wouldn't be able to continue the conversation. Wanting to prevent that, Joanna walked away. Using a back entrance, she let herself out into the parking lot. Once inside the Yukon, she locked the doors and then sat there with her eyes closed, taking deep breaths and trying to think.

She had understood what was behind the little bastard's last self-satisfied ugly grin. He knew exactly where Ruth was, and he wouldn't tell, no matter what. Joanna suspected that, in all probability, Ruth was already dead, but what if she wasn't? What if there was a chance that she had been injured but was still clinging to life? It was almost noon. If she'd already been gone for most of a day, that meant time was running out.

Chief Bernard had told Joanna that Fred Harding had found a single strand of purple hair in the trunk of Rebecca's wrecked Mazda. A strand of hair in the passenger compartment of the car meant nothing, but in the trunk? People didn't climb into trunks of cars of their own volition. Ruth had been in the trunk of her mother's car because she had been placed there by someone else. It wasn't hard to imagine that she had been unconscious at the time.

All right, Joanna told herself, trying to marshal her thoughts. Lucas put Ruth in the trunk. Then what? He took her someplace and dumped her, but where? He had been at the house, seemingly alone, in the late afternoon on Sunday when Joanna had gone there to talk to him. And he had been home again when his mother came home. He wouldn't have wanted to risk letting Rebecca know that he had taken her Mazda for an unauthorized joy ride. That meant the dumping ground would have to be somewhere fairly close by, someplace Lucas was familiar with, someplace no one was likely to go looking.

And then, as suddenly as if a light had been switched on, Joanna knew. Or at least she thought she knew. The cave where they had found Junior, the one with the glory hole just inside. Lucas knew all about it. It was close by. As long as no one realized Lucas was involved in what had happened to Junior and Star, no one would think to look there. Thanks to Calvin Lee, Joanna knew better.

As soon as that series of thoughts surfaced in her brain, Joanna's fingers sought the ignition key. She swung the Yukon out onto the roadway and merged into the traffic circle. She resisted the urge to turn on the lights. If she was right, she'd arrive at the Dowdle crime scene much sooner if she didn't wait around to summon additional personnel. And if she was wrong? No one would ever know, and Ruth Nolan, wherever she was, would be no worse off than she had been before.

Joanna drove up Highway 80 behind the main business district, pulled an illegal U-turn in a no-passing zone, and parked on the shoulder of the road near where the collection of emergency vehicles had clustered the day they had retrieved Junior Dowdle's body. After turning on both her overhead lights and her emergency flashers, Joanna grabbed her Maglite, jumped out of the vehicle, and scrambled up the wash. That second clump of scrub oak seemed impossibly far away. She clipped her all-important flashlight to her belt so it wouldn't hamper her as she climbed. By the time she reached the shade of the oak grove, she was out of breath; she had a stitch in her side, and her lungs ached with effort, but she was there.

Wanting to help her eyes adjust to the coming change of light, Joanna closed one of them as she made her way through the trees. She was relieved to see that as yet no one had made any effort to repair the damage done during the removal of Junior's body. The iron bars that had been cut away from the mouth of the tunnel still leaned crookedly against the rocky cliff, looking like a pair of wrecked doors that had been knocked off their supporting hinges.

Cautiously, Joanna stepped through the opening and switched on the light. The powerful beam illuminated the whole place, rendering her precaution of closing one eye unnecessary. She moved forward carefully, listening for any sound that would betray the presence of any other being, human or otherwise. She used the powerful beam of light to explore every chink and soaring crevice of the limestone cavern. A few steps from the abyss, she paused. "Ruth," she called. "Ruth Nolan, are you in here?"

For a long moment, all she heard was the hammering of her own heart, but then there was something else—a strange humming noise that was hardly human. She eased her way over to the edge of the drop and aimed the beam of the flashlight down into the hole. At first she wasn't sure what she was seeing. Netting of some kind seemed to have been strung from one side of the hole to the other. Caught in the middle of the net, dangling over the bottom of the hole like some kind of huge landed fish, was a silver figure of some kind.

"Ruth, is that you?"

In answer the figure struggled to move. As Joanna's vision improved, she realized that the silver came from a layer of duct tape that bound the girl's legs together and held her arms imprisoned at her sides. A separate strand of tape formed the gag that covered her mouth.

"Stop!" Joanna ordered. "Do not move! I don't know what's holding the netting in place. If you wiggle around, you might dislodge it. Stay where you are. I'm going out to call for help. My cell phone doesn't have service in here."

Another unintelligible pleading sound came from the bound girl. Joanna didn't need to hear the words to know what she was saying.

"I won't leave you. I promise. I'll be right back."

Joanna had to go only as far as the cave's entrance before she had enough bars to make the call.

"Nine one one, what are you reporting?"

"Sheriff Brady here," she said. "Contact the Bisbee Fire Department. I've found Ruth Nolan. She's trapped in some netting inside the glory hole at the same location where we found Junior Dowdle's body last week. Tell them to hurry. I don't know how strong the netting is or how well it's secured."

Ending the call, she went back into the cave and peered over the edge once more. "I'm back, Ruth," Joanna assured the girl. "I've called the fire department.

They've got a team on the way to get you out of there."

Joanna knew that without the unexplained presence of that netting Ruth would have been dead.

The girl made another faint whimpering noise. This time Joanna couldn't guess what was being said, so she answered with what she knew. "Your brother is under arrest," she said. "We believe Lucas is responsible for what happened to Junior Dowdle and also what happened to you."

Twelve feet beneath the rim of the hole, Ruth nodded desperately. Turning the light away from the girl, Joanna studied the netting. It had been fashioned in such a way that anyone falling into the hole would be guided away from landing on the hard ledge ten feet below the surface. Instead, Ruth had slid past that unharmed and now dangled in the void above the remaining twenty-foot drop. Joanna could see where metal eyebolts of some kind had been drilled into the rock surface. After that, carabiners had been used to secure the netting to the bolts. It was an ingenious arrangement that had taken skill, effort, and time.

"Are you hurt?" Joanna asked.

Ruth shook her head. That could have meant either no, she wasn't hurt, or no, she didn't know. In Joanna's estimation, either answer was acceptable.

A thousand questions roiled through Joanna's head. Had Lucas carried her here or had he forced Ruth to walk on her own? If so, had she known what was coming—that he intended to shove her over the edge? Maybe he had simply rolled her into the hole. He must have been so confident of the outcome that he hadn't bothered to stick around long enough to watch her fall. Had he seen the netting, he most certainly would have attempted to cut it down.

Beyond the cave's entrance, Joanna heard a faint wail—the welcome siren from an approaching emergency vehicle.

"They're coming now," Joanna said reassuringly. "They have to climb up from the highway, but they'll be here soon."

She went to the entrance of the cave to

meet them and was not in the least surprised that Adam Wilson was the first to arrive.

"Is she alive?" he asked.

Joanna nodded. "Did you do the netting?"

He bit his lip and then shrugged. "I figured it would take the powers that be forever to get around to putting the bars back up and doing it properly. I was afraid some little kid would fall in accidentally in the meantime, so I decided to do something about it. My grandfather always says it's better to beg forgiveness than to ask permission," he added with a self-deprecating grin.

"Well, it worked," Joanna told him. "It worked like gangbusters." Standing on tiptoes, she managed to plant a kiss on the tip of Adam's chin because that was as far as she could reach. "Thank you," she added. "Thank you so much."

"So how about moving out of the way so we can get her out of here?"

He didn't have to say it twice.

CHAPTER 31

Adam and his crew had come prepared to effect a rescue. They had brought along ropes and gaff hooks, which they used to raise the netting far enough to lift the girl out of it. After Adam kicked Joanna out of the area, it took less than ten minutes before Ruth was removed from the cave and her restraints loosened. Because she was suffering from both hypothermia and dehydration, they stuck a normal saline drip in her arm and wrapped her in warming blankets before placing her in a Stokes basket for the trip down the mountain.

As the loaded ambulance set off for the hospital, Joanna's Yukon followed close behind. At the ER entrance, she made use of her badge and uniform to follow the gurney all the way to the curtained cubicle where they stashed Ruth. Seated at the girl's bedside, she waited while a nurse took the required series of readings. When the nurse left, Ruth turned to Joanna. "How did you find me?"

"Lucky guess," Joanna said. "Can you tell me what happened?"

"I think Lucas tried to kill me," Ruth said. Tears came to her eyes. "Mom left right after I finished your interview. As soon as she was gone, Lucas lit into me. He accused me of ratting him out to you. Why would he think that? Rat him out about what? I tried to tell him I didn't—that I didn't know anything to tell, but he didn't believe me. He gave me a glass of chocolate milk and made me drink all of it even though it tasted funny—bitter, like it was spoiled or something."

"Made you?" Joanna asked.

"Lucas hits me sometimes, if I don't do what he says," Ruth answered quietly. "He told me if I didn't drink it, I'd be sorry."

"You mean he beats you?"

Ruth nodded. "And he would have done it again, so I did what he said, and then I fell asleep. When I woke up, I was sick to my stomach. I was also locked in the trunk of a car—Mom's car, I guess. I fell back asleep. When I woke up again, he was taping my mouth shut."

"You believe Lucas drugged you?" Joanna asked.

Ruth shrugged. "I think so," she said. "He probably used one of Mom's pills—like the one she gave me the other day when I had the cramps. That's what it felt like anyway. When I woke up again, he was carrying me up the hill. My legs were taped. He had me over his shoulder the way firemen carry people out of burning buildings. Then he rolled me into that hole—the same hole Junior was in. I thought I was gonna die. Instead, I landed on something soft, like a hammock. I was there for a long time. It was cold. I was freezing to death, hungry, and thirsty. And then there you were."

Joanna's phone rang. Casey Ledford's name appeared in the window. "Excuse me a minute," she said. "I need to take this." She went back out through the double doors and stood under the outside portico.

"What's up?" Joanna asked. "Did you find anything?"

"You're not going to believe it," he said. "Not in a million years."

"What?"

"They both have trophy cases."

"What do you mean both?"

"Ruth and Lucas," Casey answered excitedly. "We found loose boards in the floor under the beds in both Lucas's room and in Ruth's, too. The stash in Lucas's room included a baseball bat, a cigarette lighter, razor blades, a half-used pack of smokes, three dog collars—including one for a dog named Roxie—and a pink ribbon, too. Sound familiar? Didn't the owners say that Star was wearing a pink ribbon when she disappeared?"

"Yes, they did," Joanna answered.

"Oh," Casey continued. "And a mostly used roll of duct tape."

"What about Ruth's room?" Joanna asked.

"That's where we found the rabbit's foot. It's hard to tell one rabbit's foot from another, but I'm guessing it's Junior's. We also found a Timex watch. It's engraved on the back: 'Happy Birthday, Billy.' No idea who Billy is. Or was."

It didn't matter, not right then. What mattered was that both of them were involved—two evil twins, not one good and one bad. Joanna didn't bother going back into the ER. With the phone still clutched in her hand, Joanna raced for the Yukon. She punched Alvin's number before she turned the key.

"Has Lucas asked for an attorney?"

"Not to my knowledge. Why?"

"Put him in an interview room alone and let him sit there. I'll be there in three minutes. Sooner if I can make it."

"Without a parent with him? Why? What's going on?"

"You ever hear of John E. Reid?"

"Of course," Alvin said. "He's the guy who wrote the book on modern police interrogation. Why?"

"Because I'm on my way to try my hand at a little direct confrontation."

"Okay," Alvin said. "Lucas will be waiting.

Do you want someone in the interview room with you?"

"Nope, I'll handle this one solo."

Lucas looked up curiously when Joanna entered the interview room. Then, feigning disinterest, he looked away.

"You'll never guess where I've just been," Joanna said. "At the Copper Queen Hospital—the ER—talking to Ruth." She watched how he responded to the news and was relieved to see the telltale bobbing of the Adam's apple in his scrawny little throat.

"Aren't you going to ask if she's okay?" Joanna continued. "Nah, I guess not, but that's all right. What's interesting is what she's doing right now. She's writing out a confession, Lucas, about how she helped you murder Junior Dowdle."

Lucas's eyes shot up in surprise. "No way!" he said. "I didn't kill him."

"Oh? That's not what Ruth says. And we gave her a great deal. I told her if she testifies against you, she'll probably walk. She says you planned it all in advance. Premeditation means it's likely that you'll be tried as an adult. If you're lucky, you'll get second-degree homicide rather than first, which means you'll get out of prison when you're a few years short of forty. Think about it. You'll be older than your mom."

"I didn't do it," Lucas insisted. "I already told you. Ruth's a liar. She did it and she's trying to put the blame on me."

"Did what?"

"Pushed Junior over the edge. She told him there was a kitten that was stuck in a hole up on the mountain. He fell for it. Came right out through the window, just like that. He wasn't very good at climbing, and at first he didn't want to go in the hole, but then we told him to listen for the kitten. When he heard it crying, he went right under the bars. Then, once he got inside, he was scared of the dark. He stopped just inside the door and wouldn't go any farther. That's when Ruth sort of helped him along."

"She pushed him?"

"Yeah," Lucas said. "Sort of. She kind of shoved him with the end of a baseball bat."

"Who's Billy?"

Once again, Lucas's surprise was apparent. "How do you know about Billy?" he asked.

"We found your sister's trophies. They included Billy's watch. Who is he?"

"Billy Rojas. Just a kid in Gallup," Lucas said with a shrug. "He was sort of like Junior, only worse. He was in a wheelchair. He thought Ruth was his friend. When we invited him on a picnic with us, he was glad to go because no one ever invited him to do anything. It had rained. The washes were running. His chair went off the edge, and that was it. He drowned. The cops said it was an accident."

Filled with rage, Joanna gripped the edge of the table hard enough that her knuckles turned white. For a moment she said nothing for fear she might simply explode. She had walked into the room carrying a blue-lined notebook and a pen. Forcing herself to be calm about it, she pushed the two items across the table.

Lucas looked at them and frowned. "What are these for?" he asked.

"They're for you to write down what you just told me," she said. "Write it down and sign it."

"Why should I?"

"Because the first one to confess always gets a better deal."

"But you just told me Ruth had already confessed."

"Yes, I did," Joanna said. "I guess I lied."

When Joanna buzzed to be allowed out of the interview room, Alvin Bernard was waiting outside. "I already called Matt Keller," he said. "He's on his way to the hospital right now. And I checked with the ER. They've admitted Ruth overnight for observation. We'll make the arrest there, and I'll post a guard outside her room."

"If you need any help with staffing, call me," Joanna said. "I'm sure I can spare a deputy or two overnight."

They arrived at the hospital in a multi-vehicle entourage that looked more like a parade than any kind of police activity. Matt Keller and Ernie Carpenter covered the outside exits in case someone was stupid enough to try making a run for it.

When they found Ruth's room, Rebecca was sitting next to the bed, looking out at the dull red tailings dump that rose up outside the window, blocking everything else from view. When Joanna entered, Rebecca frowned and stood up.

"What are you doing here?" Rebecca demanded. "This is a hospital room. Ruth's been through a terrible ordeal. She's supposed to be resting."

Ruth was lying on the bed with her purple hair fanned out across the pillow. She smiled brightly at Joanna. "It's okay, Mom. I told you. Sheriff Brady is the one who found me. If it weren't for her, I might be dead."

Joanna didn't smile back. "I've just been to see your brother," she said curtly. "When I left him he was writing out a full confession, explaining exactly how you lured Junior out of his room on the pretext of rescuing a kitten and then how you pushed him over the edge of the cliff with a baseball bat. Ruth Nolan, you're under arrest for the murder of Junior Dowdle."

Without a word, Alvin Bernard produced

a pair of handcuffs. He slipped one on Ruth's thin wrist and fastened the other to the metal railing on her hospital bed.

"This can't be happening," Rebecca hissed. "It's impossible. You're crazy. My kids are good kids. They would never do such a thing!"

"Lucas is lying," Ruth insisted desperately. "Lucas always does that—he does bad stuff and tries to put the blame on me."

Joanna studied her, remembering the purple-haired sweet-faced girl who had sat in the backseat of Joanna's Yukon the day before, supposedly doing an interview of the local sheriff for her innocent-sounding blog. The old story of a serial killer inserting herself into an investigation was such a cliché that Joanna almost wanted to puke.

"No such luck, sweetheart," Joanna said. "This time the blame's all on you."

CHAPTER 32

As soon as Joanna left the hospital, the shakes hit her. It was all she could do to start the SUV and put it in gear. When her cell phone rang, it took four crows of the rooster to wrestle the damned thing out of her pocket.

"Where are you?" Kristin asked.

"Just leaving the hospital. I'm going over to the restaurant to tell Moe and Daisy what's happened. I want them to hear it from me first. Then I'm coming back to the office. What's happening there?"

"Tom Hadlock is putting together a press conference. He's planning on holding it here since we have more parking than Bisbee PD does. A lot has happened this afternoon. If you have a minute, Tom would like you to give him a briefing."

"Okay," Joanna said.

"And there are some people here to see you. Liza Machett is in the break room, and Roger Stephens just went out back to have a smoke."

"Roger Stephens of the U.S. Marshals Service? What's he doing here?"

"I asked him that, but he wouldn't tell me. He said it was confidential."

"Figures," Joanna said. "He'll have to wait. I'll talk to him when I get there, but right now I've got something important for you to do. It's time to celebrate, and we're having a party. I want you to order a dozen pizzas and put them in the break room. There isn't a single person in the department who hasn't put in extra time and effort this week. Besides, I haven't eaten since breakfast, and I'm starving."

Talking to Moe and Daisy was tough. Joanna gave them the news in Daisy's little office just off the kitchen. They were relieved, of course, and Joanna had to refrain from telling them that this was barely the beginning. Signed confessions or not, it would be months or even years from now before Lucas and Ruth Nolan would be held accountable for their crimes. For Moe and Daisy there would be no closure and no way to put the terrible wrong done to their beloved Junior right.

When Joanna arrived at the Justice Center forty-five minutes later, she wasn't at all surprised to see two enormous black Cadillac Escalades idling in the no-parking zone directly in front of the sheriff department's front entrance. The passenger windows were tinted to the point that it was impossible to see if anyone was inside. A guy in a dark suit and tie stood leaning casually against the driver's door of one vehicle. A woman in a similarly dark pantsuit leaned against the tailgate of the second one.

Grumbling under her breath, Joanna drove around back only to find a man she assumed to be Roger Stephens, also dressed in a suit and tie, leaning against the building directly in front of her reserved covered parking place. A shiny pair of snakeskin boots peeked out from beneath the hem of his trousers. The sidewalk around his feet was littered with cigarette butts.

"The smoking area is around to the side of the building," she said pointedly. "Away from the doors."

"There's no shade over there," he objected.

That was true, and it was also deliberate. No shade meant less smoking.

"What do you want?"

"I have a name for you," he said. "Richard Ransom."

"Who's he?"

"A former FBI agent from Boston, Massachusetts, who's now three small steps down from the secretary of the Treasury. Seems as though, back in the early eighties, Ransom was the only one of the guys involved in the Miller mess who was considered to be squeaky clean. Turns out, that's only because no one ever came forward to rat him out. He was also on Anson Machett's payoff delivery route.

"Funniest thing, when Anson was coming into witness protection, he never blew the whistle on Richard. There isn't one mention of him in Anson's file. Shortly after Lyle came into the program, someone began putting the bite on Mr. Ransom, and he's been paying the toll ever since. He sent money to a numbered account in the Cayman Islands without ever realizing that Anson Machett was the guy on the receiving end."

"So Lyle's been living in witness protection and making money by black-mailing people?"

"By blackmailing one person only," Stephens said. "At least as far as we know right now. Lyle faked the books and laundered his ill-gotten gains by using the blackmail money to make improvements and pay salaries at the Whetstone Retreat. When Cesar Flores's report about those old bills showed up, it was passed on to Ransom as a routine report. He looked at the evidence, figured out that Anson was probably the blackmailer, and started calling in favors, trying to get a line on where he was."

Stephens paused, took one last drag on his smoke, and then tossed the butt on the ground. "How am I doing so far?"

Joanna stopped and stared at Agent Stephens. "Fine about everything but the smoking," she said. "How the hell did you put this together so fast?"

"I didn't. It turns out Ransom was already under investigation. The FBI—the new FBI—was already working a program on him in a very hush-hush fashion. As soon as I started asking questions about this overnight, it rattled their chains, and they fell all over themselves trying to help me. They had a lot of the pieces, including contacts with various known hit men. They had put most of it together, but they were waiting for the final piece to fall into place before taking Ransom down. You provided that missing piece—Lyle Morton."

"Where is he?"

"He's under guard and in one of the cars you saw parked out front," Stephens said. "People don't get to stay in witness protection if we find out they're conducting criminal enterprises. We'll be flying him back to D.C. tonight."

"What about my murder charges?"

"We've located what we believe are the two hit men who were used here. They were placed under arrest in Tucson earlier this afternoon. You'll get them as the doers for your homicide."

"If somebody in the FBI knew this was going down, why didn't they stop it before Guy Machett was murdered?"

"Sorry," Stephens said, shaking his head regretfully. "I can't answer for the FBI."

"What about bringing Ransom here to face conspiracy and homicide charges?"

Stephens grinned at her. "Not gonna happen," he said. "You'll have to take a number and get in line."

"What are you doing here, then?"

"Lyle says his daughter is here—Liza. He wanted to come here to say good-bye. We're not wheels up for another three hours. I figured what the hell? If she wants to see him, why not?"

"Does she want to see him?"

"Beats me. None of your people would talk to me or let me see her. I believe the words your detective used were 'I can't possibly divulge that information.' Was she by any chance listening in on our conversation last night?"

"It was Detective Howell's phone," Joanna told him. "It's possible we were on speaker at the time."

Joanna let herself into her office with Agent Stephens on her six. "Wait here," she said, pointing at one of the captain's chairs. "I'll see if she wants to talk to you or to Anson Machett."

Joanna left him there, then detoured into the bullpen, where she found Deb at her desk, pounding away on a keyboard.

"I heard about Lucas and Ruth," Deb said. "Great job!"

"Where's Liza Machett?"

"In the break room."

"Lyle Morton is outside."

"I know," Deb said. "The marshals have him in custody."

"Does she want to talk to him?"

Deb shrugged her shoulders. "Beats me. Ask her."

Joanna started away, then she stopped. "Before I do, what kind of cancer does she have?"

"None," Deb said. "As in not any. The bald head and the scarf are part of her disguise."

"Disguise?"

"Somebody put her in touch with a group of people, mostly long-haul truckers, I believe, who help victims of domestic violence escape their abusers. Shaving her head and wearing a scarf was an added bit of camouflage. Nobody stares at cancer patients. It's rude."

"Okay then," Joanna said.

She made her way to the break room. Liza Machett, no longer wearing her scarf, was sitting on the frayed sofa, staring up at a flat-screen TV set where Judge Judy was busy declaiming her decision and blasting the two losers who had each accused the other of skipping out on a lease agreement. She looked up as Joanna entered.

"I already know he's outside," Liza said quietly. "I know he wants to talk to me. The hell with him. He already told you that he thought I wasn't his, and the feeling's mutual. I have no idea who my father is, but it sure as hell isn't him!"

Joanna was impressed. Liza may have lost almost everything and everybody, but she hadn't lost herself. Maybe it was true—the truth had set her free.

"Okay," Joanna said. "I'll go tell him."

She reversed course.

"Wait," Liza called after her. "What about the money? Do I have to give it back?"

"Not as far as I'm concerned," Joanna said. "I have it on good authority that the guy who was looking for you and the money is about to be taken into custody."

"All right," Liza said. "Good."

"Do you know where you're staying tonight?" Joanna asked. "There's a lot to talk over."

"Deb... Detective Howell said I should stay at the Copper Queen, but I didn't know if I could—if I'd still have money."

"You have money," Joanna assured her. "Not to worry. Sleep as late as you want. We all have a funeral to attend in the morning. We'll talk in the afternoon."

Joanna went back to her office. Roger Stephens was sitting in the chair where she'd left him, dozing. He started awake when she walked into the room.

"Liza's not interested in saying good-bye. She says to tell Anson Machett to go to hell."

"Fair enough," Stephens said, rising to his feet. "Can't say I blame her."

CHAPTER 33

By eight thirty the next morning, Joanna was in her office. Dressed in her formal uniform, she was trying to sort through the masses of resulting paperwork when Kristin knocked on her door. "There's someone out here to see you," she said. "Reverend Derek Nolan."

Joanna looked up from her desk. She was a long way from geared up to face down an accused child molester, but if he was here, it was time. "Send him in," she said, rising. "Ask Detective Carbajal to join us."

She suspected that if Jaime didn't like someone messing with kittens, he would go ballistic over someone who abused children.

The man who entered Joanna's office was tall and thin, and he looked a bit timid. "I'm sorry to disturb you, Sheriff Brady," he said. "I understand you're due to go to a funeral. If this is a bad time..."

"No, it's fine," she said. "Have a seat. I've asked one of my detectives to sit in on our chat."

Derek nodded and eased himself onto one of the visitors' chairs. "That's fine. I wanted to know if it would be possible to see my children. The hospital said that Ruth was being kept under a police guard and wasn't allowed visitors. I believe Lucas is here—in your jail."

Joanna returned to her seat and faced Derek. "The charges lodged against your son are very serious, Mr. Nolan. I thought about transferring him to the juvenile detention center, but the victim, Junior Dowdle, was very well liked here in town. Feelings are running high. I thought Lucas would be more secure here than there, at least until his arraignment. He is, of course, being kept segregated from the adult jail population."

Derek nodded again. "I understand," he said. "Will I be able to see him?"

Joanna remembered the material that

Butch had unearthed in Ruth's blog—entries that indicated that both twins had most likely been subjected to sexual abuse. She was considering how to play this when Jaime tapped on the door and let himself into the room.

"This is Detective Carbajal," Joanna said, "and this is Reverend Nolan." The two men shook hands briefly.

"Will my daughter be brought here, too, when she's released from the hospital?" Derek asked.

"Most likely," Joanna said.

Joanna looked from Jaime to Derek. The man may have abused his children, but it hadn't happened here in Cochise County. If he was brought up on charges in the future, it wouldn't be her case. That meant she had nothing to lose.

"Ruth claims you abused her," Joanna said simply. "She says you molested both her and her brother."

"I'm not surprised," Derek said, nodding quietly. "I expected this. It's not the first time she's made that accusation."

"You're saying it's not true?"

"Categorically. If you'd like me to take a polygraph test, I'll be glad to. Name the time and the place."

"Why would she say such a thing if it weren't true?"

Derek Nolan sighed. "Because my daughter is evil," he said. "Utterly evil. Both my children are."

"This sounds suspiciously like an abuser attempting to push the blame off on his victims."

Derek pursed his lips. "Rebecca and I met and started dating in high school. She was a year older than I was. She went off to college a year ahead of me and went completely wild—drinking, drugs, you name it, she did it, so we broke up. A couple of years later, someone told me she'd gone through treatment and cleaned up her act. Eventually we got back together, married, and had the twins. A few years later, I was working as an accountant in Dallas when I realized that what I really wanted to do was be a minister. We moved to Missouri and I started going to seminary. That's when she fell off the wagon."

"A relapse?" Joanna asked.

"Big-time," Derek said. "And not just drinking and drugs, either. I found out she was screwing around behind my back. I started to divorce her. She begged me to take her back, so I gave her another chance. I thought when I got my first assignment and we moved away from the friends who were such a bad influence on her that things would get better. They didn't."

"Geographical cures hardly ever work," Jaime observed.

Derek nodded. "And it got worse and worse. She came into some money—a small inheritance from her grandmother—and she was off and running again. She didn't care how it looked or how it would affect me or the kids. Finally, she gave me no choice. I divorced her.

"Then one day last spring, she came into my office at the church and told me that she and her boyfriend were moving to Bisbee, Arizona. The boyfriend was bad news, a sometime silversmith with a drug habit. I told her she couldn't—that we had joint custody of the kids and that she couldn't take them out of state without my written permission, which I wasn't going to give. That night, I found this under my pillow."

He reached into the pocket of his sports jacket, pulled out a worn envelope, and handed it over. Looking at it, Joanna saw the word "Daddy" scrawled in pencil.

"Open it," Derek urged. "Read it."

Joanna opened the envelope and extracted a piece of lined notebook paper. "If you don't let us go to Arizona, I'll go to the cops and tell them you molested me and tortured Lucas. Let us go or else."

The note was unsigned. Joanna looked back at Derek when she finished reading it. "This is Ruth's handwriting?"

Derek nodded. Two tears leaked out from under his eyelids and ran down his cheeks. He brushed them away with his sleeve. "I never touched her, I swear," he said. "Not once. Not ever. And I never hurt Lucas, either. The next day, I tried to talk to her about it. Ruth looked at me with those icy blue eyes of hers and said, 'They'll believe me, Daddy. They'll never believe you.'

"That's when I realized how truly wicked she was, but I also knew she was right. I wouldn't even have to be found guilty in a court of law. Just being accused of such a thing would mean that I'd lose my job and my life. They'd never give me another church. So I signed the permission document and they left to come here."

Joanna studied his face. There was no tell—only anguish. And this was the same story Lucas had told—that Ruth lied when she didn't get her way.

"Tell me about Billy Rojas," she said quietly.

"Billy? He was one of the kids from church. A sad case—wheelchair bound, not much of a family life. I was proud when Ruth and Lucas took him under their wing, but then he died. The three of them were out in the desert behind our house. There was a flash flood. The bank gave way and Billy drowned."

"Your children are killers, Reverend Nolan," Joanna said. "They keep trophies. We found the probable murder weapon in the Dowdle case hidden under the floorboards in Lucas's room and we found the victim's rabbit's foot hidden under the floorboards in Ruth's room. We found other things there as well, including a watch that I believe belonged to Billy Rojas."

For a moment Joanna gazed at Derek's shock-stricken eyes across the expanse of desk. "They had Billy's watch?" he asked numbly.

Joanna nodded.

"You're saying they're responsible for Billy's death, too?"

"Yes."

"Oh, my God," Derek breathed, shaking his head and almost sliding off the chair in grief. "I'm sorry," he murmured over and over. "So sorry for everything. I thought I had done a better job of raising them than that."

He didn't attempt to say that his children couldn't possibly have done what she said. He didn't have to. Joanna could see that he knew they had and he believed everything she had just told him.

Eventually, Derek lurched to his feet.

"May I see Lucas now?" he asked.

Joanna nodded. Glancing at her watch, she picked up the phone and dialed Pamela Reyes, her new jail commander. "Reverend Derek Nolan is here to see his son, Lucas," she said. "I'll ask Kristin to take him over to the jail. Detective Carbajal and I have a funeral to attend."

By eleven o'clock that morning, St. Dominick's was filled to capacity, standing room only. Since Butch was one of the pallbearers, Joanna wasn't able to sit with him. Instead, she sat with Denny squirming beside her, trying to quell her frayed nerves. Joanna hadn't found out about Moe and Daisy's request until she finally got home late on Monday night. They had called the house earlier that evening to ask if Jenny would consider singing a solo at Junior's funeral. The song they wanted her to sing was his all-time favorite, "Jesus Loves Me."

Joanna hadn't admitted to anyone what Jason Radner had told her about that very song being the one Ruth Nolan had sometimes sung outside Junior's window.

For all Joanna knew, she might well have used that very song as a tool to lure the poor man to his death. Joanna's reason for keeping silent was simple—she didn't want to betray Jason Radner's confidence, and she wouldn't unless a trial made it absolutely necessary. At the moment, Arlee Jones, the county prosecutor, was lobbying for plea agreements.

When it came time in the service for Jenny to step up beside Junior's flower-draped casket, Joanna held her breath. After a moment's pause, Jenny raised a handheld mic to her lips and then, with incredible poise, began to sing a cappella. As Jenny's sweet soprano voice drifted through the church, filling it with the words of that beloved children's song, it was too much for her mother. An uncontrollable sob welled up in Joanna's throat. She tried her best to stifle it, but she didn't succeed completely. As tears rolled unchecked down her cheeks, Denny reached up and patted her face.

"It'll be okay, Mommy," he whispered in her ear. "Please don't cry."

THE OLD BLUE
LINE

A JOANNA BRADY NOVELLA

For Dale

I knew the two guys were cops the moment Matty walked them over to their booth. I usually work the bar in the afternoons and early evenings, but the daytime cook had turned up sick. In my experience, it's easier and better for my customers to bring in a substitute bartender than it is to bring in a substitute cook. Besides, that's where I started out in this particular restaurant—as a short order cook—and it wasn't much of a hardship for me to be back running the kitchen. As the two newcomers walked past, I had just put up an order and was waiting for Danielle to come pick it up.

Given that the Arizona Police Academy is just up the street, we get a lot of cops at the Roundhouse Bar and Grill. There's always a rowdy crew of newbies—the trainees. They tend to show up in groups and hang out together in the bar in the evenings after class. Next come the instructors. They're mostly older guys, some of them long retired from active police work, who tend to arrive for meals mostly in ones or twos. Not thrilled with retirement, they're glad to get out of their houses for a while and have a chance to hang out in the restaurant, drinking coffee, chewing the fat, and talking over old times.

These two gents looked to be somewhere in the middle—too old to be trainees and too young to be instructors. They were both middle-aged and severely overdressed for Peoria, Arizona. It may have been the beginning of November, but it was still plenty hot in the Valley of the Sun. These guys were decked out in a way that set them apart from the rest of my regular customers—white shirts, ties, and jackets, the whole nine yards. Yes, and cop shoes, of course. I can spot those a mile away.

After they were seated, one of them said something to Matty—a question, most likely. She looked at me over her shoulder before she answered. When she gave the men their menus, they glanced at them, shook their heads, and immediately hand-ed the menus back. As Matty headed for her hostess station she rolled her eyes in my direction. I knew what she meant. People who come into restaurants at lunch-time and occupy booth space without ordering anything more than coffee are not high on anybody's list in the restaurant biz.

I had taken a new order down from the wheel in the pass-through and was start-ing on two plates of burgers and fries when my cell phone rang. After answering it, I perched it on my shoulder and held it in place with my jaw so I could talk and still use my hands to cook. It's not easy doing two things at once, but in restaurant kitchens, sometimes you have to.

"They're cops," Matty explained unnec-essarily. "Said they'd like to have a word with you."

In my experience, cops who want to "a word" usually want a lot more than that. "What did they order?" I asked.

"They're just having coffee."

"Right," I said. "I thought so. It's lunchtime. In that case, they can take an old cold tater and wait until I'm good and ready to deal with them."

It was almost an hour later before the kitchen finally slowed down. I ventured out into the dining room, wiping my hands on my apron as I went. My overdressed friends were still drinking coffee.

"You wanted to see me?" I asked.

Just then one of my model trains zipped by overhead. In keeping with the Round-house name and theme, multiple trains run on tracks laid on a shelf that a previous owner had hung high on the walls of both the dining room and bar. The tracks come complete with tunnel entrances painted on the partition that separates the two rooms. There are three trains in all—two freight and an old fashioned passenger—all of them running at the same time. People often worry about the trains colliding, but they needn't. That's because the shelf holding the tracks is built so close to the ceiling that it's impossible for an onlooker from below to see that there are actually three separate tracks.

"What's the deal with the trains?" one of the visitors asked.

"I happen to like trains," I told him with a shrug, "and so did one of the previous owners. That's why he named the joint the Roundhouse, that and the fact that the bar in the other room is actually round. I was told you wanted to have a word. What about?"

The guy who was evidently the lead reached into his pocket, pulled out an ID wallet and held it up for my inspection, allowing me to see both his badge and his name—Detective Andrew Jamison of the Las Vegas Police Department.

"I'm Detective Jamison and this is my partner, Detective Shandrow," he explained, pocketing his ID. "We're here investigating the death of a woman named Katherine Melcher."

"Never heard of her," I said.

"I believe you and she were married at one time."

"Then there's some kind of mistake," I told him. "My ex-wife's name was Faith."

"She changed it," Jamison replied. "As I said, her name was Katherine, but she mostly went by Katy."

"She's dead?" I repeated. "Faith is dead? You're kidding. What happened to her?"

"She was murdered, Mr. Dixon," Jamison said. "This is a homicide investigation. Are you sure you want to discuss it here?"

I looked around the room. The biggest part of the lunch rush was over, but there were still plenty of diners in the joint, most of them watching with avid curiosity while the drama played itself out. Behind the counter, Danielle had just clipped another incoming order onto the wheel.

"Sorry," I said. "My cook called in sick. I've got a kitchen to run. The afternoon cook comes on at four. I can talk to you then, but I don't see why I should. What does any of this have to do with me? Faith and I have been divorced for years. She married someone else—my former best friend, actually—so why are you talking to me?"

"Because of this," Jamison said. He reached into his pocket, pulled out a piece of paper, unfolded and handed it over. It was a printed out version of an e-mail. The time stamp said it had been sent on

October 15 at 2:00 A.M., Mountain Standard Time, a little over two weeks earlier. I scanned through the text.

Dear Deeny,
If anything ever happens to me, tell them about Butch. He's been calling me lately. He's never for-given me for leaving him, and I'm afraid he'll do almost anything to get even.
Katy

Deeny. Short for DeeAnn, maybe? I remembered that Deeny had been a grade school chum of Faith's, and I also believed she was an attendant at our wedding, but that was all I knew. Obviously no matter what Faith's name was now, she and Deeny had stayed in touch.

"According to Ms. Hallowell—DeeAnn Hallowell—Katy had complained to her that you were harassing her by phone—that you'd been threatening her."

The whole idea was preposterous. "You think I did this?" I demanded, rattling the paper in the cop's face. "You think I'm responsible for Faith's murder?"

"Are you?" Jamison asked mildly, but watched me closely as he did so. "Less than a day after Katherine Melcher wrote this, she was dead. Could you tell us where you were on the night of October fifteenth?"

I could barely make sense of it. Faith was dead, but her name was Katherine Melcher now? Who the hell was Melcher? Where had he come from? And what had become of Rick Austin, my supposedly best friend, who had run off with Faith and married her the moment our divorce was final?

I handed Jamison back the computer printout, and that's when I saw the trap because, on the night in question, I had been in Las Vegas attending a mystery writers' convention—a thing called Bouchercon. I had driven up and back, stayed at the Talisman, where I had a coupon, rather than at the convention hotel out on the Strip. I had registered under the name people call me, Butch Dixon, rather than under my real name, Frederick Wilcox Dixon, because I was worried someone would notice the F.W. Dixon connection and think I was somehow related to the woman, masquerading as a man, who wrote all those old Hardy Boys books I devoured as a kid.

If Faith or Katy or whatever her name was now had died that night, and if she had accused me in advance of doing the deed, I knew I was in deep caca.

"Duty calls," I told the two cops. "I've got food to cook. You'll have to excuse me."

I spun on my heel and made for the kitchen. On the way, I stuffed both hands deep in my pockets. I could feel they were shaking, something I didn't want the visiting detectives to see.

At the end of the counter I had to dodge around Matty to get by. "Hey," she said. "Are you all right? Is something wrong?"

"Everything's fine," I muttered as I hustled past her, not much caring if she believed me or not. I snapped the order off the clip and slapped it down on the prep table. Two chili burgers with onions and cheese. I stuck two patties on the grill and stirred the pot of chili that was simmering at low heat over a burner.

Faith was Katy now, and she was dead? Maybe she had changed her name to Katy because she realized the utter hypocrisy of being called Faith while, at the same time, being utterly faithless. Maybe the irony was too much, even for her. I said her new name aloud, just to try it out. "Katy." If I learned to call her that, maybe it would help me maintain the distance I had managed to create between my hurt back then and my new life now.

Dead or alive, I was still a long way from over what the woman had done to me. She had wiped me out—emotionally, financially, and any other "ly" word you care to mention. She had made off with all our savings, maxed out our credit cards, and then filed for a divorce claiming spousal abuse. She had been allowed to stay in our condo on the condition that she keep up the maintenance and payments. She didn't, keep up the payments, that is. When she finally got around to selling it, the court decree ordered her to split the proceeds with me. Naturally, that didn't happen, either. Instead, she and my good friend Rick lived in our unit rent free for months without making any of the necessary payments. They moved out only when they were evicted, having lost the place to foreclosure. In other words, I didn't get a dime.

And then, to add insult to injury, Faith and my mother stayed in touch. More than in touch. They were pals. Even though the ink on the divorce decree was barely dry when Faith and Rick married, my parents nonetheless attended the wedding. Talk about feeling betrayed. Had I still been in Chicago, I think my head would have exploded, but by then I had taken my sad story to my grandmother—my mother's mother—and thrown myself on her mercy.

My grandmother, Agatha, and her daughter, Maggie, could not be less alike. My mother is your basic self-centered shrew. Grandma Hudson, on the other hand, was a wise and loving person—a giving person. She and Gramps had moved to Sun City years earlier, while I was still in school. A few months after they bought a place there, Grandpa took sick and died. Once he was gone, Grandma Hudson announced that she had no intention of sitting around waiting to die. Instead, she went looking for a business to run.

When she bought the restaurant, it was already called the Roundhouse. Having been badly managed, it was a run-down wreck, just up the street from the railroad tracks. She was able to buy it for a song because the previous owner just wanted to get out from under it. At the time, Peoria, Arizona, was a sleepy little burg miles from its boisterous neighbor Phoenix.

Grandma Hudson fixed the Roundhouse up and ran it by herself for ten years. She and Gramps had paid cash for their duplex home in Sun City. Once she bought the restaurant, she rented out the Sun City unit, reserving it as her "toes up" house when it came time for that. Instead, she chose to live in the two bedroom apartment above the restaurant.

By the time Faith finished cleaning me out and I came dragging my weary, demoralized butt to Arizona, Grandma Hudson was eighty-three years old. She took me in as a full partner in the business and let me share her upstairs apartment. Grandma hung around long enough to teach me the ropes before finally turning me loose while she went back to her place in Sun City to relax and retire. The problem is, she had no idea how to go about doing that. Once she hung up her apron and quit working for good, she only lasted three months. When she died, she left me as sole owner of a house I was too young to live in and a bustling restaurant in the middle of what was fast turning into a thriving community.

Matty stuck her head into the kitchen and startled me out of my unseeing stupor. "You might want to take a look at those hamburger patties," she warned. "They're starting to look like charcoal, and they smell worse."

She was right. While standing there lost in thought with the spatula in my hand, I had let the two hamburger patties burn to such a crisp that I'm surprised the smoke alarm didn't go off. I grabbed them off the grill, tossed them into the garbage, and started two more.

Pay attention, I told myself firmly, but that proved to be almost impossible. Once that initial order of chili burgers was up in the window, I called Rocky, the evening cook, and asked him to come in a couple of hours early, so I could deal with the cop issue. Serving decent food is my livelihood. I couldn't afford to turn out slop just because someone was under the mistaken impression that I had knocked off my ex-wife. Fortunately, Rocky lives just over a mile away, so he was there in no time.

Twenty minutes after returning to the kitchen, I walked back into the dining room where the pair of visiting cops had yet to break down and order some lunch.

"How about if we go into the bar," I suggested. "Early afternoons are quiet in there. We'll have a little more privacy."

While leaving the booth, the two detectives didn't bother delivering the money for their check to Matty at the cash register. Instead, they left enough to cover their coffees and a very stingy tip on their table. I was not favorably impressed. Not only were these guys cops, they were cheap cops at that.

The booths in the bar date from a much earlier era. They're Naugahyde cocoons that were built with privacy in mind. I don't much like them because the servers can't see inside them without standing directly in front of the table. The problem is, I don't want to pony up the big bucks to tear them out and start over.

That afternoon, Amanda, one of my cocktail waitresses, was manning—well, womaning, I suppose—my usual bartending shift. She looked up questioningly as we came into the room. I shook my head, letting her know to leave us be. These guys had already spent the better part of two hours occupying one of my booths, with only two cups of coffee to show for the trouble. If they thought I was going to treat them to something else, they were mistaken.

I was not in a good mood. Faith had left me in a world of trouble when she left me years earlier. This sounded like same song second verse.

"What do you want?" I asked. "And should I have an attorney present for this discussion?"

"It's just a friendly chat," Jamison assured me. "No need to be all hot and bothered."

"I am hot and bothered," I told them. "In fact, I'm downright pissed. My wife left me, wiping me out financially in the process. She ran off with my best friend, cheated me out of my share of the proceeds of our condo, left me in a world of hurt for not paying taxes, and now she's telling the world I'm the one who killed her? Please. If I were going to knock her off, I would have done it years ago—before she let our condo go into foreclosure and before I had to declare bankruptcy just to get out from under the mountains of credit card debt she ran up."

"You sound angry."

"You're damned right I'm angry. Now what do you need from me to get this straightened out? Besides, in cases like this, isn't it always the husband who did it? What about her current husband? What about Rick Austin, her ex-husband and my ex-best friend, who also happens to be a wife-stealing bastard? What about him?"

"Our records indicate that Richard Austin

and Katherine divorced three years ago when she first came to Vegas. The timing involved in the move would suggest that she came to Nevada and established residency for the purpose of obtaining a quick divorce from Mr. Austin."

"Well well," I said. "Fair enough. What goes around comes around. Couldn't happen to a nicer guy. So let's cut to the chase. How about telling me what happened?"

"Her husband, Cliff Melcher, reported his wife missing on the morning of October sixteenth when he returned home from a business trip. Her body was found two days later in her wrecked Cadillac Escalade, crashed into a gully northeast of Searchlight. The M.E. tells us she died of blunt force trauma that isn't consistent with injuries due to a car crash. She was already dead when the car went into the wash. So far we have no known suspects, but we're currently investigating all her known friends and associates."

"Including her former husband?"

Jamison nodded.

"Does that mean I'm a suspect?"

"At this point you're a person of interest," Jamison conceded. "One of several, in fact." He paused long enough to pull a tiny notebook and the stub of a pencil out of his jacket pocket. The gesture served notice that our friendly chat was no longer friendly—not in the least.

"Do you mind telling me where you were that weekend?"

There was no point in lying. I had no doubt that these two guys already knew exactly where I was the middle of October.

"I was in Las Vegas," I said, an admission that I had the opportunity to commit the crime. The cops already knew I had plenty of motive. "I was there for a convention —Bouchercon."

"What is that exactly?" Jamison asked. "And would you mind spelling it for me?"

I dictated the spelling and then explained, "It's a convention for mystery writers and readers."

"Which are you," he asked, "a writer or reader?"

"A reader so far," I admitted, "but I'd like to be a writer someday."

"A mystery writer?"

"Yes."

"As in a murder mystery writer?" From the way he verbally underscored the word murder in the question, I could tell exactly what he was getting at.

"I don't know of any other kind," I told him.

I did, actually. There are a lot of different kinds of mysteries, and I've read them all, from cozies to police procedurals, from thrillers to true crime, but it's usually always murder. Right that moment, however, I didn't feel like giving Detective Jamison an overview of crime fiction. He didn't strike me as the kind of guy who spent a lot of his time reading books of any kind, much less mysteries.

"What do people do at this convention?"

"Chat with each other, listen to authors,. go to panels, visit the booksellers, get autographs."

"What kind of panels?"

The panel entitled "Murder and How to Get Away with It" had been top on my list of must-sees. The room had been packed —standing room only. I had also enjoyed the interview session with the author of **The Poisoner's Handbook**, which turned out to be less of a how-to book and more of a history of the birth of forensic science. I attended both of those, but the thing about Bouchercon is, there's no official sign-up sheet for any of the panels or events. They give you a list of the programs and then you attend the ones that interest you. Once you show up, if there's enough space, you sit. Otherwise, you stand or go somewhere else. It occurred to me that, under the circumstances, I probably shouldn't mention my having attended the panel about getting away with murder.

"I went to several panels," I said, ticking them off one by one. "'Agents: Why You Need One,' 'Is Traditional Publishing Dead?' 'How to Win the E-book Wars,' 'Humor and Murder Do Mix,' that sort of thing."

"Which hotel?"

"The convention was at the Bohemian on the far end of the Strip," I said. "By the time I signed up, I was too late to get the convention price there, so I stayed at the Talisman a few blocks away. One of my customers had recommended it and given me a coupon for one free night."

"Anyone with you on this trip who could verify your whereabouts on the evening in question? Girlfriend maybe, or maybe a gal pal you picked up somewhere along the way?"

I knew what he meant. Jamison was wondering if I had picked up a hooker to keep me company. I hadn't.

"I went by myself," I told him. "Drove up on Friday evening, came back late Sunday afternoon, with no gal pals in the mix at all."

"You drove across Hoover Dam?"

I nodded. Ever since 9/11, they've installed all kinds of security on that road, along with plenty of surveillance cameras, too. If someone went to the trouble of checking the tapes, they'd be able to find me eventually, creeping along in the miserable traffic and driving back and forth in my old beater Honda all by my lonesome. Some day they'll open up that new bridge they're working on—a bridge that crosses the whole canyon. Until they do, crossing the Colorado River at Hoover Dam takes for-damn-ever.

"You said you stayed at the Talisman?"

Recalling the place, I cringed. My customer's idea of "great" and mine don't exactly jibe. The Talisman isn't a hotel I'll be visiting again any time soon.

"Yes," I answered. "It's a few blocks off the Strip, which means it's less expensive, but it was also close enough for me to walk back and forth to the convention. That way I didn't have to pay for parking."

"Do you remember which room you were in?"

"Do you remember hotel numbers weeks after you check out?"

He shook his head. "No," he said. "I suppose not."

"Me, neither," I told him. "Check with the desk. They'll be able to tell you which room I was in. The Talisman is a low-rise hotel. My room was on the second floor, with the swimming pool down below."

"How much did you lose?" Jamison asked.

"I didn't lose," I said. "I went to a convention. I don't gamble in Vegas. The house always wins."

"I mean, how much did you lose when your wife left you?"

"Oh, that," I said. "I lost everything."

And that was the simple truth. I'd had a restaurant off Michigan Avenue. It was called Uptown. At the time, it was a going concern. I had money in the bank, a cool condo close to downtown, and a sizable retirement account. Faith and I also had cars—a late model BMW for me and a Volvo for her. Taken altogether, it added up to more than a mil, including the equity in the condo. When Faith took off with the goods, there wasn't ever any hope of my getting it back. If she and Rick had deposited the money in a bank somewhere, maybe I might have stood a chance of recovering some of it. Instead, it all went up in smoke— literally. It doesn't take long to go through that kind of money when you and your druggie pals are all doing cocaine.

"So how'd it happen?" Jamison asked.

He didn't say, **How could you be so stupid?** He didn't have to. I've said it to myself countless times, but I never saw it coming. Not at all.

I took a deep breath before I answered, remembering back to the first day I ever laid eyes on her.

"Faith showed up in my restaurant one day. She came in at lunch with a guy in a suit and came back later that evening alone. It wasn't long before one thing led to another. She was beautiful as all get out, smart, and charming. I fell for her hook, line, and sinker. She claimed to have an MBA from Fordham, which, I found out later, was bogus, but even without that degree, she knew way more about accounting than I did. After we were married, she was only too happy to take over the bookkeeping and accounting jobs at the restaurant. That's how she met Rick Austin. He was my financial advisor and also my best friend.

"Once they hooked up, the two of them managed to drain my bank accounts—all of them. The first I knew anything at all about it was when I wrote a check to pay the next month's rent on the restaurant, and the damned thing bounced. That's about the time both the IRS and the Illinois tax collectors came calling. Even though I had dutifully signed all the tax forms Faith handed me every year, she hadn't bothered to file them, or to send along the taxes that were due, either.

"By the time I wised up, she had slapped me with a restraining order so I couldn't even go home to get my clothes, couldn't even get into the building to get my car. It was February in Chicago. I had no vehicle, no money, no working credit cards, and the tax men breathing down my neck. Fortunately, I was wearing the sheepskin coat I had bought two years earlier when we went to Vail on vacation. I ended up walking to the building where my former maitre d' lived and crashed on his couch."

"So after she wiped you out like that, I take it you hit her?" Jamison asked. "You were violent?"

"I was not," I replied hotly, feeling my blood start to boil all over again. "I never so much as raised a hand to the woman, not once, but that didn't keep her from claiming I had. She went crying to a local domestic violence shelter with some cock-and-bull story about how I had beaten the crap out of her. They helped her do the paperwork to take out a restraining order and helped her find a shark of an attorney to come after me. I ended up being ordered to pay five thousand a month in temporary support while she and Rick got to stay on in our condo. Of course, with the restaurant shuttered, I couldn't make the support payments. That's when she had me served with papers taking me to court for non-payment."

"What did you do?"

"The night I got served was the night I hit bottom. I was completely busted. I had gone from having everything to having less than nothing, and here she was threatening to take me to court for not sending her monthly support checks? What kind of deal is that? To drown my sorrows, I drank far too much of my former maitre d's easily accessible booze and very nearly threw myself off his balcony. Ten stories up would have been more than enough to do the job. Luckily for me, I passed out before I could make it happen.

"The next morning, I woke up with a terrible hangover to the sound of a ringing telephone. Grandma Hudson always claimed to be psychic, and maybe she was, because she called me that morning when I was at my lowest ebb. When I had nowhere else to turn, she offered me a lifeline. She told me to wipe the slate clean—to put it all behind me, come to Arizona, and start over. I think it's the best advice anyone has ever given me."

"So that's what you did?" Jamison asked. "You came here?"

"I left town, came to Arizona, and started over from scratch."

"Never tried to get your money back?"

"That would have taken lawyers, and lawyers cost money, which I didn't have. Besides, there was no point. From what I could tell, Faith and Rick had run through most of it by then anyway. Instead, I went to work with my grandmother here at the Roundhouse and lived rent free with her in the apartment upstairs. I filed bankruptcy to get out from under the credit card debt Faith had run up, but that didn't fix my back taxes problem. Grandma Hudson found someone here in town, a retired IRS agent, who helped me cut a deal with the tax man. It took every penny I made for the first three years I was here to pay off the back taxes.

"The restaurant I'd owned before—the Uptown—had been more of a fine dining establishment. Grandma taught me the basics of running your ordinary blue-collar diner. When she died a few years later, she left the restaurant to me—lock, stock, and barrel. By the way, I'm still driving the car she left me, too—an early nineties vintage Honda with very low mileage."

"And when's the last time you saw Kather..." Jamison hesitated and then corrected himself. "When's the last time you saw Faith?"

"The day the divorce was final—seven years ago, October thirty-first. It always seemed appropriate that we got divorced on Halloween. I was living in Arizona then, and she's the one who filed. I flew into Chicago the morning of the court appearance and flew back out again that same night. On Halloween, I always allow myself a single trick-or-treat toast in the witch's honor."

"Faith maybe cleaned you out, but it looks like you landed on your feet," Jamison suggested. "After all, you've got all this."

He sent a significant glance and an all-encompassing gesture around the bar, which was starting to fill up. A group of golfers—several foursomes, boisterous, loud, and fresh from some local course—had turned up and were busily making themselves at home by ordering drinks all around, wings, and platters of nachos.

"I already told you. My grandmother owned the Roundhouse, and she left it to me when she died. You may not realize this, but inheriting a restaurant isn't what I'd call 'landing on my feet.' It's called landing in a pile of work. The whole trick about running a restaurant is making it look easy. It isn't. It's like that duck gliding effortlessly across the water without anyone seeing that, below the surface, he's paddling like crazy. By the way, that weekend in Vegas was my first weekend off—my first days off—in months."

"At the time you went there, did you know Faith was living in Las Vegas?"

"I had no idea."

I wouldn't be surprised if my mother had known all about it. I think I mentioned earlier that she and Faith had always been chummy, and it chapped my butt that the two of them stayed friends, especially after what Faith did to me.

"You took your cell phone to Vegas?"

I noticed the sudden shift in direction. "Of course," I answered.

"Did you use it?"

"Some, but on Saturday afternoon I noticed it was running out of battery power and realized I had forgotten the charger back here in Peoria. I called the restaurant, let them know that my cell phone was out of commission. I told them that if they needed to reach me, they'd have to call the Talisman or the people in charge of the convention. At the convention, they post messages on a bulletin board near the registration desk. After that, I shut my cell off and left it off until after I got back home."

I'm not stupid. I could see clear as day where all this was going. Jamison thought I had shut off my phone so it wouldn't ping anywhere near the crime scene. That's how the cops are able to catch the occasional killer these days—by following the bad guy's cell phone signals. That way they can place the crook at the scene of the crime without his ever having made a call.

"My phone records will bear that out," I added.

"I'm sure they will. So did you use the phone in your room to make any calls?"

"No, not that I remember. Besides, who would I have called? Other than the people I met at the convention, I didn't know anyone in Vegas."

"What about the pay phone down by the swimming pool at the Talisman? Did you use that?"

"If there was a pay phone there, I didn't notice, and I certainly didn't use it."

"Who all knew you were going to that particular convention?" This was the first time the other cop, Detective Shandrow, had asked a question.

"The people at the restaurant knew I was going to Vegas," I corrected. "I doubt I mentioned anything to them about the convention. What I was doing in Vegas wasn't any of their business. You know the old saying, 'What happens in Vegas stays in Vegas.'"

My attempt at humor fell flat, at least as far as Detective Shandrow was concerned. He grimaced. "So you're saying that none of the people who work for you are aware that you're building up to writing the great American novel?" His sarcasm was duly noted.

"It's not something I talk about. People don't like it when they think you're standing with a foot in both worlds. They get nervous. I have a good crew working here at the restaurant, and I need to keep all of them."

"Unless you decide to sell," Jamison said.

That took me aback. The truth was, for months there had been considerable interest from a company hot to trot to build a hotel in order to cash in on Peoria's burgeoning Spring Training gold mine. The developer, a guy named Jones, had bought up most of the real estate on either side of me, purchasing the buildings on the cheap from the landlords who had raised the rents enough that their longtime small business tenants—engaged in a life-or-death struggle with big box stores—could no longer afford to renew their leases. Their former landlords were only too happy to make a quick buck and go on to bigger and better things. Now, months later, I remained the sole holdout.

Grandma Hudson was nobody's fool. When she bought the Roundhouse, she bought the whole thing—both the building and the parking lot, right along with the previous owner's collection of model trains. Once I came on board, I bought more trains, and better ones, too. Unlike some of the other businesses in the neighborhood, I still had a going concern. I also didn't have a money-grubbing landlord trying to bust my balls in order to get me to leave. I hadn't taken the bait at the developer's first offer or even at his second or third.

So yes, I was hoping to sell eventually—at

my price—but it wasn't something I discussed out in the open. For one thing, if my crew figured out that I might sell, they'd be gone before the next dinner service, and I'd find myself stuck being chief cook and bottle washer along with having to do everything else. Still, the fact that Jamison and Shandrow knew about my possible real estate dealings meant the two detectives had been hanging around Peoria asking questions for some time, long before they set foot in my restaurant early that afternoon to order their two bottomless cups of coffee.

"Who told you I might be interested in selling?"

Jamison shrugged. "Word gets around," he said.

"I've had some inquiries," I acknowledged. "So far there haven't been any offers out there that I couldn't walk away from. If someone's going to buy the business out from under me, they're going to have to make it worth my while."

"I notice you have a pay phone back there by the restrooms," Jamison said.

This odd observation was completely out of context, but it was also true. Even though pay phones are thin on the ground these days, the Roundhouse has one, and I do my best to keep it in good working order.

"A few of the planned communities around here aren't big on watering holes for the old guys who still like to tipple a bit," I explained. "Some of my regulars are disabled vets who arrive in those handi-capped dial-a-van things or else by cab because they're too old to drive or their physical condition makes it impossible. The younger generation may have terminal cell-phone-itis, but not all of the older generation does.

"So yes, I have a pay phone back there so those guys can call a cab or a van when it's time for them to go home. I can also tell you that having a pay phone on the premises is a pain in the neck. When this one breaks down—which it does with astonishing regularity—and stops refund-ing the change it's supposed to spit back out, people tend to get crabby. They want me to replace their missing change, and most of the time I do. I figure I can afford to lose seventy-five cents easier than some of them can."

"Whoa," Detective Shandrow observed with an ill-concealed sneer. "You're a regular philanthropist."

I wasn't too keen on Jamison, but I liked his partner even less.

"You usually work days, then?" Jamison asked.

"Mostly," I said, "I generally do the day-shift bartending, but because I'm the owner, I pitch in as needed—including serving as short-order cook on occasion, as I did today. I'm here most of the time anyway because I live right upstairs."

"If you don't mind," Shandrow interjected, "I think I'll go use the facilities."

More than ready to be rid of the jerk, I wouldn't have minded if he'd walked straight out the door. He eased his somewhat ungainly body out of the booth and then made for the corridor that led to the restrooms while Jamison put away his notebook and pencil.

"So that's it, then?" I asked.

"For the time being," he told me. "Like I said earlier, we just needed to ask you a couple of questions. Now we'll get out of your hair."

That was pretty laughable in itself because I don't have any hair. When my hairline started receding, I went for the Kojak look and shaved it all off. Jamison stood up just as Shandrow emerged from the hallway. Jamison was between us, and Shandrow was looking at his partner rather than at his reflection in the mirror. I caught the small secretive nod he sent in Jamison's direction. Since neither of them was looking at me at that precise moment, I doubt they realized I had seen it. That nod told me that Detective Shandrow had not only gone down the hall looking for something, he had found it.

"What's the deal with the trophy case and all the photos back there in the corridor?" he asked. "You got yourself one of those dimwit kids?"

I don't have any kids of my own, but I do coach a Special Olympics team, the Roundhouse Railers. When one of my athletes comes into the diner, they always eat for free, and they always want to go visit the trophy case in the restroom hallway. Hearing Shandrow call those sweet folks dimwits left me wanting to punch the man's lights out.

"Those are my athletes." I told him in tight-lipped fury. "And no, I don't have any children of my own, dim or otherwise."

They got the message, Jamison most likely more than Shandrow, and left then, while I stayed where I was. This wasn't a social call. It wasn't my job to see them out. Besides, I was so pissed at Detective Shandrow that I was afraid I'd say something to the man that I'd end up regretting. I was still sitting in the booth when Amanda came over and wiped down the table.

"Who were those assholes, and what the hell was that all about?" she demanded, both hands on her hips. "Were they from down the street?" She jerked her head in the direction of the police academy campus.

"No such luck," I said. "It turns out my ex-wife got murdered, and they're operating on the assumption that I did it."

"Right," she said. "When would you have time?"

"That's what I told them."

"You want something to drink?"

"No," I said. "Not right now. I need to take a run up the road and have a chat with an old friend of mine."

By "up the road" I meant up Highway 60 to Sun City. And by "old friend" I mean old—a spry eighty-two, or, as Tim O'Malley himself, liked to say, "Older than dirt." Tim had retired from the Chicago PD after living and working—much of it as a beat cop—through far too many Chicago winters. He and his wife Minnie had retired to Sun City and, through mere coincidence, happened to own the house next to the one my grandparents bought a couple years later. Tim and Minnie were there for my grandmother when Grandpa Hudson was sick and dying, just as, years later, Grandma was there for Tim during Minnie's slow decline through the hell of Alzheimer's.

And after that? It's difficult to call a pair of octogenarians boyfriend and girlfriend, but that's what they were. Grandma told me once that Tim was far too young for her to consider marrying. They never lived together, either. After all, propriety had to be maintained. Even so, they were good for each other, and over time Tim and I became friends if not pals. Right that minute, I needed some sage advice, and Tim's house was where I went looking for it.

He listened to the whole story in silence. When I finished, he shook his head. "Aggie always said that Faith woman was trouble," Tim commented. "She was of the opinion that anything that looks too good to be true probably is too good to be true. Unfortunately, Faith turned out to be far worse than any of us could have expected."

"I should have expected it," I muttered. "When the gorgeous blonde walks into the room and sweeps the short bald guy off his feet, anyone with half a brain should have figured out something wasn't right. By the time I did, it was far too late."

"Okay, then," Tim said, nodding impatiently. "Enough about her. Let's get back to those cops. Did they come right out and say you were a suspect? Did they read you your rights?"

"No," I answered. "Jamison insisted I was just a 'person of interest,' but I find that hard to believe. They must have been doing some serious poking around in order to learn that I'm considering selling the Roundhouse to that hotel developer. That isn't exactly common knowledge."

Tim nodded again. It was common knowledge to him because I had confided in Tim O'Malley about that, but I hadn't told anyone else.

"How long have these bozos been in town, again?" he asked.

"They didn't say."

"Vegas is a long way from here. It doesn't seem likely that they would have sent two detectives down here to question you if they thought it was some kind of wild goose chase. They must have a pretty good reason to suspect you."

"Yes, but I didn't do it," I insisted. "I had no idea Faith was living in Vegas."

"What about the guy she ran off with?"

"My old pal Rick? She evidently shed him, too, somewhere along the way. I have no idea where he is now."

"What's his name?"

"Austin—Richard Austin."

"He's the guy who stole your wife and your money?"

"I don't think he stole Faith. She probably pulled the wool over his eyes, the same way she did mine, but between the two of them, they both stole my money."

"How much money are we talking about?"

"Over a million," I said.

Tim whistled. "That's a lot of money."

"It is, but once it's gone, it's gone. That's one thing I'm grateful to Grandma Hudson for—she helped me see that it was just money, and water under the bridge besides. In order to get on with my life, I needed to let it go, and I did."

"Cops won't see it that way," Tim cautioned. "Those guys are probably thinking you're still pissed about it."

"Turns out I am still pissed," I corrected. "But not enough to kill her over it. I'm not the murdering type. So what should I do, call a lawyer?"

"Do you have one?"

"No, but..."

"You see," Tim said, "here's where those dicks have you by the short hairs. If you don't call a lawyer you look stupid, and if you do call a lawyer, you look guilty."

"What should I do, then?"

Tim considered for a long time before he answered. "For right now, go back to work. Don't stress over this. Stress is bad for your health. Let me see what I can do. I may have been off the force for a long time, but ex-cops have some pull that most civilians don't. I'll get back to you."

He glanced at his watch. He didn't say, **Here's your hat; what's your hurry,** but I got the message and left. When I got back to the Roundhouse, the parking lot was full and so was the bar. The white-haired, blue-plate special folks, sporting their walkers and canes, were wandering into the dining room. That was the other thing I didn't like about selling the place. Any hotel that might replace it—full of polished granite floors and stylish modern furniture —wouldn't be the same kind of comfortable gathering place this one had become for that particular demographic. The new establishment on the block might be slick and cool and hip, but it wouldn't do what the Roundhouse did—remind people of places back home.

I went upstairs, showered, changed into clean clothes, and came back downstairs to the bar to lend a hand. Some of the golfers, a little the worse for wear several hours later, were still there. I told Amanda to collect their car keys and make sure they called cabs before they left. That's when it hit me—all the earlier talk about pay phones. Shandrow hadn't gone down the hall to spend time looking at the Roundhouse Railers' trophy case. He had been in search of the bar's pay phone. I went down the corridor and looked at it myself. I'd had them install it low enough on the wall so it's wheelchair accessible. I stared at it for a long time, but the phone wasn't talking, at least not to me.

Grandma Hudson always claimed work was the best medicine. "It's good for what ails you," she advised me when I came dragging into Phoenix. She must have known how close I was to the abyss. She had insisted that I see a doctor for a check-up, and had seen to it that the doctor prescribed some antidepressants for me as well. Between the two medications—daily doses of hard work and the prescription drugs—I had gradually pulled out of my funk.

That night, the hard work part did the trick again. The Friday night crowd, larger than usual, was more than I had staffed for, and I helped pinch-hit in the bar. Right around midnight a guy I'd never seen before sauntered into the bar and ordered a St. Pauli Girl, N/A—nonalcoholic—the drink of choice for some of those folks who no longer care to imbibe the hard stuff. The new arrival had the nose of a heavy drinker, and the familiar way he settled his hulking figure on the bar stool told me he had spent plenty of time in bars.

"You Butch?" he asked when I brought him back his change.

"You got me," I answered. "Who are you?"

"Pop told me to look for a bald guy with a mustache," he said. "Had to be you."

"Pop?" I asked.

"Tim O'Malley. My father-in-law—used-to-be father-in law."

There was a hint of regret in that last phrase. I couldn't tell if the regret came from losing his wife or from losing Tim O'Malley as part of his family.

"Name's Charles," he told me. "Charles Rickover. Charlie to my friends. Me and Amy have been divorced for about ten years now. I still stay in touch with Pop, though. He's a good guy."

I remembered being introduced to Tim's daughter Amy at Minnie O'Malley's funeral. If I'd been told her last name back then, I didn't recall what it was.

"Yes," I agreed. "He is a good guy."

"I used to be a cop," Charles went on. "Put in my twenty. My career came to an abrupt end about the time Amy left me. Turned out she hit forty and decided she liked women more than men. That was tough on the old ego. I spent some time drowning my sorrows, if you know what I mean."

Wondering where all this was going, I nodded. Had Tim sent Charles by so we could cry on one another's shoulders about the women who had done us wrong? If that was the case, I wasn't exactly in a mood for commiserating.

I had started to walk away when Charles reached into his pocket and pulled out one of those little business card holders. He extracted a card and then lay it on the bar in front of me. When I didn't reach for it right away, he added. "Go ahead. Pick it up. It won't bite."

In the dim light of the bar, I had to pull out a pair of reading glasses to make it out: CHARLES RICKOVER. PRIVATE INVESTIGATIONS. The only other line on the card was a phone number with a 602 prefix. There was nothing else printed there—no address, city, or state, but 602 indicated the business was located somewhere in the Phoenix metropolitan area.

"Pop says he thinks you're being framed for murder and that maybe you could use my help."

I know a little about private eyes—enough

to know they don't come cheap. I wasn't of a mind to be bamboozled into hiring one.

"Look," I said, "Tim's a great guy. As I told him earlier, someone knocked off my ex-wife a couple of weeks ago. A pair of cops came by earlier today and asked me a few questions about it. That's all. I never said anything about being framed, and I don't think it's necessary for me to hire—"

"You're not hiring me," Charles said quickly. "I'm doing this for Tim. He stood by me when a lot of other people didn't. When he asks for something, I deliver. He called me this evening and mentioned the framing bit. I still have friends here and there. Between his call and now, I've made a few calls of my own, and you know what? Either you're the guy who did it, and they've got you dead to rights, or else Tim is right, and you are being framed."

"How so?" I asked.

"An old friend of mine happens to work for the Las Vegas PD, and he did some checking for me. It turns out your ex, Katherine Melcher, had received a number of threatening telephone calls in the weeks preceding her death. She had recorded two of the calls—illegally, of course. The person on the phone whispered so it's hard to tell if the caller was a man or a woman. With the right equipment, I'm sure a trained voice recognition expert will be able to sort all that out. Voices are like fingerprints, or so I'm told. The most immediate problem is this—the calls all came from a Phoenix area phone number. Wanna know which one? The pay phone you've got in your hallway there." He pointed with the tip end of his bottle. "The one right outside your crapper."

There was a long pause after that while his words sank into my consciousness. Threatening phone calls to Faith, aka Katy Melcher, had been placed from my pay phone? How could that be?

Charles slammed his empty bottle down on the counter. "Contrary to popular opinion," he said, "I believe you **do** need my help. Your ex may be the one who's dead, but Pop thinks you're the real target, and I tend to agree with him. Given all that, we need to talk. Now where can a guy get a decent cup of coffee around here?"

I walked to the far side of the bar and tapped Jason, my evening and late night barkeep, on the shoulder. "I'm done," I told him. "Will you close up?"

"No prob," he said with a nod.

Beckoning Rickover to follow me, I ducked into the dining room and grabbed the most recently made pot of coffee off the machine behind the counter, then I led the way up the narrow stairway to what is a surprisingly spacious apartment. Because the stairway is situated in the alcove between the dining room and the bar, you enter the apartment in the middle as well.

When it comes to "open concept floor plans," Grandma Hudson was a pioneer. The main room, situated over the restaurant portion of the building, is a combination living room, dining room, kitchen, and office. A master bedroom and bath as well as a guest room and bath are located over the bar. That's not the best arrangement for sleeping, especially on raucous weekend nights, but Grandma probably figured—and rightly so—that whoever lived here would be downstairs working those noisy late nights anyway.

I turned to the right and led Charles into what an enterprising real estate sales guy might refer to as the "main salon." I put the coffeepot on the warmer I keep on the kitchen counter and directed my guest past the plain oak dining table to the seating area in the center of the room. The rest of the place may have been decorated to suit my grandmother's no nonsense, spartan tastes, but the seating area consisted of two well-made easy chairs and a matching sofa. The chintz upholstery may have faded some, but the springs and cushions had held up to years of constant use. With a glass-topped coffee table in the middle, it was the perfect place to put your feet up after spending a long day doing the downstairs hustle.

When I brought the coffee—a mug for Charles and one for me, too, I found him studying his surroundings. "You live here by yourself?" he asked.

I nodded. "Once burned, twice shy."

He gave me a rueful grin. "Ain't that the

truth. So tell me the story. Pop told me some of it, but if I'm going to help you, I need to hear the whole thing—from the very beginning."

There's something demeaning about having to confess the intimate details of the worst failures of your life to complete strangers. For the second time in a single twenty-four-hour period, I found myself having to go back over that whole miserable piece of history, but I didn't hold anything back. I understood that if the threatening phone calls to Faith had originated from my place of business, then I was in deep trouble and needed all the help I could get. In that regard, Charles Rickover was the only game in town.

He didn't bother taking notes as I talked. He listened attentively but without interruption as I made my way through the whole thing, ending with a detailed description of my encounter with Detectives Jamison and Shandrow earlier that afternoon. When I went to refill our coffee cups, I returned to find him staring at the office space at the far end of the room. It consisted of an old wooden teacher's desk that Grandma Hudson had liberated from a secondhand store somewhere in front of a bank of used and abused secondhand filing cabinets.

"Is that your computer?" Charles asked, nodding toward my desk and my pride and joy, a tiny ten-inch Toshiba Portégé. The laptop sat in isolated splendor on the desk's otherwise empty surface. Having learned my lesson about allowing other people, namely Faith, handle accounting records for my business, I do those functions myself now, on the computer. The Toshiba also holds the first few chapters of my several unfinished novels.

"That's it," I said.

"Mind if I take a look?"

"Sure."

Charles walked over to the desk, slipped on a pair of gloves, and flipped up the lid on the computer. It lit up right away. He leaned over, studied the screen, and then turned back to me with a puzzled expression on his face. "Dead men don't lie?" he asked.

"It's a story," I explained. "Fiction. It's the

title for one of the novels I'm working on."

"You leave your computer sitting here like this?"

I shrugged. "Why not? I'm the only one who lives here."

"You may be the only person who lives here, but you're not the only person who has access."

That was a scary thought and one I had never considered. Since I was downstairs all day, every day, I never locked the place up except on those very rare occasions when I was out of town.

"You're saying one of my people may have been coming up here and messing with my computer behind my back?"

Charles didn't deign to respond. "Tell me about this mystery convention you went to. What's it called again?"

"Bouchercon."

"How did you register for it?"

"On line," I answered, nodding toward the computer. "On that."

Charles sat down in front of the computer and made himself at home. He typed in a few keystrokes. "Yup," he said. "Here it is in your browser history, the Bouchercon Web site. What about your hotel? What was that again, the Talisman didn't you say?"

I nodded. The man may not have been taking notes during my long recitation of woes, but he had clearly been paying attention.

"Is there anything in here about your dealings with your ex?"

I nodded again. "There's a file called Faithless Faith," I said sheepishly. "I thought that writing it down would help me put it in the past."

"Did it?" he asked.

I shook my head. "No such luck."

"Unfortunately," Charles said, "Faithless Faith seems to have found a way back into your present. What about your dealings with that developer? Are there any records of your dealings with Mr. Jones in here?"

"Yes," I replied. "There have been a number of e-mail exchanges about that."

"In other words, this computer makes your whole life an open book for anyone who cares to take a look-see. Do you happen to have one of those floppy disk drives around here?"

"It's in the top drawer on the right along with a box of extra floppies. I use those to make backup copies of the business records on the computer's hard drive. Why?"

"I want you to come over here right now and make copies of all your essential business files and anything else you want to keep, including those unfinished novels. After that, we're going to reformat your computer. When the cops come back with a search warrant—and I'm saying, when not if—they'll grab your computer and use everything on it to put you away. Not having your files won't stop them, but it'll sure as hell slow them down. Reformatting is the best way to get rid of everything you don't want anyone else to see. If they ask, tell them your computer crashed and reformatting was the only way you could reboot it. You get busy copying your files. In the meantime, give me the keys to your car."

"Why?" I asked.

"Because you're caught up in a complicated plot here, Mr. Dixon," he said, holding out his hand, "and you're about to go down for it."

Reluctantly, I fished my car keys out of my pocket and handed them over. It seemed to take ages to go through the computer, copying the necessary files. The whole time I was doing so, I couldn't believe any of this was happening. If Charles Rickover was right, one of the people who worked for me—someone I trusted—was trying to frame me for killing Faith. So who was it?

Charles came back upstairs a long time later. He was empty-handed and his face was grim. "Just as I thought," he said. "There's a bloody bat hidden under the mat in the trunk of your car. I believe I have a pretty good idea about where that blood might have come from."

"Did you get rid of it?" I asked shakily.

"Hell no," he said. "I'm pretty sure it's the murder weapon. I'm not touching it, and neither are you."

"You mean we're just going to let the cops find it?"

"Absolutely. In the meantime, you and I are going to do our damnedest to figure out who's behind this."

After returning my car keys, he picked up our empty coffee mugs and went over to the counter where he refilled them. By then I was too stunned to play host. Besides, I was still copying files. Working with floppy disks isn't exactly an instantaneous process.

"Okay," he said, handing me the cup I assumed was mine. "What's in the file cabinets? Are your personal papers there by any chance?"

I nodded. "That's where I keep paper copies of job applications, tax returns, court decrees—bankruptcy and divorce included. That's also where you'll find my birth certificate, Grandma Hudson's death certificate, and a copy of my last will and testament."

"How often do you open those files?"

"Not often, why?"

"With any kind of luck, I think there's a slight chance that those file folders may hold some fingerprints that will work in our favor, unless of course whoever is behind this was smart enough to use gloves. And if the prints are there, the only way they'll work for us is if we can point the cops in the right direction."

"Fat chance of that," I said. "If they come in with a search warrant, I'm toast."

"Not necessarily," Charles said. "While I was downstairs, I called Pop. You've got a guest room here, right?"

"Yes, but..."

"Good. Now your guest room is about to have a guest. He's another one of Pop's Sun City chums. His name's Harold Meeks. Thirty years ago he was the top defense attorney in Phoenix, and now he's yours—pro bono, by the way. Pop says Harold's too old to drive or even play golf anymore, but he's still got all his marbles. When it comes to legal maneuvers, he can't be beat. He'll be here as soon as the cab Pop called for him can drop him off. Pop says Harold may need some help getting up and down the stairs, but he'll be here to set the cops straight when they show up with their search warrant.

"Oh," Charles added, "when he gets here, I want you to give him a list of all your employees, both current and former. He'll need to know everything you know about them—approximate hiring dates, where they live, what you know about their personal lives, where they worked before, etcetera."

"Whatever information I have on my employees is on their job applications in the personnel drawer in the filing cabinet."

"Are you listening to me?" Charles demanded. "You are not to go near those filing cabinets under any circumstances! Now, are you done copying your files?"

Properly chastised, I held up a fistful of floppies.

"I'll take those for right now," he said, removing the disks from my fingers and slipping them into his jacket pocket. "Do you know how to reformat that computer?"

"Yes."

"Do it then," he ordered.

I was still reformatting the hard drive—another not-so-instantaneous process—when Charles's cell phone rang. "Okey-dokey," he said. "We'll be right down."

I glanced at my watch as we headed

downstairs. It was after two o'clock in the morning. The Roundhouse was closed up tight. The lights were off, the cleaning crew gone. After disarming the alarm, I unlocked the door and opened it. Standing outside, leaning on a walker, was a tiny, hunched over old man with a shock of white hair that stood on end, as though he'd been awakened from a sound sleep and hadn't bothered combing his wild hairdo. If the guy was a day under ninety, I'm a monkey's uncle. Behind him, carrying two old-fashioned suitcases, stood a turban-wearing cab driver.

"I'm Harold Meeks," the old guy announced in a squeaky little voice that reminded me of someone hopped up on laughing gas. "You Butch Dixon?"

I nodded. Harold turned back to the driver. "Okay," he directed. "This is the guy. Give him the bags."

The driver handed them over to me in complete silence, then he retreated to his cab and drove off into the night.

"It's cold as crap out here," Harold griped impatiently. "Are we going inside sometime soon or are we just going to stand here until our tushes freeze off?"

We went inside. As I carried the two suitcases upstairs it occurred to me that my unexpected company obviously intended to settle in for the duration. Behind me, Harold abandoned his walker in favor of letting Charles help him up the stairs. Once Harold was safely deposited on the nearest dining room chair, Charles went back down and retrieved the walker. In the darkened bar downstairs, Harold hadn't looked that bad. Now that I saw him in full light, however, I was shocked. How could this tiny, frail old guy, sitting there in a threadbare sweater and a pair of worn moccasins, possibly be my best hope for beating a murder rap? He looked like he was far more ready to show up for a summons to the pearly gates than for duking it out in an earthly court of law.

"Okay," Charles said, dusting off his hands in satisfaction. "I'm done here and need to head out. I'll leave you two to it."

When it came to my having a capable someone to lean on, Charles Rickover looked a lot more promising than Harold Meeks.

"Wait a minute," I said anxiously. "Where are you going?"

"Vegas," Charles said. "One of Pop's pals is retired Air Force. He keeps a little Cessna over at the Goodyear airport. He doesn't fly at night anymore, but he says we can be wheels up by seven A.M. That means I'd better go home and grab an hour or two of shut-eye."

Charles Rickover bailed at that point, leaving me holding the bag as well as two surprisingly heavy suitcases. "Where's my bedroom?" Harold demanded irritably.

"Down the hall and to the right," I said.

"Good," he said. "Put my stuff in there, then come back and we'll go to work. You got any coffee that's fresher than that crap on the counter? Smells like it's about three hours past its pull-by date."

Which is how I spent the next three hours in the presence of a cantankerous old man who acted as though he'd as soon chew nails as listen to my sad story. Obligingly, I went downstairs to the restaurant, fired up the coffeemaker behind the counter and

made a new pot. While I waited for it to
brew, I stood leaning against the counter
wondering how it was that my fate was
now in the hands of this gang of old men—
the lame and the halt—who, out of the
goodness of their hearts, had joined forces
to bail me out of my jam.

I knew Tim O'Malley, the guy Charles
called Pop, was responsible. That meant
that, by extension, so was Grandma
Hudson.

I took the coffee upstairs, only to be
ordered back down to retrieve cream and
sugar. Since I drink my coffee black, I
don't keep cream and sugar upstairs. At
Harold's direction, I retrieved a yellow
legal pad from the outside pocket of one
of his bags. Then sitting at the dining room
table, I began telling my story one more
time, version 3.0, while Harold took notes,
using a Mont Blanc fountain pen to cover
one page after another with a totally
indecipherable kind of shorthand.

The only time he asked questions was
when I was going over what I had said to
Jamison and Shandrow. Harold explained

that the questions they had asked would probably reveal a blueprint of the kinds of evidence they had against me. As a consequence, I told him everything in the closest thing to word-for-word as I could manage.

Next, I gave him the lowdown on my employees. Again I did it to the best of my ability, but without being able to fall back on the paperwork hidden in those forbidden file cabinets, I couldn't tell him the exact order of hiring, ages, dates of birth, physical addresses, or anything else that seemed to be of much use. Some of my employees, like Matty and Danielle, for instance, are holdovers from my grandmother's day. The most recent hire was Jason, the nighttime bartender, but he always struck me as a straight shooter. Thinking about them one by one, I couldn't focus on a single one that I would finger as the guilty party.

By the time Harold and I finished, it was six o'clock in the morning and I could hear the sounds of people downstairs coming on duty and getting ready to open for breakfast. I was bushed. Harold, on the other hand, was raring to go. It turned out his usual bedtime was five o'clock in the afternoon. So being up and going to work at two o'clock in the morning wasn't exactly a hardship for him. But six A.M. was several hours past his usual breakfast time. I went downstairs and had Maxine cook up a plate of bacon and eggs. "Make that a double order of bacon," Harold told me. "Hells bells, I'm ninety four years old. If bacon's gonna kill me, bring it on, the crisper the better."

I did exactly that—brought him his double order of crisp bacon. In the process, I told my crew downstairs that I was taking the day off. Then, after delivering Harold's breakfast and a fresh pot of coffee, I hit the hay. And slept. A bare three hours later, when Harold Meeks shook me awake, he was totally transformed. Yes, he was still pounding the floor with his walker, but he was dressed to the nines—suit, starched white shirt, and properly tied bow tie. The moccasins had been replaced by a pair of highly polished Johnston & Murphy loafers. His mane of flyaway white hair had been tamed with a layer of gel. He seemed to have shed twenty years overnight and have had a voice transplant.

"Showtime," he announced. "Up and at 'em. I just had a call from a friend of mine who volunteers at the local cop shop. He tells me the search warrant crew is on their way. That's what held everything up— obtaining the warrant. First the cops from Las Vegas had to negotiate a peace treaty with Peoria PD and let them find a warrant-friendly judge, which must not have been very easy bright and early on a Saturday morning. So get a move on. They're probably going to take you into custody, so don't take along anything you don't want stuck in a property locker at the lockup. And remember, I talk, you listen. Do not say a word. Not one. Not to anyone. Not here, not in the patrol car, and not in that jail. Got it?"

I nodded. "What if they try to take your notes?"

He grinned a yellow-toothed grin. "Can't touch 'em," he said. "Attorney/client privilege and all that. Besides, they couldn't read my notes if they tried. It's my own brand of shorthand. I've only had one secretary who could translate it. When Gloria Gray died of a heart attack thirty years ago, that's when I threw in the towel and stopped practicing law. I was too damned lazy to go to the trouble of training someone else."

By then I could hear people storming up the wooden stairway. I sleep in my underwear. Taking my attorney's good advice to heart, I slipped into a set of sweats and a pair of tennies. Then after a quick pit stop, I went to face my doom.

When I came into the hallway, Harold was stationed at the top of the steps, effectively barring any entry. "I'm Mr. Dixon's attorney of record," he told the people waiting outside. He spoke in the stentorian voice that had replaced his earlier squeak, and it was enough to make believers of the new arrivals as he bellowed his instructions. "There is no need for drawn weapons. My client is fully prepared to surrender peacefully as long as you have both a properly drawn arrest warrant as well as a search warrant. Mr. Dixon, by the way, has invoked his right to an attorney. That means you will not be allowed to speak to him outside my presence."

There was a brief pause while documents were exchanged. Harold took his own sweet time examining them.

"Very well," he said at last. "You're welcome to search Mr. Dixon's residence, but everyone involved in the search is required to wear gloves while doing so, lest evidence that might serve to exonerate him be disturbed in any fashion. In addition, anything you take away from here must be treated as evidence. I expect all items to be placed in properly bagged and tagged evidence containers. I'm particularly concerned that any files taken from Mr. Dixon's office be examined for prints. If there is even the slightest indication that the chain of evidence hasn't been properly maintained, there will be hell to pay. Is that understood?"

The response must have been in the affirmative. Having said his piece, Harold pulled his diminutive figure out of the way, and a crowd of cops rushed inside. At the head of the pack were two uniformed Peoria officers, guys who had been in and out of the Roundhouse often enough that I knew them by name without having to peer at their badges. Behind them were two plain-clothes Peoria PD guys—one I knew and one I didn't. Bringing up the rear were my old pals, Detectives Jamison and Shandrow.

"Frederick Dixon," the first cop said. "We're placing you under arrest for the homicide of Katherine Melcher. You have the right to remain silent..."

While my rights were being read, the second officer went around behind me to fasten the cuffs. "Sorry about this, Butch," he murmured in my ear as he pulled my arms together. "Those guys from Vegas are a pair of pricks."

We certainly agreed on that score, but I took Harold's advice and said nothing. This was serious. Someone was trying to send me up, and my part of the bargain was to keep my mouth shut.

"They'll be taking you to booking, Butch," Harold counseled as we went past. "Again, mum's the word. Trust me. It's gonna be fine."

I nodded, and the two uniformed officers led me down the stairs. The alcove below was crowded with people I knew, workers and customers both. Matty stood in the foreground. With her hands on both hips, she looked like she was ready to take on the cops single-handed.

"It's okay, Matty," I assured her. "This won't take long. You're second in command. It's your job to keep things running until I get back."

"But—" she began.

"Not buts," I said. "Just do it."

"Okay," she said reluctantly. "Will do."

I'd never been booked into anything before. It was a humiliating process. Before long I was printed and changed into my orange jumpsuit. Then they wrapped me in a sort of gray blanket for my mug shot. The whole time, I tried to keep Harold's reassuring words in mind, but that didn't work too well, especially when they put me in a holding cell and locked the doors. The rattle of those jailhouse doors clanging shut and closing me inside sent chills down my spine. And that's when it hit me. Faith had taken everything from me once, and now, even stone cold dead, she was doing it again.

I sank down on the narrow bench that probably served as a cot overnight. I leaned back against the gray-green cinder-block wall, closed my eyes, and gave in to what was nothing less than a fit of total despair.

They had taken my watch, which I had forgotten to remove, so there was no way to tell how much time passed. An hour? Two? Who knows? I was glad I'd made a restroom stop before all this happened. There was a stainless steel toilet bolted to the floor of the cell, but I resisted the urge to use it. Using it would have made the whole thing more real somehow, and this was already far too real to begin with.

At last a jailer came by—another of the Roundhouse's occasional customers— and opened the door. "Right this way, Mr. Dixon," he said respectfully. "We're going to an interview room just down the hall."

Said interview room would have been crowded with three people in it. With six— the two Peoria detectives, the two guys from Vegas, Harold, and finally me—it was a zoo. Harold seemed to have been transformed into a pint-sized tower of strength, and the local cops deferred to him in a way that made the out-of-towners wince. They, on the other hand, couldn't have been more dismissive.

I found out much later that while all this was happening, on the far side of Peoria a new library building was then under construction, one scheduled to be called the H.M. Meeks Branch. In the hours I'd been cooling my heels in the holding cell, someone inside city government had evidently put the local cops in the know.

"All right, gentlemen," Harold said, as if calling a business meeting to order. "Perhaps you'd like to tell us what this is all about."

I now know that's an old interrogation trick. You only ask questions to which you already know the answers, and Harold knew exactly what this was about. He already had it down in black and white... well, yellow and blue, if you want the exact truth.

Once again the story I'd been forced to tell over and over the previous day came back to me through the mouths of strangers, hinted at more than specified by the questions they asked, which on the advice of my attorney I mostly didn't answer. I could see that was part of Harold's game. He let me answer some of their inquiries—the innocuous ones—here and there, enough to keep the cops interested and enough to keep them asking more questions. All the while, I could tell by the notes Harold made, in that peculiarly indecipherable script of his, that he was gradually gleaning far more about their case than they realized.

An hour or so into the interview, Harold called a halt. Claiming he had a bad prostate, he told them he needed to use the john and suggested that I most likely needed to relieve myself as well. It was more than a need right then. It was straight out desperation, but the Peoria cops assented and allowed as how I'd be able to go to the restroom as long as a deputy accompanied me in and out. The cop stayed back by the door, while Harold and I did our duty at the urinals.

"You're doing great," he told me in a whisper covered by somebody else flushing a toilet in one of the stalls. "Not to worry."

That was far easier said than done. Back in the interview room, a tray of sandwiches had suddenly appeared, ordered in by Harold. Subway sandwiches have never been my first choice for lunchtime cuisine, but hunger is the best sauce, and I was starved. With all the people marching through my life, it had been more than twenty-four hours since I'd last eaten. Although one of the Peoria guys dissected my twelve-inch tuna/pepper-jack sub before allowing me to eat it, he found no contraband inside, and no escape-enabling metal file, either.

The interview went on for another hour or so after lunch. It ended with Harold laying into Detectives Jamison and Shandrow and letting them know that he would be opposing any efforts made to extradite me to the state of Nevada. After that another jailer led me back to the holding cell area.

The Peoria Police Department has two

holding cells. Before I went to the inter-view, the cell across from mine had been occupied by a pair of drunks peacefully sleeping it off, both of them snoring loud enough to wake the dead. When I returned, the drunks were gone. Now the cells held two new arrivals, a pair of scrawny old guys —both of them north of eighty and both wearing outlandish golf attire. Each was dressed in extremely loud plaid pants with a matching shirt. One was in orange, the other in brilliant chartreuse. They stood at the bars of the cells like a pair of colorful old parrots, yelling at each other across the polished concrete corridor that separated them.

"You're a lowdown cheat," one of them called. "You've always been a lowdown cheat. Why I ever agreed to play another round of golf with you, I'll never know. I saw you move that ball out of the rough, plain as day. The Florsheim club."

"The hell you say," the other replied. "I never kicked a ball in my life. And even if I did, that's no reason for you to come after me with a frigging golf cart. You could have killed me."

"I wish I had. They could have buried you there right on the edge of the fairway under that mesquite tree. It would have served you right. And why the hell did you have to go and crack the windshield of the golf cart with your seven iron?"

"To get you to stop, you stupid old fart!"

"When they come after me to pay for the damages, I'm coming after you, and if you know what's good for you, you'll pay up or else."

Their fight, one that had most likely started on a golf course hours earlier, was still in full swing. No wonder the jailers had placed them in separate cells. From what had been said, I suspected they would soon face charges of assaults with a deadly weapon—a golf cart and a seven-iron, respectively. Any other time that might have been screamingly funny. Not right then.

"Settle down, boys," the jailer cautioned. "You both need to cool off. I understand your attorney should be here soon. He's evidently been delayed."

The jailer opened the door that led into

the cell occupied by Mr. Green Pants. The guard ushered me inside and then slammed the door shut behind me. There was that awful, ominous clang again. The metallic noise the locking door made rattled my nerves and chilled my soul. Leaving the two old guys to continue their shouting match, I went over to the stainless steel bench and sank down on it. I had barely closed my eyes when the shouting ceased suddenly as someone walked past me and joined me on the bench.

"You two take your golf way too seriously," I said without opening my eyes. "It's dumb to land in jail over a stupid golf game."

"Well," he said, "look who's talking?"

That actually made me laugh. He was right, of course. Since I was in jail, too, I didn't have much room to point fingers.

"My name's Roger," he said. "And don't worry about Matt and me. Harold will have us out of here in jig time."

"Harold?" I asked. "You mean Harold Meeks?"

"That's the one. He's an old pal of ours. He doesn't play anymore because of his walker, but he usually rides along, drives one of the carts, and helps keep score. He called us when we were about to tee off on the third hole—the par five—after the cops took you away. He asked if I thought Matt and me could figure out a way to get ourselves locked up for the day so we could have a private chat. He said to wait for about an hour, so we staged the whole thing on the par three on the back nine. How'd we do?"

I remembered what Harold had said about not talking to anyone in the slammer. Had the Peoria detectives gone so far as to hire a couple of retirees as jailhouse snitches? That seemed unlikely, but still...

"Great," I allowed. "But why would Harold do something like that, and why would you two go along with it?"

"Like I said, we've all been friends for a long time, and he asked us to do it as a favor. Said he forgot to ask you a question before they took you away, and he didn't want to ask it when any of the cops might be listening in."

"I thought conversations between

attorneys and clients were supposed to be private."

"Sometimes what's supposed to be doesn't match up with what is," Roger replied somberly.

"What's the question?"

"Do you have a cleaning lady?"

I could see that in focusing on the employees of the restaurant, I had forgotten the one person who had total access to my home once a week, usually when I was downstairs working. Marina would show up early in the day, wrestling her vacuum cleaner and cleaning supplies up the stairs. When she finished, my apartment would be spotless. She would pick up the hundred dollar bill I usually left for her on the dining room table and disappear, sometimes without my having even laid eyes on her. But the idea that Marina would be spying on me or going through my files? That was ridiculous. For one thing, she barely speaks English.

"Yes," I answered. "Yes, I do."

"What's her name?"

"Marina Ochoa."

"Where does she live?"

"In Glendale somewhere."

"You don't have her address?"

"No, I don't. I pay her in cash. There's never been any paperwork."

"No references, no nothing?" my interrogator asked.

"Look," I said, "my other cleaning lady quit several months ago. I was getting ready to place an ad for another one when Marina showed up asking for a job cleaning the bar and the restaurant. She spoke so little English that I had to have one of the dishwashers interpret for us. I explained that I have a commercial company that comes in to do the heavy cleaning in both the bar and the restaurant.

"When I told her that, she looked absolutely crushed and burst into tears— she was that desperate to find a job. Turns out she's a single mom supporting two little kids, ages five and three. I couldn't help but feel sorry for her, and with her right there, ready and willing to work, I was happy to dodge the agony of having to place an ad and interview people. I asked her if she'd consider cleaning my apartment and hired her on the spot. She's been cleaning my place ever since and doing a great job of it."

"Tears," Roger muttered. "They'll sucker a poor guy every single time. How long has she worked for you?"

"Three months now, maybe. She started toward the end of August."

"What days?"

"Sometimes on Fridays, sometimes on Thursdays, depending on her kids' schedules. It doesn't matter to me which day as long as she comes once a week. And like I said, she leaves the place spotless."

"Who lets her in and out?"

That's when I realized Roger wasn't just an old duffer—he was a smart old duffer, too, just like his pal Harold.

"You were a cop, weren't you?" I said.

He grinned. "Used to be," he said, "homicide, but that was a long time ago. Harold and me used to be on opposite sides of the fence. He won more times than I thought he should have. I always suspected that he cheated, and now I know that for sure. These days, though, when someone needs a hand, we usually work together."

"To help me?"

"Hell, I barely know who you are, you little whippersnapper. To help Tim, of course. Us old law enforcement types have to stick together—cops, attorneys, judges —you name it. The older you get, the less those old divisions matter. When somebody runs up the flag, we're all there, Johnny-on-the-spot. So stop stalling and answer the question. Who lets your undocumented alien cleaning lady in and out of your apartment?"

"She parks out behind the restaurant, comes in through the kitchen, and goes up the stairs."

"Is the upstairs door locked or unlocked?"

"Usually it's unlocked. Look," I added, sounding exasperated, "I'm right there the whole time."

Roger replied by asking yet another question. "Does Marina have a cell phone?"

"Probably, but I don't have the number. No point in my calling her. I don't speak

Spanish."

"Which day did she come do the cleaning for the past several weeks?"

"She was there on Thursday this past week. I'm not sure about the others."

"You got surveillance cameras?"

"You bet. Top of the line. They cover the front door, the back door, and both parking lots. There are also cameras over the bar and over the cash register in the dining room."

"How long do you keep the files?"

"They go to my security company. As far as I know, they keep them indefinitely. After all, they're just computer files. It's not like the old days when there were miles of physical tapes taking up space."

"Which security company?"

I gave him the name. If I'd had either my phone or my computer with my address book in it, I could have given him the phone number and the account number. Sitting in a jail cell, I didn't have access to either one.

A new jailer came down the hallway. "All right, Mr. Holmes and Mr. Palmer. Someone has posted your bail. Can the two of you leave together, or do I need to take you out separately?"

"Don't bother," Roger said. "We'll be fine, won't we, Matt? We've cooled our heels long enough to bury the hatchet."

A pretend hatchet, I thought, as the two old codgers were led away to report their findings to their pal and mine, Harold Meeks. Once they left, I fell asleep—on the metal bench, with no pillow necessary. They woke me up at what the clock in an office outside the cell block said was three and led me into a courtroom in the building across the way to be arraigned. I pleaded innocent, of course, and then came the bail hearing.

Even though I could see Harold was tiring, he stood up, leaning on his walker, and made a good case for my being allowed out on bail. He told them I was an upstanding citizen with close ties to the community. He insisted that since my vehicle had been hauled away to the impound lot by the CSI investigators and since my passport had been confiscated as well, I was in no danger of fleeing the area to avoid prosecution. The upshot was, I was allowed to post a $500,000 bond, courtesy of Tim O'Malley. After that, they let me change clothes and gave me back my goods.

When it came time to leave the building, I walked out expecting to have to call for a cab. (Where's a decent pay phone when you need one?) Instead, I found a spit-and-polished venerable old Lincoln Town Car complete with a uniformed driver waiting out front. The driver got out of the vehicle and hurried to meet me.

"Mr. Dixon?"

I nodded.

"This way, please."

When he opened the back door for me, I slid onto the backseat and found Harold sitting slumped next to the far window. Out of sight of the detectives and the judge, he seemed to have shrunk. When he glanced at his watch, I followed suit and looked at mine, too. It was four-fifteen.

"Way past my bedtime," he announced. "Let's get me back to your place. I need my beauty sleep."

In other words, I still had an overnight guest.

"By the way," he added, "when we get back to the Roundhouse, your people are going to be full of questions. You can't afford to talk to them anymore than you can afford to talk to the cops. I've got operatives looking into the Marina Ochoa situation, but we can't risk taking any of your other employees off the list of suspects just yet. If they ask, tell them you've been advised not to discuss it."

"Yes, sir," I said. "Will do."

In less than twenty-four hours of dealing with Harold Meeks, he had made a believer of me, right along with that search warrant crew he had held at bay on the stairway outside my apartment.

It turns out he was right to have warned me to keep quiet. The people at the Roundhouse greeted us as though we were the second coming with cheers, hugs, handshakes, and tears all around. I helped Harold up the stairs and into the guest room. When I turned around, expecting to go back down to fetch his walker, I discovered Matty had beaten me to the punch and brought it upstairs.

"It was on the noon news," she said. "They're saying you murdered your ex-wife. I didn't even know you had an ex-wife."

"That's because it's not something I like to discuss. And my attorney—Harold here," I said, gesturing over my shoulder toward the guest room, "says I'm not to talk about it now with anyone."

"Mum's the word, then," she said, giving me a second fierce hug. "All I can say about Mr. Meeks is bless his heart."

She left then. I went into the bedroom and showered. I needed to scrub the feel of that holding cell off my skin and out of my soul. No need to rub it out of my hair.

When I came back out to the living room, Charles Rickover had let himself in and made himself at home on the chintz sofa. He had somehow managed to talk his way around Matty and come upstairs with a cup of freshly brewed coffee in hand. Maybe I did need to keep my apartment door locked.

"What are you doing here?" I asked. "I

thought you were going to Vegas."

"Did," he replied. "Flew there and back, chop-chop. You ever hear of the Wright brothers?"

"So what's up?"

"Katherine Melcher's husband—her most recent husband—is in the clear, at least as far as doing the deed himself. He was out of the country on business. I've got airline records, car rental receipts, and passport control stamps coming and going. He could have hired someone to do it, I suppose, but as far as I can tell, Katherine had landed herself a fat cat and was determined to hang onto this one. According to him, after ditching the drugs, she became really serious about working her program. That's when she changed her name from Faith to Katherine—when the two of them married. It was part of a joint effort on their part to put her past in the past. By the way, my reading on Melcher is that he really is heartbroken."

"The woman would have dumped him sooner or later, and cleaned him out, too, in the process," I said. "Knowing Faith the way I do, up close and personal, I suspect her husband probably just dodged a bullet."

"Speaking of husbands," Charles said. "I also checked on your old pal Rick Austin."

"What about him? Where's he?"

"Deceased. Katherine—she was still Faith back then—married him shortly after she left you. That was followed by a time when they both did a serious amount of coke. She ended up in rehab, cleaned up her act, and left him high and dry. Austin blew his brains out after she left."

Karma's a bitch. Much as I thought Rick deserved everything he got, I couldn't help having a moment of sympathy for the guy. After all, there but for the love of Grandma Hudson would go I.

"By the way," Charles said, "I managed to lay hands on the vic's telephone records."

"How did you do that?"

"Don't ask, don't tell. Harold can subpoena them later if he needs to, but it's always better to know what they're going to say before you do that. I've got the dates and times for all the calls that were placed from the pay phone downstairs. I've also got a record of the call to her cell phone that was placed from the swimming pool pay phone at the Talisman at 2:05 A.M.

"Katherine took the call. It lasted for over three minutes. Twenty minutes later she is seen on surveillance tapes leaving her building. That's the last record I've been able to find of her, although I've got someone in Vegas looking at the surveillance tapes of all the hotels along the Strip. Talk about looking for a needle in the haystack, but we have a little better idea of what we're looking for now. It'll turn up. As for the Talisman? What a dog of a hotel! They may have surveillance cameras hanging on ceilings all over the place, but that's just for show. The problem is, not one of them works."

"In other words, the surveillance tape that might have caught the killer and exonerated me doesn't exist?"

Charles nodded. "That's the way it looks. So, are you ready to take a ride?"

I wasn't so sure. My most recent experience with being given a ride hadn't turned out very well.

"Where to?"

"I want to show you something."

"Can't you just tell me?"

"Showing's better than telling. Come on."

Not particularly happy about it, I headed for the stairs. Out in the parking lot I was surprised to discover that Charles's ride was a fire-engine-red Corvette. Not brand new, but new enough to make a statement. The man may have hit bottom years earlier, when Tim O'Malley's daughter had walked out on him for another woman, but that had most likely been the beginning of a long upward path for which Pop O'Malley was most likely largely responsible. I wondered what Tim would think if I called him by that handle, too. Somehow I suspected that he wouldn't mind.

As Charles and I headed down Highway 60 and turned onto the 101, I was dying to ask where we were going, but I stifled. Both highways were clotted with late afternoon traffic. Inching along in the HOV lane, we drove across the near north end of the city—not the real north end because the city has now expanded northward far beyond where those traditional boundaries used to lay. On the far side of Scottsdale and still on the 101, we turned south, exiting toward downtown Scottsdale on East Chaparral, just north of Camelback. Charles turned left onto Scottsdale Road, drove past Goldwater, and pulled into a parking garage at Fashion Square. Instead of parking in a space on one of the lower levels, he drove all the way up to the roof and pulled into a spot at the far edge of the lot, looking north.

"What do you see?" he asked.

I looked at the mid-rise across the street. It obviously housed high-end condos. The spacious balconies were filled with plants in wildly colorful pots and furnished with equally high-end deck chairs and tables. The grounds around the base of the building were meticulously landscaped with towering palms, a carpet of lush green grass, and flower beds thick with recently planted petunias. Clearly this was a building where the residents weren't the least bit concerned about the high cost of water in the Valley of the Sun.

"It's a building," I said grumpily, annoyed at being forced to play a guessing game. "Condos for the rich and famous."

"Rich and infamous maybe," Charles replied with a sly grin. "Who do you suppose lives here?"

"I have no idea."

"Your cleaning lady," he said. "Marina Ochoa. That's not the name she goes by here. Folks in the condo complex know her as Maria Fuentes, but believe me, this is where the woman known to you as Marina Ochoa lives. By the way, she doesn't have any kids. None at all."

I'm sure my jaw dropped. "You're kidding."

"Wish I was," Charles answered. "I got the license of her work car from the surveillance tapes at your security agency. That's an old Buick, and she doesn't park it here. She's got a sweet little SLK that she drives back and forth between Scottsdale and Peoria. The Buick is what she drives when she comes to see you. She keeps it parked, complete with her vacuum cleaner and tray of cleaning supplies stowed in the trunk, in a garage over in Peoria just a few blocks from the Roundhouse."

"I don't understand," I said. "How could she possibly afford to live here?"

"I'm sure her boyfriend pays the freight. Does the name Jeffrey Jones sound familiar?"

My jaw dropped again. Or maybe still. "She's hooked up with the hotel developer, the one who's trying to buy me out?"

"That's right. One and the same. I believe that's what Jones and Ochoa have been after this whole time—they've been trying to get the goods on you for months now. Jones must have finally realized that he wouldn't be able to convince you to sell at what he wanted to pay, so he sent Marina to you along with her hard luck story in order to gain access to your private life. One or the other of them came up with the brilliant idea that if you were in jail facing homicide charges with the possibility of a long prison sentence, you might be more inclined to be reasonable."

"But I thought..."

"I know what you thought," Charles said. "You believed Marina's sob story about being an illegal immigrant and about her working her poor little fingers to the bone in order to support her poor fatherless children. Guess again. Her parents immigrated from Mexico long before she was born. She's a U.S. citizen with an honors degree in history and English from ASU. She went on to get an MBA from Thunderbird over in Glendale. That's where she and Jeffrey hooked up. He divorced his first wife—his starter wife—shortly thereafter."

"But she worked for me for months," I objected.

"True," Charles agreed, "and they must have been looking to make a huge score, considering she was willing to do that much hard physical labor just to have unlimited access to your private life. Believe me, the Maria Fuentes who lives here has a cleaning lady of her own. The really good news for us is that before she and Jeffrey became a couple, Maria spent several years working in the securities field. That means her fingerprints are on file. I'm hoping the criminalists dusting your file folders for prints will not only find hers, but they'll find them where we need them."

"Finding her prints won't mean anything," I objected. "She cleans my apartment. Her fingerprints are bound to be there."

"In your apartment maybe, but not on the file folders containing your private documents. I can't imagine you expected her to dust the file with your divorce decree in it on a regular basis."

"But what if she wore gloves?" I objected, thinking about the gloves Charles put on his hands before touching my computer keyboard.

"Crooks like these are arrogant," Charles said. "It won't ever have occurred to them that we're this smart. She's probably been snooping through your computer the whole time she's been working for you, looking for something they could use to bring you to heel. Then two things happened. First they found out that Faith Dixon had turned into Katherine Melcher who was living in Las Vegas. Then you decided to go to Vegas for that writing convention. What's it called again?"

"Bouchercon."

"Yes, Bouchercon. At that point they must have thought they hit the jackpot because it all seemed to fall into place. At some point along the way your sweet little Marina made a copy of your car keys—the trunk key anyway. I checked the tapes. The week of October fifteenth, the week Katy Melcher died, Marina cleaned your apartment on Thursday rather than Friday. I'm pretty sure she and Jeffrey drove to Vegas together the next day to scope out the situation. I'm sure they used the old Twelfth Step ruse to lure Katy out of the house at that hour of the morning. According to Katy's widower, she took late night calls from addicts trying to kick their drug and alcohol habits."

That was way more than I could get my head around. The idea of Faith or Katy or whoever she was going out on a late night mission of mercy and being murdered for it seemed utterly unlikely.

"What about the threatening phone calls?" I asked.

"They came on days when Marina Ochoa would have been working for you. They must have figured that would make your situation a slam dunk. Threatening calls come from the victim's ex before she's murdered? What could be better?"

"What about the e-mail from Deeny?" I asked.

"That's apparently legit," Charles said. "Because of the phone calls, Katy Melcher really was worried that you were coming after her."

"In other words, Marina and Jeffrey expected that the local cops would focus on me to the exclusion of anyone else."

"Exactly," Charles Rickover agreed. "It might have gone just that way had it not been for Pop. Without him, you would have been a goner. Had you decided to forgo a public defender in favor of hiring your own defense attorney, you would have been forced to sell the Roundhouse to the first available buyer just to cover legal fees. You'd be amazed to know how much a top flight homicide defense team costs these days."

Evening was settling in. Across the street, lights switched on in various units as people came home from work or whatever it was they did during the day.

"So what happens now?"

"The two cops from Las Vegas..." he paused.

"Detectives Jamison and Shandrow," I supplied.

"They may be a bit slow on the uptake, but they're not stupid. Bright and early tomorrow morning, I expect Harold will point them in the right direction. It may take a few weeks to straighten all this up, but sooner or later your name will be cleared, as though nothing ever happened, and Jeffrey and Maria Fuentes will be up in Vegas facing first degree murder charges— both murder and conspiracy to commit. They're the ones who are goners now."

Rickover reached down, turned the ignition, and the Corvette rumbled to life.

"Where to?" he asked. "Back home?"

"If you don't mind, I'd like to stop off in

Sun City on the way. I need to see Tim O'Malley and tell him thank-you."

"Great," Charles said. "I was hoping you'd say that."

When Tim let us into his house that night, I shook his hand and said, "Thank you, Pop. It was the first time I ever called him that—the first but not the last.

"How on earth did you find all those guys?" I asked. "Harold, Roger, Matt, and even old Charlie here."

Charles Rickover and I had been through enough together that I thought my calling him Charlie was...well...long overdue.

Tim and Charlie both grinned. "You've heard of how cops used to be called the Thin Blue Line?" Tim asked.

I nodded.

"Our little group calls itself the Old Blue Line," Tim said. "Some of us are thinner than we ought to be and others are wider, but when one or the other of us has a problem and runs up the flag, we all come on the double."

"Thank you," I said again. "More than you know."

Pop served us iced tea and apologized that he'd already eaten his TV dinner and didn't have any food to offer. I said I knew a place where we could find some grub if we needed it.

Later, as we were leaving, Pop gripped my hand with both of his. "Aggie would be so happy about this," he said, "so very happy."

And I knew it to be true. Grandma Agatha Hudson would have been pleased as punch.

I took Charlie back to the Roundhouse and treated both of us to the biggest and best steaks we had in the kitchen. When I came upstairs, much later, there was no sound from the guest room and no sign of a light under the door, either. I tiptoed past, hoping not to disturb Harold Meeks. He had worked his tail off for me that day, and he deserved a good night's sleep.

It turns out, so did I. I crawled into bed and slept like a baby. It was ungodly early when I woke up the next morning. Staring at the clock, I saw it was 5:30 A.M. What had awakened me was the unaccustomed sound of people talking away in my apartment. Out in the main room I discovered Harold Meeks was up, dressed in his preferred courtroom attire, and chatting up an enthralled Matty, who had just brought his breakfast up from the kitchen —two fried eggs and a double helping of bacon along with his own pot of freshly brewed coffee.

"It's about time you showed up," Harold growled at me. "We've got places to go and things to do."

"I'll need to see if I can rent a car," I said. "I didn't have time to do that yesterday."

He shook his head as though dealing with a recalcitrant toddler. "I've got a driver and a limo," he said. "We'll take that. And when we leave here, I'd like you to bring along my two suitcases. By later this afternoon I think we'll have this little difficulty well in hand and I'll be able to go back home."

The next few days passed in a blur. Just as Charlie Rickover had predicted, once Harold pointed Jamison and Shandrow in the right direction, they ran with it. The woman named Marina Ochoa never came back to clean my apartment. She and Jeffrey Jones were arrested the following Wednesday. They fought extradition, but it didn't work, despite the fact that they had hired a high profile defense guy from California. It wasn't a surprise that Jeffrey suddenly had to liquidate his real estate holdings in order to pony up attorney's fees.

Life seemed to get back to normal at the Roundhouse Bar and Grill. I hired a new cleaning lady—the sister-in-law of one of my dishwashers. (No, Helena isn't an illegal, and her English is just fine, thank you very much.)

After jumping through all kinds of hoops, I finally got my Honda sedan back, and wished I hadn't. The bloody bat had been found in the trunk, almost in plain sight, but the CSIs had torn the whole interior of the car to pieces looking for trace evidence. The car was already old before that happened. When the insurance adjustor looked at it, he shook his head, said it was totaled, and gave me a check that was just enough to buy myself a slightly used Honda Gold Wing.

Shortly after that, a new batch of police officer recruits turned up at the police academy next door. One day a couple of weeks later my life changed forever when a little red-haired ball of fire named Joanna Brady—the newly minted Sheriff of Cochise County—marched into the Roundhouse, stepped up to my bar, and ordered herself a Diet Coke.

While attending the academy, she was also in the process of looking out for some poor guy from Douglas, a guy name Jorge, who was about to be given the shaft.

As soon as I met her, I was done for. She may have been a lot slower to come around, but as far as I was concerned, it was love at first sight. The fact that she went out on a limb to bail Jorge out of a pot of hot water didn't hurt things, either, at least not for me. Having recently been bailed out of my own pot of hot water, that was one thing about her that I really appreciated.

But what is it they say about once burned, twice shy? I had fallen head over heels once before, and I was determined that if Joanna was the one for me, I was going to take things slow and easy. I could see that she liked me—at least I thought she did— but that was about as far as things went before she finished up her academy training and went back home to Bisbee.

That's when my life took another un- expected turn. In the middle of December a guy named Clark Ashton showed up at the Roundhouse with an offer to buy me out. He had bought up all of Jeffrey Jones's properties as well as his permits and plans, and he was eager to get his new hotel building under way as soon as possible. We dickered back and forth for a time, but not that much, not that hard, and not that long, because Ashton wanted to buy, and by then I wanted to sell.

Bisbee's a little over two hundred miles to the southeast from Peoria. When you're head over heels in love, two hundred miles is entirely too much distance.

It took time for me to convince Joanna

Brady that I was the new man in her life. She wasn't an easy sell. And I didn't tell her about someone trying to frame me for murder until much later in our relationship because I didn't want to spook her. It wasn't, in fact, until after Charlie called to let me know that Pop O'Malley had passed away in his sleep that I finally got up my nerve and told her the whole story once and for all.

"Tim O'Malley and his friends did all that?" she marveled once I had finished.

I nodded.

"And now I can't even meet the man long enough tell him thank-you?"

"No, I'm afraid you can't," I said, shaking my head. "Sorry."

"I'm sorry, too," she told me, wiping a tear from her eye. "He and your Grandma Hudson must have been quite a pair."

Thinking of the two of them together made me smile. "You're right," I said. "They certainly were."

ABOUT THE AUTHOR

J. A. JANCE is the **New York Times** bestselling author of the J. P. Beaumont series, the Joanna Brady series, the Ali Reynolds series, and four interrelated thrillers about the Walker family, as well as a volume of poetry. Born in South Dakota and brought up in Bisbee, Arizona, Jance lives with her husband in Seattle, Washington, and Tucson, Arizona.

Information Services Today

Information Services Today

AN INTRODUCTION

EDITED BY

Sandra Hirsh

ROWMAN & LITTLEFIELD
Lanham • Boulder • New York • London

Published by Rowman & Littlefield
A wholly owned subsidary of The Rowman & Littlefield Publishing Group, Inc.
4501 Forbes Boulevard, Suite 200, Lanham, Maryland 20706
www.rowman.com

Unit A, Whitacre Mews, 26-34 Stannary Street, London SE11 4AB

British Library Cataloguing in Publication Information Available

Library of Congress Cataloging-in-Publication Data
Information services today : an introduction / edited by Sandra Hirsh.
      pages cm
   Includes bibliographical references and index.
   ISBN 978-1-4422-3957-9 (cloth : alk. paper) — ISBN 978-1-4422-3958-6 (pbk. : alk. paper) —
ISBN 978-1-4422-3959-3 (ebook)
   1. Libraries—Aims and objectives.   2. Library administration.   3. Public services (Libraries)
4. Library users.   5. Libraries—Information technology.   6. Libraries and electronic publishing.
7. Library science—Vocational guidance.   8. Librarians—Effect of technological innovations on.
9. Information services.   10. Information resources.   I. Hirsh, Sandra, 1965–
   Z678.I515 2015
   027—dc23   2014044550

∞™ The paper used in this publication meets the minimum requirements of American National Standard for Information Sciences—Permanence of Paper for Printed Library Materials, ANSI/NISO Z39.48-1992.

Printed in the United States of America

For
My husband Jay and daughters Hayley and Leah
for their inspiration and support
and
Gail Schlachter
my role model and mom

Contents

Contents   **ix**

Editorial Advisory Board

List of Figures and Tables

Figures

Tables

List of Appendixes

List of Abbreviations

AACU	American Association of Colleges and Universities
AASL	American Association of School Librarians
ACRL	Association of College and Research Libraries
ACRL-IS	Association of College and Research Libraries Instruction Section
ADA	American Disabilities Act
ADA	Archive of Digital Art
ADDIE	Analysis Design Development Implementation Evaluation
AECT	Association for Educational Communications and Technology
AIC	American Institute for Conservation
AIIP	Association of Independent Information Professionals
AILA	American Indian Library Association
ALA	American Library Association
ALSC	Association for Library Service to Children
ANSI	American National Standards Institute (ANSI)
APALA	Asian-Pacific American Librarians Association
APEC	Asia-Pacific Economic Cooperation
API	application programming interface
ARL	Association of Research Libraries
ARMA	Association of Records Managers and Administrators
ASCLA	Association of Specialized and Cooperative Library Agencies
ASLIB	Association for Information Management
ASP	application service providers
ASRS	automated storage and retrieval system
AV	audiovisual
BBDO	Batten, Barton, Durstine & Osborn worldwide advertising agency network
BCALA	Black Caucus of the American Library Association
CALA	Chinese American Librarians Association
CC	Creative Commons
CC BY	Creative Commons Attribution Only
CCSDS	Consultative Committee for Space Data Systems
CI	competitive (or competitor) intelligence
CLR	Council on Library Resources
CMI	copyright management information
COLA	cost of living adjustment
COPPA	Children's Online Privacy Protection Act
COSLA	Chief Officers of State Library Agencies
COUNTER	counting online usage of networked electronic resource
CTIA	Cellular Telecommunications Industry Association—Wireless Association

DAM	digital asset management
DCC	Digital Curation Centre
DMCA	Digital Millennium Copyright Act
DPLA	Digital Public Library of America
DPN	Digital Preservation Network
DPOE	digital preservation outreach and education
DRM	digital rights management
ELA	English language arts
ERIAL	Ethnographic Research in Illinois Academic Libraries
FACT Act	Fair and Accurate Credit Transactions Act
FCC	Federal Communications Commission
FCRA	Fair Credit Reporting Act
FERPA	Family Educational Rights and Privacy Act
FIPPs	Fair Information Practice Principles
FISA	Foreign Intelligence Surveillance Act
FISMA	Federal Information Security Management Act
FOIA	Freedom of Information Act
FTC	Federal Trade Commission
FTE	full-time enrollment
GIS	geographic information systems
GKPF	Global Knowledge Partnership Foundation
GLBT	gay, lesbian, bisexual, and transgender
GWLA	Greater Western Library Alliance
HIPAA	Health Insurance Portability and Accountability Act
HR	human resources
IADIS	International Association for Development of the Information Society
ICT	information and communication technologies
IFLA	International Federation of Library Associations and Institutions
ILL	interlibrary loan
ILN	International Librarians Network
ILS	integrated library system
IMLS	Institute of Museum and Library Services
INALJ	Originally "I Need a Library Job." Now only known as INALJ.
IP	intellectual property
IPTF	(U.S. Department of Commerce's) Internet Policy Task Force
IR	institutional repository
ISIS	International Society for Information Studies (ISIS)
ISO	International Standards Organization
ISTE	International Society for Technology in Education
ITU	International Telecommunication Union
LGBT	lesbian, gay, bisexual, and transgender
LIRT	Library Instruction Roundtable
LIS	library and information science
LLAMA	Library Leadership and Management Association
LMS	learning management system

LOCKSS	lots of copies keep stuff safe
LOEX	library orientation exchange
LSA	Library Services Act
LSCA	Library Services and Construction Act
LSTA	Library Services and Technology Act
MARC	machine-readable cataloging
MIS	master of information science
MLIS	master of library and information science
MODS	metadata object description schema
MOOC	massive open online course
NDIIPP	National Digital Information Infrastructure and Preservation Program
NEDCC	Northeast Document Conservation Center
NETS	National Educational Technology Standards
NIH	National Institutes of Health
NISO	National Information Standards Organization
NLM	National Library of Medicine
NMC	New Media Consortium
NSA	National Security Agency
NSF	National Science Foundation
NSL	National Security Letter
OA	open access
OAI-PMH	Open Archives Initiative–Protocol for Metadata Harvesting
OAIS	open archival information system
OCLC	Online Computer Library Center
OECD	Organization for Economic Co-operation and Development
OLA	Office for Library Advocacy
OLOS	Office for Library Outreach Services
OPAC	online public access catalog
OSF	Open Society Foundations
PDA/DDA	patron-driven acquisitions/data-driven acquisitions
PHI	protected health information
PII	personally identifiable information
PIPEDA	Personal Information Protection and Electronic Documents Act of 2000
PLA	Public Library Association
PLN	personal learning network
PPRA	Protection of Pupil Rights Amendment
PR	public relations
PREMIS	Preservation Metadata Implementation Strategies
PTSD	posttraumatic stress disorder
QR	quick response
RDA	resource description and access
RDF	resource description framework
RFP	request for proposal
RLG	Research Libraries Group
RM	records management

ROE	return on effort
ROI	return on investment
RUSA	Reference and User Services Association
SAA	Society of American Archivists
SaaS	Software as a Service
SERU	shared e-resource understanding
SIP	submission information package
SLA	Special Libraries Association
SME	small and medium-sized enterprises
STEAM	science, technology, engineering, arts, and mathematics (disciplines)
STEM	science, technology, engineering, and math (disciplines)
UKSG	originally stood for United Kingdom Serials Group
UNESCO	United Nations Educational, Scientific and Cultural Organization
USER	Understand Structure Engage Reflect
UXD	user experience design
VPAT	voluntary product accessibility template
W3C	World Wide Web Consortium
WIPO	World Intellectual Property Organization
WPA	Works Progress Administration (in 1939 renamed as Work Projects Administration)
XML	extensible markup language
YA	young adult
YALSA	Young Adults Services Association

List of Online Materials

Six archived webcasts aligned with this book that are moderated by editor Sandra Hirsh and feature selected chapter authors are available at https://libraryjournal.com/hirshondemand.

Accompanying this textbook is a comprehensive online supplement, which provides readers information about additional readings, online resources, websites and blogs, and more. In addition, the online supplement also provides the following components to extend the text printed in the chapter.

Online supplement link: https://rowman.com/page/hirshsupplement

Foreword

Those of us who educate information professionals face two kinds of meta-challenges to providing high-quality experiences to our students. First is the challenge of rapid change. Our field is evolving dramatically as new technologies accelerate the creation, flow, and management of information assets. Coping with these changes demands ongoing curriculum and course revisions as well as personal commitments to staying abreast of new trends and techniques in practice. Second is the challenge of broad scope. Because all aspects of modern life depend on information assets, our field applies to all disciplines and human enterprises. As Marcia Bates has argued, we are a meta-discipline.[1]

Rapid Change

Libraries have long acted as change agents for patrons by providing them with high-quality and contemporary information products and services that allow them to learn and grow. Libraries themselves have been undergoing fundamental changes in several waves over the decades. For example, the automation of library catalogs took more than a decade to achieve in the 1970s and 1980s as libraries undertook retrospective conversion projects. This, in turn, changed the work processes for technical service librarians and eventually for reference librarians and library patrons. The web and e-books have driven subsequent waves of technical changes that, in turn, change the way that librarians work. In fact, these waves of change in libraries are a subset of the changes that have taken place in all offices and other information-intensive enterprises. In effect, the nature of information work continues to evolve—whether the information professional works in a corporation, small startup, government agency, or library.

These waves of change demand that professional education adapt so that graduates are not only prepared to work in today's information environments, but also to drive and adapt to changes in those environments over time. Like all professional education, information education must support both original credentialing as students earn their degrees as well as continuing education programs to help working professionals adapt to change and drive new innovations. It is especially important that educators have access to timely materials to use in their courses.

Broad Scope

Information pervades human activity. The creativity and complexity of human activity manifests in myriad forms and in turn spawns broad arrays of information products and services. Classical components of library work such as material management (e.g., books, journals, catalogs) and services such as reference, cataloging, and preservation have long served as well-defined organizing boundaries for the library field, and in turn have served to distinguish courses in library curricula. Changes in technology and in representation (e.g., electronic, digital) have blurred these boundaries in both practice and education for libraries of all kinds. More importantly, the demands of organization, management, transfer, and preservation of information assets have become core interests of all kinds of enterprises and entities, ranging from small business and community groups to major corporations and government agencies. All kinds of enterprises have begun to recognize that the skills of librarians are crucial to their success. In effect, library and information educators are being asked to train information professionals who can work in all kinds of enterprises. Where once it was possible to organize curricula so that core courses such as general reference was followed by specialized courses in subject bibliography (e.g., humanities, science, social science) or type of library (e.g., school, public, academic, special), the scope of applications has exploded to include all kinds of enterprises, cultures, and disciplines.

The broadening scope of information work demands that professional education adapt so that graduates are prepared to work in a diverse mix of industries and enterprises. Programs must grapple with the challenges of breadth and depth—potentially allowing students to follow highly general paths that give them the flexibility to follow opportunities, while allowing others to develop deep specializations in particular industries or subfields (e.g., the various informatics subfields). It is especially important that educators have access to instructional materials and perspectives that represent this breadth of scope.

Information Services Today: An Introduction and associated resources aim to address the two desiderata of change and scope. The authors provide a pragmatic overview of the diverse kinds of roles that information professionals play in a variety of settings. The volume is mainly by and for practitioners with a wide range of experiences and will serve as a useful resource for students beginning their professional study, for midcareer professionals who want a broad refresher on the state of the information professions, and for general audiences who want to understand the breadth of information work. The thirty-nine chapters are organized into seven parts devoted to (1) the history and importance of diverse communities and information needs; (2) the different kinds of library and allied enterprises; (3) the different kinds of service functions information professionals provide; (4) a sample of user needs; (5) the management issues and techniques used in libraries and information centers; (6) the social, legal, and economic issues related to information assets; and (7) trends and overarching themes of information professionalism. It is impossible to include all aspects of the field, but the collection of chapters provides a purposive sample of the state of the field. The chapters together demonstrate the broad scope of information and the many career paths that information professionals may take in libraries and broader information-intensive enterprises.

The challenge of rapid change is treated on two fronts: first, the chapters themselves represent contemporary point estimates of modern information work. The topics for discussion suggested in most chapters are structured to not only stimulate students to reflect on the status quo of the chapter's focus but also to consider the core principles associated with the topic—principles that will carry through even as technology and work practices evolve over time. Second, the text has associated online materials that have the potential to allow topics to be updated and new cases or examples to be added to keep the materials fresh over time. Overall, this textbook will serve to introduce students who are preparing for information careers to appreciate the broad scope and rapid changes in our field.

—Gary Marchionini,
University of North Carolina at Chapel Hill

Note

1. Bates, Marcia, "An Operational Definition of the Information Disciplines," *iConference 2010 Proceedings*, University of Illinois, Champaign, IL, 2010, 19–25.

Preface

Information Services Today: An Introduction is not your typical introductory textbook in that it extends beyond what it means to be an information professional in today's complex world to provide instructors, students, and information professionals a forward-thinking foundation of the key issues, challenges, and opportunities on the horizon for the information profession.

The book addresses current topics and trends in the information field, including demonstrating value and the role of data analytics, open access, creation culture and makerspaces, user experience, licensing, copyright and creative commons, marketing, global information environments, infinite learning, privacy and cybersecurity, as well as many other essential areas for today's information professional.

This book's intention is to provoke discussion, engagement, and interaction in ways that will help facilitate the learning process. The book's content and the supplemental materials—discussion questions, rich sets of online supplemental materials, and multimedia webcast interviews featuring authors from this book discussing the trends and issues in their respective areas—give readers the opportunity to go beyond the content presented and develop a deeper understanding of the topics. Additionally, this book recognizes the broad range of environments that people with master of library and information science (MLIS) degrees work in, which include both libraries and other information environments. Thus, this book does not only focus on libraries, but instead encompasses *all* kinds of information organizations.

Purpose

Information Services Today: An Introduction addresses the complex environments, professional roles, and critical issues facing any environment that serves information-using communities. Specifically, the book

- provides a thorough introduction and overall state of the field,
- gives a global perspective on what it means to be a library and information professional today,
- addresses why information organizations are more important today than ever before,
- discusses how technology has influenced the ways that information professionals provide information resources and services in today's digital and global environment,
- highlights current issues and trends and provides expert insight into the emerging challenges and opportunities of the future, and
- identifies career-management strategies and leadership opportunities in the information profession.

The book begins with a historical overview of what it means to be an information professional today and highlights the transformation of libraries as the information and technology hubs within their communities. The historical role of the "library" is defined and its definition expanded to include all places that manage, create, store, or provide information as "information organizations." Similarly, the term "librarian" is expanded to "information professional," as this term more accurately reflects the varied roles, skill sets, and competencies demonstrated and required today. The book is organized into seven independent parts:

- *Part I: Information Landscapes: Cultural and Technological Influences*—focuses on the transformative, complex, and diverse communities that engage with information and are served by information organizations; a historical overview is also provided.
- *Part II: Information Professions: Physical and Virtual Environments*—focuses on the evolving landscape of information services, the various types of information organizations, and the roles information professionals perform within those organizations.
- *Part III: Information Services: Roles in the Digital Age*—focuses on the diverse ways information organizations serve the needs of information users. Topics include access and technical services, as well as information and technology literacy instruction.
- *Part IV: Information Users: Engaging, Creating, and Collaborating via Technology*—focuses on how today's users engage, learn, and create in information environments and how information services are now provided anytime and anywhere.
- *Part V: Information Organizations: Management Skills for the Information Professional*—focuses on all aspects of managing information organizations, including technology, facilities, human resources, budgets, and collections.
- *Part VI: Information Issues: Influences and Consequences*—focuses on key issues faced by information organizations and professionals today, including intellectual freedom, information ethics and policy, copyright, licensing, open access, as well as cybersecurity and information privacy.
- *Part VII: Information Horizons: Career Management and Leadership Strategies*—focuses on forward-thinking aspects and strategies for the successful information professional, with topics addressing the importance of career management, the value of global networks, and the role of leadership.

Audience

The book has four different audiences.

First and foremost, it is aimed at the new student in an information school or a library and information science program who is learning the foundational core of a library and information science (LIS) curriculum. Students will gain a solid foundation in the types of environments information professionals work in, the type of work they do, the influence of technology and how communities access and use information, and the many special issues (e.g., intellectual freedom, copyright, information privacy) that define the information landscape and will likely have implications for them during their career as an information professional. From the book's first chapter highlighting essential competencies for today's information professional to its concluding chapters on career strategies, global networking, and leadership, students will gain insight into the various opportunities—both academic and professional—that are available to them. Students will also benefit from one of the primary themes addressed throughout the book: the value and significance of lifelong learning, which is highlighted as an essential component of success in the information profession.

Second, with the continuous expansion of technological and cultural influence on how information professionals store, access, and use information, the book is also aimed at current information professionals. In order to remain essential to the organizations and the communities they serve, information professionals must continuously stay abreast of the current issues and emerging trends within the field. This book serves as a "refresher course" for information professionals committed to their own professional development. The authors provide effective strategies for addressing the needs of information users today, while forecasting the issues, challenges, and opportunities on the horizon. Awareness of these issues helps information professionals keep current and their organizations adapt to change in the future. The ongoing and future success of information organizations is reliant on the ongoing professional development and advanced skill sets of the individuals who work in them; this book addresses that need.

Third, this textbook targets the non-LIS professional. It provides a snapshot of what the field of library and information science is, defines the information organization and its various functions, and highlights the essential roles that information professionals perform in the community, business world, educational system, and even the global environment. In a nutshell, this book provides any reader with a glimpse of what libraries, information organizations, and information professionals "do" and provides an overall understanding of the complex, technological, and global information environment we all live in.

Finally, the book is written for instructors of core foundation courses at information schools and schools of library and information science. With leading industry and academic experts represented throughout the book, accompanied by discussion questions, examples, and case studies—in addition to the instructor's supplement that includes additional discussion questions, exercises, and webcasts—the book provides instructors of foundational LIS courses with a practical guide for their curriculum development and, more importantly, their students.

Expertise

The editor of this collective edition draws on her extensive and varied expertise and experience as a library and information science educator, leader, researcher, and professional both in library and other information environments to identify the key themes and topics that are addressed in this textbook, as well as the best experts to address them. She has applied her own library and information science skill set to work for more than a decade in leading Silicon Valley companies in user experience and research and development—giving her a firsthand realization of the range of possibilities for information professionals to work in many different environments in a variety of positions. As the director of the School of Information at San José State University, she works with leading professionals and educators from around the world on developing new curriculum covering the important topics facing the information profession today. Such topics include, but are not limited to, emerging technologies, changes in information user behavior, big data, cybersecurity, change management, online learning, community engagement, global communities, and more. Each of these topics has been introduced in this book by today's leading experts.

Of tremendous value to this book are its contributing authors. These authors were specifically chosen for their expertise, passion, and commitment—not only to the field of information science, but also to the professional development of tomorrow's information leaders. The authors collectively represent some of the largest programs in library and information in the United States (both iSchools and LIS schools), as library directors, library consultants, and information professionals from the profession's most valued organizations, such as the American Library Association, Educopia Institute, Digital Public Library, LYRASIS, and more. These authors were further selected for their global perspectives, which is demonstrated in some cases by residing in non-U.S. countries and, in other cases, by working on global initiatives as part of their day-to-day work. Together, these contributing authors weave their unique expertise and perspectives to address the key themes of the book.

Key Themes and Learning Objectives

Key themes were identified to provide a thorough, yet broad, introduction to the field of information science and to address the issues, terminology, and resources that every information professional should know. Working with the authors on the specific scope for each chapter, the result is a cohesive collection of essential topics and key themes applicable to the work of information professionals today. As a result of reading this book, readers will gain a foundational understanding of

- the history of libraries and the emergence of information organizations,
- the emerging trends and issues that will help information professionals remain forward thinking, and
- how information organizations must find new ways to reach users wherever they are and provide information and resources whenever they need it.

Readers will also understand that

- information and technology literacy is a growing need in communities (e.g., public, academic, social, government, organizational) and remains a primary function of information organizations—and of information professionals, and that
- information organizations will remain valuable entities in their communities—but to thrive, they will need to remain creative, innovative, and technologically advanced.

Readers will be able to

- address challenges and key issues of the field and for the sustainability and essentialness of the information organization, and
- continue learning and exploring through a wealth of key resources that are provided.

Organization

Information Services Today: An Introduction is organized into seven parts, providing a clear focus on today's key issues and trends.

Part I, "Information Landscapes: Cultural and Technological Influences," begins with chapter 1, which offers an introduction about the dynamic compilation of current issues and emerging trends facing the field of information science today. This introductory chapter defines what it means to be an information professional today—providing a clear definition of the terms "information organization" (rather than just the library) and "information professional" (rather than just a librarian). This chapter then highlights the exciting opportunities that await within the field of information science and the various competencies required of information professionals today. Chapter 2 provides a comprehensive history in which the author highlights the transformation of the library from a repository to an information center. Chapter 3 defines information communities and then leads into chapter 4, which addresses the diverse communities served by information organizations and provides the reader with tools, strategies, and resources for effectively understanding and working with diverse communities.

Part II, "Information Professions: Physical and Virtual Environments," begins with chapter 5, which highlights the field of librarianship as an evolving profession and provides the reader with a wealth of resources essential for developing a comprehensive personal learning network and adapting to change through industry awareness. Chapters 6 through 10 address both the similarities and uniqueness of the different types of information organizations where information professionals work, including school libraries, academic libraries, public libraries, special libraries, and digital libraries. Each chapter addresses the organization's environment (including the physical or virtual space and the communities it serves), as well as the specific competencies needed for successfully meeting the needs of its users. The final chapter of this part, chapter 11, addresses the value of the master of library and information (MLIS) or the master of information science (MIS) in organizations beyond the library, such as government, business, and nonprofit organizations and, respectively, the essential competencies required to thrive in these environments.

Part III, "Information Services: Roles in the Digital Age," focuses on the nature of information today and how technology has changed the way information professionals store, access, and use information. Chapter 12 focuses on users and how information organizations can meet the diverse needs of their communities. Chapter 13 highlights the role of information intermediation and reference services, including how these roles have changed with digital collections, the Internet, and mobile applications. Chapter 14 presents the reader with the technical side of information organizations, including automated systems, cataloging and authority control, metadata, and a thorough glimpse into what goes on "behind the scenes" of an information organization. Chapter 15 defines access services and discusses the evolution of the concept, briefly discussing how an access services department might be organized (e.g., e-reserves, interlibrary loan, and stacks management). This section then ends with chapter 16, which addresses the essential service of providing information and technology literacy instruction, with special sections on point-of-need instruction, collaborative learning initiatives, and assessment of literacy programming.

Part IV, "Information Users: Engaging, Creating, and Collaborating via Technology," provides a thorough view of how information organizations/professionals now serve users when and where they are. It begins with chapter 17, which offers a special emphasis on users and their experience both in the physical environment (engaging with the library) and the digital environment (concepts in digital and website design). Next, in chapter 18, the model of the hyperlinked library is presented, along with a discussion of how information organizations today are providing information services via mobile technologies, social media, and even geotechnologies. Chapter 19 focuses on creation culture and redefining library space as makerspaces. Part IV then closes with chapter 20 where infinite learning is defined and its significance to both information users and information professionals is discussed.

Part V, "Information Organizations: Management Skills for the Information Professional," addresses key management skills for all aspects of managing the information organization. Chapter 21 introduces the topic more broadly by identifying the unique management skills needed to manage efficient and user-focused organizations. Chapter 22 focuses on managing budgets and the complexity of information organization budgets—including internal and external factors (e.g., governmental, economical) impacting those budgets. Chapter 23 highlights the likeliness of information professionals being placed in a management role overseeing other people's work and provides effective strategies for proactively managing and assessing information organization personnel. Chapter 24 focuses on managing the information organization as a physical space while meeting the needs of its community. Chapter 25 focuses on managing collections—both physical and digital collections—with an emphasis on how to meet the changing needs of the community effectively. Chapter 26 focuses on managing technology (e.g., computers, automated library systems, makerspaces) in a variety of information settings. Chapter 27 focuses on the importance of understanding user needs and utilizing marketing strategies to promote the information organization's services. This section then concludes with chapter 28, which focuses on the important role that assessment plays in information organizations in terms of demonstrating value.

Part VI, "Information Issues: Influences and Consequences," presents the reader with essential and key issues facing the field of information science today. Chapter 29 kicks off this section with a chapter devoted to information policy, with information ethics following this in chapter 30. While not new topics in the field of information science, these issues have become more complex with the digitization and availability of information, and the authors address these issues. Chapter 31 focuses on copyright and the Creative Commons, with information licensing immediately following in chapter 32. Chapter 33 discusses open access and the role of information professionals in preserving and providing open access. Chapter 34 provides an overview of the significance of analog and digital curation and preservation, including challenges and methods for preserving information resources. Chapters 35 and 36 conclude this section and focus on the "hot issues" of information today, including information privacy, cybersecurity, and intellectual freedom. The authors in this section highlight the information professional's responsibility in upholding the user's rights on critical issues and present the unique challenges information organizations and professionals face in doing so.

The book then concludes with part VII, "Information Horizons: Career Management and Leadership Strategies," with the aim of energizing readers as they manage their careers in the information profession. Chapter 37 provides specific career management strategies that guide readers—whether they are new to the field of information science, are changing careers, or are current LIS professionals considering a new direction in their careers—in discovering how their skill sets match up to a variety of opportunities both within and outside the field of information science. Chapter 38 provides a broader perspective of the roles information professionals perform on a global scale—specifically, the value they bring to local communities through global inspiration and how to build a global personal learning network. This section concludes with chapter 39, addressing the importance of leadership and highlighting the various opportunities that new or current information professionals can pursue.

Special Features

Each chapter is designed to engage the reader. Sidebar content has been included to provide additional context on the chapter's key points. "Check This Out" sidebars provide the reader with links to useful content where the reader can view an example supporting a concept presented in the chapter, check out an important resource mentioned in the chapter, or view a website of interest.

Discussion questions are also embedded in each chapter to facilitate discussion in the classroom setting—whether that be physically in a classroom or online via discussion boards. These questions are designed to get the reader to think more deeply about the chapter's content and discuss how the concepts may apply to real-life scenarios.

While this collection was approached purposively to build upon learning concepts presented earlier in the book, readers can also begin and end where they want to. Each chapter's content is unique and complete to its topic; however, some content will naturally overlap the content of other chapters. When a concept is presented that is addressed in more detail in another section or chapter, a cross-reference to that chapter is provided. This way, learning is adaptable to the reader's or the classroom's unique needs and can begin and end in any sequence.

Expanded Learning

One of the overlapping themes of this introductory LIS textbook is the value placed on lifelong learning. As the editor of this book and in collaborative agreement with the contributing authors, our key emphasis is that learning should not end with this textbook—nor does it end with the MLIS degree. Successful and satisfying careers in the field of information science are based on the commitment to adapt to change and to be continuously learning. Continuous learning is the only means for meeting the diverse, complex, and changing needs of the information community.

With that in mind, an online supplement has been compiled for the readers to accompany this book available at https://rowman.com/page/hirshsupplement. In addition, six archived webcasts aligned with this book that are moderated by editor Sandra Hirsh and feature selected chapter authors are available at https://libraryjournal.com/hirshondemand.

The social, technological, and global environments that information users dwell in today create exciting opportunities for the information professional across many institutional and organizational settings. To remain effective and competent in today's information environment, information professionals must not only understand the nature of information *today* but also remain cognizant that information, and the ways users access, use, and even create information, will dynamically change in the future. That change begins with every new piece of information published (in print or online), every new technology developed, and every piece of new knowledge sought; change is happening every second of every day 24/7/365. The success of information professionals in serving their information communities is dependent on their commitment to lifelong learning and professional development. *Information Services Today: An Introduction* encapsulates the knowledge and experiences of industry leaders worldwide and rewards every information professional who reads it with the foundational knowledge and resources necessary to begin—or recharge—their careers as competent, transformative, and forward-thinking information professionals.

Acknowledgments

It is with heartfelt gratitude that I acknowledge the many individuals who assisted in the writing of this book. This was a collaborative effort, and I could never have completed a book of this size and complexity without the help and support of the following people.

First and foremost, I want to acknowledge the tremendous work that my research assistant Elaine Hall did on this book. Her outstanding contributions and ideas, organizational skills, professionalism, and attention to detail are evident all throughout the book. She was a true partner on this project, and I feel extremely fortunate to have worked with someone of her caliber. Despite her own busy school and family schedule, she worked many late-night hours with me to ensure that we delivered the project on time and with the quality we both strived for. I also am very grateful to my other research assistant, Emily Agunod, for her masterful help with endnotes, bibliography, citation checking, and many other important parts of the book that I could never have completed without her.

I also want to thank Dr. Linda Main, my associate director at the San José State University School of Information. Not only is she wonderful to work with on school business, but she also provided invaluable help early on in this project—helping me brainstorm topic areas and identify possible contributors, as well as generally serving as a sounding board for the project. A huge thank-you also goes to Lisa Valdez, San José State University School of Information communication and grant development manager. The book benefited greatly from Lisa's gifted editing skills. I knew that I could always count on Lisa to provide thoughtful suggestions about ways to organize and clarify content. I also want to acknowledge the many helpful suggestions and ideas that I received from other SJSU School of Information faculty.

I appreciated working with my publisher Charles Harmon at Rowman & Littlefield. I am grateful that he approached me with the idea for this project and for all of the support he provided throughout the process. His extensive publishing experience and calm responses to issues as they arose helped me navigate this project successfully from start to finish.

I am also extremely grateful to the many contributors to this book. I am honored to have worked with so many of the great leaders, scholars, and information professionals in our field today, and I appreciate their willingness to share their expertise, passion, and commitment in writing this important foundational text for the library and information science field.

And, finally, I must thank my husband Jay and daughters Hayley and Leah for their patience and support while I worked on this book project. They kept everything moving forward in our lives while I was focused on this important work. I would also like to thank Gail Schlachter, my mom, who inspired me to enter the exciting field of library and information science. If not for her encouragement and showing me the way, I would never have pursued this rewarding career.

Part I

Information Landscapes
Cultural and Technological Influences

If you put together a big enough and diverse enough group of people and ask them to "make decisions affecting matters of general interest," that group's decisions will, over time, be "intellectually [superior] to the isolated individual," no matter how smart or well-informed he is.

—James Surowiecki (2004)

The future of libraries and information organizations is bright! Throughout history, these organizations have served complex and diverse communities by providing materials and programs to foster and support the educational and personal endeavors of the communities they serve. That mission is stronger today than ever before. Today's information organizations uphold their foundational mission to provide materials and resources to meet the educational and entertainment needs of their communities, but now expand their services by integrating new technologies and programs that foster creativity, collaboration, and connected learning.

Part I presents the historical transcendence of the information organization while demonstrating how these organizations remain true to their core mission of serving the diverse information needs of their community. It also highlights the heart of the information organization's existence—the information professionals—and their innate understanding of community. Information organizations have become the dynamic and essential hub of their communities. It is the diversity of those communities and the ability of the information organization to meet those diverse needs that enriches the learning journey for everyone.

Welcome to *Part I—Information Landscapes: Cultural and Technological Influences!*

1

The Transformative Information Landscape

WHAT IT MEANS TO BE AN INFORMATION PROFESSIONAL TODAY

Sandra Hirsh

The field of library and information science (LIS) is amid one of the most dynamic and transformational periods in history. With the influence of the Internet, e-books, and mobile technologies, information organizations are being challenged as their collections and services compete with the rapidly evolving digital information landscape. Information organizations are responding by adopting a vision for themselves as the technological hub of their communities—meaning they integrate technologies, they design creative spaces, and they create new opportunities for learning and exploration. Information users are now coming to the information organization—both in person and online—asking for access to information and resources, asking for technologies, and asking for instruction on how to use these technologies. Indeed, "providing technology is now libraries' top priority as they redefine their roles as digital knowledge centers."[1]

The impact of technology has exponentially changed both the role of information organizations and the professionals who work in them. In addition to maintaining the integrity of information—how it is stored, accessed, and used—information professionals today must also be technologically knowledgeable and skilled in emerging technologies and their myriad of uses. What does this mean for the vitality of information organizations in serving their communities? Which skills and competencies are needed by information professionals to help their organizations thrive in the global information market? In this chapter, and throughout this textbook, the answers to these questions are explored, and the opportunities that are available to information organizations and the professionals who work in them are defined. After completing this chapter, readers will have a better understanding of today's complex information environments, the innovative and user-defined information services provided in those environments, and

> "The impact of technology has exponentially changed both the role of information organizations and the professionals who work in them. In addition to maintaining the integrity of information—how it is stored, accessed, and used—information professionals today must also be technologically knowledgeable and skilled in emerging technologies and their myriad of uses."

the critical issues (such as copyright, information policy, and information ethics) that define not only the information organization, but also the role of the information professional.

Today's Information Services

In his book *Drive*, Daniel H. Pink said, "The secret to high performance and satisfaction—at work, at school, and at home—is the deeply human need to direct our lives, to learn and create new things, and to do better by ourselves and our world."[2] There is evidence of this "drive" in everyday life—students attending higher education, professionals seeking new opportunities, children engaging and creating with new technologies, as well as graduate students seeking an MLIS degree! This drive demonstrates the transformative nature of our communities and therefore creates the vision for information organizations.

Emerging technologies continuously redefine what it means to learn, create, and do better. Information organizations, and the professionals who work in them, must also constantly transform. Information professionals must look ahead at the technologies, opportunities, and issues that impact the development, storage, access, and use of information.

Defining Today's Information Professional

Librarians have always been the gatekeepers of information, learning, and knowledge creation.[3] Librarians worked in buildings (libraries) that stored books and provided access to information available in their buildings. With the dawn of computers and digital content, libraries expanded access to include digital and multimedia content. Communities were drawn to libraries for information they otherwise could not access. But do the terms "library" and "librarian" adequately define information service today? Textbox 1.1 defines these terms.[4]

TEXTBOX 1.1

Definitions

- *Library:* a place where books, magazines, and other materials (such as videos and musical recordings) are available for people to use or borrow.
- *Librarian:* a specialist in the care and management of a library.

The confusion with these definitions is that they are not applicable to the digital and virtual world of information today.[5] Information, information need, and information use are no longer bound to physical space or time. The information professional, therefore, is no longer bound to the "library"—their expertise is needed in every school, organization, community center, home, and even on every mobile device. In this book, the terms "library" and "librarian" have been expanded to "information organization" and "information professional" to highlight the wide range of information environments—in both library and nonlibrary settings (e.g., academic, public, school, nonprofit, government, corporate)—that information professionals work in to provide important information services.

Key Trends Impacting Information Service

Information professionals must constantly survey the information and technology landscape to identify trends that have implications for the information field. Adapting to these continuous changes is part of what makes being an information professional so interesting and exciting. A few of the key global, technology, and other current and emerging trends that impact today's information services are discussed (see also chapter 5, "Librarianship: A Continuously Evolving Profession").

Global Trends

The *2013 IFLA Trends Report*[6] forecasted key trends that will impact the global information economy, and consequently information organizations. These trends include emerging technologies that expand and limit access to information, online education that democratizes and disrupts global learning, and the emergence of hyperconnected societies. The consequence of these trends is a higher, more universal value for information literacy skills; a rapid expansion of online education resources; and the "proliferation of hyper-connected mobile devices . . . that will transform the global information economy."[7]

Technology Trends

When considering technology, it is essential to remember that "time moves quickly,"[8] meaning that today's technologies will be put to the wayside as new technologies emerge at an exponential rate. But what are "emerging technologies"? *The Horizon Report*[9] annually evaluates and reports on the next emerging technologies that will be implemented by information organizations. In 2013, they reported on the immediate upswing of

- *massive open online courses (MOOCs):* targeting large-scale participation and open access via the web;
- *mobile apps:* engaging information users via microphones, touch screens, sensors, and maps via mobile technology; and
- *tablet computing:* facilitating educational, social, and professional endeavors anywhere/anytime.[10]

In 2014, *The Horizon Report—Library Edition*[11] reported a growing development of information organizations providing mobile technologies to deliver information services. Not only are information organizations building websites, apps, online catalogs, and e-book collections to access content online; they are even providing patrons with the devices (tablets, e-readers, laptops, etc.) to engage with information services—when and where they need to (see also part IV, "Information Users: Engaging, Creating, and Collaborating via Technology"). These emerging technologies have already demonstrated their impact on the information profession. Indeed, information organizations can serve as portals to these technologies in response to patrons' requests for access to MOOCs via computers as well as provide "on-the-go" access to information resources via mobile apps on smart phones and tablets.

Technology has impacted every aspect of information services. Social and mobile technologies define not only how users access or use information, but also how they communicate and engage within the digital landscape. Information users today are asking for the "flexibility, geographic independence, speed of response, time shifting, interactivity, multitasking, and time savings provided by the technology they use daily."[12]

Current and Emerging Trends

As technologies change, new areas emerge that create challenges and opportunities for information professionals. Several of these current and emerging areas are included in this book. To name a few:

- *Infinite Learning:* addressed in terms of the important role that information professionals play in providing lifelong learning opportunities where and when people need them through new technologies, such as MOOCs (see also chapter 20, "Infinite Learning");

- *Data Analytics:* addressed in terms of how analyzing big data sets can help make decisions, demonstrate value, and answer complex questions for information organizations (see also chapter 28, "Demonstrating Value: Assessment");
- *Creation Culture and Makerspaces:* addressed in terms of how information professionals create maker learning communities as well as opportunities that delight, motivate, and inspire communities (see also chapter 19, "Creation Culture and Makerspaces");
- *User Experience:* addressed in terms of presenting a range of techniques that can be applied to understand user needs and wants and to create great experiences for information users (see also chapter 17, "User Experience");
- *Privacy and Cybersecurity:* addressed in terms of threats to personal data from online activities, the role of government in improving cybersecurity, and basic measures information professionals can take to help ensure information privacy and security (see also chapter 35, "Information Privacy and Cybersecurity").

Information professionals who learn about how these trends impact (positively and negatively) the information community will become tomorrow's leaders. Libraries, nonprofit organizations, businesses, and governments alike need information professionals who are knowledgeable about the trends, opportunities, issues, and concerns of the information landscape today. Furthermore, these information professionals demonstrate an ability to help organizations adapt to change in the future: another essential quality of the information professional!

Implications for Today's Information Professionals

The information organization's value and relevance is dependent on its ability to identify and effectively adapt to new technologies and the influence it has on how society engages and communicates with both technology and information.[13] In order to compete in this global information economy, information organizations need to

- become the essential, one-stop resource for information and technical literacy instruction,
- provide access to mobile and online learning resources,
- integrate as many emerging technologies into their services as possible, and
- provide an environment of exploration and play to learn these new technologies.

"Information organizations have the unique opportunity to develop themselves as the technological hub of their communities. No other organization has the opportunity to simultaneously offer free access to both physical and digital collections, creative learning spaces for technological exploration, and staff who are knowledgeable about new technologies and their various applications."

Information organizations have the unique opportunity to develop themselves as the technological hub of their communities. No other organization has the opportunity to simultaneously offer free access to both physical and digital collections, creative learning spaces for technological exploration, and staff who are knowledgeable about new technologies and their various applications. Nor is there any other organization that can provide all this without the boundaries of physical space.

Access to basic information and communication technologies (ICTs) must be a high priority for information organizations and is the "most important function" underlying the organization's existing resources.[14] Access begins with free speech and the freedom to share ideas with others—but it does not end there. "When access is paired with the tools and skills for understanding and using" information, agency—the capacity of individuals to act independently and to make their own choices—is built. The "pairing of access + agency = a sweet spot for [information organizations]."[15] Information organizations need to integrate ICTs, design creative and engaging learning spaces, and expand opportunities for learning and exploration.[16] Consequently, today's information professionals need the skills to

- develop initiatives that blend information literacy with social media,
- make library tools available at the point of need for users,
- enable users to interface with information in a natural and personalized manner, and
- allow [users] to design their own learning outcomes.[17]

New Competencies for the Information Professional

To meet the needs of the changing information environment, information organizations need to hire and sustain professional staff who are knowledgeable and competent in emerging technologies and their applications. Library and information science education is, therefore, the essential resource for information professionals—not only for attaining an MLIS degree, but also for sustained learning opportunities long afterward through certificate programs, workshops, online workshops and seminars, virtual conferences, and more!

What are the specific skills, knowledge, and competencies required of information professionals today? Various studies are regularly performed to identify the evolving roles of information professionals and the competencies required to effectively provide information services to the communities—or organizations—they serve. A recent career trends study[18] demonstrated specific duties that information professionals today perform, which include

- cataloging and metadata, as well as electronic collections management (e.g., born-digital materials);
- working with integrated library systems;
- digitization, data migration/conversion, repository, and database tasks;
- support for distance and virtual patrons;
- evaluation and improvement of current systems and workflow;
- tracking and reporting data;
- anticipation and implementation of future or emerging needs and changes; and
- troubleshooting for hardware and software across all levels of patron, instruction, and digital access.

The same study also identified the competencies most often sought in today's information professionals. These include

- reference skills;
- technology proficiency (e.g., working with networks, metadata, digital assets, database management, website development);

- management skills (e.g. managing facilities, budgets, personnel, technology);
- statistics/analysis skills;
- teaching/instruction;
- knowledge of emerging trends/technologies; and
- ability to lead digitization projects, integrated library systems, and others.

In addition to these core skills, it is also important to have excellent "soft skills" such as effective written and verbal communication skills, a passion for continuous learning, and adaptability to new technology.[19]

TEXTBOX 1.3

Topic for Discussion

What professional skills or competencies do you already have that can be applied as an information professional? What competencies do you feel are the *most essential* to building a thriving professional career as an information professional? And what competencies do you feel would bring the *most value* to your role in serving your information community?

Adapting to Change through Lifelong Learning

Learning does not end with the MLIS. "This [is] made clear through the innumerable 'what I didn't learn in library school' articles and blog posts as well as the range and number of webinars, online short-courses, post-degree certifications, conference workshops, and so on, offered by RUSA and other divisions of ALA as well as the state library."[20] The ability to change and the readiness to receive new knowledge has been reported as the most important competencies desired of LIS professionals.[21] The good news is that many students and graduates of LIS programs realize that their skills must remain relevant and they must remain knowledgeable and skilled in the latest technologies.

Information professionals must always be learning. To advance professionally while also assuring that the information organization remains an essential and vibrant information/technological hub in the community, information professionals must access professional development opportunities, must explore (and play with) new technologies, and must remain current on user behavior—particularly as it relates to digital content and mobile technologies.

Conclusion

While challenges continue to exist in the information organization's ability to expand and integrate new technology in the information setting, the future of information organizations is bright as patrons, who have relied solely on the Internet for their information needs, redirect their attention back to the organization to access, learn, and interact with information as well as emerging technologies. Information professionals have a unique opportunity today to integrate new technologies into their organizations and therefore become the technological hub of their communities. In doing so, the community will identify the organization as an essential resource to access and interact with technology and digital resources. Consequently, the community will come to the information organization to learn, explore, play, and create. It is an exciting time for information organizations. It is an even more exciting time to become an information professional!

Sandra Hirsh

Notes

1. J. McKendrick, *Libraries: At the Epicenter of the Digital Disruption; The Library Guide Benchmark Study on 2013/14 Library Spending Plans* (Medford, NJ: Information Today, 2013).
2. Daniel Pink, *Drive* (New York: Riverhead Publishing, 2011).
3. Sue Myburgh, *The New Information Professional: How to Thrive in the Information Age Doing What You Love* (Oxford, UK: Chandos Publishing, 2005).
4. "Library," Merriam-Webster.com, n.d., http://www.merriam-webster.com/dictionary/library?show=0&t =1410888178; "Librarian," Merriam-Webster.com, n.d., http://www.merriam-webster.com/dictionary/ librarian.
5. Myburgh, *The New Information Professional*, 2005.
6. IFLA, *Riding the Waves or Caught in the Tide? Navigating the Evolving Information Environment: Insights from the IFLA Trend Report* (The Hague, NL: IFLA, 2013), http://trends.ifla.org/files/trends/assets/ insights-from-the-ifla-trend-report_v3.pdf.
7. Ibid.
8. L. Johnson, S. Adams Becker, M. Cummins, V. Estrada, A. Freeman, and H. Austin Ludgate, *NMC Horizon Report: 2013 Higher Education Edition* (Austin, TX: New Media Consortium, 2013), http://net.educause. edu/ir/library/pdf/HR2013.pdf.
9. "NMC Horizon Project," New Media Consortium, last modified July 1, 2014, http://www.nmc.org/ horizon-project.
10. Johnson et al., *NMC Horizon Report*, 2013.
11. L. Johnson, S. Adams Becker, M. Cummins, V. Estrada, and A. Freeman, *NMC Horizon Report: 2014 Library Edition* (Austin, TX: New Media Consortium, 2014), http://cdn.nmc.org/media/2014-nmc-horizon -report-library-EN.pdf.
12. Kayla L. Quinney, Sara D. Smith, and Quinn Galbraith, "Bridging the Gap: Self-Directed Staff Technology Training," *Information Technology and Libraries*, December 2010, 205–206, http://ejournals.bc.edu/ojs/ index.php/ital/article/viewFile/3131/2746.
13. S. Hirsh, R. Metz, S. Brown, L. Serrano, and S. Gurtu, "Developing a Technology Integration Residency Model: The Catalyst Project Report," *Faculty Publications*, Paper 1, 2012, http://scholarworks.sjsu.edu/ slis_pub/1.
14. B. Mehra, K. Black, V. Singh, and J. Nolt, "What Is the Value of LIS Education? A Qualitative Study of the Perspectives of Tennessee's Rural Librarians," *Journal of Education for Library and Information Science* 52, no. 4 (2011): 265–278.
15. Jill Bourne, "Finding the Sweet Spot for Libraries in the Digital Age," *Knight Blog*, last modified September 11, 2014, http://www.knightfoundation.org/blogs/knightblog/2014/9/11/finding-sweet -spot-libraries-digital-age.
16. McKendrick, *Libraries*, 2013.
17. A. Bolorizadeh, M. Brannen, R. Gibbs, and T. Mack, "Making Instruction Mobile," *Reference Librarian* 53, no. 4 (2012): 373–383, doi:10.1080/02763877.2012.707488.
18. "Emerging Career Trends for Information Professionals: Snapshot of Job Titles in Summer 2013," *San José State University*, last modified August 14, 2014, http://slisweb.sjsu.edu/about-slis/publications/ emerging-career-trends-information-professionals-snapshot-job-titles.
19. Ibid.
20. M. Kern, "Continuity and Change, or, Will I Ever Be Prepared for What Comes Next?" *Reference and User Services Quarterly* 53, no. 4 (2014): 282–285.
21. S. Hirsh, "Preparing Future Professionals through Broad Competency Planning," *Information Outlook* 16, no. 1 (2012): 9–11, https://slisweb.sjsu.edu/downloads/future_professionals.pdf.

2

Libraries and Information Organizations

TWO CENTURIES OF EXPERIENCE

Christine Pawley

Modern institutional libraries are an invention of the last two hundred years; their current shape can best be understood in the light of their origins in the nineteenth century and continuing development in the twentieth century. For more than one hundred years, public libraries led the way in establishing core principles of librarianship (e.g., cataloging, classification, and reference work), and also in creating outreach programs and introducing user-centered innovations. In the second half of the twentieth century, academic libraries became technologically advanced and developed into forward-looking organizations focused primarily on their users. Although now technically able more than ever to reach patrons beyond their physical walls, public and academic libraries find that patrons continue to value their spaces as a vital part of their local communities.

This chapter addresses the transformation of libraries from their creation in the nineteenth century to their development—including their challenges—during the twentieth century and how that shaped the way the library is defined today in the twenty-first century. After completing this chapter, the reader should have an understanding of the history of libraries and the communities they serve.

Part 1: Nineteenth-Century Beginnings

In 1800, the Reverend William Bentley (1759–1819) of Salem, Massachusetts, embodied the republican ideal of an informed citizen.[1] Fluent in twenty languages and knowledgeable about local and global affairs, he was often deep in conversation with men and women from all walks of life. His personal library of four thousand volumes was one of the largest in the country, and he himself was a kind of walking encyclopedia. He was a consummate generalist of a breed whom an expansion of knowledge, print, and literacy would soon render obsolete as people came to see knowledge as situated in texts, rather than individuals, and that these texts numbered far more than any single person could own. The story of how libraries developed into the public institutions that are known today is entwined with shifting meanings of information and community, as well as of citizenship.

> "The story of how libraries developed into the public institutions that are known today is entwined with shifting meanings of information and community, as well as of citizenship."

Development of the Institutional Library

The development of institutional libraries was influenced by many of the same forces that shaped the century as a whole. In Bentley's day, America was largely rural, reliant on free white labor in the north and enslaved black labor in the south. The school system was patchy, and favored boys, while colleges largely existed to educate the all-male clergy. Politically dominated by affluent white men, mostly of British descent, the success of the republic was believed to depend on the participation of well-informed citizens—free, white, property-owning men with the education and ability to elect the best representatives. By the end of the century, America was an industrial giant, its population swollen by immigrants from Europe and Asia. Native American resistance to white settlement had been crushed, and many Native groups banished to remote reservations. After the devastating Civil War (1861–1865), slavery was outlawed, but the failure of postwar Reconstruction ensured the continued political and economic subjugation of African Americans. Citizens were normalized as white, of European descent; it would be the 1940s and 1950s before Asians were permitted citizenship, and the 1960s and 1970s before African Americans could fully exercise their constitutional right to vote.

In the industrial North, capitalism created a burgeoning middle class of clerical and professional workers, but during the Gilded Age (1870s–1880s), an enormous gulf appeared between the very rich and the working class. Nearly 40 percent of Americans resided in cities where the poor often lived and worked in unhealthy and even dangerous conditions. Between 1890 and 1920 (the Progressive Era), federal, state, and municipal governments began to regulate aspects of life such as child labor, weights and measures, public health, transportation, and sanitation in an effort to combat the effects of such stark inequality. Women could not vote; but free schooling for white girls and boys had become the norm, and literacy rates were high. Many colleges had sprung up for men and women, most with a focus on secular education. High literacy and industrialization had produced an explosion in publications of all kinds, from newspapers and other ephemera to solid reference tomes. Fiction was enormously popular, though considered dangerous by some cultural authorities who worried about the effects of unmediated radical and even immoral ideas on an impressionable population. Modern libraries began in this century of rapid change, sponsored by the developing middle class.

Academic Libraries Develop Slowly

Academic libraries played only a minor part in the expansion of higher education, reflecting a system that still relied largely on memorization from textbooks and where little original research took place. South Carolina College constructed the first purpose-built academic library in 1840, Harvard in 1841. Only thirty colleges had holdings of at least a thousand volumes.[2] In 1871, the library of the University of Wisconsin held just over four thousand books and was open for only half an hour on four afternoons a week. Commented a visitor, "I think the library of the University is a disgrace to the state."[3] Fifty years later, in 1932, a survey of college libraries revealed that, at more than two hundred four-year liberal arts colleges, over half the book collections contained fewer than thirty thousand volumes, and only thirty-three institutions contained more than sixty thousand.[4] Not until after the mid-twentieth century did most college and university libraries transform themselves from underused storehouses into dynamic learning spaces. Instead, the library movement drew inspiration from the free public libraries that emerged out of an earlier mix of social and school libraries.

The Emergence of Public Libraries

In Bentley's time, "public" libraries were those not owned by private individuals, and included social, circulating, and school libraries as well as college libraries. Books were expensive, and in the colonial era some townspeople formed clubs to share books, based on subscription or share purchase.[5] Such social libraries became common in New England and Mid-Atlantic states, and by 1850, there were more than one thousand[6] public libraries. This model spread west with Yankee settlers; the same leading families who established banks, schools, churches, and voluntary organizations in the developing towns and cities also formed social libraries. Typically open for short hours, with restricted membership, strict limits on borrowing, and outdated collections, most survived for only a short period.[7] "Community" for these libraries referred to the social elite. But groups of African Americans also founded reading rooms, libraries, and literary societies where people gathered to share texts read aloud. For black readers as well as white, reading was an exercise for the good of the community, rather than primarily for individual self-improvement.[8] Circulating libraries were another early form of the institutional library. These commercial enterprises rented out books to whoever could afford to pay. Dependent on popular appeal for their survival, collections were heavily weighted toward novels and romances. By 1820, more than half their collections consisted of fiction, which made them suspect in the eyes of those who ran their nonprofit counterparts.[9]

Public Funding for Libraries

> "According to the library faith, reading was seen as a useful and moral behavior, and public libraries were a means of democratic progress because of their relationship to books and reading."

School libraries began in New York State in 1835 where libraries could be set up for general use in local communities, funded through taxes.[10] In 1849, New Hampshire transformed the school library idea when it allowed municipalities to levy taxes for a free public library. Massachusetts followed in 1851. The 1854 opening of the Boston Public Library boosted public library development elsewhere, and by 1875 all New England states had passed public library enabling laws.[11] Other states passed similar laws later in the nineteenth century, and gradually the public library idea took hold, as establishing a local library became one of the ways in which pioneering communities put down roots and proclaimed their own value.[12] For inspiration, public libraries drew on what some were calling the library "faith" or "spirit." According to the library faith, reading was seen as a useful and moral behavior, and public libraries were a means of democratic progress because of their relationship to books and reading.[13] As tax-supported institutions, though, they, like the circulating libraries, depended on popular appeal. Despite some leading librarians' disapproval, many filled a local demand and heavily stocked their shelves with fiction.[14] Public libraries had quickly learned to be responsive to their communities.

A New Role for Libraries: Self-Improvement and Social Harmony

Some free public libraries emerged out of older social libraries, but often it was a local women's group that established a new public library. Most women's clubs promoted individual self-improvement in an era when women's access to higher education was limited.[15] Like social libraries, the new public libraries tended to have restricted opening hours and outdated collections occupying cramped and inadequate quarters, usually rented. In 1854, the Boston Public Library occupied a former schoolhouse. In 1873, the Chicago Public Library (CPL) opened in an old rented water tower, known as the Tank. By the end of the century, cities were replacing these makeshift spaces with architect-designed libraries, some on a grand scale. Echoing halls, high vaulted ceilings, and imposing staircases were a suitable setting, some thought, for practicing the library faith. But not all agreed. The CPL's first director, William Frederick Poole, complained that such buildings wasted space and presented a fire hazard.[16] Competing for library funds were "branch" libraries—small-scale subsidiaries situated in neighborhoods. Boston Public Library opened its first branch in 1871, and by 1875 had five more.

Christine Pawley

Some branches started as "delivery stations," located in stores, where readers could order books for pickup.[17] The CPL started a deposit station system in 1884, and by 1912, over one hundred dotted the city. In 1890, the library opened its first branch reading room, and its first branch library in 1904.[18] In 1909, the new director, Henry Legler, made branch libraries a priority, seeing them as a way to make libraries "accessible to the entire community."[19] The CPL's branch libraries also provided books in seventeen languages.[20]

Rural communities lagged behind in providing purpose-built libraries, but between 1886 and 1917, the Carnegie Corporation systematically funded 1,689 public and academic library buildings in the United States. Disparaging monumental libraries as wasteful, its secretary, James Bertram, devised a pamphlet that included sample plans and suggested functional design features, such as an open plan, low bookcases, and glass partitions that drew inspiration from department stores and factories.[21] States that benefited most lay in the Midwest and the West, where many communities were keen to demonstrate values of self-help and independence. In cities and villages across America, the public library, providing free access to books and information, along with quiet, clean, well-lit, and heated space for reading (itself a luxury for many living in cramped and noisy accommodations) became a familiar institution. Often packed with readers and enjoying widespread support, many public libraries had become a cornerstone of their communities. Although library leaders might appeal rhetorically to the library faith, at the local level, librarians and patrons understood public libraries as spaces for the fostering of what historian Wayne Wiegand calls "social harmony" through demonstrating acceptable behaviors and providing "collections and services" that offered citizens "models for successful living, solving problems, and achieving an orderly life at the same time that they mediated in peaceful ways a set of ever-shifting cultural values."[22] In the century that followed, these functions would continue to evolve, as Americans broadened their understanding of "community" and "citizenship" to include people often ignored—or worse, discriminated against—during the previous era.

> TEXTBOX 2.1
>
> **Topic for Discussion**
>
> How have concepts of "community" and "information" shifted in ways relevant to libraries over the past 200 years?

Part 2: Twentieth Century–Early Twenty-First Century: Growth and Development

By 1900, the building blocks of the library profession were in place. Leading librarians had formed the American Library Association (ALA), founded the *Library Journal* in 1876, and were laying down principles of information storage, retrieval, and reference service. A central figure in these processes was Melvil Dewey (1851–1931), creator of the Dewey Decimal Classification system, a founding member of the ALA, and the first editor of *Library Journal*. Librarians saw themselves as mediators of "wholesome" literature; the ALA's motto, coined by Dewey and adopted in 1879, was "The best reading for the largest number at the least cost." Library education was taking place in colleges (Columbia University was the first to offer courses in librarianship, under Dewey's direction) and large public libraries. No government funding for libraries yet existed, but some states were establishing library commissions or state libraries to provide advice to communities. Topics that would preoccupy librarians for much of the twentieth century were already matters of professional concern.

New Technologies Lead to Information Overload

New technologies prompted discussion of information overload. In 1924, William S. Learned noted a "phenomenal improvement in speed and accuracy of communication" and complained that "even the trained student finds the time required thoroughly to examine a topic in an unfamiliar field almost prohibitive."[23] He suggested a solution, already adopted by "many progressive cities": a "central intelligence service . . . not only for 'polite' literature, but for every commercial and vocational field of information."[24] Essential components of the proposed service already existed in such public libraries as that of Cleveland, Ohio: open shelves, adult education, children's and youth services, and branches and delivery stations in schools and neighborhoods. Other specialized services included the Business Library at Newark, New Jersey; the Teachers' Library in Indianapolis; and technology departments in cities like Detroit and Pittsburgh.[25] At the same time, corporations and government agencies were beginning to set up specialized information services. In the early 1900s, for example, Wisconsin's Charles McCarthy set up the first legislative reference library as a state agency, an idea that spread to other states and prompted Congress to establish the Legislative Reference Service in 1914.[26]

Libraries Develop Creative Solutions to Serve New User Groups

Public libraries were reaching out to new user groups. Some library commissions set up traveling libraries—boxes of books deposited in homes, stores, and post offices, some in foreign languages—to reach readers in remote areas. The first horse-drawn bookmobiles were already in operation in the early 1900s.[27] Public libraries had generally excluded children under the age of twelve, but in the 1880s and 1890s, Caroline Hewins and Anne Carroll Moore led a new field in which librarians managed specially designed children's rooms and services such as storytelling and became cultural authorities in the rapidly growing area of children's publishing.[28] The new building of the New York Public Library (opened in 1911) allocated over three thousand square feet to children's services; this room circulated over two and a half million books in its first year of operation.[29] Librarians also worked enthusiastically to "assimilate" European immigrants. Large urban libraries routinely collected books in foreign languages. By 1913, 10 percent of the New York Public Library's holdings were printed in twenty-five foreign languages.[30] Even in the sparsely populated West, librarians provided foreign-language materials to reach diverse audiences.[31]

But African Americans, Native Americans, and Asian immigrants were still poorly served. In the 1940s, about 44 percent of whites living in thirteen southern states had access to free library service, but the percentage for black Americans was less than half that, and the services themselves were generally much inferior.[32]

New Forms of Funding for Libraries

Dependent on local taxes, many public libraries struggled for funding and reached a crisis with the onset of the Great Depression in 1929. The advent of the New Deal[33] persuaded the ALA that federal funding was the answer, since many libraries benefited from the 1935 creation of the Works Progress Administration (WPA). In Kentucky, "pack horse librarians" distributed books in remote mountain areas.[34] In New York City, workers ran open-air reading spaces and bookmobile services, and in Philadelphia, workers contributed five million cards to a union catalog project.[35] Following World War II (1941–1945), the ALA repeatedly tried to persuade Congress to pass legislation allocating federal funds to state public library initiatives. Finally, in 1956, the Library Services Act (LSA) passed, providing funds, mostly to rural communities, to fund books, salaries, and equipment, but not buildings or land. In the following five years, over two hundred new bookmobiles were added, serving rural schools as well as the general public.[36] In recognition of the aging stock of library buildings, in 1964, the LSA was renewed as the Library Services and Construction Act (LSCA) and renewed again in 1996 as the Library Services and Technology Act (LSTA), a significant name change reflecting a shift in emphasis from buildings to bytes. Further federal aid came in the form of E-rate (or Universal Service[37]) legislation, also passed in 1996, which helped provide network connections to libraries and schools at a discounted rate. In 1995, the Bill and Melinda Gates Foundation helped provide computers to public

Christine Pawley

libraries in disadvantaged areas, and extended the program in 1997 to all state-library-certified public libraries that served low-income communities.[38]

Libraries Develop Collaborative Units

At the state or county level, libraries formed collaborative units, such as multicounty library systems, to save money and increase efficiency. However, in the late 1970s, a new threat to local funding escalated: a tax revolt that originally emerged out of southern white resistance to desegregation and spread to the rest of the United States.[39] In Fresno County, California, for example, an LSCA grant had bought a bookmobile to serve mostly Mexican American farmworkers in the San Joaquin Valley, called "La Biblioteca Ambulante" and staffed with Spanish-speaking librarians. But with passage in 1978 of California's tax-cutting Proposition 13, the program fell victim to successive budget reductions. By 1989, only two part-time library assistants staffed the bookmobile department, one of whom, Owen Smith, also worked half time with the Fresno Corrections Department. "What I see in the jail is, of course," he said, "the result of migrants not being able to acquire the information they need to learn English, to learn to read, and to cope with the system adequately. . . . A lot of library work can be done for what it costs to keep someone in jail for a year."[40]

Libraries Embrace Intellectual Freedom

Librarians gradually moved away from their earlier prescriptive role in steering patrons toward "wholesome" reading, and toward an embrace of intellectual freedom (see also chapter 36, "Intellectual Freedom"). During World War I, librarians had assumed an even more active censorship role, as anti-German sentiment resulted in the outright suppression of German-language reading materials.[41] During the 1930s, however, they had begun to change their stance on censorship by passing the first version of the Library Bill of Rights in 1939, and in the postwar period resisting McCarthyism. In the mid-1960s, the ALA opened its Office for Intellectual Freedom, with the aim of helping librarians and others withstand censorship, while educating the public about the right to read.[42] Although formally embracing intellectual freedom, some librarians practiced passive censorship, and issues of intellectual freedom continued to present others with professional moral dilemmas as their value for intellectual freedom clashed with local demands for restrictions, especially on books for children.[43] Librarians also debated as to whether they should accept a primarily consumerist (give them what they want) or educative (give them what they need) role. In the 1970s, libraries learned to acknowledge the importance of the "library in the life of the user" rather than the "user in the life of the library."[44]

> "In the 1970s, libraries learned to acknowledge the importance of the 'library in the life of the user' rather than the 'user in the life of the library.'"

Libraries Embrace Multicultural Values

Passage of the LSCA had fitted well with President Lyndon Johnson's Great Society initiative, which, with the civil rights movement of the 1950s and 1960s, helped pave the way for a fundamental shift toward an active embrace of multicultural values in libraries. Children's services led the way. In the 1930s, Charlemae Hill Rollins, an African American children's librarian, had issued a call for children's books that reflected black children in a positive light.[45] Now in the 1970s and 1980s, public librarians serving adults as well as children began to learn the language of diversity (see also chapter 4, "Diversity, Cultures, and Equity of Access"), although not all agreed that it was valuable. In a debate in *American Journal* in 2007, Todd Douglas Quesada argued that restricting Spanish-language materials would affect at least sixteen million legal residents or citizens, and would alienate them from free and open information access. But Julia Stephens complained that by creating bilingual collections, librarians were "contributing to a divided America" and "undermining the American democracy that has created one nation for all."[46]

The Library without Walls

In the 1990s, new digital technologies spawned a new rhetoric: the library without walls. Commentators speculated about the possible demise of the "traditional" library, threatened with becoming obsolete as access to books and information was increasingly privatized through an elaborate array of information technologies, from television to the Internet.[47] Nevertheless, cities large and small continued to build libraries. In Chicago, the city constructed a new downtown library in 1991 and saw its investment rewarded in higher circulation as well as higher in-library use. The CPL also built new branches. In *Better Together: Restoring the American Community*, expressing a common myth about former public libraries as "a passive repository of books," Robert D. Putnam commented, "No longer . . . an outpost of culture, quiet, and decorum in a noisy world, the new library is an active and responsive part of the community and an agent of change. In addition, the Internet, which seemed to threaten its reason for being, turns out to be one of the things that bring people to the library."[48] Putnam described the new Near North branch (located between the mostly white and affluent Gold Coast and the mostly African American and poor Cabrini Green) as a vibrant space where residents of all ages would come to use the Internet, hold book club meetings, take job-skills classes, do their homework, display artwork, and borrow books. Both downtown and in Cabrini Green, the new libraries have been at the forefront of neighborhood renewals.[49]

TEXTBOX 2.2

Topic for Discussion

The idea of service beyond the library's walls is not new. How has it developed since the early twentieth century?

Reenvisioning School and Academic Libraries

The postwar period saw an expansion of education. Thousands of small school districts consolidated, and in the larger multigrade schools, school libraries became the norm (see also chapter 6, "Literacy and Media Centers in the Twenty-First Century: School Libraries"). With the passage of the GI Bill that made college affordable to millions of veterans, and the enormous increase in research activity, colleges and universities vastly expanded their programs and facilities, including their libraries (see also chapter 7, "The Learning and Research Institution: Academic Libraries"). Teaching methods shifted to reflect the new emphasis on research, as federal funds for science, engineering, and technology flowed onto campuses in the years of educational expansion during the 1960s and early 1970s. Education for librarianship became the sole preserve of colleges and universities, and between 1961 and 1976, twenty-three new schools were founded. However, the expansion did not last; between 1978 and 1991, fifteen schools closed.[50] The first library school to incorporate the term "information" into its title was Syracuse in 1974. More and more schools followed in the 1980s: the generally accepted term was "library and information science," but by the mid-1990s, some LIS schools were beginning to drop the "L word."

Libraries Become Early Adopters of New Information Technologies

Academic libraries became early adopters of new information technologies; in 1967, for example, one group formed the Ohio College Library Center (OCLC, now the Online Computer Library Center).

OCLC went on to form a worldwide cooperative cataloging and bibliographic utility that emblemized a growing dependence on interlibrary collaboration and consortium building in the second half of the twentieth century. Academic libraries also adopted increasingly user-friendly policies, like open stacks, unrestricted circulation, and group meeting spaces. As the financial situation worsened from the late 1970s on, libraries maintained their newly valued status on campus. Far from the "disgrace" of the nineteenth century, academic libraries had become campus showcases designed to attract students (and their parents) in an era of increasing interinstitutional competition. In the early twenty-first century, libraries facilitated mobile use of information through first wired and then wireless access to electronic resources, but still invested heavily in physical space devoted to physical texts and their readers. In 2011, for example, at the cost of eighty-one million dollars, the University of Chicago opened its Mansueto Library—a domelike reading room situated above an underground storage system designed to hold 3.5 million volumes.[51]

A New Role for Libraries: Information Literacy

As academic library collections shifted emphasis to electronic resources and the Internet became more and more accessible to students, academic libraries led the way in establishing a new subfield of librarianship: information literacy (see also chapter 16, "Teaching Users: Information and Technology Literacy Instruction"). Public librarians, too, accepted the need for information literacy among the general population, and some states began to identify information literacy as a key competency for all K–12 students. Librarians frequently appealed for justification to values for citizen empowerment and democracy. In 2000, the Association of College and Research Libraries (ACRL) Information Literacy Competency Standards for Higher Education, for example, included the goal of creating "a more informed citizenry." Far from setting up the long-dead William Bentley as an ideal, they were referring to skills of critical evaluation, efficient access, and understanding ethical aspects of information use.[52]

Conclusion

Today, in the early twenty-first century, although now technically able more than ever to reach patrons beyond their physical walls, libraries find that patrons continue to prize their spaces as a vital contribution to the public life of their local communities. Colleges and universities still prioritize library buildings as places where students and faculty can find academic resources, and where individually and in groups they can read, study, and share ideas. Cities, towns, and villages still vote to fund public libraries as places where all are welcome, and where commercial transactions are not a priority. The voluntary nature of library use means, though, that information organizations will continue to have to justify both their existence and their operating principles, to balance competing needs, and above all to be knowledgeable about changing technological, social and cultural, economic, and environmental conditions. As always, a key to their institutional success will be an information profession composed of individuals who are skilled, knowledgeable, flexible, and ethical. Unlike William Bentley, they will often serve as information providers beyond their immediate surroundings, but at the same time they will also be highly accomplished at face-to-face interactions rooted in their communal localities—the hallmark of Bentley's own achievement.

> "The voluntary nature of library use means, though, that information organizations will continue to have to justify both their existence and their operating principles, to balance competing needs, and above all to be knowledgeable about changing technological, social and cultural, economic, and environmental conditions."

Notes

1. Richard D. Brown, "William Bentley and the Ideal of Universal Information in the Enlightened Republic," in *Knowledge Is Power: The Diffusion of Information in Early America, 1700-1865* (New York: Oxford University Press, 1989), 197-217.
2. Dean Groszins and Leon Jackson, "Colleges and Print Culture," in *An Extensive Republic: Print, Culture, and Society in the New Nation*, ed. Robert A. Gross and Mary Kelley (Chapel Hill: University of North Carolina Press, 2010), 322.
3. Merle Curti and Vernon Carstensen, *The University of Wisconsin: A History*, vol. 1 (Madison: University of Wisconsin Press, 1949), 348-349, http://digicoll.library.wisc.edu/cgi-bin/UW/UW -idx?type=header&id=UW.UWHist18481925v1.
4. Neil Radford, *The Carnegie Corporation and the Development of American Academic Libraries, 1928-1941* (Chicago, IL: American Library Association, 1984), 14.
5. David S. Shields, "Eighteenth-Century Literary Culture," in *The Colonial Book in the Atlantic World*, ed. Hugh Amory and David D. Hall (Chapel Hill: University of North Carolina Press, 2007), 474-475.
6. Jesse Shera, *Foundations of the Public Library: The Origins of the Public Library Movement in New England, 1629-1855* (Chicago, IL: University of Chicago Press, 1949), 69.
7. Kenneth E. Carpenter, "Libraries," in *An Extensive Republic: Print, Culture, and Society in the New Nation*, ed. Robert A. Gross and Mary Kelley (Chapel Hill: University of North Carolina Press, 2010), 279.
8. Elizabeth McHenry, "'An Association of Kindred Spirits': Black Readers and Their Reading Rooms," in *Institutions of Reading: The Social Life of Libraries in the United States*, ed. Thomas Augst and Kenneth Carpenter (University of Massachusetts Press, 2007), 107.
9. Carpenter, "Libraries," 278.
10. Haynes McMullen, *American Libraries before 1876* (Westport, CT: Greenwood, 2000), 124-125.
11. Sidney Ditzion, *Arsenals of a Democratic Culture: A Social History of the Public Library Movement in New England and the Middle States from 1850 to 1900* (Chicago, IL: American Library Association, 1947), 30, http://archive.org/stream/arsenalsofademoc006465mbp/arsenalsofademoc006465mbp_djvu.txt.
12. For an account of the public library's role in one such community, see Christine Pawley, *Reading on the Middle Border: The Culture of Print in Late Nineteenth Century Osage, Iowa* (Amherst: University of Massachusetts Press, 2001), esp. 61-116.
13. Douglas Raber, *Librarianship and Legitimacy: The Ideology of the Public Library Inquiry* (Westport, CT: Greenwood, 1997), 39, 67.
14. Wayne A. Wiegand, *Main Street Public Library: Community Places and Reading Spaces in the Rural Heartland, 1876-1956* (Iowa City: University of Iowa Press, 2011), 148.
15. Paula D. Watson, "Founding Mothers: The Contribution of Women's Organizations to Public Library Development in the United States," *Library Quarterly* 64, no. 3 (1994): 233-269, http://www.jstor.org/stable/4308944.
16. William. F. Poole, "Progress of Library Architecture," *Library Journal* 7, no. 134 (1882): 1908-1909.
17. Walter Muir Whitehill. *Boston Public Library: A Centennial History* (Cambridge, MA: Harvard University Press, 1956), 195, https://archive.org/details/bostonpubliclibr010132mbp.
18. Carleton Bruns Joeckel and Leon Carnovsky, *A Metropolitan Library in Action: A Survey of the Chicago Public Library* (Chicago, IL: University of Chicago Press, 1940), 34-35.
19. Chicago Public Library, *38th Annual Report* (1909-1910), 17.
20. Chicago Public Library, *42nd Annual Report* (1913-1914), 23, 27-28.
21. Abigail Van Slyck, *Free to All: Carnegie Libraries and American Culture, 1890-1920* (Chicago, IL: University of Chicago Press, 1995), 34-40.
22. Wiegand, *Main Street Public Library*, 186.
23. William S. Learned, *The American Public Library and the Diffusion of Knowledge* (New York: Harcourt, Brace, 1924), 8, 12, https://archive.org/details/americanpublicli007473mbp.
24. Ibid., 12.
25. Ibid. See especially chapter 2, "The Tax-Supported Public Library as an Agency for the Systematic Diffusion of Knowledge among Adults," 26-56.
26. Paul D. Healey, "Go and Tell the World: Charles R. McCarthy and the Evolution of the Legislative Reference Movement, 1901-1917," *Law Library Journal* 99, no. 1 (2007): 36, http://www.aallnet.org/main-menu/Publications/llj/LLJ-Archives/Vol-99/pub_llj_v99n01/2007-02.pdf.

Christine Pawley

27. Christine Pawley, *Reading Places: Literacy, Democracy, and the Public Library in Cold War America* (Amherst: University of Massachusetts Press, 2010), 68–72.

28. Anne Lundin, "Anne Carroll Moore: 'I Have Spun out a Long Thread,'" in *Reclaiming the American Library Past: Writing the Women In*, ed. Suzanne Hildenbrand (Norwood, NJ: Ablex, 1996), 187–204.

29. Jacalyn Eddy, *Bookwomen: Creating an Empire in Children's Book Publishing, 1919–1939* (Madison: University of Wisconsin Press, 2006), 31.

30. Dee Garrison, *Apostles of Culture: The Public Librarian and American Society, 1876–1920* (Madison: University of Wisconsin Press, 2003), 217.

31. Joanne E. Passet, *Cultural Crusaders: Women Librarians in the American West, 1900–1917* (Albuquerque: University of New Mexico Press, 1994), 154.

32. Eliza Atkins Gleason, *The Southern Negro and the Public Library: A Study of the Government and Administration of Public Library Service to Negroes in the South* (Chicago, IL: University of Chicago Press, 1941).

33. "The New Deal," *United States History*, last modified August 9, 2014, http://www.u-s-history.com/pages/h1851.html.

34. Donald C. Boyd, "The Book Women of Kentucky: The WPA Pack Horse Library Project, 1935–1943," *Libraries and the Cultural Record* 42, no. 2 (2007): 111–128.

35. Martha H. Swain, "A New Deal in Libraries; Federal Relief Work and Library Service, 1933–43," *Libraries & Culture* 30, no. 3 (Summer 1995): 268–270.

36. Pawley, *Reading Places*, 259–260.

37. "Universal Service," Federal Communications Commission, last updated September 30, 2014, http://www.fcc.gov/encyclopedia/universal-servic.

38. John Carlo Bertot, Charles R. McClure, and Joe Ryan, "Impact of External Technology Funding Programs for Public Libraries: A Study of LSTA, E-rate, Gates, and Others," *Public Libraries* 41, no. 3 (May/June 2002): 166–171.

39. Kevin M. Kruse, *White Flight: Atlanta and the Making of Modern Conservatism* (Princeton, NJ: Princeton University Press, 2007).

40. Rachael Naismith, "Library Service to Migrant Farm Workers," *Library Journal* 114, no. 4 (1989): 54.

41. Wayne A. Wiegand, *An Active Instrument for Propaganda: The American Public Library during World War I* (New York: Greenwood, 1989).

42. Louise S. Robbins, *Censorship and the American Library: The American Library Association's Response to Threats to Intellectual Freedom, 1939–1969* (Westport, CT: Greenwood, 1996), esp. chaps. 3 and 4.

43. Emily Knox, "The Challengers of West Bend: The Library as a Community Institution," in *Libraries and the Reading Public in Twentieth Century America*, ed. Christine Pawley and Louise S. Robbins (Madison: University of Wisconsin Press, 2013).

44. Douglas L. Zweizig, "Predicting Amount of Library Use: An Empirical Study of the Public Library in the Life of the Adult Public" (PhD diss., Syracuse University, 1973).

45. Charlemae Hill Rollins, *We Build Together: A Reader's Guide to Negro Life and Literature for Elementary and High School Use* (Chicago, IL: National Council for Teachers of English, 1941).

46. Julia Stephens, "English Spoken Here," *American Libraries* 38, no. 10 (November 2007): 41, 43–44.

47. Jorge Reina Schement and Terry Curtis, *Tendencies and Tensions of the Information Age: The Production and Distribution of Information in the United States* (New Brunswick, NJ: Transaction Publishers, 1995), esp. 104–117.

48. Robert D. Putnam, *Better Together: Restoring the American Community* (New York: Simon and Schuster, 2003), 35.

49. Ibid., 36–37, 41–42.

50. Margaret F. Stieg, *Change and Challenge in Library and Information Science Education* (Chicago, IL: American Library Association, 1991), 28–29.

51. Marc Parry, "A High-Tech Library Keeps Books at Faculty Fingertips—with Robot Help," *Chronicle of Higher Education* 57, no. 42 (July 24, 2011): A12–A13.

52. Association of College and Research Libraries (ACRL), "Information Literacy Competency Standards for Higher Education," last modified July 12, 2014, http://www.ala.org/acrl/standards/informationliteracycompetency.

3

Information Communities

DEFINING THE FOCUS OF INFORMATION SERVICE

Karen E. Fisher and Ann P. Bishop

Community is one of the most profound concepts in information science because community needs, behaviors, and assets should drive the development, implementation, and evaluation of information services. Community can be thought of as the engine by which information services are developed and delivered; indeed, community is part of the information system itself. But what is community? There are probably as many responses as there are people to ask. The purpose of this chapter is to discuss the importance of community in information services. After completing this chapter, the reader should have an understanding of the ways that community is defined, how community has been approached historically in information services, how information communities differ from information grounds, and the different roles that information professionals may play therein.

Definitions of Community

At first blush, the notion of "community" seems simple. When asked, most would think of a group of people who share a lot of things in common, and the implications for information professionals would be to identify, design, deliver, and support services and systems that facilitate the exchange and growth of knowledge among those groups of people; however, it gets more complicated when one thinks deeply around the nature of those commonalities. Are they shared interests? Shared location? Shared ancestry? Who is excluded from the community, and what are the impacts of not belonging? And then the situation grows more complicated by considering additional factors. Do the people have to share these commonalities by choice (in the case of blood ties, one does not really get to choose)? Does it matter how often they communicate? Does it matter whether they use multiple modalities to communicate (e.g., in person, online, etc.), how close they feel to one another, or whether they share more than one commonalty? Indeed, Hillary noted ninety-four definitions of community, with three broad strands: geography, social interaction, and ties.[1]

In the introduction to their classic multivolume series, *Encyclopedia of Community: From the Village to the Virtual World*, Christen and Levinson describe how community can be approached from four key angles:[2]

- *Affinity:* Membership is based on common interests (e.g., book clubs, hobby groups, artists' colonies).
- *Instrumental:* Membership is based on a shared desire to achieve specific goals, whether political, economic, or other (e.g., an activist network such as from Amnesty International to Neo-Nazis, a set of hospice workers, a professional association, a political party).
- *Primordial:* Membership is based on ties of blood, kinship, race, ethnicity, or deeply held shared beliefs (e.g., the Asian American community, monastic communities).
- *Proximate:* Membership is based on residence in a particular place (e.g., a shantytown, a condominium complex, a neighborhood, a city).

Four Angles of "Community"
• Affinity
• Instrumental
• Primordial
• Proximate

These angles, of course, are not mutually exclusive, and some communities may exist along several of these dimensions simultaneously. For example, the community of humanities undergraduates at a university may have commonalities of affinity (interest in the humanities), instrument (getting a degree, having fun), and proximity (living in the same set of dorms). The community of model train enthusiasts may have commonalities of affinity (interest in trains) and instrument (learning about and building model trains). The community of Hmong refugees in Merced, California, share a primordial (ethnic and cultural) bond, as well as proximity.

These days, communities are often thought of as enabled by and primarily existing through digital technologies: virtual, electronic, or online communities, or social networks like Facebook or Twitter. Komito argues that only two types of community—moral communities characterized by egalitarian values and reciprocal relations, and norm-based communities based on a system of shared rules and meanings—are generally possible in a virtual sense.[3] Youth, in particular, who have grown up surrounded by and using digital media, seem to form communities in which much of the action takes place online. Cyberbullying is but one reminder that communities can have a dark side.

Development of a Community Approach in LIS

Historically, information services and research were concerned primarily with serving user communities based in the sciences. Pauline Atherton Cochrane[4] is among those well known for the early emphasis on the community context (e.g., their work settings, relationships, and norms as a group) underlying the information needs and uses of scientists and engineers, in order to create usable and useful information services and technologies for them. Today, such "socially grounded" approaches to system design and evaluation in professional communities are common. While public libraries have a long history of targeting particular groups for their services, such as children, the "working man," or immigrants, public librarianship and the general community were not considered as carrying the same gravitas as the hard sciences and business until the 1960s when research began to open up to focus on studying the everyday information needs of the general public (see also chapter 8, "Community Anchors for Lifelong Learning: Public Libraries"). Moreover, concern for the information communities of underserved, disenfranchised, marginalized, and vulnerable people has gradually come to the fore for noted researchers in LIS.

Sanford Berman's wide influence as a "radical librarian" began in 1971[5] with the publication of *Prejudices and Antipathies: A Tract on the LC Subject Heads Concerning People*; this publication signaled a long career devoted to fighting for standardized cataloging and classification systems to employ terms that were common in everyday use, as well as socially and culturally equitable, rather than biased toward majority and privileged perspectives. In 1975, Thomas Childers published the seminal book *The Information-Poor in America*, commissioned as a comprehensive review of the literature by the Bureau of Libraries and Learning Resources in the U.S. Office of Education.[6] Brenda Dervin has employed disciplinary approaches from communications in her research on information communities in everyday life and among vulnerable groups such as those suffering from cancer; since the 1980s, her work has been used in LIS to develop theory on "sense making," evaluate services, and design new systems, both on- and off-line.[7] A pioneer in using ethnography in LIS, beginning with her dissertation in 1984 on the working poor, Elfreda Chatman[8] developed theory around "small-world" information practices and concepts such as information poverty and life in the round, drawing from the information communities of incarcerated women, the elderly, and janitors. Roma M. Harris and Patricia Dewdney's seminal research on the information communities of battered women in the 1990s[9] has been particularly productive in its application to information services.

While the term "information communities" may not appear explicitly, as a phenomenon it is evident in the work of these pioneering researchers in that they focus on the needs and behaviors of groups of people who have a shared stake in mobilizing information resources. This research focus flourishes today, continues to bring innovative—especially qualitative—research methods and theory to LIS, and relates to cognate phenomena, such as "information ecologies," popularized by Bonnie Nardi and Vicki O'Day.[10] Considering the broad context of health, for example, information communities are reflected in the work of such LIS researchers as S. Leigh Star, Jeffrey Huber, Lynn Westbrook, Lynda Baker, and Tiffany Veinot. Across other domains of everyday life, there is a growing number of exemplary LIS researchers who have made major contributions with studies that break new ground in theory and methods for understanding diverse information communities, including Lynne McKechnie, Reijo Savolainen, Crystal Fulton, and Pamela McKenzie.

Information Communities

Information communities share some of the elements of community, plus they have the additional element of focusing on the role of information. It would be overly simplistic to assume an information community as just a particular target population or user group for an information service. As Joan Durrance, a pioneer in the information community field, explains, information communities form primarily around people's needs to get and use information.[11] She thus defined information communities as "constituencies united by a common interest in building and increasing access to a set of dynamic, linked, and varying information resources." She further elaborated how information communities can be

> "Information Communities share some of the elements of community, plus they have the additional element of focusing on the role of information."

> a partnership of institutions and individuals forming and cultivating a community of interest around the provision and exchange of information, or knowledge, aimed at increasing access to that information or increasing communication, and thereby increasing that knowledge.[12]

Thus, an information community is a group of entities that blurs the boundaries between information seekers, users, and providers, recognizing that a single person or institution can embody multiple segments of the information life cycle.

Research has shown that effective information communities have five characteristics:

1. emphasis on collaboration among diverse information providers,
2. capacity to form around people's needs to access and use information,

Karen E. Fisher and Ann P. Bishop

3. capacity to exploit the information-sharing qualities of emerging technologies,
4. ability to transcend barriers to information sharing, and
5. capacity to foster social connectedness.[13]

While not all of these characteristics will necessarily be met to the same degree in every information community, they are illustrative of the factors that make one community rich in information flow and social cohesion over another.

The information communities first studied by Durrance, Fisher, and Unruh were online community networks or free-nets that involved public libraries as key partners along with other agencies focused on community service in a particular geographic area. The framework's elasticity makes it relevant a decade later, when society has grown more complex and technology has grown more ubiquitous, where people of all ages create and search for information themselves and yet still rely on institutions for assistance. Three contemporary examples suggest the diversity of information communities today. One is FemTechNet:

Check This Out

Examples of Current Community Networks
SkokieNet
http://www.skokienet.org
and
The Blacksburg Electronic Village
http://www.bev.net

FemTechNet is an activated network of scholars, artists, and students who work on, with, and at the borders of technology, science and feminism. . . . Members in the network collaborate on the design and creation of projects of feminist technological innovation for the purposes of engaging the interests of colleagues and students on advanced topics in feminist science-technology studies. This project seeks to engender a set of digital practices among women and girls, to teach and encourage their participation in writing the technocultural histories of the future by becoming active participants in the creation of global digital archives.[14]

FemTechNet uses Wordpress blogs, Vimeo, videoconferencing, and digital course management systems, among other technologies for sharing, creating, and archiving its work.

Another example of a contemporary information community is Paseo Boricua, a vibrant, low-income neighborhood in Chicago whose motto is "Live and help others to live." Led by the Puerto Rican Cultural Center,[15] Paseo Boricua boasts a high school with one of the highest graduation rates for Latino students in the country and rooftop greenhouses that provide the community with one of its only sources of fresh vegetables; a highly successful HIV/AIDS prevention center and housing for homeless transgender youth; nationally recognized health programs focusing on diabetes and heart disease; and many other innovative cultural, health, educational, and economic activities—all designed and led by community residents themselves. The information that is the lifeblood of the Paseo Boricua community's accomplishments is generated and shared face to face in the local bakery, classrooms, and spoken word performances, as well as digitally through, for example, an electronic newspaper, listservs, a YouTube channel, a digital archive, electronic books and digitally produced posters and leaflets, and cell phones.[16]

A final example of an information community is the network of immigrants and refugees that forms and operates in many places across the globe today. The InfoMe program, based in the Seattle area, is studying and facilitating the information work of immigrant teens who serve as information intermediaries for their families, friends, and even complete strangers.[17] InfoMe is identifying how and why youth help others with information and technology, a phenomenon based on the fact that it is immigrant youth who learn the language and culture of their new country the quickest. Thus, immigrant youth are called upon to help their families navigate the health-care system, their schools orient more recently arrived immigrants, their friends feel less isolated, and their churches alleviate the hardships of those coming to live in an unfamiliar place, with few resources.

TEXTBOX 3.1

Topic for Discussion

What are your information communities? What different roles do people play in these information communities? What are the implications of these roles for information flow?

Information Grounds

Information communities comprise large sets of complementary stakeholders and last for long periods of times. These characteristics suggest design specifications for information service providers. Information grounds are another important conceptual framing that intersects with community and is rooted in information science; however, it focuses on the spaces and places where information is encountered.

Information grounds are informal social settings where people experience information, where they create, remix, curate, and share everyday information, all while attending to another activity: at cafés and pubs, on the metro, at casinos, at hair and tattoo salons, in bus queues, at the grocery store, at football games, in waiting rooms, at parks, at libraries and book stores, by luggage carousels, while flying, while waiting for a class, and at the beach, and in online settings too, including World of Warcraft, Etsy, Instagram, OKCupid, Facebook, and more (see also part IV, "Information Users: Engaging, Creating, and Collaborating via Technology").

"By understanding their characteristics—people, information, and place—information grounds can be facilitated to optimize people's everyday life situations and overall happiness."

Everyone has her or his own information grounds. They may spring up in an ad hoc manner, or be places people frequent routinely. They may represent a place where they are hoping to mingle with others or a place where they want to remain anonymous. It might be a situation in which people have been "trapped" together, like in an elevator that is stuck or a doctor's waiting room—also known as hostage settings. Information grounds also spring up during times of crisis, disaster, and displacement. By understanding their characteristics—people, information, and place—information grounds can be facilitated to optimize people's everyday life situations and overall happiness. The findings of information grounds research can be used powerfully for designing information technology, services, and policy.

The information grounds framework was developed by Fisher (née Pettigrew) in the 1990s based on her research on community health clinics in Canada. Researchers and professionals have used it extensively worldwide for understanding the role of informal social settings in information flow. She originally defined information grounds as "environment(s) temporarily created when people come together for a singular purpose but from whose behavior emerges a social atmosphere that fosters the spontaneous and serendipitous sharing of information."[18]

Information grounds have seven properties:[19]

1. Information grounds can occur anywhere, in any type of temporal setting and are predicated on the presence of individuals.
2. People gather at information grounds for a primary, instrumental purpose other than information sharing.

Karen E. Fisher and Ann P. Bishop

3. Information grounds are attended by different social types, most if not all of whom play expected and important, albeit different, roles in information flow.
4. Social interaction is a primary activity at information grounds such that information flow is a by-product.
5. People engage in formal and informal information sharing, and information flow occurs in many directions.
6. People use information obtained at information grounds in alternative ways, and benefit along physical, social, affective, and cognitive dimensions.
7. Many subcontexts exist within an information grounds and are based on people's perspectives and physical factors; together these subcontexts form a grand context.

To facilitate designing ways of analyzing and supporting people's information grounds, the people-information-place framework developed by Fisher, Landry, and Naumer is frequently used.[20] It comprises fifteen facets or characteristics, grouped under three main headings:

- *Information:* significance, frequency discussed, how created/shared, topics
- *People:* membership size, membership type, familiarity, actor roles, motivation
- *Place:* focal activities, conviviality, creature comfort, location and permanence, privacy, ambient noise

The premise is that the information professional can use these fifteen facets as a lens or sliding scale to understand the functioning nature of a particular information ground, specifically to understand who the people are, the role of the place where they meet, and how they experience information there. Through analyzing these factors, the information professional can identify ways of supporting the information ground.

For example, maybe information about a particular topic would be more efficiently disseminated by improving the "place" factors such as making coffee and muffins available, acquiring plants, or providing better lighting. If an information ground has excellent place factors, then it may signal opportunities for disseminating a broader array of information, such as providing health or financial information via a hair salon. There are many technology devices and training techniques with salon staff that could be integrated here to expand their information role beyond the realm of beauty advice. Sometimes places where people feel most anonymous are where they are most receptive to sharing and experiencing information; thus ambient noise and unfamiliarity can work in a positive way.

Information service providers have an opportunity when it comes to information grounds; the ones people find themselves in most frequently are not necessarily their favorite nor the best designed for information tasks. In the InfoMe project, their most frequent information grounds are their friends' homes, schools, places of worship, and local hangouts, such as sports fields or malls. The teen participants in InfoMe have been active collaborators in the design of new technologies and services that would vastly improve their ability to get and give information in the places where they spend most of their time. These are just a few examples of the powerful ways information grounds facilitate information flow in communities.

TEXTBOX 3.2

Topic for Discussion

How do information grounds differ from information communities? What roles do people play in information grounds? What are the implications of these different roles?

Conclusion

In this chapter, "community" was shown to be a complex, broad concept that could be addressed from many different perspectives. Information communities is a powerful concept, unique to information science, that is used to describe a group of organizations and individuals who share a commonality and work together toward sharing information in support of that commonality in an optimal way. Information grounds, another community, place-based framework unique to information science, refers to informal social settings where people experience information while attending to another activity. Though Information communities and information grounds differ in many ways, they both present gateways for guiding the work of information professionals that are based on a holistic and complete view of people's lives and the context in which they experience information services.

Notes

1. G. A. Hillary, "Definitions of Community: Areas of Agreement," *Rural Sociology* 20 (1999): 111–123.
2. "Introduction & Reader's Guide," in *Encyclopedia of Community: From the Village to the Virtual World*, ed. K. Christensen and D. Levinson (Thousand Oaks, CA: Sage Reference, 2003), pp. xxxi–xxiiii.
3. L. Komita, "Electronic Communities in an Information Society: Paradise, Mirage, or Malaise?" *Journal of Documentation* 57, no. 1 (January 2001): 115–129.
4. P. Atherton, D. King, and R. R. Freeman, *Evaluation of the Retrieval of Nuclear Science Document References Using the Universal Decimal Classification in a Computer-Based System*, AIP-UDC-8 (New York: American Institute of Physics, 1968).
5. S. Berman, *Prejudices and Antipathies: A Tract on the LC Subject Heads Concerning People*, reprint ed. (Jefferson, NC: McFarland, 2013).
6. T. Childers, *The Information-Poor in America* (Metuchen, NJ: Scarecrow Press, 1975).
7. B. Dervin, L. Foreman-Wernet, and E. Lauterbach, eds., *Sense-Making Methodology Reader: Selected Writings of Brenda Dervin* (Cresskill, NJ: Hampton Press).
8. E. A. Chatman, "Framing Social Life in Theory and Research," *New Review of Information Behaviour Research* 1 (2000): 3–18.
9. P. Dewdney and R. M. Harris, *Barriers to Information: How Formal Help Systems Fail Battered Women* (Santa Barbara, CA: Praeger, 1994).
10. B. A. Nardi and V. O'Day, *Information Ecologies: Using Technology with Heart* (Cambridge, MA: MIT Press, 2000).
11. J. C. Durrance, "The Vital Role of Librarians in Creating Information Communities: Strategies for Success," *Library Administration and Management* 15, no. 3 (2001): 161–168.
12. Ibid., 164.
13. K. E. Fisher, K. T. Unruh, and J. C. Durrance, "Information Communities: Characteristics Gleaned from Studies of Three Online Networks," in *Proceedings of the 66th Annual Meeting of the American Society for Information Science & Technology*, ed. R. J. Todd, 299–305 (Medford, NJ: Information Today, 2003).
14. "Home," *FemTechNet Commons*, last modified August 17, 2104, http://femtechnet.org.
15. Puerto Rican Cultural Center, last modified November 17, 2013, http://prcc-chgo.org.
16. P. W. Berry, A. Cavallaro, E. Vázquez, C. R. DeJesús, and N. García, "(Re)voicing Teaching, Learning, and Possibility in Paseo Boricua," in *Youth Community Inquiry: New Media for Community and Personal Growth*, ed. B. C. Bruce, A. Bishop, and N. R. Budhathoki (New York: Peter Lang International Academic Publishers, 2014).
17. "Home," *InfoMe Program*, last modified October 3, 2013, http://infome.uw.edu.
18. K. E. Pettigrew, "Waiting for Chiropody: Contextual Results from an Ethnographic Study of the Information Behavior among Attendees at Community Clinics," *Information Processing & Management* 35, no. 6 (1999): 801–817.
19. K. E. Fisher, J. C. Durrance, and M. B. Hinton, "Information Grounds and the Use of Need-Based Services by Immigrants in Queens, NY: A Context-Based, Outcome Evaluation Approach," *Journal of the American Society for Information Science & Technology* 55, no. 8 (2004): 754–766.
20. K. E. Fisher, C. F. Landry, and C. M. Naumer, "Social Spaces, Casual Interactions, Meaningful Exchanges: An Information Ground Typology Based on the College Student Experience," *Information Research* 12, no. 2 (2007), http://informationr.net/ir/12-2/paper291.html.

4

Diversity, Cultures, and Equity of Access

Patty Wong and Miguel Figueroa

This chapter starts from the basic belief that difference—and the differences between people and groups—strengthens organizations and communities when those differences are respected and acknowledged. Research shows that organizations that leverage multiple, diverse perspectives can experience better business performance[1] and have access to alternative ways of thinking and behaving that advance innovation.[2] Information organizations have tremendous opportunities to work with diverse professionals within their organization and diverse populations in their communities. Through these efforts, information organizations can strengthen their work preserving and contributing to the creation of information and ultimately improve their communities.

This chapter introduces diversity as a concept integral to the missions and values of information organizations and information professionals. It provides an overview of what the terms "diverse" and "diversity" mean, the characteristics that are commonly addressed by diversity work and diversity efforts, and the relationship of diversity to other tenets of the profession. After completing this chapter, the reader should have an understanding about intercultural communications and collaboration, cultural competencies within the organization, and developing with and from work with diverse communities.

What Do We Mean by Diversity?

Inevitably, conversations about diversity and diverse communities include three key terms—"diversity," "inclusion," and "multiculturalism." Each term is important and represents a specific approach to and activities for addressing differences among groups of people. But truly strategic organizations use a specific term intentionally based on culture, priorities, and aspirations. To help clarify how diversity is used in this chapter—and to benefit future discussions about diversity, inclusion, and multiculturalism—it is important to define them.

Multiculturalism

While less frequently used as a strategic goal or priority, multicultural or multiculturalism remains an important concept in developing services and programs. In 2005, the American Association of Colleges and Universities (AACU) released a series of three papers as part of its Making Excellence Inclusive Initiative. In one of the papers, "Making Diversity Work on Campus: A Research-Based Perspective," authors Jeffrey F. Millem, Mitchell Chang, and Anthony L. Antonio provided a simple definition of multiculturalism as "recognition or celebration of different cultures."[3] Monthlong cultural celebrations, cross-cultural dialogues, or rotating exhibits of different cultures embody some of the most popular multiculturalism efforts.

Inclusion

Inclusion assumes that an organization or community is composed of many different talents and perspectives, and so inclusion efforts seek to create an environment where those unique skills, perspectives, and experiences are valued. Inclusion efforts reinforce individuals' worth and dignity by creating a strong sense of involvement and belonging.

Diversity

The AACU paper mentioned above includes a useful definition for diversity, reading,

> In addition to conceiving of diversity in terms of composition and as an exploration of differences, we would add to the definition an interest in opposing unfair forms of exclusion, prejudice, and discrimination. . . . Indeed, perhaps more importantly for our definition of diversity, we firmly believe that diversity is fundamentally about work—very time-consuming and difficult work.[4]

Diversity initiatives focus on groups that have previously been excluded or experienced prejudice or discrimination and adopt active, significant, and intentional efforts to overturn or correct these experiences (see appendix 4.1, "Most Common Characteristics of Diversity").

TEXTBOX 4.1

Topic for Discussion

Given the definitions provided for diversity, inclusion, and multiculturalism, share some examples of programs or services that align with these terms. Explain how the service or program aligned with the concepts of diversity, multiculturalism, or inclusion as defined in the chapter.

Why Diversity?

This chapter intentionally uses the terms "diversity" and "diverse" to acknowledge that exclusion, prejudice, and discrimination still exist in communities throughout the world. The use of "diversity" is also acknowledgment that information organizations and information professionals can actively work to upend these realities.

What Characteristics Do Diversity Efforts Address?

Diversity efforts usually respond to or address the needs of specific groups or cultures within the larger community. These groups form around shared characteristics of difference. What are currently considered the most apparent characteristics for diversity efforts—gender, race and ethnicity, physical and mental ability, age, and sexual orientation—have evolved as societal and cultural changes brought to light the unique experiences of people who shared a common characteristic of difference. Efforts focused on gender diversity that sought to address differences in experiences between men and women have expanded to understand the social construct of gender and now may consider gender expression rather than an either/or approach to male and female. Understandings of groups can also change, as has been the case with revisions to organizations' understanding of Hispanic populations or distinctions between Asian populations and Pacific Island populations. The work of diversity changes as awareness of unique experiences and the exclusion, prejudice, or discrimination experienced by groups of people becomes more widely known and acknowledged.

> "The work of diversity changes as awareness of unique experiences and the exclusion, prejudice, or discrimination experienced by groups of people becomes more widely known and acknowledged."

In addition to the characteristics mentioned above, increasingly there is acknowledgment of the unique experiences resulting from differences in economic status, educational attainment (e.g., first-generation college experience), family or relationship composition (e.g., single parent, adoptive or foster, multigenerational families, single, married, partnered), immigrant experience, geography (e.g., rural, urban, suburban), work experience, linguistic abilities, and religious beliefs. To help broaden understandings of diversity and diversity efforts, many organizations use a "diversity wheel." Figure 4.1, "Diversity Wheel," illustrates the multitude of experiences through which people experience their lives. The diversity wheel helps illustrate that people do not experience life through a single dimension, but rather through multiple perspectives (e.g., their economic background and their race and ethnicity, and their gender identity, and, and . . .), each of which influences their experience.

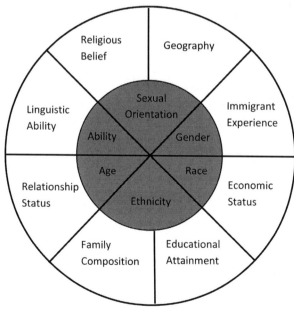

Figure 4.1 Diversity Wheel

It is important to remember that diversity work should be responsive to the community being served. As an organization considers its community, it may identify prominent community characteristics and seek to better understand the experiences of those individuals. For example, an information system that covers a large service area might prioritize the differences in experience between rural and urban users. Organizations may also determine that certain characteristics need to be better refined. For example, in a large and diverse Asian or Hispanic population, differences in national origin may be particularly important. Diversity is work; it must be responsive and adaptive, not static adherence to any set of definitions.

Diversity, Intellectual Freedom, and Equity of Access

Diversity connects with, complements, and advances two key principles of the information profession—intellectual freedom and equity of access (see also chapter 36, "Intellectual Freedom").

Information professionals' commitment to intellectual freedom compels them to support and protect information users' rights to read, seek information, and speak freely.[5] Understandings of different user needs (see also chapter 12, "Information Needs: Understanding and Responding to Today's Information User") have informed numerous intellectual freedom policies supported by the American Library Association, including diversity in collection development,[6] universal right to free expression,[7] access to resources and services regardless of gender identity or sexual orientation,[8] services to persons with disabilities,[9] and linguistic pluralism.[10] These policies advise information professionals to not only collect a diverse set of materials, but also to develop a diverse set of services to actively provide information to the many different people that need it.

> "Diversity connects with, complements, and advances two key principles of the information profession—intellectual freedom and equity of access."

Equity of access builds upon what information organizations have traditionally termed outreach, where organizations develop special programs or projects for under- or unserved—and often diverse—populations (e.g., adult new and nonreaders, the incarcerated, people experiencing poverty or homelessness, the differently abled, racially and ethnically diverse communities, immigrants, the geographically isolated, the elderly, and homebound populations). Many outreach services see great success, but too often depend on special funding or specialists dedicated to the work. Changes in staffing, funding, or priorities can disrupt the services and end the relationship with the particular community. Equitable access encourages a shift from developing special services for specific user groups to sustaining quality services for all user groups at all times by actively and regularly considering the multiple perspectives by which individuals encounter the information organization and its services.[11] Equitable access seeks to recognize the diversity of users and develop information services responsive to their unique experiences. Equitable services and policies are developed through an appraisal of the diverse landscape in which information users operate.

Intercultural Communication and Collaboration

Among the most important diversity work information organizations can undertake is the provision of equitable access to information through the inclusion of diverse communities in the design and delivery of programs and services. It is the information professional's responsibility and goal to learn about their community's diversity by becoming more familiar

> "Among the most important diversity work information organizations can undertake is the provision of equitable access to information through the inclusion of diverse communities in the design and delivery of programs and services."

Patty Wong and Miguel Figueroa

with linguistic preferences, social customs, and cultural norms and to develop strategies to best serve the full community. Professionals can meet individuals where they are and work collaboratively with community representatives to address those needs in an effective and positively impactful way. Including representatives from diverse communities can improve understanding and discussion of cultural values—and there is no better method of learning about a community than through direct participation. Community outreach is also critical, as service development should be accompanied by trusted and respected activities that demonstrate genuine interest and engagement, and ultimately cultural interchange.

The complexity of communication and its importance is only heightened when communicating across diverse communities. Effectiveness is much preferred over efficiency. Active listening and awareness of the individual or group dynamic is essential to establish a trusted and reliable dialogue and connection with the audience. See textbox 4.2.

TEXTBOX 4.2

Effective Communication Strategies for Serving Diverse Communities

1. Leave your ego at the door: Colleagues often have the best ideas, resources, and solutions; the optimal role of information professionals is often one of active listener and facilitator. A healthy appreciation for continual learning and humility offers greater depth to cultural development as an individual and within one's organization.
2. Check assumptions related to privilege and class: Everyone comes with a set of ideals and lessons intrinsic to his or her environment and experience. Information professionals should remove any presumptions and assumptions that stem from a certain position or societal standing; these factors may influence the information professional's intent and motivation in determining service delivery needs for others.
3. Filter out the centrist lens: Other, perhaps less traditional, perspectives can be valuable in analysis and operational considerations.
4. Develop a knowledge base: Increasing one's personal and professional awareness, perception, and understanding of the demographic framework are hallmarks of culturally engaged agencies.

Language

Language is an incredibly important element in cultural competency, especially when working with ethnic diversity. There are many factors involved in one's choice and preference of language—where and how one develops linguistic skills, the social context, and common use of language at home compared to other environments. When learning more about the demographics in a service community, knowledge of the many languages spoken at home, immigration factors, and birthplace can influence communication. Consider the differences between Castilian Spanish and conversational Spanish or the many dialects of Cantonese and the distinction between Taiwanese and Mandarin. Even within a common language, understanding language preferences of diverse communities can be incredibly important. The uses of "differently abled" or "disabled" or "Hispanic" or "Latino" may vary across communities.

Distinctions in language apply to both oral and written communication. Word choice and translations of library card registration forms or fliers, room signage, and other public information should be considered carefully and determined with community members' input. Ultimately, there is no substitute for actual knowledge of the community and reliable interpretation with experts from the community.

Social Customs

"Familiarity with social customs demonstrates respect and authentic interest in developing services that reflect community values."

Familiarity with social customs demonstrates respect and authentic interest in developing services that reflect community values. Customs may include everything from meal preparation to gift giving to taking off one's shoes before entering a facility to offering the oldest member of the group the choicest morsels of the meal before others. Becoming familiar with social customs and being mindful of differences and similarities in customs deepens understanding and appreciation of diverse communities. As with language, respecting a culture's ownership of a custom and acknowledging their right to share and define customs, their appropriate use, and their significance is important.

Cultural Norms

Activities that may be commonplace for some may be unusual for others. These situations may include behavior related to family communication and hierarchy, discipline, and cultural pride. Diverse communities may maintain cultural practices and norms that are unfamiliar to the larger community. Simultaneously, customs of the larger community may be foreign to diverse communities. For example, the concept of information or educational materials available for borrowing may be new to first- or even second-generation immigrant communities who had no similar experiences in their home country. Current cultural norms may also be a combination of traditional and contemporary practices, influenced and shaped by larger community expectations.

Contributing to a Culturally Competent Organization

Developing culturally competent organizations is key to information organizations' diversity efforts. Cultural competence is defined as a set of congruent behaviors, attitudes, and policies that come together and enable a system, agency, or professionals to work effectively in cross-cultural situations.[12] Textbox 4.3 lists five essential elements that should be present at every level of an organization, including policy making, administration, and practice, and should be reflected in the attitudes, structures, policies, and services of the organization.[13]

TEXTBOX 4.3

Five Essential Elements for a Culturally Competent Organization

1. Valuing diversity
2. Having the capacity for cultural self-assessment
3. Being conscious of the dynamics inherent when cultures interact
4. Having institutionalized cultural knowledge
5. Having developed adaptations of service delivery reflecting an understanding of cultural diversity

---

Leading Cultural Competency

An organization's leadership provides support and sets expectations for cultural awareness and acumen. Change most often happens when beginning with a review of organization mission, vision, and values and organizational goals and priorities to reflect a commitment to diversity.

Patty Wong and Miguel Figueroa

Transformative change can only take place if the organization creates safety and structures to learn through deeper engaged conversations about strengths, values, assumptions and biases, fears, class and privilege, and expectations. The resulting dialogue breaks down barriers to full understanding and stronger personal and professional revelation, leading to organizational cultural competence.

Building an organization that is culturally competent is a progressive, transformative process, requiring systematic engagement and change. It involves taking risks, allowing for learning through failure, commitment, and perseverance.

Diversity Committees and Employee/Community Interest Groups

Moving an organization toward a more diverse and inclusive system requires opportunities for engagement. Information professionals bring their own cultural values and experiences into an organization, and these can benefit the organization and be shared with the community. Bringing people together, both within the organization and across the community, around shared characteristics of difference or across differences, can help strengthen diversity efforts and engage new allies and supporters.

A diversity committee or group should be developed formally with a name and scope that is focused on inclusion as an organizational value. Groups should have goals and objectives that reflect cultural competencies as a system process. It should never be assumed that staff or community members from diverse backgrounds automatically participate in these efforts; allow people to contribute as they deem appropriate. (See also chapter 4, "Outreach and Partnership Resources" in the online supplement.)

Partnerships

Information professionals have no shortage of community-based and professionally based organizations to reach out to and partner with to improve diversity efforts.

There are many community-based organizations dedicated to the support and advancement of diverse communities. Immediate resources are usually available among advocates and supporters (e.g., friends groups, board members, trustees, administrators, or elected officials). Other approaches to working with community-based organizations include surveying local organizations, including nonprofits, faith communities, campus or city offices, and social clubs or gathering places; identifying potential allies and developing relationships (initially through information exchange and later through mutually beneficial service design and delivery); and becoming engaged in local organizations at whatever active level is available to demonstrate interest and commitment. Effective partnering includes building relationships based on trust, respect, and common ground.

There are a number of organizations within the information profession that actively promote service to diverse communities. State libraries and state library associations are particularly key for understanding the local community and environment. Ethnic library associations—the American Indian Library Association (AILA), the Asian-Pacific American Librarians Association (APALA), the Black Caucus of the American Library Association (BCALA), the Chinese American Librarians Association (CALA), and the National Association to Promote Library & Information Services to Latinos and the Spanish Speaking (REFORMA)—are all nationally focused, but with many local chapters. The American Library Association, including its policy offices, divisions, and roundtables, provides numerous communities focused on diversity efforts.

Valuable partners and resources may also exist outside of the information profession in organizations supporting allied professions, such as educators, social workers, medical professionals, and government or nonprofit professionals (see also chapter 4, "Diversity Information Resources" in the online supplement).

Talent Management

As with other skills, developing cultural competency requires a talent management plan that includes training and evaluation, performance measures, mentoring and coaching, and structured and informal communication. Organizations can work to identify information or talent gaps in staffing or operations and work to address them through staff training, meetings, and sharing opportunities that advance cultural competencies.

Recruitment, selection, and retention efforts are particularly important in fostering cultural competency as individual perspectives and experiences are valued. Leaders can work with human resources departments to develop job descriptions that convey the organization's commitment to diversity. Specific recruitment strategies might include the use of supplemental questions that focus on work with diverse communities, prioritization of multilingual and multicultural skills and abilities, participation of community representatives in the selection process, and promotion of opportunities through diversity advocates and organizations.

Shared Leadership: Boards, Friends, and Volunteers

Cultural competency extends to the shared leadership of an organization, including boards, friends groups, and volunteers. An informed and educated leadership and governance structure is critical to advancing cultural competency. Training opportunities can be shared with an organization's community leadership and support bodies, including volunteers and even elected officials. Engaging leaders in goal setting, planning, and implementation of efforts toward a culturally competent and inclusive organization is incredibly important.

Information Organizations and Community Development

Information organizations have a unique opportunity to provide a venue and forum to focus on shared opportunities, highlight attention, and broaden understanding pertaining to community and diversity.

Information Organizations Support Communities

Through collections, programs, and services, information organizations contribute to the community, and with these contributions come opportunities to serve and support diverse communities. Within collections, many information organizations allocate funding specifically for the purpose of purchasing bilingual and multilingual materials relevant to the community. By including materials in a variety of formats, featuring a diversity of authors and illustrators, and addressing subjects in all areas, information organizations can reflect the diversity of the community. Information organizations can establish collection development policies for selection and purchasing that are reflective of the community's diverse needs. Community members can contribute to the development of collections through input in selection and even organization and promotion of materials (see also chapter 25, "Managing Collections").

Programming that highlights and reflects the community's diverse cultural values is a key step toward a more inclusive organization and community. Programs and services can be community driven and community created through partnerships with community-based organizations. Programming can also advance engagement at a community-wide level through conversations that advance cultural exchange. As a respected institution, an information organization can facilitate important discussions around what might be difficult topics, such as race, social justice, and cultural values.

Recruitment to community leadership positions, including boards, friends groups, and volunteers, should include considerations of diversity both to advance diversity efforts in the community and as a means to strengthen the organization through the inclusion of multiple perspectives and talents. Outreach, promotion, and partnerships provide additional opportunities to advance diversity efforts. Dedicating staff time and operational funding to maintaining a broad community presence across a range of community members is critical. Additionally, sharing communications through these connections and channels creates true ownership, respect, and involvement across the community.

TEXTBOX 4.4

Topic for Discussion

As information professionals and as persons with unique perspectives and experiences, what personal contributions can be made to an information organization's diversity efforts?

Communities Support Information Organizations

As communities become more actively engaged in the production of knowledge and information, they can turn to information organizations as not only sources for content, but also as repositories for the information and resources they themselves create. By actively engaging in diversity efforts, information organizations can be at the forefront of knowledge and information cocreation with members of the community. Partnerships with diverse communities can result in unique and valuable local cultural history resources, artistic collaborations, or even social or entrepreneurial projects.

Diverse communities can support information organizations' role in preservation and access. Involvement from diverse communities can help ensure that information organizations collect and preserve the materials that are most important to documenting a community and its members. Information organizations that fail to engage diverse communities are likely also to fail to preserve their historical records. Diverse communities can work with information organizations to acquire and contextualize unique collections that advance research and guarantee future access to materials for future generations.

Finally, information organizations that engage diverse communities remain relevant across their communities. Diverse communities provide efficient systems for the sharing of information. As individuals gather around shared differences, they also share experiences and insights with their peers. The information organization that engages a diverse community ensures that its services, programs, and value are promoted within that community.

Conclusion

Information organizations and information professionals are well positioned to serve diverse individuals and advance diversity efforts within their communities. Diversity efforts strengthen the work of information professionals and ultimately improve the position of the information organization in its community. The efforts involved, including understanding a community's characteristics of difference, engaging in intercultural communication and collaboration, and developing cultural competency within the organization, require time, skill, and attention. The ultimate rewards, however, include greater support for the information organization and information professionals, and greater advancement toward the organization's mission and goals.

"Diversity efforts strengthen the work of information professionals and ultimately improve the position of the information organization in its community."

Appendix 4.1: Most Common Characteristics of Diversity

Provided below is a list of the most common characteristics of diversity, with brief descriptions of how these differences are currently conceived and how they might evolve in the future.

Gender

Gender diversity (or gender equality) efforts usually focus on traditional male and female understandings of gender and seek to advance the representation of women in traditionally male-dominated programs or services. As the understanding of gender increases, gender diversity may also expand beyond the common gender norms. Nonbinary gender diversity includes understanding for individuals' gender identity (self-concept), gender expression (outward gender expression), and gender role (place within society's male/female gender assignments). This expanded understanding of gender may also intersect with efforts to address differences in sexuality or sexual orientation.

Race and Ethnicity

In the United States, diversity efforts focused on race and ethnicity have traditionally aligned with the race and ethnicity (Hispanic or Latino) categories identified in the U.S. Census as standardized by the U.S. Office of Management and Budget (OMB). The current race question in the U.S. census asks individuals to self-identify using the following terms:

*   *White:* A person having origins in any of the original peoples of Europe, the Middle East, or North Africa.
*   *Black or African American:* A person having origins in any of the Black racial groups of Africa.
*   *American Indian or Alaska Native:* A person having origins in any of the original peoples of North and South America (including Central America) and who maintains tribal affiliation or community attachment.
*   *Asian:* A person having origins in any of the original peoples of the Far East, Southeast Asia, or the Indian subcontinent including, for example, Cambodia, China, India, Japan, Korea, Malaysia, Pakistan, the Philippine Islands, Thailand, and Vietnam.
*   *Native Hawaiian or Other Pacific Islander:* A person having origins in any of the original peoples of Hawaii, Guam, Samoa, or other Pacific Islands.

Individuals are provided the opportunity to report more than one race.

Additionally, the U.S. Office of Management and Budget requires agencies to use a minimum of two ethnicities in collecting and reporting data: Hispanic or Latino and Not Hispanic or Latino.

*   *Hispanic or Latino:* A person of Cuban, Mexican, Puerto Rican, South or Central American, or other Spanish culture or origin regardless of race.
*   *Specific Categories:* Individuals reporting Hispanic or Latino ethnicity may also report specific categories—Mexican, Mexican American, Chicano; Puerto Rican; Cuban; another Hispanic, Latino, or Spanish origin; and write-in answers.

Diversity efforts designed to address race and ethnicity usually focus on advancing the representation and participation of non-White individuals in programs and services.

Physical and Mental Ability

Differences in physical and mental ability vary greatly among individuals, making it difficult to clearly identify all of the characteristics that could be a priority for diversity efforts focused on physical and mental ability. The Americans with Disabilities Act (ADA), one of the most comprehensive pieces of civil rights legislation that prohibits discrimination and guarantees equal opportunities for people with disabilities, does not specifically list the impairments or differences that the legislation addresses. Rather, the ADA defines disability as "a physical or mental impairment that substantially limits one or more major life activities, a person who has a history or records of such an impairment, or a person who is perceived by others as having such an impairment."[14]

Many current discussions of difference in physical and mental abilities address visible and invisible differences and permanent and temporary differences. Because of the range of differences, many advocates encourage allowing individuals to express their physical or mental difference as they define it rather than assigning a specific category to a perceived physical or mental difference.

Diversity efforts designed to address physical and mental ability usually seek opportunities to include, accommodate, or design for persons with different abilities in programs and services. These efforts also seek to ensure the participation and representation of people with different abilities in decision-making bodies and organizations.

Age

The multiple generations represented in today's communities and organizations carry with them different experiences and perspectives. Generational differences may become even more apparent in communities as baby boomers (born 1946–1964) begin to enter retirement and as younger generations, raised in the midst of significant technological change, emerge as independent decision and taste makers. Generational differences can include differences in values, communication styles, work expectations, and political and social beliefs.

In the workplace, diversity efforts focused on age seek to offset age discrimination, which is often experienced by older adults, but also by young and emerging professionals. In organizations and communities, diversity efforts focused on age can help encourage participation and representation from across generational lines.

Sexual Orientation

The unique experiences of gay, lesbian, bisexual, and transgender people form a final—and still emerging—category of diversity that is frequently addressed by organizations. Sexual orientation is based on an individual's attraction to people from the opposite, the same, or both sexes. As mentioned above, gender identity (self-concept), gender expression (outward gender expression), and gender role (place within society's male/female gender assignments) may also be included in this area of difference. Society's changing understanding of sexual orientation and the personal nature of this category of difference make it difficult to fully define the range of difference contained within this category. Relying on an individual's personal expression or self-definition may provide the greatest understanding.

In the workplace, diversity efforts focused on sexual orientation seek to offset the discrimination faced by GLBT (gay, lesbian, bisexual, and transgender) employees and patrons. In organizations and communities, diversity efforts focused on sexual orientation can help encourage participation and representation from across the spectrum of experiences. These efforts may be especially important for older populations, which might be particularly vulnerable to discrimination and exclusion based on sexual orientation; GLBT parents and families, which may face exclusion or prejudice due to perceived nonconformity to the "normal" family composition; and children and young people, where the pressures of dealing with emerging sexuality or self-discovery are compounded by a sense of difference from their peers.

Notes

1. Cedric Herring, "Does Diversity Pay? Race, Gender and the Business Case for Diversity," *American Sociological Review* 74, no. 2 (April 2009).
2. Ronald S. Burt, "Social Origins of Good Ideas," *American Journal of Sociology* 110, no. 2 (September 2004), http://web.upcomillas.es/personal/rgimeno/doctorado/SOGI.pdf.
3. Jeffrey F. Millem, Mitchell J. Chang, and Anthony Lising Antonio, "Making Diversity Work on Campus: A Research-Based Perspective," Making Excellence Inclusive Initiative, Association of American Colleges and Universities, 2005, http://www.aacu.org/inclusive_excellence/documents/Milem_et_al.pdf.
4. Ibid.
5. "Intellectual Freedom," American Library Association, last modified September 17, 2014, http://www.ala.org/advocacy/intfreedom.
6. "Policy B.2.1.11 Diversity in Collection Development," in *American Library Association Policy Manual* (Chicago, IL: ALA Council, 2013), http://www.ala.org/aboutala/governance/policymanual.
7. "Policy B.2.1.12 Universal Right to Free Expression," in *American Library Association Policy Manual* (Chicago, IL: ALA Council, 2013), http://www.ala.org/aboutala/governance/policymanual.
8. "Policy B.2.1.15 Access to Library Resources and Services Regardless of Sex, Gender Identity, Gender Expression, or Sexual Orientation," in *American Library Association Policy Manual* (Chicago, IL: ALA Council, 2013), http://www.ala.org/aboutala/governance/policymanual.
9. "Policy B.2.1.20 Services to Persons with Disabilities." in American Library Association Policy Manual (Chicago, IL: ALA Council, 2013), http://www.ala.org/aboutala/governance/policymanual.
10. "Policy B.2.3.1 Linguistic Pluralism," in *American Library Association Policy Manual* (Chicago, IL: ALA Council, 2013), http://www.ala.org/aboutala/governance/policymanual.
11. Satia Marshall Orange and Robin Osborne, "Introduction," in *From Outreach to Equity: Innovative Models of Library Policy and Practice* (Chicago, IL: American Library Association, 2004).
12. T. Cross, B. Bazron, K. Dennis, and M. Isaacs, *Toward a Culturally Competent System of Care*, vol. 1 (Washington, DC: Georgetown University, 1989).
13. Ibid.
14. U.S. Department of Justice Civil Rights Division, "Introduction to the ADA," *Information and Technical Assistance on the Americans with Disabilities Act*, last modified August 10, 2014, http://www.ada.gov/ada_intro.htm.

Part II

Information Professions
Physical and Virtual Environments

The library is a community center, a place for lifelong learning, a place for early childhood, emergent literacy, a creator space, and perhaps most subtly, a statement of community value.

—James LaRue (2014)

In a profession that is experiencing continuous change, it is not surprising that the work being done by today's information professionals is quite different from what it was in the past, and clearly this phenomenon will continue into the future. As a consequence of the changing information landscape, the roles of information professionals have become complex as they creatively find new ways to meet the evolving needs of their communities. It is up to information professionals to demonstrate the value of the work they do and advocate for the changing needs of the communities they serve.

Part II examines changes in specific information environments, including those that serve students through school and academic libraries, serve business clients through special libraries, and serve each member of the community through public libraries. And since information services are no longer limited to physical spaces, a new type of information organization—the digital library (as either part of a larger organization or as its own service entity)—is also discussed. A valuable takeaway of part II is the identification of various career pathways across these types of information organization for today's information professional. Many opportunities—both within and outside the library setting—are now available and explored in this section.

Welcome to *Part II—Information Professions: Physical and Virtual Environments!*

5

Librarianship

A CONTINUOUSLY EVOLVING PROFESSION

Stephen Abram

"Change Is Our Tradition" was the theme of the 2000 Special Libraries Association (SLA) conference, and nothing could be truer. All types of information organizations have continuously adapted to changing environments and technology—with collections evolving from scrolls to the codex, card catalogs to online catalogs, print indexes to full-text databases, and in-person reference support to virtual reference services.

From their beginning, information organizations grappled with the concept of "free or fee," the idea of limited membership libraries, and the growth of universal literacy and their role therein. As society grappled with new issues, information organizations wrestled with the same challenges, such as whether information organizations should be places where racial segregation was practiced. Information organizations evolved, not just as a reflection of society, but as leaders in community and research spaces.

This chapter explores the evolutionary trends of information organizations and information professionals in the late twentieth and early twenty-first centuries. After completing this chapter, the reader should have an understanding of how information professionals must continuously adapt to change in order to not only survive, but also thrive as agents of change. These changes are about much more than e-books or the web. Instead, they represent a fundamental challenge to the underpinnings of the profession's values and the basic business models and missions of information organizations.

While technology gets most of the attention when change is discussed, it is changes in human behavior that are frequently the main thrust of change in information communities. Some changes are easy to see (e.g., new technology), while other changes—such as social behaviors that impact information organizations (e.g., web-savvy users who demand virtual access to resources) are harder to identify. Despite its complexity, change is important to the history of information organizations. The byword for information professionals must be "adapt or die," since change is our tradition. As a wise person once said, the dinosaurs did not die out because of climate change; they died out because they failed to adapt.

Change and Adaptation in the Information Profession

The history of the information profession is characterized by the need to adapt to change. Historically, it has been easier to adapt since change was achieved over a longer period and society and technology did not transform as rapidly as it does today. For example, it took centuries for the book format, global literacy, and universal education to spread widely, and indeed, early technologies like television and the telephone took many decades to widely penetrate the market. Such is not the case today, when the penetration of technological change can be achieved in mere years. And with each technological change, human behavior also changes—changes that can no longer be defined by generation. As with all species, humans are adaptive animals and respond to environmental changes such as the technological climate.

Information professionals used to have time to respond and evolve, but the information revolution is just that—a revolution where things change rapidly. This requires a stronger set of competencies and leadership skills to steer the institution and its staff. Bureaucratic processes, which traditionally comprised best practices in the public sector to protect the public purse, have become the enemy of the nimbleness needed in this environment. As professionals who often work in the public sector, there is a need for cultural change within the information organization. Reactivity versus proactivity is one place to start. Information professionals need to do more than just see the changes currently happening; they need to get out in front of them—forecasting what is to come and proactively moving ahead to adapt to these changes.

> "Information professionals need to do more than just see the changes currently happening; they need to get out in front of them—forecasting what is to come and proactively moving ahead to adapt to these changes."

There is a dynamic tension in the information field between conservative approaches to change and those who want a more aggressive approach. Balancing these tensions and having the ability to identify trends and adapt to change are rare and important attributes of leaders in the information profession. Some of the critical and difficult questions that the profession's leaders struggle with every day include

- What trends are "real," and which ones are fads?
- Which trends are relevant to information organizations and worth an investment of time and effort to explore?
- Which trends are more important than others, and how do information professionals set priorities?
- What strategies can be used to bring staff, management, and communities along the curve of innovation, especially when the future opportunities and threats are clear to some but not to others?

There are definite benefits to spotting trends early. As an example, those who saw the Internet, mobile devices, or smart phones as opportunities early in the transformation were better prepared to respond to these trends. Similarly, the profession's innovators who jumped in with both feet to the Second Life 3-D immersive environment or QR codes gained experience that helped them evaluate future gamification, geolocation, near-field communication (such as iBeacons for mobile phones), and 3-D learning environments. Today, for example, information professionals experiment with drones, Google Glass, visualization tools, and linked data. Each will follow its own arc; some will reach critical mass adoption, and some will be evolutionary distractions. Learning happens every step of the way, and the learning curve is usually too steep to start too late.

The right strategy is to explore opportunities and take risks in a careful and controlled way through betas, pilots, experiments, and trials. One strategy is to work in partnership with vendors as they research and experiment. Another is to work through associations, collaboratives, and consortia to share the expense and the effort (and the risk) with others. Information professionals can also pilot new ideas with small groups of targeted end users to get feedback on their ideas and innovations.

The Value of the Information Professional

Lewis Carroll wrote in *Alice in Wonderland* that "if you don't know where you are going then any road will get you there." Two things help professionals choose to evolve: a focus on the core values that never change, and knowledge regarding the distinct value they deliver better than anyone else in their community.

Information professionals are fundamentally about transforming lives. Information professionals who focus on information transactions (e.g., circulating collections, answering in-person reference questions) are missing the opportunity to communicate the true contributions they provide to their communities. If information organizations define themselves solely based on their collections and services (e.g., web search engines, e-books, podcasts), they threaten the very foundations of information organizations. Instead, the focus should be on the impact of information professionals on people's lives. As such, the role of information professionals continues to evolve beyond the physical setting to one where they are positioned as drivers of change. They will serve as advocates on important issues, such as the right to read, academic and intellectual freedom, digital rights and copyright, and censorship.

> "If information organizations define themselves solely based on their collections and services (e.g., web search engines, e-books, podcasts), they threaten the very foundations of information organizations. Instead, the focus should be on the impact of information professionals on people's lives."

Drivers of Evolution

To what extent are information organizations aligned with user expectations, trends, and best practices? What must change to better position the information organization to face the challenges of the next ten to fifteen years and to ensure that the organization continues to be a relevant and meaningful community institution? These are critical questions to consider in ensuring that the information profession continues to evolve and thrive in the future.

One way to critically assess the organization's capacity to anticipate and respond to a changing world is through strategic planning (see also chapter 21, "Management Skills"). Strategic planning is about abandoning outdated practices and embracing change. If a strategic plan does not chart a bold new direction for the organization that is consistent with the changing needs of users (and, perhaps more importantly, nonusers), it will not be a useful tool for managing future service delivery.

Looking at the big picture, major changes to the information profession are already taking place. The functions and roles of information organizations are changing with the surge of information and technologies. These organizations are no longer simply "warehouses" for print material that is borrowed by residents for off-site use—if they ever really were. Increasingly, these organizations are information, program, and cultural centers supporting a wide range of community, business, or research activities and objectives. In addition, the ways people are using information is also shifting, with physical access plateauing and remote access increasing. The function and design of information organizations is evolving in response to these changing roles and demographic shifts, emerging technologies, and increasing consumer expectations for what they want out of the organization's service portfolio.[1]

Looking more specifically at the significant trends affecting information professionals and organizations today, these changes are grouped into three areas: (1) lifestyle and societal trends, (2) technology trends, and (3) library facility and service trends—and are listed in table 5.1.

Table 5.1. Significant Trends Affecting the Information Profession

Lifestyle and Society Trends	Technology Trends	Facility and Service Trends
Accessibility	Online learning	Libraries are destinations
Digital divide	Wireless expectations	Multiservice
Discretionary time deficit	Digital download kiosks	Community engagement
Desired use of leisure time	Mobile device arena	Makerspaces
Environmental and "green" concerns	Live-streaming	Little free libraries
Family structure and dynamics	E-book readership	Customer-first focus
Health and wellness	User-created content	
Immigration	"Cloud" computing	
Information literacy	Computer training space	
Labor trends	3-D printers	
Partnership and collaboration	Virtual libraries	
"Smart" device expectations		
Web-savvy users		

Lifestyle and societal trends have significant implications for ways that information organizations need to evolve. For example, changes in family structures and dynamics (e.g., the rise of nontraditional family structures, the declining predominance of two working-parent households, a rise in commuter lifestyles, increased urbanization, and shared households) have implications for information organizations in terms of hours of operation, asynchronous (virtual) programming, and the delivery of library programs and services.[2] (See appendix 5.1, "Lifestyle and Societal Trends," for a more comprehensive explanation of these trends.)

Technology trends are constantly and rapidly developing, making them hard to predict. One key trend, the growth of online learning (especially massive open online courses, or MOOCs), has created issues that, to date, have largely affected academic libraries. However, MOOCs are starting to influence services in public libraries too. For example, in the United States, the Atlanta-Fulton Public Library system has created eCampus, a resource that offers users access to e-learning programs for adults and high school students. (See appendix 5.2, "Technology Trends," for a more comprehensive explanation of these trends.)

Facility and service trends generally point to an information organization that is much more integrated in the affairs of the community. The makerspace movement (see also chapter 19, "Creation Culture and Makerspaces") is a good example of trends in this category, with information organizations providing spaces for users to collaborate, learn hands-on skills, and create and produce something such as music, videos, jewelry, games, robotics, and electronics. (See appendix 5.3, "Facility and Service Trends," for a more comprehensive explanation of these trends.)

TEXTBOX 5.1

Topic for Discussion

What are the three trends information professionals and leaders *must* address? What are the least important?

Forecast: Emerging Trends and Issues

The future trends and issues mentioned above will require information professionals to remain forward thinking—both for their organizations as well as for their own professional development. How will information professionals evolve and adapt in the coming years?

In his report "Confronting the Future," Roger Levien addresses the major issues facing public information organizations in the future and provides a framework for envisioning the future (see figure 5.1). Levien introduces four "dimensions," each of which consists of a continuum of choices that lies between two extremes.[3]

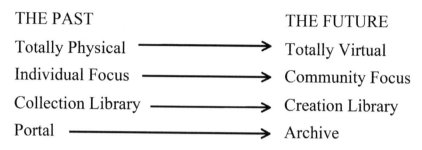

Figure 5.1 Four Dimensions for Envisioning the Future

While the framework was specifically designed for public libraries, these dimensions can also be applied to other information organizations. To meet the challenges they will face in the future, information organizations must make strategic choices concerning their place on each of the four dimensions identified by Levien. These four dimensions are described below.

Dimension 1: Physical to Virtual

This dimension relates to the form of the library as a facility, and the form of the library's collection. On one end of this spectrum is a purely physical organization; however, this sort of organization is no longer considered realistic. On the other end is the virtual organization—a space on the web that hosts all of the library's services and collections, and which is accessible to users through the library's web presence anywhere over the Internet. On this spectrum, most modern libraries are somewhere in the middle, still offering a physical building and collection, while increasingly providing virtual features, such as e-books and online services.

Dimension 2: Individual Focus to Community Focus

This second dimension deals with the type of service provided by the library and the point of focus for its users. The extremes in this case are individual-focused organizations and community-focused organizations. Organizations that focus on the individual seek to accommodate each user independently (with quiet study space, privacy, comfort, and minimal distractions). In this scenario, the primary relationship is between the information professional and the individual user. Those organizations that focus on the community look to provide space for community interaction and group work. These libraries invest considerable resources in a broad range of services, events, and programs that engage the community. These organizations are "community centers." In addition, these organizations often contain archives of local records, artifacts, memoirs, and memorabilia.

Dimension 3: Collection to Creation

This third dimension involves the way in which libraries interact with and engage their users. On one end of the spectrum is the collection-focused library, where users come to enjoy and experience the materials in the library's collection. This organization is a repository of intellectual and recreational information available for the user to explore. The other extreme is an organization where, instead of simply exploring the works of others, users are encouraged to see the organization as a creative space where equipment and facilities are provided to produce their own creative products.

Dimension 4: Portal to Archive

This fourth dimension of Levien's report looks at the ownership of the collection. In the portal model, the materials available to users are not the property of the library. Instead, the library acts as a facilitator between the user and resources that are available through other organizations. On the other end of the spectrum is an archive model, where the library's role is to possess documentary materials in a range of genres and mediums. In the archive model, the library has an important role to play in assembling and disseminating local information (and not simply historical information). This library is a living community resource that tells the community's story—past, present, and future.

Sustainability of Twenty-First-Century Information Organizations

> "Information professionals must develop the leadership capabilities necessary to thrive in this dynamically changing environment, encouraging staff to embrace change, and fighting the need for too much control in an increasingly ambiguous future."

Some challenges regarding the value and sustainability of information organizations remain—especially in terms of taking risks and influencing decision makers, building cooperative relationships, and ensuring adequate funding. While some information professionals are able to adapt and evolve to meet the challenges of a changing environment, too many information professionals are still risk averse, avoid confrontation, and lack strong ties to decision makers. Information professionals must develop the leadership capabilities necessary to thrive in this dynamically changing environment, encouraging staff to embrace change and fighting the need for too much control in an increasingly ambiguous future (see also chapter 39, "Leadership for Today and Tomorrow"). Information professionals also need to develop effective soft management skills (e.g., vision, influence, presentation skills, professional networking, change and risk-management strategies, strategic budgeting, and marketing) in order to improve their influence and positioning.

Another significant challenge is cooperation on a sustainable and scalable basis. Information organizations had a huge vision when OCLC (http://www.oclc.org) was created in the 1970s. This not-for-profit collaborative redefined the cataloging and metadata space and is a key part of such services as Amazon and Google Books. However, since then, no other entities have been created on a global scale to effectively address the challenges of scalability, creating content, systems, apps, websites, and more. Consortia struggle with issues of scale. To get the best prices through cooperative buying, they must get bigger and more powerful as they bring information organizations to the table as buyers. The technological changes happening in the information field provide opportunities for consortia to become major infrastructure players for the information sector.

One cannot discuss sustainability of information organizations without mentioning funding. Unfortunately, recent financial trends typically involve reduced funding for information organizations, while expecting the same level of services, or even expanded services. This situation puts information organizations in a difficult position. The solution to this problem is both complicated and complex. Some organizations and jurisdictions have been able to clearly articulate the case for adequate funding, and as a result, they thrived, while some have been forced to reduce services or close due to lack of funding. The long-term solution rests in better communication, advocacy, and relationships with decision makers, as well as efforts to drive productivity enhancements and cost efficiencies. While libraries, for example, tend not to be businesses, they must behave in a businesslike fashion (using expected best practices) in today's public funding environment.

TEXTBOX 5.2

Topic for Discussion

Describe the information organization of the future and the information professional who works there. Pick a year more than ten years from now. What are information professionals like? What competencies are most critical?

Essential Resources to Stay Ahead of the Curve

So how can information professionals stay ahead of the curve and avoid fighting fires? How should information professionals learn about the future? It is simple, really—in two words, *read widely*. Do not just stick to the library and information science literature and sources—also consider following publications in focused subject fields (such as user experience, copyright law, etc.) as well as experts in popular culture, technology, education, and other areas that are of interest. Print is rarely the right medium for exploring trends. Blogs, discussion boards, and conferences are where the real action is taking place.

What resources, blogs, readings, strategies, and social media should be in the professional's personal learning network (PLN)? (Learn more about personal learning networks in chapter 38, "Global Learning Networks"). While the real transformative trends tend to happen on the fringes, it is useful to read a variety of resources to gain insight regarding how innovators and early adopters are experimenting and pioneering with new methods, technologies, and ideas. Some examples of quality research organizations that cover the information profession are described below, and additional resources are covered in the book's online supplement.

- *The NMC Horizon Reports:* The NMC Horizon Project charts the landscape of emerging technologies for teaching, learning, research, and creative inquiry. Their reports cover trends in higher education, K–12 education, technology, museums, and now academic libraries.[4]
- *Pew Research Center's Internet & American Life Reports:* The Pew Research Center's Internet & American Life Project examines how U.S. residents use the Internet, and for the past three years, they have tracked trends regarding views on the nation's libraries. The project's reports are based on nationwide surveys and qualitative research, including data collected from government agencies, technology firms, academia, and other expert venues.[5]
- *OCLC Research:* OCLC Research is an organization that focuses on helping libraries, archives, museums, and other cultural heritage institutions better understand a range of trends. For example, some of the organization's recent research activities focus on metadata management, technology, user behavior, standards, scholarly publishing, digitization, and collection sharing.[6]
- *Statistics:* There are many primary sources for statistics related to libraries and other types of information centers, offering a rich source of information to explore. (See also chapter 5, "Statistical Data Sets for Information Organizations" in the online supplement).

Conclusion

The chapter emphasizes a call to action for continuing evolution—with some revolutionary aspects. Today's information professionals are charged with taking the reins of strategy and leading the charge for change. Hallmarks of dynamic information professionals in the twenty-first century include the ability to envision a better future, manage and lead change, and participate with their "tribe" of like-minded colleagues in building a better future—not just for their organizations but also for all information users. Choosing to make an impact is the first step. The resources described in this chapter can help professionals remain in a mode of continuous learning—another hallmark of a great information professional.

Ultimately, in order for information professionals to remain what they are—essential hubs of their communities—they must change. If they do not evolve and change to address the continuous changes in the world around them, then they will no longer be that vital community resource.

Appendix 5.1: Lifestyle and Societal Trends

The following list of lifestyle and societal trends is not intended to be exhaustive but provides a flavor of some of the more prevalent trends and emerging issues that may impact information organizations (see also chapter 4, "Diversity, Cultures, and Equity of Access").

- *Accessibility:* Accessibility is the umbrella term for the ability to serve all users, including those with visual, auditory, learning, or mobility challenges. These issues will be at the forefront of information service delivery for many years to come—especially as equitable access to digital resources increases in importance.
- *Digital Divide:* Digital divide refers to differential access to digital resources and services caused by demographic, economic (poverty), geographic, and other issues. It is a complex issue that encompasses physical access, education, affordability, education, and more. Information users range from those who are the most intensive and capable web users (e.g., creating websites, writing blogs, uploading videos and producing digital content) to those who are "inactive" participants who may be online but do not participate in social media or interactive content. Digital, semidigital, and nondigital users will create tensions in equitable organizational strategies.
- *Discretionary Time Deficit:* Trends over the past ten or more years suggest that "lack of time" continues to be a barrier to participation in all "discretionary" activities, including information usage. The growth in leisure time that was forecast in the 1970s has not materialized, and people are increasingly pressed for time.
- *Desired Use of Leisure Time:* While commentators disagree on the extent to which people will have more leisure time in the future, they generally predict a significant shift in the ways in which they will use their leisure time.[7] These projections see a relative decline in traditional recreational activities and a significant increase in social networking, entertainment, and virtual experiences in free time. Information organizations need strategies that tie their leisure collections beyond books on hobbies and recreational reading into a diversified program package.
- *Environmental and "Green" Concerns:* There is a heightened awareness in everything "eco-friendly" and "green." This may have significant implications for all aspects of information service delivery including facility development and design, program development and delivery, materials development and processing, and information dissemination.
- *Family Structure and Dynamics:* Statistical trends indicate a rise in nontraditional family structures (e.g., single parent, divorced parents, multiple households, same-sex marriage), the declining predominance of two working-parent households, a rise in commuter lifestyles, increased urbanization, and more shared households. These dynamics have implications for hours of operation, asynchronous (virtual) programming, and the delivery of library programs and services.[8]

Stephen Abram

- *Health and Wellness:* These concerns will continue to be a top-of-mind issue/concern to society and an increasing focus for government spending in the coming years. North American society has simultaneously an aging population with the attendant health and aging issues and a very large, young millennial population in their child-rearing years. Information professionals that can provide accessible, high-quality health/wellness resources or electronic information or links to other health information providers will be well positioned to meet growing demands for this type of information.
- *Immigration:* New immigrants in search of affordable housing will continue to locate in communities on the periphery of a country's largest cities. Research has shown that immigrants may have different expectations of information organizations, public and social services, and technology. The public library and its partners will have a key role to play in orienting newcomers to the community and the range of services available. Information organizations are working on new-immigrant orientation and partnerships with settlement agencies to drive program awareness and cardholder growth.
- *Information Literacy—Beyond Reading:* Information organizations have a long-standing role in providing access to information and ensuring information literacy (i.e., teaching proficiency in finding information and assessing its relevance, authoritativeness, and value). There is no question about the need for information literacy in a generally unregulated and ever-expanding digital universe. Information organizations need to develop strategies for information fluency, including the full range of digital literacies, reading literacies for all ages, and the ability to sift information in a too-much-information world for quality and usefulness (see also chapter 16, "Teaching Users: Information and Technology Literacy Instruction").
- *Labor Trends:* Growing employment opportunities tend to be in knowledge industries in North America, including in health care, technology/computer systems, professional services, and small/entrepreneurial businesses. Information organizations that can partner with other agencies to provide training and employment services and other collaborations in these areas will increase their profile and relevance in the community.
- *Partnership and Collaboration:* Organizational partnerships are evolving and expanding, and the organization's role in helping users navigate through the plethora of content and information available will continue to be an important one. Information organizations can make sense of multiple levels of government for citizens and residents to access the services their tax dollars pay for.
- *Private Schools, Alternative Schools, and Homeschooling:* These options appear to be on the rise. This challenges many information organizations as the support systems for homework and learning. Some U.S. states have passed legislation requiring public schools to support home learners. That said, homework help is a growing part of the service portfolio for many information organizations as school library hours are cut or are diminished altogether.
- *"Smart" Device Expectations:* Smart devices go beyond smart phones and include tablets, phablets, and the internet of things. Those under the age of twenty-five now are not "passive recipients" of education, media, or technologies; they learn differently and seek and use information differently than previous generations—having grown up in a twenty-first-century web world. The challenge for information organizations will be to engage the mobile user and adopt responsive design strategies.
- *Web-Savvy Information Users:* Information users are increasingly participating in a variety of Internet-based activities: browsing, borrowing, retrieving, downloading, and interacting with web content. The majority of Internet users are experienced web users, and most have been online for more than five years. These experienced users have higher expectations of all types of information organizations. On the other hand, they may dismiss the need for information organizations altogether if they have an unclear view of how information organizations and information professionals can add value and deliver the goods.

- *"Zoomers"*: The aging of the population is resulting in a new wave of older adults with different expectations, needs, and interests than the previous generation. Traditionally seniors have been a key niche segment for many information organizations, and this generation of retired boomers will demand more. Information organizations must meet that challenge.

Appendix 5.2: Technology Trends

With rapid developments in the field of computers and information technology, predicting the future of technology as it affects information services is particularly challenging. Current trends, however, indicate that access to all forms of information and content will become increasingly associated with smaller, more powerful, and more versatile handheld wireless devices (see also chapter 26, "Managing Technology"). Some current and emerging trends and their implications for information organizations follow:

- *Online Learning:* Although MOOCs (massive open online courses) are creating issues that largely affect academic libraries, increasing opportunities are developing for public libraries. In the United States, the Atlanta-Fulton Public Library system has created eCampus, a resource that offers users online learning through access to e-learning programs, including Gale Cengage's Gale Courses (online adult e-learning) and their accredited online high school that is offered though public libraries.
- *Wireless Expectations:* People expect all public areas, including information organizations, to have free Wi-Fi. Worktables with plug-ins for laptops or other mobile devices will be increasingly needed, and group workspaces wired for laptops are in high demand. Some information organizations are now lending wireless hotspots.
- *Digital Download Kiosks:* These are a relatively new feature in information organizations, requiring power outlets and a connection to the organization's network. Some of these kiosks allow users to download e-books, audiobooks, videos, music, and games directly to their MP3 players and handheld devices or laptops. Others, like LibraryBox, can create a hotspot with content without the need for electricity or Internet access.
- *Mobile Device Arena:* The explosion of mobile device usage is replacing the laptop/desktop model and creating a post-PC era where BYOD, or "Bring Your Own Device," is common.
- *Increasing Demand for Audio and Video Live-Streaming:* These growing demands require reliable high-speed access. Users are increasingly downloading and/or transferring video and audio content to their own devices while video is set to dominate web traffic.
- *E-Book Readership and Sales:* Recent Pew Research indicates a huge increase in e-book readership. This phenomenon of print versus e-book sales seen over the last few years has started to slow and appears to have reached a plateau, indicating that there will be a hybrid market for many more years.
- *Publishers, Information Organizations, and e-Books:* There have been some promising pilots concerning evolving relationships between publishers and information organizations, but the challenges of accessing, owning, leasing, and affording "book" content is still a struggle.
- *User Created Content:* Information users are not only browsing, borrowing, and downloading, but they are increasingly creating and interacting with content available through the web. The information organization as publisher is an emergent trend.
- *"Cloud" Computing:* Cloud computing is a major technology trend that promises to reduce costs of technology ownership but drive library systems to increase cooperation.
- *Hardware Size Shrinking but Space Needs Growing:* Although computer hardware is becoming more compact, the total amount of space for a computer workstation is not significantly reduced.
- *Computer Training Space and Equipment:* The information organization's role as a training center for hands-on instruction in the use of computers, application software, and Internet-based resources will continue to grow.

Stephen Abram

- *Latest Technology Tools:* 3-D printing has now reached the consumer market; consumers can buy their own 3-D printers at retailers like Staples. This technology is being implemented in many makerspaces in information organizations (see also chapter 19, "Creation Culture and Makerspaces"). The maker movement aligns well with North American STEAM education goals (STEAM = science, technology, engineering, arts, and mathematics).
- *Information Organizations as Centers for Technology and Innovation:* The advent of the "virtual library" and technology in general has changed the way in which core information services are being delivered, and will continue to have a major impact on future services (see also chapter 10, "Digital Resources: Digital Libraries"). Information organizations are offering more services online (and doing so at an accelerating rate by taking advantage of consortia to negotiate universal access), including virtual/digital reference services, electronic databases, and e-books (see also chapter 13, "Finding Information: Information Intermediation and Reference Services"). Most libraries find that the majority of their usage is now virtual, but the type of usage is different. It is evolving.

Appendix 5.3: Facility and Service Trends

The facility and service trends discussed in this section are closely interrelated with other trends above (see also chapter 24, "Managing Facilities"). They generally point to an information organization that is much more integrated in the affairs of the community. It is an outward-looking information organization that is heavily invested in all aspects of community life and very closely linked to other community service providers. The key trends can be briefly listed as follows:

- *Information Organizations are Destinations:* Place-making refers to both the process and philosophy of planning and creating a public space within a community—with a lot of thought given to cultural tourism, or "cultural capital," and architectural design.
- *Information Organizations as Multiservice Providers:* Information organizations are increasingly forums for community learning and expression, serving as technological, employment, business development, cultural, art, and heritage centers for their communities.
- *Information Organizations Fostering Community Engagement:* While information organizations have always been disseminators of information, innovative organizations are no longer content with one-way communication. Information organizations strengthen neighborhoods and communities by creating connections and understanding needs, going beyond traditional boundaries out into their communities, and fostering collaborative relationships to build relevant and responsive information services (see also chapter 18, "Hyperlinked Libraries").
- *Information Organizations with Makerspaces:* Provided with the space, tools, and encouragement, information organization users can come together in makerspaces to collaborate, learn hands-on skills, and create and produce music, videos, jewelry, games, robotics, and electronics—and anything in between.
- *Information Organizations That Break the Box:* A number of pilot initiatives are challenging the idea of information space. These include the Little Free Library movement, information organizations as vending machines in any location for borrowing content, bookmobiles that become book bicycles, book burros, or wireless access from a hybrid traveling car.
- *Information Organizations with a Customer-First Focus:* Today's information organizations are adopting a customer-first focus. For many, this has resulted in

  o   improved hours of operation;
  o   self-checkout technology;
  o   online booking systems to pay fines, register for programs and computers, and renew and reserve items;

- o quiet spaces for study and work;
- o comfortable spaces for socializing;
- o light food and beverage services;
- o expanded programming and dedicated resources for target groups (e.g., children, teens, seniors, cultural groups, students, etc.);
- o helpful, available staff who engage with the user in the information organization ("walk the floor"); and
- o information-rich technology and training opportunities.

Not only do these improvements better serve the organization's customers; they also result in an operationally efficient organization and a functional work environment for staff.

Notes

1. Association of College and Research Libraries (ACRL), "Academic Library Statistics," last modified August 3, 2014, http://www.ala.org/acrl/publications/trends; Association of Research Libraries (ARL), "Statistics and Assessment Surveys (Canada & US)," last modified July 13, 2014, http://www.arl.org/focus-areas/statistics-assessment#.U8kbAPlznTo; Institute of Museum and Library Services (IMLS), "Research Data Collection," last modified June 30, 2014, http://www.imls.gov/research/data_collection.aspx; National Center for Education Statistics (NCES), "Surveys and Programs," last modified September 8, 2014, http://nces.ed.gov; Public Library Association (PLA), "PLDS and PLAmetrics," last modified August 13, 2014, http://www.ala.org/pla/publications/plds. Counting Opinions, last modified July 15, 2014, http://www.countingopinions.com. In the United States and Canada, Counting Opinions is a private-sector consulting service that specializes in library data and satisfaction and effectiveness studies.
2. MarketingCharts, "American Households Are Getting Smaller—and Headed by Older Adults," last modified November 27, 2012, http://www.marketingcharts.com/traditional/american-households-are-getting-smaller-and-headed-by-older-adults-24981.
3. Roger Levien, "Confronting the Future: Strategic Visions for the 21st Century Public Library," American Library Association, Policy Brief No. 4, June 2011, http://www.ala.org/offices/sites/ala.org.offices/files/content/oitp/publications/policybriefs/confronting_the_futu.pdf.
4. New Media Consortium, "NMC Horizon Project," last modified July 1, 2014, http://www.nmc.org/horizon-project.
5. Pew Research American and Life Project, "Libraries," last modified July 13, 2014, http://libraries.pewinternet.org.
6. Online Computer Library Center, "OCLC Research," last modified August 14, 2014, http://oclc.org/research.html.
7. Mark Aguiar and Eric Hunt, "Measuring Trends in Libraries: The Allocation of Time over Five Decades," *Quarterly Journal of Economics* 122, no. 3 (August 2007): 969–1006.
8. MarketingCharts, "American Households Are Getting Smaller."

6

Literacy and Media Centers in the Twenty-First Century

SCHOOL LIBRARIES

Mary Ann Harlan

In the information age, school libraries meet a broad range of learning needs. School libraries are learning centers filled with resources, tools, and instructional support to a school. This allows members of the school community to pursue their academic and personal learning needs.

Traditionally, the mission of a school library is to support the school's mission to educate youth in a core curriculum. However, school libraries have a broader mission than merely supporting the academic curriculum of the school. They provide a variety of resources and tools, which teachers and students can use to access and create information. As an environment, the school library also provides opportunities for quiet study, as well as collaborative learning. Most importantly, the school library staff supports, instructs, mentors, and coaches the school community in inquiry-based, connected learning.

The role of the school librarian is varied and continues to evolve. The primary responsibility of a school librarian is as teacher; however, school librarians wear many hats and have varied responsibilities. Teaching in a school library requires expertise in information literacy, basic literacy, and technological literacy. Additionally, as teachers, school librarians are also curriculum generalists, having knowledge of the school curriculum as a whole. Further responsibilities include the development and maintenance of a collection that meets the needs of a diverse school community. They develop and maintain policies, manage staff, and oversee day-to-day operations. Perhaps most important, school librarians model lifelong learning.

After completing this chapter, the reader should have an understanding of how the purpose of school libraries continues to evolve, as well as the changing role of school librarians.

Roles of School Librarians

Today's roles for school librarians are based in traditional roles dating back one hundred years. In the twenty-first century, school librarian responsibilities range from program manager, to literacy expert (e.g., reading, information, digital), to collaborator working with classroom teachers in curriculum planning and instruction, to mentor providing individual mentoring to the school community. In the sections below, both the traditional and emergent roles of school librarians are outlined.

Serving as Program Manager

As program managers, school librarians are responsible for running the library. They develop policies and processes, in collaboration with the school community and with approval by the school board, to uphold the values of information access and user privacy, such as those related to selecting materials and dealing with challenged materials. School librarians also maintain and manage a budget that allows the program to grow; this often includes seeking out funds and advocating for the program. They are responsible for managing a collection, selecting appropriate materials, and organizing the collection for use (see also chapter 25, "Managing Collections"). They oversee a staff that includes student and parent volunteers, as well as paraprofessional support (see also chapter 23, "Managing Personnel"). Maintenance of the program is also the responsibility of the school librarian.

Promoting Reading and Basic Literacy

The most traditional role for school librarians is reading promotion. As far back as the earliest mention of school libraries in the 1920s, the library was seen as a place for students to obtain personal reading materials.[1] School libraries have long had a role of providing students not only with print materials to support the curriculum, but also books that students read for pleasure. School librarians model a love of reading through reading-related activities and by promoting reading materials. Even in the information age, with format changes such as the availability of audio- or e-books, this focus on reading promotion remains an important role for school librarians.

> "Even in the information age, with format changes such as the availability of audio- or e-books, this focus on reading promotion remains an important role for school librarians."

This traditional focus on supporting and promoting reading has evolved into today's role for school librarians, who act as literacy experts. The role of literacy expert is especially significant in the twenty-first century, as literacy is a complex notion that includes the ability to decode, comprehend, and create a variety of types of texts, including both print, visual, and video text (see also chapter 16, "Teaching Users: Information and Technology Literacy Instruction"). Furthermore, the emerging emphasis on complex texts found in Common Core standards (discussed in detail below) has reemphasized the role of school librarians in developing textual literacy and their expertise in reading strategies. Although today's school librarians often contribute their expertise in areas such as textual literacy and reading strategies, the practice of school librarians is primarily in the area of information literacy skills.

Teaching and Modeling Information Literacy

The information literacy role of school librarians expands beyond supporting the basic literacy of reading to teaching students to access, evaluate, and use information, both within their academic environment and as citizens of a democracy. Upon entering the information age, school librarians began to develop practices to teach students skills in accessing information. The practices were not guided by instructional or content standards in the ways of other core content areas such as English language arts, science, or social science. These core subject standards were developed as schools and teachers began to recognize the role of organized benchmarks that highlighted the tasks necessary to achieve understanding

> "The information literacy role of school librarians expands beyond supporting the basic literacy of reading to teaching students to access, evaluate, and use information, both within their academic environment and as citizens of a democracy."

Mary Ann Harlan

of a skill or content. The benchmarks were organized in an interconnected list and guided students to skills and content mastery. This list became standards that outlined what students needed to know. School librarians understood that the teaching of information skills needed standards to guide their practices, and an identification of the skills necessary to become democratic citizens.

In 1998, new national learning standards were established, providing librarians with an important set of instructional benchmarks regarding information literacy. The American Association of School Librarians (AASL), along with the Association for Educational Communications and Technology (AECT), published *Information Power*,[2] a report that describes nine student learning standards. These learning standards guided instructional goals in school libraries as students, teachers, and school librarians began to navigate a new era of information abundance. The AASL standards were consistent with the definition of information literacy provided by the American Library Association (ALA) published a year later, defining information literacy as the ability "to recognize when information is needed and have the ability to locate, evaluate, and use effectively the needed information."[3][4] In 2007, AASL updated the student learning standards to reflect twenty-first-century trends, publishing *Student Learning Standards for the 21st-Century Learner*.[5] AASL recognized four student learning standards—each with multiple benchmarks. See textbox 6.1: "AASL Student Learning Standards."

TEXTBOX 6.1

AASL Student Learning Standards

1. Inquire, think critically, and gain knowledge
2. Draw conclusions, make informed decisions, apply knowledge to new situations, and create new knowledge.
3. Share knowledge and participate ethically and productively as members of our democratic society.
4. Pursue personal and aesthetic growth.

Each standard addresses four types of knowledge needed by students: skills, dispositions, responsibilities, and self-assessment. The AASL's 21st-Century Student Learning Standards recognize that learning requires engaging deeply with information, students are responsible for being ethical users of information, and learning is lifelong and does not only occur in a classroom. The benchmarks provide a road map of learning goals as students develop information skills. They reflect the importance of inquiry learning, the responsibility of the learner, and information skills. They also acknowledge the need for communication, collaboration, creativity, and critical thinking in the new millennium.[6]

Developing Digital Literacies

Embedded in the AASL student learning standards are references to technology as a tool to access, use, and create information. Thus, the AASL standards highlight another key role of school librarians—to develop students' digital literacy. Digital literacy is defined here as the ability to use technology to learn and to contribute to the global community. Digital literacy assumes that knowing the tool is not enough; it is also important to know how to use the tool to be a member of the digital community and to enhance and transform one's learning.

While AASL 21st-Century Student Learning Standards are the basis for instruction practices in school libraries, these practices are also informed by standards developed by other organizations, such as the International Society of Technology in Education (ISTE).[7] In 2007, ISTE updated their

National Educational Technology Standards (NETS) for students, teachers, and administrators. Similar to the 21st-Century Student Learning Standards issued by the AASL, the NETS standards emphasize creativity and innovation, communication and collaboration, research and information fluency, critical thinking and problem solving, and digital literacy (National Educational Technology Standards (NETS•S) and Performance Indicators for Students). These standards also include technology operations and concepts, including the ability to use and troubleshoot software applications and the use of different technological hardware.

> "As school librarians are often the education technology experts in their schools, they need to keep current on new technologies, evolving techniques for embedding technologies in classrooms to transform teaching and learning, and issues related to privacy and safety."

There are many overlaps between the student learning standards published by ISTE and the AASL, but both standards help guide school librarian practices that encourage instruction regarding technology literacy. For teachers, the ISTE standards for students can shape the focus on pedagogy. The ISTE standards have an additional component: standards for teachers. As school librarians are often the education technology experts in their schools, they need to keep current on new technologies, evolving techniques for embedding technologies in classrooms to transform teaching and learning, and issues related to privacy and safety. The ISTE standards for teachers can help school librarians maintain their expertise, as they participate in lifelong learning to stay current in emerging digital practices.

Teaching as Curriculum Generalists

Additional national core subject area standards have shaped the practice of school librarians, providing new opportunities for them to collaborate with classroom teachers in curriculum planning and instruction. One major transition in practice occurred following the introduction of the Common Core standards. The Common Core standards are national curriculum standards for K–12 students that have been broadly adopted in the United States. The Common Core standards for math and English language arts curriculum were introduced in 2009[8] and have since been adopted by forty-three states. The Common Core English Language Arts (ELA) standards[9] are especially significant to the practice of school librarians as they include literacy standards for history/social science, science, and technical subjects and emphasize textual literacy—be it digital, print, visual, or audio.

Because the Common Core standards emphasize building knowledge through interaction with information, they provide opportunities for school librarians to collaborate with classroom teachers to foster this type of learning.[10] For example, a Common Core standard for writing emphasizes the need for students to learn to conduct research, including research projects based on focused research questions.[11] School librarians have expertise identifying a student's information needs and helping students develop research questions; find and evaluate information based on quality, accuracy, and relevance; and determine how to present the answer so that others may benefit, doing so in an ethical manner. This new emphasis on these important steps in research projects presents opportunities for school librarians to collaborate with classroom teachers to team-teach and model information literacy skills. With this transition to new learning expectations for students under the Common Core, both students and teachers need support and instruction in modern information practices.

> "With this transition to new learning expectations for students under the Common Core, both students and teachers need support and instruction in modern information practices."

Another Common Core standard that has shaped the practice of school librarians in recent years

Mary Ann Harlan

emphasizes the ability to use and analyze complex, real-world texts. Complex texts are the types of texts students encounter in their everyday lives and their classrooms. They include primary source documents, news reports, research papers, journal articles, policy briefs, narrative nonfiction, and informational texts. As literacy experts and collection developers, school librarians provide both the resources necessary for teachers to use complex texts in their classes, as well as professional development for teachers regarding how to help their students analyze and engage a complex text. As they develop the school's collection and plan ways to address this standard in each class, school librarians bring their knowledge regarding how to evaluate a text both for quantitative and qualitative reading levels, how to assess the text's appropriateness for a student, and how the text relates to a subject. School librarians build their collection with complex, real-world texts that extend beyond print items and include audio, visual, and digital texts.

Another fairly recent national standards movement has influenced the practice of school librarians and shifted their role to be more involved in curriculum planning and instruction. The Next Generation Science Standards[12] were developed by a coalition consisting of the National Research Council, the National Science Teachers Association, the American Association for the Advancement of Science, and Achieve. They were introduced in 2011 and promote a national approach to science standards. While the science standards are not a part of Common Core, they adopt similar approaches to student learning. The Next Generation Science Standards include an emphasis on student performance rather than content knowledge, student inquiry in building and applying scientific knowledge, and an integrated approach throughout K–12. School librarians can support science teachers and students by facilitating inquiry, making connections in the curriculum, and teaching skills related to demonstrating knowledge.

As curriculum generalists, school librarians have a basic understanding of each of the content area standards and an in-depth awareness of how teachers teach, or implement, content area standards in their classrooms. This is a key element to being a school librarian.

> "The Next Gen standards include an emphasis on student performance rather than content knowledge, student inquiry in building and applying scientific knowledge, and an integrated approach throughout K–12."

Instructional Models in School Libraries

As school librarians increasingly focus on instruction, they engage with students through three different schedules of student contact with the library: fixed, flexible, and mixed. Fixed schedules are based on students coming to the library with their class once a week or every two weeks. Flexible schedules occur when teachers schedule class time in the library as needed. Mixed schedules combine fixed and flexible scheduling. Within the three schedules, there are different instructional models including direct instruction or programming such as story time, inquiry-based learning models, and connected learning models. This chapter focuses on inquiry-based learning and connected learning as emerging models of instruction in school libraries.

Inquiry-Based Learning

Over the last several decades, some K–12 teachers and librarians have implemented inquiry-based learning at their schools. Although policies implemented under the era of No Child Left Behind and Race to the Top (2001–2011) emphasized basic skills needed for success in high-stakes student testing and curtailed widespread implementation of inquiry-based learning, the more recent transition to Common Core standards and its focus on helping students develop real-world skills needed for college and careers has returned the focus of K–12 schools to inquiry-based learning. Inquiry-based learning involves several key components (see textbox 6.2).

> TEXTBOX 6.2
>
> **Inquiry-Based Learning**
>
> 1. Real-world, relevant questions or problems
> 2. Questions and investigations that build on students' interests and prior knowledge, connecting school-based learning with out-of-school experiences
> 3. Iterative investigation using a variety of resources, including experts in the field, primary and secondary sources, investigation in the field, construction and presentation of new knowledge, and reflection

There are several models of inquiry-based learning.

- *Problem-Based Learning:* Students investigate and design a solution to a real-world problem, often derived from their community. Example: designing a program to address bullying in their school.
- *Project-Based Learning:* Students engage in a project that solves or addresses real-world concerns. Example: designing and producing an alternative energy source for their neighborhood.
- *Guided Inquiry:* Students select a topic relevant to their lives and are guided through an in-depth research process. Example: students engage in an academic research paper and are guided through the process of developing an essential question, planning a course of action in gathering information from primary and secondary sources, using information to shape and refine their initial question, gathering supporting information, and planning a presentation that is shaped for a specific audience (e.g., Ted Talk, written paper, website).

> "The key to inquiry-based learning is student ownership of the learning process, shifting the role of the teaching team to that of coach and model."

The key to inquiry-based learning is student ownership of the learning process, shifting the role of the teaching team to that of coach and model. As information specialists, school librarians can be at the forefront of implementing opportunities for inquiry-based learning, with its emphasis on twenty-first-century skills, such as collaboration, communication, creativity, and critical thinking (also emphasized in the Common Core standards).

Connected Learning

Another learning model that has impacted school libraries is connected learning.[13] Connected learning is based on three learning principles and three design principles. See table 6.1: "Connected Learning."

As an emerging framework for learning, school librarians that design learning opportunities using the three design principles of connected learning support both inquiry-based learning and the focus of the Common Core standards. For example, production-centered learning relates to Common Core standards associated with the presentation of knowledge and ideas. The principle of openly networked learning allows school librarians to address the ethical use of information in the presentation of knowledge, an important component of the AASL 21st-Century Student Learning Standards. By focusing on a shared purpose in designing learning opportunities, students need to develop the skills necessary to be successful in collaboration, a strand in both Common Core standards and emphasized in the

Table 6.1. Connected Learning

Learning Principles	Design Principles
Interest Powered: Students pursue areas of interest or that are personally relevant, fostering motivation.	*Production Centered:* Learning opportunities include actively producing, creating, experimenting, and designing content for a global audience.
Peer Supported: Students engage in communities of peers and friends that contribute ideas and feedback to build collective knowledge.	*Open Networked:* Learning opportunities cross the contexts of school, home, and community.
Academically Oriented: Students develop academic skills through engaging in learning opportunities designed on the three design principles.	*Shared Purpose:* Learning opportunities are cross-cultural, cross-generational, and focused on common goals.

21st-Century Student Learning Standards. Connected learning imagines a world in which education is the responsibility of a distributed network[14]—embracing learning as occurring in different contexts throughout one's life.

In designing learning opportunities, school librarians should recognize the principles of learning and how they relate to familiar learning models, such as inquiry-based learning approaches. In emphasizing the interest-powered learning youth engage in, this is recognizing the role of intrinsic motivation in learning. This deepens the inquiry-based learning models of project-based and problem-based learning by allowing students to engage in projects of personal relevance. For example, collaborative groups can focus on community projects that are of deep interest to the participants while still connecting to core academic content. In recognizing the role of peers in supporting learning, school librarians can encourage connections between learners with similar interests while empowering youth to demonstrate their expertise. School librarians identify, support, and encourage the development of academic skills while students are engaged in learning opportunities. By identifying the skills students develop, school librarians help students develop reflective practices that allow for the transference of skills between disciplines.

As curriculum generalists, school librarians bridge the subject areas for a multidisciplinary approach. As information specialists, they instruct and mentor students in inquiry-based and connected learning. This is a unique role within the school.

School Libraries as "Third Place"

Why does the connected learning framework matter to school libraries, and what does it mean within the constraints of a school's mission? While third-place theory deserves more attention than provided in this chapter, the significance to school libraries lies in the idea that there are three spheres of learning: the home sphere, the work or school sphere, and an additional space in a public environment that is a community anchor, including public libraries. School libraries traditionally have been seen as falling firmly in the school space. However, in both traditional constructions of school libraries and in learning commons, the environment of the school library can also act as third places.

School libraries support individual inquiry, individual reading interests, and individual pursuits in ways that traditional classrooms do not necessarily provide. This suggests that school libraries can be places of connected learning for interests beyond classroom curriculum. In other words, despite the location of school libraries on school campuses, they support a much broader type of learning. School libraries support interest-driven, peer-supported, product-oriented, and openly networked learning. Connected learning positions school libraries as third places for students to pursue their own interests in constructing knowledge.

The third place of the school library has an additional benefit for students. It is a place of refuge—a space where an individual can pursue information needs and interests that they may not be able to explore in other environments due to perceived risk. School librarians must strive to provide safe, welcoming spaces for students in need of quiet time and space. School libraries that have implemented the learning commons model, which includes space for collaboration, should consider how to also provide space for quiet contemplation, study, and reading.

TEXTBOX 6.3

Topic for Discussion

Discuss the mission of the school library and how a focus on inquiry-based learning or connected learning supports this mission.

School Libraries as Learning Commons

As inquiry-based learning takes hold in schools, school libraries are beginning to reshape how their space and their resources are used to serve the learning community. Many are now defined as learning commons, challenging traditional ideas of school libraries solely as repositories of materials and places for independent learning.

Learning commons are defined as learning, project, and research spaces. In a single space, they combine elements typically associated with libraries, computer labs, and collaboration areas. Learning commons offer a flexible space, which can easily be reconfigured for use as a performance space, for small-group collaborative work, or for independent study. Additionally, learning commons are trending toward incorporating elements of makerspaces, particularly media and digital makerspaces, equipped with project-oriented tools, such as cameras, editing hardware and software, and robotics and electronic equipment (see also chapter 19, "Creation Culture and Makerspaces"). The philosophy of a learning commons invites students to construct their own understandings and design their own work.

School libraries are well suited to serve as school learning commons. They have existing research resources, computers for accessing information, and furniture that encourages collaboration, such as tables. School learning commons are improving their spaces by adding tools and resources for learners, such as the addition of design-based software, peripherals necessary to create digital media, and space to celebrate and perform both online and offline. Additionally, school learning commons offer 24/7 access to learning. Virtual learning commons are more than school websites. While they provide traditional access to databases, online catalogs, links to recommended sources, and tutorials in information skills, they are also providing interactive space. Students and teachers can build and contribute to a learning commons, providing collaborative knowledge-building opportunities, peer expertise, and mentoring. As they produce work in this online space, students engage in real-world publication and the global community.

"School learning commons are the heart of the school, the place where students, teachers, curriculum, and interests come together, but also reach out beyond school walls to participate in inquiry."

Mary Ann Harlan

Perhaps the most important element of the learning commons that school librarians can provide is modeling lifelong learning and mentoring community members in information skills. As information literacy experts who understand how to use technology to present learning, school librarians are well situated to manage the environment of a learning commons. They act as liaisons to experts in the community, both local and global. Learning commons incorporate the whole school learning community; they do not exist as separate entities based in individual classrooms. School learning commons are the heart of the school, the place where students, teachers, curriculum, and interests come together, but also reach out beyond school walls to participate in inquiry.

> **TEXTBOX 6.4**
>
> **Topic for Discussion**
>
> How does a learning commons model support and encourage connected learning?

Conclusion

In the information age, school libraries are the hub of learning. They provide instruction, mentoring, resources, tools, and connections to support inquiry both for class curriculum and informal learning. They are integral to a school community, and the school librarian has the opportunity to impact learning and teaching and to infuse information literacy skills into students' experiences while supporting curriculum and content standards. They develop unique relationships with learners and model lifelong learning in spaces that provide a multitude of activities.

Notes

1. Blanche Woolls, Ann C. Weeks, and Sharon Coatney, *The School Library Manager*, 5th ed. (Santa Barbara, CA: Libraries Unlimited, 2013).
2. Excerpt from chapter 1: "The Vision," in *Information Power: Building Partnerships for Learning* (Chicago, IL: American Library Association and Association of Educational Communication and Technology, 1998), http://www.d91.net/LRC/LRCPDF/Attachment%201-A.pdf.
3. American Association of School Librarians (AASL) and Association for Educational Communications and Technology (AECT), *Information Literacy Standards for Student Learning* (Chicago, IL: American Library Association, 1998), http://umanitoba.ca/libraries/units/education/media/InformationLiteracy Standards_final.pdf.
4. American Association of School Librarians (AASL), *Standards for the 21st Century Learner* (Chicago, IL: American Association of School Librarians, 2007), http://www.ala.org/aasl/sites/ala.org.aasl/files/content/guidelinesandstandards/learningstandards/AASL_Learning_Standards_2007.pdf.
5. P21 Framework Definitions, *Partnership for 21st Century Skills*, December 2009, http://www.p21.org/storage/documents/P21_Framework_Definitions.pdf.
6. "Standards," International Standards for Technology in Education (ISTE), last updated September 3, 2014, http://www.iste.org/standards.
7. "About the Standards," Common Core State Standards Initiative, last modified September 12, 2014, http://www.corestandards.org.
8. "English Language Arts Standards," Common Core State Standards Initiative, last modified September 12, 2014, http://www.corestandards.org/ELA-Literacy.
9. Ibid.
10. Ibid.
11. Next Generation Science Standards, "About the Standards," last modified June 25, 2014, http://www.nextgenscience.org/about-standards-development-process.
12. Mimi Ito, Kris Gutierrez, Sonia Livingstone, et al., *Connected Learning: An Agenda for Research and Design* (Irvine, CA: Digital Media and Learning Research Hub), http://dmlhub.net/sites/default/files/ConnectedLearning_report.pdf.
13. Ibid.
14. Herring, James E., "Year 7 Students, Information Literacy, and Transfer: A Grounded Theory," *School Library Media Research* 14 (2011).

7

The Learning and Research Institution

ACADEMIC LIBRARIES

Todd Gilman

Academic librarians perform many of the same duties as school, public, and special librarians: reference, outreach, collection development, collection maintenance, cataloging, archival processing, digitization of rare and unique materials, preservation, conservation, interlibrary loan and document delivery, and cultivating relationships with donors. As members of academic communities and employees of academic libraries, however, they serve different constituencies and perform different duties than their counterparts in school, public, and special libraries do. Librarians in junior colleges, community colleges, and four-year colleges serve undergraduates, faculty, and staff, both on campus and virtually. Librarians in research universities, by contrast, serve graduate students among these constituencies, again both on campus and online. Academic librarians often hold subject master's degrees or doctorates in addition to the MLIS degree. Many enjoy tenure-track faculty status.

The purpose of this chapter is both to elucidate the roles and responsibilities academic librarians assume today and to forecast trends and issues that will require them to continuously and creatively adapt to the inevitably evolving roles that the future of academic libraries will require. After completing this chapter, the reader should have an understanding of the many and varied activities in which academic librarians engage and duties they perform, as well as the challenges they face given the current climate of higher education in North America.

Academic Librarians Today

Academic librarians work closely with students, faculty, and staff in colleges and universities. Because they serve in a higher education environment, they are typically expected to have more, or more specialized, formal education than other information professionals. Job postings for academic library positions frequently require a subject master's degree or a doctorate in addition to, or in some cases instead of, the MLIS, because of the often specialized nature of the duties they must perform. For example, a subject specialist in Western European humanities at a research university might be expected to hold a PhD in history or literature in addition to having proficiency in one or more Romance languages in addition to German. This is because such a position typically entails collection development work in multiple languages and research consultations with teaching faculty and graduate students.[1]

Many colleges and universities grant faculty status to their librarians (whether tenure track or non-tenure track) since they are expected to demonstrate achievements on a par with teaching faculty, including conducting research that leads to presentations at professional conferences or publication or both. Librarians with so-called academic appointments, by contrast, often must advance through one or more promotion review cycles before being granted continuing (or permanent) status. These librarians may or may not be required to conduct research and publish; in many such cases, a record of excellent service and evidence of a strong commitment to professional development are sufficient to earn a continuing appointment.

Emerging Roles for Academic Librarians

Many academic librarians today offer expertise in instructional technology, GIS (geographic information systems), and informatics. Instructional technology skills enable librarians to create research or subject guides to library resources that support academic courses, topics, or disciplines taught in colleges and universities. These guides, often known as LibGuides, allow students and faculty to gain access to library resources without having to ask a librarian for assistance. The examples below are from Yale University Library:

* English Language and Literature Research Guide (http://guides.library.yale.edu/english?hs=a)
* U.S. History and American Studies (http://guides.library.yale.edu/ushistory?hs=a)
* European History (http://guides.library.yale.edu/content.php?pid=607882)

Those with training in GIS may work with computer programs and geographic data sets to organize and display information related to land that can be used by researchers. GIS specialists might assist faculty and students with, for example, creating interactive digital mapping programs or analyzing spatial data.

TEXTBOX 7.1

GIS in the Works: Photogrammer

Photogrammer[1] (http://photogrammar.yale.edu) is a project that Yale University Library GIS specialist Stacey Maples collaborated on with Professor Laura Wexler. They created a visualization and exploration platform for the Library of Congress Farm Security Administration/Office of War Information photo collection (170,000 images).[2] There is more information on the site about its genesis. Maples worked on all geocoding and map visualization in the platform. He has also been working to stand up and stabilize two critical pieces of Spatial Data Infrastructure, GeoData@Yale[3] and GeoServer.[4]

---

1. "Welcome," Photogrammar, last modified September 20, 2014, http://photogrammar.yale.edu.
2. Library of Congress, Farm Security Administration/Office of War Administration, n.d., http://www.loc.gov/pictures/collection/fsa.
3. GeoData@Yale, n.d., http://geoportal.library.yale.edu.
4. GeoServer, n.d., http://geodata.library.yale.edu:8080/geoserver/web.

Data curation constitutes one of the newest and increasingly important evolving roles for academic librarians, and experts in informatics might help faculty and students with digital humanities data curation or e-science projects.[2] Digital humanities data curation involves working with metadata, text encoding, format and encoding management, technical aspects of data repository systems, data description, and digital preservation (see also chapter 34, "Analog and Digital Curation and

Preservation"). The research activities of e-science involve what is often referred to as "big data" and focus on developing new computational tools and infrastructures to support scientific discovery. In a particularly urgent development, funding agencies, such as the National Science Foundation (NSF) and National Institutes of Health (NIH), now require scientists to provide open access to the under-lying data gathered as a result of grant-funded research (see also chapter 33, "Open Access"). Since January 2011, proposals submitted to NSF must include a data management plan. In response, some academic libraries are already helping campus scientists comply with the requirements to create the plans and to archive and share the gathered data. For example, according to Spencer D. C. Keralis and associates, "in the libraries at the University of Illinois at Urbana-Champaign, the liaison librarians serve the disciplines most affected by the NSF mandate, and they drive support for data management. The life sciences librarian developed a links web page to give researchers access to information from funding agencies, information about data repositories, and a list of services, including help in devel-oping a data curation profile for research projects using Purdue's Data Curation Profile Toolkit (origi-nally developed in partnership with the UIUC Graduate School of Library and Information Science)."[3]

With the growth of the larger open access move-ment, a proposed solution to the high cost of access to research materials whereby authors make the results of their research free to all, the concept of the institutional repository (IR) has become compelling to colleges and universities in the past decade. At campuses that have adopted a formal open access policy, academic librar-ians now work to set up and populate electronic IRs for faculty and staff publications and data sets. Materials in IRs can have different levels of access: some are avail-able only to the campus community, for example; others, to the larger scholarly community or to anyone with access to a computer. Many of these digital ef-forts raise new copyright questions, so academic libraries now recruit or train specialists who can field faculty and staff questions about which materials can and cannot be shared freely.[4]

TEXTBOX 7.2

Topic for Discussion

Are academic librarians much different from other information professionals? If so, how? If not, why not?

Information and Technology Literacy Instruction

Check This Out
ACRL's Information Literacy Competency Standards for Higher Education
Visit:
http://www.ala.org/acrl/standards/informationliteracycompetency

Accreditation commissions and colleges and universities have acknowledged the importance of devel-oping students' capacity for critical thinking. As a result, many academic librarians who work in public services offer information literacy and technology literacy instruction for undergraduates and graduate students (see also chapter 16, "Teaching Users: Information and Technology Literacy Instruction"). Information literacy instruction typically involves helping students to identify a need for information, locate the needed information, evaluate the quality of the information found, and use the information effectively, legally, and ethically. Some librarians work diligently to follow the Association of College and Research Libraries' (ACRL) Information Literacy Competency Standards for Higher Education, a set of five standards and related performance indicators,[5] when they work with students. Others take a more informal approach, seeking mainly to impress upon students the hazards of relying solely on Google and Wikipedia for college-level research and explaining and demonstrating alternatives, such as librarian-authored research guides, bibliographies, indexes, and other scholarly resources, including academic monographs and essay collections and peer-reviewed journal articles. Technology literacy instruction typically involves training students in the use of computers (including iPads or other tablets) and a variety of software, from electronic library catalogs and archival finding aids to free and fee-based bibliographic and full-text databases, to mobile apps, to citation management programs such as RefWorks, Zotero, EndNote, or Mendeley.

Those who teach information literacy and technology literacy often perform these duties in their capacity as library liaisons to academic departments. In the past decade or so, a model of service known as the embedded librarian or, in a purely virtual environment, as the so-called embedded e-brarian has become popular. Embedded librarians seek to reach students where they are rather than wait for students to come to them. They might serve as a co-teacher by means of a virtual presence in an online course offered to their institution's students or to students enrolled in a faculty member's MOOC (massive open online course); hold office hours in an academic department, student union, cafeteria, or writing center; or offer brief introductory visits to face-to-face classrooms at the invitation of teaching faculty[6] (see also part IV, "Information Users: Engaging, Creating, and Collaborating via Technology").

> "Embedded librarians seek to reach students where they are rather than wait for students to come to them. They might serve as a co-teacher by means of a virtual presence in an online course offered to their institution's students or to students enrolled in a faculty member's MOOC (Massive Open Online Course); hold office hours in an academic department, student union, cafeteria, or writing center; or offer brief introductory visits to face-to-face classrooms at the invitation of teaching faculty."

Service to the University and Profession

Academic librarians also serve on campus, state, and national committees. If they have faculty status, they may be involved in campus governance, enjoying a place at the table alongside members of the teaching faculty and the central administration. Librarians serving on statewide library or education committees might act as advocates for the implementation of educational standards involving information and technology literacy in state college and university systems. Librarians serving on committees sponsored by the Association of Research Libraries (ARL) or ACRL develop guidelines and standards for adoption by academic library professionals nationwide. These guidelines and standards address professional concerns ranging from best practices in fair use for academic and research libraries; to screening and appointment of academic librarians; to services to undergraduate students; to interlibrary loan of rare and unique materials; to preservation, security, and theft in special collections; to distance-learning library services; to recommended competencies for special collections professionals.

Research and Publication

Academic librarians also conduct research and publish articles and books on both discipline-specific and LIS subjects. Librarians with tenure-track faculty status are typically required to do so in order to achieve promotion and tenure. Publication expectations of tenure-track librarians might not in all cases be as rigorous as those for teaching faculty, since librarians devote most of their professional time to the performance of primary job responsibilities and typically hold twelve-month appointments. Still, expectations are high, and promotion and tenure is either granted or denied after five to seven years of service based on a thorough review of all aspects of performance. Librarians with non-tenure-track status or administrative appointments (managerial and professional staff with nonfaculty status) are often encouraged to conduct research and publish, but they have other means of demonstrating professional competency, such as excellent service to library users, building collections, and committee work, that allow them to advance through the ranks without research and publication. There is no one-size-fits-all model when it comes to research and publication among academic librarians.

New Models for Reference Service

Academic librarians today face a significantly decreased demand for traditional reference service. The growth of the web has made academic library users more self-sufficient. As a result, many reference desks in colleges and universities have been either eliminated or merged with other service points such as circulation or computing services; others have moved to a tiered model, in which frontline staff might be students or nonprofessional library workers. Members of the frontline staff are trained to answer basic questions and to refer more advanced questions to professional librarians. Related to this development, another new model of service has sprung up: the so-called learning commons, information commons, or digital commons. Based in part on the concept of "one-stop shopping," this is a full-service learning, research, and project space typically combining library resources such as expert help with a computer lab and moveable furniture in a repurposed space designed to facilitate both individual and group work.[7] Professional librarians working under these new service models are now able to focus more on high-level research questions, consultations, and outreach to faculty and students (see also chapter 13, "Finding Information: Information Intermediation and Reference Services").

Collection Development, Access, and Preservation

Materials costs for academic libraries have risen so dramatically in recent decades that most libraries cannot keep up and have been forced to introduce drastic cost-cutting measures. While costs for print books rise steadily, particularly challenging are the exorbitant prices of so-called Big Deal electronic serials packages (large bundles of electronic journals) offered by publishers such as Elsevier, Emerald, Sage, Springer, Taylor & Francis, and Wiley in the STEM fields.[8] To make matters worse, these prices increase each year by a fixed amount (e.g., 5 percent). If academic libraries back out of a big deal, they can lose 60 percent of their access to content while still paying more for individual subscriptions than they were paying before. However, even print journals have high costs associated with them since they must be checked in, bound, stored, and reshelved after patron use.

Many libraries have adopted a policy prioritizing electronic format for journals (sometimes known as an "e-priority policy" for short) and canceling print subscriptions whenever possible in order to avoid duplication and its attendant costs. Most academic libraries have become comfortable with deaccessioning or moving their print journal collections to off-site storage once they have secured reliable digital surrogates for these materials (see also chapter 25, "Managing Collections").

As another efficiency measure, patron-driven or data-driven acquisitions (PDA/DDA) are also on the rise. Under this acquisitions model, e-book vendors allow libraries to load records into their online catalogs for e-books and e-journals that the library has not yet purchased, enabling discovery by the libraries' patrons. If a patron uses an e-book or journal article beyond a certain agreed-upon threshold (for example, he or she reads a given number of e-book pages or downloads an article), the text is acquired by and charged to the library. In this way libraries only pay for what their patrons actually use.

Still, the question of long-term electronic preservation remains an issue. Most e-book vendors have not addressed this question adequately, forcing libraries to rely on partial solutions such as the Digital Preservation Network (DPN)[9] and HathiTrust.[10] Even combined, DPN and HathiTrust leave much digital library material vulnerable to permanent loss (see also chapter 10, "Digital Resources: Digital Libraries").

Todd Gilman

Since separate library systems cannot typically share access to electronic journals or books between them because of copyright and licensing restrictions (e.g., Columbia University cannot share its licensed electronic holdings with Yale), many academic libraries have banded together in recent decades to form consortia in order to share print materials as efficiently and at as low a cost as possible. The Ivy League's Borrow Direct[11] (http://www.borrowdirect.org) system is one such consortial arrangement. All the Ivies (i.e., Brown, Columbia, Cornell, Dartmouth, Harvard, University of Pennsylvania, Princeton, and Yale) plus MIT, the University of Chicago, and Johns Hopkins now freely share their materials using a patron-initiated rapid book request and delivery system. Similarly, the Greater Western Library Alliance (GWLA),[12] a consortium of thirty-three research libraries located in the central and western United States, offers interlibrary loan reciprocity between its members. (GWLA members also realize cost savings on library materials thanks to cooperative negotiation of discounts and licensing agreements). Cooperative collection development constitutes a related initiative that many academic libraries are considering as a cost-saving measure. In this model of collection development, partner libraries agree to divide up collecting areas between them (such as African or central Asian materials or small-press books) in order to build complementary rather than duplicative collections and share their acquisitions freely with each other.[13]

TEXTBOX 7.3

Topic for Discussion

What can academic librarians do to help increase open access for scholarly materials?

Assessment in the Academic Library

In an effort to continuously demonstrate the library's value to campus stakeholders, academic librarians frequently concern themselves with assessment (see also chapter 28, "Demonstrating Value: Assessment"). Assessment is a process used by libraries to learn about the needs of users in order to improve academic programs, teaching, student learning, and the library's role in the research activities of students and faculty.[14] Many academic libraries now employ a dedicated assessment librarian or head of assessment who oversees the library's assessment activities by collecting, analyzing, and reporting assessment data and developing a data-driven approach to achieving strategic objectives. Library assessment uses various research methods, including website usability testing, observation, focus groups, interviews, and surveys. The most widely adopted library satisfaction survey is LibQUAL+, a service-quality survey developed by ARL. Ideally, assessment plans should be driven by and linked to the larger institution's mission, vision, and values, and all goals and outcomes should be agreed upon, specific, and measurable.

Library Programs Considered for Assessment
• Reference
• Information literacy
• Technology literacy
• Library collections
• Scholarly programs and services
• Library liaison programs
• Library design and furnishings
• Library technology
• In-house access
• Remote access
• Distance-education resources
• Library value

A major driver of assessment in colleges and universities is accreditation. Accrediting agencies perform two primary duties: quality assurance and institutional improvement. They formulate guidelines for continuous assessment and ask colleges to define goals and prove that they are using these goals to seek and respond effectively to feedback. Accrediting bodies typically value information literacy outcomes, so academic librarians are encouraged to identify information literacy language in accreditation documents and use it to integrate information literacy skills into teaching and assessment activities across campus. More generally, academic librarians should monitor their users' understanding of the role of the library in their teaching, learning, and research, and their users' success in gaining access to needed materials.

Conclusion

It should be apparent from this chapter that perhaps the most important overall issue facing academic libraries today is their sustainability. With so many competing, freely available sources of information open to students and faculty, academic librarians have to constantly communicate and demonstrate that library resources are worth paying for. Yet even if they do so, in light of rising materials costs, many academic libraries simply cannot afford to provide all the books, journals, and databases their faculty and students need; they risk patron dissatisfaction as a result. Given the lightning-fast pace of technological innovations in libraries, academic librarians also have to constantly learn new skills or risk becoming obsolete. Finally, with higher education itself in a period of flux as a result of unaffordable tuition, a trillion-dollar national student loan burden, and stakeholders (especially parents) demanding a significant "return on investment," academic libraries must show that they remain critical to the mission of the institutions they serve.

Notes

1. Thea Lindquist and Todd Gilman, "Academic/Research Librarians with Subject Doctorates; Data and Trends 1965-2006," *portal: Libraries and the Academy* 8, no. 1 (2008): 31-52; Todd Gilman and Thea Lindquist, "Academic/Research Librarians with Subject Doctorates: Experiences and Perceptions, 1965-2006," *portal: Libraries and the Academy* 10, no. 4 (2010): 399-412.
2. Joyce L. Ogburn, "The Imperative for Data Curation," *portal: Libraries and the Academy* 10, no. 2 (April 2010): 241-246, http://muse.jhu.edu/journals/pla/summary/v010/10.2.ogburn.html.
3. Spencer D. C. Keralis, Shannon Stark, Martin Halber, and William E. Moen, "Research Data Management in Policy and Practice: The DataRes Project," in *Research Data Management: Principles, Practices, and Prospects* (Washington, DC: Council on Library and Information Resources, 2013), 26.
4. See an extensive list of U.S. college and university IRs here: "College and University Institutional Repositories," Digital Commons, last modified September 13, 2014, http://digitalcommons.bepress.com/institutional-repository-colleges.
5. Association of College and Research Libraries, "Information Literacy Competency Standards for Higher Education," last modified July 12, 2014, http://www.ala.org/acrl/standards/information literacycompetency.

Todd Gilman

6. Alice L. Daugherty and Michael F. Russo, eds., *Embedded Librarianship: What Every Academic Librarian Should Know* (Santa Barbara, CA: Libraries Unlimited, 2013).

7. Laurie A. MacWhinnie, "The Information Commons: The Academic Library of the Future," *portal: Libraries and the Academy* 3, no. 2 (2003): 241–257.

8. Karla L. Strieb and Julia C. Blixrud, "Unwrapping the Bundle: An Examination of Research Libraries and the 'Big Deal,'" *portal: Libraries and the Academy* 14, no. 4 (2014, in press).

9. "The Digital Preservation Network," Digital Preservation Network (DPN), last modified July 7, 2014, http://www.dpn.org.

10. "Our Digital Library," HathiTrust, last modified September 24, 2014, http://www.hathitrust.org/digital_library.

11. "Home," Borrow Direct, last modified September 3, 2014, http://www.borrowdirect.org.

12. "Home," Greater Western Library Alliance, last modified July 9, 2014, http://www.gwla.org.

13. Association of Research Libraries, "21st-Century Collections: Calibration of Investment and Collaborative Action," ARL Issue Brief (Washington, DC: Association of Research Libraries, March 10, 2012). http://www.arl.org/storage/documents/publications/issue-brief-21st-century-collections-2012.pdf.

14. Joseph R. Matthews, *The Evaluation and Measurement of Library Services* (Westport, CT: Libraries Unlimited, 2007); Peter Hernon and Ellen Altman, *Assessing Service Quality: Satisfying the Expectations of Library Customers* (Chicago, IL: American Library Association, 1998).

8

Community Anchors for Lifelong Learning

PUBLIC LIBRARIES

Kathleen de la Peña McCook

For more than two centuries, public libraries in the United States have been the heart of their villages, towns, cities, or counties. The public library is the community's anchor institution that supports community improvement and provides lifelong learning opportunities through access to books and media in all formats, as well as a wide range of programs and services—all designed to meet the community's needs for education, information, and personal development.[1] And, as a result of the Stafford Disaster Relief and Emergency Assistance Act of 2011, the public library's function as a safe haven is now formally recognized, designating public libraries as facilities eligible for federal assistance following a major disaster[2] (see textbox 8.1).

In 2014, a public libraries survey reported that there are 16,415 public library outlets and 695 bookmobiles. Urban libraries in cities such as Boston, New York, Chicago, Denver, Los Angeles, and Seattle serve millions of people from dozens of service points with hundreds of staff. Yet most public

---

TEXTBOX 8.1

U.S. Federal Definition of a Public Library

A public library is an entity that is established under state enabling laws or regulations to serve a community, district, or region, and that provides at least the following:

1. an organized collection of printed or other library materials, or a combination thereof;
2. paid staff;
3. an established schedule in which services of the staff are available to the public;
4. the facilities necessary to support such a collection, staff, and schedule; and
5. is supported in whole or in part with public funds.[1]

---

1. Institute of Museum and Library Services, *Public Libraries in the United States Survey: Fiscal Year 2011* (Washington, DC: Institute of Museum and Library Services, 2014), p. 2.

libraries serve communities with less than twenty-five thousand residents. Only 6.1 percent of public libraries serve populations over one hundred thousand.[3]

The scope of today's public library services is also extremely diverse. For example, public libraries offer literacy programs, access to technology, downloadable digital media, cultural events, and programs to meet the needs of a broad range of patrons, including job seekers, recent immigrants, and veterans. This spectrum of capacity, service area, and different governing structures presents a complex, challenging, and ever-evolving organization that defines librarianship for the majority of people in the United States.[4] After completing this chapter, the reader will have an understanding of the history of U.S. public libraries, including how they have evolved into the complex institutions that serve as today's community learning hubs. Readers will also gain insight regarding how public libraries are administered and funded, followed by an exploration of the scope of services offered by today's libraries.

History of Public Libraries in the United States

The forerunners of the nation's public libraries appeared in the early 1700s, and a century later, the first tax-supported public libraries were established. A range of factors influenced the rapid expansion of public libraries across the United States and the scope of services they provided. See figure 8.1.

1854	1896	1924	1943	1956	1966	1996
• The first tax-supported library was established in Boston.	• Nearly 1,000 U.S. public libraries established.	• ALA begins its support for the expansion of public libraries.	• Post-War Standars Report recommends that public library services should be available in the U.S.	• Library Services Act funds expansion of public library services to rural areas.	• LSCA expands scope of public library services and addresses the needs of underserved groups.	• IMLS established, and the mission of public libraries is expanded to include lifelong learning.

Figure 8.1 History of Public Libraries

Establishment of the First Public Libraries in the Nineteenth Century

The role of New England in the development of public libraries looms large in library history. The two major forerunners of the tax-supported public library were the social library and the circulating library. Early examples of each were in existence by the early 1700s. Social library collections emphasized literature, history, science, and theology, while circulating library collections reflected popular reading with an emphasis on fiction (as distinguished from literature).[5] Arguments for the creation of school district libraries provided additional impetus for the foundation of tax-supported public libraries.[6]

The social and economic factors that came together in New England to create the context in which people could visualize the idea and gather support for public libraries are discussed in Jesse H. Shera's book, *Foundations of the Public Library*, which provides a social history covering 1629 to 1855. He concludes that seven diverse factors contributed to the emergence of tax-supported public libraries:

- Economic resources in the community
- Scholarship, historical research, and the urge for conservation
- Local pride
- Social importance of universal public education

- Self-education and the lyceum movement
- Vocational influence
- Religion, morality, and the church[7]

While there are earlier examples of free public libraries—such as the Peterborough Town Library in New Hampshire (1833)—the establishment of the Boston Public Library, which opened in 1854, marks the beginning of the public library movement from which the key principles for tax-supported public libraries emerged.[8]

In 1851, Boston mayor Benjamin Seaver declared that the city should hold an election to create a board of trustees to move the idea of a tax-supported public library to fruition. Their work resulted in the *Report of the Trustees of the Public Library to the City of Boston* in 1852, a seminal document in the history of public librarianship in the United States.[9] The report begins with a compelling justification for the library as an institution, describes how the opportunity for public education ends after formal schooling is complete, and notes that there is no provision to put books within the reach of young men and women. In October 1852, a Boston city ordinance was passed and laid the foundation for public libraries throughout the United States to adopt the board plan of administrative management.

Public Library Growth between 1876 and World War I

> "Each public library established in a community is a story in itself."

Massachusetts took the lead in establishing a state library commission, which led to other states enacting library legislation and the formation of many state library commissions.[10] As a result, by 1896, nearly one thousand public libraries had been founded. Each public library established in a community is a story in itself.[11] Many factors account for the growth in the number of public libraries established between 1876 and World War I, but three factors were especially noteworthy:

1. the contribution of women's organizations;[12]
2. philanthropy, including more than forty-one million dollars contributed by Andrew Carnegie to build 1,679 libraries in 1,412 communities across the United States between 1898 and 1919;[13] and
3. the establishment of state commissions and traveling libraries.[14]

Public Libraries during World War I and World War II

World War I marked a turning point for library development. In his study of librarians during World War I, Wiegand described the state of libraries prior to the war as consisting of thousands of local libraries scattered across the United States staffed by women and men who developed high-quality collections but who longed for a consolidation of their position within the community.[15] At the close of the war, the U.S. public library achieved integration into the fabric of life by close association with the war effort. By 1918, public libraries were generally accepted as a standard component of municipal services.

A 1924 report, *The American Public Library and the Diffusion of Knowledge*, included the observation that "the free public library is already an accepted and cherished figure in American intellectual life" and put forth the suggestion that the American Library Association (ALA) should provide support for the growth and expansion of libraries.[16] The concept of the library as an agency of ongoing education for adults became firmly established in U.S. society.

As World War II began, the ALA's Committee on Post-War Planning issued Post-War Standards for Public Libraries in 1943.[17] Part of a national effort to help make the world a better place in which to live, the postwar standards asserted the importance of the public library and recommended that public

Kathleen de la Peña McCook

library services should be universally available in the United States. These standards were followed by another ALA report, a *National Plan for Public Library Service*, published in 1948.[18]

Public Libraries in the Second Half of the Twentieth Century

Between 1947 and 1952, a multipart project called the Public Library Inquiry[19] contributed to the reformulation of the public library's service mission during the 1950s, acting as one of many catalysts that stimulated the innovative outreach efforts of the late 1960s and early 1970s.[20] Initially public librarians had relied upon statistics and checklists to establish models that could be used when defining local service, with standards for public libraries issued in 1933, 1943, 1956, and 1966, which implied that meeting numerical goals would establish quality.[21]

But much changed from 1955 to 1966, following passage of the Library Services Act (LSA) in 1956. The LSA provided funds to establish library service in areas unserved, especially in rural parts of the country. It also required that each state submit a plan for library development before it was eligible to receive federal aid.[22] In 1964, the LSA was amended and expanded to include urban libraries and construction and was retitled the Library Services and Construction Act (LSCA).

In 1966, LSCA modifications stimulated development of a wide variety of innovative library services as well as services to the elderly and homebound, literacy services, services to tribal communities, and child-care centers for latchkey children.[23] Additionally, prior to civil rights legislation in the 1960s, segregation prevailed in libraries throughout much of the United States. Writers such as E. J. Josey, Alma Dawson, John Mark Tucker, Patterson Toby Graham, and David Battles have constructed histories on the manifestation of segregation in various states and regions.[24] The ALA Office for Literacy and Outreach Services was established in 1970 in response to these new national priorities for public libraries and focused on addressing the needs of underserved groups.[25]

New legislation passed in 1996; the Library Services and Technology Act (LSTA) moved the administration of federal aid to public libraries from the Department of Education to a new agency, the Institute of Museum and Library Services (IMLS). The LSTA built on the strengths of previous federal library programs but included some major differences. While it retained the state-based approach from previous legislation, it sharpened the focus to two key priorities for libraries—information access through technology and information empowerment through special services. By locating federal support for libraries within the Institute of Museum and Library Services, since 1996, the government now emphasizes the community-based role of libraries and includes lifelong learning in the mission of the public library. For example, the LSTA statement of purpose includes a description of the ways that library services were changing, including a transition from their traditional focus on collecting and circulating physical holdings to a mission focused on providing "access to computers, software, and a host of new services, including an ever-increasing pool of digital information services."[26]

Over the last fifty years, the Public Library Association has focused on strengthening public libraries and their contribution to the communities they serve.[27] The PLA published five planning guides (see also "Chapter 8—Planning Guides for Public Libraries" in the online supplement), which reflect the concerns and priorities of public library managers and boards at the time they were written between 1980 and 2008; these provide an overview of fifty years of library development, sharing examples of how public library priorities have changed over the decades.[28]

TEXTBOX 8.2

Topic for Discussion

Library services continue to evolve and expand. What skills and knowledge do you think an information professional needs in order to be an effective leader in a public library environment today?

Administration of Public Libraries

"Public librarians are inescapably a part of government and involved in 'politics,'" asserted Oliver Garceau in his 1949 classic study, *The Public Library in the Political Process*.[29] Operating a public library requires an awareness of the social, political, and economic factors that affect library services. Librarians must scan and assess the national, state, regional, and local political environment because public policy and legislation at all these levels influence each library's funding and governance.

Organization and Funding

More than 50 percent of U.S. public libraries fall under the jurisdiction of municipal government, but the legal basis for some public libraries is county government (approximately 10 percent), library district units (approximately 15 percent), and other types of units, such as multicounty agencies.[30]

Check This Out

Current access to the library statutes of most states can be found on the website for Chief Officer of State Library Agencies (COSLA), which lists a profile of each state library, including the current website and links to the legislation for libraries currently in force for the state.[1]

1. Chief Officers of State Library Agencies (COSLA), http://www.cosla.org/profiles.

The legal basis for public libraries resides in state laws that grant a city, town, village, or district the right to establish a library, authorize the power to levy taxes, and determine the structure and powers of the library board. In addition to state law, many municipalities and counties have passed local ordinances relating to library governance.[31] The primary source of funding for public libraries is local tax dollars (see also chapter 22, "Managing Budgets").

Public libraries are overseen by a group of citizens—usually called a board of trustees or board of directors. Commonly appointed by a governing body, but sometimes elected, the library board is responsible for a range of functions: hiring, recommending, and evaluating the public library director; developing community support for bond issues and taxation; budget and policy review and approval; commitment to freedom of inquiry and expression; and long-range planning.[32]

The federal government is also an important source of public library funding and governance. The federal program that provides funding to libraries is the Library Services and Technology Act (LSTA).[33] The LSTA is administered by the IMLS through grants to state library agencies.

Other federal legislation impacts public libraries. For example, in 2014, the Workforce Innovation and Opportunity Act included funding for public libraries to be considered one-stop partners. The act authorized adult education and literacy activities provided by public libraries as an allowable statewide employment and training activity.[34] The ALA's Office for Government Relations, located in Washington, D.C., monitors and works to influence legislation, policy, and regulatory issues of importance to the library field and its public, including federal legislation that may impact library funding.[35]

Management and Staffing

The management and staffing of public libraries is governed by the municipal, county, or district that oversees the library. As such, local civil service policies specify the conditions of employment, and they usually differ from community to community. Directors most often report to a library board that is authorized by state statute, but there are many variations on the organizational structure of public libraries.

Kathleen de la Peña McCook

The library director works closely with the library board to establish the public library mission, develop long-range plans, and implement policies for the library's operations (see also chapter 21, "Management Skills"). The director works at the nexus of community and staff. Directors are expected to handle numerous responsibilities, such as leading planning cycles; organizing human resources (see also chapter 23, "Managing Personnel"); representing the library in the community; overseeing financial operations; interacting with local, state, and national library entities; developing the library's fiscal base through development and fund-raising; managing facilities and technology (see also chapter 24, "Managing Facilities," and chapter 26, "Managing Technology"); and planning, designing, and evaluating services[36] (see also chapter 28, "Demonstrating Value: Assessment").

Public library staffing is structured in response to community needs. For example, since public libraries serve users of all ages, they usually hire youth librarians and adult services librarians. Increasingly librarians with digital and electronic skill sets are in demand to meet the changing needs of their communities. Libraries configure divisions depending on the local situation.

Check This Out

The Public Library Data Service (PLDS) includes longitudinal data—staffing, operating, finances, output measures, interlibrary load, and technology—from more than 1,100 North American libraries.[1] Visit: http://www.ala.org/pla/publication/plds.

_____

1. Ian Reid, "The Public Library Data Service 2012 Statistical Report," *Public Libraries* 5, no. 6 (2012): 36–46.

Volunteer organizations that support public libraries are called Friends of the Library groups, and they provide additional support for library operations. Friends extend a library's capacity through financial contributions, volunteer and program support, and advocacy.[37] In addition to staff, volunteers comprise a significant portion of workers in public library settings.

The Public Library as Community Anchor

"Why Build Libraries?" asked Colorado library director James LaRue in the July/August 2014 issue of *Public Libraries*. Because, he states, "the library is a community center, a place for lifelong learning, a place for early childhood, emergent literacy, a creator space, and perhaps most subtly, a statement of community value."[38]

It is important for public librarians to understand the role of the public library to the community's sense of self-identity. The public library is simultaneously a tangible representation of humanity's ideals and a place where library services are delivered. The library can be a public space that inspires, sustains, and anchors a community's educational and cultural self-perception.[39]

The library as place is an important concept. According to a 2014 report published by the Aspen Institute entitled *Rising to the Challenge: Re-Envisioning Public Libraries*, "today's library is both a physical and virtual place, but it continues to be the physical presence of the library that anchors it most firmly in the community." The authors of the report assert that physical library spaces are community assets that "provide a safe and trusted location for community services such as health clinics, emergency response centers, small business incubators, workforce development centers, and immigrant resource centers."[40] Library spaces offer opportunities for people to connect, create, and collaborate (see also part IV, "Information Users: Engaging, Creating, and Collaborating via Technology"). As library services continue to evolve, library space must also evolve, being flexible enough to adapt to changing community needs.

The history of public library buildings in Oregon from 1893 to 2014, described by Jim Scheppke,[41] is emblematic of the development of library buildings across the United States. Several factors combined to create Oregon's statewide commitment to public libraries that continues today, including major donations, the Carnegie building program, library associations, charitable foundations, and local engagement.

Public Library Services

Public libraries in the twenty-first century are anchor institutions, centers of community reinvention, lifelines to surviving in a complex economic climate, and the heart of a community's lifelong learning. In addition to books in multiple formats, today's public library services include new directions in response to evolving technologies. Services can be configured to meet each community's needs and to address unique characteristics of local residents, such as age, language, and culture.

The Public Library Association (PLA) emphasizes this focus on developing services aimed at addressing local needs. In 1980, the PLA changed its approach to defining "excellent service" to a planning context based on three assumptions:

- Excellence must be defined locally. It results when library services match community needs, interests, and priorities.
- Excellence is possible for both small and large libraries. It rests more on commitment than on unlimited resources.
- Excellence is a moving target.[42]

Service Roles for Libraries

The Public Library Association identified eighteen service roles for libraries, offering an overview of the changing nature of public library services (see textbox 8.3).[43] For each of these roles, libraries develop collections or services to address their communities' needs.

In their book *Public Libraries and Internet Service Roles*, McClure and Jaeger describe the public library as the "place for public access to the Internet." They note that "for a majority of communities, the public library is the only place where free access to the Internet is available." To deliver these services, the library needs staff who are trained to help users locate the resources available to them. The library also needs to have a high-quality technology infrastructure, such as adequate workstations, bandwidth, and up-to-date equipment and software.[44]

The National Medal for Museum and Library Service celebrates libraries that make a difference in their communities. A review of recent honorees is an indicator of the scope and range of today's public library services.[45] For example, services provided by 2014 award winners include the following:

- free access to books, digital resources, downloadable media, and online databases;
- access to computers, Internet connectivity, 3-D printers, media labs, and other tools to create and share content;
- lifelong learning programs, including early literacy programs and tutoring for students, as well as financial literacy, health literacy, and digital literacy services for individuals of all ages;
- programs to serve specific local needs, such as the needs of job seekers, veterans, and small-business entrepreneurs;
- cultural programs, such as art exhibits and artist receptions, lectures, author visits, cultural film screenings, and poetry contests; and
- cultural preservation activities, including collections of local artifacts and oral histories.

Kathleen de la Peña McCook

TEXTBOX 8.3

Service Roles for Public Libraries

1. Be an informed citizen: local, national and world affairs
2. Build successful enterprises: business and nonprofit support
3. Celebrate diversity: cultural awareness
4. Connect to the online world: public Internet access
5. Create young readers: early literacy
6. Discover your roots: genealogy and local history
7. Express creativity: create and share content
8. Get facts fast: ready reference
9. Know your community: community resources and services
10. Learn to read and write: adults, teens, and family literature
11. Make career choices: job and career development
12. Make informed decisions: health, wealth, and other life choices
13. Satisfy curiosity: lifelong learning
14. Stimulate imagination: reading, viewing, and listening for pleasure
15. Succeed in school: homework help
16. Understand how to find, evaluate, and use information: information fluency
17. Visit a comfortable place: physical and virtual spaces
18. Welcome to the United States: services for new immigrants

Offering Inclusive Services

As described in the PLA's eighteen service roles for libraries, today's public libraries need to provide equitable access to services that are inclusive of traditionally underserved populations, including native and tribal peoples, new and nonreaders, older adults, people geographically isolated, people with disabilities, rural and urban poor people, and people generally discriminated against based on race, ethnicity, sexual orientation, age, language, and social class (see also chapter 4, "Diversity, Cultures, and Equity of Access"). The ALA Office for Literacy and Outreach Services provides support for public libraries' efforts in these areas.[46]

> "Today's public libraries need to provide equitable access to services that are inclusive of traditionally underserved populations."

Today's public libraries also provide service to people in institutions, provide resources for people with Alzheimer's and related dementias, serve the deaf, serve individuals in correctional facilities or immigration facilities, and offer assistive technology and accessibility services for people with visual or physical disabilities. The Association of Specialized and Cooperative Library Agencies (ASCLA) offers guidelines for providing these types of service.[47]

Young people are another key audience of public library services, accounting for one-third of public library circulation.[48] This group is served by librarians with special expertise as defined by the Association for Library Service to Children (ALSC) and the Young Adults Services Association (YALSA). Both associations have identified competencies for librarians serving children or young adults.[49] Additionally, associations at the national and state level cooperate on childhood literacy projects, such as Every Child Ready to Read at Your Library.[50]

Looking to the Future: Community Transformation, Inclusion, and Human Rights

In the future, public libraries will increasingly emphasize social inclusion and community transformation and address challenges that result in deeper commitment to issues of human rights (see also chapter 5, "Librarianship: A Continuously Evolving Profession"). These values have been expounded by librarians such as Pateman and Williment, who describe how public libraries can tackle social exclusion, contribute to community engagement, and work for social justice.[51]

To these ends, the literature of public librarianship is in a time of self-analysis of mission and future directions. Great shifts in service have been explored in studies such as *Transforming Libraries, Building Communities*[52] and *Public Libraries and Resilient Cities*.[53] There is widespread recognition of the growing role of technology in collaborative community services.[54]

But the biggest shift has been a turn to values of human rights as drivers of service for public libraries—concepts defined and articulated by Toni Samek in 2007 and reenforced by McCook and Phenix in 2011.[55] The concept of human rights as an overarching vision will continue to be a compass for librarians.[56] "Where do universal human rights begin?" asked Eleanor Roosevelt at the United Nations in 1953. "In small places, close to home," she noted. A small place, close to home—like the public library.[57]

Conclusion

The journey of public libraries from Boston's first public library, which opened in 1854, to today's public libraries, which offer access to digital resources and technology, is a glimpse into what makes public libraries such an important part of their communities. They are a community anchor—a place where lifelong learning is fostered and where important collaboration takes place. They offer access to a range of resources for individuals who otherwise would have no way to go online, access government benefits, or compete in today's economy. And they support the information needs of groups that are often on the margins of our society, helping to ensure inclusion and address human rights. Because public libraries serve every community member, they are a critical community asset.

No discussion of public libraries would be complete without mentioning the librarians who work there. These committed individuals wrestle to address shifting funding challenges, changing community demographics, and the need to update technology as it rapidly evolves in the digital age (see also chapter 1, "The Transformative Information Landscape: What It Means to Be an Information Professional Today"). The competencies they need continue to expand as they take on a broader range of roles. For example, they need to interact effectively with library users from all walks of life, both in person and online. They need to be able to quickly adapt to new situations. They also need to be able to measure the impact of their services and demonstrate the library's value to the community. At the core, they are information professionals who seek to meet the lifelong learning needs of their communities.

Kathleen de la Peña McCook

Notes

1. Kathleen de la Peña McCook and Katharine J. Phenix, "Public Librarianship," in *Encyclopedia of Library and Information Sciences*, 3rd ed. (London: Taylor and Routledge, 2010).
2. FEMA, Robert T. Stafford Disaster Relief and Emergency Assistance Act (Public Law 93-288), as amended, https://www.fema.gov/robert-t-stafford-disaster-relief-and-emergency-assistance-act -public-law-93-288-amended; Deborah D. Halsted, Shari Clifton, and Daniel T. Wilson, *Library as Safe Haven: Disaster Planning, Response, and Recovery* (Chicago, IL: American Library Association, 2014).
3. Institute of Museum and Library Services, "Number and Percentage of Libraries by Select Characteristics," in *Public Libraries in the United States Survey: Fiscal Year 2011* (Washington, DC: Institute of Museum and Library Services, 2014), http://www.imls.gov/research/public_libraries_in_the_us_fy_2011_tables.aspx.
4. See also the ALA annual report, "Public Library Use," http://www.ala.org/tools/libfactsheets/ alalibraryfactsheet06.
5. James Raven, "Social Libraries and Library Societies in Eighteenth-Century North America," in *Institutions of Reading: The Social Life of Libraries in the United States*, ed. Thomas Augst and Kenneth Carpenter, 24–52 (Amherst: University of Massachusetts Press, 2007).
6. Elaine Fain, "The Library and American Education: Education through Secondary School," *Library Trends* 27 (Winter 1979): 327–352.
7. Carleton Joeckel, *Post-War Standards for Public Libraries* (Chicago, IL: American Library Association, 1943).
8. Jesse H. Shera, *Foundations of the Public Library: The Origins of the Public Library Movement in New England, 1629–1855* (Chicago, IL: University of Chicago Press, 1949).
9. Kathleen de la Peña McCook, "Brahmins, Bequests, and Determined Women: The Beginnings to 1918," in *Introduction to Public Librarianship*, 2nd ed., 17–34 (New York: Neal-Schuman, 2011).
10. Boston Public Library, *Report of the Trustees of the Public Library to the City of Boston*, 1852, http:// www.bpl.org/govinfo/online-collections/regional-boston-and-massachusetts/boston-public-library -documents-1852-1998.
11. Paula D. Watson, "Valleys without Sunsets: Women's Clubs and Traveling Libraries," in *Libraries to the People: Histories of Outreach*, ed. Robert S. Freeman and David M. Hovde, 73–95 (Jefferson, NC: McFarland, 2003).
12. See, for example, Phyllis P. Dain, *The New York Public Library: A History of Its Founding and Early* Years (New York: New York Public Library, 1972); Ray E. Held, *The Rise of the Public Library in California* (Chicago, IL: American Library Association, 1973); Christine Pawley, "Advocate of Access: Lutie Stearns and the Traveling Libraries of the Wisconsin Free Library Commission: 1895–1914," *Libraries and Culture* 35 (Summer 2000): 434–458.
13. Paula D. Watson, "Founding Mothers: The Contribution of Women's Organizations to Public Library Development in the United States," *Library Quarterly* 64 (July 1994): 23; Suzanne Hildenbrand, ed., *Reclaiming the American Library Past: Writing the Women In* (Norwood, NJ: Ablex, 1996).
14. George S. Bobinski, *Carnegie Libraries: Their History and Impact on American Library Development* (Chicago, IL: American Library Association, 1969).
15. Wayne A. Wiegand, *An Active Instrument for Propaganda: The American Public Library during World War I* (Westport, CT: Greenwood, 1989).
16. William S. Learned, *The American Public Library and the Diffusion of Knowledge* (New York: Harcourt, 1924).
17. Carleton Joeckel, *Post-War Standards for Public Libraries* (Chicago, IL: American Library Association, 1943).
18. Carleton B. Joeckel and Amy Winslow, *A National Plan for Public Library Service* (Chicago, IL: American Library Association, 1948).
19. Douglas Raber, *Librarianship and Legitimacy: The Ideology of the Public Library Inquiry* (Westport, CT: Greenwood, 1997).
20. Mary Niles Maack, "Public Libraries in Transition: Ideals, Strategies and Research," *Libraries and Culture* 29 (Winter 1994): 79.
21. Kathleen de la Peña McCook, "Statistics, Standards, Planning, Results, and Quality of Life," *Introduction to Public Librarianship*, 2nd ed., 76–82 (New York: Neal-Schuman, 2011).

22. Genevieve M. Casey, ed., "Federal Aid to Libraries: Its History, Impact, Future," *Library Trends* 24 (July 1975).

23. Bridget L. Lamont, "The Legacy of the Library Services & Construction Act in Illinois," *Illinois Libraries* 80 (Summer 1998): 93-184.

24. David. M. Battles, *The History of Public Library Access for African Americans in the South or Leaving behind the Plow* (Lanham, MD: Scarecrow Press, 2009); Alma Dawson, "Celebrating African-American Librarians and Librarianship," *Library Trends* 49 (Summer 2000): 49-87; Patterson Toby Graham, *A Right to Read: Segregation and Civil Rights in Alabama's Public Libraries, 1900-1965* (Tuscaloosa: University of Alabama Press, 2002); E. J. Josey, *The Black Librarian in America* (Metuchen, NJ: Scarecrow Press, 1970); John M. Tucker, *Untold Stories: Civil Rights, Libraries and Black Librarianship* (Champaign, IL: University of Illinois Press, 1998).

25. This was a landmark in national focus. See American Library Association Archives, http://archives.library.illinois.edu/alaarchon/?p=creators/creator&id=3476. On July 3, 1970, the Office for Library Service to the Disadvantaged and Unserved was established, and on July 3, 1980, the name was changed to Office for Library Outreach Services (OLOS). The purpose of OLOS was (1) to promote the provision of library service to the urban and rural poor, of all ages, and to those people who are discriminated against because they belong to minority groups; (2) to encourage the development of user-oriented informational and educational library services to meet the needs of the urban and rural poor, ethnic minorities, the underemployed, school dropouts, the semiliterate and illiterate, and those isolated by cultural differences; and (3) to ensure that librarians and others have information, access to technical assistance, and continuing education opportunities to assist them in developing effective outreach programs. The Jean E. Coleman Lecture was established to commemorate the work of the founding director, http://www.ala.org/offices/olos/olosprograms/jeanecoleman/jeanecoleman.

26. "Grants to State Library Administrative Agencies," Institute of Museum and Library Services, last modified October 28, 2014, http://www.imls.gov/programs.

27. "Strategic Plan," Public Library Association, last modified April 14, 2014, http://www.ala.org/pla/about/strategicplan.

28. Public libraries have been an important community asset in recent centuries, although their focus has shifted as the needs of their communities have changed. What key lessons can you draw from the history of public libraries that can help you be better prepared to serve patrons in the future? Vernon Palmour, Marcia C. Bellassai, and Nancy V. DeWath, *A Planning Process for Public Libraries* (Chicago, IL: American Library Association, 1980); Charles R. McClure et al., *Planning and Role-Setting for Public Libraries: A Manual of Options and Procedures* (Chicago, IL: American Library Association, 1987); Ethel Himmel and William James Wilson, *Planning for Results: A Public Library Transformation Process* (Chicago, IL: American Library Association, 1998); Sandra Nelson, *The New Planning for Results: A Streamlined Approach* (Chicago, IL: American Library Association, 2001); Sandra Nelson, *Strategic Planning for Results* (Chicago, IL: American Library Association, 2008).

29. Oliver Garceau, *The Public Library in the Political Process: A Report of the Public Library Inquiry* (New York: Columbia University Press, 1949).

30. Institute of Museum and Library Services (U.S.), "Table 5: Percentage Distribution of Public Libraries, by Type of Legal Basis and State: Fiscal Year 2011," in *Public Libraries in the United States Survey: Fiscal Year 2011* (Washington, DC: Institute of Museum and Library Services, 2014), http://www.imls.gov/research/public_libraries_in_the_us_fy_2011_tables.aspx.

31. Kathleen de la Peña McCook, "Organization, Law, Advocacy, Funding and Politics," in *Introduction to Public Librarianship*, 2nd ed., 101-130 (New York: Neal-Schuman, 2011).

32. Sally Gardner Reed and Jillian Kalonick, *The Complete Library Trustee Handbook* (New York: Neal-Schuman, 2010).

33. "Legislation and Budget," Institute of Museum and Library Services (U.S.), last modified October 28, 2014, http://www.imls.gov/about/legislation_and_budget.aspx.

34. "Libraries and Workforce Development," U.S. Department of Labor, last modified July 7, 2014, http://www.doleta.gov/usworkforce/uswf_nav.cfm.

35. "Office of Government Relations," American Library Association, last modified October 10, 2014, http://www.ala.org/offices/ogr.

36. Kathleen de la Peña McCook, "Administration and Staffing," in *Introduction to Public Librarianship*, 2nd ed., 137–140 (New York: Neal-Schuman, 2011).

37. Sally Gardner Reed, *Libraries Need Friends United for Libraries: The Association of Library Trustees, Advocates, Friends and Foundations*, 2012, http://www.ala.org/united/sites/ala.org.united/files/content/friends zone/toolkits/libraries-need-friends-1.pdf.

38. James LaRue, "Why Build Libraries?" *Public Libraries* 53 (July/August 2014): 12–17.

39. Kathleen de la Peña McCook, "Structure and Infrastructure," *Introduction to Public Librarianship*, 2nd ed., 159–198 (New York: Neal-Schuman, 2011).

40. Amy Garmer, *Rising to the Challenge: Re-Envisioning Public Libraries* (Washington, DC: Aspen Institute, October 2014).

41. Jim Scheppke. "Public Library Buildings in Oregon: A Historical Sketch," *OPL Quarterly* 15, no. 3 (2014): 8–11.

42. Nelson, *Strategic Planning for Results*, 143–217.

43. P. T. Jaeger, et al., "The Public Library in the Local Political Process," in *Public Libraries, Public Policies, and Political Processes: Serving and Transforming Communities in Times of Economic and Political Constraint*, 131–149 (Lanham, MD: Rowman & Littlefield, 2014).

44. Charles R. McClure and Paul T. Jaeger, *Public Libraries and Internet Service Roles: Measuring and Maximizing Internet Services* (Chicago, IL: American Library Association, 2009).

45. Institute of Museum and Library Services (U.S.), *National Medal for Museum and Library Service*, 2014, http://www.imls.gov/assets/1/AssetManager/Medals2014Brochure.pdf.

46. Office for Literacy and Outreach Services, "Mission," last modified October 9, 2104, http://www.ala.org/offices/olos; John Gehner, "Libraries, Low-Income People, and Social Exclusion," *Public Library Quarterly* 29, no. 1 (2010): 39–47.

47. Association of Specialized and Cooperative Library Agencies (ASCLA), last modified July 8, 2014, http://www.ala.org/ascla/asclaourassoc/asclainterest/list.

48. Institute of Museum and Library Services (U.S.), "Table 8: Number of Public Library Services, by Type of Service and State: Fiscal Year 2011," in *Public Libraries in the United States Survey: Fiscal Year 2011* (Washington, DC: Institute of Museum and Library Services, 2014), http://www.imls.gov/assets/1/AssetManager/FY2011_PLS_Tables_8-17A.pdf.

49. Association for Library Services to Children (ALSC), "Competencies for Librarians Serving Children in Public Libraries," 2009, http://www.ala.org/alsc/edcareeers/alsccorecomps; Sarah Flowers, *Young Adults Deserve the Best: YALSA's Competencies in Action* (Chicago, IL: American Library Association, 2011).

50. Association for Library Services to Children (ALSC) and Public Library Association (PLA), "Every Child Ready to Read at Your Library," 2010, http://www.everychildreadytoread.org.

51. John Pateman and Ken Williment, *Developing Community-Led Public Libraries* (Surrey, UK: Ashgate, 2013).

52. Julie Biando Edwards, Melissa Rauseo, and Kelley Rae Unger, *Transforming Libraries, Building Communities: The Community Centered Library* (Lanham, MD: Scarecrow Press, 2013).

53. Michael Dudley, *Public Libraries and Resilient Cities* (Chicago, IL: American Library Association, 2013).

54. N. G. Taylor, U. Gorham, P. T. Jaeger, and J. C. Bertot, "IT and Collaborative Community Services: The Roles of the Public Library, Local Government, and Nonprofit Entity Partnerships," *International Journal of Public Administration in the Digital Age* 1, no. 1 (2014): 91–107.

55. See *Progressive Librarian*, 1990–present, available full text at http://progressivelibrariansguild.org/PL_Jnl/jnl_contents.shtml.

56. Toni Samek, *Librarianship and Human Rights* (Oxford: Chandos, 2007); Kathleen de la Peña McCook and Katharine J. Phenix, "The Future of Public Libraries in the Twenty-First Century: Human Rights and Human Capabilities," in *Introduction to Public Librarianship*, 339–360 (New York: Neal-Schuman, 2011); P. T. Jaeger, N. G. Taylor, and U. Gorham, *Libraries, Human Rights, and Social Justice: Enabling Access and Promoting Inclusion* (Lanham, MD: Rowman & Littlefield, in press).

57. See the very poignant essay by Glen Holt, "Exploring Public Library Contributions to Urban Resiliency," in *Public Libraries and Resilient Cities*, 37–56 (Chicago, IL: American Library Association, 2013).

9

Information Centers

SPECIAL LIBRARIES

Cheryl R. Dee, Stephen Abram, and Deb Hunt

Special libraries differ from other libraries in that they uniquely focus on diverse and specialized resources with a limited subject scope, serve specialized and limited users (typically called customers or clients in special libraries), and often deliver technologically advanced specialized services. Special libraries develop their mission and goals based on their parent organization and provide services to meet the organization's goals. They acquire, provide, and often archive information resources aligned with the parent organization's specialization. Some of the distinguishing characteristics of the information professional in the special library setting are highlighted by the Special Libraries Association (SLA) core values: leadership, service, innovation and continuous learning, results and accountability, and collaboration and partnering.[1]

> "Although diverse, special libraries have significant unifying characteristics, particularly the philosophy of service tailored to the specific information needs of each customer."

The special library offers information access and specialized custom services to ensure rapid delivery of information to meet customers' unique information needs. Technological developments significantly influence the role of special libraries and provide the means to rapidly and proactively deliver information. Information professionals are often the leaders of these organizations with their creative, innovative uses of technology. After completing this chapter, the reader should have an understanding of the origin of special libraries; the work environment; the roles, responsibilities, and competencies of information professionals in the special library environment; and the opportunities and challenges that are unique to special libraries.

History

Special libraries began as personal, religious, or scholarly society libraries. Their prominence, however, arose in Great Britain and the United States as more industries developed associations for special libraries to fulfill their unique information needs.[2]

By the early twentieth century, John Cotton Dana, head of the Newark (NJ) Public Library, recognized special librarianship's distinct role to provide practical and utilitarian information to meet the needs of the special library's users.[3] In 1909, Dana and F. B. Deberard met with a group of information professionals on the Mt. Washington Hotel veranda to discuss the creation of a new type of organization. "The participants in this 'Veranda Conference' . . . decided that the demands of their job had actually created a new kind of librarianship—

that of library service geared to meet the needs of specialized situations."[4] Dana and his colleagues founded the Special Libraries Association, created and directed toward the specific needs of those seeking information, knowledge, and strategic learning in pursuit of their practical goals.[5] Dana served as SLA's first president. The inclusiveness and diversity of SLA's membership was established as a primary characteristic of the association, as stated in the association's 1909 constitution, with the objective to promote the interests of a wide range of special libraries in a variety of venues.[6] The global spread of special libraries began in 1924 when information professionals in Great Britain formed the Association for Information Management (ASLIB).[7] Further globalization is recognized by the existence of the Division of Special Libraries within the International Federation of Library Associations and Institutions (IFLA).[8] Today, the Special Library Association's divisions, caucuses, and student groups encompass the depth and breadth of the field of special libraries (see table 9.1).

The SLA is organized into fifty-five geographic chapters on every continent except Antarctica.[9]

Table 9.1. Special Libraries Association Divisions and Sections

Special Libraries Association	

Academic and Scholarly
Biomedical and Life Sciences
• Medical Section
Business and Finance
• Advertising and Marketing
• Corporate Information Centers
• College and University Business Libraries
• Financial Services
Chemistry
• Material Research and Manufacturing
Competitive Intelligence
Education
Engineering
• Aerospace Section
Architecture, Building Engineering,
   Construction, and Design
Environmental and Resource Management
• Forestry and Forest Products
• Food, Agriculture, and Nutrition
Government Information
Information Technology
• Communications and Social Media
• Information Systems
• Technical Services
• Web Management
	Knowledge Management and
	   Records Management
	Legal
	Leadership and Management
	• Consulting
	• Content Buying
	• Marketing
	Military Libraries
	Museums, Arts, and Humanities
	News
	Petroleum and Energy Resources
	Pharmaceutical and Health Technology
	• Devices and Diagnostics
	Physics—Astronomy—Mathematics
	Science—Technology
	Social Science
	• Geography and Maps
	• International Relations
	• Nonprofit Sector
	• Public Policy
	• Labor Issues
	Solo Librarians
	Taxonomy
	Transportation

Special Library Environments

There is a special library for just about any subject area or organizational type that exists. From architectural materials libraries (flooring, siding, and paint chip samples) to electrical engineering specifications, to button and shoe collections in a fashion library, one will find that there is a library collection and information professionals who meet all the knowledge and research needs of their customers.

Special libraries are staffed and curated by information professionals or subject specialists who usually have a master of library and information science (MLIS) and often a second subject-related master's degree with expertise in their organization's subject areas or extensive continuing education and training. More and more, information professionals are embedded in their organization's operating units and thus are familiar with the knowledge needs of their customers. Special libraries range in size from small operations administered by one person within an organization to large institutions within their own buildings with hundreds of staff members.[10]

In the for-profit world, special libraries are generally not called libraries at all—if they even exist as a physical space. They often go by other names, such as "corporate knowledge center" or "corporate information commons." Often, there is no designated library location or space, but the information professionals are embedded in departments and teams within the organization. Corporate information professionals tend to work long hours that match those of their customers and often are issued a company mobile phone and laptop so they can be contacted when research and intelligence are needed. In today's world of global business, they may be on call 24/7/365. It is often a demanding job requiring information professionals to stay on top of the trends and information in the organization's sphere of business, but it can also be an exciting career path where information professionals can have significance and influence.[11]

Information Professionals' Role in Special Libraries

Information professionals who work in special libraries wear many hats. They work with specialized types of information, provide specialized information services, manage internal and external resources, and offer programs (e.g., competitive intelligence programs) that benefit organizations.

Working with Specialized Types of Information

Special libraries require deep, narrowly focused, and specialized types of information to meet the specific interests and needs of the customers in the sponsoring organization. Traditional broader-scope information organizational systems (e.g., OCLC Incorporated) do not provide enough differentiation for most special libraries' highly detailed and technical subject matter. Information professionals often prepare in-house classification and cataloging systems or contract with specialized commercial companies with specialized thesauri (e.g., the U.S. National Library of Medicine's [NLM] own NLM Classification;[12] NLM's Medical Subject Headings [MeSH];[13] and the NLM Unified Medical Language System [UMLS], Metathesaurus).[14] Special library resources vary according to the focus of the organization and the type of special library (see appendix 9.1, "Mastering Special Library Resources").

Organizations often have repositories or assets that are outside the more traditional library collection of print and e-resources. These can include archival and records management assets that preserve the history of an organization and/or may be legally mandated to be kept for certain periods of time. Archives can range from an organization's articles of incorporation to membership records to photographs or collections of works by one distinguished individual of the organization.[15] Records management can include physical records, electronic records, and SharePoint repositories. Today's born-digital assets can be a challenge to organize as they often reside in unstructured shared online folders or on computer desktops.

Cheryl R. Dee, Stephen Abram, and Deb Hunt

Professional organizations such as the Society of American Archivists[1] and ARMA International[2] offer many resources about careers in archival and records management.

───────────

1. Society of American Archivists, http://www2.archivists.org.
2. ARMA International, http://www.arma.org.

Providing Specialized Information Services

Information professionals have a service philosophy that is less focused on teaching their customers how to find the information themselves and instead aims to provide research deliverables to customers with whom they work regularly. Rapid response time in the delivery of relevant, up-to-date information is often critical. For example, because of the need to meet urgent point-of-care medical questions, the National Library of Medicine is often at the technological forefront to develop tools for rapid research[16] and the delivery of medical information.[17] Information professionals in special libraries must often go beyond factual ready-reference answers to provide in-depth research services and extensive bibliographies using specialized resources. This type of work requires careful prioritization of the research tasks.

> "Information professionals who work in special libraries typically serve a limited population and become acquainted with their customers and their ongoing information needs; this allows the information professionals to anticipate and proactively deliver narrowly defined, customized information on a specific topic."

Information professionals who work in special libraries typically serve a limited population and become acquainted with their customers and their ongoing information needs; this allows the information professionals to anticipate and proactively deliver narrowly defined, customized information on a specific topic, including customized electronically accessible tables of contents prepared by a publisher or in-house by the information professional, with subsequent delivery of full-text articles.

Managing Internal Information

Information professionals in other sectors of the information profession usually work with externally published information in many forms. In the special library setting, hosted in corporations and other specialized environments, the information and answers demanded by customers is often a hybrid of both internal and external information. In addition to the publicly available external information found in books, in databases, on the web, and in other physical resources, completion of the customer's request often involves seeking information through internal, private, or confidential files and databases. Sometimes this material is under the control and management of the special library, and sometimes it involves working with other units of the organization to access information (e.g., archives, records, legal conflicts files, lab notebooks, photo libraries, medical records, human resources files for expertise databases). This content is not limited to just textual information; it also includes data, visuals, charts, x-rays, and more. The special library often builds some of this content (e.g., competitive intelligence files, current awareness services, issues tracking, patent or FDA approval tracking, or tracking press mentions in social and other mainstream media).

Organizations have a hard time keeping track of, sharing, and finding certain types of knowledge—the type that often exists only in the memories and experiences of its employees. This is the practice of knowledge management, which leverages information that is tacit rather than explicit. Tacit knowledge, which typically lives only in people's heads, is difficult to transfer to another person. Often tacit knowledge is what employees of an organization need in order to do their job, start a new project, or launch a new product. However, tacit knowledge is difficult to share, and frequently this valuable form of knowledge is lost when someone leaves an organization to retire or pursue other career opportunities. Information professionals are well poised to become knowledge managers of tacit knowledge for the benefit of the organization and scholars. The emergence of the institutional or corporate intranet as a private, employees-only virtual space delivered to the desktop and mobile devices has increased the trend toward fuller information being made available in an integrated fashion to key employees and professionals. The ability to access corporate "memory" is a critical advantage in organizations that operate in a competitive framework or where efficient access to knowledge is a key success factor.

Offering Special Library Programs

> "While the special library often has as its foundation specialized hard copy and digital collections, the real value of the special librarian comes through in the programs and services that special librarians provide—above and beyond standard professional reference and research support activities."

While the special library often has as its foundation specialized hard-copy and digital collections, the real value of information professionals comes through in the programs and services that they provide—above and beyond standard professional reference and research support activities. Studies have found that most people seeking information in special libraries possess only very basic research skills. For example, Dow Jones Factiva discovered that knowledge workers spend 15 to 35 percent of their time searching and not finding information they need. Forty percent of corporate workers reported that they could not find what they wanted on their intranets.[18] IDC found that only 21 percent of respondents said they found the information they needed 85 percent to 100 percent of the time, and Butler Group reported that up to 10 percent of staff costs are lost because employees cannot find the right information to do their jobs.[19] Therefore, users in special library environments frequently turn to their fellow workers and colleagues in their area of specialization who are perceived as experts on the topic to ask them specific questions to meet their information needs.[20] Clearly information literacy needs to be an immediate goal, as does getting the word out within the organization about the value of utilizing information professionals to provide on-target research.

To teach research and database-searching skills to customers, information professionals provide internal professional development programs on searching, finding, and honing intranet skills; learning related to device and app usage; expanding database awareness; and other topics to improve decision-making quality and enhance employee productivity.

Competitive intelligence (CI) services are unique in special libraries and are aligned with other current awareness services on special topics, issues, laws/patents, companies, or other topics critical to the host organization. CI has kept up with the rapid changes in technology by adopting innovations in e-mail, RSS, blogs, dashboards, tweets, and more. Many information professionals maintain a plethora of dashboards on critical topics that are updated by hand and/or automatically and are often highly valued by their customers. Monitoring the competition is essential, and information professionals fill this space.

TEXTBOX 9.1

Topic for Discussion

How do special libraries and the services they provide differ from other library types (public, academic, and school)?

Cheryl R. Dee, Stephen Abram, and Deb Hunt

Professional Competencies Required for Working in Special Libraries

Information professionals who work in special libraries use information in strategic ways to help the mission of the organization they work in. The Special Libraries Association defines the competencies as the ability to

- develop and maintain information services that meet the customer's and organization's needs,
- identify and access relevant information resources that meet customer needs,
- find evidence to inform and help decision making within the organization,
- help clients in the organization stay current and make sure they are aware of critical trends that impact their business,
- ensure that the value of the special library is appreciated by key stakeholders, and
- be an active contributor and provider of information to inform management decisions and strategies.[21]

Check This Out

Check out SLA's Competencies for Information Professionals of the 21st Century
Visit:
http://www.sla.org/about-sla/competencies

Information professionals apply their specialized skills and competencies to resolve challenges within enterprises and other organizations. Their information organization skills may also be applied to the intranet for building enterprise-specific taxonomies, ontologies, and metadata practices that meet the needs of the organization to reduce the time-to-access of critical information in their knowledge management strategies.

Success Strategies for Information Professionals

The special library manager aligns the library with the mission, vision, and strategic plan of the parent organization. To demonstrate the special library's value to the company, the library must contribute to the attainment of the parent organization's goals and objectives. The placement of the special library on the organizational chart is critical to the library. Optimally, the manager of the special library reports to the manager of the organization; this allows the information professional direct access to knowledge regarding organizational developments, thus facilitating the alignment of the library—its services, budget, and strategic plan—to the organization's goals and developments. Information professionals' participation on teams and committees, especially strategic planning committees, also prepares information professionals to proactively respond to the organization's information needs and heightens the information professionals' visibility within the organization. Two key strategies for information professionals working in special libraries include marketing and advocacy.

Marketing

Marketing is especially critical in the special library environment (see also chapter 27, "Managing Communications, Marketing, and Outreach"). The information professional must communicate the value of the special library—its services, activities, and potential to add value throughout the entire organization. The information professional *is* the product in terms of providing information in the specialized context

> "The information professional 'is' the product in terms of providing information in the specialized context of special libraries."

of special libraries. This affects everything about the marketing plan and strategies employed by information professionals who work in these environments.

Promoting information services is done in a variety of ways—from using more traditional communication channels to establishing relationships (see appendix 9.2, "Strategic Positioning Messages"). Information services are marketed within the organization using internal e-mail lists, intranets, printed employee magazines and newsletters, exhibits, posters, social gatherings in the library, training sessions, employee orientations, and a variety of social media.

Social media also plays a role in the specialized context. LinkedIn[22] is a key tool used in special library and organizational settings for maintaining networks and finding people for research, recruitment, and partnership opportunities. There are also private social media software providers that allow defined groups of users to share conversations and information outside of the public realm. Tools such as Yammer,[23] SalesForce.com,[24] and other internal social networks can be tied to the small-group or enterprise workplace, thereby maintaining the organization's ability to keep these discussions "inside the tent" for competitive and confidentiality reasons. "Inside the tent" is a concept where conversations are held between only those authorized to participate (e.g., team members, employees only, or management only). Some information professionals also maintain networks of contacts on social media tools, such as Facebook,[25] to bring together networks of experts.

Relationship Building

Building on the importance of marketing, it is especially critical to highlight that, without the personal respect, allegiance, and support of strong relationships and champions built over time, information professionals, and the entire special library, can be at risk of being cut when budgets get tight. One way to safeguard against this is to ensure that the information professional is strongly positioned in the organization (see appendix 9.3, "Evidence of the Strongly Positioned Information Professional").[26]

Developing ongoing deep relationships with key clients and serving as critical contributors on strategic projects are especially effective techniques that help to demonstrate the value of the informational professional. In fact, every interaction—every research task, hallway conversation, chance meeting, and corporate/institutional event—is an important marketing opportunity! The critical challenge every information professional faces in the special library environment is the constant building of personal relationships and development of ongoing trust, awareness, and understanding. Information professionals also engage in specific partnerships and relationship-building activities with other related units in the organization (e.g., information technology and systems, human resources, records management, intranet management or webmasters, and marketing). Solid relationships must be maintained in order for the information professional to have a strong impact on enterprise strategies and decision quality in his or her host organization.

> TEXTBOX 9.2
>
> **Topic for Discussion**
>
> How do information professionals in the special library environment add value to the services and expertise they provide their customers?

Looking Forward: Opportunities and Challenges in Special Librarianship

Special library environments have been hotbeds of innovation (see appendix 9.4, "Trends in Special Libraries"). Listed below are a few key things that represent critical challenges and opportunities to information professionals in the second decade of the twenty-first century. These include

Cheryl R. Dee, Stephen Abram, and Deb Hunt

- *ROI:* Clearly defining the return on effort and investment (ROE or ROI) of special libraries, intranets, and information acquisition and use is an ongoing challenge (see also chapter 22, "Managing Budgets"). The general perception among too many corporate end users is that they can survive on "good enough," which is often low-quality, free web-based information. Methods to define and market the value of information professionals to executives and corporate leaders were the focus of SLA's alignment research in 2008–2009.[27]
- *Intranets:* Over the coming years, information professionals in special libraries will work to adapt their organizational intranets to integrate more seamlessly into their customers' lives—less of a destination site and more of an information partner in your pocket (see also part IV, "Information Users: Engaging, Creating, and Collaborating via Technology"). Information professionals will continue to innovate in a number of ways: building more advanced dashboards of critical information for specialized teams; building knowledge portals (as opposed to mere information portals) that are tied to the decision-making behaviors demanded by the organization; adding a diverse range of content to their intranets; moving better mobile services to smart phones; growing discovery systems and specialized search tools and visualization tools that display information results for higher impact; adapting to increased nontext content like streaming media, e-learning, and MOOC offerings; increasing digitization of corporate memory from older records management systems; performing data mining on intranet use for expertise database development to identify staff talents and intranet strategy improvements; and more.[28]
- *Embedding:* There are challenges and key issues for the sustainability of the special library model as a stand-alone library, as most enterprise content no longer requires physical space in a digital world. The trend is toward repositioning information professionals within organizational teams—often peppered throughout the organization. SLA has supported research on embedded information professionalship.[29]
- *Disintermediation:* The belief that information professionals—as gateways or gatekeepers—are in the way needs to be addressed. The SLA alignment research, referenced above, showed that executive decision makers felt the information professional's single worst weakness is that their processes and services are too "slow," with expectations driven by a Google world. This challenge is addressed by some successful information professionals who have moved the positioning of their role to be more specialized—to one at either end of a spectrum—rather than in the middle as a generalist. One end is as an infrastructure expert, using the skills of modern digital information organization and user experience expertise, and the other end is as a guide-on-the-side and training and research support partner on embedded teams. Again, specialization in the digital content and service enterprise environment is less likely to be tied to a physical facility as the primary indication of its value.[30]

Conclusion

Special libraries are uniquely positioned to provide technologically innovative and diverse resources with highly personalized, customer-specific services to a digital, and global, environment. Marketing the value of these resources and services to the parent organizations will ensure the survival of special libraries, but only if information professionals take the lead in providing proactive, innovative services their customers want and need.

Appendix 9.1: Mastering Special Library Resources

Special library resources vary according to the focus of the organization and the type of special library. Two examples are provided here—medical and legal.

- *Medical:* The National Library of Medicine (NLM) provides a wide array of health science data-bases for health-care professionals, information professionals, researchers, consumers, and pa-tients.[31] One example is PubMed,[32] which is a database of citations and abstracts in the fields of medicine, nursing, dentistry, veterinary medicine, and more. Links to full-text articles are found in PubMed Central.[33] TOXNET Toxicology Data Network[34] databases cover chemicals and drugs. Cancer.gov[35] provides cancer-related information. MedlinePlus[36] is NLM's main portal for reliable consumer health information. The Medical Library Association (MLA) provides the "MLA's List of the Top Ten Most Useful Health Websites."[37] Medical librarians are charged with the task to educate health-care professionals and consumers to find and use high-quality databases.[38]
- *Legal:* Many different types of law libraries exist to serve different constituencies. Academic law libraries have a broad range of materials: primary legal materials (court opinions, statutes, and administrative regulations) and secondary materials (legal encyclopedias, practice guides, forms, and rules of procedure) in print and electronic formats, plus databases (e.g., Westlaw Next, LexisNexis Advance, Bloomberg [for business law], and Kluwer Arbitration). Law firm li-braries tend to concentrate their collection on the legal practice area and needs of their attorneys. County, state, and federal law libraries vary greatly depending on need and budget. County law libraries tend to serve the public and therefore focus on free,[39] self-help, and more practical re-sources. State and federal libraries tend to have a dual mission of serving the public but also the state or federal legislature. Court libraries tend to focus on the primary legal materials (the law itself) and procedural rules for the particular jurisdiction of the court.[40]

Appendix 9.2: Strategic Positioning Messages

- *Personal Relationships:* Being on a first-name basis with every significant and recurring user and knowing their needs is very important in special libraries compared to other types of libraries that must serve people on a community-wide scale.
- *Understanding Organizational Context:* Understanding the core business and the context of special-ized users and becoming an expert at understanding the company, industry, and the enterprise's goals for very specific research needs, strategies, and profit/loss measurements is essential. The information professional often gets deeper into understanding the needs of a specific profession like engineering, medicine, or the law.
- *Being on the "Team":* Teamwork skills are essential for information professionals when the teams are not library-centric but organization-centric. Serving as part of the larger organizational team of diverse professionals and client teams on specific projects provides a vehicle to contribute specific skills and insights. Representing the information professional's skills as part of a larger multifunctional team is a key communication and relationship skill.
- *Performance Measurement:* Measuring performance based on a different—more personal—scale ties performance contracts to very specific goals and agendas. Information professionals are often measured on their individual contributions to enterprise goals in addition to their teamwork.

Appendix 9.3: Evidence of the Strongly Positioned Information Professional

- *Respect:* Look for evidence of visible respect, awareness of information professional's personal competencies and trust, referrals, and testimonials as individuals and not just solely the generic library operation.
- *Communication:* Seek verification from clients of the transformational value that information pro-fessionals add on a personal relationship level, the impact of research tasks, and in specific inter-actions and projects—not just on an enterprise basis.

Cheryl R. Dee, Stephen Abram, and Deb Hunt

- *Acknowledgment:* Collect and share management acknowledgments of the contributions of the information professionals on teams and to external clients, special projects, corporate strategies, and strategic investments; recognition of the value of the information professional's advice and consulting skills and not just for getting information quickly on a transactional basis. Determine how respect is seen for information professionals not to be viewed as mere "support staff" as evidenced by the reporting relationship and flexibility to spending decisions and budget.
- *Impact:* Research and communicate with clarity the information professional's measurable impact on such organizational issues as white-collar productivity, research success, timeliness, and decision-making quality.
- *Proofs:* Communicate proofs of the information professional's ability to determine their customers' information needs and their satisfaction with the library's services using the results of surveys, customer comment forms, narrative story and testimonial collections, and frequent discussions with the library's customers—with whom they are well acquainted.

Appendix 9.4: Trends in Special Libraries

- Social media use is increasing (e.g., for employees networking internally within organizations and for actively monitoring what is being said externally about the company's reputation).
- Intranets are a private weblike service available usually only to employees within an organization that integrate access to internal information, records, news, policies, licensed resources, and so forth. The ability to access both internal and external digital information is provided by approved devices using specialized search tools, thus adapting to the mobile revolution and responsive design needs. Information professionals also contribute to the organization, information architecture, and taxonomic needs of intranet initiatives.
- E-learning for staff with staff training and development strategies is a key trend to reduce the cost of employee development and scale learning on a global or organization-wide basis. Organizations can license learning content that provides opportunities for nontextual information to be delivered throughout the organization.
- Staff in-house communication vehicles are mostly electronic (blogs, intranet dashboards, Yammer, discussion lists, Twitter, etc.), and information professionals often manage and archive this information.
- Mobile strategies for content and communication with smart phones provided by the employer (as well as tablets and/or laptops) are challenging organizations on many fronts, offering roles for information professionals in security, licensing, and content design and delivery.
- Quality digital resources of both internal and external content are expanding far beyond the traditional text-based resources into images, learning objects, streaming media, and more.
- Private content and personal networks behind intranet or firewall barriers are creating roles in repositories, archives, and content vaults that lead to a competitive advantage.

Notes

1. "Vision, Mission, and Core Values Statements," Special Libraries Association, last modified August 2, 2014, http://www.sla.org/about-sla/vision-mission-core-value.
2. Alma C. Mitchell, *Special Libraries Association: Its First Fifty Years, 1909–1959* (New York: Special Libraries Association, 1959).
3. Guy St. Clair, Andrew Berner, and Rebecca Vargha, "Special Libraries (SLA)," in *Encyclopedia of Library and Information Science*, 3rd ed. (Boca Raton, FL: CRC Press, 2009).
4. E. Ferguson, "Association Highlights," in *Special Library Association: Its First 50 Years, 1909–1959* (New York: Special Libraries Association, 1959).
5. St. Clair et al., "Special Libraries."

6. Constitution of Special Libraries Association, *Special Libraries* 1, no. 1 (January 1910): 1, 8.
7. "About Us," ASLIB Association for Information Management, last modified July 17, 2014, http://aslib.com/about/about_us.htm.
8. International Federation of Library Associations and Institutions (IFLA), last modified July 17, 2014, http://www.ifla.org.
9. "Chapters," Special Libraries Association, last modified November 25, 2013, http://www.sla.org/get-involved/chapters.
10. Ellis Mount and Renee Massoud, *Special Libraries and Information Centers: An Introductory Text* (New York: Special Libraries Association, 1999).
11. Deborah Hunt and David Grossman, *The Librarian's Skillbook: 51 Essential Skills for Information Professionals* (San Leandro, CA: Information Edge, 2013).
12. "Fact Sheet: NLM Classification," NIH U.S. National Library of Medicine, last modified July 5, 2014, http://www.nlm.nih.gov/pubs/factsheets/nlmclassif.html.
13. "Fact Sheet: Medical Subject Headings (MeSH®)," NIH U.S. National Library of Medicine, last modified July 5, 2014, http://www.nlm.nih.gov/pubs/factsheets/mesh.html.
14. "Fact Sheet: Unified Medical Language System® (UMLS®) Metathesaurus®," NIH U.S. National Library of Medicine, last modified July 5, 2014, http://www.nlm.nih.gov/pubs/factsheets/umlsmeta.html.
15. "In His Own Words: Martin Cummings and the NLM," *History of Medicine: NIH U.S. National Library of Medicine*, last modified July 5, 2014, http://www.nlm.nih.gov/hmd/digicolls/cummings/index.html; Cheryl R. Dee and K. A. Smith, "Martin M. Cummings MD, 1920–2011," obituary, *Journal of the Medical Library Association* 100, no. 3 (July 2012): 157–160, http://www.ncbi.nlm.nih.gov/pmc/articles/PMC3411258.
16. PubMed, National Library of Medicine, http://www.ncbi.nlm.nih.gov/pubmed; Cheryl R. Dee, "MEDLARS: Development of MEDLARS (Medical Literature Analysis and Retrieval System)," *Journal of the Medical Library Association* 95, no. 4 (2007): 416–425, http://www.pubmedcentral.nih.gov/tocrender.fcgi?iid=150885.
17. "DOCLINE," NIH: U.S. National Library of Medicine, last modified December 19, 2013, http://www.nlm.nih.gov/pubs/factsheets/docline.html.
18. Mary Ellen Bates. *The True Value of Information: Making the Case for Value-Added Aggregators*, Factiva Institute, 2011, http://www.dowjones.com/factiva/institutefiles/14-The%20True%20Value%20of%20Information%20e-Book.pdf.
19. Denise Dubie, "Time Spent Searching Cuts into Company Productivity," *Networkworld*, last modified October 20, 2006, http://www.networkworld.com/article/2300548/infrastructure-management/time-spent-searching-cuts-into-company-productivity.html.
20. Jenny Taylor, "Studying Your Users to Improve Services," *Information Outlook* 18, no. 2 (2014): 10–12; Cheryl R. Dee and R. Blazek, "Information Needs of Rural Physicians: A Descriptive Study," *Bulletin of the Medical Library Association* 81, no. 3 (1993): 259–264, http://www.pubmedcentral.nih.gov/picrender.fcgi?artid=225785&blobtype=pdf.
21. Special Libraries Association, "About Information Professionals," https://www.sla.org/career-center/about-information-professionals.
22. LinkedIn, https://www.linkedin.com.
23. Yammer, https://www.yammer.com.
24. SalesForce.com, https://www.salesforce.com.
25. Facebook, https://www.facebook.com.
26. Stephen Abram, "Post-Information Age Positioning for Special Librarians," in *Out Front with Stephen Abram: A Guide for Information Leaders* (Chicago, IL: American Library Association, 2007).
27. Special Libraries Association, "Alignment Project, 2008–2009," http://dbiosla.org/Alignment%20Project%20Article.pdf.
28. Stephen Abram, *Stephen's Lighthouse* (blog), http://stephenslighthouse.com.
29. David Shumaker, *Models of Embedded Librarianship: Final Report* (Washington, DC: SLA, 2009), http://hq.sla.org/pdfs/EmbeddedLibrarianshipFinalRptRev.pdf.
30. Abram, "Stephen's Lighthouse."

31. Chery R. Dee and J. Rankin, "Medical and Allied Health Sciences Literatures and Their Users," in *Encyclopedia of Library and Information Sciences*, ed. Marcia Bates (Abingdon: Taylor & Francis, 2009).

32. "PubMed," NIH U.S. National Library of Medicine, last modified July 27, 2014, http://www.ncbi.nlm.nih.gov/pubmed.

33. "PubMed Central," NIH U.S. National Library of Medicine, last modified July 27, 2014, http://www.ncbi.nlm.nih.gov/pmc.

34. "TOXNET: Toxicology Data Network," NIH U.S. National Library of Medicine, http://toxnet.nlm.nih.gov/cgi-bin/sis/htmlgen?TOXLINE.

35. "Cancer.gov," National Cancer Institute, http://cancer.gov.

36. "MedlinePlus," NIH U.S. National Library of Medicine, last modified July 26, 2014, http://www.nlm.nih.gov/medlineplus.

37. "MLA Top Health Websites," Medical Library Association, last modified July 8, 2014, https://www.mlanet.org/resources/medspeak/topten.html.

38. Cheryl R. Dee and J. Rankin, "Health Science Professional Literatures and Their Users," in *Encyclopedia of Library and Information Sciences*, ed. Marcia Bates and Mary Niles Maack (Boca Raton, FL: CRC Press, 2009).

39. "Federal Digital System," U.S. Government Printing Office, last modified July 15, 2014, http://www.gpo.gov/fdsys.

40. Wanita Scroggs, JD, MLS, personal communication, June 8, 2014.

10

Digital Resources

DIGITAL LIBRARIES

Lisa Gregory and Amy Rudersdorf

As today's information professionals survey their workplaces, what they see is in some ways a world apart from those who staffed their same offices just a few decades ago. With the advent of networked computing, shared digital resources, and the ubiquity of technology in the lives of many people, the boundaries of information organizations have become fluid, far reaching, and at times hard to define. In their passion to understand and meet users' needs, information professionals are increasingly embracing and adapting to this challenge, even as it demands rigorous training, personal flexibility, and shifting resources.

> "The digital library goes by many names, but generally involves information products and services that are organized, described, and delivered through technology."

The digital library goes by many names but generally involves information products and services that are organized, described, and delivered through technology. The same core tenets of the information professions in past decades undergird the profession today—organizing information for easy retrieval and guiding information seekers to appropriate resources. What differs are the challenges and opportunities afforded by technology, whether in creating resources, managing them, or communicating about them to users. While information organizations are diverse and serve different needs based on their locations, materials, access to resources, and users' needs, there are a number of overarching issues that are common to most digital libraries.

This chapter focuses on the day-to-day challenges and benefits that technology has introduced into the information profession. It begins by describing some of the overarching demands common to many digital libraries. Following that, it explores the varying roles of a digital librarian. After completing this chapter, the reader should have an understanding of both the big ideas and specific tasks an information professional will confront and negotiate while managing a digital library, as well as the types of skills a digital librarian must bring to the table to be successful.

Managing the Demands Facing Digital Libraries

Today's digital libraries face a formidable array of challenges, requiring leaders who understand the challenges and know how to address them. To manage expectations means finding ways to understand the digital library's primary virtual audience. It means making hard choices about allocating funds to new ventures while sustaining old ones. It means planning strategically for a rapidly changing technological future, while advocating to administrators that the institution and staff should be abreast of that change instead of overwhelmed by it. It means making sure the digital librarian's skill set is diverse and technology based.

Managing Users' Needs and Expectations

Through its website, electronic resources, and e-mail and chat reference services, information organizations reach users every day who are often anonymous and geographically disparate. Users of today's information organizations are no longer limited to those who are local enough to set foot in the door. While on-site services are extremely important,[1] an information organization's most frequent and fervent users may in fact live miles away, and may never speak directly to a staff member or touch a physical item.

This situation presents challenges as information professionals try to understand a relatively unknown audience, particularly when it comes to choosing what the information organization offers online and how to deliver virtual services. Both passive (web analytics) and active (surveys and focus groups) methods of gaining user data can provide a lot of information regarding an information organization's audience. However, it can be difficult to fully identify and reach the users who may benefit most from an institution's services and resources. It can also be challenging to describe this audience in terms that appeal to those decision makers who provide an information organization with its funding.

These digital library users, both known and unknown, are part of a technologically demanding public. As of 2014, 87 percent of U.S. adults use the Internet, with 68 percent of those doing so at some point with mobile devices.[2] Both the casual information seeker and the most rigorous researcher expect resources and services to be made digitally accessible. When it comes to public libraries, users rank "free access to computers and the Internet" as well as "research resources" as important for libraries to offer.[3] In the academic library sphere, the "speed and convenience" of immediate access to resources is highly desirable, and "more digital content of all kinds and formats is almost uniformly seen as better."[4] Government agencies, schools, cultural institutions, and corporations help reinforce this expectation with the delivery of crucial information online. As providers of broadband access, lenders of mobile devices, and hubs for technological training, information organizations are asked and strive to meet the needs of the technologically demanding public while maintaining more traditional services.

> "Libraries strive to meet the needs of the technologically demanding public while maintaining more traditional services."

Managing Resources

Information professionals have embraced technology vigorously, weaving e-resources and digital services into their institutions wholeheartedly in an effort to meet users' needs as efficiently and robustly as possible. Often, new technology expands an information organization's services in exciting ways, whether it is offering full-text search of journals or engaging with young users via social media. Information organizations with rare or unique materials address the demands of researchers by digitizing and offering those materials online.

As these new services are added, staffing, financial resources, and institutional strategy have to shift to accommodate them. Catalogers become trained in linked data. Infrastructure expands in order to preserve and deliver digital materials. Administrators must decide how to position their institutions in their communities to help make the case for continued funding in a Google world. In a climate of static and shrinking budgets,[5] it can be hard to shift money from long-established print priorities to cover digital resources, with associated costs that seem to grow exponentially. While digital libraries are no longer a new concept, many institutions are still in the thick of an ongoing transition from discrete and/or grant-funded digital library projects to stable and sustainable digital library programs.[6] Whether the digital library is part of a larger institution with an array of competing priorities or is establishing itself on its own as a new endeavor, finding trained staff and sustainable financial resources can be a challenge.

Managing Information

Three Types of Digital Information
- Licensed content
- Content self-created
- Content donated by others

Information organizations today steward three types of digital information: licensed content, content they create themselves, and content donated by others. In some ways, these three types of digital resources have a lot in common with their print equivalents. For e-books and e-journals, purchasing agreements are made and content is cataloged. Digitized content requires reference support just as its analog counterparts do. Donations still involve establishing donor relationships and agreements. These similarities belie the many ways information organizations have had to expand or adapt existing resources to manage digital information. As a result, information organizations can end up working with outdated systems that accommodate traditional inventory functions while taking on new systems for digital content.[7] The rights and responsibilities attendant to licensed content as well as content an information organization creates through digitization or accepts via donation encompass a wider spectrum than before, within a rapidly evolving landscape full of stakeholders ranging from publishers, to authors, to users.

"Information professionals find themselves weighing risks and rewards when deciding whether or not items in their collections can be made available digitally, considering privacy concerns, copyright law, and the needs of both item creators and users."

In addition, there are practical issues that put an information organization in a mediating position between users and content providers, negotiating new rules for digital surrogates of print items. Information professionals find themselves weighing risks and rewards when deciding whether or not items in their collections can be made available digitally, considering privacy concerns, copyright law, and the needs of both item creators and users. From course reserves to historic photographs, information professionals attempt to discover the best way to organize and present the information their users need while respecting legal concerns. This negotiation often demands a suite of new skills, many of which will be discussed later on in this chapter.

Managing Expectations of Stakeholders

Information professionals working within parent organizations inevitably end up advocating for their services with those who are unfamiliar with libraries, archives, or information management. Information professionals try to quantify the value of these services in a way that all can understand,[8] in an attempt to justify increasing expenditures when many believe "everything's online already" and that digital is less expensive than analog. Because the growing digital library requires implementing new technology, increasing infrastructure, and ongoing training, those managing digital libraries find they also must excel at managing expectations to support this growth. It can be especially difficult to report on and to explain parallels and discrepancies between physical metrics like foot traffic versus

Lisa Gregory and Amy Rudersdorf

virtual metrics like website page views. How much is a "visit" to a digital library worth? What is the return on investment for a digitized annual report, the on-website use of which might be only the beginning of how it serves the public? It can also be difficult when, as mentioned above, the information organization's user base could almost be said to encompass the entire planet.

TEXTBOX 10.1

Topic for Discussion

Digital libraries must balance a number of competing priorities with limited funds. Would you advocate for publishing content specifically requested by your current audience? Or for selecting content that has historically been popular with on-site visitors?

The Digital Librarian's Vital Roles

When reading job postings for a digital librarian, data curator, metadata librarian, or scholarly publishing coordinator, one may wonder how one person could be expected to do and know everything outlined in the posting. Yet, as far back as 2006, Choi and Rasmussen predicted that "digital professionals will be required to have more breadth and depth of knowledge and skills across the dimensions of traditional library knowledge, technology, and human relations."[9]

While the skill set for digital librarians is in many ways unique when compared to the skill sets needed by others in the field of information management, some digital librarian skills are readily found in the collective information professional tool kit. Responsibilities like project management, collaboration, outreach, education, and resource description are as important to the digital librarian as to many others in the field. But, along with those abilities, it is especially important that digital librarians remain up to date in their knowledge of technological change. For example, they need to understand how technological changes impact repositories; online applications and software; metadata; digitization, digital curation and preservation; digital scholarship and publishing; and much more. And, as more content and services move into the online environment, digital librarians must maintain a firm grasp on the complexities of intellectual property and copyright, and the organizations like Creative Commons that are working within the legal realm to open up access to born-digital and digitized content.

It is fair to say that the digital librarian's required skill set is varied and long. In one recent study, it was reported that "current students as well as practicing information professionals [should] seek out additional non-curricular opportunities to build competency in the technical areas represented . . . if they are or expect to be marketable."[10] In an attempt to succinctly encapsulate this broad range of skills, the most valuable skill sets needed by digital librarians are highlighted into eight generalized roles.

Eight Roles of the Digital Librarian

Cataloger
Collector
Educator
Legal Expert
Manager
Negotiator
Researcher
Technologist

Cataloger

It may seem unusual to see cataloging among the skills that a twenty-first-century information professional should have. As one of the oldest roles that librarians have held—along with reference, circulation, and collection development—cataloging may conjure up visions of dusty stacks and paper cards in wooden boxes. But the twenty-first century has become one in which metadata has taken a central role in how libraries do business (see also chapter 14, "Organizing Information: Technical Services").

Digital librarians create metadata application profiles and describe archival and special collections materials using a variety of metadata standards and controlled vocabularies. They also generate online finding aids to point researchers to important historic and scholarly collections, and they aggregate data through protocols for metadata harvesting and, increasingly, through linked open data. This use of metadata enables machines to use library vocabularies to logically connect information about the same topic with unique identifiers instead of mining data for similar terms. Linked data is how Google can tell the difference between Venus (painting), Venus (planet), and Venus (tennis player). Even "traditional" catalogers describe content in digital formats and manage the circulation of e-readers, personal hotspots, and similar connective devices. Many catalogers are leading their institution's transition from their MARC-based OPACs to RDA-driven discovery systems.

Check This Out

Ontologies now available as linked open data (LOD):
Library of Congress
Subject Headings
Visit: http://id.loc.gov

Getty Research Institute's
Art and Architecture Thesaurus
Visit: http://www.getty.edu/research/tools/vocabularies/aat

These types of information professionals may be referred to as metadata librarians, data technologists, or digital catalogers.

Collector

Digital library collections are conceived of in much the same way as the collections that reside in stacks and archival boxes, although they are stored in digital or institutional repositories, in the cloud and data grids, on servers and hard drives, and in dark archives. Their long-term maintenance is equally important and often far more complicated than their physical counterparts, which in most cases are relatively safe on stable shelves in temperature- and humidity-controlled environments. While digital collections may not be organized by Library of Congress classification number, digital objects are typically assembled logically—often by format (photography collections), topic (Kennedy assassination papers), or even geography (Minnesota Digital Library).

Whether they are working with born-digital data or digitized copies of physical objects, digital librarians must understand how to identify the best means of describing, storing, and providing access to that content today, and evolve those processes to maintain the integrity of the content over time. In effect, collectors must think like digital forecasters, exploring how to preserve and provide ongoing access to digital content into an unknown future environment (see also chapter 25, "Managing Collections").

These types of information professionals may be called digital curators, digital archivists, digital stewards, digital preservationists, or plain old digital librarians.

Lisa Gregory and Amy Rudersdorf

Educator

The term "library educators" may describe professors or reference staff who perform bibliographic instruction. But for the digital librarian, "education" encompasses many roles and requires a variety of surprising skill sets. In the digital realm, education is often equated with outreach or even marketing, and information professionals may find themselves responsible for designing, managing, and creating content for an institution's website, exhibits and online galleries, blogs, or social media presence. This may require a combination of design, server management, or web scripting skills, as well as knowledge of exhibit curation, writing for the web, and social media platforms.

As educators, digital librarians must think like digital natives, creating tools to guide users in navigating the challenges of researching, finding, and using appropriate information resources. Equally important is the digital librarian's role in providing guidance to digital nonnatives, be they patrons or colleagues, who may not be as comfortable within the digital information environment (see also chapter 16, "Teaching Users: Information and Technology Literacy Instruction").

Digital librarians must be willing to maintain the currency of their own knowledge in a quickly changing information landscape even as they are writing, teaching, and presenting about it. In fact, unlike information professionals working in roles better understood by administrators, digital librarians often must educate decision makers about the work they do and the staffing, technologies, and knowledge required, *even before* they can advocate for resources to support this work.

Educator is a role that is part of most digital librarians' job responsibilities and is not specific to a single type of digital professional.

> "Digital librarians must be willing to maintain the currency of their own knowledge in a quickly changing information landscape."

Legal Expert

Understanding the intricacy of copyright law is probably not something many imagine as a requirement of an information professional's daily work (see also chapter 31, "Copyright and Creative Commons"). A digital librarian or digital archivist not only needs to have a solid grasp of the copyright status of the items in their collections to assign legally viable, understandable, and actionable copyright statements, but they also may need to play a leadership role in educating administrators about concepts like fair use, public domain, and orphan works. Equally important is establishing the level of risk their institution is willing to take, either to avert or to address takedown requests or actions. Advocating for greater access to content, educating colleagues and patrons about organizations like Creative Commons that are working to make copyrighted content more openly available, and participating in the open access movement are all important roles that digital librarians can play to affect positive change for patrons today and into the future (see also chapter 33, "Open Access").

Information professionals responsible for preservation, including digital reformatting and the preservation of born-digital objects, also need to understand the implications of copy making, one of the many important components of preservation librarianship (see also chapter 34, "Analog and Digital Curation and Preservation"). Those working in the fields of digital scholarship and publishing must be able to understand and translate author contracts. At a minimum, these information professionals must have a basic understanding of the types of rights an author might retain or lose depending on the academic publisher with which they choose to work. These information professionals are often tasked with guiding colleagues, faculty, students, and other authors of academic papers through the complexities of peer review and restricted versus open access publishing.

While many larger academic libraries now staff lawyers or lawyer-librarians in their scholarly publishing units, information professionals without legal training may be responsible for some of the tasks listed here. They may be referred to as digital publishing librarians, digital scholarship librarians, or some combination thereof. Some roles identified in this section will also be part of the total skill set of any number of information professionals working in digital libraries.

Manager

The role of manager is not unique to digital librarians; however, how and what digital librarians manage is unique. The digital library is inherently technology based, so staff must be able to identify the best, most stable, open source (hopefully), easy-to-launch, secure technology with the lowest impact on staff and financial resources (see also chapter 26, "Managing Technology"). Managing grants, including staffing, budgets, and reporting, and ensuring that timelines are met are also necessary qualities for an information professional working in a typically project-based digital library world (see also chapter 22, "Managing Budgets," and chapter 23, "Managing Personnel").

The "stuff" that digital librarians manage (or "steward" or "curate") is data accessed from unseen servers in a cold, windowless room behind a door that few ever enter. This can cause a disconnect for those who are more familiar with the management of physical objects. When objects have form, the expenditures for their long-term care may be better understood. Storage shelves and Mylar sleeves are more easily conceptualized than cloud storage and data grids. Because these costly requirements for data management may not be readily apparent, it becomes the digital librarian's job to advocate for the resources to meet the challenge of long-term access and stewardship.

An added complexity for the digital library manager is that this costly IT-project work is often done in collaboration with other units within the information organization, or even, as is the case with statewide and national programs like the North Carolina Digital Heritage Center and the Digital Public Library of America, with geographically dispersed institutions. The skills required for the successful digital library manager in this distributed paradigm are many—financial planner, IT analyst, human resources specialist, fund-raiser, and cat herder—and are often not those taught to digital librarians in school.[11] Like many of the other categories listed here, many who are not in administrative roles may share some subset of managerial duties.

Actual management titles might include head of, coordinator, director, or manager of a data/digital/virtual/scholarly unit within an information organization.

> **Check This Out**
> North Carolina
> Digital Heritage Center
> Visit: http://www.digitalnc.org
>
> Digital Public Library
> of America
> Visit: http://dp.la

Negotiator

Digital librarian, metadata librarian, and data curator are all positions in the information profession that have not been around for long. Many who were hired into a job with that title over the last decade and a half were the first of their kind in the institution where they worked. Young, energetic, with a job title that few understand—this situation can lead to exciting new adventures as well as some tough negotiations for a first-time information professional. For many of these digital pioneers, explaining to administrators and colleagues what they do all day and why it takes so long is just part of the job. Still, this can be demanding, and it requires calm and thoughtful responses and reminders that everyone is learning together.

Digital librarians must learn early on the art of negotiating these types of complexities, because many aspects of what they do affect, or are affected by, the work of their colleagues. For example, in some institutions, digital reformatting services are a stand-alone unit that works with resources

Lisa Gregory and Amy Rudersdorf

managed by other departments, namely archives, special collections, and preservation. Metadata description may be performed by another department—perhaps cataloging or technical services. Yet another department, IT, may be responsible for digital preservation storage. Traversing the needs, personalities, and unique cultures within each of these units requires the digital librarian to be an excellent communicator with deft management skills.

Finally, digital librarians often work with vendors to outsource reformatting or metadata production, design and build websites, or purchase computing hardware and repository software. Purchasing negotiations can be as straightforward as choosing the lowest bidder in a request-for-proposal (RFP) process or as complex as going head to head with e-journal bundlers to get the best price for subscriptions. The information professionals responsible for this type of work must research options, competition, and pricing and understand local needs and resources before entering into negotiations with a vendor whose product they likely will work with for a very long time.

Negotiator is a role that is part of most digital librarians' job responsibilities and is not specific to a single professional position.

Researcher

Research is an integral part of what all information professionals do. So, what types of research do digital librarians perform? For one, it tends to be done in support of resources that are produced for all patrons. As examples, the outcomes of the digital librarian's research provide historical context for online exhibits, ensure long-term access to digital heritage, or offer advice on making faculty authorship open access.

Second, because so much of digital librarians' output is freely and publicly accessible, understanding how users (want to) interact with these resources is integral. Usability, and research on user behavior, should be fundamental to the design and production of any online resource. Usability research can take many forms: one-on-one interviews, focus groups, recorded navigation testing, and use cases and surveys are just some of the ways that usability is researched and tested. Whatever type of usability testing is performed, the data that is produced will provide deep insight and guide decisions for improving online resources.

Decisions about what to produce based on large-scale information gathering is a third key aspect of digital librarians' research. Data-driven decision making involves gathering and analyzing information to make informed decisions about which resources to produce, how to produce them and for whom, and even how much staffing and funding to provide to their creation. User studies, like those mentioned above, are perfect examples of data-driven decision making. This informed decision-making process is a guiding principle behind much of what digital librarians do and why they do it.

TEXTBOX 10.2

Topic for Discussion

This chapter posits the idea that a digital librarian must take on multiple roles. Do you see this as different from the roles of information professionals before the digital age? Why or why not?

Technologist

The last skill that is required—and probably the most obvious—is a strong aptitude for and comfort with technology. Not everyone needs to know how to program in Python or do crash recovery on a laptop, but increasingly, digital library jobs require some web scripting knowledge such as a basic facility with PHP or JavaScript. At the very minimum, a digital librarian working with digital collections, websites, or online exhibit building must be comfortable working with HTML and style sheets. Information professionals responsible for building or maintaining digital repositories and creating digital content must have a strong understanding of metadata standards (e.g., Dublin Core, MODS, VRA Core), structured data (e.g., XML, RDF), and data-sharing protocols (e.g., the Open Archives Initiative Protocol for Metadata Harvesting [OAI-PMH] or the HathiTrust data API). Digital curation librarians must have knowledge of a variety of analog and digital media formats (or know where to go to learn them), their storage and reformatting needs, and the ability to steward and evolve digital preservation administration and technologies.

Digital librarians typically work closely with IT professionals who may or may not have library backgrounds. Communicating with these programmers and systems administrators can sometimes be a challenge. Just like information professionals, IT professionals have their domain-specific vocabulary. In fact the term "library" itself has a fundamentally different meaning in the programming world. (Basically, it is a collection of scripts that can be referred to from the central code so that the same lines of code do not have to be produced over and over.) When building technologies or communicating technical requirements, digital librarians should use vocabularies appropriate to the task. This approach will increase the likelihood of greater respect and collegiality and better support for the digital librarian's technology needs.

> "Most digital librarians should—at the minimum—have a basic understanding of content management systems, databases, some metadata standards, and web technologies."

The technology skill sets needed by digital librarians are as varied as the technologies that surround us. However, most digital librarians should—at the minimum—have a basic understanding of content management systems, databases, some metadata standards, and web technologies.

Conclusion

There are few information organizations in the United States today that do not interact with their audiences in one digital way or another. The challenges faced by information professionals working with digital content require skills apart from the ones needed fifty or even twenty years ago. The good news is that the realm of digital libraries is large, and much has been done already. Many best practices have been established, and many trends have been identified that will need to be monitored over the next few years. Technology affords professionals the opportunity to stay well in touch with others tackling the same problems; indeed, it is crucial for the digital librarian to collaborate, not only to avoid reinventing the wheel but also to strengthen the community's common mandates and ends. Information professionals owe it to their audiences to be transparent about their ethics and their passionate goals for digital information literacy, and to be rigorous in their professional standards so that they can ensure the virtual future lives up to the foundation laid by information professionals of the past. See appendix 10.1, "Case Study: Staffing a National Digital Library Initiative," and appendix 10.2, "Case Study: Planning for Distributed Digital Preservation."

Appendix 10.1: Case Study—Staffing a National Digital Library Initiative

The Digital Public Library of America (DPLA) brings together the riches of America's libraries, archives, and museums and makes them freely available to the world. It strives to contain the full breadth of human expression, from the written word, to works of art and culture, to records of America's heritage, to the efforts and data of science. DPLA aims to expand this crucial realm of openly available materials

Lisa Gregory and Amy Rudersdorf

and make those riches more easily discovered and more widely usable and used. At publication, the DPLA contains nearly eight million resources from twenty direct partners that represent almost 1,500 contributing institutions across the United States.

DPLA has a staff of eleven professionals, including eight with LIS degrees. Of the remaining three, one has a bachelor of science in liberal arts/film studies and two have PhDs in history and are active members or leaders in the field of digital humanities. The organizational structure of the DPLA includes an administrative team and two defined units: the content team (three staff) and the technology team (four staff). The remaining staff reports directly to the executive director. Focusing on the content team will provide insight into how the skill set above can be practically applied.

The content team's responsibilities include identifying and developing partner relationships and guiding the establishment of local collaborations in the support of growing the DPLA partner network into one that represents every state in the United States. Additionally, the content team maintains digitization partnerships and related workflows, is integral to metadata normalization and shareability, and coordinates community engagement to promote the DPLA as a resource for research and learning. The three members of the content team have a combined experience of nearly forty years working with digitized and born-digital content, the technical and administrative systems that provide access to that content, and the users who engage with it. All three began their work creating content—digitizing and managing the creation of metadata—but also developing systems for large-scale digital reformatting, designing online delivery technologies, and creating systems for the long-term management of digital content to ensure ongoing access and preservation. While none of the content team is a programmer or web scripter, all are very familiar with the relevant library technologies. For example, the director was formerly the associate dean for digital scholarship and technology at a Research I institution; the assistant director ran the digital information management program at a state library. Each of the DPLA content team positions requires experience in nearly all of the skills listed in this chapter. And while each staff member fulfills a different need within the organization, a general overview of how the skill set described above can be applied to the DPLA content team's roles can be instructive.

As catalogers, the content team helps establish systems for structuring metadata, analyzes the data received from partners, maps that data to the DPLA metadata structure, and performs quality control. By definition, the content team staff are collectors; they are responsible for identifying partners and growing the DPLA collections. They are technologists who daily use complex systems to manage and analyze data, including OAI-PMH and API feeds, and who work closely with the DPLA technology team and partners to identify issues with the portal interface, metadata crosswalks, and so forth.

Their roles as researchers are conveyed through their work developing a national-scale model for aggregation and service support that considers the needs of cultural heritage institutions of all sizes. Because nothing like the DPLA has been undertaken before, modeling the network requires intensive study and assessment. They are legal experts sharing their knowledge of copyright law, which is both essential and extremely challenging for many digital librarians to apply appropriately to their research and cultural heritage materials. Maintaining good relationships with twenty partners across the United States, who themselves aggregate content from nearly 1,500 contributors, means that everyone involved—not just the staff of the content team—has to be a great negotiator. Their management roles may vary, but each applies this skill every day. The director not only manages her staff, but also the development of the DPLA networks; she also cultivates and leads multimillion-dollar grant projects, in addition to helping to coordinate the development of statewide and regional collaborations. Likewise, the assistant director manages ongoing partner relations, metadata workflows, and the development of technical documentation and assists with grant reporting and assessment. And finally, as leaders of a national-scale initiative, a significant portion of their time is spent as educators, writing, talking, and presenting on the topics listed here to audiences as varied as librarians, archivists, and museum professionals, as well as LIS students, genealogists, teachers, researchers, and other interested users.

Within the DPLA content team can be found many of the skills identified in the second section of this chapter. But it must be noted that the job titles that fall under the umbrella of digital librarianship are nearly as varied as the roles that do not, and many have received only passing mention here. Our profession must prepare for the field of digital librarianship to continue to grow, and ensure that all have the necessary skills needed to succeed as data curators, scholarly publishers, metadata librarians, or whatever new positions the digital future holds.

Appendix 10.2: Case Study—Planning for Distributed Digital Preservation

Since 2004, MetaArchive Cooperative has been providing a distributed storage system that allows institutions to preserve their digital content in a way that adheres to accepted best practices. Taking advantage of the LOCKSS (Lots of Copies Keep Stuff Safe)[12] system, the cooperative leverages the geographically distributed locations of its partners to create a redundant network of servers. Institutions sustain the cooperative by taking responsibility for a portion of the technology infrastructure. Partners must host a server, and in turn their content is automatically replicated to seven other servers, one of which is located at the Library of Congress. Content is not overwritten—instead, new versions are kept alongside originals in case unintentional changes occur.

One of the core values of the cooperative is to empower and encourage institutions "to build their own preservation infrastructures and knowledge rather than outsourcing this core service to external vendors." Truly, as an institution accumulates digital materials, the preservation of those materials must become a core service. Following established digital preservation best practices means thoughtful stewardship, detailed planning, and full infrastructure support. "In the digital area, benign neglect fails, and fails spectacularly." With a service like the MetaArchive Cooperative, individual institutions can take advantage of the knowledge of their cohort. Preservation problems can be addressed by the group, instead of tackled by a single location. The investment of multiple partners can help ensure long-term sustainability. Costs are kept lower when shared by the many.

The cooperative is a tailor-made example of successful and sustainable collaboration in digital library services. It demonstrates the capacity of institutions to find a digital solution that upholds their responsibility to their users and materials, follows industry best practices, and stewards limited resources in a strategic way.

Notes

1. Katherine Zickuhr, Lee Rainie, Kristen Purcell, and Maeve Duggan, "Section 2," in *How Americans Value Public Libraries in Their Communities* (Pew Research Center, December 2013), http://libraries.pew internet.org/files/legacy-pdf/PIP_Libraries%20in%20communities.pdf.
2. Susannah Fox and Lee Rainie, "The Web at 25 in the U.S.," *Pew Research Internet Project*, last modified February 27, 2014, http://www.pewinternet.org/2014/02/27/the-web-at-25-in-the-u-s.
3. Zickuhr et al., "Section 2," in *How Americans Value Public Libraries*.
4. Lynn S. Connaway and Timothy J. Dickey, *Digital Information Seeker: Report of Findings from Selected OCLC, RIN and JISC User Behaviour Projects*, Document No. 706, Version 1.1, (March 2010), http://www.jisc .ac.uk/media/documents/publications/reports/2010/digitalinformationseekerreport.pdf.
5. Judy Hoffman, John Carlo Bertot, and Denise M. Davis, "Libraries Connect Communities: Public Library Funding & Technology Access Study 2011–2012," digital supplement, *American Libraries*, Summer 2012, http://viewer.zmags.com/publication/4673a369; Michael Kelley, "The New Normal," *Library Journal*, last modified January 16, 2012, http://lj.libraryjournal.com/2012/01/funding/ the-new-normal-annual-library-budgets-survey-2012.
6. Blue Ribbon Task Force on Sustainable Digital Preservation and Access, *Sustainable Economics for a Digital Planet: Ensuring Long-Term Access to Digital Information*, Final Report of the Blue Ribbon Task Force, 2010.

7. Marshall Breeding, "Forging Ahead through Times of Major Transitions," *Computers in Libraries* 31, no. 10 (December 2011): 26–29.

8. Megan Oakleaf, *The Value of Academic Libraries: A Comprehensive Research Review and Report* (Chicago, IL: Association of College and Research Libraries, 2010), http://www.ala.org/acrl/sites/ala.org.acrl/files/content/issues/value/val_report.pdf; Betsy Kelly, Claire Hamasu, and Barbara Jones, "Applying Return on Investment (ROI) in Libraries," *Journal of Library Administration* 52, no. 8 (November 2012): 656–671, doi:10.1080/01930826.2012.747383.

9. Choi Youngok and Edie Rasmussen, "What Is Needed to Educate Future Digital Librarians: A Study of Current Practice and Staffing Patterns in Academic and Research Libraries," *D-lib Magazine* 12, no. 9 (2006): 3.

10. Elías Tzoc and John Millard, "Technical Skills for New Digital Librarians," *Library Hi Tech News* 28, no. 8 (2011): 11–15.

11. John N. Gathegi, *The Digital Librarian's Legal Handbook* (Chicago, IL: Neal-Schumann, 2011).

12. In 2000 (ARL); Karen S. Croneis and Pat Henderson, "Electronic and Digital Librarian Positions: A Content Analysis of Announcements from 1900 through 2000" (2002); and Youngok and Henderson, "What Is Needed to Educate Future Digital Librarians" (2006), "workplace studies revealed a high demand for *new professionals for leading* [italics ours] digital library efforts in traditional libraries," including "policies and procedures, collaboration, planning, supervision."

11

Expanding the Horizon of the MLIS

Melissa Fraser-Arnott

What kinds of jobs are available to graduates of library and information (LIS) programs? There was a time when LIS programs were structured as professional training programs for librarians. Although LIS programs are still educating librarians, LIS programs provide their graduates with a valuable set of skills and an understanding of how to find, evaluate, organize, and disseminate information that is applicable to a wide range of roles and industry sectors. In choosing to pursue an LIS degree, individuals are undertaking a professional degree with the potential to open many opportunities in the modern information economy. This chapter explores some of those opportunities and provides examples of job postings in various industry sectors that are appropriate for information professionals. Additionally, insights are shared about the motivations of information professionals who have pursued positions in information environments outside of the library. Finally, this chapter discusses some of the transferable competencies held by information professionals and ways in which information professionals can translate their skills to work in a variety of industry sectors. After completing this chapter, the reader should have an understanding of the variety of opportunities available to information professionals outside of libraries and ways in which information professionals have obtained these positions.

Information Professionals Working across Industry Sectors

People naturally associate library and information science (LIS) programs with jobs in the library sector. LIS programs are, however, educating people for more than library jobs. Information professionals work in nearly every sector of the economy. In fact, information professionals working outside of libraries may outnumber those who work within them. A brief search of LinkedIn indicates the spread of information professionals across industries. Of the 1,149,155 people in LinkedIn with the word "library" in their profile in August 2014, 137,108 or 12 percent were listed as having jobs in the library industry. The remaining 88 percent were listed as employed in a wide range of industries, with the largest concentrations working in the industry sectors of museums and institutions, information services, writing and editing, publishing, computer software, higher education, international affairs, research, semiconductors, fund-raising, information technology and services, public relations, and nonprofit organization management.

Some studies have provided numbers for the percentage of information professionals working outside of libraries, sometime referred to as "alternate careers." Weech and Konieczny,[1] for example, cited a 2007 *Library Journal* placement survey that suggested that 10 percent of information professionals do not work in libraries or for library vendors. Shongwe and Ocholla[2] in 2011 found, in a tracer study of African information professionals, that thirty of the fifty participants had job titles that did not include the word "librarian" in their job title. Taylor and associates[3] in 2010 found that there is a trend toward increased employment of information professionals in settings outside of libraries. Although determining the exact number of information professionals who build a career outside of libraries is challenging, numerous studies have found that a significant number of graduates, ranging from 10 percent to more than 50 percent of graduates, take roles outside of libraries.

TEXTBOX 11.1

Case Study: MLIS Internship Programs Provide Exposure to Career Options

Many ALA-accredited MLIS programs provide their students with the opportunity to participate in internships or co-op placements that allow them to gain exposure working in different library and information organization settings. This can open up new career opportunities. Take, for example, a government information manager who credited his career choice to the internship he completed as a library school student. After completing an internship working in government information, he was hired by his internship employer. Like many of his classmates, he had entered library school with the intention of becoming an academic librarian; his only previous experiences had been with school, public, and academic libraries, and he had no exposure to other career possibilities. This internship launched his career as an information professional in government information.

This example came from interviews conducted by the author in 2014 with LIS graduates working outside of libraries.

What Motivates LIS Professionals to Seek Jobs Outside the Library?

ALA-accredited master's programs in North America provide courses that appeal to information professionals both within the library as well as outside of it. Some students enter an LIS program intending to work outside of libraries; others get exposure to these careers while they are in their LIS program. Many LIS programs also provide students with research assistantships, co-op placements, or internships exposing them to work opportunities that they did not realize existed initially. For some LIS students, therefore, an interest in the "information science" side of the library and information science degree, combined with taking a variety of courses, pursuing research opportunities, and/or working in internships in settings outside the library, has led to expanded career options. See textbox 11.1.

Some people are attracted to careers outside of libraries because of the benefits that these careers offer. Higher pay and prestige in these workplaces[4] are some of the reasons why information professionals might pursue a career outside of libraries. Salaries for information professionals working outside of the library sector can, in fact, be significantly higher than those of information professionals working in libraries. See table 11.1, "Average Annual Salaries for Information Professionals." For example, a taxonomist working in a high-tech company may make twenty thousand dollars more per year than a cataloger working in a library, even though the skill sets required for these two jobs are very similar. Careers outside of libraries can therefore be highly rewarding opportunities for information professionals.

Table 11.1. Average Annual Salaries for Information Professionals

Occupation Name	2012 Median Annual Pay
Archivists, curators, and museum workers	$44,410
Fundraisers	$50,680
Editors	$53,880
Public relations specialists	$54,170
Librarians	$55,370
Writers and authors	$55,940
Market research analysts	$60,300
Web developers	$62,500
Budget analysts	$69,280
Network and computer systems administrators	$72,560
Statisticians	$75,560
Financial analysts	$76,950
Database administrators	$77,080
Management analysts	$78,600
Computer systems analysts	$79,680
Administrative services managers	$81,080
Political scientists	$102,000
Computer and information research scientists	$102,190
Computer and information systems managers	$120,950

Source: Bureau of Labor Statistics, "Occupational Outlook Handbook," 2014, http://www.bls.gov/ooh.

Another reason why some information professionals choose to pursue careers outside of libraries is because they can provide opportunities to help and influence the library community. Some information professionals use their experience to develop consulting practices in which they provide support and advice to information organizations. Other information professionals use the skills they develop during their LIS education to pursue jobs in the high-tech sector. Information professionals are employed in some of the largest and emerging information technology companies that are producing tools that change the way people experience their world.

TEXTBOX 11.2

Case Study: A Research Assistantship Leads Directly to a Career in the High-Tech Sector

Research assistantship positions are another way in which MLIS students can gain skills and practical experience that can lead to a career. Take, for example, one information professional who leveraged the skills she developed as a research assistant into a career in the high-tech sector. She used the hands-on experience she gained from her research assistantship that involved creating a taxonomy for a collection of digital resources to apply for a position focused on developing directories for an Internet search company. The experience of having created taxonomies gave her an advantage as a job candidate.

This example came from interviews conducted in 2014 with LIS graduates working outside of libraries.

Melissa Fraser-Arnott

The Intrepid Information Professional

So, if they are not working as librarians in libraries, what types of employment are information professionals pursuing? This is a question that has been asked in the LIS literature for approximately the past thirty years. A variety of job titles and types of employment have arisen as strong "alternatives" for information professionals, including information brokering, research consulting, publishing, information management, knowledge management, webmasters, competitive intelligence, and user needs analysis.[5]

Information professionals find jobs in every industry sector, as they possess highly sought-after skills, competencies, and values that can help organizations manage their information and knowledge resources in today's modern information economy. Table 11.2 shows a list of the ten most commonly requested competencies in job postings for both library jobs and jobs outside the library.[6]

Table 11.2. Most Commonly Requested Competencies

Most Commonly Requested Competencies in Job Announcements	
Library Jobs	**Jobs Outside the Library**
Communication skills	Knowledge of subject areas or job tasks
Analytical, problem-solving, and critical-thinking skills	Preparing/producing documents (briefing materials, correspondence, reports, memoranda, etc.)
Knowledge of metadata schemes or standards	Providing strategic advice, guidance, and recommendations
Delivering training, instruction, or teaching (instructional skills)	Experience with particular skills or tasks
Innovative technologies, applications, and social media	Analytical ability/skills/thinking
Time management, multitasking, meeting deadlines, managing workloads	Project or program implementation, coordination, and administration
Business software skills (Microsoft Office)	Finance, budget, and resource management
General qualifications (no criminal record, ability to travel, driver's license, etc.)	Liaising, consulting, and negotiating
Research skills	Management and leadership
Interpersonal skills	Business planning/Strategic planning

Source: Melissa Fraser-Arnott, "Library and Information Science (LIS) Transferable Competencies," *Partnership: The Canadian Journal of Library and Information Practice and Research* 8, no. 2 (2013).

The fact that there is a significant amount of overlap between these lists suggests that information professionals have a skill set that could allow them to apply for a wide variety of jobs. The rest of this section highlights some of the most essential attributes (e.g., skills) information professionals possess that are highly desired across a multitude of industries.

Desired Attributes of the LIS Professional

- *Customer Service:* Information professionals encompass the ability to provide relevant information to people and connect people with the information that they need. Information professionals tend to be user focused, and this helps them to have strong customer service skills. This combination, a desire to connect people with information and a strong customer service ethic, may allow information professionals to take on research or policy analysis roles. Organizations, such as government departments, think tanks, research institutes, and consulting firms, hire research and policy analysts to develop reports to help guide public- and private-sector entities to address important business or social issues.

- *Information Needs:* Information professionals understand how to accurately identify a client's information needs. This ability is obtained through the reference interview training in LIS programs that builds critical competencies, such as active listening, questioning techniques, and analytical thinking. These skills may be used by information professionals who wish to become information brokers or information consultants. Information consulting requires an individual to be able to quickly identify and understand a client's information needs. Such a person must be able to analyze information obtained through documentary sources (e.g., corporate reports), through systems (e.g., file plans, databases), and from people (e.g., through individual or face-to-face interviews). Absorbing information quickly and asking the right questions are essential skills that are needed to do this job.

- *Information Organization:* Information professionals bring an ability to organize information. These organizational skills can be applied to data management, information management, and knowledge management projects. Organizations produce vast amounts of information, and the ability of employees to find the information they need to complete their work in a timely manner can mean the difference in making deadlines and winning contracts. An information manager can help organizations to organize the information that they have created, enabling employees to find the information they need quickly. Information professionals may also help organizations to meet their legal or regulatory obligations by establishing systems and procedures that ensure that the organization's information holdings are complete, accurate, and up to date.

> "Technological abilities, combined with active listening skills and commitment to customer service, give information professionals the potential to serve as valuable members of teams dedicated to the implementation of new technologies."

- *Information Technology:* Information professionals offer potential employers a competence in the use of information technology (IT). IT classes are an important part of many LIS program curricula, with courses such as web design and development, databases, information architecture, informatics, systems design, information visualization, usability, social media, human–computer interaction, digital asset management, big data, data mining, telecommunications, and geographic information systems. Technological abilities, combined with active listening skills and commitment to customer service, give information professionals the potential to serve as valuable members of teams dedicated to the implementation of new technologies. They can serve as intermediaries between information technology professionals and end users, playing the valuable role of ensuring that end-user perspectives are incorporated into technology development and developing and delivering training.

- *Teamwork:* Information professionals also possess a strong competency in teamwork. Information professionals develop this competency both during and after their LIS studies. LIS programs provide students with the opportunity to work with their peers on group projects, and this helps to develop their teamwork skills. The fact that many LIS programs offer distance learning provides students with the added benefit of learning how to work with virtual teams and use collaborative tools, such as wikis and synchronous or asynchronous communication systems. Those who have worked in library settings also bring teamwork skills to new job settings; they often gain teamwork

Melissa Fraser-Arnott

experience by working with coworkers in the library setting, as well as through building partnerships in their communities.

- *Communication:* Information professionals encompass transferable communication skills—both verbal and written. The ability to express one's ideas clearly and succinctly in writing is a vital skill in a variety of settings in an individual's personal and professional life. Despite its universal importance, it is a skill that has not been universally mastered. The LIS degree helps students develop their writing skills through a variety of writing assignments, including research papers, annotated bibliographies, pathfinders, content for websites, and management reports. This range of tools encourages information professionals to think about writing for a variety of audiences. Additionally, students often write these assignments on very short deadlines, and this prepares them for the fast pace of many work settings.

This section outlined a few of the competencies and attributes that LIS graduates bring to their professional roles. These skills are highly desirable by companies in a variety of industry sectors and open up many potential opportunities for LIS graduates.[7]

Job Opportunities for Information Professionals

Information professionals have a number of avenues for finding jobs. In addition to their personal networks, social media listings, and general job resources such as Monster.com, one of the most common methods of job seeking is to use the job boards provided by LIS programs and professional associations for information professionals. These job boards often focus on jobs in library settings, but more and more often, they include jobs from other industries (see also "Key Resources—LIS Job Boards" in the online supplement). These positions are located in the financial, government, insurance, and corporate sectors and represent just a few examples of jobs that are available to information professionals (see also appendix 11.1, "Job Opportunities for Information Professionals").

Everyone's career path is unique, and there is no "secret sauce" to career success. There are a few observations, however, that should be of interest to information professionals who are considering a career outside of libraries. The first and most important of these is learning how to articulate the value that an information professional brings to an organization as a result of LIS training.

TEXTBOX 11.4

Case Study: Moving to a Second Career

Maria had developed a successful career working as a cataloger in several types of libraries. When working in a special library setting, members of the corporate services team approached the library director for advice on developing the information architecture for the company's new intranet. Her library director approached Maria—given her experience in cataloging and library systems—and asked her to take on this project. Maria took on the intranet design project and effectively demonstrated how the skills she developed organizing information in a library setting were broadly applicable in the corporate setting. She found the assignment so satisfying that she went on to a second career in information architecture consulting.

This account is based on an interview conducted by the author as part of a study on the professional identities of LIS graduates working outside of libraries. The name of the participant has been changed.

Conclusion

People are increasingly recognizing the value of information as currency, and this is opening up a range of new opportunities for information professionals that did not exist in the past. There are now a myriad different ways to be an information professional. Graduates of library and information science programs are taking their skills and applying them to a wide variety of job settings and are undertaking a wide range of job tasks. The proliferation of information and communication technologies and the tsunami of informational objects that these technologies have created are making information professionals more, rather than less, important. Information professionals are taking on a variety of roles in private- and public-sector organizations in which they are able to help connect people to the information that they need. They are also sitting at the wave front, creating new tools and new ways of finding, creating, organizing, and delivering information. The LIS degree has applications well beyond the world of libraries. There are countless employment possibilities available to information professionals who are able to think abstractly about the skills they developed and can articulate the value of those skills to potential employers.

> **TEXTBOX 11.5**
>
> **Topic for Discussion**
>
> How can an LIS graduate describe his or her skills to a potential employer without an LIS background?

Appendix 11.1: Job Opportunities for Information Professionals

The following are examples of job advertisements for information professionals situated outside the library sector.

Senior Prospect Research Analyst

RESPONSIBILITIES

- Interpret, analyze, and synthesize biographical and financial information
- Assist fund-raisers with linking donors' areas of philanthropic interest
- Contribute ideas and manage projects
- Assist with portfolio development
- Facilitate individualized strategy meetings
- Share best practices and provide training

QUALIFICATIONS

- Bachelor's degree and a minimum of three years of prospect research
- Strong understanding of the goals and guiding principles of the fund-raising profession
- Demonstrated proficiency in conducting prospect research and data analysis
- Significant expertise in using research resources
- Familiarity with data mining
- Ability to foster a collaborative, customer-oriented working environment
- Ability to work independently and as part of a team
- Ability to establish priorities, balance multiple assignments, and work under time constraints
- Excellent written and oral communication skills
- Strong attention to detail
- Demonstrated record of professionalism, initiative, problem solving, and adaptability
- Skills in the use of Microsoft Office applications

Melissa Fraser-Arnott

Support Analyst

RESPONSIBILITIES

- First point of contact for all inbound customer inquiries and problems
- Provide support for most issues
- Maintain close contact and open communications with customers
- Create detailed work logs
- Create flows of procedures and troubleshooting
- Follow documented technical procedures

QUALIFICATIONS

- Experience in library service
- Knowledge of Unix and/or Oracle
- Excellent written and verbal communication skills
- Ability to deliver outstanding customer service
- Ability to work collaboratively with employees
- Strong troubleshooting skills and ability to evaluate and manage changes
- Must be able to work well with stringent deadlines
- Good organizational skills
- Must follow predefined guidelines, protocols, and procedures
- Detail oriented with a strong work ethic
- Possess the ability to learn, retain, and apply new information and new products

Research Consultant

RESPONSIBILITIES

- Conduct client research consultation, including prospecting, market intelligence, and portfolio research
- Pitch engagements or compete for business
- Execute deals/transactions
- Support the training, growth, and development of junior members of the team
- Regularly consult with clients
- Administrative initiatives and other special projects including web development, workflow queue oversight, marketing, training, outreach and relationships, and vendor management and development

QUALIFICATIONS

- Four-plus years of reporting and analytical experience
- Master of library and information science (MLIS) with investigative and research skills
- Knowledge of online sources
- Proficiency with MS Office, Internet, and other web applications
- Experience in researching across a broad range of industries and entities
- Broad knowledge of capital markets deal-execution processes and standards
- Motivated self-starter, proactive, high level of maturity and professionalism

Competitive Intelligence Research Specialist

RESPONSIBILITIES

- Create briefing documents for client planning meetings
- Provide in-depth and complex research and reference assistance
- Support practice area marketing activities through competitive analysis and review of business and industry trends
- Evaluate sources of competitive intelligence information and new products/tools for use in intelligence research
- Keep abreast of new technologies

QUALIFICATIONS

- Ability to organize and prioritize numerous tasks
- Results oriented yet flexible and creative
- Solid organization, problem-solving, and multitasking skills
- Ability to work well independently and as part of a team
- Interpersonal skills
- Ability to perform complex research projects
- Proficiency in MS Office software

Communications Analyst

RESPONSIBILITIES

- Support knowledge management needs
- Monitor industry developments
- Assist with developing training materials
- Prepare status updates regarding various industry matters
- Maintain a system to track license and regulatory filing deadlines
- Monitor current industry and legal developments
- Conduct market research
- Provide training related to communications industry regulatory issues and current legal developments
- Assist with the development of technology products
- Design and develop content for practice-related databases

QUALIFICATIONS

- Organizational and communication skills
- Well-developed and professional interpersonal skills
- Familiarity with communications industry terminology
- Strong organizational skills

Manager, Records and Retention

RESPONSIBILITIES

- Manage all aspects of the records management team, including hiring, training, workload, and professional development

- Assist with budgeting and expense management
- Manage working relationships with vendors
- Establish policies and procedures for efficient completion of records management tasks
- Ensure the standardization of filing procedures across the firm
- Lead projects to roll out new or improved technologies

QUALIFICATIONS

- Strong organizational and interpersonal skills
- Strong verbal and written communication skills
- Detail oriented and accurate
- Ability to multitask
- Flexible and self-motivated
- Proficient in Excel and Word
- Independent thinker with proven team-building skills
- Expertise in using the resources and tools specific to the records management function

Notes

1. Terry L. Weech and Alison M. Konieczny, "Alternative Careers for Graduates of LIS Schools: The North American Perspective—an Analysis of the Literature," *Journal of Librarianship and Information Science* 39, no. 2 (2007): 67–78.
2. Mzwandile Shongwe and Dennis N. Ocholla, "A Tracer Study of LIS Graduates at the University of Zululand, 2000–2009," *Mousaison* 29, no. 2 (2011): 227–248.
3. Stephanie D. Taylor, R. Alexander Perry, Jessica L. Barton, and Brett Spencer, "A Follow-Up Study of the Factors Shaping the Career Choices of Library School Students at the University of Alabama," *Reference & User Services Quarterly* 50, no. 1 (2010): 35–47.
4. Ibid.
5. See, for example, Ken Haycock and Carla Garner, "The Bunheads Are Dead: Discovering High-Tech, High-Touch Opportunities in Library and Information Science," *American Libraries Digital Supplement Winter 2009*, 2009, 6–10, http://www.eslarp.uiuc.edu/news/AmericanLibraries2009.pdf; Christopher Soo-Guan Khoo, "Competencies for New Era Librarians and Information Professionals," in *International Conference on Libraries* (ICOL, 2005), 14–16, http://www.ibrarian.net/navon/paper/COMPETENCIES_FOR_NEW_ERA_LIBRARIANS_AND_INFORMATI.pdf?paperid=11070448; Briana Hovendick, "What I Learned about the Value of an MLIS Degree: An LIS Student's Perspective," *Fast Facts—Recent Statistics from the Library Research Service*, ED3/110.10, no. 271 (2009), http://www.lrs.org/documents/fastfacts/271_Student_Perspective.pdf; or Lisa M. Stronski, "Thinking Outside the Library: Employment Trends of Special Libraries Association Members" (master's paper, University of North Carolina–Chapel Hill, 2004), https://cdr.lib.unc.edu/indexablecontent/uuid:c6ba86cf-f78c-4329-8aa1-710e893c5da1?dl=true.
6. Melissa Fraser-Arnott, "Library and Information Science (LIS) Transferable Competencies," *Partnership: The Canadian Journal of Library and Information Practice and Research* 8, no. 2 (2013), https://journal.lib.uoguelph.ca/index.php/perj/article/view/2595#.U_qXBmPHTpw.
7. San José State University, "Emerging Career Trends for Information Professionals: A Snapshot of Job Titles in Summer 2013" (San José, CA: San José State University, 2013), http://ischool.sjsu.edu/downloads/emerging_trends_2012.pdf.

Part III

Information Services
Roles in the Digital Age

[Information professionals] have the opportunity to develop initiatives that blend information literacy with social media, make library tools available at the point of need for users, enable users to interface with information in a natural and personalized manner, and allow [users] to design their own learning outcomes.

—Bolorizadeh, Brannen, Gibbs, and Mack (2012)

To become effective contributors in society, information users need the skills to not only recognize their information needs, but also to best access and use information suitable to their needs. Information professionals are the essential guide in helping users gain the knowledge and skills on how to access, evaluate, and effectively use and engage with the information they retrieve.

Part III highlights the various roles—both in person and behind the scenes—that guide users through the information-seeking process. Behind the scenes, information professionals work to acquire, organize, and describe information so that it is readily available and easy to find. These technical services are complemented by what are often known as access services, which involve facilitating access to material, whether it is a printed book checked out in a physical building or a digital resource downloaded from an online portal. At the core of these roles is the information professional's function as an educator who provides information and technology literacy instruction to assist the user when navigating today's complex information environments.

Welcome to *Part III—Information Services: Roles in the Digital Age!*

12

Information Needs

UNDERSTANDING AND RESPONDING TO TODAY'S INFORMATION USER

Heather O'Brien and Devon Greyson

Information need is a fundamental concept in library and information science (LIS). Human information needs form the basis of many types of information work. Anticipating and meeting the information needs of specific user groups through programs and services is key to success in information organizations. Understanding information needs is the aim of a substantial stream of LIS research and professional work.

Information needs, like information users, are diverse. The experienced (or perceived) needs of individuals and groups in different circumstances and social locations vary, and the needs of individuals change over time. Consider the following scenarios:

- A fifth-grade student in an inner-city American school asks friends for help finding a good book about which to write a book report.
- A lawyer involved in an international biopatent case asks her staff to research precedent for gene patents in various jurisdictions.
- A young father in rural Canada, worried about his baby's fever, looks online for guidance regarding whether to embark on the hour-long trip to a hospital.

In the above scenarios, there are differences in the individuals' motivations and strategies for information seeking. These differences are based on individual ("micro-level") characteristics such as age or geographic location; relational factors ("meso-level") such as who is available to help fill information needs; higher-level ("macro-level") influences such as IT infrastructure and cultural values; and task-specific factors such as the currency of the requested information. All information needs are temporal and may shift and evolve over time and place as people interact with, interpret, and make sense of information.

This chapter examines and unpacks the construct "information need," using a combination of theoretical approaches, a multilevel model, and four case studies. The case studies feature information professionals striving to assess and meet the needs of multiple user populations in a variety of settings, and emphasize how the micro-, meso-, and macro-levels, combined with task-specific factors, act and interact to inform information needs in those cases. After completing this chapter, the reader should have an understanding of information needs and the various individual and contextual factors that shape them, as well as how information professionals work to identify and meet information needs in their work.

Defining Information Needs

"What is an information need?" For some, information needs are responses to a problem situation. Needs stem from recognizing a "problem" that is preventing an individual from moving forward. Information seeking is a natural course of action to reduce uncertainty,[1] fill a knowledge gap, or make sense of one's world.[2] The problem-centered view sees information behavior as a process whereby people encounter situations that prompt them to acquire knowledge or skills, seek specific information, and engage in decision making and sense making as they determine how well the located information meets their needs.

This perspective has been contested, as it assumes that seeking information is the natural course of action resulting from a need. Yet people who need information may not seek it; rather, they might engage in information avoidance, lack the skills or motivation to seek useful information, or not recognize what others (e.g., librarians, friends) perceive as a need.

Further, not all information acquisitions are needs-driven; for example, casual information encounters (e.g., channel surfing, checking social media) do not have an imperative "need" for information.[3] The relationship between needs and seeking is further complicated by the lack of clarity around the basic definition of information need. Who determines whether and when an individual or group has a need for information, and (how) do information professionals distinguish needs from what a person wants, demands, or expects?[4] There is a great deal of ambiguity around the definition of information need, and around the relationship between information needs and other activities such as seeking.

How might information professionals define an information need? An outcome-oriented definition is that an information need is "the information that individuals ought to have to do their job effectively, solve a problem satisfactorily, or pursue a hobby or interest happily."[5] By using simple language, it acknowledges potential constraints (micro, meso, and macro) to obtaining information and takes into account a variety of tasks and contexts of use.

While some might argue that information needs are only needs when they are perceived by users, the above definition is noncommittal on this point, and others have suggested that there is a state of "incognizance"[6] in which people do not know enough to understand or articulate what their needs are. Information professionals cannot always make decisions about programs, systems, and services based on well-articulated information needs; these may be the "tip of the iceberg" when it comes to the full information need of the user.

> "Information professionals must take seriously, and strive to meet, information needs articulated by their users. Even trivial-seeming requests may be relationship building, paving the way for more significant queries down the line."

Information professionals must take seriously, and strive to meet, information needs articulated by their users. Even trivial-seeming requests may be relationship building, paving the way for more significant queries down the line. However, receiving articulated information requests is rarely sufficient for fully assessing, understanding, and meeting the information needs of a user group. In addition to the information needs of specific users, information professionals must strive to understand the many factors that structure and influence information needs. Further, they must work to anticipate the needs of communities based on larger societal trends before related needs are perceived and expressed if information services and organizations are to stay ahead of the information curve.

Heather O'Brien and Devon Greyson

Theoretical Approaches to Information Needs

Wilson defines the domain of information behavior as "the totality of human behavior in relation to sources and channels of information, including both passive and active information seeking, and information use."[7] In his *Theory of Information Need*,[8] Cole identifies three dominant perspectives within information needs research:

1. information needs are inferred from behaviors that imply a need for information;
2. contextual factors give rise to information needs; and
3. information needs are a normative part of the human condition.

Information Needs as Implied by Information Behaviors

Information needs not only motivate information activities[9] but may be analyzed according to the information behaviors they initiate. Information needs themselves are not observable[10] and therefore represent a "black box."[11] By examining how people interact with formal (e.g., information databases) or informal (e.g., friends and family) information systems, information professionals can infer needs.

"By examining how people interact with formal (e.g., information databases) or informal (e.g., friends and family) information systems, information professionals can infer needs."

There are two main critiques of this approach. First, it does not account for what people are thinking and feeling, only what they are doing. When people recognize, articulate, and try to fulfill a need, they not only engage in different activities (e.g., consulting others, targeted searching), but also cognitive processes (e.g., perceiving, interpreting)[12] and affective states (e.g., uncertainty, frustration).[13] In the last decade, there has been an increase in research on the value of understanding, measuring, and designing for affective or emotional informational experiences.[14]

Second, behavior may allow us to predict or typify information needs in our organizations, but it does not help us understand and engage with individuals, in their own contexts, around their complete and current information needs.

Information Needs and Context

Information needs are highly contextual; different social and material contexts give rise to different information needs (see also chapter 4, "Diversity, Cultures, and Equity of Access"). Therefore, information needs may be approached according to "the user's life world."[15] The life world is made up of various subworlds (e.g., home, school): each subworld contains different reference groups (e.g., peers, teachers) and human and/or technological information systems with which to interact. Information needs arise from situations in the subworld, and from the social roles individuals assume in specific contexts.[16]

This may be why there is such an abundance of research based on occupation (e.g., lawyers, physicians), demographics (e.g., age, socioeconomic status), and role (e.g., patient, hobbyist).[17] It is likely impossible to arrive at a universal method for assessing and evaluating information needs, but it is manageable to consider a specific setting and the information needs that evolve for the people operating within that setting. For example, what kinds of tasks do pediatric nurses perform that require them to seek or use information? What types of information skills and resources will first-year college students require to complete their first academic paper? The contextual perspective allows information professionals to consider various factors related to individuals, their circumstances, and their workplaces or communities that precipitate and influence their information needs.

Information Needs and the Human Condition

Lastly, information need as part of the human condition is rooted in positive psychology. Maslow's *Theory of Human Motivation* (1943)[18] represents needs as a pyramid, with basic needs (i.e., food, shelter, security) grounding the hierarchy. As basic needs are satisfied, people pursue higher-level needs such as love, esteem, and, ultimately, self-actualization. Whether "information need" is a fundamental human need is an unresolved issue. Nonetheless, there are aspects of Maslow's work that have been adapted in LIS to inform thinking around information needs. Taylor[19] built on Maslow's position that needs are conscious and unconscious by proposing that people move through stages of recognizing they have an information need (visceral), articulating that need in their own minds (conscious), and then determining how to turn that need into a question (formalized). Taylor's stages were developed in the context of libraries, and his work forms the backbone of the reference interview (see also chapter 13, "Finding Information: Information Intermediation and Reference Services"). It is a key task of information intermediaries (e.g., librarians) to help people articulate their information needs as queries in order to obtain an optimal outcome.

TEXTBOX 12.1

Topic for Discussion

What is the relationship between information needs and information-seeking behaviors? Can you think of instances where a need might not lead to seeking?

A Multilevel Framework for Considering Information Needs

"Information professionals must both 'zoom in' on the individual user and his or her specific problem situation, cognitive and affective state, and end goals, and then 'zoom out' to the level of the group, organization, or community to consider the broader expectations, access and resource constraints, and emerging technologies that will impact current and future information needs."

This chapter has considered what an information need is, as well as behavioral, contextual, and psychological components thereof. Next, it will explore the information needs of diverse users as encountered in various settings. Information professionals must both "zoom in" on the individual user and his or her specific problem situation, cognitive and affective state, and end goals, and then "zoom out" to the level of the group, organization, or community to consider the broader expectations, access and resource constraints, and emerging technologies that will impact current and future information needs. As such, ecological systems theory[20] is useful for adopting a multilevel view in which information needs are shaped by:

- *Individual Factors:* socioeconomic status, literacy level, cultural background, motivation, interest, social role, prior topical knowledge, technology proficiency, and affect
- *Relational Factors:* the extent of one's social and/or professional network
- *Environmental (Community or Societal) Factors:* technology infrastructure, norms and values, culturally specific "ways of knowing" and communicating
- *Task- and Situation-Specific Factors:* the purpose for which information is sought and the characteristics of information and resources that are prioritized and valued (e.g., accuracy, timeliness, format)
- *Temporal Factors:* the passage of time influences and changes information needs within an individual and society

Heather O'Brien and Devon Greyson

These multiple layers of factors influence a given information need, and also interact with each other, creating a dynamic ecological system in which information needs arise, and ideally are resolved. Figure 12.1, "Understanding and Addressing Information Needs," illustrates a simplified ecological systems model adapted for understanding and addressing user information needs.

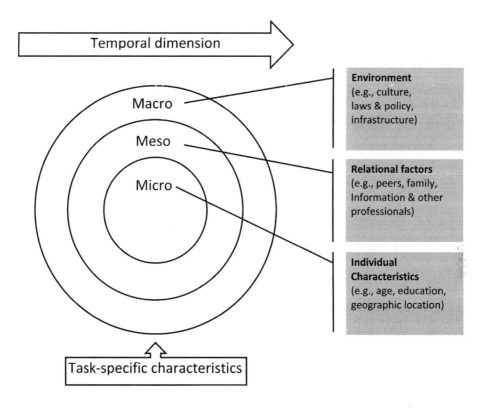

Figure 12.1 Understanding and Addressing Information Needs

To connect the theoretical discussion with "real-world" application, real-life examples of information needs and efforts to meet them are presented below. These case studies[21] represent four information professionals working in the United States and Canada—a public teen services librarian, a systems librarian working in a nonlibrary organization, a special health librarian, and a virtual academic librarian—who vary in terms of years of experience, communities served, geographic location, and type of organization for which they work. Their voices provide concrete examples of how information professionals are assessing, meeting, and evaluating diverse and ever-changing information needs. Within these examples, it is evident that multiple levels of factors are at work shaping information needs, and that meeting these needs is important for the sustainability of information organizations and services.

Case Study 1: Teens in a Public Library

Aubri Keleman, a public teen services librarian for over six years, notes that sometimes teens approach the library for help solving a specific information need. At other times, it is the job of library staff to get to know local youth and key community members or organizations in order to assess potential unexpressed needs. Specific to teen populations, she finds that "keeping up on pop culture does help with a certain number of kids," but that it is most important to build trusting relationships with youth and local youth service providers in order to stay in touch with the ever-evolving local youth culture. Additionally, teen librarians should bear in mind the interaction between teen development and information needs,[22] including sensitive treatment of personal and potentially stigmatized needs (e.g., sexuality).[23]

Aubri describes a successful teen program her library initiated in response to information needs that were observed in the community:

> There was a certain period of time where the teenagers at one of our rural libraries were in conflict with the police, and also were doing things like skipping out on court dates . . . so it seemed like we needed to talk to kids both about what rights they had, and ways that they could make things go smoother for themselves.

In response to this observed need for information among local youth, the library invited a lawyer in to give a workshop about legal rights and procedures in order to clarify and demystify for the teens what to expect from the police, as well as the consequences of resisting arrest.

The information need in this case was influenced by individual characteristics (e.g., a population of rural minors), relational factors (e.g., negative relationships between youth and the law, neutral or positive relationships between youth and the library), and environmental factors (e.g., lack of access to legal information, possibly a conflict of cultural values and norms). It was timely, as court dates are time-sensitive and the community was experiencing an escalation in negative teen–police interactions. The library staff crafted a program aimed at meeting the observed information need. Aubri says that in this case, "I think it was clear from what happened after that, that there was less conflict. And again we had that relationship with the teens so we could say, you know, 'Are you showing up for your court date? What's going on? Do you have any more questions?'"

While Aubri encourages information professionals to try new programs to meet perceived information needs, she cautions not to be too hung up on every program being a success. "I think it's important that we don't, as professionals, decide that there's an information need, and then become frustrated because people . . . don't feel that information need in their life."

Case Study 2: Systems Librarianship and Serving Students with Print Disabilities

Systems librarian Tara Robertson works for a government-funded organization with a mandate to format-shift academic materials (e.g., textbooks) for use by students with print disabilities. As she puts it, on an individual level, "we're using technology to solve a user's need." On a higher level, "education can be a really transformative force. Or it can keep people out. So I think we're kind of a bridge."

While students come to Tara via a formal referral process, this does not mean it's always simple to elicit or assess user needs. Some people come knowing exactly what they need (e.g., a textbook turned into an audiobook), while others may not know what format would be best for them. Tara explains that a personal conversation is required: "With students, if they don't know what they want I'll ask them about how their print disability impacts their reading, or impacts their studying. And that seems to be the right question to ask. At the beginning I wasn't really sure how to ask it."

Such a conversation allows the information professional not only to discover micro-level factors such as how a student's specific disability affects his/her reading, but also makes space for other factors that might influence the particular need. These include meso-level factors (e.g., students' relationship with their school's disability coordinators), temporal factors (e.g., when they need the materials), and task-specific factors unique to the material or field of study.

Tara also observes macro-level factors that influence student information needs. These include budgetary constraints for postsecondary education and support services, provincial policies encouraging certain types of education over others, and the stigma around having a disability. Understanding these is less likely to come out of direct conversation with users and more likely to arise from experience with the community.

Tara emphasizes the essential nature of collecting multiple forms of data when designing information systems. Specific methods include card-sorting exercises with staff and students, "guerilla user testing" with members of the target group (in one case this involved taking chocolate bars to a high-traffic student area as an incentive to provide website feedback), analytics, and library statistics such as circulation and database usage. While many of these methods are quantitative, Tara also stresses the importance of qualitative information via focus groups, surveys, and one-on-one follow-ups to validate the quantitative statistics:

> You can't just look at the data without asking people—because you could see a big drop and go, "Oh, okay, so that's not a useful resource." And it's like, "Oh, someone drove a truck through the front of the library that day and it was closed." And if you talk to someone, they'll tell you that, and it makes the data make sense, or contextualizes it.

Tara cautions against relying on library staff perceptions of what is working to meet user needs. In a previous systems job where she was transitioning a library to a new integrated library system (ILS) and website, she recalls, "I had quite a few disagreements with the reference librarians, because the way that they thought things were happening, the data suggested the opposite." She stresses the importance of welcoming negative feedback, as it can be useful for helping information organizations improve their ability to meet user needs.

> We rarely get [comments] that say, "Your service sucked" or "It didn't work for me." So that's the piece that we're missing. And I think everyone here is really keen to figure out more, like we get really enthusiastic when we get negative feedback [laughs] because we're like, "Okay! What went wrong? Let's track it!"

While this emphasis on continual assessment of how well a system is meeting user needs is time intensive, Tara reminds us that if what an information service is doing is not helping, "all that time is wasted." Assessment of a service's success at meeting user needs is essential for sustainability and funding advocacy within many organizations. Tara's organization reports to the government annually, and she finds that solid assessment results can be a useful advocacy tool for organizational funding and support.

> "Assessment of a service's success meeting user needs is essential for sustainability and funding advocacy within many organizations."

Case Study 3: Medical Professionals in a Special Library Setting

Diane (pseudonym), a health information specialist for twelve years in special and hospital libraries, is currently the librarian for 150 staff within a health organization. She supports diverse user needs through the provision of resources, instruction and referrals, maintenance of a health policy database, and archival records management. Diane's users are professionals with work-related information needs and seeking; therefore she works within an "embedded" model of health librarianship.[24]

Diane takes a task-based approach to anticipating and meeting employees' needs, where specific types of needs are typically associated with specific units. Understanding the work being done within the organization and its individual departments is key:

It takes time to get a sense of organization and individual needs. Conversations and requests by individual staff members help me to know individual needs. Working on projects, organization communications or strategies, and team meetings are all ways in which I gain knowledge of information needs.

> "Without proactive work on the part of the information professional, employees may not recognize the role the library can play in assisting them with their work."

Diane emphasizes that gathering intelligence about information needs is also part of sustaining library services within the organization. Without proactive work on the part of the information professional, employees may not recognize the role the library can play in assisting them with their work. She relayed an example of a staff member who thought "you could get everything on the Internet for free," but now sees the value of library resources. Building relationships with users means assessing and meeting user needs is an ongoing conversation:

> It's about knowing the client and following through with them. For example, after doing a literature search for someone, you might come across further information that you forward along—"I read this article and thought you would be interested" and "Here's the abstract. Let me know if you would like the full text."

One challenge that Diane encounters is how to fulfill information needs given macro-level and temporal constraints. For example, she sees information literacy instruction as a growth area for the library, but it is a challenge to figure out how to deliver instruction effectively given employees' time limitations and the existing institutional professional development framework. Additionally, working to foster relationships across departments is difficult. Current struggles include educating the information technology (IT) unit about the information needs the library fulfills and trying to better support organizational records management needs with limited staff resources. Of determining needs, she says,

> sometimes this is simple and straightforward. Sometimes it involves more of an iterative process to determine the real need. Sometimes it involves providing options. It still involves good reference skills. It involves getting to know client needs.

Yet trying to meet these needs involves negotiating within the larger macro-level of the organization's structure, culture, and technological infrastructure (see also chapter 9, "Information Centers: Special Libraries").

Case Study 4: Virtual University Students

Students represent one of the most studied user populations in LIS.[25] Currently, there is much emphasis on virtual learning (e.g., flexible learning, flipped classrooms) in higher education and the information needs of online learners. Samantha Sinanan, manager of library instruction with Virtual Librarian Service (VLS), provides library and information services to online universities in the United States.

For Samantha, academic librarians have a very clear role in working with educational institutions to assess and meet students' information needs: "[We] break down this massive amount of information into digestible chunks" and give students skills they can "carry through their academic program and into their professional lives." Another responsibility is staying abreast of current trends. Recently, for example, she's been looking at mobile applications, because we need to "be creative in the ways we reach students" and to choose "instructional supports and strategies" that are relevant to them and meet them where they are.

Heather O'Brien and Devon Greyson

Meeting the students where they are emphasizes the technological affordances of the online environment. VLS relies on asynchronous communication with students, which has both challenges and benefits:

> We really need to work harder at the point of contact to make sure we get it right. But we know that for many of the students in an online environment, the asynchronous mode works for them. It allows us to sit down and carefully think about our response, and we have the opportunity to follow up with the student.

There are also collections management issues—embargos placed on recent content and items not available in electronic format. Virtual librarians "don't have a choice" but to be literate and comfortable with IT. Since beginning her job three years ago, Samantha has had to "fearlessly embrace technology" and learn the skills to work with new systems and software.

A major question is how to provide instruction and information in the virtual environment. Samantha asks, "We are designing instructional supports, but are the students using them?" and "How do we deliver information in manageable, understandable chunks without compromising our mission, or oversimplifying it [the information]?" The students with whom Samantha interacts have chosen online education because it fits their lives. In typical reference encounters, Samantha looks at micro-level factors—program of study, student status (new versus advanced student)—and the complexity of the information need being presented. She tries to deliver the right amount of information to students—not too little and not too much—and pitch it at the right level. For example, a student in a nursing diploma program will require a different level of information than a doctoral student in nursing.

Getting a sense of students' information literacy is paramount. Although information literacy "lay[s] the foundation for the student's entire academic experience," Samantha feels that some students are not conscious of this need, and that these skills are not encouraged in the "age of Google where in many cases you put in a string of words and get back what you want." In addition, they tend to focus on immediate needs for tangible information, rather than the building blocks for locating and evaluating it. At the macro-level, VLS serves numerous online universities, each with "their own culture" and a diversity of programs. This impacts instructional tools, such as LibGuides: "Do we create one overarching guide [for a subject] or hundreds [for each school]?" VLS liaises with faculty, program directors, and student success coordinators at the universities, and this collaboration is based on a common goal: "everybody wants the students to succeed." Part of this collective effort is working toward student retention. This is a concern for the library itself (i.e., What happens to the students who don't come back? Did we serve them successfully, or were they completely confused?), and for the institutions that VLS supports. Samantha says, "We all have our part to play, including the library. . . . We don't want 'students lost in cyberspace' or 'dropping out and fading away' or feeling unsupported."

TEXTBOX 12.2

Topic for Discussion

Consider a specific user group with whom you work or would like to work. Brainstorm individual (micro), relational (meso), and environmental (macro) factors that might shape the needs of those users.

Conclusion

Human information need is a "fuzzy" concept, yet central to the existence and mission of information organizations. Needs relate to information behaviors, such as seeking, avoidance, and assessment, and are highly context sensitive. Information needs may be known and specifically addressed by users, or they may be unclear or unacknowledged until identified and met by an information professional.

Expressed information needs must be taken at face value, but other needs are more effectively met when the information professional attempts to gain an understanding of the factors that create and influence specific needs.

Aubri's case study highlights the importance of being in touch with a user community, through direct observation/interaction and via networks of service providers. Tara's story emphasizes the importance of using data to challenge librarians' perceptions of user needs and how well they are being met, as well as of adopting a mentality of continuous assessment. Diane's message is that the special library must demonstrate value through collaboration and formal and informal means of assessing organizational and individual information needs. Samantha stressed meeting students where they are and fulfilling articulated needs while also working on latent information literacy needs to promote student success and retention.

Information professionals working with different groups and communities encounter diverse user needs. While the specific needs, as well as strategies to meet them, vary greatly depending on the context and user, it is imperative to assess information needs *and* how well we are meeting them. The sustainability of information organizations depends on it.

Acknowledgments

We appreciate our interviewees: Aubri Keleman, Tara Robertson, "Diane," and Samantha Sinanan for sharing their insights and experiences for this chapter.

Notes

1. Carol C. Kuhlthau, "Inside the Search Process: Information Seeking from the User's Perspective," *Journal of the American Society for Information Science* 42, no. 5 (1991): 261–271, http://ptarpp2.uitm.edu.my/silibus/insidesearch2.pdf.
2. Brenda Dervin, "What Methodology Does to Theory: Sense-Making Methodology as Exemplar," in *Theories of Information Behavior*, ed. Karen E. Fisher, Sandra Erdelez, and Lynne E. F. McKechnie (Medford, NJ: Information Today, 2005).
3. David Elsweiler, Max L. Wilson, and Brian K. Lund, "Understanding Casual-Leisure Information Behavior," in *New Directions in Information Behavior*, ed. Amanda Spink and Jannica Heinström (Bingley, UK: Emerald Group, 2011).
4. Thomas D. Wilson. "On User Studies and Information Needs," *Journal of Documentation* 37, no. 1 (1981): 5.
5. David Nicholas, *Assessing Information Needs: Tools, Techniques and Concepts for the Internet Age* (London: ASLIB, 2000), 20.
6. Beth St. Jean, "'I Just Don't Know What I Don't Know!': A Longitudinal Investigation of the Perceived Usefulness of Information to People with Type 2 Diabetes," *Proceedings of the American Society for Information Science and Technology* 49, no. 1 (2012): 1–10.
7. Thomas D. Wilson, "Models in Information Behavior Research," *Journal of Documentation* 55, no. 3 (1999): 249.
8. Charles Cole, *Information Need: A Theory Connecting Information Search to Knowledge Formation* (Medford, NJ: Information Today, 2012).
9. Charles Naumer and Karen E. Fisher, "Information Needs," in *Encyclopedia of Library and Information Sciences*, 3rd ed. (Abingdon, UK: Taylor & Francis, 2009), 2452–2458.
10. Nicholas J. Belkin and Alina Vickery, *Interaction in Information Systems: A Review of Research from Document Retrieval to Knowledge-Based Systems* (London: British Library, 1985).
11. Cole, *Information Need*, 65.
12. Robert S. Taylor. "Question-Negotiation and Information Seeking in Libraries," *College & Research Libraries* 29, no. 3 (1968): 178–194, http://crl.acrl.org/content/29/3/178.full.pdf; Kuhlthau, "Inside the Search Process."

13. Kuhlthau, "Inside the Search Process: Information Seeking from the User's Perspective."
14. Wilson, "On User Studies and Information Needs," 5–6.
15. D. Nahl and D. Bilal, "The Centrality of Affect in Information Behavior," in *Information and Emotion: The Emergent Affective Paradigm in Information Behavior Research and Theory* (Medford, NJ: Information Today, 2007).
16. Wilson, "On User Studies and Information Needs," 9.
17. Donald O. Case, *Looking for Information: A Survey of Research on Information Seeking, Needs and Behavior* (Bingley, UK: Emerald Group, 2012).
18. Abraham H. Maslow, "A Theory of Human Motivation," *Psychological Review* 50 (1943).
19. Robert S. Taylor, "Question-Negotiation and Information Seeking in Libraries."
20. Urie Bronfenbrenner, *The Ecology of Human Development: Experiments by Nature and Design* (Cambridge, MA: Harvard University Press, 1979).
21. Aubri Keleman, Tara Robertson, "Diane," and Samantha Sinanan, telephone interviews by Diane O'Brien and Devon Greyson, June 2014.
22. Denise E. Agosto and Sandra Hughes-Hassell, "Toward a Model of the Everyday Life Information Needs of Urban Teenagers, Part 1," *Journal of the American Society for Information Science and Technology* 57, no. 10 (2006): 1394–1403.
23. Jennifer Burek Pierce, "Young Adult Sexual and Reproductive Health Information Needs," in *Youth Information-Seeking Behavior II: Context, Theories, Models, and Issues*, ed. Mary K. Chelton and Colleen Cool (Lanham, MD: Scarecrow Press, 2007).
24. Devon Greyson, Soleil Surette, Liz Dennett, and Trish Chatterley, "'You're Just One of the Group When You're Embedded': Report from a Mixed-Method Investigation of the Research-Embedded Health Librarian Experience," *Journal of the Medical Library Association* 101, no. 4 (2013): 287.
25. Case, *Looking for Information*, 301.

13

Finding Information

INFORMATION INTERMEDIATION AND REFERENCE SERVICES

Michelle Holschuh Simmons

Connecting people with information is at the heart of information professionals' work. This essential task is divided into many discrete tasks, including organizing information for efficient access through database design, preserving access to information through digital curation, and managing information centers through effective and visionary leadership, all of which are covered in other chapters of this book. This chapter addresses the actual point of contact between the information professional and the user. It focuses on how information professionals directly assist users in formulating their information questions and finding relevant and accurate information.

Like so many other parts of the information profession, the work of an information intermediator (e.g., the reference librarian) is becoming increasingly decentralized, distributed, and diverse in its delivery. Historically, if users needed assistance in finding information, they were required to initiate contact with an information professional by physically moving into the organization's space (i.e., approaching the reference desk). This limitation was mitigated somewhat with the adoption of phone and e-mail reference interactions in the 1980s and 1990s; however, the patrons were still actively initiating contact and moving into the information professional's space, even if doing so virtually via e-mail, chat, or phone. Reference services of today still encompass these more traditional, reactive methods of providing service, but more and more, information professionals are implementing service models that are proactive and decentralized. Information intermediators are meeting users at their point of need in their own space, both physically and virtually. After completing this chapter, the reader should have an understanding of the many ways that information intermediators are providing these distributed, decentralized services to connect users with information.

Constants in Reference Services

As much as reference services have evolved in the last few decades, the foundational principles and practices have remained central to the task of connecting people with information, regardless of medium. Quality of service (including conducting an effective reference interview), knowledge of the information search process, and user education are all aspects of information intermediation that remain, irrespective of the medium or technology.

To encourage quality of service through standardized assessment of reference interactions, the Reference and User Services Association (RUSA) developed the *Guidelines for Behavioral Performance of Reference and Information Service Providers.*[1] RUSA, a division of the American Library Association (ALA) dedicated to reference services, originally developed the guidelines in 1996 and revised and reapproved them in 2013. These guidelines articulate the essential behavioral attributes of information intermediators: approachability, interest, listening/inquiring, searching, and follow-up.

Essential Behavioral Attributes of Information Intermediators
- Approachability
- Interest
- Listening/inquiring searching
- Follow-up

RUSA's *Guidelines for Behavioral Performance of Reference and Information Service Providers* (available via the online supplement).

Central to the RUSA guideline of listening/inquiring is the reference interview. The reference interview is a questioning technique discussed widely in the professional literature, with Brenda Dervin's work on neutral questioning as the foundation.[2] The purpose of the reference interview is for the information professional to understand the questioner's query fully before embarking on the searching segment of the reference interaction. By using neutral questioning techniques, the information professional is able to determine the precise information need from the patron without the information professional's own assumptions affecting the result.

In addition to using the RUSA guidelines to improve service, information professionals use their knowledge of information-seeking behaviors to assist individuals who have information needs. Carol Kuhlthau's work on the information search process is especially useful in that it articulates common intellectual and affective stages that seekers of information typically experience, thereby allowing information professionals to intervene with appropriate assistance at each stage, no matter the technology or the medium of service delivery.[3]

Another consistent aspect of reference service regardless of medium is user education or information literacy instruction. Dating back to Samuel Swett Green's recommendations in 1876 that educating patrons was one of four goals for reference librarians,[4] user education remains an integral part of reference service. James Elmborg articulated the continued centrality of information literacy instruction in reference service in his oft-cited article "Teaching at the Desk: Toward a Reference Pedagogy."[5] Indeed, as information has become more readily available to users through the Internet, the information professional's role in teaching users to find, use, and evaluate information has become ever more pressing.

TEXTBOX 13.1

Topic for Discussion

The RUSA guidelines can be used to evaluate an information professional's performance in any reference interaction. How might these guidelines need to be supplemented or adapted for use with virtual reference interactions? What considerations might be more important in a virtual reference setting that are less important in a physical setting? What considerations might be less important in a virtual reference setting that are more important in a physical setting?

The Changing Nature of Reference Collections

As information intermediators are increasingly reaching their patrons through electronic means (such as chat reference) and using electronic resources (such as online databases), the need for a substantial physical space for the reference desk and the reference collection is diminishing. More and more, information organizations are reducing dramatically the number of print volumes in their reference collections,[6] and in fact, some are almost or completely eliminating the print reference collection through a combination of weeding and reshelving in the circulating collection (see also chapter 25, "Managing Collections").[7] Typically, the physical space previously consumed by the print reference stacks is now being repurposed for a variety of patron-centered functions.

This trend away from print reference collections in favor of patron-centered spaces is happening in both academic and public libraries. For example, at the main library at the University of Iowa, the substantial print reference collection was weeded and relocated to make room for the learning commons. According to the University of Iowa, the learning commons is a "tech-infused comfortable and flexible learning space and one-stop academic and information help center . . . with good coffee! The commons includes space for group collaboration and individual study with modern technology amenities and high-quality assistance with information and technology resources."[8] Notable in this description is the emphasis on technology, collaboration, and learning, with the simultaneous deemphasis on physical information sources. In this model, the university's students are content creators using information and technology tools with the help of "high-quality assistance," presumably by information professionals (see also chapter 19, "Creation Culture and Makerspaces").

Similarly, in the White Plains (New York) Public Library, print resources were relocated to make room for a three-thousand-square-foot space for teens called the Edge, which is divided into three areas: "The Living Room—a space for socializing and gaming; The Mixing Area—a place for research and homework; and The Digital Media Lab—a flexible space for workshops, classes, and collaboration."[9] In both the academic library and the public library examples, the physical reference collection and the traditional reference desk were relocated or dissolved in favor of spaces that allow for collaboration and creation with the support of information professionals who need to be nimble and flexible in the way they provide service.

Meeting Users through Physical Presence

Concurrent with changes in physical reference collections, physical reference services are changing as well. An overall trend in reference service is one of meeting users where they are (either physically or virtually), instead of requiring users to initiate contact with the information professional in the professional's space (i.e., approaching the reference desk to speak with the information professional).

Service Models within Information Centers

While the traditional model of a reference librarian seated at a reference desk waiting for patrons to approach with questions does still exist, an expanding variety of other organizational models are being employed. For example, many information organizations have collapsed the circulation desk and the reference desk into a single service point, where patrons can seek assistance with borrowing materials as well as with information queries. Often in this service model, the information professional is "on call," so when a patron approaches the desk with an information query, the staff person alerts the information professional on call, who then attends to the patron's question. Also called "tiered reference," this model is efficient in terms of budgeting and professional staff time; however, it requires substantial coordination and marketing to ensure that patrons know that professional information assistance is available.[10]

Michelle Holschuh Simmons

In an effort to make information professionals more visible and more available to patrons when and where they need assistance, some organizations have begun roving reference programs, such as at Southern Illinois University at Carbondale.[11] Facilitated by increasingly mobile electronic devices, roving reference has become more and more feasible since its introduction into the professional literature in the early to mid-2000s.[12] In a roving reference model, information professionals are not tethered to a reference desk but instead move around the information organization, often with a mobile device such as an iPad, offering assistance to those who need it. Smith and Pietraszewski argue that roving reference makes information professionals seem more approachable and provides opportunities for more in-depth assistance than often occurs at the desk.[13] For a roving reference program to be successful, information professionals must provide extensive marketing so patrons understand that the service is available. Additionally, the information professional needs to possess personality traits, such as openness and friendliness, so that patrons are willing to seek assistance.

Service Points Outside the Information Center

ROVING REFERENCE

A logical extension from the roving reference initiatives has been for the information professional to rove outside the organization's walls—allowing them to meet users at their points of need and in their space more fully. This has been done in a variety of settings successfully, thereby extending the reach of the information organization's services to patrons who never set foot in the information organization itself. For example, the information professionals at the University of Maryland, Baltimore County (UMBC), have implemented a roving reference program in high-traffic areas on campus, such as the commuter lounge, the university center (student union), and the women's center.[14] Information professionals at UMBC used social media outlets such as the organization's Twitter feed to announce at which location on campus they would be present and at what times. Ironically, the location that had the fewest reference questions was the library itself: at the library's twenty-four-hour study space! They found that students "were mostly at this location for group study and did not typically have reference questions."[15] Equipped with an iPad, a laptop stand, and a prominent sign advertising the service, these information professionals sought to meet their users where they were, providing assistance in using information resources without the physical space of the information organization at all.

Other information organizations have experimented with creative models of roving reference, such as locating an information professional regularly in a coffee shop or similar social space. The information professionals at the University at Albany, State University of New York, have implemented a "Librarians with a Latte" initiative in an on-campus coffee shop for one-on-one reference assistance.[16] The website for Librarians with a Latte emphasizes that students should look for the "Librarian with a Latte" sign and stop by anytime; registration or RSVP is not necessary.

EMBEDDED LIBRARIANSHIP

Related to roving reference is the concept of embedded librarianship. Whereas roving reference is intended to locate an information professional in a highly trafficked area where patrons who need assistance might happen upon the information professional, embedded librarianship is intended for the information professional to be an integrated member of a community outside of the information organization. Coined in 2004 by Barbara Dewey,[17] the term "embedded librarian" has come to mean an information professional who is focused "on the needs of one or more specific groups, building relationships with these groups, developing a deep understanding of their work, and providing information services that are highly customized and targeted to their greatest needs."[18] David Shumaker has written a thorough overview of embedded librarianship in his book *The Embedded Librarian: Innovative*

Strategies for Taking Knowledge Where It's Needed.[19] Information professionals have applied the concept of embedded librarianship in a wide range of settings, in all types of information centers.

Academia is perhaps the most common setting for embedded librarianship, both for faculty and student support. For example, in a serendipitous accident due to a library renovation, the office of a librarian at California State University, Stanislaus, was relocated within the College of Education's faculty offices. This inadvertent embedding resulted in a successful opportunity to build relationships with both faculty and students.[20] Similarly, though perhaps more intentionally, several information professionals at Washington University in St. Louis are embedded in academic departments and hold office hours within academic departments for several hours each week.[21]

In addition to placements in academic departments, other information professionals are embedding themselves within other campus units especially to provide research assistance to students. At the University of Alberta, for example, one information professional spends weekly office hours within the computer lab of the campus's Specialized Support and Disability Services center.[22] At the University of North Texas, an information professional took his role as an embedded librarian to an unprecedented level by participating in the Faculty-in-Residence program and living with students in a residence hall.[23] He provided research assistance through designated "Homework Help" hours in the lobby and in the cafeteria to students who lived in the residence hall. By becoming a full residential member of the community, this information professional was able to reach students in a way that would be unlikely within the walls of an information organization, such as the campus library.

Outside of academia, embedded librarianship is being implemented in a wide range of settings. For example, embedded hospital librarians can play an important role in the care of patients, delivering targeted information within a clinical setting at the point of care.[24] Embedded librarians are also working in consumer health environments, not just clinical environments, such as in Bay Area Cancer Connections, a nonprofit organization dedicated to supporting people affected by breast and ovarian cancer.[25]

Public librarians have also begun embedding themselves within their communities outside of the organization's walls. For example, the Douglas County (Colorado) Libraries (DCL) found that the number of traditional reference questions asked at the reference desk was declining, so the information professionals moved into the community, where the questions actually were. The DCL staff are embedded "throughout the county in local schools, city councils, metro districts, economic development councils, and even a local women's crisis center."[26] Clearly, information professionals are finding places within their communities where they are welcomed and valued for providing reference services outside the walls of their organizations.

TEXTBOX 13.2

Topic for Discussion

Embedded librarianship depends on full integration into a community. The advantages of embedded librarianship are many for the community. However, what are possible drawbacks of information professionals being fully integrated into a patron community and apart from other information professionals? What might be lost by having the librarians dispersed among patron communities?

Meeting Users through Virtual Presence

A major expansion in reference librarians' responsibilities has been beyond physical interactions to virtual reference interactions. While the various technologies used in virtual reference bring their own set of challenges and opportunities, the foundational service principles and practices explained earlier

Michelle Holschuh Simmons

in this chapter remain relevant and useful. Indeed, the RUSA guidelines that provide standards for behavior attributes for reference librarians can be applied to physical or virtual reference interactions, regardless of the communication technology.

Virtual Reference via Chat and Text

Starting with phone and then e-mail reference services decades ago, information professionals have long used communication technologies to provide reference services to their users.[27] Presently, information organizations are providing reference through an ever-expanding range of technologies in direct response to users' regard for convenience as a primary criterion in their choice of information source. Perhaps most widely used is chat reference through services such as OCLC's QuestionPoint cooperative reference service.[28] Co-browsing capabilities (in which the information professional can see what the patron has on his or her computer screen) in services such as QuestionPoint provide an opportunity for information professionals to incorporate information literacy instruction into the virtual reference interaction, since the information professional is able to show the user how to find the information so that the user can replicate the search skills learned for a future information need.

Check This Out

Learn more about OCLC's 24/7 cooperative reference service "QuestionPoint"
Visit: http://www.questionpoint.org

As texting via cell phones has become increasingly pervasive as a communication medium, information professionals have introduced reference services via text messages. Similar to QuestionPoint for chat reference, MyInfoQuest is a nationwide collaborative text reference service.[29] Due to the limit of 160 characters in a text message, texting for reference interactions tends to be used by patrons for ready reference questions for which the answers are relatively brief.[30] Due to the succinct nature of these reference transactions, most text reference interactions do not involve a full reference interview. As Luo and Weak concluded, it is important for text reference librarians to "strike a good balance between being concise and being informative."[31]

Embedded Virtual Information Professionals

Just as embedded information professionals integrate themselves into their physical community, virtual embedded information professionals integrate themselves into a virtual space to provide service to members of a community. A thorough treatment of virtually embedded librarians is available in the edited volume by Elizabeth Leonard and Erin McCaffrey titled *Virtually Embedded: The Librarian in an Online Environment*.[32] Included here are a few of the many ways information professionals can become embedded within a virtual environment to provide reference service.

Perhaps the most common example of an embedded information professional in a virtual space is an academic librarian who has a presence within a class in a learning management system (LMS), such as Blackboard, D2L, or Canvas. An embedded information professional might offer highly integrated services, such as leading discussion boards about research questions, providing a widget for live video chat about research questions, or being involved with the assessment of student assignments.[33] The embedded information professional maintains a consistent virtual presence in the class and contributes to the learning objectives of the course.

While an information professional embedded within a class's LMS might be able to provide highly personalized, high-involvement service for a limited number of classes and students, this task becomes much more daunting when the class is a massive open online course (MOOC) with potentially thousands of students. In this setting, the level of involvement might be low-investment strategies, such as providing a link within the class site to the information organization's website or to a relevant LibGuide or subject research guide, or providing instructional screencasts or other learning objects. Additionally, the embedded information professional might be more directly involved with the instructor than with the students, by providing instructional design consultation, assisting in finding open access materials for the MOOC, or providing media expertise in audio or video recording.[34]

Through these many ways of providing reference service in virtual environments, through virtual reference and through being virtually embedded, reference librarians can extend the reach of their influence across geographic and temporal bounds. Without meeting these patrons face to face, virtual information professionals can provide high-quality service that connects people with information.

Conclusion

Information and communication technologies (ICT) have dramatically changed the work of information professionals in the last several decades; reference librarians of a half century ago would hardly recognize the work of a reference librarian of today. However, throughout all of these developments, the reference librarian's goal of efficiently connecting users with accurate information has been consistent. Challenges that might have seemed insurmountable have become opportunities for innovation, thereby keeping the field of reference services relevant, nimble, and entrepreneurial.

And yet significant challenges remain. Scalability is a persistent problem for highly personalized initiatives, such as many of those mentioned in this chapter. While a single information professional might be able to be an active presence in a handful of classes within the LMS, for example, he or she simply cannot maintain the same level of involvement in hundreds of classes, as there likely would be in a large academic institution. Similarly, a single information professional might be embedded within an academic department—offering office hours and one-on-one assistance—but it would be challenging to provide comparable staffing for every academic department in a large university when library budgets are shrinking. Thus, being innovative about ways to do more with less will continue to be a significant challenge.

An additional challenge related to tight budgets is the threat of not being recognized for the valuable reference work that information professionals do. It is necessary to demonstrate and articulate how the work contributes to the goals of the larger organization. Being cognizant of the larger institution's mission, and understanding how the work is in support of that larger mission, is an important step in ensuring that the work is valued. Further, at a time when Internet sites like Wikipedia (www.wikipedia.com) and services like Quora (www.quora.com) boast that they are the best sources for information, users often do not understand the role of the information professional, and thus might not seek assistance.

And finally, a continuing challenge for the field of reference services is to stay on top of the technological changes that are affecting patrons' worlds and consequently reference librarians' work. It is imperative that reference librarians keep current with trends and developments so that they are not left behind at the reference desk, wondering where the patrons are.

The days have passed when information professionals could sit behind the desk, waiting for patrons to approach with questions. Information professionals of today must seize the opportunities for innovation to engage with patrons in new and pioneering ways. They must meet patrons where they are, either physically or virtually, to connect them with information.

Michelle Holschuh Simmons

Notes

1. Reference and User Services Association, "Guidelines for Behavioral Performance of Reference and Information Service Providers," 1996.
2. Brenda Dervin and Patricia Dewdney, "Neutral Questioning: A New Approach to the Reference Interview," *RQ* 25, no. 4 (1986): 506–513.
3. Carol Collier Kuhlthau, "Inside the Search Process: Information Seeking from the User's Perspective," *Journal of the American Society for Information Science* 42, no. 5 (1991): 361–371, http://ptarpp2.uitm.edu .my/silibus/insidesearch2.pdf.
4. Samuel Swett Green, "Personal Relations between Librarians and Readers," *American Library Journal* 1, no. 1 (1876): 74–81, http://pacificreference.pbworks.com/f/Personal%20Relations%20Between%20 Librarians%20and%20Readers.pdf.
5. James K. Elmborg, "Teaching at the Desk: Toward a Reference Pedagogy," *portal: Libraries & the Academy* 2, no. 3 (2002): 455–464.
6. See, for example, Mary Francis, "Weeding the Reference Collection: A Case Study of Collection Management," *Reference Librarian* 53, no. 2 (2012): 219–234; Nathaniel King, "Nice vs. Necessary: Reference Collections in ARL Member Libraries," *Reference Librarian* 53, no. 2 (2012): 138–55. doi:10.108 0/02763877.2011.607415.
7. See, for example, Brian Herzog. "Update on Eliminating Our Reference Collection," *Swiss Army Librarian Blog*, last modified April 7, 2011, http://www.swissarmylibrarian.net/2011/04/07/update-on -eliminating-our-reference-collection.
8. "Learning Commons," University of Iowa Libraries, last modified August 22, 2014, http://www.lib.uiowa .edu/commons.
9. Michael Dardano, "Grand Opening of the Edge at the White Plains Public Library," *White Plains Patch*, last modified December 11, 2013, http://whiteplains.patch.com/groups/announcements/p/ grand-opening-of-the-edge-at-the-white-plains-public-library_613afe1e.
10. For an overview of reference service models, see David A. Tyckoson, "Issues and Trends in the Management of Reference Services: A Historical Perspective," *Journal of Library Administration* 52, nos. 6-7 (December 11, 2013): 581–600. doi:10.1080/01930826.2012.707953.
11. Megan Lotts and Stephanie Graves, "Using the iPad for Reference Services: Librarians Go Mobile," *College & Research Libraries News* 72, no. 4 (2011): 217–220, http://crln.acrl.org/content/72/4/217.full .pdf+html.
12. See, for example, Martin P. Courtois and Maira Liriano, "Tips for Roving Reference: How to Best Serve Library Users," *College & Research Libraries News* 61, no. 4 (2000): 289–315; Michael M. Smith and Barbara A. Pietraszewski, "Enabling the Roving Reference Librarian: Wireless Access with Tablet PCs," *Reference Services Review* 32, no. 3 (2004): 249–255. doi:10.1108/00907320410553650.
13. Smith and Pietraszewski, "Enabling the Roving Reference Librarian."
14. Joanna Gadsby and Shu Qian, "Using an iPad to Redefine Roving Reference Service in an Academic Library," *Library Hi Tech News* 29, no. 4 (2012): 1–5. doi:10.1108/07419051211249446.
15. Ibid.
16. "'Librarians with a Latte' Can Help!" *University Libraries: The University at Albany State University of New York Blog*, blog post by John Pardavila, posted on November 13, 2013, http://liblogs.albany.edu/ librarynews/2013/04/got_questions_got_research_anx.html.
17. Barbara I. Dewey, "The Embedded Librarian," *Resource Sharing & Information Networks* 17, nos. 1-2 (2004): 5–17. doi:10.1300/J121v17n01_02.
18. David Shumaker, "Who Let the Librarians Out? Embedded Librarianship and the Library Manager," *Reference & User Services Quarterly* 48, no. 3 (2009): 239–257.
19. David Shumaker, *The Embedded Librarian: Innovative Strategies for Taking Knowledge Where It's Needed* (Medford, NJ: Information Today, 2012).
20. Warren N. Jacobs, "Embedded Librarianship Is a Winning Proposition," *Education Libraries* 33, no. 2 (2010): 3–10.
21. Brian Vetruba, "Embedded Librarian: Meeting Users on Their Turf," Slideshare presentation, posted February 20, 2011, http://www.slideshare.net/bvetruba/embedded-librarian-meeting-users-on-their-turf.

22. "Embedded Librarian at SSDS for Winter 2014 Term," University of Alberta Student Success Centre Specialized Support and Disability Services, last modified November 13, 2013, http://www.ssds .ualberta.ca/en/News/2013/November/EmbeddedLibrarianatSSDS.aspx.

23. "Faculty-in-Residence: Taking Embedded Librarianship to a New Level," *College and University Libraries Division*, last modified November 28, 2013, http://culd.wordpress.com/2013/08/23/ faculty-in-residence-taking-embedded-librarianship-to-a-new-level.

24. Colleen Kenefick, "The Case for Embedded Hospital Librarianship," *Journal of Hospital Librarianship* 11, no. 2 (2011): 195–199. doi:10.1080/15323269.2011.558407.

25. "Medical Information Services," Bay Area Cancer Connections, last modified August 17, 2014, http:// bcconnections.org/our-services/understanding-cancer.

26. Colbe Galston, Elizabeth Kelsen Huber, Katherine Johnson, and Amy Long, "Community Reference: Making Libraries Indispensable in a New Way," *American Libraries*, last modified June 13, 2012, http://www.amer icanlibrariesmagazine.org/article/community-reference-making-libraries-indispensable-new-way.

27. Lynn A. Connaway, Timothy Dickey, and Marie L. Radford, "'If It Is Too Inconvenient, I'm Not Going After It.' Convenience as Critical Factor in Information-Seeking Behaviors," *Library and Information Science Research* 33, no. 3 (2011): 179–190. doi:10.1016/j.lisr.21010.12.002.

28. "QuestionPoint," OCLC, last modified November 26, 2013, http://oclc.org/questionpoint.en.html.

29. "Welcome to My Info Quest—Txt 4 Answers!" MyInfoQuest, last modified September 3, 2014, http:// www.myinfoquest.info.

30. Lili Luo and Emily Weak, "Texting 4 Answers: What Questions Do People Ask?" *Reference & User Services Quarterly* 51, no. 2 (2011): 133–142.

31. Ibid., 141.

32. *Virtually Embedded: The Librarian in an Online Environment*, ed. Elizabeth Leonard and Erin McCaffrey (Chicago, IL: American Library Association, 2014).

33. Amy R. Hofer and Karen Munro, "Embedding in the LMS: Faculty Evaluations of a Low-Touch Widget," in *Virtually Embedded: The Librarian in an Online Environment*, ed. Elizabeth Leonard and Erin McCaffrey (Chicago, IL: American Library Association, 2014), Kindle edition, location 4003.

34. Elizabeth Leonard and Erin McCaffrey, "MOOCs: Getting Involved," in *Virtually Embedded: The Librarian in an Online Environment*, ed. Elizabeth Leonard and Erin McCaffrey (Chicago, IL: American Library Association, 2014), Kindle edition, location 4921.

Michelle Holschuh Simmons

14

Organizing Information

TECHNICAL SERVICES

Sylvia D. Hall-Ellis

The technical services mission is to acquire, catalog, and process items for addition to the library or information center collection. The emergence of metadata schema and implementation of resource description and access (RDA) in early 2013 changed the technical services workplace environment and demands. In order to meet these expectations, technical services staff need to be familiar with basic and advanced cataloging, classification schemes, bibliographic utilities, electronic resources, Internet tools, integrated library systems, interoperability technologies, human–computer interactions, layered discovery tools, and the crosswalks needed to migrate data among schema. Technical services staff work collaboratively with public services staff (information professionals who work in reference and other public-facing areas). After completing this chapter, the reader should have an understanding of the technical services functions, the emergence of metadata schemas, and the importance of collaborative activities with public services staff.

The Process of Organizing Information

Human learning is based upon the ability to analyze and organize data, information, and knowledge. Organizing is a human activity that facilitates the ability to find things, locate information, and assemble and maintain a usable record of human endeavors. Information professionals organize information that is based on metadata and bibliographic data. Technical services staff construct, edit, and enhance descriptions of both tangible and electronic works and information. Patrons seek, identify, retrieve, and use these descriptions compiled in online public access catalogs (OPACs) and via the Internet during the discovery (also known as search) process. The user enters a query into the online public access catalog in order to find a specific title, works by a particular author, or materials about a subject.

Technical services personnel gather and organize data during the cataloging and metadata transcription

> "Organizing is a human activity that facilitates the ability to find things, locate information, and assemble and maintain a usable record of human endeavors."

processes. These data are entered into a standardized database framework (e.g., MARC, BIBFRAME, a metadata schema) and assembled to provide access points to information packages. Understanding search strategies that users employ during the information-seeking and discovery processes enables technical services staff to identify specific names, titles, subjects, keywords, and related data that will provide access to the surrogate or metadata record and retrieval of the item. Regardless of format, each resource goes through the process of description for the bibliographic universe in which all information is recorded. The goal is to provide personal and corporate body names, titles and subtitles, subjects, keywords, and other access points in all descriptions. The technical services team adds the surrogate records (i.e., metadata) for all print, electronic, and digital resources to the OPAC.

Who Benefits from Organized Information?

Information professionals rely on an organized collection of resources. Their familiarity and knowledge of a dynamic environment of print, electronic, and digital assets enables reference librarians to work with users during the information-seeking and discovery processes. Research and information-seeking experience developed through education and training prepares the reference librarians to use specialized materials and databases. They can navigate the structured arrangement of resources in the library or information center.

The traditional practice for a standardized arrangement of resources within the physical plant provides continuity for users and public services staff. While the locations of shelving and special collections differ, the basic categorization of resources is predictable among organizations. For example,

- Print items are customarily arranged according to the classification scheme (e.g., Library of Congress, Dewey Decimal, National Library of Medicine) in neat rows on utilitarian shelving.
- Specialized display racks and lower shelving for highlighted collections or children's materials can be found in strategic locations.
- Special collections, whether selected by topic or physical format, can be found in rooms, alcoves, or sections of shelving.
- Fiction collections are filed alphabetically by the author's surname; subgroupings by genre (e.g., science fiction, mystery, westerns) can be found adjacent to the general fiction collection.

The customary physical location of print materials provides a method for the information organization to make available all types of resources to its users. Specialized shelving or display racks accommodate particular formats (e.g., DVDs, CDs). Information professionals

- organize items within collections to determine the works contained within information packages or parts of them;
- assemble information packages into collections in libraries, archives, museums, Internet files, and depositories;
- produce lists of information packages prepared according to standard citation rules;
- construct data elements for access to information packages; and
- provide the means of locating an item.

The uses of bibliographic data and metadata vary among different types of information organizations. See table 14.1, "Bibliographic Data and Metadata by Type of Information Organization."

Sylvia D. Hall-Ellis

Table 14.1. Bibliographic Data and Metadata by Type of Information Organization

Users and Public Services Professionals	Archivists	Museum Staff
• create robust cataloging records • determine shelving arrangement and organization • deliver reference and information discovery services • load and maintain accurate and high-quality data in integrated library systems • connect with the Internet for resource sharing and access to geographically remote information organizations	• describe unique items • arrange and describe groups of assets • convey the provenance for specific items • preserve the original order within a collection • create an accession record • build finding aids • maintain catalog records	• describe visual materials • create accession records for purchases, gifts, and loans • build a registration file • convey the provenance for items within the collection • provide subject analysis to specific collections and unique items • interpret discrete objects • maintain local terminology, references, and organization

Meeting Patrons' Needs through Public Services and Technical Services Partnerships

The symbiotic partnership between public services and technical services serves as the critical convergence of the skills, competencies, and services that information organizations offer. Public services, which include reference staff, work with users, building their knowledge, technical skills, and competencies. Technical services staff work in nonpublic areas to order, acquire, catalog, and process resources for the organization's collection. It is helpful for technical services staff to understand the information-seeking behaviors and search strategies that public services staff and users follow because this enables the catalogers and metadata specialists to enrich bibliographic data and increase access points to meet local users' demands.

Information professionals may share responsibilities for discovery and reference in information centers of all types and sizes. Teams of reference librarians, in consultation with technical services colleagues, may select materials. When technical services staff work with users and query the OPAC to identify resources, these experiences bring into focus the importance of accuracy to enable quick and appropriate discovery of resources and help reference librarians identify deficiencies and shortcomings in the catalog. Both public and technical services staff can use these experiences to discuss challenges and formulate appropriate strategies to resolve them. Technical services staff have opportunities to share perspectives related to cataloging, classifying, and arranging items in the collection with their reference services colleagues, and this can lead to improved experiences for users. Understanding the ways in which the online catalog

> "Technical services staff have opportunities to share perspectives related to cataloging, classifying, and arranging items in the collection with their reference services colleagues, and this can lead to improved experiences for users."

TEXTBOX 14.1

Topic for Discussion

What is the role of bibliographic and metadata records in the information discovery process?

is queried and resources are retrieved can be used to modify or increase access points. Improving the accuracy of the search, query, and retrieval process results in a higher level of satisfaction for information professionals and users. Gaining an appreciation for the work that colleagues do contributes to the organizational goal to serve users and respond to their information needs.

Technical Services: Inside the Backroom in the Library

The majority of work that technical services staff do happens out of public view. A technical services department focuses efforts on the ordering, purchasing, receiving, cataloging, classifying, and processing of new and selected donations for the collection. Materials may include print, electronic, and digital resources in a variety of languages for a diverse group of users. The technical services team includes paraprofessionals and professional staff. The work is typically divided into one or more of these functions: acquisitions, cataloging, processing, and database maintenance and authority control.

> "The majority of work that technical services staff do happens out of public view. A technical services department focuses efforts on the ordering, purchasing, receiving, cataloging, classifying, and processing of new and selected donations for the collection."

Acquisitions

Information professionals build and maintain collections by purchasing and licensing information resources. They learn about information resources that they may want to select for their information organization's collection by reading announcements, publishers' catalogs, and reviews about newly published resources in a variety of formats and languages. In addition to acquiring new information resources, the acquisitions process is also used to purchase replacements for missing or damaged items and additional copies of high-demand resources. Materials may be purchased at a significant discount from a jobber or wholesaler specializing in the sale of items to libraries, information organizations, and bookstores. Jobbers offer deep discounts, online ordering, expedited delivery, and cataloging services. Major jobbers include Baker & Taylor,[1] Yankee Book Peddlar,[2] Ingram Content Group,[3] and Follett Titlewave.[4]

Selected electronic resources (e.g., databases, e-books) are not offered for sale but rather can be acquired under a licensing agreement (see also chapter 32, "Information Licensing"). A member of the acquisitions staff originates a purchase requisition that is reviewed by the legal advisors for the organization. At the conclusion of this purchasing process, a license for a defined period of time and user group is acquired. Licensed content is not owned by the information organization—the publisher or creator retains ownership—and the license must be renewed at the end of the contract or else the licensed content is no longer available to the information organization.

Cataloging and Metadata Creation

Cataloging and metadata creation is a three-step process: preparation of a descriptive bibliographic record, assignment of subject headings, and classification.

STEP 1: PREPARATION OF A DESCRIPTIVE BIBLIOGRAPHIC RECORD

The first step is the preparation of a descriptive bibliographic record. Each resource in the collection is represented by a machine-readable record (also called a surrogate record). If the bibliographic records will be added to the online public access catalog, they are prepared according to the MAchine-Readable Cataloging (MARC) standard.[5] The majority of printed materials, databases, and electronic resources are cataloged and described using internationally adopted rules and conventions. Currently,

Sylvia D. Hall-Ellis

legacy resources have been cataloged using the *Anglo-American Cataloging Rules*.[6] New resources are described according to the rules in *RDA: Resource Description and Access*[7] (also called *RDA*), which was adopted in March 2013.

The technical services department may subscribe to a bibliographic utility (such as OCLC, Bibliofile, or Sky River) to obtain MARC bibliographic records. If a paraprofessional staff member searches the database and locates a bibliographic record with correct data, subject headings, and a classification number, the individual may select the record and add it to the online catalog. This process is called copy cataloging. Because a significant number of new titles can be found in bibliographic utilities, many libraries and information centers use this process to control costs and move items through technical services quickly and efficiently. When an item cannot be located in a bibliographic database, an original bibliographic record will need to be prepared by a cataloger.

Printed resources and digital assets in special collections may be cataloged and described in a non-MARC metadata schema. The variety and number of metadata schemas available for use in special libraries, collections, libraries, and information organizations continue to grow.[8] Libraries and information centers adopted metadata schemas to meet the needs of describing special collections, archives, digitized materials, and resources that were "born digital." The proliferation of digitization projects resulted in growing popularity of several metadata schemas. The most popular metadata schemas used by historical societies, special collections, archives, and libraries include Dublin Core, EAD, MODS, ContentDM, and METS.[9]

> "The most popular metadata schemas used by historical societies, special collections, archives, and libraries include Dublin Core, EAD, MODS, ContentDM, and METS."

STEP 2: ASSIGNMENT OF SUBJECT HEADINGS

The second step in the process is the assignment of subject headings. Subject analysis is the process of discerning the concepts addressed in a document as a precursor to assigning subject headings and index terms for efficient retrieval. Catalogers use standardized lists of precoordinated subjects like the Library of Congress Subject Headings[10] to facilitate access to items in the collection that pertain to a particular subject. These subject headings are predefined and lead the user from broad to specific topics through the addition of subdivisions. This standardized list can be supplemented through the addition of subject headings of local interest or that represent a genre or type of material. The standardized list includes topical, geographical, and chronological subject headings. The use of hyperlinked and faceted subjects in online public access catalogs is designed as a less expensive way to search and features postcoordinated headings. The user determines which topical subject terms to enter or coordinate.

STEP 3: CLASSIFICATION

Classification is the third step in the process. Each nonfiction item in the collection is associated with a subject that is represented by the classification number and places the item into a given hierarchy. The assignment of a notation associates the item with the proper level of the hierarchy. Libraries and information centers may choose to follow one of the following three popular classification schemes:

- *Library of Congress Classification Scheme:* Adopted by many academic, special, and large public libraries and information centers.[11]
- *Dewey Decimal Classification:* Devised by Melvil Dewey in the nineteenth century; it has been adopted by school and public libraries and selected information centers.[12]
- *National Library of Medicine Classification Scheme:* Adopted for classifying medical collections.[13]

Processing

After items pass through the cataloging and metadata creation process, they are processed and made ready for shelving or housing. Labels are generated and affixed to the item, packaging, or container. The item will be bar-coded, and this unique identifier will be linked to the bibliographic record in the OPAC. Book trucks or boxes are filled with the new, shelf-ready resources and delivered to the public services or circulation staff for shelving or displays.

Technical services staff may elect to purchase print or electronic precataloged materials. Each item arrives from the supplier with an accompanying machine-readable record, a spine label, and information for checkout. The technical services staff can quickly verify the order, properly stamp the item, attach a barcode, and load the record into the OPAC.

Selected organizations may elect to use an automated materials handling process. These systems significantly reduce the need for human intervention to check in, sort, check out, or move materials. Materials move through technical services on a conveyor belt so that the barcode can be read by a scanner and directed to the appropriate location. Elaborate automated materials handling systems may include chutes, bins, sorters, stackers, and unstackers. Users may use an automated station for checking in and checking out materials.

Database Maintenance and Authority Control

Database maintenance and authority control tasks are the responsibility of the technical services department. Staff strive to maintain the highest-quality bibliographic database that contains authenticated headings for access points and is free of errors or problems that impede retrieval. Each work is represented by a single bibliographic record for distinct formats; holdings are attached for each item. The database contains comprehensive bibliographic records, which contain standardized numbers (e.g., OCLC control number, Library of Congress control number, publisher's number). These standardized numbers are valuable for the ability to search for an exact match that can be used for ordering, updating, and maintaining database quality and integrity.

The staff makes reasonable efforts to update the database so that it reflects additional copies, new locations, added volumes, location transfers, withdrawals, duplicates, and notations of materials in storage or considered for transfer to a shared off-site storage facility or repository. When an information organization withdraws an item from the collection, technical staff personnel delete the holdings records and the bibliographic records if no copies remain.

TEXTBOX 14.2

Topic for Discussion

Why do libraries and information centers organize their collections?

The Process of Collection Building and Management

The collection development plan typically includes policies to guide material selection, the replacement of worn or lost materials, weeding, planning for expanded collections, and cooperative decision making based on agreements with other sister organizations or consortia (see also chapter 25, "Managing Collections"). Information professionals consider reviews of new print and electronic publications, suggestions from colleagues in the organization, and requests from members of the user community. A team of information professionals compiles the suggestions for purchase, reviews current resources in the collection, and anticipates user demands. After careful evaluation of the suggestions and the collection development plan and a review of the acquisition budget available, decisions are made. Purchasing the selected items becomes the responsibility of the technical services department.

Sylvia D. Hall-Ellis

When shipments of new resources arrive, the acquisitions staff receives the items, verifies the accurate receipt of materials, makes claims for missing or damaged items, and authorizes payments.

Building Information Collections

The acquisitions staff serves as the intermediary between the collection development team and the catalogers. Charged with the mission to acquire resources for the library or information center at the lowest costs, the acquisition staff seeks to acquire print, electronic, and other materials efficiently and quickly while maintaining a high degree of accuracy. The acquisitions staff develops and maintains cordial working relationships with departments in the organization, suppliers, and vendors. In order to purchase the array of materials required to build, enrich, and maintain the collection, the acquisitions staff use several strategies. Materials are acquired for the legacy print collection, online resources, and digital assets.

LEGACY PRINT COLLECTIONS

Legacy print collections may be purchased, selected through approval plans, accessed through rental agreements, or procured by other means. Works for the legacy print collection that are identified specifically by title are typically purchased directly from a jobber or subscription agency. Items in specific categories can be acquired through standing-order plans (e.g., annual volumes of a particular series or set). Approval plans provide new titles in specific subject areas that are sent automatically to the acquisitions department for review. After a hands-on examination by the collection development team, titles are purchased or returned. The acquisitions staff may use blanket orders through a contract with a publisher or vendor that guarantees the purchase of everything available on one or more topics. A small group of short-term, high-demand titles (e.g., *New York Times Best Seller List*) can be rented or leased. These items can be purchased or returned at the end of the contract period. The acquisitions staff may accept and examine gifts or donations from individuals. Items given to the organization that are not selected for addition to the collection may be exchanged or donated to another library or information center.

ONLINE RESOURCES

Online resources may be purchased, leased, or obtained through a subscription. Online resources are leased through contracts for a specified number of users for a stated period of time. Leases are commonly used to acquire databases, current and back files of journals, and web-based materials. The library or information center pays for access to the electronic resource but does not have ownership. Subscriptions are used to purchase journals, newspapers, or other serials. The acquisitions staff uses a contract with a subscription agency, vendor, or publisher to receive copies of printed and electronic issues as they are published. Subscriptions run for one or more years and must be renewed in order to have continued access to the journal or database.

DIGITAL ASSETS

Digital assets include the purchase of resources and artifacts that have been digitized. Cultural heritage resources can be grouped in three categories: textual content (digital assets), images (media assets), and multimedia (media assets). Textual content is derived from documents and publications that were originally written or published as printed materials. Media assets include images originally published in printed form and digitized or those created using computer graphics, a video game, or visual effect. Libraries and information centers include digitized photographs, maps, and other images in digital asset collections.

Collection Management

Collection management involves technical services personnel in the following three activities: weeding, binding and repair, and preparing items for transfer to remote facilities. Each of these time-consuming tasks requires specialized knowledge and skills. The carrying out and completion of these tasks may impact the bibliographic metadata records and holdings information that represent the collection.

WEEDING

Weeding is an ongoing process that occurs as part of collection development. Users expect to see a current, well-maintained, and useful collection. The public service and technical services staffs need to work together so that this goal is achieved. Based on their experience and subject expertise, public service professionals work in assigned collection areas and review the available resources. They make decisions about the currency and condition of items as well as recommend titles for updating, replacing, and withdrawing from the collection. Items that are worn or in poor physical condition may be replaced if demand warrants or replaced with more recent publications or new editions. This ongoing process is reflected in the catalog so that users and public services staff can search confidently for specific resources and subject materials and know that the library or information center owns and can supply the desired items. Withdrawn materials are handled in accordance with a routine process of removing ownership marks and discarding.

BINDING AND REPAIR

The technical services staff may identify specific items for binding and repair. These practices are used to repair damage so that the affected volume can be retained. Rebinding is customarily done by specialty firms hired through contract. Decisions to rebind items are made if a replacement copy cannot be acquired and the public service staff determines that keeping the work in the collection merits the investment of time and expense. Print copies of journals are frequently bound into annual volumes for ease of retrieval and shelving.

PREPARING ITEMS FOR TRANSFER

Collections can grow to exceed the physical space in the information organization. Rather than reduce the collection size, sometimes staff work to identify potential remote facilities that are either owned by the information organization or shared by consortia. When part of a consortium, staffing and operation costs for the remote storage facility are shared by the participating institutions. State-of-the-art storage and high-density facilities are temperature and humidity controlled and feature thousands of shelf feet of compact storage.

Remote facilities are not set up for visits from the public. Materials are received and sorted according to size rather than classification number or location designation. Items in a remote storage facility remain the property of the information organization that sent them and agree to share them with other participants through resource-sharing agreements. Users can identify needed resources and request that they be sent to the owning institution for checkout. Following use by a patron in an information organization, the item is returned to the remote storage facility.

Serials Processing

Serials are available in print and electronically. Describing magazines and journals requires that the bibliographic data reflect holdings in print and electronically. Casual readers of magazines frequently

Sylvia D. Hall-Ellis

visit a local library or information center to browse recent issues of their favorite titles. Users may seek specific articles for research or specific queries. The format in which the article is delivered to the user may not be significant. Consequently, libraries and information centers participate in local, regional, and national resource-sharing networks, which enable interlibrary loan personnel to request articles that will be delivered electronically to the user as an e-mail attachment.

There are two general types of serials that technical services staff handle: magazines/journals and hardcover collections. Magazines and journals are described in the OPAC, frequently with links to the electronic databases in which they are available. Access through the subscription customarily requires entering a user name or card number. Hardcover volumes that are published regularly or irregularly as serials are described so that users can discover them in the catalog and locate them within the collection. Determining whether to treat monographic serials as individual volumes or as sets requires discussion with the public services staff. Decisions are made on a case-by-case basis. Regardless of the decision, the technical services staff orders, catalogs, and processes each item for the collection.

Online Public Access Catalog—A Unique Resource

The online public access catalog (OPAC) is the most unique and valuable resource in the information organization.[14] Built over decades through the addition of bibliographic records that represent the legacy and print collections, the OPAC of the twenty-first century also includes metadata for electronic resources and digital cultural heritage assets. With the adoption of *RDA*, catalogers and metadata specialists determined that enhancing bibliographic records to conform to the new rules was not practical without machine intervention and data manipulation. Therefore, the materials that had been cataloged according to *AACR2* were retained, and these older records were termed the "legacy collection."

Initially built through the transcription of bibliographic data from paper catalog cards into an online system, early OPACs had limited searching and retrieval capabilities. A significant number of information organizations designed and assembled their own OPACs to save investment costs. By the 1980s, commercial integrated library systems (ILSs) were available. Early ILSs focused on circulation functions, and developers quickly expanded them to include basic bibliographic data. New capabilities included more sophisticated searching, the use of Boolean operators and keywords, placement of items on hold, and the preparation of overdue notices and fine calculations. Boolean operators enabled users to combine or exclude terms through the use of "and," "or," and "not" when searching databases. By the 1990s, the desire to incorporate sophisticated search engines similar to those found on the Internet prompted system developers to enhance OPACs.

OPACs were the initial search engines that a large portion of users used. As users became more sophisticated, they demanded that OPACs provide newer next-generation catalogs. These ILSs featured more sophisticated search technologies reflecting intuitive relationships (such as ProQuest's AquaBrowser[15]), relevancy ranking, and limited faceted searching. The user interfaces reflected an understanding of human–computer interactions and demands for increased customization of the ILS. As search engines for the Internet became more powerful, users wanted and expected OPACs to work in a similar manner.[16] The use of icons became popular as a strategy to differentiate different formats for the same work. Libraries and information centers added social media portals (such as Facebook and Twitter) and collaborative software (such as chats and instant messaging) to their websites.

The contemporary generation of library catalogs allow for the synchronization of data between traditional ILSs and new catalog systems built by enterprise search companies and open source projects. These emerging systems may also be organization led to maximize customization and control development and investment costs.

The online catalog supports public service and technical services functions. Public service functions include resource discovery and access, the creation of bibliographies, finding aids, special collections, and resource sharing among consortia. Technical service functions include original and copy cataloging, sharing bibliographic data within a cooperative, authority control, comprehensive inventory to determine lost or missing items, the status of items in circulation or on order, and the creation of metadata in non-MARC schemas for special collection.

Conclusion

Technical services personnel work behind the public scenes to acquire, organize, describe, and prepare print, electronic, and digital resources for the information organization of which it is a part. The goal of the technical services department is to create and maintain organization of resources with authenticated, standardized access points for rapid, efficient discovery to locate materials and answer information queries. Known historically as the creators of bibliographic data and guardians of resources, technical services staff dedicate their efforts to support their public service colleagues who work with users seeking answers to topical questions and help them locate specific titles and resources.

Notes

1. "Home," Baker & Taylor: The Future Delivered, last modified September 19, 2014, http://www.baker-taylor.com.
2. "Home," YBP Library Services, last modified July 4, 2014, http://www.ybp.com.
3. "Home," Ingram, last modified September 22, 2014, http://www.ingramcontent.com/pages/home.aspx.
4. "Follett Titlewave," Titlewave, last modified March 29, 2013, https://www.titlewave.com/login.
5. "MARC Documentation," Library of Congress, last modified July 17, 2014, http://www.loc.gov/marc/marcdocz.html.
6. American Library Association, *Anglo-American Cataloging Rules*, 2nd ed. (Chicago, IL: American Library Association, 2009).
7. American Library Association, *RDA: Resource Description and Access* (Chicago, IL: American Library Association, 2013).
8. "Guide: Putting Things in Order; A Directory of Metadata Schemas and Related Standards," JISC Digital Media, last modified July 14, 2014, http://www.jiscdigitalmedia.ac.uk/guide/putting-things-in-order-links-to-metadata-schemas-and-related-standards.
9. Sylvia D. Hall-Ellis, "Metadata Competencies for Entry-Level Positions: What Employers Expect as Reflected in Position Descriptions, 2000–2013," *Journal of Library Metadata* (in press).
10. "Library of Congress Subject Headings PDF Files," Library of Congress, last modified August 20, 2014, http://www.loc.gov/aba/publications/FreeLCSH/freelcsh.html.
11. "Library of Congress Classification," Library of Congress, last modified July 24, 2014, http://www.loc.gov/catdir/cpso/lcc.html.
12. Melvil Dewey, *A Classification and Subject Index for Cataloging and Arranging the Books and Pamphlets in the Library (Dewey Decimal Classification)*, facsimile, Project Gutenberg, http://www.gutenberg.org/files/12513/12513-h/12513-h.htm.
13. "NLM Classification 2014," NLM NIH, last modified July 7, 2014, http://www.nlm.nih.gov/class.
14. Lorcan Dempsey, *Thirteen Ways of Looking at Libraries, Discovery, and the Catalog: Scale, Workflow, Attention*, last modified December 10, 2012, http://www.educause.edu/ero/article/thirteen-ways-looking-libraries-discovery-and-catalog-scale-workflow-attention.
15. "AquaBrowser," ProQuest, n.d., http://www.proquest.com/products-services/AquaBrowser.html.
16. Mary O'Kelly and Colleen Lyon, "Google Like a Librarian: Sharing Skills for Search Success," *College and Research Libraries News*, http://crln.acrl.org/content/72/6/330.full.

15

Accessing Information Anywhere and Anytime

ACCESS SERVICES

Michael J. Krasulski

Access services is the administrative umbrella under which the circulation, reserves, interlibrary loan, stacks maintenance, and related functions typically reside within an information organization.[1] See appendix 15.1, "Access Services Functions and Tasks." These often unseen or unnoticed functions are central to an information organization's daily operations, yet the grouping of them together into one administrative unit is a relatively recent innovation. The exact impetus for the creation of access services departments is unclear. The best evidence suggests that a departmental grouping centered on circulation functions grew out of the mid-1970s Association of Research Libraries (ARL) Library Management Review and Analysis Program.[2] The first known advertisement for the position to lead an access services department appeared in 1977.[3] The creation of access services placed "more emphasis on the user as a consumer of information who needs access to information in a variety of formats."[4] The implications are that access services can help facilitate access to materials users need in a timely matter regardless of the source. After completing this chapter, the reader should have an understanding of the basic concepts of access services.

The Disparate Parts of Access Services

Access services is a sum of many disparate parts, and its encompassed operations impact every user of the information organization. As James Neal, vice president for information services and university librarian, Columbia University, remarked,

> Access services opens the library in the morning and secures it at night. It serves as our essential link to campus operations, like building maintenance, security, and food services. It oversees the quality and usability of library space. It manages our physical collections. . . . It circulates materials and technologies and supports the special facilities for distinctive formats, for group and class use. . . . It supports teaching and learning through traditional and electronic reserves, enabling a strong presence for libraries in course management systems and online education. It is the front line of our consortial relationships, managing an expanding array of regional, national and global interlibrary loan and document delivery services that support quality scholarship. It is the early

warning system for building environmental issues and collection preservation and damage problems. It is the gatekeeper for the authorization and authentication of library users to the vast array of electronic resources we have leased and acquired. Access services is essential, fundamental, and pervasive.[5]

The functions that Neal enumerates above are indeed essential to, fundamental to, and pervasive within the information organization, although the full impact of access services may not always be present on the organizational chart. Absence of an access services department does not signal the absence of access services functions from the information organization. Rather, access services functions can be diffused administratively across and throughout the organizational structure. Regardless of the label on an organizational chart, the various functions described in this chapter can be found in the vast majority of information organizations regardless of type.

"The fluidity of access services means being all things to everyone."

For those organizations that have access services departments, the organization of these departments says more about the needs of the parent organization than about larger access services trends in the information profession. In some ways, it is best to think about access services as "circulation-plus" since access services can appear to assume the persona of a refuge for services and functions that do not fall clearly under any other category.[6] This is an important point to remember for those who seek careers in access services—the fluidity of access services means being all things to everyone. For simplicity's sake, this chapter will explore the circulation, stacks maintenance, interlibrary loan (ILL), reserves, and building management functions that are most typical in access services departments and how these functions contribute to the success of the information organization.[7]

TEXTBOX 15.1

Topic for Discussion

Why does the access services area often assume the persona of "all things to all people"?

Circulation

Circulation, or more precisely the circulation desk, and access services are often used interchangeably. Circulation fulfills the dual role of facilitating the access to physical items between the information organization and the user and of being able to identify the location of any item in the physical collection at all times. These dual roles are administered through the information organization's integrated library system (ILS). The ILS has different modules to handle various functions (e.g., acquisitions, cataloging). The circulation module tracks what items have been loaned out, to whom, and when those items are due back, as well as the location of items within the building. Additionally, the ILS can manage fines, renewals, and simple communications to users concerning overdue and recalled material via e-mail or short message service (SMS). The ILS is not just for managing traditional book and journal collections. Information organizations that circulate e-reading devices, laptops, audiovisual materials, and even Wi-Fi hotspots can track these materials in the ILS.[8] Each information organization has its own, potentially complex loan rules and policies that govern who can borrow what and for how long. The ILS takes the guesswork out of managing, administering, and remembering these rules and policies since the ILS is customizable to handle such institutional variability. The ILS also demonstrates the interdependency of access services with other departments within the information organization. For example, cataloging and acquisitions, often labeled together as technical services, process materials into the ILS, and the systems department administers the ILS.

Michael J. Krasulski

In many information organizations, the circulation desk is located at or near the main entry/exit point. Consequently, the access services department—and the circulation desk in particular—is the first, and often only, point of contact between the majority of users and the organization.[9] To state this reality another way, the circulation desk *is* the information organization's original user interface. It is here that perceptions about the information organization are formed. Consider the variety of interactions at any circulation desk in any information organization on a given day. There is the potential for an interaction to go wrong—for a negative situation to arise. Such situations may be the result of a serious user infraction, like theft or mutilation of organizational property. Others are more benign, like enforcing fine policies. It is imperative for access services staff to be trained in creating a positive user experience. Negative user interactions reflect poorly on the information organization. As corporations have learned in our digitally connected age, negative customer interactions can become viral thanks to various Web 2.0 technologies such as blogging, Twitter, and Facebook. Experiences with access services staff often shape how users view the organization.

"Even though the circulation desk is the original information organization user interface, the increased availability of electronic resources and the decline in book circulation have led many organizations to rethink the role of the circulation desk."

Even though the circulation desk is the original information organization user interface, the increased availability of electronic resources and the decline in book circulation have led many organizations to rethink the role of the circulation desk. There has been a movement toward one-stop shopping, particularly in information organizations connected to colleges and universities, by combining the circulation desk with the reference or information desk. The goals are to eliminate patron confusion, streamline service, and free staff to do other things. Streamlining service and freeing staff to do other things have been reasons for organizations to add self-check terminals at circulation desks, a change that can also improve service. These terminals allow users to check out materials without, or with little, staff involvement. However, no system is foolproof; errors may occur, and staff intervention may be needed. Thus, self-check machines are typically placed in close proximity to the circulation desk. While technologies, such as the ILS and self-check, have drastically changed how a circulation department operates, what has remained the same is the need for outstanding user interactions—whether that interaction is in person, over the telephone, or online. See table 15.1, "Keys to a Successful Circulation Operation." Simply put, a successful circulation operation is one where the organization's collection is accounted for, the organization's circulation records are in good order, and a positive user experience is provided.

Table 15.1. Keys to a Successful Circulation Operation[1]

Successful Circulation
Collection is accounted for.
Circulation records are in good order.
Positive user experience is provided.

1. Michael J. Krasulski, "'Where Do They Come From, and How Are They Trained?': Professional Education and Training of Access Services Librarians in Academic Libraries," *Journal of Access Services* 11, no. 1 (2013): 22-23.

Stacks Maintenance

The storage, retrieval, and maintenance of the organization's physical collections, also known as stacks maintenance, is a vital access services function. Depending upon the organization, stacks maintenance functions may fall to volunteers, student workers, or paraprofessional staff. Regardless of the type of employee designated to do shelving work, there are three key functions in this area:

- shelving returned items or new items added to the collection;
- checking, from time to time, the items on the shelves to ensure that items are shelved properly, often referred to as shelf-reading; and
- adjusting items already on the shelves to accommodate changes in collection size, often referred to as shifting.

Recent Innovations in Stacks Management

Physical collections take up valuable space within the information organization. The decline of book circulation and the call to repurpose space for other uses have given rise to various storage techniques for the collections that do remain. Three common techniques are compact shelving, remote storage, and automated storage and retrieval systems (ASRSs).

COMPACT SHELVING

Compact shelving is a slight change from traditional shelving in that the space between the shelving units is largely eliminated. Think about having the entire book stacks compressed together and then having the ability to open a section of stacks to retrieve a needed book or journal. That is essentially how compact shelving works. Users still go to the shelves, call number in hand, and retrieve the item. However, instead of walking into the stacks, the users will operate a manual or automatic shelving system to open up the exact area where the needed item is located.

REMOTE STORAGE

Remote storage, as the term suggests, is the removal of physical collections to a site located away from the information organization's facility. Users locate items in the catalog, request them, and then have those items delivered to a service point, likely the circulation desk, for pickup. Remote storage meets the goal of opening space for other purposes; however, users lose the ability to browse the shelves and may experience a delay between the placement of the request and the delivery of the item.[10]

AUTOMATED STORAGE AND RETRIEVAL SYSTEMS (ASRSs)

The recent introduction of ASRSs has brought a technological solution to the shelving and housing of physical collections. The first installation of such a system was at California State University, Northridge. The James B. Hunt Library at North Carolina State University is another example; it opened in January 2013 to much excitement. Because the building was designed to have more open and collaborative study and work space, the book stacks are largely removed and out of sight. Items are kept in a high-density storage facility within the library and retrieved using bookBot. BookBot is a robotic, automated book delivery system. Users select the item they wish to use in the online catalog, and within minutes, the item is available for pickup near the library's entrance. The online catalog permits virtual browsing so that users can view like items that would be on the shelves around the item requested. The remaining bound journal collection also utilizes the bookBot system. Users can place a request for an article, and the article will be delivered by e-mail in about twenty-four hours. ASRS technology allows the Hunt Library collection to take up about one-ninth the space it would if the same items were stored on traditional shelves.[11] Another notable example of ASRS technology at work can be found at the Joe and Rika Mansueto Library at the University of Chicago.

Interlibrary Loan (ILL)

ILL is the process that supplies users with materials not readily available at their own institution. A user places a request for a desired item. If the item is owned by another information organization, a request to borrow the item is sent; when the item is received, it is checked out to the patron for a loan period determined by the lending organization. ILL complements materials owned by the information organization since the information needs of users are enhanced by the ability to obtain items outside those in their local collections. Increasingly, users are also allowed to request items that are owned in their local collections but that are otherwise unavailable. This allows multiple users to research the same topic without competing for resources.[12]

> "ILL complements materials owned by the information organization since the information needs of users are enhanced by the ability to obtain items outside those in their local collections."

ILL requires a significant investment on the part of the information organization in both human and financial resources. Staff intervention is often required to locate desired items. Additionally, the arranging, tracking, and managing of requests can be labor intensive, and most large information organizations invest in an ILL management system to administer these tasks. Shipping costs, fees to acquire items, and fees for lost or overdue items are often absorbed by the information organization.

Declining book circulation may lead one to conclude that ILL is also in decline. Yet, paradoxically, it is not. For example, in academic information organizations, book circulation has declined since the mid-1990s, while interlibrary loan usage simultaneously has skyrocketed. The reason for this paradox rests in the fact that users want to use the information organization and its services, but not necessarily the materials provided for them on the shelves, often thanks to users finding obscure citations through Internet searches. Additionally, advances in ILL processing have often reduced ILL turnaround time from days to mere hours.

Reserves

ILL services are available in any information organization, while reserves tend to be prevalent in college and university settings. Reserves can be either physical objects available at a service desk (traditional reserves) or digital resources available remotely, typically through a password-protected portal (e-reserves). Traditional reserves require access services staff to purchase new or retrieve already owned materials from the stacks at the request of faculty members and to place them in a restricted area, often behind a service desk. The materials are added to the faculty members' course listing, and students can retrieve the items at the information organization. The loan period is generally short, typically no more than a few hours, and often accompanied by the threat of high late fees to ensure prompt return. Formats can include books, journal articles, videos, CDs, DVDs, and, at the author's institution, even anatomical models. Reserves can also facilitate the academic information organization's laptop and e-reader or other nontraditional-format lending programs (should such programs be locally available). Placing materials on reserve provides an ideal solution to the problem of managing materials in high demand. The service allows users equal access to the same materials.

TEXTBOX 15.2

Topic for Discussion

How can reserves and interlibrary loan (ILL) violate copyright law?

Since the late 1990s, academic libraries have focused their efforts on providing remote access to reserve materials in digital form. In terms of process, electronic reserves differ considerably from print reserves. Professors still identify library materials (or provide their own) to be placed on reserve, but instead of photocopying those materials and housing them behind a service point, information organization staff make digital copies and place them on a server or similar storage device or link directly to e-resource holdings.[13] The materials are still associated with each professor's course listing; however, staff intervention is not necessary, as users can access the materials from anywhere online.

Building Management Functions

The role of access services as being all things to all people is perhaps best evidenced through its responsibility for building management functions (see also chapter 24, "Managing Facilities"). As the department that is present during all the operating hours of the information organization, access services often serves as the liaison between the information organization and the institution's facilities or physical plant department. Problems with the building are typically reported to access services staff first.[14] Additionally, access services staff can possess a unique perspective from their frontline service point and are able to oversee certain facility-related issues within an information organization operation—for example, 24/7 staffing and the creation of signage for effective way-finding.

Just as an information organization's electronic resources are available twenty-four hours a day, the demand for access to physical collections has resulted in many academic organizations remaining open for twenty-four hours for five, or in some cases seven, days a week. Providing twenty-four-hour access is no small undertaking. The barrier to providing such a service often comes down to staffing these overnight hours. Sometimes it is full-time access services staff, or the responsibility may fall to student assistants or students receiving work-study funding. If few or no services are provided in these wee hours, a member of the organization's security department may be utilized to provide adequate staffing. The solution chosen is, naturally, decided based on local conditions, including funding and building design considerations.[15]

The creation and subsequent revisions of signage for the organization can fall to access services. Responsibility for signage is a result of maintaining the signage at the ends of ranges of shelving units indicating the first and last call numbers of each row. Additionally, think about signage as a response to frequently asked questions. Clearly worded and well-placed signage can greatly reduce the number of directional questions received at service points and serve to communicate a welcoming and inclusive atmosphere.[16]

Michael J. Krasulski

Assessing Access Services

The above sections serve as an introduction to the various access services functions and illustrate ways that access services contribute to the success of the information organization. However, contributing to the success of the information organization is no longer enough to remain vital or essential since the continuing relevance of information organizations is being questioned as never before in many arenas (e.g., academia,

> "Every function or department in the information organization, access services included, must demonstrate and document their contributions in purposeful and meaningful ways."

local and state government). Every function or department in the information organization, access services included, must demonstrate and document their contributions in purposeful and meaningful ways. The process of systematically evaluating and demonstrating success and implementing improvement as needed is called assessment (see also chapter 28, "Demonstrating Value: Assessment"). As information organizations strive to become more user-centric, they are paying increasing attention to assessing user needs and designing services to meet those needs. Access services functions are often at the center of these assessment efforts. Additionally, academic organizations, for example, are being required to participate in formalized assessment efforts across their campuses since accrediting bodies mandate that institutions of higher learning organize, document, and sustain assessment activities in order to, as the Middle States Commission on Higher Education has instructed its member institutions, "[use] the results of those assessments to improve programs and services . . . with appropriate links to the institution's ongoing planning and resource allocations processes."[17]

The most basic assessment measure is documenting use—that is, how and to what extent the services and functions of the information organization are being used. Put simply, gauging use involves gathering usage totals from various functions over a period of time, typically a year, compiling these data in a chart or table, and then comparing them to the data from the previous period. Such data can be gathered in a variety of ways, including entrance and exit counts or lending and borrowing statistics from both circulation and ILL.

Gauging use and tracking such use over time are important; however, such data do not tell if users are satisfied with the services or quality of services provided. User satisfaction studies can answer such questions, and user satisfaction studies usually take the form of surveys. Information organizations may choose to develop their own survey instrument or elect to use a standardized survey. Each has its own advantages. An instrument developed in-house is certainly cheaper and can ask for very specific information germane to the information organization. While a standardized survey is more expensive, such tools have the advantage of allowing for benchmarking across organizations. The two major survey instruments available are LibQUAL+ and LibSat. LibQUAL was developed by ARL and asks respondents to rate the information organization on twenty-one different qualities that focus around quality of service, information access, and the information organization as place. Respondents are also asked to rate the minimum level of service they would expect versus the actual level received. ARL administers LibQUAL and provides initial analysis of the results for the information organization. LibSat was developed by Counting Opinions with public information organizations in mind. LibSat is a continuous survey tool that measures user satisfaction and expectations and the importance of those expectations to users. Regardless of which instrument is used, user satisfaction studies provide valuable data that cannot be extrapolated from usage statistics.[18]

Now that the data are collected, the information organization should close the assessment loop, that is, use the results to improve, change, or realign services. For example, knowing when users come to the building can be helpful in determining how much staffing is needed at a service point. Additionally, these data can be useful in setting appropriate service hours or in demonstrating the appropriateness of current levels of service, should there be a clamor for additional service. User satisfaction data may reveal that underused services need to be promoted more heavily or are no longer needed. The utilization of assessment data varies from one information organization to the next. If improvements are made, communicate those changes to the user. Let the user know he or she was heard.

Leading Access Services

Access services can be a stand-alone department or diffused across the organizational chart. Those tasked with leading access services may be paraprofessionals with significant experience or information professionals who have library and information science degrees. Generally speaking, a dedicated course in access services is not taught in ALA-accredited library and information science graduate programs, though aspects of access services may be covered elsewhere in the curriculum.[19] A recent study has shown that access services professionals typically learn the skills directly related to access services on the job.[20] That is not to suggest, however, that library and information science education has no role in the development of access services professionals.

The same study showed that higher-order managerial skills are equally important as access-services-specific skills to the success of the access services information professional. The overwhelming majority of respondents reported that the abilities to formulate policies, delegate responsibilities, determine priorities, supervise and evaluate staff, utilize existing resources effectively, and collect, calculate, and analyze statistics were important to the success of the access services professional.[21] Practitioners are likely to be exposed to these types of management and statistical skills during their library and information science educational experience.

Additionally, respondents were asked about their professional backgrounds in information organizations before becoming access services professionals. The study found no clear path to becoming an access services professional.[22] Some of the respondents began their careers in access services paraprofessional positions and then moved into more administrative roles, while others began in other areas of the information organization, typically in reference or technical services, and moved into access services after sharpening their administrative skills. Hands-on work experience and theoretical course work are equally important to the success of the access services practitioner.

Conclusion

Access services has moved well beyond the circulation desk to fill vital roles in the continued success of our information organizations by connecting users with resources. As Trevor A. Dawes and the author have argued, the present state of access services can be best summed up as "Like always, like never before," in the short-lived tag line to the mid-2000s Saturn automobile commercial—"like always" because access services retains its historical roots in circulation and stacks management, and "like never before" because access services continues to meld and change in response to technological and institutional changes.[23]

These types of changes will continue as the information organization continues to find its place in a twenty-first-century reality. However, there appear to be several clear trends in access services that are worth noting:

- Expect to see more coupling of information or reference desks and circulation desks into one service point. In those organizations that have coupled their service points, information professionals do not staff the desk but tend to be available for in-depth resource consultations.
- ILL will increase in importance while book circulation will continue to decline.
- Print reserves in academic information organizations will decline.
- Access services work will become more collaborative as staff will be trained to do a variety of access services tasks.
- Excellent customer service skills will remain paramount.[24]

Regardless of whether these predications prove correct, one can be assured that access services will continue to grow, change, and adapt to meet the needs of a robust twenty-first-century information organization, and it will continue to assume and subsume new responsibilities, sometimes finding itself in unfamiliar territory.

Appendix 15.1: Access Services Functions and Tasks

Function	Tasks
Circulation	Check in/check out materials
	Answer directional questions
	Process holds and renewals
	Administer overdue fines
	Provide superior customer service
Stacks Management	Sort and shelve materials
	Shift collections
	Shelf-read
	Provide superior customer service
Interlibrary Loan	Process ILL requests from users
	Process ILL requests from other libraries
	Monitor copyright issues
	Provide superior customer service
Reserves	Process reserve requests from faculty
	Check in/check out reserve materials
	Post e-reserves materials in locally available platform
	Instruct users in how to use reserves
	Provide superior customer service
Building Management	Liaise with facilities department or physical plant
	Liaise with security department
	Manage physical structure during all operating hours
	Maintain signage

Notes

1. Duane Wilson, "Reenvisioning Access Services: A Survey of Access Services Departments in ARL Libraries," *Journal of Access Services* 10, no. 3 (2013): 153.
2. Mary Anne Hansen, Jakob Harnest, Virginia Steel, Joan Ellen Stein, and Pat Weaver-Myers, "A Question and Answer Forum on the Origin, Evolution and Future of Access Services," *Journal of Access Services* 1, no. 1 (2003): 12.
3. Linda Frederiksen, "Access Services Librarians: A Content Analysis of Job Advertisements, 1977–2004," *Journal of Access Services* 3, no. 2 (2005): 15.
4. Hansen et al., "Question and Answer Forum," 10.

5. James Neal, "Foreword," in *Twenty-First-Century Access Services,* ed. Michael J. Krasulski and Trevor A. Dawes (Chicago, IL: Association of College and Research Libraries, 2013), vii.

6. Nora Dethloff and Paul Sharpe, "Access Services and the Success of the Academic Library," in Krasulski and Dawes, *Twenty-First-Century Access Services,* 174.

7. Bradley Tolppanen, "A Survey of Current Tasks and Future Trends in Access Services," *Journal of Access Services* 2, no. 3 (2004): 7–8.

8. Jenny Xie, "Two Major Public Library Systems Are About to Start Lending Wi-Fi Hotspots," CityLab, June 23, 2014, http://www.citylab.com/cityfixer/2014/06/two-major-public-library-systems-are-about-to-start-lending-wi-fi-hotspots/373233.

9. Pixey A. Mosley, "Assessing User Interactions at the Desk Nearest the Front Door," *Reference & User Services Quarterly* 47, no. 2 (2007): 160.

10. Jay Price, "NCSU's Hyper-Modern James B. Hunt Jr. Library Poised to Open," *News Observer,* December 18, 2012, http://www.newsobserver.com/2012/12/18/2553438/ncsus-hyper-modern-new-james-b.html.

11. Dethloff and Sharpe, "Access Services," 180–181.

12. Tolppanen, "A Survey of Current Tasks," 10.

13. Steven J. Bell and Michael J. Krasulski, "Electronic Reserves, Library Databases and Courseware: A Complementary Relationship," *Journal of Interlibrary Loan, Document Delivery, & Electronic Reserves* 15, no. 1 (2004): 85.

14. Stephanie Atkins Sharpe, "Access Services within Campus and Library Organizations," in Krasulski and Dawes, *Twenty-First-Century Access Services,* 129–130.

15. David W. Bottorff, Katherine Furlong, and David McCaslin, "Building Management Responsibilities for Access Services," in Krasulski and Dawes, *Twenty-First-Century Access Services,* 88–89.

16. Ibid., 90–91.

17. Middle States Commission on Higher Education, *Characteristics of Excellence in Higher Education* (Philadelphia: Middle States Commission on Higher Education, 2011), 25.

18. David K. Larsen, "Assessing and Benchmarking Access Services," in Krasulski and Dawes, *Twenty-First-Century Access Services,* 196–197.

19. David McCaslin, "Access Services Education in Library and Information Science Programs," *Journal of Access Services* 6, no. 4 (2009): 485.

20. Michael J. Krasulski, "'Where Do They Come From, and How Are They Trained?' Professional Education and Training of Access Services Librarians in Academic Libraries," *Journal of Access Services* 11, no. 1 (2014): 23.

21. Ibid., 21.

22. Ibid., 24.

23. Trevor A. Dawes and Michael J. Krasulski, "Conclusion," in Krasulski and Dawes, *Twenty-First-Century Access Services,* 243.

24. Ibid., 244–245.

16

Teaching Users

INFORMATION AND TECHNOLOGY LITERACY INSTRUCTION

April D. Cunningham and Stephanie Rosenblatt

One of an information professional's core roles is teaching information users. Information professionals not only make sure that users know how to get the most they can from the organization's collections, but also ensure that users develop effective information behaviors that apply in any environment. This chapter describes the development of information professionals' work as educators in various types of information organizations. It also argues for the continuing value of information and technology literacy in the twenty-first century. After completing this chapter, the reader should have an understanding of how information professionals entering the field can embrace their role as teachers and ensure that they achieve the goals of "new librarianship" by "facilitating knowledge creation in their communities."[1]

Definition of Information and Technology Literacy

In 1989, the American Library Association (ALA) formally defined information literacy as a person's ability "to recognize when information is needed and have the ability to locate, evaluate, and use effectively the needed information."[2]

This simple definition has been used by a number of organizations, such as the American Association of School Librarians (AASL),[3] the Association of College and Research Libraries (ACRL),[4] and the Public Library Association (PLA),[5] to define the skills and conceptual knowledge that information professionals should be teaching users at their institutions. Using this definition, these associations have developed sets of criteria used for planning and assessing the acquisition of information and technological literacy. These criteria, often presented as standards and performance objectives, and lately as threshold concepts, have informed the way information professionals have done their jobs, formalizing the information professional's teaching role and, more recently, adding an assessment component to the information professional's work.

Many organizations outside libraries have adopted the above definition of information literacy in order to legitimize their own conceptualizations of the intellectual skills needed by the populations they serve. Examples of these organizations include UNESCO,[6] the National Council of Teachers of English,[7] and the Association of American Colleges and Universities.[8]

Alternate Terms for Information Literacy Instruction
- User education
- Bibliographic instruction
- Library orientation
- Library instruction
- Information literacy instruction

Alternate Terms for Information Literacy
- Critical thinking
- Metaliteracy
- Information fluency

Alternate Term for Technology Literacy
- Digital literacy

The core concepts that define information literacy have largely remained constant, and there is evidence that information literacy was being taught in libraries for at least a century before ALA's definition was adopted.[9] However, the terms used to describe the ability to find and use information effectively have changed over time, as have the criteria used to identify the acquisition of this ability. These additional terms reflect growing concerns that citizens should be able to navigate and evaluate a wide range of resources both in and out of the library so that they are able to participate in today's information society by creating as well as consuming information (see also part IV, "Information Users: Engaging, Creating, and Collaborating via Technology"). These changes have also influenced how information professionals have tried to explain the concepts of information literacy to themselves and to outside groups.

Multiple parties, including a task force of the ACRL, have chafed at the limitations they see in the 1989 definition of information literacy and the instructional standards that followed and have begun devising different ways of conceptualizing the content and scope of what patrons should learn about finding and using information, especially in light of the read/write web, commonly referred to as Web 2.0. These concerns have produced documents such as the draft *Framework for Information Literacy for Higher Education*[10] and have sparked discussions about what information professionals should be teaching, resulting in information professionals coalescing around the term "critical information literacy."[11]

Critical information literacy recognizes that the practices/processes/intellectual products that define the academic information environment are politically and socially constructed, so they can be changed, questioned, and contravened. Instead of just socializing students into current academic discourse, the information professional should teach students to also question its underlying principles.[12]

Information and Technology Instruction in Various Settings

Libraries in the United States have traditionally garnered support by tapping into the belief that people have an unlimited capacity to improve themselves through self-education. In 1757, Benjamin Franklin describes the importance of social or subscription libraries to the birth of the new American republic:

> These libraries have improved the general conversation of Americans, made the common tradesmen and farmers as intelligent as most gentlemen from other countries, and perhaps have contributed to some degree to the stand so generally made through the colonies in defense of their privileges.[13]

While information professionals have been consistently recognized as coaches for adults engaged in independent self-study, partners in developing collections supporting formal educational institutions, and champions for youth and adult literacy, their role as formal instructors of information users did not begin to be widely documented until the beginning of the twentieth century (see figure 16.1).[14] Support for information professionals as formal instructors waxed and waned during the middle of the century. Public librarians largely began to retreat from this role—with the exception of continuing to provide literacy-related programming for children and adults.[15]

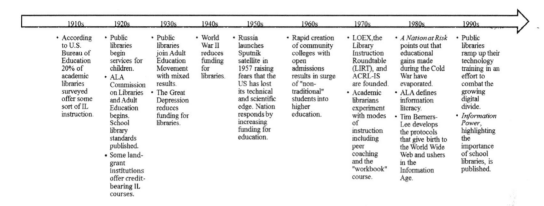

1910s	1920s	1930s	1940s	1950s	1960s	1970s	1980s	1990s
• According to U.S. Bureau of Education 20% of academic libraries surveyed offer some sort of IL instruction.	• Public libraries begin services for children. • ALA Commission on Libraries and Adult Education begins. School library standards published. • Some land-grant institutions offer credit-bearing IL courses.	• Public libraries join Adult Education Movement with mixed results. • The Great Depression reduces funding for libraries.	• World War II reduces funding for libraries.	• Russia launches Sputnik satellite in 1957 raising fears that the US has lost its technical and scientific edge. Nation responds by increasing funding for education.	• Rapid creation of community colleges with open admissions results in surge of "non-traditional" students into higher education.	• LOEX, the Library Instruction Roundtable (LIRT), and ACRL-IS are founded. • Academic librarians experiment with modes of instruction including peer coaching and the "workbook" course.	• *A Nation at Risk* points out that educational gains made during the Cold War have evaporated. • ALA defines information literacy. • Tim Berners-Lee develops the protocols that give birth to the World Wide Web and ushers in the Information Age.	• Public libraries ramp up their technology training in an effort to combat the growing digital divide. • *Information Power*, highlighting the importance of school libraries, is published.

Figure 16.1 Teaching Users in the Twentieth Century

In 1983, the National Commission on Excellence in Education report, *A Nation at Risk*, sounded the alarm about the tide of mediocrity flooding American education since the height of Cold War-era investment, and voiced fears that the country would soon lose its dominance in the world economy, baldly stating, "If an unfriendly foreign power had attempted to impose on America the mediocre educational performance that exists today, we might well have viewed it as an act of war."[16] ALA's *Presidential Committee on Information Literacy: Final Report*, which formally defined information literacy in 1989, directly responded to *A Nation at Risk* and proposed information literacy as the solution to the threat the National Commission identified.

Academic libraries, school libraries, and, to a lesser extent, public libraries used the release of the presidential report to galvanize efforts to prove libraries' relevance in the new information age born with the creation of the World Wide Web. ACRL released the *Information Literacy Competency Standards for Higher Education* in 2000.[17] AASL continued to promote best practices in school library service and teaching with *Information Power: Building Partnerships for Learning* in 1998.[18] School and academic librarians began renewed efforts to collaborate with other faculty members to infuse information literacy across the curriculum. Colleges and universities showed support for information literacy programs by adding library instruction classrooms—dedicated computer labs, with projectors, and local area networks (LANs)—to their buildings. Public libraries continued to provide the same types of programming as earlier in the century, but added programs to provide computer-use instruction and technology training.

> "Information literacy is a survival skill in the Information Age."

Information literacy is a survival skill in the Information Age. Just as public libraries were once a means of education and a better life for many of the over twenty million immigrants of the late 1800s and early 1900s, they remain today as the potentially strongest and most far-reaching community resource for lifelong learning[19] (see also chapter 20, "Infinite Learning"). Instead of drowning in the abundance of information that floods their lives, information-literate people know how to find, evaluate, and use information effectively to solve a particular problem or make a decision—whether the information they select comes from a computer, a book, a government agency, a film, or any number of other possible resources. Libraries, which provide a significant public access point to such information and usually at no cost, must play a key role in preparing people for the demands of today's information society.

TEXTBOX 16.1

Topic for Discussion

Should information professionals teach at all? Why should they teach?

The Growing Need for Information and Technology Literacy in Communities

Increasing people's access to information has not resulted in all the positive social outcomes that commentators of the twentieth century had hoped to see.[20] Instead, the current information environment has raised new concerns about how people think and learn, communicate with one another, and evaluate the information they find.[21]

The Digital Divide

The term "digital divide" first came to prominence in 1995 when the National Telecommunications and Information Administration published its study on the disparity in access to the Internet;[22] this rapidly changed what it meant to be connected.[23] The causes of the digital divide have often been attributed to structural inequalities leading to disparities in socioeconomic status, which are further complicated by inequalities related to ethnicity and gender.[24] Other dimensions of the digital divide besides access include disparities in the skills,[25] knowledge,[26] and interest[27] to use information technology and the web.

Twenty-First-Century Literacies

"Recent surveys of employers show that information literacy and solving problems using information remain vital competencies for success in many fields, whether in the professional, service, or manufacturing sectors."

Our nation's need for a highly skilled workforce has been one of the driving concerns behind efforts to reduce the effects of the digital divide. Influential reports like *What Work Requires of Schools*, prepared by the Secretary's Commission on Achieving Necessary Skills in 1991 (SCANS), have identified the job skills that employers prize most.[28] These job skills include knowing how to acquire, evaluate, and communicate information, as well as how to use "efficient learning techniques to acquire and apply new knowledge and skills."[29] These skills also have strong connections to the fundamental attributes of information literacy as defined by ALA in 1989. Recent surveys of employers[30] show that information literacy and solving problems using information remain vital competencies for success in many fields, whether in the professional, service, or manufacturing sectors. Efforts to define the value of a college degree in the first two decades of the twenty-first century have focused on these core competencies that all students should expect to develop before graduation, regardless of their location,

April D. Cunningham and Stephanie Rosenblatt

major, preparation, or standing. The *Degree Qualifications Profile*, developed in 2011 and updated in 2014 by the Lumina Foundation as part of its efforts to increase college attendance and completion, defines the proficiencies that come from an effective undergraduate education. These include the intellectual skills associated with information literacy, such as analytical inquiry, using information resources, "engaging diverse perspectives, ethical reasoning, quantitative fluency, and communicative fluency."[31]

Accountability Movement

Widespread concern about maintaining U.S. prominence in the global economy has resulted in increased scrutiny and control of educational and nonprofit organizations by the government and by reformers.[32] In the field of information science, the accountability movement inspired ACRL to commission the *Value of Academic Libraries Report* in 2010.[33] This report was a large-scale review of the existing research about the impact of academic libraries on higher education. Many of its recommendations call upon academic librarians to investigate the effects of their teaching on users by comparing students who have had library instruction against students who have not. See textbox 16.2.

In 2014, the AASL launched a national assessment initiative to gather evidence of the impact of school libraries on students' success.[34]

> TEXTBOX 16.2
>
> **Recommended Areas for Demonstrating Academic Libraries' Value**
>
> - Student enrollment
> - Student retention and graduation rates
> - Student learning
> - Student achievement (e.g., GPA)
> - Student experience
> - Student success after graduation

Contemporary Examples of Teaching in Libraries

When information professionals talk about teaching, they are most often referring to formal teaching, such as when learners enroll in a course or attend a class or workshop taught by an information professional or staff member. In addition to formal teaching, there is also informal teaching, such as when information professionals teach patrons at their moment of need (see also chapter 13, "Finding Information: Information Intermediation and Reference Services"). Often referred to as "reference" by public services staff, instruction librarians widely consider these services to be instructional, and they include the work that information professionals do at the reference desk, in research consultations, or via online tutorials and videos that learners access when they get stuck in the course of conducting their research.

Literacy Training at Public Libraries

Information professionals recognize that reading is a foundational skill that facilitates all other learning.[35] Although not usually taught by information professionals, adult literacy training in libraries ensures that libraries are fulfilling one of their core roles. Many public policies that provide funding for adult literacy programs in libraries are supported because literacy has a social value as a work skill.[36]

TEXTBOX 16.3

Examples of Public Libraries Promoting Early Literacy and Family Literacy

- Alameda County Public Library has a state-supported literacy program for immigrants that is part of the Bay Area Literacy Network.[1]
- The Casa Grande Public Library in Arizona used grant funding to begin a story time using e-readers and promoted participation by reaching out to parents who were least likely to have access to e-readers themselves and were most likely to be looking for ways to give their children a chance to experience this new technology.[2]
- The San Diego Public Library offers a family literacy program throughout its branches where parents can attend with their children. The sessions introduce techniques parents can use when reading to their children, families receive free books to begin an in-home library, and parents learn about nutrition and healthy media habits for children.[3]

---

1. Luis Kong, "Failing to Read Well: The Role of Public Libraries in Adult Literacy, Immigrant Community Building, and Free Access to Learning," *Public Libraries Online* 52, no. 1 (January/February 2013), http://publiclibrariesonline.org/2013/03/failing-to-read-well-the-role-of-public-libraries-in-adult-literacy-immigrant-community-building-and-free-access-to-learning.
2. "Digital Storytime Means Serious Fun—and Vital Learning—for Arizona Toddlers," *Institute of Museum and Library Services* (n.d.), http://www.imls.gov/digital_storytime_means_serious_fun_and_vital_learning_for_arizona_toddlers.aspx?CategoryId=2&pg=5.
3. "San Diego Public Library's Award-Winning Literacy Services," *Support My Library San Diego* (February 22, 2011), https://supportmylibrary.org/?attachment_id=516.

Technology Literacy Training: Public and Academic Libraries

Though closely related, information literacy and technology literacy are not synonymous. Technology literacy addresses users' abilities to problem-solve and build confidence with new technologies. There is an assumption that everyone now has the computer skills and Internet access they need to complete basic tasks like applying for jobs, signing up for health insurance, and interacting with government agencies online. As a result, technology literacy is more important than ever. Despite wider dissemination of information technologies across populations in the United States, public libraries still play a significant role in reducing the negative effects of the digital divide by providing access to computers and other hardware for users.[37] Information professionals observe that library users are often five to ten years behind in developing the skills they need to effectively use all of the tools now available to them.[38] In order to make these tools more useful for creating and sharing knowledge, information professionals train users and teach them about the social practices around information technology.[39] Ever since personal computers became ubiquitous, public librarians have been offering basic sessions on using them for word processing and accessing the Internet. Lafayette Public Library and Hennepin County Library, for example, also offer classes on creating websites, designing video games, editing photos, and using 3-D printers.[40]

In higher education, library users often already have access to personal computers, so information professionals focus on emerging technologies instead. When Google Glass was first released in 2013, most people had no chance to try it out, so a handful of academic libraries became early adopters. Claremont College, for example, organized class visits, a lecture program, and symposia about Google Glass where users not only had a chance to encounter the technology but also to consider its meaning for their community.[41]

Information Literacy and Research Training

SCHOOL LIBRARIES

The Common Core standards, initiated in 2010 and widely adopted by 2015, changed elementary and secondary education in the name of increasing students' readiness for careers and college. The standards required students to conduct research and integrate sources into their writing across content areas and much earlier in their education than they had in the past.[42] Although these new standards emphasized students' use of information, it made no provision for additional funding for school libraries or school librarians. Severely underresourced libraries remained a pressing issue in states without a minimum requirement for school library staffing. The school librarians already on-site used the new Common Core curriculum to continue their work with classroom teachers to ensure that libraries had materials to support students' inquiry and provided training to teachers, staff, and students about research fundamentals (see also chapter 6, "Literacy and Media Centers in the Twenty-First Century: School Libraries").[43] Many school librarians implemented or adapted existing models like iSearch and Big6 to support students' growth as researchers.

PUBLIC LIBRARIES

Public librarians teach users how to do research using the public library's more specialized collections (see also chapter 8, "Community Anchors for Lifelong Learning: Public Libraries"). Two common examples are business research and genealogical research. This instruction makes the library's collections more valuable to users, who might not know how to get the most out of them or how to access them at all. This improves the library's return on investment by bringing more users to some of the collections that are costly for the library to maintain, providing information professionals with data that shows why the funding should continue.

ACADEMIC LIBRARIES

Academic librarians introduce novice researchers to advanced techniques for thinking about information, framing questions for inquiry, and making meaning of what they find (see also chapter 7, "The Learning and Research Institution: Academic Librarians").[44] Recent surveys show that college professors and academic library directors highly value academic librarians' efforts to develop undergraduates' information literacy, including research and analysis, ranking it ahead of the support the library provides for faculty research.[45] Academic librarians also provide research instruction for graduate students and teaching assistants to ensure that they have the skills they need to complete their own research and support their students' development.

> "Recent surveys show that college professors and academic library directors highly value academic librarians' efforts to develop undergraduates' information literacy, including research and analysis, ranking it ahead of the support the library provides for faculty research."

When professors request information literacy instruction to prepare students to successfully complete specific assignments, communication is essential to ensure that the instruction will be relevant to students' needs. If faculty do not provide sufficient information to plan effective instruction, it is academic librarians' responsibility to educate professors about their expectations, demonstrating to faculty how more collaboration will result in better learning.[46] At many institutions, academic librarians train new faculty about information literacy, library resources, and the standards information professionals have set for instruction.[47]

Communication between information professionals and faculty about research instruction can be as simple as brief e-mails or conversations to plan one-shot sessions that meet the information professional's and the professor's goals for students' learning.[48] But sometimes information professionals and faculty work more closely together to plan instruction. In these cases, information professionals may make suggestions to improve assignment instructions or may create new assignments for students to support their development as researchers and lifelong learners.[49] Academic librarians have also adapted a concept from special libraries called embedded librarianship.[50] Embedded librarians provide ongoing support to students and faculty by integrating themselves into learning environments, like courses and fieldwork, where they have more opportunities to intervene in students' learning and create experiences that reinforce positive research habits.[51]

Many academic librarians also teach for-credit courses. Research suggests that taking an information literacy course in college can improve students' graduation rates.[52] Some colleges and universities require students to take a course entirely on information literacy, while other campuses have identified one or more courses where information literacy is integrated into existing curriculum in other disciplines. Some information professionals have found a middle path by co-teaching courses with other faculty or teaching in paired classes where their course is linked to a course in another discipline.[53]

Educational Principles

All instruction librarians, regardless of the setting in which they work, need to apply the same basic instructional design principles when planning learning experiences (see textbox 16.4).

TEXTBOX 16.4

Instructional Design Principles

- Identify the audience/students that will be taught.
- Determine the information needs of the students.
- Decide what will be taught.
- Decide how to formally or informally assess what the students have learned.
- Design the instructional experience.
- Reflect on the teaching.

Deciding what will be taught and how to assess the acquisition of the skill/concept before planning the instructional experience is common to all methods of instructional design. Models of instructional design commonly used by information professionals include Wiggins and McTighe's backward design method,[54] the ADDIE method,[55] and Char Booth's USER method.[56]

One of the key steps to deciding what to teach a particular group of students is identifying desired outcomes for the class based on the users' immediate information needs as connected to broader ideas about information literacy. Identifying outcomes helps information professionals prioritize what to focus on during the lesson. This is especially important for information literacy instruction, as the majority of the teaching by information professionals still takes place in a one-shot session without any follow-up contact.

Assessing Instruction

One of the biggest changes in the work of instruction librarians in the twenty-first century is the increased expectation that information professionals will be able to document and assess the learning that takes place through their teaching efforts (see also chapter 28, "Demonstrating Value: Assessment"). Most often, information professionals assess users' learning during instruction or immediately after. When information professionals assess users' learning during the instruction session, often called formative assessment, the information professional can use what he/she discovers about learners' understanding to make informed decisions about what to emphasize or deemphasize during the rest of the session. When information professionals assess users' learning at the end of the session, often called summative assessment, the information professional gains a sense of what users learned overall. Both of these types of assessment give the information professional the opportunity to find out if users can demonstrate the skills and knowledge that were the focus of the instruction. Direct assessments, which require the learner to practice the new skill or apply the new knowledge, create the most meaningful evidence.

There are many types of activities that get learners to engage with the content of instruction. Many educators share their active learning techniques online. Information professionals can also find examples in books and in professional periodicals like *College & Research Libraries News*. The foundational work on classroom assessment by Angelo and Cross, *Classroom Assessment Techniques: A Handbook for College Teachers*, provides an overview of the rationale behind classroom assessment, as well as strategies that can be adapted for the classroom.[57] The decision about the type of assessment methods to use in a classroom should be based on what the information professional wants to know about students' learning and how they plan to use that knowledge. Assessment should be an ongoing process of learning about the information professional's effect on users and applying that learning to keep improving instructional efforts.

Pursuing Professional Excellence

It is impossible to become an effective instruction librarian without dedicating time and energy to professional development. Most information professionals learn how to teach by observing more experienced teachers, reading the professional literature, attending conferences that focus on information and technology literacy instruction, and joining local or national organizations for instruction librarians. A good method for ensuring continuing improvement is to set aside time annually to reflect on satisfying and uncomfortable teaching experiences to identify areas of strength and those in need of improvement. Once one or two goals for improvement are identified, make time for additional training to help meet those goals.

Opportunities and Challenges

Scaling Up

Attention on information literacy development is increasing in the early twenty-first century. Evidence of this includes the 2014 UNESCO declaration on media and information literacy,[58] higher-education accreditation standards that identify information literacy as a core outcome of a college education,[59] national policies that name the library as a site of workforce development because of the lifelong learning skills that librarians encourage,[60] and employer surveys that demonstrate their expectation that employees will apply advanced information processing and communication skills.[61] This presents an opportunity for information professionals because they have been developing their capacity for teaching users this set of skills that is now so sought after. In order to benefit from this opportunity, however, some information professionals have already found that they need to meet the challenge of scaling up their efforts to reach more users without additional staff or increased funding.[62] Online instruction, particularly through web-based tutorials, has been embraced by many information professionals as a method for providing instruction to self-directed learners and learners who are looking for instruction just in time as they are encountering the limits of their research skills.

> "In order to get the most benefit from online instructional materials that information professionals create, professors, teachers, and employers must further facilitate users' learning by deliberately connecting the content the information professionals made to performance requirements in classes and on the job."

Research suggests that online and in-person instruction on information literacy skills result in similar learning gains.[63] Yet drawbacks remain. One drawback to online instruction is that some users do not have access to the technology they need to access the materials. Another is that some do not prefer to learn online. Additionally, if users do not apply what they learn from these tutorials, it will not lead to lasting changes in their skills or habits. In order to get the most benefit from online instructional materials that information professionals create, professors, teachers, and employers must further facilitate users' learning by deliberately connecting the content the information professionals made to performance requirements in classes and on the job.

For information professionals, another drawback to online instruction is that developing effective tutorials requires significant up-front investments of staff training and time, as well as ongoing maintenance to make adjustments based on assessment results and to keep the content and appearance up to date. Although being able to provide a mix of in-person and online instruction may be ideal for meeting users' needs, in reality the libraries with well-developed online instruction have either had to divert resources that were previously dedicated to other services or seek new funding streams from grants or other sources. The pressure to make library instruction more efficient will continue as the trend of increasing access and decreasing costs intensifies in higher education and government services. Information professionals' interest in adopting new technologies and finding creative solutions to problems will be invaluable assets for the foreseeable future.

Stepping Up

In order to sustain instruction programs, information professionals will need the ability to see opportunities to enter what has been called in organizational research the "arena of confrontation."[64] This is the location, sometimes physical and sometimes only symbolic, where institutional priorities are weighed and decisions are made about allocating limited resources. For information professionals who teach in public libraries, the arena of confrontation may be management meetings at their library or city council meetings where elected officials make budget decisions that will either enhance or hinder the library's ability to provide learning opportunities for users. In academic settings, information professionals benefit from volunteering for campus-level service opportunities, like organizing accreditation self-studies or serving on first-year-experience committees, because these are the sites where the values of the institution are defined and information professionals can influence decisions to benefit students' information literacy. School librarians can enter the arena of confrontation by accepting leadership roles on their campus and in their district, including becoming a teacher on special assignment who is responsible for building colleagues' skills through professional development. Information professionals must not wait to be asked to step into these roles but should seek them out. In every case, entering the arena of confrontation requires information professionals to transcend their day-to-day role and allows them to demonstrate their value to their institution. By challenging others' assumptions about the place of the information professional in their institution, information professionals gain power and influence that they can use to create the circumstances that will result in the biggest benefit to users' learning.

TEXTBOX 16.5

Topic for Discussion

What types of information and technology have you received? Who taught you? What were the strengths and weakness of the teaching you observed?

April D. Cunningham and Stephanie Rosenblatt

Conclusion

The future holds exciting possibilities for information professionals who teach. Education is considered a growth area for information professionals.[65] Some believe that soon the buildings and collections that have traditionally constituted libraries themselves will no longer be the purpose and focus of information professionals' work.[66] The profession may already be in the process of orienting itself toward facilitating learning and communication, regardless of where users are finding information.[67] Teaching users in the future may prove to be one of the most stable aspects of a profession that no longer has to warehouse materials just in case they are needed. The value information professionals add to users' abilities to create knowledge in their own communities[68] and strengthen "civic ecologies"[69] may become our most recognizable trait. This chapter has offered background, examples, and suggested techniques for teaching that information professionals will use as the foundation on which to build the future of librarianship.

Notes

1. R. David Lankes, *The Atlas of New Librarianship* (Cambridge, MA: MIT Press, 2011).
2. Association of College and Research Libraries, *Presidential Committee on Information Literacy: Final Report*, last modified January 10, 1989, http://www.ala.org/acrl/publications/whitepapers/presidential.
3. American Association of School Librarians, *Information Power: Guidelines for School Library Media Programs* (Chicago, IL: American Library Association, 1988), http://files.eric.ed.gov/fulltext/ED315028.pdf.
4. American Association of School Librarians, *Standards for the 21st Century Learner* (Chicago, IL: American Association of School Librarians, 2007), http://www.ala.org/aasl/sites/ala.org.aasl/files/content/guidelinesandstandards/learningstandards/AASL_Learning_Standards_2007.pdf.
5. June Garcia and Sandra Nelson, *2007 Public Library Service Responses* (Public Library Association, 2007), http://ryepubliclibrary.org/wp-content/uploads/2012/05/ALAserviceresponses.pdf.
6. Forest Woody Horton Jr., *Understanding Information Literacy: A Primer* (Paris: UNESCO, 2007), http://unesdoc.unesco.org/images/0015/001570/157020e.pdf.
7. "The NCTE Definition of 21st Century Literacies," National Council of Teachers of English, last modified February 5, 2013, http://www.ncte.org/positions/statements/21stcentdefinition.
8. "Information Literacy Value Rubric," in *VALUE: Valid Assessment of Learning in Undergraduate Education*, American Association of Colleges and Universities, last modified March 14, 2013, http://www.aacu.org/value/rubrics/InformationLiteracy.cfm.
9. Otis H. Robinson, "College Library Administration," in *Public Libraries in the United States: Their Condition and Management; Special Report, Department of the Interior, Bureau of Education, Part 1* 35, no. 1187 (Washington, DC: Government Printing Office, 1876), 520–525, facsimile of the first edition with an introduction by Francis Keppel; Jacquelyn M. Morris, *Bibliographic Instruction in Academic Libraries: A Review of the Literature and Selected Bibliography* (Champaign, IL: University of Illinois, 1979), 1–48, http://files.eric.ed.gov/fulltext/ED180505.pdf.
10. "Framework for Information Literacy for Higher Education," *Association of College & Research Libraries*, last modified June 17, 2014, http://acrl.ala.org/ilstandards/?page_id=133.
11. James Elmborg, "Critical Information Literacy: Implications for Instructional Practice," *Journal of Academic Librarianship* 32, no. 2 (2006): 192–199, doi:10.1016/j.calib.2005.12.004.
12. Ibid.; Jim Elmborg, "Literacies, Narratives, and Adult Learning and Libraries," *New Directions for Adult and Continuing Education*, no. 127 (2010): 67–76, doi:10.1002/ace.382; Heidi L. M. Jacobs, "Information Literacy and Reflective Pedagogical Praxis," *Journal of Academic Librarianship* 34, no. 5 (2008): 256–262, doi:10.1016/j.acalib.2008.03.009; Debra Hoffman and Amy Wallace, "Intentional Informationists: Re-Envisioning Information Literacy and Re-Designing Instructional Programs around Faculty Librarians' Strength as Campus Connectors, Information Professionals, and Course Designers," *Journal of Academic Librarianship* 39, no. 6 (2013): 546–551, doi:10.1016/j.acalib.2013.06.004.
13. Benjamin Franklin, *The Autobiography of Benjamin Franklin* (Charlottesville, VA: University of Virginia Library, 1995), 36.

14. Henry L. Cecil and Willard A. Heaps, *School Library Service in the United States: An Interpretive Survey* (New York: H. W. Wilson, 1940), reprinted in Melvin M. Bowie, *Historic Documents of School Libraries*, 175–191 (Fayetteville, AR: Hi Willow Research & Publishing, 1986); Robert Ellis Lee, *Continuing Education for Adults through the American Public Library, 1833–1864* (Chicago, IL: American Library Association, 1966), 1–13; Elise A. Rogers Halliday Okobi, "History and Development of Adult Services," in *Library Services for Adults in the 21st Century* (Santa Barbara, CA: Libraries Unlimited, 2014), 19–28; Jesse H. Shera, "The Social Library, I: Origins, Form, and Economic Backgrounds," in *Foundations of the Public Library* (Chicago, IL: University of Chicago Press, 1949), 68–85; John Mark Tucker, "User Education in Academic Libraries: A Century in Retrospect," *Library Trends* 29, no. 1 (1980): 9–27.
15. Okobi, *Library Services for Adults in the 21st Century.*
16. David P. Gardner and the United States National Commission on Excellence in Education, *A Nation at Risk: The Imperative for Educational Reform; A Report to the Nation and the Secretary of Education* (Washington, DC: Government Printing Office, 1983), 5, http://www.eric.ed.gov/contentdelivery/servlet/ERICServlet?accno=ED226006.
17. American Library Association, "Information Literacy Competency Standards for Higher Education," American Library Association, 2000.
18. American Association of School Librarians and Association for Educational Communications, *Information Power: Building Partnerships for Learning* (Chicago, IL: American Library Association, 1998).
19. American Association of College and Research Libraries, *Presidential Committee on Information Literacy: Final Report.*
20. Vannevar Bush, "As We May Think," *Atlantic*, July 1, 1945, http://www.theatlantic.com/magazine/archive/1945/07/as-we-may-think/303881/?single_page=true.
21. Siva Vaidhyanathan, *The Googlization of Everything (and Why We Should Worry)* (Berkeley: University of California Press, 2012); David Weinberger, *Too Big to Know: Rethinking Knowledge Now That Facts Aren't Facts, Experts Are Everywhere, and the Smartest Person in the Room is the Room* (New York: Basic Books, 2011).
22. "Falling through the Net: A Survey of the 'Have Nots' in Rural and Urban America," National Telecommunications & Information Administration, United States Department of Commerce, last modified February 22, 2014, http://www.ntia.doc.gov/ntiahome/fallingthru.html.
23. Svanhild Aabø, "The Role and Value of Public Libraries in the Age of Digital Technologies," *Journal of Librarianship and Information Science* 37, no. 4 (2005): 205–210, doi:10.1177/0961000605057855.
24. Eszter Hargittai, "Second-Level Digital Divide: Differences in People's Online Skills," *First Monday* 7, no. 4 (2002), doi:10.5210/fm.v7i4.942.
25. Hargittai, "Second-Level Digital Divide."
26. Mun-Cho Kim and Jong-Kil Kim, "Digital Divide: Conceptual Discussions and Prospect," in *The Human Society and the Internet: Internet-Related Socio-Economic Issues* (Berlin: Springer, 2001), 78–91.
27. Michael Kende, *Internet Society Global Internet Report 2014*, 2014, http://www.internetsociety.org/sites/default/files/Global_Internet_Report_2014_0.pdf.
28. The Secretary's Commission on Achieving Necessary Skills (SCANS), *What Work Requires of Schools: A SCANS Report for America 2000*, U.S. Department of Labor, 1991, http://wdr.doleta.gov/SCANS/what work/whatwork.pdf.
29. SCANS, "What Work Requires of Schools," 14.
30. Hart Research Associates, *It Takes More than a Major: Employer Priorities for College Learning and Student Success: A National Survey of Business and Non Profit Leaders*, American Association of Colleges and Universities, 2013, http://www.aacu.org/leap/documents/2013_EmployerSurvey.pdf; Alison J. Head et al., "What Information Competencies Matter in Today's Workplace?" *Library and Information Research* 37, no. 114 (May 2013): 75–104, http://www.lirgjournal.org.uk/lir/ojs/index.php/lir/article/view/557/593.
31. *The Degree Qualifications Profile 2.0: Defining U.S. Degrees through Demonstration and Documentation of College Learning*, Lumina Foundation, 2014, 19–23, http://www.luminafoundation.org/publications/DQP/DQP2.0-draft.pdf.
32. F. King Alexander, "The Changing Face of Accountability: Monitoring and Assessing Institutional Performance in Higher Education," *Journal of Higher Education* 71, no. 4 (July/August, 2000): 411–431, http://www.jstor.org/stable/2649146.

April D. Cunningham and Stephanie Rosenblatt

33. Megan Oakleaf, *Value of Academic Libraries: A Comprehensive Research Review and Report* (Chicago, IL: American Library Association, 2010), http://www.ala.org/acrl/sites/ala.org.acrl/files/content/issues/value/val_report.pdf.

34. American Association of School Libraries National Research Forum, "Causality: School Libraries and Student Success," American Library Association, 2014, http://www.ala.org/aasl/sites/ala.org.aasl/files/content/researchandstatistics/CLASSWhitePaper_6-24-14_DRAFT.pdf.

35. Erlene Bishop Killeen, "Yesterday, Today, and Tomorrow: Transitions of the Work but not the Mission," *Teacher Librarian* 36, no. 5 (2009): 8-13.

36. Kathleen de la Peña McCook and Peggy Barber, "Public Policy as a Factor Influencing Adult Lifelong Learning, Adult Literacy and Public Libraries," *Reference & User Services Quarterly* 42, no. 1 (2002): 66-75.

37. Paul T. Jaeger, et al., "The Intersection of Public Policy and Public Access: Digital Divides, Digital Literacy, Digital Inclusion, and Public Libraries," *Public Library Quarterly* 31, no. 1 (2012): 1-20, doi:10.1080/01616846.2012.654728.

38. Joseph McKendrick, *Funding and Priorities: The Library Resource Guide Benchmark Study on 2011 Library Spending Plans* (Chatham, NJ: Unisphere Research, 2011), http://lgdata.s3-website-us-east-1.amazonaws.com/docs/231/215960/Funding-and-PrioritiesThe-Library-Resource-Guide-Benchmark-Study-on-2011-Library-Spending-Plans.pdf.

39. Kimberly Pendell et al., "Tutor-facilitated Adult Digital Literacy Learning: Insights from a Case Study," *Internet Reference Services Quarterly* 18, no. 2 (2013): 105-125.

40. Cynthia Matthias and Christy Mulligan, "Hennepin County Library's Teen Tech Squad: Youth Leadership and Technology Free-for-All," *Young Adult Library Services* 8, no. 2 (2010): 13-16; Richard Burgess, "South Regional Library to Give 3-D Printing, Electronic Kits Trial Run over Summer," *The Advocate*, May 23, 2014, http://theadvocate.com/news/9184745-123/south-regional-library-to-give.

41. Char Booth and Dani Brecher, "OK, Library: Implications and Opportunities for Google Glass," *College & Research Libraries News* 75, no. 5 (May 2014): 234-239, http://crln.acrl.org/content/75/5/234.full.pdf+html.

42. Liz Deskins, "Inquiry Studies: Needed Skills," *School Library Monthly* 28, no. 5 (February 2012): 20-23, http://clearviewregional.edu/docs/hs/libra/inquiryskills.pdf.

43. American Association of School Librarians, *Implementing the Common Core State Standards: The Role of the School Librarian*, American Library Association, November 2013, http://www.ala.org/aasl/sites/ala.org.aasl/files/content/externalrelations/CCSSLibrariansBrief_FINAL.pdf.

44. Barbara Fister, "Smoke and Mirrors: Finding Order in a Chaotic World," *Research Strategies* 20, no. 3 (2005): 99-107, http://homepages.gac.edu/~fister/WILU2005.html.

45. Ross Housewright, Roger C. Schonfeld, and Kate Wulfson, *Ithaka S+R US Faculty Survey*, April 8, 2013, 69, http://www.sr.ithaka.org/sites/default/files/reports/Ithaka_SR_US_Faculty_Survey_2012_FINAL.pdf.

46. Yvonne Nalani Meulemans and Allison Carr, "Not at Your Service: Building Genuine Faculty-Librarian Partnerships," *Reference Services Review* 41, no. 1 (2013): 80-90, doi:10.1108/00907321311300893.

47. Betsy Baker, "Bibliographic Instruction: Building the Librarian/Faculty Partnership," *Reference Librarian* 24 (1989): 311-328, http://www.tandfonline.com/doi/abs/10.1300/J120v10n24_25#preview.

48. Joan R. Kaplowitz, *Transforming Information Literacy Instruction Using Learner-Centered Teaching* (New York: Neal-Schuman, 2012); Ryan Sittler and Douglas Cook, *The Library Instruction Cookbook* (Chicago, IL: Association of College and Research Libraries, 2009).

49. Daniel Brendle-Moczuk, "Encouraging Students' Lifelong Learning through Graded Information Literacy Assignments," *Reference Services Review* 34, no. 4 (2006): 498-508, doi:10.1108/00907320610716404.

50. David Shumaker, *The Embedded Librarian* (Medford, NJ: Information Today, 2012).

51. Cassandra Kvenlid and Kaijsa Calkins, *Embedded Librarians: Moving Beyond One-Shot Instruction* (Chicago, IL: Association of College and Research Libraries, 2011); Amy Van Epps and Megan Sapp Nelson, "One-Shot or Embedded? Assessing Different Delivery Timing for Information Resources Relevant to Assignments," *Evidence Based Library and Information Practice* 8, no. 1 (2013): 4-18, http://ejournals.library.ualberta.ca/index.php/EBLIP/article/view/18027/14793.

52. Jean Marie Cook, "A Library Credit Course and Student Success Rates: A Longitudinal Study," *College & Research Libraries* 75 (May 2014): 272-283, http://crl.acrl.org/content/early/2012/12/19/crl12-424.full.pdf+html.

53. Hoffman and Wallace, "Intentional Informationists."
54. Grant Wiggins and Jay McTighe, *Understanding by Design* (Upper Saddle River, NJ: Merrill Prentice Hall, 1998).
55. Steven J. Bell and John D. Shank, *Academic Librarianship by Design: A Blended Librarian's Guide to the Tools and Techniques* (Chicago, IL: American Library Association, 2007).
56. Char Booth, *Reflective Teaching, Effective Learning: Instructional Literacy for Library Educators* (Chicago, IL: American Library Association: 2011).
57. Thomas A. Angelo and K. Patricia Cross, *Classroom Assessment Techniques: A Handbook for College Teachers* (San Francisco, CA: Jossey-Bass, 1993).
58. UNESCO, *Paris Declaration on Media and Information Literacy in the Digital Era*, 2014, http://www.unesco.org/new/fileadmin/MULTIMEDIA/HQ/CI/CI/pdf /news/paris_mil_declaration.pdf.
59. Western Association of Schools and Colleges, *Core Competency FAQs*, Senior College and University Commission, June 2014, http://www.wascsenior.org/content/core-competency-faqs.
60. American Library Association, "Workforce Investment Act (WIA)," last modified May 13, 2014, http://www.ala.org/advocacy/workforce-investment-act-wia.
61. Hart Research Associates, "It Takes More than a Major"; Head et al., "What Information Competencies Matter in Today's Workplace?"
62. Lisa Kammerlocher et al., "Information Literacy in Learning Landscapes: Flexible, Adaptable, Low-Cost Solutions," *Reference Services Review* 39, no. 3 (2011): 390–400.
63. Kenneth J. Burhanna, Tammy J. Eschedor Voelker, and Julie A. Gedeon, "Virtually the Same: Comparing the Effectiveness of Online Versus In-Person Library Tours," *Public Services Quarterly* 4, no. 4 (2008): 317–338, doi:10.1080/15228950802461616; Joanna M. Burkhardt, Jim Kinnie, and Carina M. Cournoyer, "Information Literacy Successes Compared: Online vs. Face to Face," *Journal of Library Administration* 48, nos. 3/4 (2008): 379–389, http://gcls2.cmich.edu/conference/presentations/kinnie.pdf; Yvonne Mery, Jill Newby, and Ke Peng, "Why One-Shot Information Literacy Sessions Are not the Future of Instruction: A Case for Online Credit Courses," *College & Research Libraries* 73, no. 4 (2012): 366–377, http://crl.acrl.org/content/early/2011/08/26/crl-271.full.pdf+html.
64. Michel Crozier and Erhard Friedberg, "Actors and Systems: The Politics of Collective Action," trans. Arthur Goldhammer, *Humboldt Journal of Social Relations* 11, no. 2 (Arcata, CA: Humboldt State University, 1980): 163–168, http://www.jstor.org/stable/23261843.
65. Nancy Bolt, "Libraries from Now On: Imagining the Future of Libraries; ALA Summit on the Future of Libraries—Report to ALA Membership," *ALA Connect*, May 19, 2014, http://connect.ala.org/node/223667.
66. Barbara Fister, "Critical Assets: Academic Libraries, a View from the Administration Building," *Library Journal*, May 29, 2010, http://lj.libraryjournal.com/2010/05/academic-libraries/critical-assets-academic-libraries-a-view-from-the-administration-building/#; Lankes, *The Atlas of New Librarianship*; Brian Mathews, "Librarian as Futurist: Change the Way Libraries Think about the Future," *portal: Libraries and the Academy* 14, no. 3 (2014): 453–462, http://vtechworks.lib.vt.edu/handle/10919/49667.
67. Brian Mathews, "Librarian as Futurist: Change the Way Libraries Think about the Future"; Frank Menchaca, "Start a New Fire: Measuring the Value of Academic Libraries in Undergraduate Learning," *portal: Libraries and the Academy* 14, no. 3 (2014): 353–367, doi:10.135/pla.2014.0020; Kelly E. Miller, "Imagine! On the Future of Teaching and Learning and the Academic Research Library," *portal: Libraries and the Academy* 14, no. 3 (2014): 329–351, doi:10.1353/pla.2014.0018.
68. Lankes, *The Atlas of New Librarianship*.
69. Aspen Institute, "Dialogue on Public Libraries: Aspen Ideas Festival—'The Public Library Reimagined,'" last updated August 28, 2014, http://www.aspeninstitute.org/policy-work/communications-society/our-work/dialogue-public-libraries.

Part IV
Information Users
Engaging, Creating, and Collaborating via Technology

"When asked what I see for the future of libraries—all kinds of libraries—I imagine a space where users will connect, collaborate, create, and care."

—Michael Stephens (2011)

That future is now! While information organizations offer a range of resources, including physical and virtual collections, at the heart of the work done by today's information professionals is the information user. The needs of these users are extremely varied, and the ways information organizations fulfill those needs varies as well. With user needs firmly in mind, information professionals can forge ahead and address users' evolving needs, such as the need for more open, participatory services that are available anywhere, at any time, and programs that meet the lifelong learning needs of users. Information organizations become spaces for creation, discovery, and collaboration that inspire their communities.

Part IV begins with an overview of key concepts that information professionals need to understand in order to meet users' needs and to create an information environment and experiences that users want and are excited to use. The concept of user-centered design that takes the user's experience into account is presented, as are the models of the hyperlinked library, creation culture, and makerspaces. Encompassing the focus on the user's information need is the quest of infinite learning—where learning and exploration take place anytime and anywhere, 24/7/365 and beyond—which is defined in greater detail throughout this section.

Welcome to *Part IV—Information Users: Engaging, Creating, and Collaborating via Technology!*

17

User Experience

Aaron Schmidt

User experience (UX) design is an unparalleled framework for thinking about and improving any type of information organization, of any size. From a problem as granular as "What word should we use to label this content on the website?" all the way to "What is the purpose of our organization and what sort of services should we provide?" UX can help information organizations make the right choices.

If information organizations are to remain relevant, trusted institutions, they must be useful, usable, and desirable. UX design can help information professionals achieve this goal by focusing on the information users and the communities they serve. Whether an information organization is part of a town, school, university, or corporation, UX (as a user-centered design process) instructs information professionals to take the needs, desires, and preferences of their users into account in the services they provide, the facilities they build, and the products they develop. By focusing on interaction design and thinking about the user's purpose, information organizations can improve the experience that their users have.

After completing this chapter, the reader should have an understanding of the UX design process and why information organizations need to be concerned with designing the user experience they provide. By employing UX design, information professionals can create information organizations that people want to use and are excited about using.

The Importance of User Experience for Information Organizations

Information professionals strive to meet user needs, and UX provides a framework to develop a deeper understanding of these needs and helps information professionals develop useful, usable, and desirable information organizations and services. UX also can serve as a form of advocacy for the information organization. Even though she does not use the term, Eleanor Jo Rogers' "What's a Library Worth" is one of the best articles about user experience for information organizations. The article reminds information professionals that no information organization exists in a vacuum. All information organizations are part of a larger ecosystem. Rogers states that libraries, instead of focusing on doing what is good for the library, need to focus on doing what is right for their host ecosystems.[1] This has two positive effects. What is good for the ecosystem is good for the information organization. If an information organization can make its community better off, the information organization will be better off.

What is more, if an information organization successfully contributes to the vitality of the ecosystem, the information organization will be recognized as an important, positive force. Stakeholders will value the information organization for the role it plays and be more likely to support it. This is a deep form of advocacy for information organizations, and its outward focus meshes tightly with the principles of UX design.

Interaction Design in Information Organizations

Whether it is confusing classification systems, locked-down computers, or electronic interfaces that seem user hostile, information organizations have not always been designed with usability in mind. Aside from being difficult to use, information organizations sometimes lack appeal. Things like uncomfortable furniture, signage that does not consider the rules of graphic design, and stacks of dusty books can all contribute to a less than appealing vibe. All of the elements that people come into contact with to use an information organization—all of the touch points—impact the experience that people have. Thinking about UX can help information organizations assess and improve all touch points.

Optimizing Touch Points

The aim of user experience design is to intentionally craft and optimize all aspects of a user's interactions with a product or service.

TEXTBOX 17.1

Two-Step Process to Creating a Good User Experience

1. Consider all of the elements that impact the overall UX.
2. Optimize these elements so that they meet the needs and desires of users.

TEXTBOX 17.2

Tasks Involved with Attending a Library Event

- Learn about an event in the library newsletter.
- Register for the event online.
- Read a confirmation e-mail.
- Lock up bike at a library bike rack.
- Walk into the building.
- Ask a library worker a directional question.
- See directional sign.
- Find the event space.
- Attend the event.
- Browse materials after the event.
- Exit the building.
- Unlock bike at the bike rack.

Easier said than done, right? Information organizations are complicated organizations with diverse offerings. They consist of many different touch points—ways in which people interact with the organization. The typical information-seeking task requires someone to interact with the information organization in many different ways. See textbox 17.2.

Examined with scrutiny, the complexity of this seemingly simple task of attending a library event becomes apparent. Information organizations must think critically about all of these touch points for each user task to provide good experiences. This gets even more complicated when considering that information organizations aim to provide services not only in their buildings, but also online via desktop computers and also mobile devices.

Aaron Schmidt

The Existential Woe of the Information Organization

Just what is an information organization, anyway? Is it a building that contains a lot of books? Is it a place to get tax forms? Is it a place where information professionals read to groups of children?

Information organizations have traditionally been places that facilitate access to information, often providing a solution to information scarcity. In today's society, though, information is not as scarce as it was once, and people have unprecedented access to books, movies, and music, often via the devices they carry on a regular basis. This provides information professionals with an opportunity to expand their service solutions and to consider the information and entertainment needs of their communities. R. David Lankes, in his *Atlas of New Librarianship*, states that the mission of information professionals is "to improve society through facilitating knowledge creation in their communities."[2] This broad statement is useful and liberates information professionals to think about fulfilling the mission in a variety of ways.

Beyond Optimization

Optimizing touch points improves usability, and that is a very important thing. Who likes things that are difficult to use, right? But information organizations must do more than just become easier to use. A good user experience is one that not only is easy, but is also meaningful. Information organizations must learn about the communities, such as the town, university, or business, they serve to create programs and services that meet their needs. While this task might be

> "A good user experience is one that not only is easy, but is also meaningful. Information organizations must learn about the communities, such as the town, university, or business, they serve to create programs and services that meet their needs."

more difficult than optimizing touch points, it is also more important. After all, it does not matter how easy it is to use an information organization if no one wants to use it.

The key to both improving touch points and creating meaningful services is developing empathy for information users. Without considering the preferences, desires, needs, and motivations of information users, it is impossible to create a good user experience. Information professionals are trained to think about information users. Examples include

- buying materials that are relevant to their communities, and
- planning and hosting a series of events that their community will attend.

There are a lot of moving parts to deal with when designing a great user experience: touch points, user behavior, user goals, the organization's goals, and capacity too. UX design provides a framework for learning about and analyzing all of these things.

UX Techniques

There are a variety of techniques that can be used to understand information user experience efforts, such as experience safaris, UX audits, UX partnerships,

TEXTBOX 17.3

Topic for Discussion

What are the top three information organization touch points most likely to benefit from UX improvements? What prevents information organizations from making these points?

contextual inquiries, experience mapping, usability testing, content audits, and user interviews. These can be used alone or, even better, used in combination to learn user needs and desires.

Experience Safaris

It is often useful for information professionals to get outside of the information organization and go on an experience safari at a café, restaurant, park, museum, or retail store. Experience safaris can happen online too. Why is getting outside of the organization useful? People working in the information organization see their organization day in and day out. This much exposure can dull one's perspective and prevent someone from seeing something with fresh eyes.

During an experience safari, information professionals record their observations about all the touch points that they encounter. Observations typically focus on the following prompts:

- What is the goal of this experience?
- What was good about this experience? What could have been better?
- Describe the customer service.
- Was the temperature comfortable?
- Describe the facility. Was it clean? Busy?
- What was the noise level?

During a debrief meeting with other colleagues, give everyone a chance to talk about their observations. Information professionals might be tempted to apply what they have observed to their information organization. While there may be some direct takeaways that can be applied, the real value of experience safaris is practicing how to observe and communicate about experiences.

The UX Audit

Once information professionals are comfortable describing and analyzing experiences, it is time for them to turn their eyes toward their information organization. The UX audit records every touch point in (and out of) the information organization, including digital touch points. If possible, it is useful to approach this in a systematic fashion and divide the work among the UX team. If the information professional has a large enough UX team, it is valuable to have more than one person independently look at certain touch points. The differences and similarities in analysis can make for fruitful discussion.

UX Partners

Forming a UX partnership with another organization takes the benefits of a UX audit to the next level. Find a like-minded institution and conduct an audit of each other's UX. This will take some trust and tact, but it is worthwhile developing a good relationship to reap the benefits of an outsider's perspective.

Contextual Inquiry

This technique, borrowed from the field of anthropology, is slightly different than conducting a UX audit. Instead of creating a descriptive analysis of the UX in the information organization, during a contextual inquiry, the information professional observes the behavior of people in the information organization. This is important for a couple of reasons. Making these observations, the information professional can learn how the building and services are—or are not—aligned with people's behavior. The information professional can also use data from a contextual inquiry as the basis for improving touch points. For example, if the information professional is interested in improving the library's reading room, it makes sense to learn about how people are currently using it. A contextual inquiry can be a great start.

During a contextual inquiry, the information professional observes behavior around the touch point in question and records everything that is observed. Sessions of thirty or forty-five minutes are easy to fit in. It is recommended that the information professional do this at a few different times during the week, and also have colleagues do the same. When the information professional records behavior, analyzing the data should be reserved for later. Once the data is collected, the information professional aggregates the data and starts combining to look for patterns. The patterns that develop will give the information professional a good idea of how people are behaving around this touch point. Based on what has been learned, the information professional can then design the touch point to create a better experience.

Experience Mapping

Once the information professional is comfortable discussing and analyzing experiences, and once the information professional has observed people using the information organization, it is a good time to create some experience maps. An experience map—also known as a customer journey map—is a visualization of all the steps it takes someone to complete a task. These diagrams are very useful because they break down complicated activities into discrete steps. When tasks can be digested as granular activities, they—as well as the overall task—can be assessed and improved. It is often helpful to assess each step of the journey by asking the following questions:

- How might a user feel during this step?
- What is the purpose of this step?
- What is good about this step? What is not working? Can it be improved? Is it necessary?

Answering these questions can help information professionals think differently about both the individual steps and the task as a whole.

To see the start of a very basic journey map for a common library task—attending a library program—see textbox 17.2. To see a more fully fleshed-out journey map, see "The Anatomy of an Experience Map" by Adaptive Path.[3] While a detailed experience map can be worthwhile, making a simple list and answering the above questions can be a great way to get started.

Usability Testing

Usability testing—watching people complete tasks on the information organization's website—is a great way to get started with user research. It is fairly simple to do, is always illuminating, and can help communicate the value of doing user research. In this way, usability testing is like a "gateway" user research project that can drive the information organization to learn more about its users. Usability testing is also an invaluable tool. Watching people complete tasks on the organization's site will make the team aware of where users are encountering problems and how the site could better facilitate their task-completion rate.

To conduct usability tests, the information professional needs to find users who agree to test the website. Almost anyone who is not working as an information professional can participate in the usability test. To run the test, task scenarios need to be written for the testers to complete. It is critical to make sure that the scenarios do not use any leading language that gives the testers hints about how to complete the task. After reading the scenarios to the testers, the information professional observes their behavior. It is also possible to share the screen and have coworkers observe in another room. After the tests are complete, a debriefing meeting is held to discuss what was observed during the tests and to create an improvement plan.

Content Audits

Content audits are a fantastic way to get a grip on an information organization's huge, sprawling website. This is a great place for catalogers to help with UX because, in a content audit, information professionals will essentially be cataloging the website. Every page on the site should be entered into a spreadsheet, with some quantitative elements (such as an assigned page ID and URL) and some qualitative elements (such as assessments about accuracy, quality of writing, and usefulness). Take a look at Kristina Halvorson and Melissa Rach's *Content Strategy for the Web*[4] for more about content audits.

User Interviews

All of the above techniques are useful for assessing and analyzing an information organization's UX (see also chapter 28, "Demonstrating Value: Assessment"). This is very important, but it is not the full picture. Central to the design process—and improving the information organization's UX—is turning the focus outward and learning about information users. It is impossible to create a meaningful and engaging organization without knowing a lot about the people who are being served. This should come as no surprise. In fact, one of the profession's foundational statements—Ranganathan's five laws of library science[5]—implores information professionals to know about their users, an early precursor to the user-centered design concept. There are many ways that this focus on the user is evident in the information profession, such as in how information organizations attempt to develop collections and host programs that are of interest to their communities.

The more information professionals focus on learning about their communities, the more successful they will be. A foundational research technique for learning about people is the user interview. Simply put, user interviews are lightly directed conversations between researchers and someone they want to learn about. The process is very similar to conducting reference interviews, something with which many information professionals have experience (see also chapter 13, "Finding Information: Information Intermediation and Reference Services"). During a user interview, the job of the interviewer is to listen and to ask prompting, open-ended questions. When conducting an interview, the scope of the conversation will depend on what the information professional is trying to learn. But regardless, the emphasis should be on listening to what people have to say about their lives. While it is tempting to ask people directly about their information use or their opinions about the organization, information professionals should remember that the goal is to learn about the users' lives, not to learn about their opinions about the information organization.

Improving UX

While assessing the organization's UX, information professionals may find some touch points that are pain points—elements that are detracting from a great user experience. Assuming there is a list of things that the organization would like to improve, it is time to start improving them. On occasion, it will become clear what needs to be done, and the information professional can do it rather easily. For instance, something as simple as removing a few unnecessary signs might declutter and improve a space. On other occasions, information professionals know what needs to be done, but it will take some effort to carry out the work. For instance, creating and implementing an entire new graphic identity for the information organization would take considerably more work than just removing a few signs.

Aaron Schmidt

But what happens when something needs to be fixed but the information professional does not know how to fix it? For instance, what if the book checkout process in the information organization is cumbersome and confusing, takes a long time, and generally gets low marks from users? The solution might not be apparent. Install self-check machines? Relocate the circulation desk? Hire more staff? All of the above? Employing a systematic design process can help information professionals answer questions like these and ensure they are serving users in a way that makes sense to them.

TEXTBOX 17.4

Topic for Discussion

What are some strategies or activities that an information organization can employ to ensure its staff understands the value of adopting a user-centered perspective?

Information Professionals Are Designers

The first step in improving the information organization's UX is to realize that when trying to improve a pain point, a design decision is being made. The information professional becomes the designer. Whether it is determining where a photocopier should be placed, creating a poster, or purchasing an online resource, information professionals make design decisions on a daily basis. These decisions have a big impact on the organization's UX, so these decisions need to be taken seriously. And as a designer, the information professional can learn about the problem that needs to be solved and create great solutions.

> "The first step in improving the information organization's UX is to realize that when trying to improve a pain point, a design decision is being made. The information professional becomes the designer."

How Can Information Professionals Be Good Designers?

It is not uncommon for information professionals to say, "How can I be a designer? I am not very creative." What they really mean is that they have not practiced being creative in a safe environment in a long time, possibly since they were a child. Creativity is a skill that everyone can practice and get better at. Sharpening creative skills and doing great design work does not require us to sit alone in a room, sketching and being contemplative. Good design *can* happen that way, but there is a better way for information professionals to get some practice. When recognizing design as a process, information professionals can let the process guide their design. This process is often described as design thinking. See textbox 17.5.[6]

TEXTBOX 17.5

Design Thinking Process

- Empathize.
- Understand the people being served.
- Define.
- Express the problem that needs to be solved.
- Ideate.
- Explore solutions to the problem.
- Prototype.
- Manifest potential solutions in the real world.
- Test.
- Evaluate the prototypes to see what works.
- Identify what could be improved.

This framework can help information organizations put some structure on the touch points they are trying to improve.

Examples of Good UX for Information Organizations

Here are some examples of interesting and user-focused information organization services and programs. These programs either reconceptualize traditional information organization offerings and/or serve their users in interesting, meaningful ways as a result.

- *Baltimarket:* In an attempt to help solve the problem of food deserts in Baltimore, the Enoch Pratt Free Library has partnered with Baltimarket,[7] a program that provides healthful groceries where they are not readily available. People can now pick up their groceries in the library.
- *Literary Lots:* Bringing books to life in vacant lots around Cleveland, Literary Lots[8] creates displays related to children's books with which people can interact. Cleveland Public Library is one of the project's many partners.
- *LibraryFarm:* The Northern Onondaga Public Library has a very interesting item in their collection: a half-acre parcel of land divided into plots that library members can check out.[9] They are providing access to something that members might not have access to otherwise, and they enrich the offering with programming and activities.
- *Chicago Public Library Hotspots:* Taking their mandate to provide access to information seriously, Chicago Public Library is circulating Wi-Fi hotspots in neighborhoods that lack broadband access. Patrons can take home a hotspot—and a laptop—for three weeks.[10] This is a great example of serving people where they want to be served.
- *Multnomah County Library My Librarian:* This readers' advisory service facilitates building relationships between library users and librarians. And it accomplishes this without requiring people to visit the library. Patrons can choose to interact with their librarian via telephone, e-mail, chat, or Skype.[11]
- *Vancouver Public Branch and YWCA Housing:* A forthcoming branch of the Vancouver (BC) Public Library will reallocate space with housing for low-income mothers and their children. This is a surefire way to positively impact the lives of people in need.[12]

Conclusion

Information organizations have a history of user-centered design. Take the words of Gratia Countryman from her opening address of a 1905 Minnesota Library Association meeting:

> The whole building at all times should be managed in the broadest spirit of hospitality; the atmosphere should be as gracious, kindly and sympathetic as one's own home. Then do away with all unnecessary restrictions, take down all the bars, and try to put face to face our friends the books and our friends the people. Introduce them cordially, then stand aside and let them make each other's blessed acquaintance.[13]

While her whole address is worth reading, this section in particular is quite moving. It is a warm and informative mandate that is as meaningful now as it was in 1905. Information professionals should build on this history and focus on making great information organizations.

In sum, good UX is everyone's job, and everyone working in an information organization must be on board and realize that the decisions they make impact users. Only when staff align and actively aim to improve the user experience their information organization provides will an information organization become useful, usable, and desirable.

Notes

1. Eleanor J. Rodger, "What's a Library Worth," *American Libraries* 38, no. 8 (September 1, 2007): 58–61.
2. David R. Lankes, *The Atlas of New Librarianship* (Cambridge, MA: MIT Press, 2011), 31.
3. Chris Risdon, "The Anatomy of an Experience Map," last modified November 30, 2011, http://www .adaptivepath.com/ideas/the-anatomy-of-an-experience-map.
4. Kristina Halvorson and Melissa Rach, *Content Strategy for the Web* (Berkeley, CA: New Riders, 2009).
5. S. R. Ranganathan, *The Five Laws of Library Science* (Madras, IN: Madras Library Association, 1931).
6. The dSchool Institute of Design at Stanford, *Bootcamp Bootleg* 2 (2010), http://dschool.stanford.edu/ wp-content/uploads/2011/03/BootcampBootleg2010v2SLIM.pdf.
7. "Baltimarket: The Virtual Supermarket Project," Enoch Pratt Free Library, http://www.prattlibrary.org/ home/index.aspx?id=61972 (accessed July 14, 2014).
8. Literary Lots, last modified July 28, 2014, http://literarylots.org.
9. "LibraryFarm," Northern Onodaga Public Library, last modified September 11, 2014, http://www.nopl .org/library-farm.
10. Matt Enis, "CPL, NYPL WiFi Hotspot Lending Programs Funded by Knight Foundation Grants," Digital Shift, last modified June 25, 2014, http://www.thedigitalshift.com/2014/06/digital-divide/ cpl-nypl-wifi-hotspot-lending-programs-funded-knight-foundation-grants.
11. "My Librarian," Multnomah County Library, last modified July 3, 2014, https://multcolib.org/my-librarian.
12. "FAQ: VPL Branch and YWCA Housing," Vancouver Public Library, last modified October 15, 2012, http://www.vpl.ca/news/details/faq_vpl_branch_and_ywca_housing.
13. "The Library as Social Centre," *Library Juice* 3, no. 12 (2012), http://libr.org/juice/issues/vol3/LJ_3.12 .html#13.

18

Hyperlinked Libraries

Michael Stephens

Emerging mechanisms for global communication and collaboration are changing the world and the way the world works. Businesses no longer demand employees and customers to be in any particular physical location to provide and receive premium services. Organizational charts are becoming flatter and more team based. Individuals are constantly engaged in conversation and expect to have their information needs satisfied immediately, on any device, and wherever they happen to be. Information is no longer bound to a form or a place. Information organizations, such as libraries, housing unique and valuable collections, works and artifacts of local significance, and information sources not yet digitized must find ways to reach out to a public that will never have the opportunity to visit their buildings and who may never easily happen upon their websites. Information organizations that are already providing online services and digital content must constantly watch for innovative solutions that could be included in their information center processes, designs, and web presences.

Historically, libraries have been advocates for the protection and expansion of information access, but now libraries have become one of the only inclusive spaces for the public to experiment with and use technological tools. Information professionals must extend their knowledge and training into the online space—sharing, collaborating, and reflecting. Information professionals must think and act outside their organization, community, and even national boundaries to seek inspiration and support. In a report by Wells, industry analysts predict that by 2020, more than fifty billion mobile devices will be connected worldwide.[1] In the next few years, the world will be using mobile services and devices that cannot be imagined today. The information organization that builds value and thrives will be fluid enough to anticipate and quickly respond to new technologies and user expectations. One such model, the hyperlinked library model, builds this value by being welcoming, open, and participatory, and by incorporating user input and creativity. The hyperlinked library is human, and its communications and conversations, externally and internally, are in a human voice. It is a playful model emphasizing collections and spaces that evolve via user and staff participation in a transformational anytime, anywhere service dynamic.

> "The hyperlinked library is human, and its communications and conversations, externally and internally, are in a human voice. It is a playful model emphasizing collections and spaces that evolve via user and staff participation in a transformational anytime, anywhere service dynamic."

After completing this chapter, the reader should have an understanding of the hyperlinked library model and its qualities of transparency, openness, and participation; the current landscape of digital connectivity; influences of mobile technologies on information organizations and information services; and examples of hyperlinked library technologies—cloud computing, professional development on demand, mobile apps, and processes on the horizon.

The Hyperlinked Library

The author has worked for several years researching, refining, and teaching a model of information service called "the hyperlinked library." This model is synthesized from data collected on emerging societal trends and burgeoning technologies used in information service, as well as the writings of such authors as David Weinberger, Clay Shirky, and Seth Godin. Glenn[2] calls the methodology used to build the evolving model "futures research," which is a blend of horizon scanning, trend research, and scenario planning. In an article for *Serials Review*, the hyperlinked library model is defined as "an open, participatory institution that welcomes user input and creativity. It is built on human connections and conversations. The organizational chart is flatter and team-based. The collections grow and thrive via user involvement. Information professionals are tapped in to user spaces and places online to interact, have presence, and point the way."[3]

> "Hyperlinked library services are born from the constant, positive, and purposeful adaptation to change that is based on thoughtful planning and grounded in the mission of libraries."

Hyperlinked library services are born from the constant, positive, and purposeful adaptation to change that is based on thoughtful planning and grounded in the mission of libraries. Information professionals embracing the hyperlinked model practice careful trend spotting and apply the tenets of librarianship along with an informed understanding of emerging technologies' societal and cultural impact. Information professionals communicate with patrons and potential users via open and transparent conversations using a wide variety of technologies across many platforms.

The hyperlinked library model flourishes in both physical and virtual spaces by offering collections, activities, trainings, and events that actively transform spectators into participants. In participatory cultures, everyone is in the business of advancing knowledge and increasing skill levels. The community is integrated into the structure of change and improvement.

The hyperlinked library is transparent when it talks and listens, practices inclusion, and keeps no secrets. The information organization activates processes to gather as much input from the entire community as possible, which heightens in patrons the expectation that communications with the information organization will be open and equitable. The hyperlinked library encourages all types of conversation and feedback about the organization. It is a move toward greater transparency when users are invited to share their opinions about how an information organization is performing, and when the information organization listens and responds. Management shows evidence of active listening and responding to users and staff by implementing requested changes and launching new services, using careful testing as part of the plan for solid, incremental growth.

Because of the easy and ubiquitous communications possible with mobile devices, these technologies make transparency more attainable than ever. Information organizations can share information about current plans and solicit feedback on social networks, which utilize the more naturally transparent and trusted conversation channels developed among peers and families. Published updates, calls

> "Because of the easy and ubiquitous communications possible with mobile devices, these technologies make transparency more attainable than ever."

for community input, and beta tests of new services delivered to the devices in users' hands enable the hyperlinking of all stakeholders anytime and anywhere.

Continuous Computing and Participation

The current landscape is one of continuous computing and of always being in conversation. Information has an active social life; creating and sharing ideas plays out across networks and social sites. World populations are moving toward this ubiquitous digital connectivity with anytime, everywhere access, mainly via mobile devices such as tablets or phones. Organizations no longer have a monopoly on packaging information, and information control is decentralized and distributed. Anyone can curate information and publish collections from anywhere, deliver content anytime, and share on a wide selection of devices in many different formats and in multiple languages. User preferences for particular technologies are unpredictable; the heavily promoted complex nanocomputers, head-mounted displays, and other experimental devices may never make it to mainstream adoption, but handheld devices of all kinds have become the norm for connectivity. ITU, the United Nations agency that collects telecommunications data from two hundred economies, estimates the number of mobile-cellular subscriptions at seven billion. According to CTIA Wireless Association CEO Meredith Baker, an average of 3.6 million text messages and almost 183,000 video and photo messages were sent every minute in 2013, which is an increase of 120 percent over the previous year.[4]

In addition to the increases in personal messaging on handheld devices worldwide, groups, institutions, and businesses are increasingly publishing and distributing communications via mobile apps. Information professionals who establish free, open, and well-publicized communication channels on mobile platforms and who build these channels for user interaction will be rewarded with a growing, engaged community base. With patrons and potential users thinking and interacting on the move, information professionals must constantly study how information services are discovered, accessed, and used. Communications have evolved from simple two-way interchanges into interconnected, multilayered flows. Adopting a hyperlinked library model and collaboratively designing spaces for these new information-sharing practices calls for a flattening of organizational structure. Adopting the hyperlinked library model means inviting patrons to partner with information professionals to revisit mission and values statements, set revised goals and objectives, and discuss the big ideas behind information services and the field of information science.

Throughout *Too Big to Know*, David Weinberger argues that the smartest person in the room is not the biggest brain or the whole group of people in the room, but the room itself. A poorly constructed room can result in echo chambers and groupthink, while a well-constructed room can enable constructive conversations and continuous knowledge discovery. Weinberger (2012) suggests five foundational concepts to "help make the networking of knowledge the blessing it should be" (see textbox 18.1).[5]

These tenets should guide the building of new outreach services with mobile technologies as well as participatory online spaces created by information professionals for their constituents.

TEXTBOX 18.1

Five Concepts of Knowledge Networking

- Open up access.
- Provide the hooks for intelligence (metadata).
- Link everything.
- Leave no institutional knowledge behind.
- Teach everyone.

Influence of Mobile Technologies

A hotel bartender chatted with the author about his mobile device and said, "I have everything I need here: I have my web, I have my e-mail, I have my text, I have my video, and I have my music: I have the world of information in my hand." His remark resonated, and the story has been told in many of the author's presentations and articles ever since, because it is indicative of the way that people think about their devices. The Pew Research Internet Project, in a survey with 2,008 adults, found that 29 percent could not imagine living without their cell phones, 44 percent sleep with their phones, and 67 percent regularly check for notifications without being alerted.[6] The main findings in "Cell Internet Use 2013" provide further evidence that mobile devices are ingrained in our lives.[7] Maeve Duggan and Aaron Smith, senior researchers at the Pew Research Internet Project, reported that younger adults, nonwhites, the less educated, and less affluent Americans use cell phones as the primary device for accessing online content much more often than older, white, college-educated, and more affluent Americans—a development that has particular relevance to organizations seeking to reach these groups.

A joint study by AOL and advertising firm BBDO[8] reported that 68 percent of individual mobile phone use happens within the home and also found seven primary motivations. The descriptors include self-expression, discovery, preparation (planning a trip, etc.), and accomplishment of a task (mobile banking, etc.). The highest use, however, at 46 percent, is what the researchers call "me time," or accessing relaxing or entertaining content that will help to pass the time. The study, aimed at marketers, should also inspire information organizations and information professionals to offer virtual experiences in which users can indulge and enjoy themselves.

The *NMC Horizon Report 2012* explored mobile access to learning, and authors Johnson, Adams, and Cummins noted that mobile apps make it possible for people to work, learn, study, and play whenever and wherever they want to.[9] When services and opportunities for learning are not available on the go, the term "place based" is used to describe the limitations that confront both students and library users. For example, administrators might ask, "How many of your processes require people to visit your location?" "How many could be accomplished via the web or mobile technology?" Delivering learning opportunities and access to collections and services on mobile devices seamlessly and without barriers is a positive response to this trend.

The Hyperlinked Library Gone Mobile

When exploring the hyperlinked library model, the current state of continuous participatory computing, and the affordances of mobile technologies, information professionals must focus on what information organizations could develop as strategies for mobile access and participation. What avenues should be explored in relation to hyperlinked mobile services? How can information professionals find a place inside these emerging environments?

Collections Everywhere

A few years ago, the author discovered that a university library with a unique artifact from a songwriter in its special collection had digitized and showcased only one page of the lyrics on the library website. The rest is only available for visitors who travel to this distant institution. The university cited concerns about preservation and copyright as reasons why these documents could not be accessed digitally. Counter that unfortunate barrier to access with the impressive collection-focused apps from the British Library and the work done at New York Public Library highlighting various parts of the collection via iPad apps. The hyperlinked library offers collections and access anywhere—especially an information organization's most unique and interesting offerings. Mobile apps expand the process of discovery into virtual worlds, and information collections need to be where the users are exploring.

Information Professionals in the Cloud

As users spend more computing time on mobile devices and become increasingly familiar with saving and sharing content on cloud-based services, the emerging participatory culture will need

> "As users spend more computing time on mobile devices and become increasingly familiar with saving and sharing content on cloud-based services, the emerging participatory culture will need the traditional foundations of literacy (research skills and critical analysis) along with skills in networking, problem solving, and exploratory play."

the traditional foundations of literacy (research skills and critical analysis) along with skills in networking, problem solving, and exploratory play. Information professionals can expand their practice by becoming knowledgeable guides in these new cloud landscapes. They can teach others to build and maintain personal learning networks (PLN) and exploration spaces.[10] They can harness the power of the data stored in the cloud to answer questions, share information, and collaborate with users. Huge amounts of data—images, status updates, reviews, and more—become a set of resources at our fingertips. The groups and collections thriving at the image- and resource-sharing communities, Flickr, DeviantART, Instagram, and Pinterest, are examples of environments that hold opportunities for cloud content curation and management. For example, Flickr's The Commons partners with many organizations, including the Smithsonian Institution, to share photos and encourage users to tag, comment, and reuse the images.

Professional Development on Demand

With the continuing evolution of cloud resources and mobile technologies, many information organizations must provide opportunities for staff training before expanding services and initiating programs with the public. The 23 Mobile Things program, spun off from the incredibly popular Learning 2.0 programs that originated in libraries in 2006, cultivates an enthusiasm for experimenting with emerging and unfamiliar technologies by providing a simple, adaptable framework of exploration, one app at a time. The program's clear focus on immersion into mobile technologies allows 23 Mobile Things participants to use the learning and practice for all aspects of information service. 23 Mobile Things' program adaptations by the international information community can introduce administration and staff to variations in practices and technologies that will spark more experimentation (see also chapter 38, "Global Learning Networks"). This participatory platform also brings professionals together from all over the world to explore and discuss the future of mobile and the technologies that will expand and enrich communications. Research demonstrates the efficacy and success rates of Learning 2.0 and Mobile 23 Things programs, concluding that staff who participate experience more comfort and confidence with emerging technologies.[11]

TEXTBOX 18.2

Topic for Discussion

What are the challenges to experimentation and adoption of mobile technologies?

On the Horizon

Mobile trends and technologies on the horizon provide a glimpse into the future of information services and sharing. Geo-social apps allow users to share location and find local information. Adding gamification, or gamelike elements, to apps offers further engagement. Users who consume media while also using a mobile device can share and participate with others watching the same content. Information professionals may find roles in these emerging trends: curating local data aligned to geographic location or embedding themselves into information environments. The following sections describe these trends further.

Michael Stephens

Hyperlinked and Hyperlocal

An increasing number of the new social sharing apps on mobile devices incorporate geolocation in surprising and innovative ways. The interfaces can be messy, weird, and kind of silly, but mapping content to location offers a promise of discovering hidden relationships within content that can be used to spot trends and expand information services. With the most rudimentary location-based apps, it is easy to find specialty menu restaurants within specific distances from any geographic point via localized search. It is also possible to tap into the wisdom of nearby hikers while exploring a national park via app services like "Find Twitter users near me." However, deciding how much information to share about personal location and situation on open platforms is an important privacy consideration (see also chapter 35, "Information Privacy and Cybersecurity"). Information professionals need to develop more understanding about how much is too much and how little is too little.

Gamification

The *NMC Horizon Report: 2014 Higher Education Edition* placed the time-to-adoption for applying gaming dynamics to learning and research environments at two to three years.[12] Game play has become a portable activity, which utilizes the combination of particular elements, mechanics, and frameworks to increase productivity, creativity, and problem solving. Information organizations can take advantage of game play's ability to increase engagement by creating online environments with level-up properties that reward users. Information users can interact in experimental gamified spaces or become involved with larger regional, national, or even international gaming groups within the information organization. Information professionals can participate as on-demand expert scouts and guides. In a discussion of gamifying library experiences in *ACRL TechConnect*, Kim reported that applying game dynamics has the potential to raise levels of engagement with library services, especially when the objectives of games are not particular outcomes, but fun and enjoyable experiences.[13] An example of a gamified library service is Librarygame, "a bespoke library enhancement product that adds game elements directly into the library experience to make it more fun, engaging and delightful."[14] Libraries in the United Kingdom are experimenting with and implementing these types of service to promote a sense of play and excitement.

Second Screen Sharing

Social sharing apps related to television, movies, and other popular cultural interests have led to the use of mobile devices while consuming entertainment. Second screen sharing describes a participatory process in which users might tweet, post to social sites, or interact while watching broadcast programs and events. This process might also involve active searching for information related to the content of the show, movie, or event. Sharing entertainment experiences becomes easy and fun with apps such as tvtag (formerly Get Glue), and participation will only become more immersive with new apps that are certainly in development. Closely related to the entertainment-sharing apps are social sites devoted to readers in conversation about books and other textual material. Social reading and second screen sharing are trends that will only increase over time.

Geo-Social Curation and Stewardship

Within immersive, participatory environments, who is better equipped to curate and manage content associated with geographic locations than the information professional? And who is better prepared to organize historical information linked to specific geographic locations than local history librarians? Who might best oversee a hyperlinked tour of data-rich points of interest around town, a campus, or corporate headquarters? Information professionals aware of mobile app development requirements and versed in information architecture concepts fit the bill nicely. Partnering with museum and historical society staff would bring even more depth and range to app contents and user experiences.

Embedded Local Experts

Is it too far out to imagine a time when someone might be able to link up with a local expert via a geo-social Twitter-like app, such as Localmind, and ask research questions in addition to making requests for simple recommendations? What if, for example, while using the National Park Service Independence Mobile App to explore points of interest near the Liberty Bell in Philadelphia, PA, someone could directly link to Revolutionary War experts chatting live during scheduled times and ask them questions? What if someone could stand in Independence Hall and listen to live debates about pressing constitutional issues and participate in the dialogue?

> **TEXTBOX 18.3**
>
> **Topic for Discussion**
>
> How must information professionals adapt to the concept of learning everywhere?

Conclusion

Learning via mobile devices happens in an entirely new landscape, infinite in every direction. Access to information through mobile devices has unbundled learning from the traditional forms imposed by time and space. It has made anytime, anywhere collaboration and feedback possible. It has fostered impromptu conversations without concerns for language and cultural differences. All levels of learners, from beginners to experts, participate in the formation of knowledge networks that offer direct connections and rapid expansion. These virtual exchange spaces can offer endless opportunities for future-thinking information professionals who develop skills as online learning experience curators and engagement developers.

> "Information organizations continue to evolve and adapt as sociotechnological changes occur. Exploring the hyperlinked library model as a mobile platform for discovery, interaction, and participation is just one facet of the rich and varied possibilities for the future."

Information organizations continue to evolve and adapt as sociotechnological changes occur. Exploring the hyperlinked library model as a mobile platform for discovery, interaction, and participation is just one facet of the rich and varied possibilities for the future. Delivering easy-to-use, unique, and just-in-time services to the palm of a user's hand, however, may be one of the most important goals addressed as information professionals.

Notes

1. Mark Wells, "A Growing World of Connected Devices," YouTube video, posted by CTIA The Wireless Association, May 5, 2014, https://www.youtube.com/watch?v=HxK46CFsJeM&list=PLE53CB584A01349B5.
2. Jerome C. Glenn, "Introduction to the Futures Research Methods Series," in *The Millennium Project Futures Research Methodology Version 2.0*, ed. Jerome C. Glenn and Theodore J. Gordon, last modified August 21, 2009, http://www.millennium-project.org/millennium/FRM-v2.html.
3. Michael Stephens and Michael Collins, "Web 2.0, Library 2.0, and the Hyperlinked Library," *Serials Review* 33, no. 4 (2007): 253–256.

4. Meredith Attwell Baker, "Why Consumers Care about Spectrum," YouTube video posted by CTIA The Wireless Association, July 8, 2014, https://www.youtube.com/watch?v=XA16b_H-ah0.
5. David Weinberger, *Too Big to Know: Rethinking Knowledge Now That the Facts Aren't the Facts, Experts Are Everywhere, and the Smartest Person in the Room Is the Room* (New York: Basic Books, 2012).
6. "Mobile Technology Fact Sheet," Pew Research Internet Project, last modified October 1, 2014, http://www.pewinternet.org/fact-sheets/mobile-technology-fact-sheet.
7. Maeve Duggan and Aaron Smith, "Cell Internet Use 2013," Pew Research Center, last modified September 22, 2014, http://www.pewinternet.org/2013/09/16/cell-internet-use-2013.
8. AOL, "Joint Study from AOL and BBDO Turns Traditional View of Mobile Space on Its Head" (press release, October 3, 2012).
9. Larry Johnson, Samantha Adams, and M. Cummins, *The NMC Horizon Report: 2012 Higher Education Edition* (Austin, TX: New Media Consortium, 2012), http://www.nmc.org/pdf/2012-horizon-report-HE.pdf.
10. Michael Stephens, "Learning Everywhere," *ACCESS* 26, no. 4 (2012): 4–6.
11. Michael Stephens, "Exemplary Practice for Learning 2.0," *Reference & User Services Quarterly* 53, no. 2 (2013): 129–139.
12. Larry Johnson, Samantha Adams Becker, V. Estrada, and A. Freeman, *NMC Horizon Report: 2014 Higher Education Edition* (Austin, TX: New Media Consortium, 2014), http://www.nmc.org/pdf/2014-nmc-horizon-report-he-EN.pdf.
13. Bohyun Kim, "Harnessing the Power of Game Dynamics," *College & Research Libraries News* 73, no. 8 (2012): 465–469.
14. "Engaging Libraries with Library Game," Library Game, last modified July 6, 2014, http://librarygame.co.uk.

19

Creation Culture and Makerspaces

Kristin Fontichiaro

The urge to set hands and minds in motion is a basic human need, and today's information organizations are poised to expand their traditional knowledge-building services to include a culture of creation. "Creation culture," the democratization of digital tools—in addition to low-cost, low-barrier access to the Internet—makes it possible for everyone to not only create for enjoyment, but also to share those creations online. This ease of sharing has given birth to new opportunities to reenergize and restimulate the creative impulses in patrons and citizens. Carving out spaces and activities for creation, many information organizations are experimenting with novel avenues for drawing in new patrons or providing a wider range of services for existing patrons. After completing this chapter, the reader should have an understanding of the big ideas behind the creation culture and how makerspaces can fulfill long-term strategic planning that supersedes fads or novel technology.

Makers and Makerspaces

Many generations grew up learning about Leonardo da Vinci, who could sketch, create scientifically correct diagrams, build inventions, paint frescoes, and more. For generations, da Vinci has been called the Renaissance man: someone who could blend art and science in potent and powerful ways. Today, he might be called a "maker."

"All of us are makers," says Maker Media founder and CEO Dale Dougherty[1] Whether stitching, soldering, cooking, carpentering, plumbing, programming, crafting, tinkering, inventing, drawing, wiring, or sketching, the need to create is an inherent human instinct. As once-costly tools like microcontrollers, 3-D printers, and other digital fabrication tools dropped dramatically in price, interest across information organizations in creating spaces and programming that reflected this instinct grew.

> "Maker is an inclusive term for anyone who sews, solders, welds, creates, tinkers, prototypes, designs, cooks, codes, gardens, or otherwise transforms one set of materials into another."

"Maker" is an inclusive term for anyone who sews, solders, welds, creates, tinkers, prototypes, designs, cooks, codes, gardens, or otherwise transforms one set of materials into another (see also chapter 19, "What's Your Patron's Dream Makerspace?" in the online supplement). One need only wander into the nonfiction section of a public library to see titles that reflect these traditional and new interests. From creating Halloween pumpkins to HTML, the possibilities have sat on library shelves for decades. What is different in today's information environment? A new sense of place and people.

Massimo Banzi, world renowned for his work codeveloping the Arduino microcontroller—a low-cost, open source microcontroller or "brain" that acts as home base for sensors, lights, and other future inventions—says, "The whole idea of being a maker involves concepts of collaboration, community, and working with other people. It is very hard to be a maker and be by yourself locked in a room or even in a lab. It is really something that involves a lot of collaborations at different levels."[2] This collaborative spirit is key to makerspace culture. Just as the information organization's resources help patrons bring together multiple perspectives, face-to-face making lets them merge their knowledge and experiences with others. This does not mean lockstep work in which everyone does the same thing at the same time; rather, as in the Renaissance guilds and studios, some may be novices and others masters. The goal is for patrons to feel they are working at their "center of gravity"[3]—pursuing their interests and curiosities in a safe environment. Safety to explore new tools and methods, to envision new creations, and to keep trying when early prototypes and attempts do not succeed are key in aligning the information organization with the goals of creation culture.

Melvil Dewey said, "The new library is active, an aggressive, educating force in the community."[4] School libraries have always fulfilled this role, as have academic libraries (see also chapter 6, "Literacy and Media Centers in the Twenty-First Century: School Libraries," and chapter 7, "The Learning and Research Institution: Academic Libraries"). Public libraries, too, build on long traditions as learning institutions via story times, book clubs, informational lectures, film showings, concerts, knitting circles, quilt guilds, digital literacy initiatives, and more (see also chapter 8: "Community Anchors for Lifelong Learning: Public Libraries"). Makerspaces do not replace these activities; they build on them and provide an overarching narrative that all making—from robots to running stitches—has value in satisfying the personal need to create and, perhaps, jump-starting new economic opportunities.

Beginning around 2011, many information organizations leveraged past authority as resource providers and extended into providing experiences in-house, shifting from "check out our DIY materials and leave" to "check out and linger." Forming spaces that may be named makerspaces, digital labs, or production studios, along with activities for creators known as "makers," many information organizations are experimenting with how to invite in new patrons while expanding services for existing patrons. Chicago Public Library's YouMedia and Maker Labs, the Free Library of Philadelphia's MakerJawn initiatives, Westport Library's Makerspace, the University of Michigan Library's 3-D Lab, and the piles of recycled materials in a corner of Leslie Preddy's Perry Meridian (IN) Middle School are each unique in square footage, budget, and materials, but each shares a commitment to putting minds, hands, and imaginations to work.

> "Makerspaces do not replace these activities: they build on them and provide an overarching narrative that all making—from robots to running stitches—has value in satisfying the personal need to create and, perhaps, jump-starting new economic opportunities."

TEXTBOX 19.1

Topic for Discussion

Some communities see making as a fun hobby; others see it as a career pathway to innovation that a community could leverage for new invention, entrepreneurship, and economic opportunity. How would you assess the needs of your community?

Developing Dynamic Makerspaces in the Information Environment

When developing a new makerspace, it can be easy to look to influential blog posts or conference presentations featuring shining tools and assume that assembling a new coterie of equipment will convert the information organization into a thriving, collaborative space. Experienced "makers" know that it takes planning, attunement to community needs and wants, and patience to create a sustainable space that supports creative, collaborative practice—even after the novelty of a new 3-D printer or tool has faded.

Identify Makerspace Goals and Expectations

When information professionals purchase books, multimedia, or online resources, they rely on their collection development policy to guide their selections. When planning to buy maker tools, similar guidelines help to unify expectations and desired outcomes. Key questions to ask include

- What is the core mission of having a makerspace in the organization?
- Is the mission to provide a series of entertaining, fun, hands-on activities?
- Is the mission to provide ongoing education in a specific area, such as circuits, digital design, garment construction, or bonsai?
- Is the information organization the only makerspace in town, or does it serve, as Mark Anderson[5] has noted, as an "on-ramp," a place to explore a variety of activities before moving on to formal education or a higher-end makerspace?

The answers to these questions help define the goals and expectations of the makerspace and need to be documented in a charter or other planning document.[6] Not only is this a useful reference for sharing plans with supervisors and board members, but it also provides essential talking points for employees, marketing staff, and potential donors.

Starting Small and Expanding Based on Patron Wants and Needs

A quick look through the Chicago Public Library Maker Lab's Flickr stream[7] or Maui Makers' photo documentation of the Westport Library space[8] can catapult one's dreams to a new zenith. Keep in mind, however, that these are some of the profession's most established makerspaces. It is important to think big—but start small. For example, the Michigan Makers' service-learning project through the University of Michigan School of Information partners graduate student mentors with K–12 makers in underserved communities; graduate students work with the same student maker cohort all year long. Developing a supportive community is a top priority. One strategy is to offer just three to five options per week (makers need choices!) that are low-tech activities such as origami, Snap Circuits kits,[9] Little Bits,[10] Squishy Circuits,[11] friendship bracelets, or junk box creations. These activities cluster makers around tables, maximizing eye contact and potential conversation. Conversations with mentors often reveal future topics of interest that the participants would like to explore—providing direct insight to the selection of future directions.

Embrace Open Source Thinking

Many information professionals are familiar with the concept of Creative Commons licensing (see also chapter 31, "Copyright and Creative Commons"), which allows writers, photographers, and multimedia creators to retain copyright but signal in advance that their creations may be reused, remixed, or adapted under particular circumstances. Makers often do the same under the "open source" label. Blueprints, design plans, and computer code can all be labeled as open source, meaning that they can be used, reused, added to, and adapted without gaining permission or paying royalties. One of the maker movement's most ubiquitous tools, the Arduino microcontroller mentioned earlier, is open source. Although they are available for purchase for about thirty-five dollars, one can construct an Arduino from scratch using freely available plans online or adapt the provided plan in new ways, as long as the new plans are released similarly. Not only is the hardware open source, but Arduino's code is as well. If a maker wants to make a plant sensor that tweets when it needs water, existing construction plans and open source programming code just might be available online, shared by another maker. By sharing code and construction plans, future tinkerers can accelerate their growth because they build on the existing work of others—legally. As Banzi writes, "We believe in the open source movement and everyone should be really aware that it can develop successfully if everyone takes from it, but especially if people and companies contribute back. That's why it's important to highlight who creates a positive loop and nurture knowledge sharing and collaboration."[12]

Partner, Do Not Compete

There is an aphorism that says "The rising tide lifts all boats." Makers feel the same, realizing that it is by helping fellow makers and maker-interested organizations grow that the entire ecosystem for making improves. As information professionals consider beginning or expanding the maker work in their organizations, seeking out maker partners can produce valuable results. For example, who in the community designs video games, comics, or yarn-bombing campaigns and would be willing to mentor others? These makers may be interested in partnering to expand outreach, promotion, learning, and community engagement.

Community makerspaces provide potential colleagues for makerspaces in information centers, not competitors. Partnering to seek funding and swap expertise and resources is a smart move forward. Often information organizations have space, and makers have skills; by trading, both institutions grow. Information organizations also often have access to grants that for-profit makerspaces do not. There is opportunity and advantage in seeing community makerspaces as colleagues, not as competition.

Seek Mash-Ups

Traditional programming in information organizations has relied on scheduling one activity at a time: Minecraft on Monday and weaving on Wednesday. Part of the excitement and innovation that makerspaces can create comes from putting people of diverse backgrounds and skill sets together at the same time and in the same place (see also chapter 12, "Information Needs: Understanding and Responding to Today's Information User"). Real makerspaces are never single-activity workshops; thriving makerspaces encompass different people working on different things simultaneously. Partnering two or more activities at once can create new cross-disciplinary creations. For example, kids who like to sew stuffed animals, plus programmers who love to control sensors with an Arduino, plus circuitry buffs could discover that, by merging their skills, they could end up with a cuddly object that automatically illuminates when it gets dark, or a stuffed animal that senses the temperature of a sick child or can measure the muscle strength of a child recuperating from a broken wrist when squeezed. It is the twenty-first-century version of those 1980s Reese's Peanut Butter Cup commercials where a peanut butter lover's jar bumped into a chocolate fan's bar, yielding a tasty new creation: "Two great tastes that taste great together!"

Cast a Wide Net: Welcome All Kinds of Makers

At the 2013 FabLearn conference at Stanford University, Leah Buechley shared some startling statistics regarding the cover photos for *Make* magazine, the leading popular magazine for makers. By her analysis of the then forty people who had been featured on covers, 85 percent were male and none were people of color. Her analysis of *Make* editorial staff showed a similar homogeneity: 87 percent men, none of whom were of color. Buechley also found that the content of the photos showed a narrow range of maker activities. She found that just over half featured electronics: vehicles 31 percent, robots 22 percent, rockets 8 percent, and music 5 percent.[13]

Certainly, some makers will be interested and intrigued by those topics. However, an information organization has a responsibility to serve all. The first tenet of the American Library Association code of ethics states, "We provide the highest level of service to *all* library users through appropriate and usefully organized resources; equitable service policies; equitable access"[14] (see also chapter 30, "Information Ethics"). Therefore, consider broadening the range of activities in order to welcome a broader swath of the population. Seeing something familiar reassures people that it is safe to enter the room to try something new. Once they are in the room, they may migrate to something new that would have been off-putting from the outside. A philosophy of having "something for everyone"[15] provides more inclusion. Often, a tool predicted to interest one gender may interest both. For example, sewing machines are more popular among boys than girls in the Michigan Makers project!

Embrace the concept of "windows and mirrors" when planning formal maker programming. Formal programming is a great introduction to making, but so is "open lab" time in which people put their new skills into practice on their own timeline and in their own way. Mirrors are makerspace activities that reflect existing patron/community interests. For example, the community may have an existing group of drop-spindle aficionados, wood-carvers, or weavers; early programming that welcomes and recognizes those activities brings early engagement. Window activities, on the other hand, introduce less familiar, less established, or newly launched activities. 3-D modeling, the process of designing objects that can be represented in multiple dimensions by a 3-D printer, is an example of a window in most communities. So are activities that add unfamiliar elements to familiar objects, such as weaving circuits into paper books or digitizing images for use on electronic embroidery machines.

Another way to welcome all makers is to balance short- and long-term projects for skills acquisition. Especially in underresourced communities, some patrons may feel intimidated by novel materials or uncertainty about their ability to achieve success. Activities that can be completed in a single visit can help minimize frustration and eliminate the challenge of returning multiple times to create a product. Some short-term tasks—like learning to fold an origami cup or decorating unfinished pottery—can be accomplished in a single sitting. These can boost confidence and demonstrate to novices that they are capable of success in new arenas. As success and interests grow, makers may become more willing to take on new challenges that take longer to accomplish, such as learning HTML code, building a robot, or tackling alterations. Additionally, some people are more comfortable in formal learning settings than others. Some like to putter independently while watching others out of the corner of their eye, so having some activities that require no instruction at all or for which videos or instructional sheets are provided is an effective strategy for makerspaces (see also chapter 20, "Infinite Learning").

TEXTBOX 19.2

Topic for Discussion

Many maker activities, like programming, app design, and graphic design, require computer-age skills. Others call on traditional skills like electrical wiring, carpentry, or sewing. Still others are experts in aesthetics and art. Mashing up old and new, right-brain and left-brain can yield new creative opportunities, like sweatshirts that light up or lights that turn on when certain temperatures are sensed. Who in your community possesses these skills? How could you partner up diverse skills in formal or informal ways to ignite innovative designs in your information organization?

Another way to promote inclusivity is by embracing peer mentorship and leadership. Rather than avoiding certain maker activities because staff are not experts, look to the community of makers and tap them for expertise. Teens with parental permission can teach Minecraft, for example. In a makerspace, experience determines expertise, not age. And the more sharing of expertise that is developed among the participants, the more sustainable the makerspace will be. Peer mentorship is key in developing a community of learners in the information organization.

Celebrate Progress

Along with the collective enthusiasm for making among makers, celebrating the patron's achievements along the way promotes the organization's services and provides openings for newcomers to join in. Design challenges, in which participants are asked to solve a problem or put unusual materials to work, offer a short-term involvement for familiar faces and new ones. For kids, Rachelle Doorley of Tinkerlab has an archive of challenges[16] for one-off events, such as creating something new from cupcake liners. Hackathon challenges focus on using computer programming to solve a problem, and there are emerging trends in designing challenges around low-cost prosthetics design and other world-changing maker practices.

Information organizations need to establish a formal sharing time both during workshops and in showcase events. Each community is different in this regard, and the desire to share publicly can vary, so choose a sharing pathway that feels right to patrons—and is designed with their input. Some groups enjoy taking the last five to ten minutes of a workshop to see how everyone else interpreted a new task. Lay completed projects out on a table or sit in a circle to admire what has been made, depending on the size of the creation. Other recommendations include

- keeping a photo board of inspiring works in progress or completed objects;
- taking advantage of social sharing platforms like the organization's Facebook page, Flickr site, blog, or Instagram feed; and
- setting up a semiannual maker event, such as a Maker Media–licensed Maker Faire[17] or a customized MakerFest event (for which no licensing agreement is required).

These efforts can garner attention from the wider community of makers and those who admire their efforts. See table 19.1, "Strategies for Developing Successful Makerspaces."

Table 19.1. Strategies for Developing Successful Makerspaces

Developing a Makerspace	
Find a Partner	Seek help from partners who have expertise and networks you do not.
Identify Resource	Create the resource that people want.
Develop a Vision	Imagine the dream outcome that could happen while stashing away a plan B for when the worst does.
Stay Inspired	Remember that around the country, there are many maker mentors and sites that can provide guidance.

Source: Molly Rubenstein, "How to Make a Makerspace," *Make*, August 14, 2014, http://makezine.com/magazine/make-40/how-to-make-a-makerspace.

Conclusion

This chapter explored creation culture, with the main focus on makerspaces, and considered the questions and issues that boost makerspace success. (Check out the chapter 19, "Makerspace Virtual Tour" in the online supplement.) Information organizations have a long tradition of supporting a community's intellectual and personal interests through rich collections available for checkout and through interactive activities online and in the physical space. By unifying the how-to collections of the information organization with the let's-do energy of the community, information organizations can create maker learning communities and opportunities that delight, motivate, and inspire communities.

Notes

1. Dale Dougherty, "We Are Makers," TED Talks video, January 2011, http://www.ted.com/talks/dale_dougherty_we_are_makers.
2. Massimo Banzi, "Making Is Best When It's Done Together," *Make* blog, last modified February 7, 2014, http://makezine.com/magazine/making-is-best-when-its-done-together.
3. John Dewey, "The School and the Life of the Child," *School and Society: Being Three Lectures* (Chicago, IL: University of Chicago Press, 1900), http://books.google.com/books?id=QWYWAAAAIAAJ.
4. Melvil Dewey, "Why a Library Does or Does Not Succeed," in *Library Notes: Improved Methods and Labor-Savers for Librarians, Readers and Writers* (Boston, MA: Library Bureau, 1887), 47.
5. Mark Anderson, personal communication, September 23, 2013.
6. Kristin Fontichiaro, "A Charter for Your School Makerspace?" *Active Learning* blog, September 4, 2014, http://www.fontichiaro.com/activelearning/2014/09/04/a-charter-for-your-school-makerspace.
7. Flickr, "Chicago Public Library Makerspace," n.d., https://www.flickr.com/photos/cpl_makerspace/sets.
8. Flickr, "Westport Library Maker Space," n.d., https://www.flickr.com/photos/mauimakers/sets/72157644802128769.
9. Snapcircuits, "Home," last modified August 19, 2014, http://www.snapcircuits.net.
10. LittleBits Electronics, "Home," last modified September 12, 2014, http://littlebits.cc.
11. Squishy Circuits, "Squishy Circuits Project Page," last modified July 26, 2014, http://courseweb.stthomas.edu/apthomas/SquishyCircuits.
12. Banzi, "Making Is Best When It's Done Together," 2014.
13. Christina Quattrochi, "MAKE'ing More Diverse Makers," *EdSurge*, last modified October 29, 2013, https://www.edsurge.com/n/2013-10-29-make-ing-more-diverse-makers.
14. American Library Association, "Code of Ethics of the American Library Association," last modified January 22, 2008, http://www.ala.org/advocacy/proethics/codeofethics/codeethics.
15. Kristin Fontichiaro, "Reflections on North Quad MakerFest," *Active Learning* blog, last modified December 18, 2013, http://www.fontichiaro.com/activelearning/2013/12/18/reflections-on-north-quad-makerfest.
16. Tinkerlab, "Challenges," last modified June 25, 2014, http://tinkerlab.com/challenges.
17. Maker Faire, "How to Make a Maker Faire," last modified July 2, 2014, http://makerfaire.com/mini.

20

Infinite Learning

Paul Signorelli

Information users' learning needs are not determined by the information organization's hours of operation, nor are those needs determined by where the buildings are located. Learners in many parts of the world have come to expect that learning will occur when and where they need it. This chapter explores some of the ways information professionals combine traditional and innovative approaches to serve communities through the use of information organizations such as on-site and online lifelong learning centers. After reading this chapter, readers will have a better understanding of how information organizations support infinite learning in the evolving nature of the contemporary lifelong learning landscape.

Defining Infinite Learning

People often think of lifelong learning as something that begins after the completion of formal academic education. However, learning actually begins with the first moments of life and extends up to the moment of death. It is important, therefore, to examine and understand how information and other learning organizations interact. Retaining an image of the learning environment as broken into discrete segments (i.e., preschool, K–12, undergraduate education, graduate/postgraduate education) makes people miss the ways that learning organizations work together to produce an overall lifelong learning environment. Michael Stephens, in his "Office Hours"[1] column in *Library Journal*, discusses the importance of this type of learning, especially the ability to learn anytime and anywhere, and the role that information professionals play in supporting learners using a range of technologies; he calls this infinite learning. "Across all types of libraries, the librarian as community learning connector and collaborator might support learners on platforms that offer endless opportunities."[2]

Information organizations, working either alone or in formal and informal partnerships with other learning organizations, often are part of this infinite learning or can contribute to the overall learning landscape at every stage of an individual's life. By examining some of the more frequently discussed elements in the learning landscape (e.g., formal and informal learning; synchronous and asynchronous learning; face-to-face, online, and blended learning; and mobile learning), information professionals can begin to see how these elements increasingly overlap and how information professionals can support information users in their learning endeavors.

Formal Learning

Formal learning, such as when people pursue a master's degree, is what most frequently comes to mind when people think about learning and education. It implies a start-to-finish course of study that generally culminates with an official moment of graduation. Information professionals meet and serve these formal-learning users in school, college and university, public, and special libraries and information organizations—both face to face and online.

Informal learning

Informal learning, a term commonly used to describe what is learned outside of formal workshops and course work in workplaces, comprises anywhere from 50 to 80 percent of the learning that takes place in those settings, according to various studies that have been completed. The information organization, its resources, and its staff are important parts of the informal learning landscape. Information professionals working within information organizations are also information users, and those not working within information organizations learn informally through interactions with staff members and other information users.

Synchronous and Asynchronous Learning

Synchronous and asynchronous learning are terms defined by whether the learning takes place in real time (e.g., in a live on-site or online session with a learning facilitator) or is available to be pursued by learners regardless of whether a learning facilitator is engaged in live interactions with the learners. The distinctions between synchronous and asynchronous are not new; however, the formats for delivering learning content have changed. For example, learners in previous generations were involved in asynchronous learning through correspondence by mail, recorded learning sessions broadcast over public television stations, and other means; the contemporary version is learning delivered via recorded webcasts and learning management systems. Furthermore, information organizations today continue to meet their users at the moment of need by offering synchronous learning sessions on topics ranging from basic Internet instruction and how-to-use-the-library sessions to more pressing adult learning needs including how to write resumes, how to use social media to find employment, and how to create social media strategies for businesses.

Blended Learning

Blended learning, sometimes called hybrid learning, covers those situations in which learning takes place both on-site and online, synchronously and asynchronously. Blended learning is an area of learning that offers exciting possibilities as teleconferencing tools continue to expand the ability for information professionals to be where information users are. Information professionals who are equally comfortable interacting with learners on-site and online are in a key position to effectively serve those users—regardless of time and place. Live online sessions take the information professional wherever the learners are and make it easy for the learner to reach them; recordings of those sessions, if placed online in ways that make them easy to find, help information professionals to be available in a way many have not previously considered possible.

Mobile Learning

Mobile learning is any learning opportunity that is made possible through the use of mobile devices. Information organizations are very involved in facilitating mobile learning—meeting their users through the use of mobile devices and using social media and other online collaborative tools in ways that foster learning (see also chapter 18, "Hyperlinked Libraries"). The question no longer is whether information organizations are ready to engage in mobile learning. The question now is, what are information organizations doing to best meet and serve their learners through mobile devices?

TEXTBOX 20.1

Topic for Discussion

What does the term "infinite learning" imply to you? How does it fit—or not fit—into what information organizations provide to members of their on-site and online communities?

The Roles Information Organizations Play in the Infinite Learning Process

Anyone who doubts the long-standing, long-term commitment of information organizations and information professionals to be involved in the learning process needs to look no further than the American Library Association's strategic plan. The mission statement on the second page of the plan includes an explicit reference to learning: "The mission of the American Library Association is to provide leadership for the development, promotion and improvement of library and information services and the profession of librarianship in order to enhance learning and ensure access to information for all" (ALA Policy 1.2).[3] The plan, one page later, further—and explicitly—describes what that means: "The association provides opportunities for the professional development and education of all library staff members and trustees; it promotes continuous, lifelong learning for all people through library and information services of every type."[4]

It is also common to see references to lifelong learning in the mission statements of individual or system-wide organizations. In fact, there are a growing number of learning opportunities within information organizations; the breadth and depth of these offerings are evident, even with just a cursory search of the calendars of events. Information professionals are increasingly designing and facilitating learning sessions, for colleagues and information seekers, rather than relying exclusively on others to provide those learning opportunities. Information professionals who want to fully meet the learner's needs must be engaged in the learning process as trainers-teachers-learners.

Information professionals are familiar with many of the traditional terms applied in learning settings (e.g., teacher, instructor, professor, and trainer) and are also becoming familiar with terms, such as "learning facilitator," that imply a different role for them in the learning process. Additionally, information professionals are seeing shifts in how professionals outside the field of library and information science (LIS) are describing facets of the information professional's work (e.g., "talent development" in place of "training" or "workplace learning and performance" for workplace-based training). For example, the change of an association's name from the American Society for Training and Development to the Association for Talent Development in May 2014 demonstrates this shift.

Regardless of what they call themselves, information professionals must recognize that what they do through their organizations to facilitate infinite learning and meet and serve information users in their learning moments of need is multifaceted and will continue to evolve as learning continues to evolve.

> "Regardless of what they call themselves, information professionals must recognize that what they do through their organizations to facilitate infinite learning and meet and serve information users in their learning moments of need is multifaceted and will continue to evolve as learning continues to evolve."

Furthermore, it is helpful to consider the nuances of the term "trainer-teacher-learner"; if any of these three words were omitted, an essential element of what prepares information professionals for the roles they play in the information organization's lifelong learning offerings would also be omitted.

The learning approach information professionals take makes a tremendous difference in how well they meet the learners' needs. A teacher-centric approach is one in which information professionals place themselves as the most important figure in a learning space; a typical example of this approach is the centuries-old model of lecture hall delivery. In contrast, a learner-centric approach is one in which information professionals see themselves as part of a community of learning and where the learners themselves contribute to the learning process; a great example of this approach is working in makerspaces (see also chapter 19, "Creation Culture and Makerspaces"). The learner-centric approach empowers learners by encouraging them to play dynamic roles in fostering their own learning process. This approach is far from new. Well-known educators, such as Malcolm Knowles[5] (*The Adult Learner*) and Carl Rogers[6] (*Freedom to Learn*), are among those who long ago found that engaging learners, by placing them at the center of the learning process, produces magnificent results.

In the makerspace learning environment, for example, information professionals are learners themselves and are not expected to have mastered every element in a makerspace; they actually make themselves part of the learning community that learns from everyone in the learning space. This realization can alleviate fear and stress for facilitators, who sometimes unrealistically expect to have completely mastered an ever-growing body of knowledge.

Information organizations and professionals foster learning when and where it is needed by providing flexible, adaptable learning spaces on-site and online. These flexible on-site spaces currently include information commons, media labs, and "innovation centers"—spaces where everything can be reconfigured quickly to provide the best possible setting to encourage learning for groups of learners (see also part II, "Information Professions: Physical and Virtual Environments," to learn more about specific types of learning environments).

The best of these spaces allow learners to gather in circles for whole-group discussions and then quickly rearrange furniture for breakout sessions in which learners break into smaller groups for discussions and collaborative learning activities. Flexible online spaces, still currently in the early stages of development, include access to online courses provided by outside vendors, access to online learning objects ranging from videos to PDFs and PowerPoint presentations, and interactions via Skype and Google+ Hangouts.

By remaining open to a combination of formal (planned) and informal (impromptu) learning opportunities, information organizations can meet information users' learning needs regardless of where and when the need arises. Providing learning spaces that encourage and support connected learning— where learners are the focus, where traditional as well as digital resources are integral to the learning experience, and where making-creating-producing is part of an experiential learning process—works well in meeting learners' needs at the moment of need. This approach to learning has the additional benefit of removing some of the pressure information professionals often feel to be the sole providers of learning in their information organizations.

> "Providing learning spaces that encourage and support connected learning—where learners are the focus, where traditional as well as digital resources are integral to the learning experience, and where making-creating-producing is part of an experiential learning process— works well in meeting learners' needs at the moment of need."

Information professionals who find creative ways to integrate collection components and resources raise the bar in meeting users at their point of need. As an example, many educational institutions have introduced massive open online courses (MOOCs) into their learning landscape. Their involvement ranges from encouraging local participants in a MOOC, to gathering face to face within information organization facilities to discuss and engage in completing their course work, to helping MOOC developers draw upon the information professional's teaching, technology, and information management skills to more effectively create online learning content. Another example of this is how Los Angeles Public Library offers MOOCs to adult students wanting to get a high school diploma; these learners also use the library for assistance and as a place to meet and interact with each other.

Blended Learning: When Learning Trumps Time and Space

Trainers-teachers-learners, both within and outside of information organizations, still have a lot to understand before they are comfortable with infinite learning and the possibilities that educational technology provides. Nevertheless, maintaining a commitment to engage in every aspect of the training-teaching-learning process creates opportunities for them and for their users' information and learning needs.

One example of an information organization's exploration of blended learning sessions and spaces comes from an exercise used to help library directors in Virginia explore what would be involved in creating a social learning experience with resources that are currently available. Using a large rectangular meeting space with wireless routers, they set out to create a learning space that brought together the directors in the room and several colleagues who were elsewhere in the United States. When the session started, two facilitators initiated a live chat via Twitter, had the live Twitter feed displayed on a screen visible to the on-site participants, and facilitated the conversation by having one facilitator interacting with the on-site participants and the other facilitating the exchanges between on-site and online participants via Twitter. While the session was not flawless, it was an effective learning experience, and the result was a session that helped everyone see how this level of blended learning could produce engaging opportunities for everyone—both for those who were on-site and those who were online.

Another example for exploring this currently extreme level of blended learning comes through a session where learners were together in an on-site space and one of the learning facilitators was off-site. With little more than a blank wall, a projector and small mobile sound system hooked up to a laptop, and a laptop with a built-in webcam, information professionals were able to have the off-site facilitator see and interact with the on-site participants and have the on-site participants see and interact with the learning facilitator directly. Those who could see a life-size image of the presenter on that blank wall and hear her through the speaker system confirmed that they soon forgot that she was not physically in the room; it was the same effect audiences have, in well-designed movie theaters, when the sound and visual elements are so compelling that viewers are completely drawn into the action and set aside any cues that they are somehow separated from what is happening in the moment.

Technology continues to increase the opportunities that information organizations have for being where and when information users and learners need them to be. For example, information professionals can

* conduct learning sessions, such as live virtual office hours, via the chat function in Facebook via a private or public group within that social media tool;
* have synchronous and asynchronous learning sessions through a Google+ Community established by information professionals or other members of a learning community;
* connect with their information users "face to face" through the audio and video capabilities of Google+ Hangouts or Hangouts on Air (sessions that are set up in advance so they are recorded and archived the moment the sessions end);

- schedule and facilitate live chats via Twitter by creating specific hashtags to be used during those live learning sessions, and then see the learning continue through postsession asynchronous exchanges via Twitter with the same hashtag; and
- keep up with ed-tech developments through online resources including the Horizon Reports produced throughout the year by the New Media Consortium. The inaugural Library Horizon Report was published in August 2014.

Collaborations in Learning

There is no reason to talk only to others within the information world; the more interactions information professionals have with others involved in the training-teaching-learning process regardless of their professional affiliations, the better prepared they are as partners in the lifelong learning process. Many opportunities for collaboration exist, including

- becoming active with the Association for Talent Development, which is the premier workplace learning and performance staff training organization in the United States and beyond, and
- actively engaging in educational technology organizations tracking trends, challenges, and technology developments related to lifelong learning.

The New Media Consortium (NMC) is one example of the numerous resources and communities of learning available and demonstrates how large and well connected the on-site/online learning landscape is. What it does—among many other achievements—is document trends, challenges, and developments in educational technology through its Horizon Project reports. These reports, which now include specific editions for K–12 schools, higher education, museums, and libraries, along with attention given to community colleges and trade schools, draw attention to the expansive network of training-teaching-learning colleagues and organizations available to information professionals. These reports show how libraries-as-learning-facilitators interact with museums-as-learning-facilitators. They document how information organizations interact with K–12 and higher education and are often embedded in learning institutions. It starts with a commitment to being part of the learning landscape, builds upon decades of experience in training-teaching-learning, and continues with the information profession's commitment to explore and keep up with ed-tech developments.

"There are numerous reasons to believe that information professionals have a bright future in collaborating to meet the infinite, lifelong learning needs within the communities they serve, for they are as much in need of infinite, lifelong learning as everyone else within those communities."

All of this suggests that there are numerous reasons to believe that information professionals have a bright future in collaborating to meet the infinite, lifelong learning needs within the communities they serve, for they are as much in need of infinite, lifelong learning as everyone else within those communities. Information professionals must not forget, however, that they have to serve information users on their terms, in their locations, and within their time frames to remain effective partners in learning.

Conclusion

The idea that information organizations are a part of the lifelong learning landscape is far from new. Information organizations have more than 150 years of experience serving as "the people's university" and are now finding new ways to fulfill that role every time technological developments place new tools in our hands. Information organizations are overtly, and quite publically, embracing and claiming their place in the lifelong learning landscape. While they are beginning to brand themselves as lifelong learning centers, information organizations are not abandoning any of the other critically important roles they play in the on-site and online communities they serve. It is an exciting time to be entering and working within information organizations. If information professionals continue to embrace infinite learning and a commitment to fostering it for information users when and where they need it, the present and future of information organizations is even brighter than many already believe it is.

Notes

1. Michael Stephens, "Infinite Learning: Office Hours," *Library Journal*, last modified October 23, 2013, http://lj.libraryjournal.com/2013/10/opinion/michael-stephens/infinite-learning-office-hours/#_.
2. Ibid.
3. American Library Association, *Strategic Plan 2011–2015*, 2010, 2, http://www.ala.org/aboutala/sites/ala.org.aboutala/files/content/missionhistory/plan/strategic%20plan%202015%20documents/strategic_plan_2.pdf.
4. Ibid., 3.
5. Malcolm Knowles, Elwood F. Holton III, and Richard A. Swanson, *The Adult Learner: The Definitive Classic in Adult Education and Human Resource Development*, 6th ed. (Burlington, VT: Elsevier, 2005).
6. Carl Rogers, *Freedom to Learn: A Vision of What Education Might Become* (Columbus, OH: C. E. Merrill, 1969).

Part V

Information Organizations

Management Skills for the Information Professional

Business leaders should keep their organizational strategies updated in the face of continually evolving technologies, ensure that their organizations continue to look ahead, and use technologies to improve internal performance.

—Manyika et al. (2013)

Perhaps the most important skills in the information professional's tool kit are those aimed at helping the organization ensure that it can sustain its services and continue to evolve. Information professionals need to manage collections (including the procurement, classification, and preservation materials) and manage systems that provide easy access to information in a variety of formats. Information professionals need to manage, motivate, and inspire personnel. They also need to manage physical facilities and the technology within those facilities. And, importantly, they need to be able to assess the efficacy of their services, market new and continuing services, and communicate the organization's value effectively to stakeholders.

Part V provides information professionals an overview of the key management issues and strategies for the information organization. Spanning across the organizational department of personnel, budgets, facilities, collections, and technology, this section highlights the critical issues in effectively running an information organization. It also discusses the multifaceted and rigorous strategies for assessing services and presents marketing strategies that permit information professionals to better meet their customers' needs.

Welcome to *Part V—Information Organizations: Management Skills for the Information Professional!*

21

Management Skills

Janine Golden

Managers and leaders both play critical but different roles in today's information organizations. Yet every great leader must own some management skills, and every great manager should possess leadership qualities.[1] To help identify and distinguish between the two, the Library Leadership and Management Association (LLAMA), a division of the American Library Association (ALA), formed a competencies committee. This committee established a definition for each role as a first step before identifying the competencies:

Manager: a person in a position of authority in an organization who is responsible for employing human and material resources to accomplish the organization's purpose. A manager is task oriented. Managers are knowledgeable and proficient at a set of well-known processes, such as planning, budgeting, staffing, measuring performance, and problem solving. Their role is to help the organization meet the needs of their community in the most high quality and cost effective way possible.

Leader: a person who influences others to adhere to his or her ideas, values, and models of behavior. A leader is behavior oriented. Leaders are inspirational. They have the skills and abilities to move an organization forward by looking for creative ways to solve problems, motivate others to achieve, and create new opportunities while also staying focused on the mission of the organization.[2]

Using these role identifications, the committee used the ALA-based Core Competencies, primarily section 8, "Administration and Management," as a skeleton structure to help identify, develop, evaluate, and review leadership and management competencies for information organizations (see also chapter 39, "Leadership for Today and Tomorrow"). Section 8 of the ALA Core Competencies[3] helps guide the managerial skill sets included within this chapter. The topics introduced address organizational management authority and responsibility, change management, the planning process, the importance of collaboratives, and the value of advocacy. After completing this chapter, the reader should have an understanding of the complex and interrelated functions that comprise all levels of management and supervision required for the operation of information service organizations.

> **TEXTBOX 21.1**
>
> **Topic for Discussion**
>
> Are there additional sections, other than section 8, in the ALA core competencies that apply to managers of information professions?

Authority

A simplistic understanding of a management position is described as an authoritative role where managers take responsibility for running their organizations. An acceptable addition is the recognition that power and control are necessary components of managers who possess authority within an organization.

Power

The first component, power, is defined as "the capacity or ability to direct or influence the behavior of others or the course of events . . . political or social authority or control."[4] In 1959, social psychologists French and Raven identified the existence of power "sources":

- *Legitimate:* having the ability to prescribe behavior because of being elected or appointed to a position of responsibility.
- *Reward:* having the ability to reward and/or to remove negative consequences.
- *Coercive:* having the ability to punish if there is nonconformance to demands made.
- *Expert:* possessing distinctive knowledge, ability, and skills.
- *Referent:* owning a desire to emulate a person who has power.
- *Informational:* controlling the information needed by others in order to reach a goal.

The sources of power are provided by the organization (position) and developed by the leader (personal). Legitimate, reward, and coercive powers are provided by the organization; expert and referent powers are personal.[5] In 1965, Raven added a sixth base, informational power, which is a personal power.[6]

Control

The second component of an authoritative role is control. Since all activities within an organization do not always function smoothly, there exists a need for control. The process of control has three basic requirements: establishing standards, monitoring results and comparing them to standards, and correcting deviations.[7] Rue and Byars explain that controls are necessary so that a manager can be forewarned either of an existing or a potential problem. Management controls are used to "prevent crises, standardize outputs, appraise employee performance, update plans, and protect an organization's assets."[8]

Working within the culture of an organization, both terms—power and control—can connote a negative perception, depending on a manager's working style. Goleman outlines six management styles, each one having a distinct effect on the organization:[9]

Organizational Controls
- Budgets
- Financial
- Direct observations
- Written reports
- Electronic monitors
- Management by objectives
- Balanced scoreboards
- Management information systems
- Audits
- Break event charts
- Time-related charts

- *Directive:* is coercive, and amounts to do-it-the-way-that-I-tell-you-to-do-it
- *Affiliative:* places people first and the task second
- *Pacesetting:* includes managers who tend to do tasks him/herself
- *Authoritative:* includes managers who tend to be firm but fair

Janine Golden

- *Participative:* is more democratic, with managers who participate and also encourage the staff to participate as well
- *Coaching:* includes managers who help employees to develop into their full potential

Each style has its own pros and cons but nevertheless can impact how an informational organization is run.

Responsibility

Well-renowned management consultant Peter Drucker believed that if a manager claims authority, then along with that authority comes responsibility. Similarly, if a manager assumes responsibility, he/she claims to be the authority. Illustrating otherwise are two examples taken from the writings of Herbert S. White, distinguished professor emeritus, Indiana University.

White's first example concerns whether a particularly volatile issue should be brought to the board for policy resolution. Some individuals believe that the board does not like to be bothered by such potentially embarrassing problems. However, while this may be true, board members do not want to learn from the local newspaper that the organization is being sued. Their strategy is authority without responsibility.

A second example concerns individuals who live in one agency's taxing district but use an information center near where they work, the imbalance being that residents of bedroom communities travel into the city for their jobs, then go back to the suburbs where they live. They are given the authority via public user privileges, whether it is computer use, the ability to reference the collection, or perhaps attend a program. However, they own no responsibility since the organization is city operated, and they live in the outskirts of the city's taxing district.

Change Management

A main responsibility of a manager is to recognize the signs as to whether or not the organization can and should be improved. Most efforts at planned change include a diagnosis as to whether change is needed, a planning process for conducting the change, conducting the actual process with accompanying education, and finally an evaluation of the change process. Change can actually be considered as a component of organizational development since change is a process that hopefully increases the organization's performance. Because of the challenges that information organizations face in keeping pace with current information technology, the economy, the move toward evidence-based decision making, as well as maintaining a committed staff, more and more information organizations are finding the need to redevelop their services.

Change vs. Stability

Organizations often need to bring about change to ensure long-term sustainability. What needs to be kept in mind, however, is that there are certain aspects of the organization that need to be preserved in order to accommodate both continuity and change. Managers need to recognize the need to retain aspects of their behavioral practices, core values, philosophies, learning, and knowledge that contributed to their past success. "In short, they need to change, but at the same time they need to maintain some of those stabilizing elements that served them well in the past and may preserve them in the future."[10]

Decision Making

Authority and responsibility demand a manager's ability to make decisions. Depending on the management style, and the amount of authority and responsibility held by the manager, the resultant effects of a decision may differ. Variables such as the actual process of making a decision, the type of decision making used (e.g., group decision making), and the delegation of that decision all impact the outcome. The role of managers at all levels is to make decisions among alternatives, which at times can be painful. Managers need to understand what is workable in the organization while recognizing the need to empower the staff to take possible risks.

While the manager is typically the decision maker, the real emphasis "needs to be placed on the decision making, and the flow of information within organizations that instructs, informs, and supports the decision making processes."[11]

TEXTBOX 21.2

Four-Step Decision-Making Process

1. *Intelligence Gathering:* collecting pertinent information by knowing what information is needed, finding the best sources of this information, and then figuring how to go about getting this information.
2. *Design:* identifying several possible courses of action, noting all possible and desirable alternatives and evaluating each one based on which has the higher potential to assist with reaching the goal.
3. *Choice:* selecting the alternative that seems to be best suited to make the decision, realizing that the choice may be a combination of alternatives.
4. *Review:* examining the results of the decision and evaluating whether or not it has resolved the need initially identified. If the decision has not resolved the identified need, the process, or some steps of the process, may be repeated in order to make a new decision.

Implementation of Change

Change needs to involve top management, including the board and various stakeholders. Change also typically involves the process of unfreezing, change, and refreezing, which is a model that makes the steps involved in organizational or social change easily understandable.[12]

- *Step 1—Unfreezing:* makes an organization receptive to change
- *Step 2—Change:* when actual change is made
- *Step 3—Refreezing:* ensures that the change that was made becomes a permanent part of the organization

Because change in the organization typically involves the application of these three steps, it is usually best carried out as a team-wide effort. To make an impact when change occurs, a manager within the organization must be closely aligned with the current culture of the organization. Resistance is most people's first reaction to announced changes, but surmounting the obstacles presented by change is vital to an organization that wishes to survive.[13]

"Recognizing that staff will want to know why change is necessary and what the new goals or expectations are, the best approach for a manager is through supportive leadership, openness, integrity, and trust."

Many times the reason for this resistance during the transition is due to staff finding it difficult to let go of the past and not fully recognizing how the change will personally affect them. Recognizing that staff will want to know why change is necessary and what the new goals or expectations are, the best approach for a manager is through supportive leadership, openness, integrity, and trust.[14]

Janine Golden

Planning

One of the responsibilities of a manager involves planning and charting a direction for the information organization. Planning is generally known as a process of determining meaningful, achievable, and quantifiable objectives that an organization needs to pursue and then identifying what is needed to implement them. This involves data collection and analysis, evaluation, and decision making. Considerations include

- why the plan is needed,
- if the plan should occur on a formal or informal basis,
- how long the plan needs to be and whether the plan needs to be updated annually,
- whether the entire organizational staff should be involved,
- who should be involved and the identification of the stakeholders,
- why community assessment is necessary in the strategic planning process.

Without utilizing the planning process, managers may tend to organize, reorganize, and then organize again sooner than expected. Planning is critical, and it enables a manager to proactively affect the future. Without planning, organizations risk having to react to what others have already decided, for example in terms of budgets and staffing, and then "planning" to make the best of their reactive situation.

Strategic Planning vs. Long-Range Planning

Plans are often classified by function (or use) and emphasis. Two major types of planning strategies used by information organization managers are long-range planning and strategic planning. These strategies are different, even though many times the two are confused as meaning the same.

LONG-RANGE PLANNING

Long-range planning is the development of a plan of action by an organization in order to create a long-term direction. A set of agreed-upon goals are developed to guide the direction of the organization over a period of several years. This type of planning is data driven and can be done assuming that a manager knows enough based on current data about the stability of existing conditions and is able to reasonably project into the future. Included within this process is a subtype of planning called short-term planning. This is generally done annually and provides checks and balances for the long-range plan. Long-range plans generally consist of a vision, mission statement, goals, and objectives and include additional functional plans including staff development, collection development, technology, and marketing. A short-term plan may be the calculation of one year's budget, which is expressed in operational terms.

STRATEGIC PLANNING

Strategic planning, first emerging in the 1970s and 1980s, is used to help an organization "focus its energy, to ensure that members of the organization are working toward the same goals, to assess and adjust the organization's direction in response to a changing environment"[15]—the key words here being "assess and adjust the organization's direction." "Strategic planning looks at doing the right things (effectiveness) over doing things right (efficiency)."[16] It assists in examining the whole organization to see how each internal unit relates and ideally to help establish priorities and improve organizational performance. There are many ways that a manager can carry out a strategic plan. Some of the varied considerations might include using an analytical approach that uses scientific analysis, or using a customer-centered approach that focuses on the needs and desires of members of the community. Regardless of the approach used, three distinct levels exist: the strategic level, the action level, and the assessment level. At each level, what needs to be noted is the direction of the process (strategy), the effective implementation and knowing that everyone understands the process (action), and finally the evaluation of the measures and outcomes (assessment), which is critical to an organization's accountability. See figure 21.1.

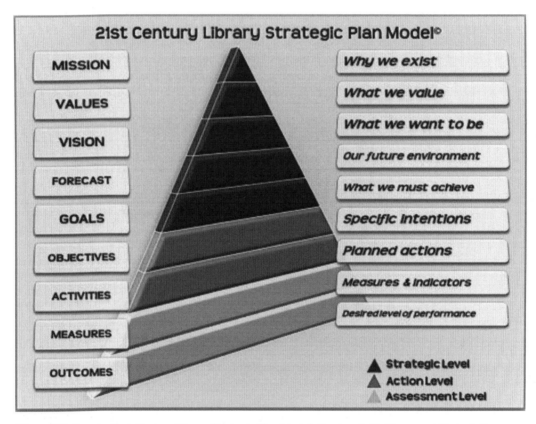

Figure 21.1 Twenty-First-Century Library Strategic Plan Model. *Stephen A. Matthews and Kimberly D. Matthews, Crash Course in Strategic Planning (Santa Barbara, CA: Libraries Unlimited, 2013), 8.*

In these days of accountability, outcome-based planning, which uses audience needs and desired results for plan design, is gaining in popularity. Penna and Phillips describe eight outcome models used in outcome planning, noting that one of the most widely used is the logic model. Here the organization provides a graphic overview of a program and outlines the anticipated outcomes and how they are to be achieved. This model identifies the target audience, the resources to be used, the activities, and the objectives.[17] Outcome-based planning frames the information organization's planning process in the selection of core outcomes. Key to the core outcomes are the selection of strategies, resources, and action planning. An accountability and evaluation framework created at the beginning of the planning process provides the basis for achievement-focused, accountable, and realistic plans.

Janine Golden

Topic for Discussion

Strategic management is an activity that must emanate from top management. Given this, why should a first-line or middle manager be concerned with it?

Assessment and Evaluation

Assessment and evaluation are critical to the planning process. Both focus on inputs, outputs, and outcomes. An organization can choose to use a formal assessment model that is structured and uses techniques such as a pretested survey or a focus group led by a facilitator following a script. An organization can also choose an informal method of assessment, which requires minimal resources and can be used for investigating single issues or gathering feedback. Examples of these are gathering information through comment forms and face-to-face interactions with customers at the reference desk.[18] Assessment needs to contain many elements:

- a set of performance standards based on the values of the organization, a predetermined set of questions generated by those standards, appropriate data-gathering tools whether it be focus groups or surveys, etc.;
- a defined plan for use of the data;
- a collection of data through different methods of assessment in order to corroborate the results;
- a strong attempt to maintain validity; and
- data collection instruments that have been pretested.[19]

By comparing the outcomes with the data noted in the assessment, managers then can easily form the basis of their evaluation.

Standards

"Standards are established criteria against which subsequent performance can be compared and evaluations can be made."[20] According to the U.S. Office of Personnel Management, organizations generally use one or both classes of standards: (1) those relating to materials and performance (including quality, quantity, cost, and time), and (2) those relating to moral aspects (including the organization's value system and ethical criteria that may be used to establish some sort of code of ethics). Standards are formulated during the planning process and in turn are key in the assessment of outcomes measurement.[21]

Adopted standards must be established, and then agreed upon, within individual information organizations. Once the standards have been accepted, then some sort of analysis must be performed in order to measure any activity against these standards. What is important to realize is that standards serve as important guides for information organization managers—a kind of benchmark.

Collaboration

Collaboration is the act of working together cooperatively for a common purpose to achieve benefit for all organizations involved. When organizations serve the same community and share the same vision, ideally the managers of those organizations form a collaborative. This happens particularly because the need for outreach by information organizations is stronger than ever. Many organizations, such as those providing similar services to the community, coordinate their efforts to save time, leverage resources, and integrate activities or services.

A few examples of these shared services include shared programming, technology, collections, electronic resources, and space. One of the most popular collaboratives involves libraries, archives, and museums. According to the Institute of Museum and Library Services (IMLS), researchers observe that "collaboration may enable . . . museums and libraries to strengthen their public standing, improve their services and programs, and better meet the needs of larger and more diverse cross-sections of learners, especially underserved learners."[22] In addition, more schools are also getting involved, and some are physically cojoined with public and academic libraries.

Check This Out

IMLS provides many examples of collaboratives on their website.
Visit: http://www.imls.gov/about/national_initiatives.aspx

Effective collaboration involves:

- an awareness of shared purpose, motivation to drive consensus, self-synchronization as individuals to decide when things need to happen, and participation by all;
- mediation as negotiation and collaboration;
- reciprocity through sharing;
- reflection to consider alternatives; and
- proactive engagement.[23]

One of the biggest challenges to collaboratives revolves around establishing outcomes. Each organization has its own outcomes and appraisal systems; however, there is also a set of shared, common outcomes established by the collaborative. The key element for an individual member of a collaborative is to assess individual performance without undermining the "essence" of the collaborative.[24]

Advocacy

Advocacy is "public support for or recommendation of a particular cause or policy."[25] For information organizations, this could lead to turning passive support into educated action for the organization's program that coincides with the agenda and priorities of stakeholders. Simply stated, advocacy's main function is to increase awareness and support for libraries and other information organizations through increased visibility. Information organizations overall are struggling to gain sufficient support; in particular, they are consistently being challenged to do more with less money, less staff, and less time. These factors impact the services that information organizations perform, illustrating the need for information professionals, staff members, trustees, and others with a vested interest in their organization to convey to their communities the value of the information organization. There can be specific times when an organization may want to target specific advocacy campaigns, such as to gain support for a new information facility, pass a tax referendum, or increase the information organization's overall budget.

Many national as well as international organizations are involved with advocating for information organization movements. One of the most well known in the United States is the American Library Association (ALA); the Office for Library Advocacy (OLA) was created to assist and support information organization advocacy by providing a network, resources, and training for advocates at all governmental levels. Many resultant ALA initiatives have been developed, some as a result of ALA presidents' platforms. ALA also has formed a political action committee (PAC) to assist ALA members in promoting their libraries at the local, state, and national levels. See appendix 21.1, "Grassroots and Frontline Advocacy."

Check This Out

America's Right to Libraries is one of the most recent campaigns stemming from ALA's past president Barbara Stripling's Libraries Change Lives initiative. Visit: http://www.ala.org/advocacy/declaration-right-libraries

---

Strategies

Advocacy is about building relationships, increasing the perceived value of the information organization, and creating support for the organization. Targeting, timing, and tactics are key advocacy strategies. Relationships—including personal relationships with customers and relationships with influencers, funders, or decision makers—are essential for information organization advocacy. In an advocacy campaign, decision makers, such as local, state, and national legislators, are identified and prioritized in order to develop a credible relationship. Visiting and providing the decision makers with updates throughout the year assists with this. ALA-sponsored annual National Library Legislative Day held in Washington, D.C., provides the opportunity for information professionals and their advocates to talk to congressional staff and policy makers at key foundations and organizations about the vital role information organizations and their staff play in communities. ALA also suggests the use of a legislator scorecard, which outlines votes and support of legislation that is important to and has an impact on the organization's community. Organizations need not operate in a vacuum when advocating for their organizations. There are additional organizations that can help libraries with advocacy strategies. One example is Every Library, a national nonprofit social welfare organization, which is dedicated to assisting organizations with political action at a local level to create, renew, and protect public funding for libraries of all types.[26] The key point is that information professionals be able to identify and make use of tools provided by library and information professional associations on the national, state, and local levels.

Conclusion

Information organization managers must understand their role if they are to maintain their organization's presence as a viable entity in their communities. The ability to recognize and acknowledge challenges and key issues of the field is essential in order for managers to sustain an effective internal and external organization.

Using the ALA Core Competencies, the LLAMA Competencies Committee summarized the knowledge, skills, and abilities that define the role of a manager. This report emphasizes that an information organization manager should know and, where appropriate, be able to employ

- the principles and procedures of planning and budgeting;
- the principles of effective personnel practices and human resources development (see also chapter 23, "Managing Personnel");
- the concepts behind, and methods for, assessment and evaluation of information services and their outcomes (see also chapter 28, "Demonstrating Value: Assessment");

- the concepts behind, and methods for, developing partnerships, collaborations, networks, and other structures with all stakeholders and within communities served; and
- the following concepts and methods—vision, interpersonal effectiveness, and managerial effectiveness.

It is through the understanding and mastery of these competencies that a manager should have the skill set necessary to successfully perform the complex and interrelated functions that comprise all levels of management and supervision required for the operation of information service organizations.

Appendix 21.1: Grassroots and Frontline Advocacy

Advocacy campaigns assist with connecting libraries and information organizations to value systems, particularly in the areas of literacy, innovation, and community engagement. Two common approaches used by organizations include grassroots advocacy and frontline advocacy.

Grassroots advocacy involves the use of a network of individuals who stand ready, sometimes even at a moment's notice, to assist with raising the level of awareness of information organization issues at the local, state, or national level. Strong networks of trusting relationships provide a context in which advocacy can be addressed effectively. This core of individuals from the general public (who are not professional lobbyists) act in support of the information organization when the time comes to contact legislators and other government officials regarding specific issues.

Their strategies involve researching whom the advocacy campaign needs to address and at what level (targeting), knowing when to connect with their target (timing), and planning what methods to use (tactics). Two major ways that this type of advocacy can be used is gathering signatures for a petition to stop an organization's budget cuts, or perhaps mobilizing numbers to attend a public hearing. Social capital is one of the most powerful predictors of outcomes for individuals and communities. Communication is commonly through mass mailing, e-mail, and social media; social media is especially effective in mobilizing a large portion of their membership base quickly, sometimes within minutes. Mobilizing people toward a common goal with events, such as a rally, a march, a read-in, or letter-writing campaigns, energizes support and demonstrates advocacy for the organization.

Strong networks of trusting relationships and an inclination of citizens to participate provide a context in which other community priorities can be addressed effectively. Grassroots advocacy can also be labeled as guerilla advocacy; this occurs when grassroots advocates use unconventional tactics, such as flash mob presentations, targeted promotional-driven encounters in public places, and viral marketing campaigns.

Frontline advocacy differs from grassroots advocacy mainly because the frontline organization staff is performing the advocacy, so it is done on a daily basis while serving the community both inside and outside of the information agency.[27] The focus is not necessarily on getting the message out to elected official and decision makers, but to users daily. During ALA past president Camila Alire's 2009–2010 presidency, she created the Libraries: The Heart of All Communities initiative. To help frontline organization staff identify the opportunities to advocate for the value of libraries and their own value on a daily basis, ALA provides tool kits created by frontline public, school, academic, and special librarians with those specific audiences in mind.

Notes

1. Brooke E. Sheldon, "Another Look at Leadership," in *The Portable MLIS: Insights from the Experts*, ed. Ken Haycock and Brooke E. Sheldon (Westport, CT: Libraries Unlimited, 2008), 59.
2. LLAMA Competency Task Force, *LLAMA Competencies Committee Report 2013–2014*, report to LLAMA Board, ALA conference, Las Vegas, Nevada, 2014.

3. "Section 8, Administration and Management," in the ALA Core Competencies, http://www.ala.org/educationcareers/careers/corecomp/corecompetences.
4. "Power," Oxford Dictionaries, http://www.oxforddictionaries.com (accessed August 1, 2014).
5. John R. P. French Jr. and Bertram H. Raven, "The Bases of Social Power," in *Studies in Social Power*, ed. Dorwin Cartwright (Ann Arbor, MI: Institute for Social Research, 1959), 150-167.
6. Bertram H. Raven, "Social Influence and Power," in *Current Studies in Social Psychology*, ed. Ivan Dale Steiner and Martin Fishbein (York, UK: Holt, Rinehart, Winston, 1965), 371-382.
7. Ibid., 398.
8. Ibid., 397.
9. Daniel Goleman, "Leadership That Gets Results," *Harvard Business Review*, March–April 2000, 78-90.
10. Noel Burchell and Darl Kolb, "Stability and Change for Sustainability." *Business Review* (University of Auckland Business School) 8, no. 2 (2006): 3.
11. Herbert A. Simon, *Administrative Behavior* (New York: Free Press, 1997), xvii.
12. Bernard Burnes, "Kurt Lewin and the Planned Approach to Change: A Re-appraisal," *Journal of Management Studies* 41, no. 6 (September 2004): 977-1002.
13. Samuel Olu Adeyoyin, Imam Abayomi, and Taofik Olatunde Bello, "Management of Change in the 21st Century Libraries and Information Centres," *Library Philosophy & Practice*, paper 695, 2012, http://digitalcommons.unl.edu/libphilprac/695.
14. Petra Düren, "Leadership in Libraries in Times of Change," *IFLA Journal* 39, no. 2 (2013): 134-139.
15. John M. Bryson, *Strategic Planning for Public and Nonprofit Organizations: A Guide to Strengthening and Sustaining Organizational Achievement* (San Francisco, CA: Jossey-Bass, 1995).
16. Peter Drucker, *Management: Tasks, Responsibilities, Practices* (New York: HarperCollins, 1973).
17. Robert Penna and William Phillips, "Promising Practices: Eight Outcome Models," *Evaluation Exchange* 11, no. 2 (Summer 2005), http://www.hfrp.org/evaluation/the-evaluation-exchange/issue-archive/evaluation-methodology/eight-outcome-models (accessed September 28, 2014).
18. Jeanne M. Brown, "Informal Assessment for Library Middle Managers," *Library Leadership and Management* 24, no. 1 (Winter 2010): 18-22.
19. Lisa R. Horowitz, "Assessing Library Services: A Practical Guide for the Non-expert," *Library Leadership and Management* 25, no. 4 (2009): 193-203.
20. Robert D. Stueart and Barbara B. Moran, *Library and Information Center Management* (Westport, CT: Libraries Unlimited, 2002), 420.
21. U.S. Office of Personnel Management, "Developing Performance Standards," last modified August 3, 2014, http://www.opm.gov/policy-data-oversight/performance-management/performance-management-cycle/planning/developing-performance-standards.
22. Alexandra Yarrow, Barbara Clubb, and Jennifer-Lynn Draper, "Public Libraries, Archives and Museums: Trends in Collaboration and Cooperation," *IFLA Professional Reports* 5 (2008), http://archive.ifla.org/VII/s8/pub/Profrep108.pdf (accessed August 1, 2014).
23. "What Is Collaboration?" Association for Information and Image Professionals, last modified January 15, 2014, http://www.aiim.org/What-is-Collaboration#sthash.1hDyl26v.dpuf.
24. Ibid.
25. "Advocacy," Oxford Dictionaries, http://www.oxforddictionaries.com (accessed August 1, 2014).
26. Every Library, last modified September 17, 2014, http://everylibrary.org.
27. "Frontline Advocacy Toolkit," American Library Association, last modified July 8, 2014, http://www.ala.org/advocacy/advleg/advocacyuniversity/frontline_advocacy.

22

Managing Budgets

Sara F. Jones

Managers of information organizations are not usually accountants or financial experts. Many enter the profession with no accounting training and little expertise in managing professional budgets. They often learn how to manage budgets primarily on the job, through trial and error. In light of recent challenging economic times, it has become increasingly apparent that in order to effectively manage any information organization, unit, or program, an information professional needs to be able to manage a budget effectively. The basic principles remain the same, whether managing a budget of $15 million or $1,500. After completing this chapter, the reader should have an understanding of how to plan a budget aimed at helping the organization achieve its strategic objectives.

Understanding Budgets

A budget is a plan that allocates money to specific elements of income (revenue) and expenses over a certain period of time. It is the foundation for any organization's planning process and the basic tool used to track and control spending. A budget is a fairly universal tool used by businesses, nonprofit organizations, and all forms of government.

Budgets typically cover a calendar year or a fiscal year, which for many institutions runs from July 1 through June 30, and for the federal government runs from October 1 through September 30. In some cases, budgets are biennial, which means they cover two years.

It is important to learn as much as possible and ask questions about the budgeting process. The more information professionals know about budgeting, the more they can advocate for funding aimed at meeting specific organizational objectives. Understanding budgets also makes it more likely that an information professional can take on additional leadership responsibilities, as managing budgets is a part of all leadership positions in an information organization.

Budgets and Revenue

It is a common misconception that information organizations only deal with the expense side of the budget equation. That is rarely the case. Even in an organization where the majority of income is derived from tax revenue, a budget must be used when requesting funds from a parent entity and determining how much revenue was allocated to the organization. Many information organizations (such as public libraries, academic libraries, special libraries, school libraries, etc.) are government entities that receive the majority of their funding from a parent agency, such as a city government, school district, or university.

There are two types of funds typically used to provide revenue to these publicly funded organizations, and it is important to understand the distinction. "General fund" is a term used to describe funding that supports government agencies by drawing from the parent organization's general ledger account. A special purpose fund, which some organizations have, describes funding (usually from a dedicated tax source) that is collected and set aside specifically for the organization's purposes. In a general fund, there is usually competition for scarce funding across all departments in a government organization, often including mandated public safety services like fire and police. Thus, an information organization's leader's ability to demonstrate the value of the services it provides and advocate for funding is an important part of ensuring that the organization receives adequate funding from the parent entity (see also chapter 28, "Demonstrating Value: Assessment").

> "General fund" is a term used to describe funding that supports government agencies by drawing from the parent organization's general ledger account.
>
> "Special-purpose fund" describes funding that is collected and set aside specifically for the organization's purposes.

In addition to an entity's general funds, many information organizations also benefit from supplemental types of income, which usually vary from year to year. These supplemental financial resources include contributions, such as direct donations by individuals or corporations, as well as grant funds awarded by government agencies or private foundations. In addition, several groups typically associated with information organizations either provide direct contributions or assist in raising funds for the organization. Examples include Friends of the Library organizations, a group of volunteers, and a library foundation (a nonprofit entity affiliated with the library that focuses on raising donations). Some information organizations also receive revenue through fines (e.g., on overdue materials) and fees (e.g., fees paid by college students used to fund an academic library).

Budgets and Expenditures

In addition to using budgets to understand and plan for revenue, budgets are tools managers can use to plan allocations prior to implementing the budget and then track and control expenditures. Through ongoing monitoring of the budget, managers can view actual amounts for each expenditure and identify any variance between the budget and the actual expenditures. Budget expenditures can be planned and controlled for the overall organization, as well as by department, location, or pro-

Budgeting Activities
- Managing employees
- Scheduling employees
- Managing hardware and software
- Ordering supplies
- Ordering books
- Reviewing materials or resources for selection
- Building management
- Programming
- Technology resources

gram. As an example, the organization might have a budget for a specific branch of an information system, or a budget for particular services or programs.

There are some activities involved in budgeting that might not seem obvious. For example, any purchasing decision involves understanding the budget, whether buying new technology, ordering books, or purchasing supplies for building maintenance. Individuals who manage employees have an impact on budget expenditures, as they schedule employees or decide to hire a new staff member (see also chapter 23, "Managing Personnel"). Decisions made regarding how many hours a building will be open to serve its clients also impact the budget. In addition, personnel are responsible for collecting and reporting data used by managers to make budget decisions, such as staff schedules and purchasing records.

Types of Budgets[1]

Line-item budgets are the most common type of budget. This type of budget lists expenses item by item, grouped by the type of expense (e.g., personnel, materials, training, travel). Line-item budgets are fairly simple to manage, as the amount of funds allocated for each line item makes it clear to the manager the total amount allocated for the line item. In addition, as managers review budget updates during the year, they can watch spending for each line item as time progresses.

Line-item budgets have several management limitations. First, when funds are spent all at once for a specific line item (e.g., purchasing a database) early in the year, it suggests that budgeting amounts are more than they should be early in the year. For the governing or oversight authority, this type of cash flow always needs explaining. They will need to know why the total amount for that line item was spent in the first month of the year. Another limitation of a line-item budget is that it gives little information linking expenses to programs or service goals. For example, salaries are usually listed together in a single line item, rather than listed by program or service, so actual costs for a program cannot be determined.

Other types of budgets include

- *Program Budgets:* Program budgets group expenses by program. An example might be a literacy program budget. The program budget then follows the line-item budget format, listing expenses such as employees' salaries, benefits, and operating expenses. In addition, program budgets include a cost allocation for shared overhead expenses, like use of facility space or utilities, and administrative functions, such as accounting and human resources. Program budgets are very effective for assessing budget allocations by program or service, which can be helpful when making budget-cut decisions or deciding to expand an existing program.
- *Performance Budgets:* Performance budgets attach funds to performance objectives. This type of budget directly connects the input of resources with the output of services. Performance budgets are used to demonstrate the link between funding provided by the public and the outcomes of services provided to the public.
- *Zero-Based Budgets*: Zero-based budgets rebuild all the budget numbers from zero. Zero-based budgeting requires managers to analyze every function within an organization to determine its needs and expenses. The largest downside of zero-based budgeting is that it can be very time consuming, and justifying every expense can be a waste of resources. The benefit of zero-based budgeting is that it prevents managers from keeping budget categories year after year; this makes it possible for managers to create budget categories that are in better alignment with the organization's current strategic objectives.

TEXTBOX 22.1

Topic for Discussion

What budget type seems most effective, and why?

The Budgeting Process

The budgeting process is ongoing and is often described as a four-phased cycle. See figure 22.1, "The Budget Cycle."

Sara F. Jones

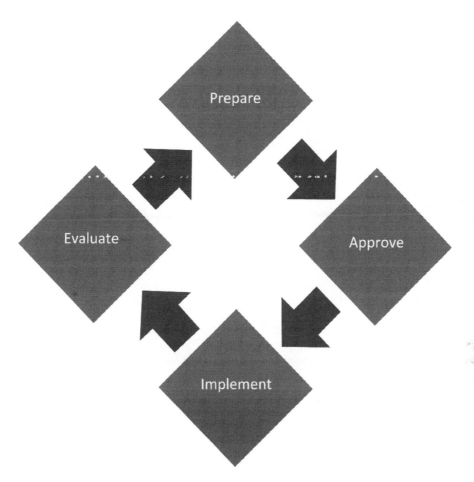

Figure 22.1 The Budget Cycle

Preparing the Budget

Good budget preparation starts with a meaningful strategic plan (see also chapter 21, "Management Skills"). Decisions regarding what to include in a budget must be based on that plan, ensuring that funds are focused on helping the organization achieve its strategic objectives. Unfortunately, some budgets are not based on updated strategic plans, but instead are created by adding a new layer to an old budget, keeping older budget items in place. Using this approach, an organization may have several budgeted items they no longer need, which remain in the budget year after year because leaders do not take the time to examine existing budget items and decide if they are still appropriate.

With a strategic plan in place before budget preparation, the plan provides guidance regarding how budget allocations can support strategic objectives and the types of expenses departments should plan for in the upcoming budget year in order to achieve those objectives. The process of generating the budget for the next year (or the next two years, if using a biennial time frame) should start with careful thought regarding what programs, services, and resources need to continue and what new initiatives fit the goals and objectives of the strategic plan. Each department provides recommendations regarding what to include in the budget and sends their requests to decision makers for inclusion in, or exclusion from, the final document.

Approving the Budget

There are a variety of ways budgets are approved, ranging from a process that may involve relatively few steps to a process that has many steps. The type of approval process is driven by the governing laws of the organization, including which parent organization (if any) is involved in the approval process.

To describe the budget-approval process simply, after the information organization finalizes the budget, it is shared with an oversight agency, which might be a library board or commission or an elected official. For public agencies, the budget is usually filed in some manner with the state government, and there are usually public hearings and notices involved. Managers responsible for budget oversight must understand the steps needed to get a budget approved, as well as the timelines, to ensure that each step is completed on time.

TEXTBOX 22.3

Typical Budget Process in a Publicly Funded Information Organization

1. Library creates the budget.
2. Library board, advisory board, or college/university official approves the budget.
3. Governing agency discusses budgets and combines all agencies in one budget package.
4. Governing authority approves the overall budget package.
5. Budget is implemented.

Implementing the Budget

Once the budget is approved, an online or printed document verifies what has been approved and provides details regarding approved expenditures. See appendix 22.1, "Types of Budget Expenditures." There are standard areas in virtually every budget, and they include

- salaries and benefits for personnel;
- services and supplies, such as purchasing materials for the collection, employee training expenses, and utilities; and
- capital expenditures for tangible assets valued over a certain amount (e.g., five thousand dollars) or building improvements.

Operating Expenditures

- Salaries and wages
- Employee benefits
- Professional services
- Programming
- Publicity
- Dues and memberships
- Leased equipment
- Lease or rent space
- Books and periodicals
- Software and databases
- Training
- Travel
- Utilities

Evaluating the Budget

A critical component of the budgeting process is ongoing evaluation. As important as it is to have a strategic plan to create a budget, it is even more important to use the strategic plan to evaluate the budget's effectiveness. This evaluation should be ongoing, occurring monthly or quarterly. Performance-based budgeting is very common for information organizations, and funding authorities often ask how funding directly affects desired performance outcomes. Ongoing budget evaluation allows a manager to explain the connection between budget expenditures and performance outcomes.

Managers at every level should spend time on budget evaluation. Since it is necessary for them to monitor the budget and make sure costs do not exceed amounts budgeted, that time can also be spent ensuring that the resources and services provided through the organization's budget are meeting expectations.

Because funding is very limited for many information organizations, it is important for managers to identify expenditures they no longer need. For example, libraries may have a line item in their budget for the preservation of books or periodicals, including tasks such as microfilming or periodical binding, when these services are no longer necessary. Managers should plan to take those unnecessary allocations out of future budgets. And during the current budget year, these unnecessary allocations can be shifted from one line item to another, ensuring that budgeted funds are reallocated to more relevant needs.

Funding Sources

Information organizations receive revenue from a variety of sources. Some of the revenue is fairly consistent, with the organization receiving stable funding levels year after year. Other types of revenue are not as stable, and the organization cannot rely on receiving this funding. In addition, some funding comes with specific restrictions regarding how it can be spent, while other funding allows the organization's leaders to determine how it is spent.

It is important for a manager to understand where revenue comes from and how much of the organization's funding comes from supplementary funding sources that may be variable in terms of how much money is received and how often it is received. The best practice is to integrate these variable resources into budget forecasts and expenditure plans, allowing managers to account for them in the budgeting process. See appendix 22.2, "Funding through Tax Revenue."

Government Funding Sources

Many information organizations rely extensively on public funding. For example, the majority of funding for public libraries, as well as publicly supported academic libraries and school libraries, comes from tax revenue. In some cases, the tax revenue is dedicated for libraries from a taxing district in the form of a rate or levy. Thus, libraries funded through a taxing district can be assured they will receive all funds raised through the levy. In other publicly funded libraries, the tax revenue is not directly raised to benefit a library, but instead it funds a range of local services, with the library representing just one entity that can receive funds. In this funding model, tax revenue is placed first in a general fund for a city, county, or state, and then decisions are made regarding how much of that revenue to allocate to library operations.

Supplementary Funding Sources

There are a wide variety of supplementary funding sources for information organizations. One type of supplementary funding is direct sources, such as fines and fees. This type of revenue is often a small portion of the budget, although it can be a more substantial portion of an academic library budget, which receives revenue from fees paid by college students. In addition to fines and fees, supplementary funding is often generated by organizations created to support the library. These include Friends of the Library organizations, volunteers dedicated to raising funds for the library, and library foundations.

Many information organizations also pursue grant funding, another source of supplementary revenue. Grant funding is typically used to develop and pilot new programs, expand or digitize collections, purchase new technology, train personnel, or update facilities. In academic libraries, grants can also be used to fund research conducted by information professionals. Grants are awarded for a short amount of time for a very specific purpose, with grant funders indicating how funds are to be allocated. Grant funders range from small, local private foundations with minimal guidelines regarding how funds are to be spent, to large national private foundations or government agencies that have very specific guidelines regarding how grant funds can be spent by the organization. Grants range from very small amounts disbursed for a single year to multiyear awards for substantial amounts. Also, proposals requesting a grant award must include a budget; thus budgeting skills are used in grant seeking as well as in administering grant awards.

A major source of federal grant funding for libraries is the Institute of Museum and Library Services[2] (IMLS). The IMLS awards grant funds directly to libraries through several highly competitive grant programs. In addition, libraries can receive grant funds through a formula-based program called the Library Services and Technology Act[3] (LSTA). State libraries receive LSTA funds from IMLS and then decide how to use the funds, either to support statewide initiatives or by distributing funds through subgrants or cooperative agreements to libraries located in their state.

Audits

It is fairly common for audits to occur. An audit is a systematic examination of financial or accounting records by a specialized inspector, called an auditor, to verify the accuracy and truthfulness of those records. Sometimes a financial audit examines a specific part of an organization's budget, such as one library program. Other audits involve a review of the entire budget for the information organization, while some audits may involve a review of certain financial information regarding the library as part of an audit of the parent organization. Audits can be a very positive part of an organization's budgeting process, as they can show a manager where funds can be managed more effectively. Audits can also foster development of good internal controls, methods that ensure all resources are used effectively and efficiently. Controls ensure that money is handled properly, including funds received (e.g., how cash and checks are handled and deposited) and how funds are spent (e.g., the purchasing process).

Financial Management Principles

It is impossible to be an effective manager of financial resources without having a comprehensive knowledge of the budgeting process. In some cases, managers are promoted within an organization and are able to learn the budgeting process incrementally and thoroughly. This gradual process to learn about budgeting provides many advantages as managers take on new oversight responsibilities and manage larger aspects of the organization's resources. However, in many cases, managers come from other organizations that take a different approach to budgeting. There is almost always some variation in budgeting processes across organizations. For example, although many public libraries may follow a similar budgeting process, the process can look quite different when comparing the process used in a public library with the budgeting process of an academic library. Regardless of the type of institution, many budgeting process elements are the same, and managers need to be competent in their knowledge and abilities to understand the process and be accountable for the financial actions of the organization.

"Another critical component of financial management is having a full awareness of the level of accountability that comes with being responsible for a budget."

Another critical component of financial management is having a full awareness of the level of accountability that comes with being responsible for a budget.

Sara F. Jones

When managers do not fully understand all the financial aspects of their organization, they are more likely to make critical mistakes. While having accounting professionals and financial departments to support managers is a tremendous asset, the ultimate responsibility for financial management still rests with the organization's top leader (e.g., a library director). Also, any leader who is part of the financial management process and has authority to approve expenditures carries the responsibility for those decisions. Mishandling public funds is a criminal offense, so budget responsibilities should not be taken lightly. All leaders who are responsible for approving expenditures must understand approved budget allocations and policies regarding how budget allocations can be disbursed. Handling public finances means being responsible and accountable to the public. Being unaware of budgeting practices or being poorly informed will never be an acceptable excuse for mismanagement of funds, whether done intentionally or as a result of incompetence.

Credibility is also a central element of successful financial management. Managing resources effectively means keeping spending within budgets. It also means following all legal requirements for purchases and making good decisions regarding any large investment, such as a major technology upgrade.

The organization needs to have one person who is ultimately responsible for budget oversight, ensuring that budget decisions help the organization achieve its strategic objectives and that resources are managed effectively. Also, having one person responsible for oversight of the organization's budget allows key stakeholders, including the public, to trust that their investment is well spent, whether the investment is tax revenue, student fees, donations, grant funds, or other resources.

Even with due diligence, budget crises can and do occur. These can come from a variety of directions, and many are outside a manager's control. Natural disasters can completely destroy collections and buildings. Many cities have been forced to declare bankruptcy, and information organizations have found it extremely challenging to continue offering services at any level. And just as there has been fraud and embezzlement in private corporations, there have been cases of fraud and embezzlement in information organizations. After a crisis, leaders must manage day-to-day operations as efficiently as possible and meet with all affected stakeholders to explore solutions aimed at returning the organization to a healthy and stable financial future.

Finally, an entire chapter could be written on handling budget cuts. In recent years, budget cuts have been a very common part of budget management for information organizations. Budget cuts can range from a few percentage points to cases where the organization needed to reduce spending by more than 50 percent. The same principles used to build budgets are used when making decisions regarding where to make budget cuts, and should begin and end with a meaningful strategic plan.

Conclusion

Budgeting is an important part of managing an effective information organization. As with any important responsibility, having a solid knowledge of the process is a critical element of success. It is also important to utilize input from every resource available and accept full accountability for decisions.

Appendix 22.1: Types of Budget Expenditures

Salaries and benefits usually require coordination with other entities. Health benefits might be handled by the organization, by the government entity, or in a pool of similar organizations. Retirement benefits also are coordinated with the public entity. In most cases, a public employment retirement system is in place that covers full-time employees and excludes them from contributing to Social Security. Part-time employees usually are included in Social Security contributions.

Employee raises for performance or a cost-of-living adjustment, often called a COLA, are also managed together. Compensation is often determined by a union agreement, so there are many factors needed to accurately calculate salaries and benefits. This portion of the budget is, in most cases, set for this type of spending and is not easily or readily moved to services and supplies spending categories.

Services and supplies line items will have a variety of categories.

Appendix 22.2: Funding through Tax Revenue

In some cases, organizations, primarily public libraries, are their own government organization and are typically called a district or special district. When funded as a district, the formation, governance, and structure are found in state law. Each state has some variations, but library districts exist in most every state. In a district, there are set taxes collected for the specific purpose of supporting the library.

There are a variety of other types of public library governance structures that dictate how they are funded, and they vary by town, township, municipality, city, county, consolidated city and county, multicounty, and a large array of possible variations. However, in the end, they are most distinctly separated by whether they have a dedicated tax stream or they compete with other parts of the government organization for their funding. In the latter case, they are funded from the parent organization's general fund.

Notes

1. National Center of Education Statistics, chapter 3: "Budgeting," in *Financial Accounting for Local and State School* Systems, 2003 ed., last modified July 2, 2013, http://nces.ed.gov/pubs2004/h2r2/ch_3.asp.
2. Institute of Museum and Library Services (IMLS), last modified August 28, 2014, http://www.imls.gov. The mission of IMLS is to inspire libraries and museums to advance innovation, lifelong learning, and cultural and civic engagement. IMLS provides leadership through research, policy development, and grant making.
3. Library Services and Technology Act (LSTA), last modified August 14, 2014, http://www.ala.org/advocacy/advleg/federallegislation/lsta. LSTA is also known as the Grants to States Program and is the largest grant program run by IMLS; it provides funds to state library administrative agencies (SLAAs) using a population-based formula. SLAAs may use federal funds to support statewide initiatives and services; they also may distribute the funds through subgrant competitions or cooperative agreements to public, academic, research, school, and special libraries in their state. The program has the benefit of building the capacity of states to develop statewide plans for library services and to evaluate those services every five years.

23

Managing Personnel

Cass Mabbott

At some point in most careers, information professionals find themselves in the position of managing other people. Sometimes it is managing other information professionals in a manager–staff relationship, other times it is managing volunteers, and still other times it is managing people on committees or spearheading a new project working with others. Even when people start out thinking that their dream is to be a children's librarian, they may end up as the children's department manager, or overseeing all of youth services, after an unpredictably short period of time. Managing personnel is challenging and requires skill in dealing with a variety of employee motivation and experience levels. In today's information environments, with many competing demands on static or shrinking budgets, it can be difficult to balance the needs of the employee, such as training and professional development, with other needs in the information organization. Understanding how to motivate personnel and manage them effectively is a critical skill. After completing this chapter, the reader will understand how managers can efficiently create a thriving staff who will contribute to the information organization's future successes. To do this, a manager needs to develop a true understanding and practice of transcendent leadership, cultural pluralism, and transactional management skills.

Transcendent Leadership: Foundation for Strong Personnel Managers

While this chapter is focused on personnel management, a transcendent leader—someone who demonstrates strong transformational and transactional management skills and practices cultural pluralism—is critical for managing people effectively within information organizations.

What Is Transcendent Leadership?

Transcendent leaders have both transformational skills (i.e., the ability to unearth the motivations of individuals and empower them to participate in cooperative relationships with colleagues, moving toward a common goal) and transactional skills (i.e., making schedules, calendars, policies, procedures, hiring and firing decisions, and day-to-day directives that keep an organization running). In addition, transcendent leaders take leadership a step further by being "reflective, value-centered, global in perspective, and a facilitator of dialogue."[1] In a global information age—where information is available anywhere, anytime, and without borders—there is little room for managers who are anything less than transcendent leaders when it comes to leading organizations that are dedicated to open-minded dialogue and perspectives. It does not matter if a manager leads a staff of four at a small rural library, oversees a staff of twenty-two in a law firm in the middle of Manhattan, or works alone as a consultant, transcendent management skills are a necessary part of sustaining the organization and meeting the needs of its stakeholders (see also chapter 39, "Leadership for Today and Tomorrow").

Transformational Skills

One of the most important transformational skills is understanding emotional intelligence. In fact, emotional intelligence and setting a good "mood" for the information organization can help employee retention and morale. Many scholars have discussed the importance of the *emotional style*[2] of leaders and the brain science behind managing one's own moods. Emotions are actually quite contagious, and a manager needs to be optimistic, sincere, and realistic. "[A] leader must first attend to the impact of his mood and behaviors before moving on to his wide panoply of other critical responsibilities."[3] A manager's mood and authenticity can impact the entire organization. This mood can be "caught" by employees and can either create harmony or dysfunction. Managers who are attuned to their own moods—being reflective—can authentically listen to colleagues and stakeholders, facilitate dialogue, serve as a model for other employees, and ultimately contribute to the health of the organization. Goleman, Boyatzis, and McKee recommend a very specific process to follow in order to be as emotionally intelligent a leader as possible. Although their approach has evolved over the years, their original idea entails following a five-part process that was created to foster a new way of thinking and feeling as a leader. See textbox 23.1.[4]

TEXTBOX 23.1

Five Steps for Leading with Emotional Intelligence

1. Who do I want to be?
2. Who am I now?
3. How do I get from here to there?
4. How do I make change stick?
5. Who can help me?

Transactional Management Skills

Transactional management skills include identifying staffing needs, training and professional development, performance appraisals, and recruiting and retaining staff. Granted, there are many more skills needed to effectively manage information professionals, but the skills discussed here represent a core of transactional management ideas. To explore this topic, check out the online supplement for more resources on managing information professionals and staff.

Identifying Staffing Needs

As a manager, it is essential to know how many people are necessary to safely and effectively run the organization. This usually comes down to how many hours of staff time it takes to minimally run a department. For example, what is the minimum number of people the organization needs to run efficiently if a colleague calls in sick, has a family emergency, or is trapped my inclement weather?

Cass Mabbott

Although each organization approaches this issue in different ways, it is important for managers to have a backup plan, know how to contact suitable substitutes, and be able to maximize—or repurpose—the skills of the available staff. And managers need to understand how employees are affected when there are not enough people for the organization to run smoothly.

Good managers must also be able to articulate to administrators why it is important to replace an employee who leaves the organization. Managers should know what the minimal and optimal levels of staffing are for each department before staffing becomes an issue and back up their assertions with data. See textbox 23.2.

TEXTBOX 23.2

Evaluating Staffing Needs

- How many people need to be routinely shelving each day so it does not get backed up?
- How many people need to be in the building so employees, volunteers, and patrons feel safe?
- What ratio of managers to staff is necessary to run each department efficiently?

Using these data, managers are equipped to make staffing recommendations based on feedback received from other supervisors, patrons, and volunteers.

TRAINING AND PROFESSIONAL DEVELOPMENT

Most information organizations offer their employees a very formal and thorough orientation and training program. Training new employees is vital to the health of any organization. It is important that key employees share a strong set of similar skills, such as how to conduct a performance appraisal, how to use databases and reference resources, and how to participate in the process to interview or hire new employees. Each employee should also have a thorough knowledge of the benefits and professional development offered by the organization.

Although the organization has a responsibility to offer training programs to its personnel, it is equally important that each employee and volunteer take responsibility for his or her own professional development, even if the organization does not provide funding for it. Managers should take an active role in educating employees about the value of developing their own personal learning network (PLN) and seeking professional development opportunities outside the organization (see also chapter 20, "Infinite Learning," and chapter 38, "Global Learning Networks"). The wealth of information that employees learn during professional development greatly enriches the organization when employees share that information and use it to better serve the community.

COACHING AND PERFORMANCE APPRAISALS

Every employee deserves a written record of his or her performance, which can be accomplished with regular performance appraisals. Nothing in a performance appraisal should ever come as a surprise if both the employee and the manager are doing their jobs.

In fact, employees should know where they stand at all times. If an incident—good or bad—should happen during the day, it is crucial to address it the same day. This type of timely feedback reinforces positive attributes of employees and identifies areas in need of change. Performance reviews open up opportunities for managers to offer coaching strategies that help employees improve performance. See textbox 23.3.

Coaching

Most people want to do a good job, and our lives can get very complex. Coaching helps empower employees and volunteers to be receptive and able to answer honestly.

- Let them know you have observed their behavior.
- Tell them what you would like to see changed.
- Ask if they have any input about your observation.
- Ask open-ended questions: Are you okay? How can I help?
- Then stop talking and just listen.

When leaders recognize employee accomplishments, either within the department or organization-wide, these efforts show the rest of the organization that the manager is paying attention and is concerned with both performance improvement as well as recognizing excellent performance. Some organizations liken this to being a good coach for an athletic team.

RECRUITING AND RETAINING STAFF

There is no stronger employee recruitment campaign than the staff and volunteers of any organization. Satisfied staff and volunteers, who are proud of the organization's accomplishments and feel well supported by organizational leaders, will be vocal advocates for the organization. They will share the organization's accomplishments and describe how much they enjoy where they work, in person and on social media. However, if employees or volunteers are unhappy, or if the organization has issues, word can get around fairly quickly. Employment candidates who hear disparaging remarks or read bad press about the organization are less likely to apply for open positions; these negative perceptions can also impact staff retention.

Professional networking websites such as LinkedIn offer unprecedented recruiting opportunities for today's hiring managers. Another tool to foster an effective climate for employee recruiting is to broadly share announcements regarding the organization's accomplishments and new personnel hired. Sharing news regarding how the organization is filling vacancies says a great deal about an organization's success, so it is important to make announcements in the local press, on the organization's website, in its newsletter, or in its blog. Remove job listings immediately after they are filled.

Topic for Discussion

How does the culture of an information organization affect the customer? How can a manager's mood affect—both positively and negatively—the working environment for his/her employees and therefore the community the organization serves? And why does this matter? What are the short- and long-term consequences of a negative organizational culture?

Cultural Pluralism

Diversity is no longer a complete description for the environments where today's information professionals work. It is a word that has been often used as a catchphrase for an organization's endgame—a goal, as in, "We want to be a diverse organization." A better term to use, and a more appropriate goal to seek, is that of cultural pluralism. In organizations that model true pluralism, leaders create an environment where nondominant groups participate fully in the dominant, established groups within the organization, while encouraging members of these nondominant groups to maintain their cultural, spiritual, ethnic, or sexual identity (see also chapter 4, "Diversity, Cultures, and Equity of Access").

Check This Out

There is a striking collection of examples at the Microaggressions Project.
Visit: http://www.microaggressions.com

Transcendent leaders empower their employees to participate in creating such a pluralistic environment. As an example, employees can help create policies that support cultural pluralism. Policies should discourage microaggression,[5] or the unintentional things people say in the workplace, perhaps without truly meaning to be racist, sexist, or prejudiced, but which nonetheless can truly be hurtful and offensive. It is important that overt prejudice and microaggressions not occur in the workplace. Employees are happier and more productive when diversity is not only tolerated but also celebrated.[6]

TEXTBOX 23.5

Topic for Discussion

What are some ways a manager can encourage teamwork and collaboration among his/her employees?

Conclusion

Managers who demonstrate their values with those they manage through authentic leadership and through meeting each new challenge with an open mind provide sustainable, solid futures for their organization. To meet the changing demands of the organization, as well as the needs brought on by the organization's staff, managers need to tune in to the cultural pluralism of their employees and be creative when it comes to resolving issues. Staff development and training make for positive attitudes and employee buy-in. With all of these skills in place, transactional management skills, such as recruiting, training, and performance appraisals, empower managers to quickly identify employee needs while also meeting the needs of the organization.

Notes

1. John Jacob Z. Gardiner and E. L. Walker, "Transcendent Leadership: Theory and Practice of an Emergent Metaphor," *International Journal of Servant-Leadership*, no. 5 (2009). See article listed in the works cited page for more information, as well as his research interests listed here: http://www.seattleu.edu/coe/edlr/Default.aspx?id=8692.
2. Daniel Goleman, Richard Boyatzis, and Annie McKee, "Primal Leadership: The Hidden Driver of Great Performance," *Harvard Business Review* 79, no. 11 (2001): 42–53, http://www.researchgate.net/publication/40964875_Primal_leadership__the_hidden_driver_of_great_performance/file/3deec52a72500dff3f.pdf.
3. Ibid., 44.
4. See textbox and Goleman, Boyatzis, and McKee article for more information.
5. The Microaggressions Project, "Microaggressions," last modified July 20, 2014, http://microaggressions.tumblr.com.
6. Harold Andrew Patrick and Vincent Raj Kumar, "Managing Workplace Diversity: Issues and Challenges," *SAGE Open* 2, no. 2 (June 2012), doi:10.1177/2158244012444615, http://classic.sgo.sagepub.com/content/2/2/2158244012444615.full.pdf+html.

24

Managing Facilities

Paul Glassman

Integrating the expertise of multiple disciplines, including architecture, engineering, interior design, and building design is a collective process. Each project comes with its own pragmatic considerations and cultural expectations. Therefore, there is no generic problem statement for a new building, facility, or space. Rather, in order to achieve a solution with nuance, depth, and complexity, each problem merits its own statement of parameters and constraints.

Thus, achieving an information organization's building design that is functional, flexible, and forgiving requires information from multiple sources. Although an integrated design process, one that empowers users and seeks their ongoing participation, would seem sensible, architects do not always develop a detailed building program based on the information that only users can provide. The most durable designs—those that allow for multiple uses, adapt to repurposing over time, and accommodate the complexity of information organization missions and operations—result from sustained and systematic collaboration among multiple constituents. User participation enables the design team to collaborate from the outset of the project to devise solutions to multiple problems.

After completing this chapter, the reader should have an understanding of

- the architectural and space design process,
- how to select appropriate tools and techniques for gathering user requirements in order to make informed design decisions,
- the articulation of needs in quantitative and qualitative terms to create a meaningful picture of user needs, and
- how to develop a disaster plan to ensure emergency preparedness.

A Paradigm for Facilities Planning and Design

Why is space planning important? With the concept of the third place, which is a social setting apart from home and the workplace, more information organizations are seen as extensions of home—as places for social interaction, discovery, collaboration, and contemplation. But to draw constituents to these spaces, they need to be perceived as comfortable, safe, neutral—even beautiful. Csikszentmihalyi and Hermanson suggest that motivation in public learning environments requires that they be supportive and "free of anxiety, fear, and other negative mental states."[1] Thus, a well-designed organization with those attributes will also be a successful learning space.

And why is user participation important? In addition to achieving buy-in for what may become a new design paradigm in the community or on the campus, there is a systemic reason: user participation can shift the basis of decisions from opinion to more measurable behavior and patterns of use.[2] A multidisciplinary team in Taiwan concluded that a collaborative design process ensures more successful buildings, especially when that process integrates the knowledge and experience of information professionals, institutional administrators, architects, and engineers—each group demonstrating respect for the other's "perspectives and priorities" and an openness to compromise.[3]

Several ethnographic methods for designing an ideal learning space leads to an outline of strategies for incorporating patrons into space planning and for soliciting feedback from information users. After describing the steps of the design process, the chapter outlines steps for assessing user needs with ethnographic methods, for expressing those needs in terms of a quantitative statement of need—the architectural program—and for safeguarding the result with an emergency preparedness plan.

The Design Process

Whether imagining the shape of a pencil sharpener or a church sanctuary, designers begin with a concept in the form of an abstract diagram or *parti* that communicates the core idea of the product. As the design materializes, the floor plan, a scale drawing of the spaces and their enclosures from above, emerges, sometimes from bubble diagrams (see appendix 24.1, "Bubble Diagram for Facility Design"), which are circles arranged on a page to indicate relative adjacencies of functional areas with no reference to scale, height, or form.

At this stage, the design is merely schematic, and ideally there will be multiple versions of the floor plan, each representing a distinct set of spatial relationships. For example, floor plans in a more finalized state represent the design development phase and provide cross sections and reflective ceiling plans (see appendix 24.2, "Sample Floor Plan"). Once feedback is integrated and a final design is produced, the architectural office produces construction documents, drawings for the builder (usually referred to as the "contractor" or "general contractor") and subcontractors, who are specialists hired by the general contractor (GC) to complete specific installations such as mechanical systems for climate control, electrical conduits, and plumbing.

Why is feedback important? As they develop, according to Peter Drucker, most successful innovations move toward an ideal by incorporating feedback.[4] But what is the source of feedback? How is it gathered? What happens if the architects do not request review during the design development phase and bypass feedback? For this reason, the establishment of a project team is critical. Architect Peter Gisolfi recommends that formation of a building committee with representation from multiple constituencies (e.g., elected officials, board of trustees, professional staff, frequent users, donors) be the first step.[5] The client representative—and even this role needs to be clarified and assigned—can assemble the team and schedule regular meetings. The client representative may be the public library director, the academic library dean or director, the college chief financial officer, or even an independent

> "A well-designed organization—'free of anxiety, fear, and other negative mental states'—will also be a successful learning space."

TEXTBOX 24.1

Topic for Discussion

How is the staff in the information organization involved in the planning and design for building design and renovation?

project manager employed by the client apart from the design professionals. Regardless of who assumes the role, the client representative plays an irreplaceable role in ensuring that there is a place for the expression of user needs (see also chapter 17, "User Experience").

Assessing User Needs

What are the key decision-making areas in the design of the information organization? Even in advance of engaging a design professional or contractor, information professionals can and should be able to justify and offer a rationale for the project with a needs assessment. Aaron Cohen and Associates have produced a survey for both public and academic libraries in which they outline present and future space allocations by activity and function: books, e-books, e-readers, computers, program rooms, magazines/periodicals, staff, group study rooms, tutoring, events, and other programs.[6]

Multiple methods exist for gathering data on user behavioral patterns and expectations. For example, at the River Campus Libraries of the University of Rochester, faculty were interviewed and video-recorded to document their work habits and environments. In another study at the same institution, students were given disposable cameras and asked to photograph a series of objects and places that revealed their emotive relation to research, academic work, and library space (see also chapter 24, "River Campus Libraries Twenty Assigned Objects and Places" in the online supplement).[7]

Although this study was not applied fundamentally to assess user needs in information organizations, nevertheless, its ethnographic method (fieldwork that observes and describes human culture) is wholly transferrable to those seeking a greater understanding of user behavior and needs in library spaces (see also chapter 12, "Information Needs: Understanding and Responding to Today's Information User").

Another important study is ERIAL (Ethnographic Research in Illinois Academic Libraries), a two-year study of how students conduct research.[8] Like the Rochester project, ERIAL's central objective is not to assess user needs in preparation for library design, but the techniques and results can still be used toward that end. See table 24.1, "Tools for Collecting User Data," for a list of instruments used in assessing user needs.

Table 24.1. Tools for Collecting User Data

Tools for Collecting User Data	
Librarian interview	Faculty in web design workshops
Librarian photo journals (visual records of activities or processes)	Librarians/staff in web design workshops
Faculty interview	Research process
Student interview	Student cognitive mapping (diagrams describing key aspects of thought processes)
Student photo journals	Student research journals (diaries of the research process)
Student mapping diaries	Research paper retrospective interviews (interviews with students after the research papers have been completed)
Students in web design workshops	Student space design workshops (workshops gathering information from students on their preferences for work spaces)

Paul Glassman

The ERIAL project also offers guidelines for administering many of these instruments, advising that, although the project will take longer than anticipated, costs are low. Consulting with a trained ethnographer (a fieldworker who observes and records human culture) is beneficial, while the members of the research team can come from a variety of disciplines and backgrounds. The project also provides a four-part structure for any project of this type: planning, data collection, analysis, and reporting and concluding. In an academic environment, an additional time consideration is the review and approval of the project by an institutional review board (IRB), which will authorize behavioral research involving human beings.[9]

Amanda Etches classifies methods for data collection into three groups: attitudinal (surveys, interviews, focus groups), behavioral (observation, walk-throughs, journey maps), and participatory (cognitive maps and reverse guided tours). By allowing for easy selection of one activity from each of the three methods, these classifications are useful for simplifying the ethnographic process.[10]

Information organizations of varying size have experimented with ethnographic studies in preparation for building planning, design, and construction. For example,

- Students enrolled in a course at Dalhousie University, in one-hour increments, observed fellow students in the library and recorded general surroundings, characteristics of student groups, duration of use, patterns of interaction, and circulation through architectural space.[11]
- At Purdue University Libraries, the planning for the construction of an integrated classroom and library building to accommodate active-learning pedagogies provided the opportunity to gather input from instructors, students, and information professionals. Using observation and interview techniques, the study aimed to gather the most significant needs and wants of each stakeholder group as they related to working in an active learning environment, both in and out of the classroom. The results of the study became a centerpiece in the academic program statement for the integrated building.
- At Seattle Pacific University, the cultivation of student participation in the design process began with identification of multiple types of student resources, from academic to social, for gathering input to align space planning with user needs. Subsequently, the library established an aesthetics team in order to evaluate and implement student recommendations on space use.
- At Sonoma State University, the user feedback strategy was linked to its pursuit of a sustainable culture of assessment, resulting in the creation of a planning tool kit for soliciting user input on a variety of design issues.

Perhaps because of the diversity of their constituencies and their government-based funding, public libraries have used different methods for establishing design and planning guidelines (see also chapter 8, "Community Anchors for Lifelong Learning: Public Libraries"). For example, New York's Center for an Urban Future has launched its Branches of Opportunity program by requesting proposals from architects and planners for prototypical designs for branch libraries, with the goal of making their spaces more open and dynamic.[12] Some public libraries employ one-page patron surveys exploring spatial prototypes, resulting in adoption of a retail prototype such as Barnes & Noble bookstores or Apple Stores.[13] Some public libraries in California (San José, Hayward, and Los Angeles County) have gone so far as to hire a retail store consulting firm to examine how readers move through and use their facilities. After the firm, Envirosell, documents the patterns of movement by patrons over several days with video recordings, those patterns are plotted onto the floor plan of the library to indicate key nodes of activity.[14]

Young adult spaces are possibly the most fertile area in public libraries for user-centered design.[15] A grant from the Institute for Museum and Library Services (IMLS) funded an exploratory study of twenty-two young adult divisions in public libraries, in which not only did the information professional in each setting record a short video tour of the young adult space, but an adolescent patron also created a video tour, thus giving the teen user a voice in evaluating renovated spaces.[16]

Expressing User Needs

Once the data is collected, analyzed, and reported, the goal is to articulate the need with quantifiable requirements by describing existing conditions, providing estimates of spatial requirements, and creating a program from that information.[17] The architectural or design program is a list of quantifiable, functional requirements. It is not a design solution; rather, it is a problem statement (i.e., a definition of the dominant objectives of the project). It can serve as a checklist after a solution is identified to ensure that functional and space needs have been addressed properly.

In 2005, Hofstra University initiated a plan to renovate and transform the public areas of the main floor of the Joan and Donald E. Axinn Library, completed in 1967 to the designs of Warner, Burns, Toan & Lunde. Renovation architects were provided and worked closely with a detailed program (see chapter 24, "Joan and Donald E. Axinn Library" in the online supplement).

In 2013, Felician College was awarded a grant from the Building Our Future Bond Act of the state of New Jersey for the renovation of the abandoned Messler Library into an education commons. (The college purchased the original campus of Fairleigh Dickinson University in Rutherford to serve as its residential campus.) In advance of commissioning Arcari + Iovino Architects, library faculty and staff members, based on interviews of faculty and students, devised a concise program areas summary, which served as the basis for the design (see chapter 24, "Felician College" in the online supplement).

In the cases of both Hofstra University and Felician College, the assertive behavior of library faculty and staff created a close collaboration with design professionals to integrate sensible and practical design parameters into the project.

Preparing for Emergencies

With the investment of time, expertise, mental energy, and financial resources into a new or carefully renovated information environment, a new or renovated environment needs to be prepared for natural and other disasters. With the Online Disaster-Planning Tool from the Northeast Document Conservation Center (NEDCC), library staff can, with reasonable time and financial outlay, create a usable emergency preparedness plan.[18]

To be useful in stressful circumstances, the document should be concise. Its key components are as follows: first-response contact information (e.g., police and fire departments, campus security and physical plant offices), locations and types of emergency supplies (e.g., wet-dry vacuum cleaners, latex gloves, freezer bags, duct tape), salvage priorities (e.g., special collections, archives, rare books), damage evaluation, procedures for various types of materials (e.g., paper-based, nonprint), and procedures for smoke and soot removal. The document typically ends with a list of local vendors or service providers, such as freeze-drying and desiccant drying, and disaster recovery firms, which usually assist with water damage, fire damage, and mold remediation.

> **TEXTBOX 24.2**
>
> **Topic for Discussion**
>
> What is the process of preparing for emergencies while assuring that current users' needs are being met?

Conclusion

Whether referred to as participatory design, cocreation, or user-driven renovation, implementing a strategy for incorporating user feedback into the design of new or renovated facilities can be of great value in identifying planning priorities. Taking into consideration the user perspective is an economically sound approach when it prevents investment in solutions of little importance to patrons.

Shaping information space is an energizing experience for those privileged to participate. Therefore, engage as many of the professional staff members as possible in the planning and design development stages. Gather and review information thoroughly. Double the time investment and be prepared to delay the completion date. And be prepared in the end to settle for less, bearing in mind that any improvement to the information organization environment adds value.

"Whether referred to as participatory design, cocreation, or user-driven renovation, implementing a strategy for incorporating user feedback into the design of new or renovated facilities can be of great value in identifying planning priorities."

Appendix 24.1: Bubble Diagram for Facility Design

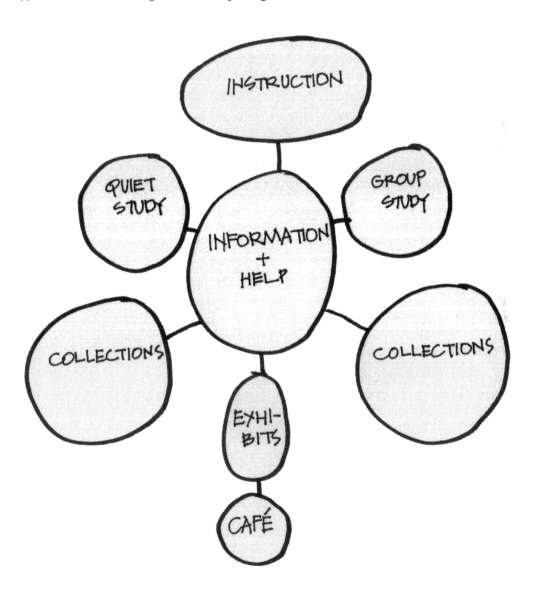

Appendix 24.2: Sample Floor Plan

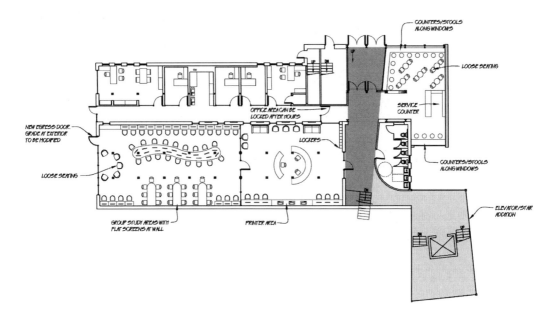

Notes

1. Mihaly Csikszentmihalyi and Kim Hermanson, "Intrinsic Motivation in Museums: What Makes Visitors Want to Learn?" *Museum News* 74, no. 3 (1995): 35.
2. Amanda Etches, "Know Thy Users," *Reference & User Services Quarterly* 53, no. 1 (2013): 14.
3. Pei-chun Lin, Kuan-nien Chen, and Sung-Shan Chang, "Before There Was a Place Called Library—Library Space as an Invisible Factor Affecting Students' Learning," *Libri: International Journal of Libraries and Information Services* 60, no. 4 (2010): 347.
4. Peter F. Drucker, *Managing for Results: Economic Tasks and Risk-Taking Decisions* (New York: Harper & Row, 1964), 141.
5. Peter Gisolfi, "Melding Minds to Make a Library: Successful Libraries Are Designed Collaboratively," *American Libraries*, September/October 2013, 40–41.
6. Alex Cohen, "Outcomes Survey for Public Libraries," Aaron Cohen Associates, 2014, https://docs .google.com/forms/d/1OQbGDkH9mKiJQLvZcoLfEZjhIgwT99x2QEhfdYqk2OU/viewform.
7. Judi Briden, "Photo Surveys: Eliciting More Than You Knew to Ask For," in *Studying Students: The Undergraduate Research Project at the University of Rochester*, ed. Nancy Fried Foster and Susan Gibbons (Washington, DC: Association of College and Research Libraries, 2007), 41.
8. Andrew Asher and Susan Miller, "So You Want to Do Anthropology in Your Library? or A Practical Guide to Ethnographic Research in Academic Libraries," ERIAL Project, http://www.erialproject.org/publications/ toolkit (accessed July 5, 2014).
9. Etches, "Know Thy Users," 2013, 14–17.
10. Ibid.
11. Linda Bedwell and Caitlin Banks, "Seeing through the Eyes of Students: Participant Observation in an Academic Library," *Partnership: The Canadian Journal of Library & Information Practice & Research* 8, no. 1 (January 2013): 4.
12. David Giles, *Branches of Opportunity*, Center for an Urban Future, January 2013, http://nycfuture.org/ pdf/Branches_of_Opportunity.pdf.

13. David Kernohan, John Gray, and John Daish, *User Participation in Building Design and Management: A Generic Approach to Building Evaluation* (Oxford: Butterworth Architecture, 1992), 129.
14. Joseph R. Matthews, *Research-Based Planning for Public Libraries: Increasing Relevance in the Digital Age* (Santa Barbara, CA: Libraries Unlimited, 2013), 145.
15. L. Meghann Kuhlmann, Denise Agosto, Jonathan P. Bell, and Anthony Bernier, "Learning from Librarians and Teens about YA Library Spaces," *Public Libraries* 53, no. 3 (2014): 24–28; Anthony Bernier and Mike Malel, "YA Spaces and the End of Postural Tyranny," *Public Libraries* 53, no. 4 (July/August 2004).
16. Kuhlmann et al., "Learning from Librarians and Teens," 2014.
17. WBDG Aesthetics Subcommittee, "Engage the Integrated Design Process," *Whole Building Design Guide*, last modified August 31, 2014, http://www.wbdg.org/design/engage_process.php.
18. Northeast Document Conservation Center, "dPlan: The Online Disaster-Planning Tool for Cultural and Civic Institutions," 2006, https://www.dplan.org.

25

Managing Collections

Wayne T. Disher

Collection management is a complex process that involves strategic planning, innovation, change management, and community analysis. This chapter discusses those responsibilities through an exploration of how collections have evolved over time and how they are likely to evolve even further in the digital future, especially as users interact with technology in new ways and have different demands and expectations regarding how they access and use collections. After completing this chapter, the reader should have an understanding of how and why collection management took its current shape. Readers will also acquire an understanding of why it is necessary for managers to create new and innovative ways to offer information collections to users. This chapter also presents recommendations to help deal with the challenging issues in developing the best possible collection. See appendix 25.1, "Basics of Building a Collection," for a summary of basic collection management activities.

How Collections Have Evolved over Time

Perhaps as far back as when Ptolemy collected papyrus scrolls and stored them at the ancient Library of Alexandria, collection developers have focused most (if not all) of their attention and budget on the printed word. Modern-day collection developers have not been immune to equating a society's cultural knowledge solely with the physical content of printed books. As technology and publishing innovation made it easier and less costly to mass produce the printed word, the number of books collected in U.S. information organizations increased exponentially. The publication of printed books went from seventy-eight thousand in 1948 to nearly two million in 2005.[1] During the same period, print collections grew at similar rates.[2]

Printed material remained the focus of collection managers, even as collections expanded in the 1950s and 1960s to include media. Although user demands for music and film certainly pressed collection managers to turn attention to alternative material formats, 85 percent of information organizations' collections were still comprised of books.[3] This occurred at a time when mass communication and media professionals like Marshall McLuhan were proclaiming the death of printed material. Collection developers most certainly saw community expectations and behavioral patterns change. However, much of the evidence suggests that they either ignored these changes or chose to collect the material they were most comfortable with providing—books.

Society changed even more drastically during the 1980s and 1990s. Television, video-gaming, and of course the Internet instilled new user behaviors that favored a preference for visual stimulation, virtual environments, and the ability to think and be entertained in a far less linear fashion than that provided by the printed word. While collection managers did begin to address community demand and shifting user preferences by adding small collections of film, music, and other formats, they did not turn their primary focus away from the printed book. In fact, the Institute of Library and Museum Services reported that, in 2010, the proportion of print materials in the information organization's collections—at least in the public library—had actually increased to 87 percent.[4] Meanwhile, in the retail world, business managers understood the need to adapt to new behaviors and were responding to the public's shifting reading habits. For example, online bookseller Amazon.com reported in 2011 that it was selling more e-books than printed ones.[5] The consumer world changed, but the information organization's collections, for the most part, did not. It seems that collection managers over the last century equated "library collections" to mean "our collection of books."

The Book Brand

Collection managers can point with at least a modicum of pride to the success of branding "the book" as a professional product. This collecting activity has taken a firm hold in the mind of information users. In 2005, the Online Computer Library Center Inc. (OCLC) conducted an extensive survey of users around the world on their perceptions of libraries.[6] The published report revealed that roughly 70 percent of respondents first thought of "books" when they thought of a library. Another more recent report[7] conducted by the Pew Research Center revealed that 80 percent of survey respondents cited books as the library's major resource. While businesses and organizations spend millions on advertising and marketing campaigns to achieve a high level of brand recognition that books already enjoy, it should pose serious concerns for information managers. If an organization relies only on one product or service, what happens when it becomes unnecessary?

Fortunately, communities also recognize the benefit information organizations play in creating an information-literate society. Whether by supporting tax measures or by visiting information organizations in record numbers, society—for the time being—respects the relationship between communities and information organizations. Information professionals have exhibited their expertise in retrieving the most useful information while teaching others to do the same, proving their positive role in the advancement of information literacy.

With the information organization's focus on information literacy (see also chapter 16, "Teaching Users: Information and Technology Literacy Instruction"), collection managers must now maintain collections that work seamlessly with their role as teachers, coaches, and partners in the information exchange process. However, by focusing most of the institution's collecting activity on the printed book, the collection manager puts the organization's commitment to advancing information and technology literacy at significant risk. Certainly the things collection managers have done in the past have been incredibly valuable—even critically important—to the successful expansion of information literacy in our society. The collecting activities that served that purpose well in the past, however, could soon reach their expiration date. At this point in time, there seems to be a need for a new approach to collection management if information collections are to remain meaningful to the communities they serve. The new approach involves a strategic planning process that includes substantial thought about new trends, technology, and changes in user behavior.

TEXTBOX 25.1

Topic for Discussion

The author emphasizes that this is not the time for managers to immediately discard everything that has to do with the printed book. Do you think this is true? When do you believe that it would be appropriate to do so?

Strategic Planning and the Collection

Studies in professional journals attest to the importance of strategic planning in organizations, including information organizations (see also chapter 21, "Management Skills"). It is a critical aspect of collection management as well. Although collection managers spend a considerable amount of time evaluating the internal value (the strengths and weaknesses) of collections, their planning efforts all too often stop there, without considering the external impact (the opportunities and threats) of their decisions. The collection manager must pay attention to external trends, such as reader preference and emerging technology, and visualize how those trends will affect what would be best to include in the collection. At the same time, an analysis of current collection practices in light of those trends should be made to determine if the way that trend is going is aligned with the collection development plan. The desired result is that the trend and current practice are converging rather than diverging.

> "The collection manager must pay attention to external trends, such as reader preference and emerging technology, and visualize how those trends will affect what would be best to include in the collection."

Divergence is exemplified in the practice of inventory control, a process that involves much labor. So much time is spent accounting for printed material that the information manager loses sight of the shift in user demands. Inventory control, although necessary to keep the collection relevant, often becomes tantamount when set alongside new trends for immediate access in any format.

Strategic planning helps collection managers recognize when user demands are shifting, enabling them to respond to those shifts by adapting their collection management plans. The lesson here is that having prior knowledge of possible new trends and thinking strategically about those trends gives one a tactical advantage. If collection management practices fail to focus on today's user needs and anticipate future trends, information organizations could be in real trouble. Managers must continuously reposition their collections and keep them viable in a technologically and information-literate society.

> **TEXTBOX 25.2**
>
> **Topic for Discussion**
>
> Strategic planning is a critical component of an information organization's success. What strategic opportunities and threats would be important for the collection manager to consider?

Tomorrow's Collections: Preparing for a Postprint World

Will the postprint world be completely paperless? The answer is not clear, and the debate rages on. The question as to whether society will (or should) become paperless can be left for others to debate. While there is still a significant user base for print collections, particularly for children, tomorrow's collections will (and should) necessarily look quite different than yesterday's collections. Current trends indicate a much larger demand for access to electronic content. Even if, or when, society becomes completely paperless and invests all its efforts in producing and exchanging informational content only in electronic form, the change will not happen quickly.

However, the change that will happen quickly (if it has not happened already) is in user perception regarding information collections. Because electronic information is delivered to almost anywhere more quickly and more conveniently than other resources, users may perceive that the electronic format is the most valuable resource for their information needs. In a postprint world, digital information resources can no longer be a secondary priority for collection managers. Furthermore, forward-thinking managers move beyond inventory control (check in, check out, shelve, and reshelve) as a primary focus and instead work to increase information literacy by helping communities access and use collections more creatively.

Community Expectations and the Role of the Collection Manager

Strategic planning and evaluation are important parts of collection management. So too is the principle that the collection's existence is to effectively serve the community that supports it. The success of the information organization, and users' perceptions of the collection's relevance, are built on understanding the user community today and anticipating its needs for tomorrow (see also chapter 3, "Information Communities: Defining the Focus of Information Service"). For example, collection managers must realize that most users want to access information without physically visiting buildings. Saving the reader's time is one of the five laws of library science proposed by S. R. Ranganathan[8] back in 1931 (see textbox 25.1).

Table 25.1. Ranganathan's Laws of Library Science

Ranganathan's Laws of Library Science
1) Books are for us.
2) Every reader his [or her] book.
3) Every book its reader
4) Save the time of the user
5) The library is a growing organism

Source: R. S. Ranganathan, *The Five Laws of Library Science* (London: Edward Goldston, 1931)

The 2012 survey of *eBook Usage in U.S. Public Libraries*[9] reported that e-book use the previous year had quadrupled. An anticipated 70 percent continued rise in demand was expected. In academic organizations, e-book collections grew more than 40 percent in 2012[10] as user demands for better access increased. Use across all information environments points to similar demands for electronic material. Such statistics illustrate that information users are placing more and more value on access to digital material in the postprint society. They expect information organizations to provide access to it, not debate its staying power.

Many collection managers are repositioning information organizations to take advantage of electronic resources and to meet the digital demand. However, the pace may be frustratingly slow for a society that has become more and more tech savvy. Collection content has become user driven. A collection manager has to convince key stakeholders to invest and support the strategic direction for the collection. The current community of information users is demanding collections with a great deal more electronic material, and the format of that material will continue to evolve rapidly. As such, managers need to be open to the evolving nature of information formats and focus on users' learning experience and information needs when making collection management decisions.

Challenges and Opportunities in Collection Management

Resources are an organization's most important asset, a means to meet its mission. The same is true with the resources available to a collection manager, which are usually scarce and must be appropriated to specific goals prudently. As has been repeatedly shown in public, academic, and school financing for information materials, the resources needed by collection managers to meet their organization's mission will likely be greater than the funds available. So how should the collection manager reconcile the gap between the need for more collection formats and the need for more money to keep the collection current and accessible? Remaining innovative and technologically advanced is the key (see also chapter 22, "Managing Budgets"). Collection managers looking toward innovation must take advantage of newer collection development models (such as patron-driven acquisition and cooperative collection development) that help meet demand, provide wider access, and increase the relevancy of an information organization's collections within the community.

With limited resources, it is critical for the collection manager to adopt a more "demand-driven" philosophy and look for collection-building processes that focus first on community demand before considering other selection criteria. Patron-driven acquisition models, while not necessarily new to the information environment, do seem to be gaining popularity with collection managers across all information environments. In adopting these models, collection managers emphasize to users that user needs and user wants are the core of their collection-building efforts.

> "With limited resources, it is critical for the collection manager to adopt a more 'demand-driven' philosophy and look for collection-building processes that focus first on community demand before considering other selection criteria."

Complex licensing policies and expensive pricing from vendors and publishers may prevent many information organizations from providing electronic content on their own. Therefore, efforts must be made to find opportunities to create collection partnerships and share information resources cooperatively as members of a consortium. Two examples of very successful collection partnerships are the California Digital Library and the Northeast Research Libraries Consortium. Both of these cooperatives provide best practices models in sharing collections, negotiating licenses, and providing optimal consortia services. Fortunately, technology advances have made participating in consortia and resource sharing easier and offer the collection manager a promising approach to build access and relinquish the burden of ownership.

Check This Out

Examples of successful collection partnerships:

California Digital Library
Visit: http://www.cdlib.org

Northeast Regional Libraries Consortium
Visit: http://www.nerl.org

Relevant Collections in a Changing World

There are more subtle changes a collection manager can make when looking toward innovation and technology. Although community expectations are not always apparent, the collection manager must be able to anticipate those changes. Business managers follow consumer and industry trends to help identify potential opportunities to advance their market share. Collection managers should do the same.

In the past, communities looked to information organizations as windows into a world they knew little about (see also chapter 3, "Information Communities: Defining the Focus of Information Service"). Users turned to information organizations as natural vehicles to increase awareness of the

Wayne T. Disher

world around them. However, today, a user's natural first step in meeting their information need is to turn to the Internet. For example, many current consumer trends reveal that community members are now embracing hyperlocalism: the clamoring for information regarding local events, local photographs, and local information as they strive to gain a local identity and perspective of their neighborhood. If the user's information need includes their immediate community and local environment, they will find a far less successful online experience. However, collection managers could well capitalize on this trend by enriching their local history offerings by providing digitalized collections of local history photographs, curated data of local events, and localized content. In doing so, they expand the way their collections meet changing community needs.

Conclusion

The twenty-first century will undoubtedly continue to be a time of great upheaval and change for institutions. As the ground shifts underneath collection managers, it is all the more important for them to remember the management skills relevant to handling change. They must now consider new formats, as well as new ways of reading and learning, for which many in the profession have not, up to this point, adequately planned. Collection managers must revisit strategic plans and chart new directions that meet the demands of a changing society. Having a strategic plan in place will increase consumer confidence that information organizations are relevant to their changing information needs.

The information professional must employ managerial skills most suited to deal with current and future collection challenges, plan strategically, embrace innovation, and analyze community trends. Collection managers can then capitalize on the organization's role in fostering information literacy, rather than solely being content providers. The collections they build accelerate learning, increase global access, improve convenience, and add value to the user experience.

Appendix 25.1: Basics of Building a Collection

What are the basic activities involved in building a collection? This section provides an overview of some of the key aspects of collection management, ranging from access to community analysis to weeding.

- *Access:* When collection development professionals talk about access, they are usually referring to how an information organization's materials are made available to its users (see also chapter 15, "Accessing Information Anywhere and Anytime: Access Services"). Traditionally, information professionals focused on providing physical access to information by placing an item on the organization's shelves—thus allowing a user to come into the facility to look at or borrow it. Technology has provided alternative ways of providing access to the organization's users. Information can now be delivered digitally over the Internet or via mobile devices (see also chapter 14, "Organizing Information: Technical Services"). Users are trending toward a preference for this type of access due to the fact that it can be delivered to them more conveniently and quickly.
- *Allocations:* Allocations is a budgeting term meant to designate the amount of money given to a particular service, product, or department. The information organization's budgeting process is usually a complex means by which the total amount of money available is distributed and allocated among the various departments and collections (see also chapter 22, "Managing Budgets"). In order to track collection expenditures in more detail, the total amount of money allocated to the organization's collection is usually subdivided into smaller allocations, with a portion of the total amount, for example, given to children's material, a portion of the total amount given to young adult material, and so on. Collection development professionals follow allocation expenditures closely, using this information to measure performance, monitor trends, and project future budget needs.

- *Collection Building:* Collection developers in information organizations are continually identifying, selecting, and acquiring materials to include as part of their collection. Oftentimes, a need arises for the information professional to select information meant for a specific purpose, a specific group of people, a specific location, and a specific time. This requires collection building, which is a more specific part of the entire collection development process focused on building specific areas of the collection on an as-needed or emergency basis. As an example, many information professionals found themselves needing to build collections to help children understand the topics of Islam and Muslims following the terrorist attacks at the World Trade Center on 9/11.
- *Collection Development:* An information organization needs a method by which it can make decisions about what material it should spend its money on. Collection development best describes this method. It is that part of the larger collection management that includes the process of identifying the strengths and weaknesses of a collection in terms of user needs and community resources and then attempting to correct any weaknesses found.
- *Collection Management:* Collection management is an all-encompassing term used to describe all the management-related processes and procedures involved in developing and building the collection, such as planning, budgeting, controlling, and evaluating.
- *Community Analysis:* An information organization does not exist for any other purpose than to serve the wants, needs, and demands of those in its community of users. In order to determine what the community's wants, needs, and demands are, a collection developer must define the community—its legal boundaries, its residents, and its demographic, economic, political, geographic, and sociological composition (see also chapter 12, "Information Needs: Understanding and Responding to Today's Information User"). By utilizing various community analysis tools, such as U.S. census data, surveys, state and local statistical analyses, and personal observations, a collection developer can qualitatively and quantitatively determine current community demands and predict future ones (see also chapter 28, "Demonstrating Value: Assessment").
- *Consortia:* A consortium is a legal partnership formed of local, regional, statewide, or interstate information organizations cooperating with one another to coordinate specific information-related activities. Information organizations use consortia to pool their resources, negotiate improved licensing agreements, and share professional expertise in order to reap service benefits for each of their user communities.
- *Digital Content:* Also known as e-content, e-resources, and virtual content, digital content refers to most any collection of data in digital format that can be stored and transmitted electronically, for example over the Internet (see also chapter 10, "Digital Resources: Digital Libraries"). Unlike print material, digital content requires another medium to store, retrieve, and/or open the digital data in order for a user to see and use it. However, digital content can be made instantly available to almost any user at any time who has the appropriate technical capability to access it. Forms of digital content include computer files, e-books, computer databases, streaming media, audio files, and websites.
- *e-Books:* One of the most popular forms of digital content, electronic books (or e-books) are digital versions of the print book that can be read using a personal computer, smart phone, or proprietary e-book readers such as a Kindle or Nook. Publishers sell the rights to their material to vendors who then transfer the book into a digital format. Information professionals work with these vendors to purchase subscriptions to popular e-book collections and license this content to allow limited access to their users via an online authentication process (see also chapter 32, "Information Licensing"). With few exceptions, e-books are exact replicas of their print versions. Trends are showing that information users prefer e-books due to the fact that they can be distributed over computer networks, thereby improving accessibility.
- *Selection:* The basic process of collection development involves information professionals looking at the immense breadth of materials available and then deciding what is (and what is not)

appropriate for the community the organization serves. In almost every case, the amount of appropriate material is still too large for any single information organization to afford, so a selection process is put in place to identify the *most* appropriate material. Collection developers utilize an established collection development policy and develop criteria for selection that often include established need, author/publisher reputation, suitability for the intended audience, authoritativeness, scope, and price.

- *Selection Tools:* Collection development professionals are often called upon to select material about which they have limited knowledge. There is some risk in spending funds to purchase material the information professional knows little about. To reduce risk, collection developers use selection tools to help obtain information about material they may be considering for addition to the organization's collection. The most common selection tool is a journal of current book reviews. Journals such as *Publisher's Weekly, Library Journal, Booklist,* and *Choice* offer current reviews of material. Information professionals, with an understanding of the needs, wants, and demands of information organizations and their users, often write reviews.

- *Weeding:* Material contained in an information collection is rarely—if ever—needed forever. Community needs, wants, and demands constantly evolve, and in order for an organization's collection to remain relevant to the users it intends to serve, information professionals must continually evaluate material contained in the facility to ensure it is still useful, in good condition, not outdated, and appropriate for the community. This process is called weeding. Collection developers develop a weeding plan that involves, in many cases, a book-by-book appraisal in which information professionals evaluate condition, use, and appropriateness. Books that do not meet preset criteria are deleted from the collection.

Notes

1. George Bobinski, *Libraries and Librarianship* (Lanham, MD: Scarecrow Press, 2007), 7.
2. Ibid., 11.
3. Ibid., 9.
4. "IMLS 2010 Public Library Survey Results Announced," last modified April 10, 2014, http://www.imls.gov/imls_2010_public_library_survey_results_announced.aspx (accessed May 31, 2014).
5. "Amazon.com Now Selling More Kindle Books than Print Books," http://phx.corporate-ir.net/phoenix.zhtml?c=176060&p=irol-newsArticle&ID=1565581&highlight (accessed June 2, 2014).
6. Cathy DeRosa, Joanne Cantrell, Diane Callentani, Janet Hawk, Lillie Jenkins, and Alane Wilson, *Perceptions of Libraries and Information Resources 2005* (Dublin, OH: OCLC, 2005), 3–31, http://www.oclc.org/content/dam/oclc/reports/pdfs/Percept_all.pdf (accessed July 6, 2014).
7. Kathryn Zickuhr, Lee Rainie, Kristine Purcell, and Maeve Dugan, *How Americans Value Public Libraries in Their Communities* (Washington, DC: Pew Research Center, 2005), http://libraries.pewinternet.org/2013/12/11/libraries-in-communities (accessed July 6, 2014).
8. R. S. Ranganathan, *The Five Laws of Library Science* (London: Edward Goldston, 1931).
9. *2012 Survey of Ebook Usage in U.S. Public Libraries* (New York: Library Journal, 2012), 5, http://www.thedigitalshift.com/research/ebook-usage-reports/public (accessed July 6, 2014).
10. The Digital Shift, "2012 Survey of Ebook Usage in U.S. Academic Libraries," *Library Journal*, 2012, 5, http://www.thedigitalshift.com/research/ebook-usage-reports/academic (accessed July 6, 2014).

26

Managing Technology

Marshall Breeding

Technology permeates almost every aspect of libraries, archives, museums, corporations, and other organizations where information professionals carry out their work. All information professionals make use of technology tools in their portfolio of responsibilities, and an understanding of how technology can be leveraged to better serve their communities will help professionals use these tools more effectively. Beyond using technology as part of their daily tasks, some information professionals are responsible for managing some aspect of their organization's technology tools and infrastructure, making it even more important for these leaders to understand the various ways technology can be used today, and how knowledge of technology trends can guide their decision making.

Technology remains in constant flux, so no discussion of trends or how technology is currently used will endure for long. While this chapter aims to provide information and insight into the current technology landscape, it can provide only a baseline that must be continually updated throughout the career of an information professional. After completing this chapter, the reader should have an understanding of the scope of technologies used to manage print and digital collections and enable discovery and access to those materials. Readers will also learn about some of the important trends in information technology that provide context for the development and architecture of these tools.

Trends that Impact How Information Organizations Manage Technology

The constantly turning cycles of technology mean that information organizations have to continually adapt to changes, including broad trends affecting all businesses, as well as technology trends specifically oriented to information organizations (see also chapter 5, "Librarianship: A Continuously Evolving Profession"). These ongoing trends have vast implications for information organizations, including the kinds of technology tools used by the organizations, the forms of content that comprise their collections, and the ways that organizations deliver access to these collections. This section discusses some of the major technology trends that currently warrant attention. While it is helpful to note the features of the current landscape, the overarching message involves continually surveying the field for each next phase of change.

Open Source Software

In the current technology environment, software applications oriented for information organizations are provided in two ways: (1) as proprietary products under the control of a specific vendor, and (2) as open source software, where users of the software can use, modify, and share it freely (see also chapter 33, "Open Access").

Proprietary software is governed by a commercial license or contract that specifies the terms under which it can be used and the fees to be paid to use it. The source code for proprietary software is usually not made available to those who use the software, and all development is under the control of the vendor.

In contrast, open source applications provide access to source code, allowing users to modify it. Rather than remaining under the control of a single vendor, many individuals and organizations can participate in developing an open source application. Some open source projects involve broad, international development efforts, while for others, activity takes place within a more limited or tight-knit community. Larger-scale applications, whether they are based on open source or proprietary software, offer application programming interfaces (APIs) that enable programmers to extend functionality and extract data.

Information professionals involved in managing technologies need to understand the differences between open source and proprietary software, as well as the varying roles of information professionals as they manage their organization's use of these tools. For example, proprietary software comes with comprehensive support from a vendor, and the contract will specify the up-front costs for the software, as well as annual software and support fees. In return for these fees, the organization will be entitled to make use of the software, receive ongoing updates made to the application, and receive help from the vendor with problem resolution. Information organizations will not be able to directly reprogram the internal workings of the software, but most major applications offer a wide set of customization options. Most vendors of proprietary software sponsor user groups that provide additional avenues for training, and many user groups develop lists of desired enhancements for the vendor to address.

Organizations that use open source applications have a wider range of opportunities to be involved in software development and may become involved in fixing bugs or creating enhancements. Some information organizations employ programmers, who become part of the development community of an open source software project. Rather than handling implementation locally, implementation of some open source products is done through support contracts with commercial companies. These commercial contracts make

---

Major Proprietary ILS
- SirsiDynix
- Millennium
- Poloris
- VTLS Virtua

Major Open Source ILS
- Koha
- Evergreen
- Content audits
- User interview

Alternative Open Source
- Ex Libris Alma
- Sierra
- ProQuest Intota
- Worldshare Management Services

Discovery Interfaces
- VuFind
- Blacklight

TEXTBOX 26.1

Topic for Discussion

What are some of the tools or technologies that an information organization can implement to provide access to its collections? How do these tools compare with those that persons use such as Google or Google Scholar to find information?

these open source applications accessible by libraries without programmers or technical staff. While proprietary applications are tied to a single vendor, open source applications allow multiple vendors to offer service and support.

Cloud Computing Technologies

The basic model for deploying technology has shifted dramatically in the last few years away from one where organizations make use of software applications installed on local servers or workstations toward those that are accessed via an entirely web-based platform. This transition from local computing to what is informally called cloud computing brings many fundamental changes in the way that information organizations manage technology.

Cloud computing includes a variety of models, each with its own distinct characteristics and functionality. These varying models of cloud computing in turn come with different implications for those responsible for managing technology for information organizations. In general, cloud technologies mean less need for the organization's personnel to deal with low-level hardware and software components. The following list provides an overview of key types of cloud computing (for additional context, see also chapter 26, "Cloud Computing Technologies" in the online supplement):

- Local computing
- Vendor hosting or application service provider
- Multitenant Software as a Service (SaaS)

Local Computing

Cloud computing in general contrasts with local computing, or the client/server architecture. This model of technology deployment depends on servers that reside on the premises of the organization. For major products, such as the integrated library system (ILS), the software would be installed on a server and accessed by information organization personnel through client software installed on their desktop or laptop computers. These systems may also have web-based interfaces that avoid this requirement to install special client software. The client/server architecture distributes the overall set of computer tasks involved for an application between what is handled by the server and others that take place within the client software.

In a local computing environment based on client/server technologies, modules operated through web-based interfaces still connect to the server component physically housed on the premises of the organization. It is also important to note that a client/server application can serve a large organization. A consortium can implement a client/server ILS that supports many libraries or branches. The server might, for example, be housed in a facility managed by the consortial office or in a lead institution within the consortium. The users of that system would connect their client applications via the local network or the Internet to that server.

Sometimes the server is not necessarily housed directly in the information organization, but it might reside in the data center of its parent organization. It is common for a university or municipal IT department to operate a data center for the applications it manages directly and those managed by other departments or units.

The model of local computing comes with a substantial burden for those who manage technology. Some of the key components of a local system requiring attention include

- *Server, Storage, and Network Hardware:* The initial deployment of the system would require the procurement, installation, and configuration of a variety of hardware components. Technical management tasks would include tasks such as physical installation of the servers in the data center, updates and configuration of firmware, configuration of storage systems, and establishing connectivity with the local network.

- *Server Operating System:* A locally managed application will run on a specific server operating system such as Microsoft Windows Server or Linux. The operating system must be installed, configured, and optimized according to the specifications of the application. Network security tasks will include the configuration of internal and external firewalls to protect the server from external attacks, malware, and other potential problems.
- *Database Engines:* High-performance business applications typically depend on third-party relational database management systems, such as the proprietary products from Oracle or open source tools like MySQL or PostgreSQL. Management tasks include basic table configuration, resource allocation, and optimization.
- *Disaster Planning and Recovery:* Any business application managed on a local server demands careful attention to implementing measures to protect data in the event of any possible hardware or software failure or through human error. Data must be backed up regularly with the ability to be quickly restored following a failure.
- *Application Management:* In addition to all the components of the operating environment mentioned above, the application itself will require significant attention. The initial installation includes tasks such as configuration of each of the modules to match the organizational structure, business rules, and circulation policies. Many libraries will have a dedicated systems librarian who manages all the technical and specialized tasks associated with its integrated library system.

With all these required areas of specialized attention, the local computing model requires significant expertise. The categories of work include hardware and network engineers, system administrators, database administrators, and systems librarians.

Vendor Hosting or Application Service Provider

One alternative to the local computing mentioned above involves the same basic configuration of system, but with the server equipment housed and managed by the vendor of the software. The fundamental architecture of how the instance of the software serves the organization remains in place, including the configuration of what information organizations and branches are served by an instance of the software. The only difference is that the server resides in the vendor's data center rather than that of the information organization. Any client software remains in place but connects via the Internet rather than the network of the information organization or consortium. The model of vendor hosting is often marketed as a form of Software as a Service (SaaS).

The application service provider model of deployment relieves the information organization of all the responsibilities that come with a locally managed server as described above. The vendor takes responsibility for the physical hardware platform and all its subsequent components, systems administration for the operating system and network connectivity, security patches, database administration, and some aspects of the management of the application itself. In most cases, the vendor will assume responsibility for disaster planning and recovery and for general data security issues.

A significant set of tasks remains in the domain of technology management in the information organization relative to the vendor-hosted model of application deployment. The systems librarian, for example, might continue to have responsibility for maintaining circulation policy tables, performing data loads, and other routine tasks.

Moving to a hosted arrangement allows the information organization to redirect its technical personnel away from low-level infrastructure management to higher-level activities that potentially focus on tasks with more direct impact on the information organization and its customers. Support for low-level technical infrastructure may not necessarily be a core competency of the information organization and can be provided more efficiently and effectively by specialized organizations that manage large numbers of server instances.

Multitenant Software as a Service

A more current flavor of cloud computing technology is based on a natively web-based platform designed to simultaneously support all the institutional or individual users of an application. Multitenant applications organize functionality in order to segregate the data and functionality of the software as needed, but all use is supported through a unified platform. A multitenant platform will rely on a large number of servers and other hardware components, but these components remain entirely transparent to its users.

The multitenant SaaS model simplifies how new versions of an application are deployed. Since there is a single instance of the software that serves all users simultaneously, the concept of needing to install updates on a given server does not apply, at least not from the perspective of the information organization or its users. The provider of the platform can apply bug fixes once that are immediately available for all users. New features can be deployed gracefully as well.

From a technology management perspective, the multitenant SaaS model comes with the least need for direct technology management support relative to other deployment models. Most of the support will be directed toward functional tasks rather than those relating to technical infrastructure. Tasks related to institutional options for business rules, customized policies, and data-loading routines may be required.

Mobile Technologies

The ever-increasing adoption of smart phones and tablets is a trend that has major implications for the ways information organizations provide access to their collections and deliver their services to their clients. When most software and content products used by information organizations were developed, they were primarily oriented toward web browsers on full-sized devices—laptop and desktop computers. Consumer technology has reshaped itself, with smart phones and tablets now dominating access to the web.

The technique of responsive design must be followed for all interfaces used by clients, including websites and online catalogs. Responsive sites are not optimized for any specific device but instead detect the size and capabilities of the device and adapt accordingly. This approach not only adjusts presentation features, such as layout, font size, and orientation, but it can also selectively present functionality according to the capability of the device.

Individuals responsible for managing their organization's use of technology must also monitor usage statistics for each of its web-based services. Either through analysis of usage logs or through services such as Google Analytics, information organizations can analyze very detailed data regarding client use by each category of mobile device and operating system. Armed with this data, technology managers can focus their attention toward ensuring that each service the organization offers is well optimized for delivery via the most popular devices.

Responsive design can be accomplished in different ways. For example, organizations that directly control their websites can modify the interfaces themselves to incorporate responsive design. This work may require some training and expertise with the content management system used to deploy the site, as well as with general web technologies and protocols, such as HTML5, JavaScript, and CSS. In addition, managers can draw upon experts or develop expertise in the domain of user experience (UX)[1] to ensure that the redesigned site can be easily understood and used (see also chapter 17, "User Experience").

Technologies for Managing Resources and Automating Operations

Information organizations rely on specialized business applications to automate many aspects of their operations and to describe and manage their collections. From the earliest years of computing, software has been developed to help information organizations automate their work. These systems have evolved through every generation of computer technology, from the early systems based on punch cards, to mainframe computers, to distributed systems based on client/server technology, and most recently to those based on cloud computing technologies.

Integrated Library Systems

The integrated library system (ILS) emerged as the basic model for information organization automation as computing technologies matured, and it continues to be a core business system used by information organizations to manage their collections. The ILS brings together multiple areas of functionality (e.g., cataloging and circulation) into a single application in order to operate as an efficient and cohesive system. The ILS emerged prior to the advent of electronic resources and thus was primarily oriented to the management of print materials. Many different vendors developed ILS products, each with a variety of distinguishing characteristics and relative strengths and weaknesses.

The ILS products available today offer very mature and sophisticated functionality, with thousands of discrete features and options. Understanding the general features of these systems provides a basic framework for identifying how information organizations can best use library automation tools and make decisions regarding which new ILS technologies to adopt.

- Cataloging modules provide the capability to create the bibliographic records that describe each item of content.
- Public catalog modules allow clients to interact with the collection.
- Circulation modules manage the lending of physical materials in the collection.
- Acquisitions modules manage the procurement of materials and include placing orders for materials, managing funds used to purchase materials, maintaining a database of current suppliers, and other transactions related to the financial component of collection management.
- Serials control modules are used to manage journals, newspapers, and other subscription-based materials.

Electronic Resource Management Systems

Since integrated library systems are primarily oriented to the management of print resources, these products are not necessarily well equipped to manage the growing number of electronic resources in the collections of most information organizations.

The management of e-journals involves specialized functionality not available in the standard feature set of the ILS. As a result of this gap in functionality, a number of vendors launched electronic resource management products that offer tools for managing procurement, analyzing use statistics, and identifying overlap of coverage among content packages from different aggregators.

Despite the gap in functionality in the ILS and the major investments in electronic resources in academic and research libraries, this genre of software saw fairly limited adoption. Many academic libraries found the products on the market cumbersome and challenging to use in parallel with their integrated library systems. The genre of electronic resource management systems as a separate application has largely given way to the inclusion of this functionality in the new genre of library services platforms discussed below.[2]

Information Service Platforms

The integrated library system was conceived to manage collections that were primarily comprised of print materials. As the universe of information resources shifts toward electronic forms of content, the framework of automation ingrained in the ILS may become strained.

A new genre of business system for information organizations was developed more recently, beginning around 2009, based on a new framework. These systems, generally termed library services platforms, aim to address the needs of organizations that manage collections comprised of materials in diverse formats, deployed using modern technology architectures. A considerable portion of the functionality available through library services platforms overlaps with integrated library systems, but there are important differences, including

- *Inherent Design to Manage Multiple Types of Information Organization Content:* Library services platforms take a comprehensive resource management approach that accommodates multiple types of formats, including different metadata formats, procurement processes, business rules, and access methods for the many different categories of print and digital materials.
- *Web-Based Multitenant Platforms:* Library services platforms are primarily deployed using web-based, multitenant platforms, aimed at serving multiple types of users.
- *Shared Metadata and Knowledge Bases:* These new systems have a sharper focus on bodies of metadata that can be shared globally among all the users of the product.
- *Service-Oriented Architecture:* Library services platforms tap into the current global IT trend toward services-oriented architecture, which means that software products are built from very small units of functionality, called services, that can be composed to assemble more complex workflows, modules, complete applications, or interoperable product suites.

Integrated library systems continue to evolve, in many cases gradually reshaping themselves into library services platforms. Organizations that continue to be primarily oriented toward the management of print collections will continue to find that integrated library systems are well suited for their requirements.

Technology Managers and Library Services Platforms

The advent of library services platforms and the ongoing viability of integrated library systems mean that information professionals involved in technology management will need to have a flexible approach relative to the strategic business applications that support the organization. They will need to understand the advantages of each product in order to choose those products that can best support the organization's strategic mission. And as is the case with other technology, leaders should anticipate other transitions in the future.

> "The advent of library services platforms and the ongoing viability of integrated library systems mean that information professionals involved in technology management will need to have a flexible approach relative to the strategic business applications that support the organization."

These evolving business applications mean that the approach to technology management for information organizations needs to change. For example, to the extent that these new products are deployed through cloud computing, technology managers will focus on higher-level functionality and services, rather than on administration of hardware, operating systems, and other infrastructure components. The new resource management models will require that technology managers think and work more collaboratively as they engage with other organizations using the platform, with less emphasis on self-sufficiency and isolation. Technology managers will need to be well versed in many different types of metadata structures, processing workflows, and other characteristics inherent in complex collections spanning diverse formats.

New Generations of Resource Discovery Tools and Patron Portals

As information organizations seek new ways to facilitate access to collections and discovery of resources by clients, new tools are continuously developed (see also chapter 26, "Examples of New Generations of Resource Discovery Tools and Patron Portals" in the online supplement).

*   *Online Catalog:* A long-standing tool for providing client access to resources. In recent years, online catalogs have been redesigned to include more intuitive interfaces. For example, many online catalogs have been extended to provide discovery and lending of e-books through integration with e-book lending platforms.
*   *Discovery Interfaces:* Tools designed to provide access to resources that are not accessible through the organization's ILS. Instead, web-based discovery interfaces rely on their own indexes or connectors with external content sources to provide access to an information organization's resources. The interfaces aim to provide a highly intuitive user experience and usually follow well-established conventions seen within other web-oriented services, such as a single search box, relevancy-ordered results lists, facets to narrow results according to applicable categories (e.g., author, subject, date, language, format). Many discovery interfaces depend on integration with the ILS, such as looking up the current status of an item in the ILS (e.g., available or checked out to another borrower). Discovery interfaces can also provide access to many other categories of content not included in the ILS, including access to other content repositories maintained by the information organization or resources maintained externally. The distinguishing characteristic of these vendor-based discovery interfaces lies in their independence from any specific ILS.
*   *Index-Based Discovery Services:* A central index that can be used to explore the broad universe of scholarly publishing and discover scholarly articles. An alternative term, "web-scale discovery services," has also been widely used to describe these products. The indexes of these products address many hundreds of millions if not billions of individual content items, represented by citations, full text, abstracts, or discipline-specific controlled vocabularies. Index-based discovery services are especially oriented to academic libraries but may be of interest to any organization that makes major investments in access to electronic scholarly content.
*   *Library Portals:* A content management environment and other specialized tools to replace the entire information organization website, not just the online catalog. These portals provide an integrated experience for information organization customers, instead of a jarring separation that is often seen between an information organization's website and its online catalog or discovery service.

TEXTBOX 26.2

Topic for Discussion

What are the key differences between library services platforms and integrated library systems? What kinds of information organizations would be best suited for a library services platform? What kinds of information organizations are best suited for integrated library systems?

Technology Managers and Resource Discovery Tools

Any product used by an information organization to offer client access to resources is a critical part of the services offered by the organization, and as such, professionals responsible for managing technology need to understand how it functions. Technology managers must therefore devote intense attention to these discovery interfaces, portals, and other related tools. This aspect of the information organization's infrastructure is subject to even more rapid change than the tools used by personnel behind the scenes. While an information organization may retain its integrated library system for a decade or two, it needs to refresh its customer-facing services on a much more accelerated schedule. Not only do client expectations continually change, such as the current movement toward using mobile technologies to access resources, but the products available in this space likewise evolve rapidly. Information professionals must be constantly vigilant to ensure that the organization's web presence remains as close as possible to the state of the art for these types of tools.

This arena of customer-facing interfaces and tools provides the greatest opportunities for information professionals charged with managing technology to make a positive impact for their institution. A variety of specialized expertise can be useful, ranging from graphic design, user experience, and information architecture, to specific technical skills such as programming languages, content management systems (e.g., Drupal), and coding standards (e.g., HTML5 and CSS). Technology managers also need an in-depth knowledge of the ILS or resource management applications in place, including how to leverage this existing technology to provide new services through the information organization's web presence.

> "This arena of customer-facing interfaces and tools provides the greatest opportunities for information professionals charged with managing technology to make a positive impact for their institution."

Managing the Transition to e-Books

The increased interest, especially among public libraries, in offering e-book lending services brings significant challenges, spanning many different areas of concern. To date, there are many levels of participation by publishers in making e-books available to information organizations for lending. Publishers have concerns that library lending could erode their business in the consumer sector. These concerns have led to several responses by publishers, including not offering their titles at all; offering only specific subsets of their catalogs in premium pricing; or setting specific limitations on lending policies, such as requiring that an information organization repurchase a title after a specified number of loans or time period.

Libraries are also interested in providing e-book lending services that are well integrated into their other lending services and are easy for clients to use. E-book lending in public libraries largely takes place through service providers that negotiate business arrangements with publishers and provide content delivery platforms to which libraries can subscribe in order to lend e-books to their clients. Typical arrangements include payment of an annual platform fee and the ability to select and pay for a collection of titles.

In the initial phase of library e-book lending, libraries included links on their websites to connect clients to the platform of their e-book lending service. Many libraries now prefer to provide a more integrated experience to their clients. This integration is accomplished by loading and indexing bibliographic records for their e-books directly in their ILS and enabling their customers to check out and download available titles through the library catalog or discovery interface. In most cases, the technical work of this integration is carried out by the vendor, and information organization personnel activate the service through the administrative tools provided by the vendor.

Marshall Breeding

In addition to subscribing to commercial e-book lending services, some libraries have implemented their own e-book lending infrastructure and work directly with authors and publishers to acquire titles to lend. As an example, the Douglas County Libraries in Colorado were an early advocate of this model, which focused on titles that can be purchased and owned by the information organization and are not subject to some of the less favorable terms of the commercial e-book lending services.[3]

Considerable progress has already been made to integrate e-books into library lending services, but considerable work remains. On the business front, libraries continue to advocate with publishers to make additional content available and at more attractive terms. While progress has been made in the technical integration of e-book lending into information organization services, this capability is not available on all library catalog and discovery products, and the integration tools offered by e-book providers have varying degrees of completeness.

Emerging Technologies and Innovation Labs

Many information organizations are relatively conservative in their decisions regarding which technologies they rely on to support their internal operations and manage their collections. The technology that supports their mission-critical infrastructure must be well proven and reliable. Although it is important to ensure that the organization's technology infrastructure is reliable, it is also essential for information professionals to be well versed in new emerging technologies so they can take advantage of useful new technology, implementing these new tools early in their development and adoption cycle. Forward-looking leaders show an interest in providing personnel with opportunities to try out new technologies and make them available to clients. After piloting and evaluating new technology, the technologies that organizations incorporate into their operations must be robust and user friendly.

Innovation labs help information professionals identify new technology that may benefit their organization and their clients, providing an opportunity to investigate how the technology could be used by the organization and its clients. For example, many libraries now have facilities where their clients and their personnel can gain hands-on experience with new and emerging technologies. Such a facility might be thought of as an innovation lab or sandbox to try out new technology products that may or may not eventually move into the mainstream. In innovation labs, explorations of new technology can spark ideas by personnel regarding new services the organization could offer that incorporate use of this new technology. Likewise, clients appreciate opportunities to try out new technologies that may not yet be widely available or affordable. In addition, an innovation lab helps position the organization as cutting edge, willing to continuously explore how to improve its services. The specific technologies that might be part of an innovation lab are naturally going to change frequently. Examples of emerging technologies of current interest to information organizations include iBeacon, which is a technology from Apple that uses low-powered transmitters to interact with persons within an indoor space, and NFC or near-field communications, which is technology that enables devices such as smart phones to carry out payments or other transactions.

A related concept comes in the form of what is often called makerspaces (see also chapter 19, "Creation Culture and Makerspaces"). These facilities provide tools that enable clients to design and create content or objects. A makerspace might include a variety of software tools for graphical or physical design, video editing or production, as well as more traditional tools for creating and editing textual information.[4]

Managing the People Who Manage Technology

All information organization employees are touched by technology due to the nature of their work. Information professionals involved directly in the support and implementation of technology naturally need to have the most in-depth skills and expertise. Some of the categories of skills that an information professional focused on technology might include in their portfolio include

- *Programming:* Information professionals should become masters in programming and scripting languages. Programming languages are flexible tools that can be applied to solve an almost infinite array of problems, such as creating customized tools for the organization or interacting with databases and other software applications deployed by the organization (e.g., the ILS).
- *Systems Administration:* Information professionals should know how to manage local server installations. These activities span multiple aspects or layers of technology, such as operating systems, network connectivity, security, and configuration of software applications that run on the server. In many organizations, an IT professional will be responsible for these categories of activities.
- *Metadata:* Information professionals should understand metadata and the general concepts and syntactical structures that might be involved in scenarios such as the exchange of data between information systems. Technologists should also have a strong understanding of XML, since it is the underlying syntactical carrier for most metadata and many forms of content.
- *Library Standards and Protocols:* Information professionals involved in technology benefit from a basic familiarity with the major standards—such as those provided by the National Information Standards Organization (NISO)—plus more detailed understanding of those that are relevant to the key systems used within the organization.
- *Web Standards and Protocols:* Information professionals involved with technology should be familiar with at least the most common and broadly implemented standards overseen by the W3C (http://www.w3.org/standards), which define the basic building blocks of the web. Good starting points are HTML, XML, and CSS, since they are used in almost all content-oriented applications.
- *Computer Architectures:* Information professionals involved in the creation of software will have detailed knowledge of the concepts and implementation details related to development frameworks, such as the services-oriented architecture.

"It is generally not feasible to achieve expert-level mastery of all aspects of technology, but a well-rounded technology professional will have both broad general knowledge in many different areas and deep expertise in a selected area of specialization."

Even a very basic introductory level of knowledge in each of these categories will foster a better understanding of how computer and information systems work. From this foundation of basic concepts, an information professional may need to selectively explore some of the technologies or concepts in more depth, according to areas of interest or focus of responsibility. It is generally not feasible to achieve expert-level mastery of all aspects of technology, but a well-rounded technology professional will have both broad general knowledge in many different areas and deep expertise in a selected area of specialization.

Conclusion

This chapter discussed a wide range of topics that information professionals involved with managing technology will face. The topics covered are not meant to be comprehensive but to give a selection of real-world examples of the categories of technology currently in place and trends that shaped the current environment. The discussion focused primarily on larger-scale technology that is especially relevant to information organizations, such as integrated library systems, library services platforms, customer-facing discovery services, and e-book lending technologies. Cloud computing has ushered in a new genre of products and services for resource management and discovery. For those charged with managing technology, cloud computing dramatically redefines the profession, shifting away from the need to manage low-level infrastructure to working at a level closer to users, both clients and the personnel in the organization who depend on these tools to carry out their work.

Just as important as the specific trends and technologies described, readers should take away the inevitability of ongoing change in technology. The chapter illustrated how some of the products and technologies in place today displaced tools used in earlier generations. Likewise, the tools in place today cannot be considered as final solutions. Rather, they are interim steps along the path to yet another phase in the ongoing quest of information professionals to leverage technologies to support their work. Practitioners in the field should expect to continually master new skills and adapt to each new cycle of technology to avoid stagnation in their career path and enable them to contribute positively to the profession.

Notes

1. Aaron Schmidt and Amanda Etches, *User Experience (UX) Design for Libraries*, Tech Set Series 18 (Chicago, IL: ALA TechSource, 2012).
2. Marshall Breeding, "The Many Facets of Managing Electronic Resources," *Computers in Libraries* 24, no. 1 (2004): 25; Marshall Breeding, "The Year of ERM," *Smart Libraries Newsletter* 25, no. 3 (2005): 2.
3. Marshall Breeding, "Technology to Empower Information Organization Control of e-Book Lending," *Smart Libraries Newsletter* 33, no. 8 (2013): 3–6.
4. Erin Fisher, "Makerspaces Move into Academic Libraries," *ACRL TechConnect Blog*, November 28, 2012, http://acrl.ala.org/techconnect/?p=2340.

27

Managing Communications, Marketing, and Outreach

Christie Koontz

Libraries and other information organizations serve markets that are unique and in a constant state of evolution and change. Successful information professionals proactively seek knowledge of what is changing so they can provide varied customer groups with the services, products, and programs they need. The primary mission of an information organization is to solve problems or resolve issues that are related to the match process between customers and information.[1]

The topic of this chapter, marketing, is the driving force for all types of organizations, including information organizations. Marketing provides a set of tools to focus on meeting customers' needs. Through marketing research, customer market segmentation, and other marketing strategies, information professionals can learn more about their customers, identify information products and services that can better meet their customers' needs, and better target these information products and services to the people who need them. In fact, marketing should be considered early on when planning for any information service. After completing this chapter, the reader should have an understanding of how

> "Through marketing research, customer market segmentation, and other marketing strategies, information professionals can learn more about their customers, identify information products and services that can better meet their customers' needs, and better target these information products and services to the people who need them."

- marketing practices work in real situations,
- marketing activities relate to one another, and
- public relations and branding can support marketing activities.

The Marketing Process

All organizations engage in marketing—whether they know it or not—though with varying degrees of success.[2] The marketing process includes four major steps: (1) marketing research; (2) market segmentation; (3) the marketing mix (the 4 Ps—product, price, place, and promotion); and (4) marketing evaluation.[3]

Step 1: Marketing Research

The first step in the marketing process is marketing research. The goal of marketing research is to find out as much as possible about the organization's actual and potential customer markets. A market, or potential market, includes all the people who may use a particular product or service or who could be expected to do so. Marketing research plays a defining role in understanding customers' attitudes and behaviors *before* moving ahead with product or service development.[4] Marketing research helps to identify different customer profiles, with each type of customer potentially having different attitudes, behaviors, and needs. Untapped and new markets can be developed through consistent marketing research.[5] Throughout the marketing process, "current, reliable and valid information is needed to make effective decisions."[6]

Marketing research of society as a whole, with a focus on local trends, is important for assessing the information, education, and entertainment needs of the customer population. For example, as government agencies implement new guidelines for receiving health-care benefits, the information-seeking needs of customers may shift as a growing number of consumers seek information regarding the new benefits.

Marketing research is also important for identifying competitors, which for the information organization includes other entities that seek to meet the information needs of the target audience. Marketing research requires understanding the other sources of information used by the target audience, such as the Internet, television, newspapers, and magazine subscriptions, as well as for-profit information brokers. In addition, it is important to understand how other public agencies compete for the same public monies. For example, often libraries compete for public funds with local schools, fire departments, and police agencies.

Research with the objective of proactive awareness of external and internal change is known as environmental scanning. Managers need methods for quickly understanding the external environment and how it interconnects with the organization's internal[7] environment. Some organizations create specific divisions or departments for environmental scanning, with professional staff gathering these data on a daily basis. Two popular environmental scanning methods include searching public information sources (print and online) and conducting brainstorming sessions with knowledgeable people (see also chapter 27, "Additional Marketing Tools" in the online supplement). Another method, which can be expensive, includes focus groups and surveys.[8] No matter what approach organizations may take, environmental scanning activities must be consistent and continuous. Things change rapidly—that is why ongoing environmental scanning is so critical.

Marketing research can help answer important questions as an organization decides which services to offer, as well as which audiences to serve and how to reach them. For example, marketing research should help information professionals answer the following questions:

- Who are the organization's current and potential customers?
- What are their needs?
- Where are they located?
- Which of their needs is the organization serving now?
- Why should they choose this organization over going somewhere else?[9]

Without research, these questions are challenging to answer. Without this information, organizations may misspend financial resources and staff time trying to reach and serve customers.

Step 2: Market Segmentation

The second step, market segmentation, is based necessarily upon market research. It is impossible to make appropriate decisions regarding which target audiences to serve without conducting marketing research.

A market segment is a group of potential customers who share similar wants and needs. This grouping is often demographic, behavioral, or geographic. Market segmentation is based on the fact that markets are heterogeneous. Managers must define and understand various markets in order to develop services aimed at meeting target market needs and to provide services effectively. The private sector learned long ago that treating all customers the same might achieve profits on some levels. But they also learned that when differences between customers are ignored, the result may be that no one is really getting what they want or need from the products or services designed for a mass market.

Typical market segmentation strategies for information organizations include

- *Demographic:* segmenting programs based on customer age, such as summer reading programs for children and job-seeking programs for adults
- *Geographic:* analyzing where actual and potential customers live for optimized facility placements and other channel decisions
- *Behavioral:* designing information literacy programs for consumers who lack access to technology or have limited knowledge regarding how to use technology

Step 3: Marketing Mix Strategy

The third step, the marketing mix strategy, involves developing optimal services and products, offered at market-bearing prices, delivered conveniently, and communicated through segment-based promotional tools and media. These services and products are targeted to various customer market segments, based upon market research, and ultimately help the organization use its limited funds in an efficient and effective manner. Like for-profit businesses, libraries and other types of information organizations are involved in the "four Ps" of the marketing mix: product, price, place, and promotion.

- *Product or Service:* Information organizations need to decide which services to deliver in response to identified needs of the target audience. As audience needs change, services should be eliminated or modified, or new services should be introduced. As an example, if a library offers a successful children's story time in English, yet market research shows that a growing number of families in the community speak Spanish at home, the library may want to consider offering bilingual story-time programs. Or, if the local economy changes and many residents are out of work, the library may respond to that change by introducing new programs for job seekers.
- *Place or Making the Service Available to Customers:* Information organizations also rely on market research to decide how best to deliver services to target audiences. Customers access information services on-site, at a physical location, as well as online. As target audience needs shift, the organization may find that it needs to adjust how it delivers services. For example, it may modify hours of service, open a branch site, or offer more online resources to patrons who cannot or do not want to visit the physical site.
- *Price or Value:* While many information organizations do not charge fees for their services, the issue of price is still relevant. For example, key stakeholders make decisions every day regarding whether or not to offer library services in their community or at their school, as they decide whether to invest tax dollars and staff time to provide these services. In response to concerns, library leaders need to be able to assess the impact of their services and demonstrate the value of those services to key stakeholders (see also chapter 28, "Demonstrating Value: Assessment"). In addition, even when customers do not pay directly for information services, they still have concerns regarding the personal cost of accessing services in terms of their time, seeking services that are convenient.
- *Promotion:* The final part of the marketing mix involves promoting services to target audiences. Many nonprofit organizations tend to focus their energy on this one piece of the marketing

process, investing resources in promoting services through social networks, print or online advertisements, news releases, television and radio announcements, seminars, websites, or personal pitches. Because promotional activities are the most visible part of the marketing process, many individuals believe that these promotional efforts represent the totality of the marketing process, when in fact efforts to promote services are only one aspect of marketing and should not occur until the other steps have been completed.

TEXTBOX 27.1

Topic for Discussion

Marketing is often confused with promotion, although effective promotion is based on market research. If explaining "marketing" to a friend or colleague, what three to five points could be made to better define the marketing process?

Promotional tools are used to make targeted customers aware of opportunities and persuade them to access or consume products or services. Typical promotional tools include advertising, sales promotions, publicity, personal selling, and direct marketing. Marketing involves deciding which tool (or combination of tools) is best used to reach the target audience, known as the promotional mix. An optimal mix of promotional tools and media channels can build awareness of the organization by sharing products and services with both actual and potential customers.[10] Organizations may choose to mix "old" media forms, such as ads in print newspapers, with "new" channels, such as social media. New skills are needed to mix the new and old successfully, especially as some of the newer channels, such as social media, are two-way channels of communication, allowing interaction between the audience and the organization, as well as interaction between audience members themselves.

> "Selecting among media options requires knowledge of the strengths and weaknesses of each type of media and the preferences of each market segment the organization wants to reach."

Selecting among media options requires knowledge of the strengths and weaknesses of each type of media and the preferences of each market segment the organization wants to reach. The marketing process involves conducting research to understand which media the targeted segments consume.[11] For example, social media or radio may be the best choices for reaching teenagers or on-the-go working adults. By contrast, area snowbirds (retirees who drift south in the winter months) may best be reached at the local senior center or retirement community. Direct mail is a good option for customers known to reside in a specific zip code. Cultural sensitivity can assure that promotional strategies are effective, especially when target markets are diverse.[12]

Step 4: Marketing Evaluation

The last step in the marketing process is evaluation. Marketing evaluation is distinctive in that it monitors the use of products or services designed for specific customer groups. It involves measuring outputs, such as the number of visits to an information center, the number of questions answered by information professionals, or the number of people who attend an event. However, to be even more valuable, marketing evaluation involves assessing outcomes for the target audience, including user satisfaction, as well changes in user behavior or knowledge, such as increased knowledge of how to apply for a job online or increased willingness to apply for a job online rather than in person.

Careful statistics gathered through marketing evaluation can also be used for justifying future expenditures in budget reports, proposing changes to the scope of services offered, or performing other program planning activities.[13] Findings from marketing evaluation can also be useful when applying for grants and other types of external funding, demonstrating that the institution understands the needs of the target audience.

Currently, because of a growing need for accountability and competition for dwindling public and donated funds, organizations are measuring output and outcomes. Ongoing evaluation allows organizations to benchmark and measure changes, both positive and negative, that indicate new trends or demonstrate the impact of services.

EVALUATING PROMOTIONAL STRATEGIES

In addition to evaluating the outcomes of the services delivered by an information organization, marketing also involves evaluating the effectiveness of efforts to promote services to target audiences. Good promotion is based upon good market research and segmentation. The organization's promotional messages and outreach material should be reviewed from a marketing perspective, considering the target audience profile. Resources (staff and money) will not be wasted if choices of media and content are substantiated through basic market research.

Evaluation of promotional strategies requires pretesting messages with members of the target market segment. This can be accomplished by having customer groups respond to a quick checklist regarding the message via a face-to-face interview, through online feedback, or through a focus group. Evaluation after messages are released must be judged by the objectives set, such as an increase in use or attendance or a measured response to a direct mail.

One expert suggests, "Make a list of all promotional tools, media, and techniques used and assess effectiveness of each. Consider these points: has the promotional tool produced good results; does the media convey the image desired; does it address the right audience and speak to their particular values and needs?"[14]

A library example would be a sales promotion (tool) for the university library's new 24/7 virtual reference. An e-mail blast (media) is sent to freshmen students during the first week of class (technique). The first 25 percent who reply within twenty-four hours after receiving the e-mail blast (one level of evaluation) will receive one dollar off a Starbucks coffee. The promotional objective set by staff is to have a 30 percent increase in contacts from new freshman in the first semester for the new 24/7 service. The latter data can be gathered with library card registration data, or other data gathered from virtual reference exchanges.[15]

TEXTBOX 27.2

Topic for Discussion

Many nonprofits offer intangible goods (services), which increases difficulty in assessing impact (i.e., how much did the child benefit from story hour, or what value is the archaeological exhibit to passing tourists?). Consider what type of data can be (reasonably) collected and how it could be presented to offset this dilemma.

Marketing's Role in Social Media Success

As with all other activities, social media should be used to advance the mission, goals, and objectives of the organization.[16] The development of relationships between customers and the organization is of utmost value. Measuring the results of these relationships is the key to quantifying success in social media. Managers often refer to measuring social media in terms of ROI—return on investment—typically looking at the impact of a social media campaign on organizational objectives of increasing profits. This same measure can also be used at the program level. In the nonprofit sector, organizational objectives could include increased participation in response to a Facebook promotion, or more web traffic to the archives' new online digitized collections. Tracking "likes," "followers," "comments," "reshares," and "subscribers" as a measure of customer relationships is useful, but by itself it is not sufficient to measure real impact. Managers will want to know "to what extent did social media activities help the organization to reach a goal or further the mission?"[17]

A plan for measuring basic indicators of social media activity should include tried-and-true steps such as these:

1. define the goal;
2. identify publics/segments (and prioritize these if there are too many);
3. determine how the social media affects the identified publics/segments by using key performance indicators such as increased visits, membership sign-ups, or click-through rates to a certain URL;
4. define benchmarks (objectives) using norms;
5. select a tool (such as web analytics, surveys, or content analysis);
6. analyze results, make recommendations, and do it all over again;
7. determine ROI through use, cost savings, earned search rankings, and social capital (long, healthy organizational life with lots of relationships).[18]

Marketing's Role in Public Relations

Public relations (PR) is charged with trying to develop a successful image for the organization. PR managers develop special events surrounding a new product or service and follow up with news conferences, "freebie" magazine and newspaper articles, and blog and social media posts. This free content is designed to gain a high level of credibility—which is more possible as it is not paid for. Publicity is essentially nonpaid-for information that targets customer groups and strives to create interest and enthusiasm for the organization's offers. Ideally, publicity efforts are built upon data derived from tried-and-true marketing.

Nonprofits traditionally depend on public relations, and they heavily rely on publicity. But true public relations must be built upon true marketing. True marketing teaches that products and services—the content for public relations efforts—must be based upon customer research and data. If the organization remains unaware of systematic marketing practices, unreliable or untested content is communicated, resulting in a devastating waste of everyone's time—especially the customers'. Marketing-related activities for public relations efforts include the following:[19]

- Creating an up-to-date list of the key stakeholders (including media contacts) of the organization—not only customers, but also others who have a vested interest in the organization.
- Analyzing readily consumable customer data resulting from the systematic marketing process. These data can provide demographic profiles and satisfaction levels or attitudes toward the organization. This information assures better crafting and targeting of media messages.
- Establishing PR goals to achieve. For example, what is the one-hundredth birthday celebration of the library really trying to accomplish? Specifically, which customer groups does the organization wish to reach, and what attitudes does it desire to maintain or change?
- Measuring accomplished PR goal—through surveys on-site, hits to the website, readership of blogs and newsletters, video or TV viewers, podcast subscribers, attendees at an event, number of media coverage stories, and more.

Marketing's Role in Branding

A brand is a "name, term, design, symbol, or any other feature that identifies one seller's good or service as distinct from those of other sellers."[20] Often during public relations or advocacy campaigns, the issue of branding comes up as organizations seek ways to change their image, boost volume of use, or perhaps impact public sentiment about an issue.

Libraries are fortunate. Libraries have huge "brand awareness" from the public already, serving for decades as the premiere community agency for learning, culture, and intellectual curiosity. Libraries' perceived mission and motto are "Everyone is welcome, and all who enter will be served." Most retailers would die for this perception, and ultimately this reputation. So this brand usually elicits high regard from customers and even those who may not even use the library. Those who do use the library and have a good experience continue to think positively and return and thus exhibit brand loyalty. This feel-good quality of the library's brand is invaluable—it is an advantage not to be tossed away lightly.[21]

> "Libraries are fortunate. Libraries have huge 'brand awareness' from the public already, serving for decades as the premiere community agency for learning, culture, and intellectual curiosity."

With this in mind, any rebranding campaign is not only risky but can also be expensive. For example, some public libraries have added "information center" to their titles—but at what benefit or cost? The organizational mission and targeted marketing research must drive any redesign. Rebranding without these two factors can lead to confusion and loss of business. Organizations are generally encouraged to stay with something that is meaningful to everyone, and stay away from rebrandings that mean nothing to anyone. At a minimum, any organization discussing rebranding should ask themselves why they are doing it and combine this with a sufficient amount of pretesting and monitoring.[22]

Marketing Strategies in Action

While some information professionals read *American Libraries* and *Library Journal* to learn more about how their colleagues are engaged in innovative activities, for more than a decade, valuable insight into the marketing process is published annually as winning examples from the International Federation of Library Associations (IFLA) International Marketing Award, sponsored by Emerald Group Publishing.[23] The award is designed as a marketing education piece that furthers the knowledge and practice of marketing among information organizations worldwide, with a glossary of definitions that are agreed upon globally.[24] First- and second-place winners from 2014 are presented here to demonstrate marketing in action. Marketing research is the basis of each example, followed by a mix strategy that targets identified audience segments. Also, each has an evaluation component—"How successful were we?"

Serving Users on the Go

The first-place winner, Jiří Mahen Library in Brno, Czech Republic, designed an innovative partnership program, Library in the Tram—Tram to the Library. The library worked with Brno's DP Public Transport company and an advertising agency to develop the program, aimed at bringing library services to a mobile user population. As part of the program, individuals who ride the tram can use Quick Response (QR) codes posted on board to sample library services, search the library catalog, or read book excerpts. Throughout the year, the library mounts thematic reading campaigns, and library volunteers riding the tram give small gifts to reading passengers. The featured book excerpts and thematic reading campaigns are based on riders' reading interests, identified through market research. Information posted on board the trams is segmented to target audiences, depending on where riders normally sit (e.g., strollers and children at the back, disabled and elderly at the front). Information such as book tips is regularly updated to engage the target audience. Approximately one thousand riders a day use the tram-based library services (per marketing evaluation of outputs). In addition to directly promoting services to tram riders via visual material located on board and interaction with volunteers, the tram service is heavily promoted through the library's web pages and social media, as well as through promotional materials displayed throughout the library system. The program has attracted media and government attention and is an example of how marketing strategies can be used to identify new types of services needed by target audiences, introduce new ways for target audiences to access information services, and develop new ways to reach consumers and promote new services as they go about their everyday business.

Promoting Library Services through Videos

Regina Qu'Appelle Health Region Health Sciences Library, Regina, Saskatchewan, Canada (second place) produced three ninety-second, amusing and effective videos to promote three much-needed services to students and faculty (market research and segmentation). The first video showed how information professionals could provide quick and thorough information retrieval from medical/scientific databases on specific topics. The second illustrated the use of apps on mobile devices to find evidence-based information at the immediate point of care, while the third pointed to e-mail alerts set up by librarians in medical/scientific databases on specific topics or electronic tables of contents for particular journals. The videos are accessible on the library's website and, handily and with humor, reach student and faculty populations. Marketing evaluation is conducted through output data gathered from number of views and website hits.

Conclusion

Marketing is a systematic planning approach that includes assessing actual and potential customer interest, imaginatively designing and delivering services and products using feedback that improves service, and using effective communication methods to promote the services to targeted market segments. Marketing involves research, segmentation, mix strategy, and evaluation. Just as other customer-based private- and public-sector agencies successfully use marketing practices to achieve their objectives, so can and must information organizations. It is critical to understand what consistent application of marketing processes can do and how marketing can be conducted most effectively.

Notes

1. Brian Arbogast and Eliza Dresang, "*Information Organizations: About the Concept*" (unpublished course materials, LIS 5408 Management of Information Organizations, Florida State University, School of Information, n.d.).
2. Philip Kotler, "Strategies for Introducing Marketing to Nonprofit Organizations," *Journal of Marketing* 43, no. 1 (1979): 40, http://www.jstor.org/stable/1250756; John Fortenberry Jr., *Nonprofit Marketing: Tools and Techniques* (Burlington, MA: Jones & Bartlett Learning, 2013), 261.
3. Christie Koontz and Lorri Mon, *Marketing and Social Media: A Guide for Libraries, Archives and Museums* (Lanham, MD: Rowman & Littlefield, 2014), 65–71.
4. Neil G. Kotler, Philip Kotler, and Wendy Kotler, *Museum Marketing & Strategy: Designing Missions, Building Audiences, Generating Revenues and Resources*, 2nd ed. (San Francisco, CA: Jossey-Bass, 2008), 249.
5. Russell D. James and Peter J. Wosh, eds., *Public Relations and Marketing for Archives: A How to Do It Manual* (Chicago, IL: Society of American Archivists, and New York: Neal-Schuman, 2011), 1109, 1119.
6. J. Paul Peter and James H. Donnelly Jr., *A Preface to Marketing Management*, 13th ed. (New York: McGraw-Hill Irwin, 2011), 19; Kotler, "Strategies for Introducing Marketing," 1979, 40.

7. J. L. Morrison, "Environmental Scanning," in *A Primer for New Institutional Researchers*, ed. M. A. Whitely, J. D. Porter, and R. H. Fenske (Tallahassee, FL: Association for Institutional Research, 1991), 2, http://horizon.unc.edu/courses/papers/enviroscan.
8. Kotler et al., *Museum Marketing & Strategy*, 2008, 47–65.
9. Anne Mathews, "Use of Marketing Principles in Library Planning," in *Marketing for Libraries and Information Agencies*, ed. Darlene E. Weingand (Norwood, NJ: Ablex Publishing, 1984), 12.
10. Fortenberry, *Nonprofit Marketing*, 2013, 261.
11. Alan R. Andreasen and Philip Kotler, *Strategic Marketing for Nonprofit Organizations*, 6th ed. (Upper Saddle River, NJ: Prentice Hall, 2003), 446.
12. Barbar Mueller, *Communicating with the Multicultural Consumer: Theoretical and Practical Perspectives* (Washington, DC: Peter Lang, 2008), discusses the influence of culture and ethical and social responsibility of selling to multicultural consumers.
13. James and Wosh, *Public Relations and Marketing for Archivists*, 2011, 29.
14. Ibid.
15. Koontz and Mon, *Marketing*, 2014, 165.
16. "How to Measure Your Nonprofit's Social Media Success," Socialbrite: Social Solutions for Nonprofits, last modified July 3, 2014, http://www.socialbrite.org/2010/12/15/how-to-measure-your-nonprofits-social-media-success.
17. Katie D. Paine, "Social Media Measurement Manifesto: Yes We CAN, and Already ARE Measuring Social Media" (white paper, Berlin, New Hampshire, 2009), http://dmabenchmarkshub.wikispaces.com/file/view/Yes+we+Can+measure+social+media+white+paper+r.pdf.
18. "Katie Delahaye Paine's New Social Media Measurement Checklist," *Measurement Standard*, last modified January 23, 2010, http://kdpaine.blogs.com/themeasurementstandard/2010/01/katie-paines-social-media-measurement-checklist.html.
19. Andreasen and Kotler, *Strategic Marketing*, 2003, 472–474.
20. "Brand," *American Marketing Association Dictionary*, https://www.ama.org/resources/Pages/Dictionary.aspx?dLetter=B&dLetter=B.
21. Koontz and Mon, *Marketing*, 2014, 265.
22. Andreasen and Kotler, *Strategic Marketing*, 2003, 177.
23. Christie Koontz, ed., "Marketing Glossary," IFLA.org, 2001, extracted with permission from *Dictionary of Marketing Terms*, ed. Peter D. Bennett, 2nd ed. (Chicago, IL: American Marketing Association; Lincolnwood, IL: NTC Publishing Group, 1995), http://archive.ifla.org/VII/s34/pubs/glossary.htm.
24. "11th IFLA International Marketing Award," IFLA.org, http://www.ifla.org/node/6922.

28

Demonstrating Value

ASSESSMENT

Cheryl Stenström

This chapter focuses on the importance of demonstrating the *value* of information organizations and their services in a rapidly changing environment. Showing internal and external stakeholders the value of the information center is just as important as other management functions involved in running an efficient and effective organization. These two aspects of management work synergistically. Without a strong organization, it can be difficult to show value, but without the ongoing support of external stakeholders and funders, it can become increasingly difficult to run an organization that meets the needs of its users. To the surprise of many managers, much of an effective leader's time is spent on ensuring that the value of the organization is apparent to stakeholders.

The chapter approaches the topic of assessing value from a management perspective and uses a variety of practical examples to illustrate key points. While assessment can be complex, in the context of this chapter, it is defined as the set of practices used to both evaluate a program, service, collection, or other offering and to show how it creates value by meeting the needs of stakeholders. After completing this chapter, the reader should have an understanding of

- why assessment is important, and the best way to approach conducting an assessment (e.g., asking the right questions, collecting the best data);
- the various strategies for demonstrating the value of an information organization and its services;
- how outcomes and impacts can help an information organization determine its value for different audiences; and
- the importance of strategically evaluating the context in which information work is situated, and of targeting decision makers with key messages.

Defining Value

There are many ways to describe value, and the most appropriate depends on the purpose of the assessment. Consider this list of different definitions of value:

- *User Satisfaction:* This measures the perception of a client, customer, user, or patron regarding whether they believe their needs have been met. Although it might seem obvious that user satisfaction should be measured, the impact of many initiatives is much more complex than considering whether or not users were satisfied. For example, the cost of running a program may be prohibitive even though many people would enjoy participating.
- *Economic Impact:* This measures the financial impact an information organization has on its immediate community. For example, a university paying salaries to library employees who then turn around and purchase goods in their local communities demonstrates both direct and indirect economic impact.

> "Although it might seem obvious that user satisfaction should be measured, the impact of many initiatives is much more complex than considering whether or not users were satisfied."

- *Social Impact:* This is multifaceted and difficult to measure—as many factors beyond the information organization can contribute to the growth or decline of an organization's social impact; however, many consider it more important than economic impact.[1] Examples include improved literacy levels, community pride, a sense of belonging, greater levels of social trust, and increased opportunities for democratic participation.

TEXTBOX 28.1

Discipline of Economics: The Value of Information

When looking at the value of information itself, rather than the value of the services provided by libraries and information centers, the discipline of economics provides helpful frameworks for consideration. For example, economic decisions always include an element of uncertainty and gaps in our knowledge. In some cases, the information needed to fill these gaps is completely unknown and impossible to predict. In other cases, the gaps can be filled by other people or information sources. Having the ability to provide information used to make economic and financially based decisions may be highly valued by those operating in uncertain environments. Within the frameworks of rationality, uncertainty, risk, and availability, information is seen as a product, or a private good. Those working in a corporate setting regularly assess the cost-benefits of providing information based on a variety of factors.[1]

---

1. H. A. Simon, "A Behavioral Model of Rational Choice," *Quarterly Journal of Economics* 69, no. 1 (1955): 99–118; D. Kahneman and A. Tversky, Prospect Theory: An Analysis of Decision under Risk, *Econometrica* 47, no. 2 (1979): 263–292; J. Stiglitz, and A. Weiss, Credit Rationing in Markets with Imperfect Information, *American Economic Review* 71, no. 3 (1981): 393–410.

The Critical Role of Assessment for Information Organizations

For managers, developing a culture of assessment in their information organization should be a priority. In an era of increasing scrutiny, and diminishing resources for some organizations, assessment plays a critical role. Assessment activities help managers evaluate the organization's performance in order to accomplish two main goals:

- to inform decision making regarding the organization's strategic directions, and
- to aid in demonstrating the value of the organization's services to its stakeholders.

Cheryl Stenström

"Value" is a complex concept and can be measured in many different ways, including user satisfaction. For example, consider the different ways researcher Carol Tenopir describes how an academic library's various users derive value from its services:

> Value to first year undergraduates may be the library's role in encouraging them to continue in school (thus factoring into retention rates), which is enhanced by having a welcoming physical space with friendly assistance. By the time those students are seniors, the value of the library may be more in helping them find high quality resources in a timely manner to improve their research papers. For a faculty member, the value of instructional services may be to help them improve the courses they teach and, at the same time, help their students do better in class assignments. For a graduate student or a faculty member's role as researcher, the value of the library may be to get access to the widest range of resources or the use of an institutional repository as a place to deposit their research datasets for long-term preservation and shared access.[2]

Understanding the various ways users perceive value is important, as is understanding options for measuring the impact of services. In the twentieth century, information organizations typically gathered statistics on all kinds of inputs and outputs, such as funding, books purchased, items circulated, or the number of visits to the building. These statistics were used to make statements like, "Last year, the average number of books borrowed by each patron of the library was 5.2." More recently, information professionals are recognizing that numbers showing outputs—such as the number of books someone borrows—are not all that meaningful. Drawing on the example above, the average borrower might find that the true value comes from the content found in those books. Indeed, the number of items borrowed might have no bearing on whether or not people have found the *right* information to meet their needs.

TEXTBOX 28.2

Topic for Discussion

Why is it important to define the purpose of assessment before gathering data?

Outcomes and Impacts

Thinking about the impact the services and collections of an information organization have on those who use them leads to a discussion of outcomes and gets much closer to the concept of value. Unlike the previous example of measuring outputs quantitatively, both qualitative and quantitative measures can and should be used to measure outcomes. Both direct and indirect value can be considered when looking at services and collections provided by an information organization:

- *Direct Value:* to the user, for example, as measured by increased skills, knowledge, enjoyment, or financial savings (with an emphasis on user satisfaction).
- *Indirect Value:* to society generally, for example, as measured by greater levels of education, generalized trust, job creation, or support of the publishing cycle and national cultural growth (with an emphasis on the broader social impact).[3]

Simply gathering output data about an organization's operations allows managers to answer questions such as, "How many hours of instruction does the library provide?" or "How many computers are available to the public?" However, these questions fall short of answering the question of how an information organization provides indirect and direct value to its users and the wider community. More significant questions allow managers to explore and express value, such as, "What impact has the library's instructional program had on student achievement?" or "In what ways did the library's public access computers enhance the quality of users' lives?"

Over the past decade, some information organization leaders have taken a different approach to demonstrate the value of their institutions. They have used a combination of direct and indirect measures to demonstrate the *financial value* provided by information organizations. Check out these examples:

- In Florida's public libraries, for every dollar spent on the libraries, more than $10.18 of value was returned to the local economy through direct and indirect spending and direct savings to users, and it was found that most library users considered the service essential.[4]
- The Martin Prosperity Institute found "for every dollar invested in the Toronto Public Library, Torontonians receive $5.63."[5] These dollar figures come from extensive examinations of a wide variety of factors; use of collections, programs, meeting space, and technology were the inputs considered to calculate the direct benefits to users, a five-hundred-dollar annual savings per member on average. Each of these inputs has the potential to greatly increase the quality of those individual's lives, but the study goes on to analyze the impact that direct spending by the library (e.g., collections, staff) and indirect spin-off spending have in the community, thus expressing the increase in the quality of life for the whole community.

Check This Out

Read more about the Martin Prosperity Institute's Report,
"So Much More: The Economic Impact of the Toronto Public Library on the City of Toronto"

Visit: http://martinprosperity.org/2013/12/06/o-much-more-the-economic
-impact-of-the-toronto-public-library-on-the-city-of-toronto

A New Era of Data

Regardless of whether one is assessing an information organization or information service, strong research skills are paramount. With more data available than ever before, information professionals must know which data sources are important and be able to critically assess data gathered from a variety of sources.

Useful data sources abound. A wealth of internal data is available to information organization managers, and internal data can be gathered at a much more granular level than ever before. For example, managers can quickly identify trends by analyzing popular search terms used by patrons to find books, articles, and other resources in the information organization's collections, or by exploring the device and operating system preferences of users as they access content. These data speak directly to the kinds of performance assessments that can be used to make decisions regarding collection development budgets, programming, and investments in new technology.

External data is also important, and a revolution in data availability is beginning. The big data movement allows correlations to be made in ways never previously imagined. For example, consider the questions that might be explored if national standardized student achievement rates were cross-referenced with the coordinates of school libraries with full-time information professionals. This type of analysis might bring to light the fact that higher test scores were clustered in areas where school libraries were staffed with full-time information professionals.

This notion of using big data to make decisions and demonstrate value speaks to data literacy and the growing importance of understanding how data are used to answer complex questions. A key step in the assessment process is developing *relevant* assessment questions and appropriately aligning

Cheryl Stenström

research methods and data to answer them. The above example of student test scores and the presence of information professionals does not on its own answer a key question, but it opens the door to investigation. Many additional factors would need to be examined before concluding that one factor (full-time information professionals in school libraries) causes a specific outcome (higher test scores).

Both within and outside the information industry, the explosion of data from cell phones, web page views, GPS systems, image captures, and more is changing the way researchers look for patterns in human behavior and networks. Already the big data movement has resulted in new insights that were impossible to see a decade ago. For example, looking at the aggregated demographics of users across jurisdictions and borders allows information center managers to devote resources to the collections and services most likely to satisfy user needs; or finding out about how people use e-books and other electronic collections (e.g., time spent on a page, search terms, average length of time it takes to read an item) helps publishers provide more responsive materials based on the new ways readers interact with these formats.

Managers have greater opportunities to ask big questions, but care must be taken to ensure that the raw data are used wisely. Consider the following questions in this context: "Will large-scale analysis of DNA help cure diseases? Or will it usher in a new wave of medical inequality? Will data analytics help make people's access to information more efficient and effective? Or will it be used to track protesters in the streets of major cities? Will it transform how we study human communication and culture, or narrow the palette of research options and alter what 'research' means? Some or all of the above?"[6]

Conveying Value

All the best research is useless unless its findings can be conveyed in a meaningful way to target audiences. To be able to truly demonstrate value, information professionals must be able to speak about data clearly and appropriately. In this regard, both qualitative and quantitative data matter, and statistical measurements can be contextualized through story.

Once a target audience has been identified, it is imperative to think about what they might already know, what they need to know, and whether or not "less is more." Consider this example of a public librarian researching different aspects of early literacy. To her boss, she presented an informal but thorough report covering the types of activities undertaken in the library, the use of preschool services, and the demographics of the city. For a group of elementary school teachers, she prepared a PowerPoint presentation that pulled out some of the most technical aspects of how preliteracy skills are acquired. Finally, she met with a group of elected town council members and simply held up a board book (the kind with the thick cardboard pages, typically read to babies and toddlers) in one hand and a calculus textbook in the other hand and said, "It is a long road from here [referring to the board book] to here [referring to the calculus text]."

A challenge in conveying the value propositions of information services lies in the complexity of the impact. Sometimes value is shown over long periods of time or in multiple ways, rather than through a single program or initiative. Caution and sense must be exercised when crafting messages. Avoid sweeping, unbelievable statements like, "Story times reduce crime; therefore money should be taken from the police force and given to children's librarians." A more appropriate way of expressing this might be, "Law enforcement personnel recognize the role high literacy rates play in reducing crime. The public library is the best place for young children to get a head start in developing strong literacy skills in their preschool years."

Recognition of the need to align the impact of the organization with the values of decision makers is growing. Local, regional, national, and international venues are important targets for demonstrating impact, and key relationships should be developed at each of these levels to ensure the message is heard. Examples of the kinds of external audience information professionals might target when talking about the value they provide include university teaching faculty; city council members; department heads with subject expertise, such as medical doctors; school superintendents; regional, national, and international policy-making bodies; and elected politicians. Internal audiences can vary widely as well, and may include supervisors, employees, and colleagues. Each audience may need a different form of assessment or a new way to frame the same data to emphasize the value that is important to the audience.

When considering their audience, the questions astute information professionals ask themselves are simple:

- Who am I trying to reach?
- What do they already know and what additional information do they need?
- How can I make my message clear and credible?
- Will this information help them? If it will cause problems, do I have solutions to propose?

TEXTBOX 28.3

The SPICE Model

A growing number of information professionals are actively publishing and promoting the movement known as "evidence-based librarianship." A pioneer in the area, Andrew Booth, suggests using the SPICE model to focus our assessment questions:[1]

(S) Setting, where?
(P) Perspective, for whom?
(I) Intervention, what?
(C) Comparison, compared with what?
(E) Evaluation, with what result?

"From the perspective of an undergraduate student (perspective) in a university library (setting), is provision of a short term loan collection (intervention) more effective than a general collection (comparison) in terms of the percentage availability of recommended texts (evaluation)?" (p. 362).

---

1. Andrew Booth, "Clear and Present Questions: Formulating Questions for Evidence Based Practice," *Library Hi Tech* 24, no. 3 (2006): 355–368.

Recent studies speak to the importance of information professionals finding ways to tailor their messages regarding value to the needs of specific audiences with whom they have previously established a level of familiarity and trust.[7] Here is an example: Perhaps a specific library program is no longer financially sustainable. Despite the fact that participation levels reveal its growing popularity over the past several years, funders have targeted it for a decrease in funding. Some managers might decide to post announcements on social media, talking about the anticipated reduction in service, how availability of collections and hours might be curtailed, and the negative effect this decision will have generally. Another manager might decide to phone contacts at the funder's office and ask if a meeting could be held to discuss concerns. At the meeting, the manager explains what impact the

TEXTBOX 28.4

Topic for Discussion

What are the most effective ways to convey value to target audiences?

Cheryl Stenström

service decrease could have on users and suggests that other avenues could be explored to see how an equivalent amount of funds could be saved in an area that is no longer a priority. Consider that both approaches provide data that can help funders make a decision, but the second approach also suggests solutions and alternatives.

Conclusion

Assessments are conducted for a variety of reasons. Sometimes managers want to examine the internal performance of an organization so they can convey findings to staff, clients, or direct funders. Perhaps the results of an assessment may form the basis of a public relations campaign highlighting user satisfaction and a refreshed image for the organization. Increasingly it is becoming more important to show positive impact to policy makers and influential decision makers.

Although there are a variety of ways to use assessments to describe value to key stakeholders, perhaps the economic and social impacts of information services provide the greatest opportunities to demonstrate value and influence decision makers. This chapter opened with a discussion of the current trend of moving from measuring outputs to outcomes and impacts. A discussion of value is not complete without considering the question, "Who is asking?" The present dominant political ideology in most Western countries places a notable emphasis on economic costs and impacts. Those working in the information profession have worked hard to align their methods of assessment with this ideology, but as this chapter has shown, the biggest impacts of information work are much greater than a simple financial calculation. Multifaceted and rigorous assessment that seeks to measure meaningful impact in appropriate ways will also prove to be the best way to demonstrate value.

> "Multifaceted and rigorous assessment that seeks to measure meaningful impact in appropriate ways will also prove to be the best way to demonstrate value."

Notes

1. See, for example, Svanhild Aabø, "The Role and Value of Public Libraries in the Age of Digital Technologies," *Journal of Librarianship and Information Science* 37, no. 4 (2005): 205.
2. Susan Imholz and Jennifer Weil Arns, "Worth Their Weight: An Assessment of the Evolving Field of Library Evaluation," *Public Library Quarterly* 26, nos. 3/4 (July 2007): 31; Andreas Varheim, "Social Capital and Public Libraries: The Need for Research," *Library & Information Science Research* 29, no. 3 (2007): 416.
3. Tracy Micka, "Demonstrating the Value of the Public Library: Economic Valuation and the Advocacy Imperative," *Student Research Journal* 3, no. 1 (2013): 6, http://scholarworks.sjsu.edu/cgi/viewcontent.cgi?article=1127&context=slissrj.
4. Florida Department of State, Division of Library & Information Services, "Return on Investment in Florida Public Libraries—2013 Study," last modified June 29, 2014, http://dlis.dos.state.fl.us/bld/roi.
5. Kevin Stolarick and Kimberly Silk, "So Much More: The Economic Impact of the Toronto Public Library on the City of Toronto" (report, Martin Prosperity Institute, 2013), http://martinprosperity.org/media/TPL%20Economic%20Impact_Dec2013_LR_FINAL.pdf.
6. Danah Boyd and Kate Crawford, "Six Provocations for Big Data," (presentation, Oxford Internet Institute's A Decade in Internet Time: Symposium on the Dynamics of the Internet and Society, Oxford, September 21, 2011), http://papers.ssrn.com/sol3/papers.cfm?abstract_id=1926431.
7. Cheryl Stenstrom and Ken Haycock, "Influence and Increased Funding in Canadian Public Libraries," *Library Quarterly* 84, no. 1 (2014): 49–68.

Part VI

Information Issues
Influences and Consequences

We significantly influence or control the selection, organization, preservation, and dissemination of information. In a political system grounded in an informed citizenry, we are members of a profession explicitly committed to intellectual freedom and the freedom of access to information. We have a special obligation to ensure the free flow of information and ideas to present and future generations.

—American Library Association, Code of Ethics (2008)

The true value of the information profession is its upholding of the principles of intellectual freedom and access to information. These issues are typically perceived as hallmarks of the information profession—key ideals that permeate all decisions. How information professionals address these issues shines a spotlight on why the profession is needed now more than ever. Today's information professionals play a critical role in shaping information policy, influencing decisions that enable civil liberties such as privacy, intellectual freedom, and equity of access to resources, and impact economic issues such as intellectual property.

Part VI examines how the ideal of intellectual freedom is more complex than ever before. It also explores the profession's ethical code, including how those principles have been challenged in the past and how they are likely to be the focus of controversy in the future. Additionally, it examines some legal issues related to information access, such as copyright and information licensing, especially licensing of digital content. Most importantly, this section focuses on the responsibilities of the information professional in upholding these values to preserve the rights of information users.

Welcome to *Part VI—Information Issues: Influences and Consequences!*

29

Information Policy

Kate Marek

Our contemporary society runs on information, from the day's weather and stock prices to details about international terrorism. It therefore stands to reason that the policies, rules, and processes that govern information—what we call information policies—are fundamental to the tenor of society.

The emergence of this information-based society has profoundly shaped the development of laws, rules, and policies that govern information use and flow. Information policies enable civil liberties such as privacy, intellectual freedom, and equity of access to resources, and they impact economic issues such as intellectual property and commercial performance. Each of these issues, however, is as complex as today's complex society and involves conflicting priorities that must be balanced simultaneously. For example, today's critical discussion of national security versus citizen privacy is an information policy issue. Another example is the economic benefit of intellectual property and the right to information ownership, which must be balanced with society's need for a healthy public domain to enable creativity. Thinking about information policy in today's dynamic world is challenging and exciting, and information professionals are called to be key contributors to the public discussion.

This chapter provides a brief introduction to information policy specifically for information professionals in an effort to provide a framework for policy analysis and awareness in key areas that are relevant to the information field. After completing this chapter, the reader will have an understanding of information policy as a concept, the role of values in policy creation, the policy creation process, frameworks for analyzing policy decisions, examples of specific information policies in the United States, and how information professionals play an important role regarding information policy issues in a democratic society.

Conceptual Elements of Information Policy Development

Information policies are the rules, regulations, laws, and tacit processes that direct and govern the information cycle: creation, ownership, dissemination and flow, access, use, and legacy storage. When considering this definition, two broad questions arise:

- What are the key value questions that need to be asked when establishing information policy?
- What are the key issues that must be addressed when establishing information policy?

For example, is information accessible by everyone, or only by a select few? Under what circumstances is information accessible, and at what price? What power do government agencies have to limit ownership of and access to information? Who owns information? Who decides what information is created and shared, and how are those decisions made? What power inequities exist as a result of decisions regarding information access and control, and to what extent are those power inequities acceptable in a democratic society?

Decisions regarding information policy can have profound impacts on daily life and may involve personal privacy, intellectual freedom, or even workplace effectiveness. For example, who has access to people's medical information? Who has access to people's electronic book purchases? What information barriers exist in people's workplace?

Values as the Foundation for Policy Formulation

Values drive the creation of information policy. Overman and Cahill list seven values that shape the information policy debate (see textbox 29.1).[1]

An examination of the strengths and limits of each of these values within the context of freedom, security, and the nation's capitalistic economic structure provides a framework for policy analysis in a democratic society.

TEXTBOX 29.1

Values Relevant to Information Policy Creation

- *Access and Freedom:* the assumption of democracy
- *Privacy:* the preservation of personal rights
- *Openness:* the public's right to know
- *Usefulness:* the pragmatist's creed
- *Cost and Benefit:* the bureaucratic necessity
- *Secrecy and Security:* the authoritative cloak
- *Ownership:* the notion of intellectual property

Information Issues that Drive Policy Formation

"A society's values provide an important context for establishing information policies, and specific types of issues must be addressed when establishing information policies. All of these issues may have conflicting priorities; may overlap; may have political, social, and bureaucratic implications; and may be temporary (ceasing to be an issue as technology and society evolve)."

A society's values provide an important context for establishing information policies, and specific types of issues must be addressed when establishing information policies. While information policy issues are always changing, textbox 29.2 provides a list, by no means exhaustive, of current information policy issues. All of these issues may have conflicting priorities; they may overlap; they may have political, social, and bureaucratic implications; and they may be temporary (ceasing to be an issue as technology and society evolve).

Policy Making in Light of Organizational Mission

Just as solutions to information policy issues differ depending on the values of society, they also differ based on the mission and goals of the information organization. An organization's institutional mission adds nuance to information policy discussions.

For example, a public library might be concerned with the chilling effect on patron privacy of national legislation, such as the USA PATRIOT Act,[2] which limits information privacy (see also chapter 8,

Examples of Information Policy Issues

- Censorship and intellectual freedom
- Information ownership, disclosure, storage, confidentiality, and privacy
- Intellectual property (copyright and copyright limits)
- Public domain (how do we ensure access to ideas?)
- Societal barriers to information access: economic, cultural, generational, and educational
- Telecommunications policy, broadcasting policies, and information infrastructure (such as broadband deployment, commercial ownership of the airwaves, and net neutrality)
- Consumer information for commerce and for privacy
- Data collection and management (commercial, personal)
- National security and surveillance
- Computer regulation and computer crime
- Fee-based information services (including propriety research)
- Universal access to information
- Media ownership and monopolies
- Medical and health information systems
- International communication policy

"Community Anchors for Lifelong Learning: Public Libraries"). Public libraries may also seek to balance a desire for patron privacy with many patrons' desire for customized information services via social media (see also chapter 35, "Information Privacy and Cybersecurity"). An academic library might be hypervigilant to government surveillance of faculty research, and also concerned with open academic content weighed against author recognition for academic tenure and review policies. Similarly, an information service within a corporate environment might be concerned with intellectual property from the perspective of protecting corporate assets, as well as with legal uses of information for competitive advantage (see also chapter 9, "Information Centers: Special Libraries").

A Framework for Evaluating Policy Decisions

One helpful framework for evaluating information policy decisions was developed by Ian Rowlands, who established a matrix of choices, allowing policy makers to better visualize the impact of their decisions. Rowlands identified two conflicting aspects of information (for the public good and as a tradable commodity) and two extremes of access (open and closed) and proposed a four-quadrant matrix.[3] Figure 29.1, "Matrix of Information Issues," depicts Rowlands's matrix, presenting the four quadrants and offering examples of current information issues in each quadrant.

Rowlands' concept of information as a public good emphasizes the perspective that information is needed for an open society. However, the matrix also represents the competing priority of limiting openness in order to ensure both personal privacy (e.g., can anyone access my Social Security number?) and national security (e.g., can anyone access our government's emergency security plans?). Information as a tradable commodity acknowledges the role of information in a capitalistic, knowledge-based society, where potential profit from information ownership must be balanced with consumer access for ongoing discovery and quality of life.

As depicted in figure 29.1, there are tensions when weighing policy decisions in light of the public good (individual rights and social justice) versus the private good (ownership and economic growth).

Information as Public Good

INFORMATION FOR CITIZENSHIP	INFORMATION PROTECTIONISM
• Free public libraries	• Restricted data access
• Open Internet	• National security
• User privacy	• Data collection / surveillance
• Information for civic discourse	• Censorship Commercial secrecy
• Barrier-free access to resources	
• Strong public domain	

Open,
Unrestricted
Information Flows

Open,
Unrestricted
Information Flows

INFORMATION FOR CONSUMER CHOICE	INFORMATION FOR COMPETITIVE ADVANTAGE
• Freedom of the press	• Intranets
• The mass media	• Competitive Intelligence
• Universal service	• Patents
• Public-private partnerships	• Strict intellectual property rights; long rights terms
• Fee-based information services and Internet	• Proprietary information
Infotainment	• Work for hire

Information as a Tradable Commodity

Figure 29.1 Matrix of Information Issues. *Adapted from Ian Rowlands, "Understanding Information Policy," Journal of Information Science 22, no. 1 (1996): 15.*

There are also tensions when evaluating policy decisions in light of the need for open/unrestricted flows of information (no cost, no limits) and closed/restricted flows (fee based, tight limits).

Information professionals will not always choose policies from the open/public good quadrant. For example, information centers within commercial organizations, particularly those developing products or which are highly competitive, will select information policies that restrict flows of information outside the organization and perhaps even will practice very restrictive information flows within the organization. It is important to consider the mission, purpose, and overall values of the organization or the society when analyzing whether a policy is appropriate.

Another twenty-first-century example of an information policy issue involving the need to address two equally desirable goals is the use of electronic surveillance and encryption, which can foster national security while sometimes limiting personal privacy. What kinds of information policies can best address this tension, maximizing national security but also ensuring citizens' civil liberties?

TEXTBOX 29.3

Topic for Discussion

Think of an example of an unwritten information policy within an organization. What are some impacts of unwritten policies regarding internal information flows in that setting? What power inequities are evidenced in your scenario?

Kate Marek

The Process of Government Policy Making

Information policies are necessary at all levels of society: global, national, regional, state, local, organizational, and personal. As already discussed, an organization's mission drives its decision making regarding information policies, and society's values impact how information issues are addressed. However, government agencies play a key role in information policy making. The policy-making process in the United States takes place within the three branches of government: executive, legislative, and judicial. Each of the branches of government may play a role in the policy process. There are five stages to the policy formulation process (see textbox 29.4).

Stage 1: Problem Identification and Agenda Setting

When an issue in society develops, an agenda or broad plan to address the issue may take shape within the government or in response to a vocal public urging government officials to take action. Values emerge as drivers of suggested government action. This stage of the process is considered the time of problem identification and agenda setting.

Stage 2: Problem Formulation/Policy Making

The next stage of the process is policy formulation, where an approach to the issue is designed and articulated. Policy formulation often includes extensive debates based on contrasting values and intended outcomes. To be effective, policy formulation must involve compromise.

In her book *Policy Paradox: The Art of Political Decision Making*, Deborah Stone describes policy formulation using the metaphor of dividing a chocolate cake for a classroom of students. The cooperative goal may be to divide the cake fairly, but disagreements arise on seemingly ceaseless aspects of the question. In particular, there are "competing values of an equitable distribution."[4] Many factors are brought into the decision-making process and are part of the values definition that precedes policy formulation, such as whether the cake should be divided equally among the students totally based on weight

> "To be effective, policy formulation must involve compromise."

and size of the pieces, or whether extenuating circumstances and preexisting external conditions should influence the definition of "equitable." Stone identifies eight potential scenarios that might influence the division of the cake, including the possibility that a student already had some chocolate cake and indeed has lots at home (external conditions), that a student contributed more actively to class discussions (merit), or that a student might or might not receive a portion despite her absence that particular day (requirements for benefits).[5]

In the United States, this policy formation stage takes place most often in the legislative branch, but it may also come from a president's executive order or from a Supreme Court ruling. For example, the Freedom of Information Act (1966)[6] was enacted by Congress and had subsequent modifications through various executive orders. An example of policy made through a Supreme Court ruling is the 1965 landmark case *Griswold v. Connecticut*,[7] where a state ban on contraceptives was declared unconstitutional based on a citizen's right to marital privacy. This decision has had broad ramifications guaranteeing Americans a constitutional right to privacy.

Stage 3: Budgeting

After policy formulation/policy making, budget issues associated with the policy need to be resolved (see also chapter 22, "Managing Budgets").

Stage 4: Policy Adoption and Implementation

The stage of policy adoption takes place when legislation is passed, when an executive order or a new regulation goes into effect, or when the Supreme Court issues a ruling. This is followed by policy implementation, which frequently happens through government agencies, individual state governments, or even local jurisdictions, depending on the nature of the policy or ruling.

Stage 5: Evaluation

The final stage of the process is evaluation, allowing decision makers to examine the impact of the policy and whether it is still relevant. For example, a policy may need to be updated or revised based on broad changes in public opinion, developments in technology or new research, or the more pragmatic basis of a cost-benefit analysis in situations where it may no longer be financially feasible to continue with the policy. When considering possible policy solutions to an issue, it is useful to think not only of the intended outcomes (e.g., welfare payments to ease hunger), but also potential unintended consequences (e.g., the welfare system perpetuates dependence on government payments rather than building self-sufficiency). Unintended negative outcomes of a policy are frequently the rationale for policy reconsideration and revision.

Information Professionals: Responsibilities and Opportunities

Information professionals' roles in the arena of information policy include awareness, advocacy, and activism. Information professionals have indeed been leaders in the fight for policies that reflect the profession's core values, such as equity of access and intellectual freedom, sometimes at great personal and professional risk (see also chapter 36, "Intellectual Freedom").

An example of one of those heroes is Ruth Brown (1891–1975), who in the mid-twentieth century took a stand on equity of access within her community. As the longtime director of the Bartlesville Oklahoma Public Library, Brown gradually but relentlessly opened the library's programming and collections to African Americans. Despite the strong support of many community members, as well as the Oklahoma Library Association, the American Library Association (ALA), and the American Civil Liberties Union (ACLU), growing political opposition cost Brown her job; she was fired in 1950.[8]

> "Information professionals have indeed been leaders in the fight for policies that reflect the profession's core values, such as equity of access and intellectual freedom, sometimes at great personal and professional risk."

Activist Zoia Horn (1918–2014) is considered a hero for her work protecting privacy rights and intellectual freedom. Horn, who worked in academic and public libraries, spent twenty days in jail in 1972 as a result of her refusal to testify against the Harrisburg Seven, priests and nuns who were peace activities and protested against involvement in the Vietnam War. She asserted that being forced to testify would violate her professional principles of privacy and intellectual freedom.[9] Throughout her

Kate Marek

life, Horn continued her activism in support of intellectual freedom and against all barriers to information services.

Something as subtle, but as fundamental, as standardized subject headings used to classify library materials can support or question a cultural point of view. The efforts in the 1970s of the ALA Task Force on Gay Liberation (now the Gay, Lesbian, Bisexual, and Transgendered Round Table) provide a case history of policy activism as it relates to simple, but highly visible, language changes. By moving the topic "homosexuality" from the Library of Congress subject heading "Sexual Deviations" to "Sexual Life" in 1972, the Library of Congress made a significant contribution to shifting cultural norms.[10] Bowker and Star explore the issue of "classification and its consequences" in depth in their book on this topic, *Sorting Things Out*.[11]

The value of information privacy came to the forefront in a 2005–2006 court case involving the "Connecticut Four," where four librarians from a Connecticut library database co-op challenged a national security letter demanding USA PATRIOT Act-sanctioned access to patron records without a court order. A significant component of the case was the mandatory gag order associated with the delivery of the national security letter and thus the broad restrictions on freedom of speech. Engaging the American Civil Liberties Union, the Connecticut Four fought the gag order and continued to fight to protect their patrons' privacy. The case, officially titled *Doe v. Gonzales*,[12] was finally resolved in 2006 when a federal court lifted the gag order, and shortly thereafter the FBI dropped its demand for the patron records. The Connecticut Four, George Christian, Barbara Bailey, Peter Chase, and Janet Nocek, were subsequently recognized by the American Library Association with the 2007 Paul Howard Award for Courage.[13]

As these examples demonstrate, information professionals benefit from knowing federal and state laws affecting information organizations, access, and use. Information professionals should also be aware of their own organization's policies and be a part of the evaluation and review of those policies. Information professionals should always consult an attorney when they are confronted with a challenge to an information policy issue. The American Library Association and each state library association also have structures to help defend citizens' rights to access and privacy.

TEXTBOX 29.5

Topic for Discussion

A society's values affect its information policies, but how should an information professional uphold policy that goes against his/her own values?

Conclusion

As the role of information in our society has expanded in recent decades, so too has the work of information professionals as information stewards. The questions regarding information policy introduced in this chapter should trigger an awareness of the critical role information professionals play in the formulation of information policy.

Advocacy happens at multiple levels, through various avenues, and with a variety of methods. Information professionals can make large and small statements, many of which will be incremental over time. When thinking of advocacy and activism, information professionals are working for core democratic values that affect citizens' rights for intellectual freedom and for access to all kinds of information, in all formats, and without barriers. If information professionals are passionate about these issues—intellectual freedom, privacy, and all citizens' right to information access—then they are essentially passionate about information policy.

Notes

1. Sam E. Overman and Anthony G. Cahill, "Information Policy: A Study of Values in the Policy Process," *Policy Studies Review* 9, no. 4 (1990): 803–818.
2. U.S.A. Patriot Act of 2001, Pub. L. No. 107-56, 115 Stat. 272 (2001), http://thomas.loc.gov/cgi-bin/query/z?c107:H.R.3162.ENR:%20.
3. Ian Rowlands, "Understanding Information Policies," *Journal of Information Science* 22, no. 1 (1996): 13–25.
4. Elizabeth Stone, *Policy Paradox: The Art of Political Decision Making*, rev. ed. (New York: Norton, 2002).
5. Ibid.
6. Freedom of Information Act of 1967, Pub. L. 89-487, 80 Stat. 250 (1967), http://www.foia.gov.
7. Griswold v. Connecticut, 381 U.S. 479 (1965), http://www.pbs.org/wnet/supremecourt/rights/landmark_griswold.html.
8. Louise S. Robbins, *The Dismissal of Miss Ruth Brown: Civil Rights, Censorship, and the American Library* (Norman, OK: University of Oklahoma Press, 2000).
9. John N. Berry III, "Library Freedom Fighter Zoia Horn Remembered," *Library Journal*, last modified August 19, 2014, http://lj.libraryjournal.com/2014/08/people/library-freedom-fighter-zoia-horn-remembered.
10. Melissa A. Adler, "The ALA Task Force on Gay Liberation: Effecting Change in Naming and Classification of GLBTQ Subjects," *Advances in Classification Research Online* 23 no. 1, (2013), https://journals.lib.washington.edu/index.php/acro/article/viewFile/14226/12086.
11. George C. Bowker and Susan L. Star, *Sorting Things Out* (Cambridge, MA: MIT Press, 2000).
12. Doe v. Gonzales, 546 U.S. 1301 (2005), http://www.supremecourt.gov/opinions/05pdf/05a295.pdf.
13. "2007 Paul Howard Award for Courage Recipient Named," ALA.org, last modified May 15, 2007, http://www.ala.org/Template.cfm?Section=archive&template=/contentmanagement/contentdisplay.cfm&ContentID=157765.

30

Information Ethics

Martin L. Garnar

Information ethics is "a field of applied ethics that addresses the uses and abuses of information, information technology, and information systems for personal, professional, and public decision making."[1] For information professionals, this subset of ethics has the most direct application to their daily work and its primary concerns are well represented in the profession's ethical statements. By understanding the ethical principles at the core of the information science profession and by referring to those principles when making decisions or facing dilemmas, information professionals can strive to ensure that their everyday actions are consistent with the field's professional values. In addition, discerning how those principles apply to new trends and situations helps keep the profession vital and relevant in a constantly changing world. After completing this chapter, the reader should be able to define the terminology for discussing ethics, explain different ethical theories, describe the principles that inform the profession's ethical codes, identify evidence of those principles, and discuss future trends and implications for ethical thinking.

Information Ethics: Key Concepts

Defining terms is the first step in understanding ethics. For the purposes of this chapter, ethics is defined as a set of principles that guide decision making in a specified setting. Ethics can be personal or shared, which impacts the source of the principles at the heart of an ethical system. Principles may also be referred to as morals, values, or beliefs—and people may have these instilled by their families, cultures, and society. People may also choose to adopt their own principles based on personal experience and study. When ethics are shared, such as in a professional setting, the underlying principles must also be shared and agreed upon by those involved. As different settings may have distinct areas of concern, there are subsets of ethics, such as information ethics, that may be tailored to various fields.

Ethical Theories

Before ethics can be approached from a professional perspective, it is important to understand different theories for applying ethics. Though there are multiple ethical theories, this chapter focuses on three dominant schools of thought: utilitarianism, deontology, and the ethics of care.

Utilitarianism

As defined by Henry R. West, utilitarianism is "the theory that actions, laws, institutions, and policies should be critically evaluated by whether they tend to produce the greatest happiness."[2] First espoused by Jeremy Bentham, utilitarianism is associated closely with John Stuart Mill, whose writings popularized the concept.[3] A layperson's approach to utilitarianism may be summed up by the exchange between Captain Kirk and Mr. Spock in *Star Trek II: The Wrath of Khan* when Spock tells Kirk why he is sacrificing his life in the damaged engine room: the needs of the many outweigh the needs of the few (or the one). Something that is beneficial for the majority is ethically acceptable if the people disadvantaged by such a decision are in the minority. Critics of utilitarianism observe that negative consequences can too easily be justified in this system of thought.

> "The utilitarianism theory emphasizes that 'something that is beneficial for the majority is ethically acceptable if the people disadvantaged by a decision are in the minority.'"

Deontology

Deontology, from the Greek *deon* meaning duty, refers to an ethical system based on adherence to rules (i.e., duty-bound to follow the rules). Immanuel Kant is considered to be the preeminent proponent of a deontological approach to ethics. In contrast to utilitarianism, deontology focuses not on the consequences of a decision, but on the rightness of the action taken. An action is ethical if the rule guiding the action depends on an underlying principle of validity as applied to everyone regardless of the consequences.[4] Deontology falls short when the choices of action are all right, leaving the actor in the difficult position of having to decide which rule to break in order to preserve another rule.

> "In contrast to utilitarianism, deontology focuses not on the consequences of a decision, but on the rightness of the action taken."

Ethics of Care

Another approach to ethical thinking is care-based ethics, which may be easily summed up with what is commonly known as the Golden Rule: "Do unto others as you would have them do unto you." Though often associated with Christianity, this tenet can be found throughout a variety of world religions and philosophical traditions, including Confucianism, Hinduism, Islam, Judaism, Buddhism, and classic Greek and Latin texts, so considering it a universal value is not beyond reason.[5] Additionally, the "ethics of care"[6] is a feminist concept offered as a corrective to the dominant paradigms of utilitarianism and deontology, as both of those approaches represent the patriarchal hegemony in modern ethical thought. Given the service orientation of the library and information science professions, a care-based approach to ethical thinking can be seen as complementary to overall goals. However, as with other approaches to ethics, flaws can be found with care-based thinking. "Do unto others" stops being effective when the other is an evildoer.

> "Given the service orientation of the library and information science professions, a care-based approach to ethical thinking can be seen as complementary to our aims."

All of the aforementioned approaches to ethics can be discredited with examples of scenarios that fall outside of their paradigms. Rather than focus on the merits or deficits of a specific ethical approach, it is helpful to know that there are multiple ways of approaching ethical dilemmas, as specific situations may require the consideration of a variety of solutions before a decision can be made.

Martin L. Garnar

Professional Ethical Codes

Having a clearly defined ethical code is a hallmark of a true profession.[7] In the library and information science profession, there are a number of ethical codes that correspond with specialties within the profession. The Code of Ethics of the American Library Association (ALA), the earliest professional code for information professionals, was first adopted in 1939 and establishes broad principles to "guide the work of librarians [and] other professionals providing information services."[8] The Code of Ethics for Archivists from the Society of American Archivists (SAA) and the Code of Ethical Business Practice from the Association of Independent Information Professionals (AIIP) cover many of the same topics, but also address issues that are unique to their respective situations.[9] A relative newcomer on the scene, the IFLA Code of Ethics for Librarians and Other Information Workers from the International Federation of Library Associations and Institutions (IFLA) was first adopted in 2012 and is the most detailed of these four examples, as it must establish some principles that are taken for granted in individual countries.[10] While these statements cannot provide guidance in every situation, they serve as reminders of the principles that are the foundation of the information profession. See textbox 30.1.

TEXTBOX 30.1

Professional Codes of Ethics

- Code of Ethics of the American Library Association: http://www.ala.org/advocacy/proethics/codeofethics/codeethics
- Code of Ethics for Archivists from the Society of American Archivists: http://www2.archivists.org/statements/saa-core-values-statement-and-code-of-ethics
- Code of Ethical Business Practice from the Association of Independent Information Professionals: http://aiip.org/content/code-ethical-business-practices
- IFLA Code of Ethics for Librarians and Other Information Workers: http://www.ifla.org/news/ifla-code-of-ethics-for-librarians-and-other-information-workers-full-version

The Profession's Shared Principles

When faced with an ethical dilemma, one of the first steps is to determine what principles are in conflict. In a professional setting, it is imperative for shared principles to be identified and articulated. Of the four professional codes mentioned previously, only the SAA Code of Ethics for Archivists is explicitly paired and presented with a statement of core values: the SAA Core Values of Archivists.[11] This statement is essential to understanding the full commitment of archivists to their principles. Though not presented in tandem with the ALA Code of Ethics, the ALA Core Values of Librarianship statement is a good starting point for a broad list of shared principles and is used here as a framework for comparing how these principles are represented in the four ethical codes.[12] Table 30.1 presents these comparisons in a side-by-side format with detailed comparisons following.

ACCESS

ALA mentions "equitable access" in the very first article, denoting its importance among principles.[13] Likewise, the first section of the IFLA code is titled "Access to Information" and details why access is so important.[14] "Access and Use" is an entire section within the SAA code and includes an acknowledgment that access may be restricted due to donor agreements based on protecting confidential information, thus highlighting how competing principles may sometimes cause an ethical dilemma.[15]

Table 30.1. Shared Principles: Side-by-Side Comparison

Shared Principles	ALA	SAA	AIIP	IFLA
Access	Y	Y	Y	Y
Confidentiality and Privacy	Y	Y	Y	Y
Democracy	Y	N	N	Y
Diversity	Y	Y	N	Y
Education and Lifelong Learning	Y	Y	N	Y
Intellectual Freedom	Y	N	N	Y
Preservation	Y	Y	N	N
Professionalism	Y	Y	Y	Y
Public Good	Y	Y	Y	Y
Service	Y	N	Y	Y
Social Responsibility	Y	Y	N	Y
Y = included principle. N = not included. Implied principles are indicated as included. Comparison of shared principles across the ALA, SAA, AIIP, and IFLA codes of ethics.				

Though access does not necessarily apply to the client of an independent information professional, AIIP's code includes "giv[ing] clients the most current and accurate information," which is similar to ensuring good access to information[16] (see also chapter 15, "Accessing Information Anywhere and Anytime: Access Services").

CONFIDENTIALITY AND PRIVACY

All four codes reference confidentiality and privacy for users regarding information use.[17] As it did with access, the SAA code spells out special responsibilities for both donor and user privacy (see also chapter 35, "Information Privacy and Cybersecurity").

DEMOCRACY

Alone among the codes, the preamble to the ALA code notes that information professionals are in a "political system grounded in an informed citizenry" and states that the profession has a "special obligation to ensure the free flow of information."[18] Given the specialized roles of archivists and independent information professionals, and given that democracy is not the only form of government in countries represented by IFLA, the absence of a specific mention in the other three codes is not a surprise. It is worth noting that the SAA Core Values of Archivists statement does make a clear reference to the relationship between democracy and archives when they document "institutional functions, activities, and decision-making" for purposes of accountability.[19]

Martin L. Garnar

DIVERSITY

The IFLA code has the only explicit reference to diversity, noting "that equitable services are provided for everyone whatever their age, citizenship, political belief, physical or mental ability, gender identity, heritage, education, income, immigration and asylum-seeking status, marital status, origin, race, religion or sexual orientation"[20] (see also chapter 4, "Diversity, Cultures, and Equity of Access"). The IFLA code also calls for respect for language minorities. Though the SAA code's preamble states that archives "provide evidence of the full range of human experience" and the ALA code mentions serving "all library users," these references to diversity are implicit at best.[21] However, the SAA core values statement includes an entire section on diversity.[22] The AIIP code does not address diversity.

EDUCATION AND LIFELONG LEARNING

Article 8 of the ALA code notes the importance of continuing education for members of the profession.[23] IFLA includes education as one of the core missions of libraries and specifically mentions increasing reading skills and teaching information literacy, and it also notes the importance of professional development.[24] Though the SAA code does not mention education and lifelong learning, it is part of the SAA core values statement[25] (see also chapter 20, "Infinite Learning").

INTELLECTUAL FREEDOM

The ALA code specifically states that "we uphold the principles of intellectual freedom," while the IFLA code references the importance of "freedom of opinion, expression and access to information"[26] (see also chapter 36, "Intellectual Freedom"). Neither the SAA code nor core values statement makes explicit reference to intellectual freedom, though elements of intellectual freedom such as privacy and access have been noted above. The AIIP code does not mention intellectual freedom.

PRESERVATION

Not surprisingly, multiple sections of the SAA code and core values statement refer to the importance of preservation[27] (see also chapter 34, "Analog and Digital Curation and Preservation"). The ALA code implies that preservation is a responsibility in its preamble when it states that librarians have "a special obligation to ensure the free flow of information and ideas to present and future generations."[28] While the need to publicize preservation policies is mentioned in the IFLA code's section on neutrality and professionalism, the purpose of preservation is not discussed.[29] The AIIP code does not include preservation.

PROFESSIONALISM

All codes include professionalism as a concept. ALA, SAA, and IFLA all call for fairness and respect when dealing with other members of the profession, while AIIP gives clear direction about respecting the rules of libraries, not accepting projects that would be "detrimental" to the profession, and upholding the profession's reputation.[30] The SAA core values statement also includes a section on professionalism.[31]

THE PUBLIC GOOD

This core value may not be easily understood without some context. The ALA core values statement affirms that "libraries are an essential public good" in light of movements to outsource and/or privatize library services.[32] In this sense, none of the codes address this value beyond previous mentions of connections to democracy. The SAA core values statement does explicitly mention the public good with reference to social responsibility, but in the context that archives have a responsibility *to* the public good, not that archives *are* a public good.[33]

SERVICE

All codes except SAA highlight service as a primary value of the profession, though SAA's core value statement does include a section devoted to service.[34]

SOCIAL RESPONSIBILITY

Like the concept of the public good, this concept may benefit from context. The ALA core values statement says that "the broad social responsibilities of the American Library Association are defined in terms of the contribution that librarianship can make in ameliorating or solving the critical problems of society."[35] The IFLA code is the only one that specifically mentions social responsibility as inherent to the profession because of the importance of information service to "social, cultural and economic well-being."[36] The SAA core values statement includes a section on social responsibility, explaining that archivists are responsible not only to their employers and institutions, but also to the greater society because of their custody of the cultural record.[37]

TEXTBOX 30.2

Topic for Discussion

The principal, in response to a parent's complaint about a book in the school library, removes the book and puts it in her office without following the official policy for handling challenges. Do you say anything? If so, what and to whom?

Reflecting on these four professional codes, the choice between brevity and detail can make a big difference in what principles or values are clearly stated and what needs to be inferred. IFLA, with the longest code at almost 1,600 words, has the most inclusive approach when it comes to explicating shared principles. The choice to pair an ethical code (of just over 800 words) with a core values statement (of just over 1,400 words) allowed SAA to have a shorter code, though some of those core values were not reflected in that shorter code. That some issues were still not covered in the combined statement shows that a specialized professional statement can get into great detail on matters of special concern while still ignoring areas of broader concern. The AIIP code shows a very different approach to a specialized statement. At 187 words, it is the shortest of the four and is focused exclusively on the concerns of this subset of the profession. Finally, the ALA code favors brevity over detail at 380 words. Twelve of those words were added in the latest revision to expand upon an issue not previously discussed in this chapter, as this topic (intellectual property) was not included in either of the core values statements. Yet three of the four codes (ALA, IFLA, and AIIP) state that information professionals should respect intellectual property, and ALA and IFLA go on to discuss the rights of information users (IFLA, of course, in much greater detail).[38] This is an example of how codes of ethics may sometimes include principles of how information professionals ought to act regarding a topic that may not be at the spiritual heart of a profession, but nevertheless is vital to the profession's work. It is also an example of how ethical codes can adjust and change in response to current trends.

Martin L. Garnar

Keeping Pace with a Changing World

As noted earlier, the ALA Code of Ethics was first created in 1939. Though it has been revised three times since its adoption to address necessary changes, is it possible that some of the values are no longer relevant? In other words, do print-based principles apply to a digital world? The short answer is yes, but not without recognizing how the world has changed or explaining why the principles are still relevant.

Digital Content

Information organizations continue to shift their collections from print/analog to digital content. While some library users provide their own devices for accessing the content, there will always be some people who need to use or borrow library-provided devices, as they do not have anything suitable (or at all). It may be technically equal access to say that everyone has the same right to download content, but the professional ethical codes call for equitable access, which means that information professionals need to bridge the gaps created by individual needs. Whether those needs take the form of equipment, skills deficits, or other barriers to accessing content, information professionals must do their best to remove those barriers. At the same time, if information organizations spend too much money on devices, they will have less money for increasingly expensive content. Meanwhile, licensing continues to supplant purchasing as the model for acquiring content, especially when it is in digital form. If information professionals leave behind the limits on copyright that allowed their organizations to lend and reproduce portions of purchased content, how are they ensuring the free flow of information to future generations?

> **TEXTBOX 30.3**
>
> **Topic for Discussion**
>
> A vendor recently changed its platform to restrict printing of documents to one page at a time. You discover a workaround that restores the ability to print in larger quantities. Do you share this information with your colleagues? Your users? The vendor?

Diversity

A 2012 study of diversity in the library profession showed a 1 percent increase (from 11 percent to 12 percent) of ethnic and racial minorities working as degreed librarians. In response, ALA president Maureen Sullivan observed that, "although the findings show some improvement in the diversity of the library workforce, [the profession] clearly has a long way to go. . . . To continue to serve the nation's increasingly diverse communities . . . libraries and the profession must reflect this diversity."[39] Is the profession actively recruiting underrepresented people? Can users truly feel they are receiving the highest level of library service when no one speaks their language or if they cannot find materials that are relevant to their communities? Is digital content accessible to those using adaptive equipment? If diversity is one of the profession's shared principles, then it is imperative the information professional move beyond statements of openness and learn how to live it.

Internet Filtering

Since the upholding of the Children's Internet Protection Act in 2003, the use of Internet filters in public and school libraries has become ubiquitous. A recent study by the American Library Association reveals a tendency for information organizations to overblock content beyond what is required by law and that the use of Internet filters has a disproportionate impact on access to information for those library users without Internet access at home.[40] Additionally, filters continue to be imperfect, blocking appropriate content and letting other materials through, so there are still concerns about censorship. How do information professionals balance the desire to save money through the E-rate discounts that come with adopting a filter with the ethical imperative to ensure equitable and unfettered access to information?

User-Created Content

Information organizations have become places where users interact with and create content rather than just consume it (see also chapter 19, "Creation Culture and Makerspaces"). If information organizations allow users to add their own reviews and comments to library materials in the catalog or through library social media outlets, is it censorship to remove a racist or sexist remark? At what point do organizations place limits on the use of 3-D printers and other makerspace equipment? When does someone's hobby turn into a library-supported business? What obligations do information professionals have to educate users about the copyright implications of their latest video mash-up made on library equipment?

Privacy

Many pundits have stated that privacy is dead, and the continuing convergence of online services and resources makes it increasingly difficult to maintain a private persona without opting out of the online world completely. Social media allows individuals to broadcast and document the minutiae of their lives, and many do so voluntarily. Yet the profession still invests significant resources and political capital in the public defense of privacy, and the public outcry over revelations of the National Security Agency's data collection practices demonstrate that not everyone undervalues privacy. Is it right for the ALA to continue to invest in educational efforts like Choose Privacy Week (www.choosepriva-cyweek.org) when its resources are stretched thin? Is it right to abandon a principle that has been enshrined in the code of ethics since its inception?

Service Models

The first article of the ALA Code of Ethics states, "We provide the highest level of service to all library users through . . . equitable service policies [and] equitable access."[41] The term "service" can be looked at in a number of ways. A move toward self-service has freed up staff to work on other projects. Some users might like the increased sense of privacy that comes with using a self-check machine, while others are concerned that their materials on open-hold shelves are identified with their names for all to see. Information organizations of all types have seen an increase in online users, including those who never step foot in a physical library. Do online users get the same level of service as walk-up users? Alternatively, if information professionals move away from the traditional reference desk to a more centralized service center, are they offering the highest level of service to the technology-averse user encouraged to "live chat" with their reference questions? How do information organizations strike a balance between supporting traditional services and testing innovative ideas? How do information professionals evaluate services and programs when funding is tight and cuts must be made?

For all of these trends, there is a common theme: rather than finding answers, more questions arise. This is usually the case with ethical dilemmas. As noted in the preamble of the ALA Code of Ethics, the "principles of this Code are expressed in broad statements to guide ethical decision making. These statements provide a framework; they cannot and do not dictate conduct to cover particular situations."[42] Therefore, being comfortable with the profession's ethical principles is important to good decision making, as is knowing when to seek assistance.

Martin L. Garnar

Getting Help

Ethical dilemmas are by nature difficult to resolve—if it is easy to resolve, it is not truly a dilemma. There are resources from ALA that can help. The Office for Intellectual Freedom offers assistance to the library profession when dealing with ethical challenges and other issues related to core principles. The ALA Committee on Professional Ethics provides guidance on ethical issues through interpretative statements of the ALA Code of Ethics in a question-and-answer format, covering such topics as social media, conflicts of interest, and workplace speech, and in 2014 it issued the first-ever interpretation of the Code of Ethics on copyright.

Check This Out

The office for Intellectual Freedom and the ALA Committee on Professional Ethics provides guidance on ethical issues through interpretative statements of the ALA Code of Ethics.

Visit: http://www.ala.org/office/oif

The best strategy for resolving ethical dilemmas is preparation. All information professionals should be aware of policies and procedures at their institutions, and regular reviews of policies and procedures serve as both a refresher on content and an opportunity to address new developments. Since professional values should be at the heart of these policies and procedures (e.g., access, privacy, balancing copyright and fair use), openly discussing these issues can educate new staff as well as remind others about what is truly important. In addition to knowing policies and procedures, an effective training method for resolving ethical dilemmas is through the use of scenarios. Participants are given a scenario that poses an ethical dilemma and are asked to discuss all the issues before making a decision on what they would do. In addition, managers should keep track of issues happening in the workplace and discuss them at regular staff meetings to evaluate what was done well and what could have been done differently. It does not have to be a life-or-death situation to be good practice of how to resolve a dilemma.

Check This Out

The Intellectual Freedom Committee of the Colorado Association of Librarians has developed a number of scenarios that are freely available through their website, along with other training materials.

Visit: www.cal-webs.org/?page=IFCTraining

Conclusion

Change is a constant in the library and information science profession. Information organizations are constantly adapting to new technologies, new demands on services, and new opportunities for serving their communities. At the same time, tradition plays an important part of what the profession represents. Collections represent the cultural heritage of society, and many information organizations have been at the heart of their communities from time immemorial. Along with the need to balance the competing needs of change and tradition comes the need to balance the competing interests of the latest ethical dilemma. Ethical codes serve as a reminder of the industry's principles, but the intentional lack of specificity requires information professionals to think before applying these principles to current situations. Reviewing past challenges and current issues demonstrates that there have been ample opportunities to apply ethical principles, and the future will surely bring new and unpredicted controversies. Information professionals can, however, depend upon these principles to remain applicable to whatever comes their way, provided they face each ethical dilemma as it comes rather than rely on past practice to supply the only answer.

Notes

1. Edwin M. Elrod and Martha M. Smith, "Information Ethics," in *Encyclopedia of Science, Technology, and Ethics* (Detroit, MI: Macmillan Reference USA, 2005).
2. Henry R. West, "J. S. Mill," in *The Oxford Handbook of the History of Ethics*, ed. Roger Crisp (New York: Oxford University Press, 2013), abstract and keywords, doi:0.1093/oxfordhb/9780199545971.013.0025.
3. John Stuart Mill, *Utilitarianism* (London: Parker, Son & Bourne, 1863).
4. Andrews Reath, "Kant's Moral Philosophy," in *The Oxford Handbook of Ethical Theory*, ed. Roger Crisp (New York: Oxford University Press, 2013), doi:10.1093/oxfordhb/9780199545971.013.0021.
5. Andrew H. Plaks, "Golden Rule," in *Encyclopedia of Religion* (Detroit, MI: Macmillan Reference USA, 2005).
6. Virginia Held, "The Ethics of Care," in *The Oxford Handbook of Ethical Theory*, ed. David Copp (New York: Oxford University Press, 2009), doi:10.1093/oxfordhb/9780195325911.003.0020.
7. Kenneth McLeish, ed., "Profession," in *Bloomsbury Guide to Human Thought* (London: Bloomsbury, 1993).
8. "Code of Ethics of the American Library Association," American Library Association, last modified January 22, 2008, http://www.ala.org/advocacy/proethics/codeofethics/codeethics.
9. "Code of Ethics for Archivists," Society of American Archivists, last modified January 2012, http://www2.archivists.org/statements/saa-core-values-statement-and-code-of-ethics; "Code of Ethical Business Practice," Association of Independent Information Professionals, last modified April 20, 2002, http://aiip.org/content/code-ethical-business-practices.
10. "IFLA Code of Ethics for Librarians and Other Information Workers," International Federation of Library Associations and Institutions, last modified August 12, 2012, http://www.ifla.org/news/ifla-code-of-ethics-for-librarians-and-other-information-workers-full-version.
11. "Core Values of Archivists," Society of American Archivists, last modified May 2011, http://www2.archivists.org/statements/saa-core-values-statement-and-code-of-ethics.
12. "Core Values of Librarianship," American Library Association, last modified June 29, 2004, http://www.ala.org/advocacy/intfreedom/statementspols/corevalues.
13. "Code of Ethics of the ALA," art. 1.
14. "IFLA Code of Ethics," art. 1.
15. "Code of Ethics for Archivists," Access and Use.
16. "Code of Ethical Business Practice."
17. "Code of Ethics of the ALA," art. 3; "IFLA Code of Ethics," art. 3; "Code of Ethics for Archivists," Privacy; "Code of Ethical Business Practice."
18. "Code of Ethics of the ALA," preamble.
19. "Code of Ethics for Archivists," preamble.
20. "IFLA Code of Ethics," art. 2.
21. "Code of Ethics for Archivists," preamble; "Code of Ethics of the ALA," art. 1.
22. "Core Values of Archivists," Diversity.
23. "Code of Ethics of the ALA," art. 8.
24. "IFLA Code of Ethics," arts. 1, 2, and 5.
25. "Core Values of Archivists," Professionalism.
26. "Code of Ethics of the ALA," art. 2; "IFLA Code of Ethics," preamble.
27. "Code of Ethics for Archivists"; "Core Values for Archivists."
28. "Code of Ethics of the ALA," preamble.

Martin L. Garnar

29. "IFLA Code of Ethics," art. 5.
30. "Code of Ethics of the ALA," art. 5; "IFLA Code of Ethics," art. 6; "Code of Ethics for Archivists," Professional Relationships; "Code of Ethical Business Practice."
31. "Core Values of Archivists," Professionalism.
32. "Core Values of Librarianship," The Public Good.
33. "Core Values of Archivists," Social Responsibility.
34. "Code of Ethics of the ALA," art. 1; "IFLA Code of Ethics," preamble, arts. 1, 2, and 5; "Code of Ethical Business Practice"; "Core Values of Archivists," Service.
35. "Core Values of Librarianship," Social Responsibility.
36. "IFLA Code of Ethics," preamble.
37. "Core Values of Archivists," Social Responsibility.
38. "Code of Ethics of the ALA," art. 5; "IFLA Code of Ethics," art. 4; "Code of Ethical Business Practice."
39. "Diversity Counts," American Library Association, last modified October 3, 2013, http://www.ala.org/offices/diversity/diversitycounts/divcounts.
40. Kristen R. Batch, "Fencing Out Knowledge: Impacts of the Children's Internet Protection Act 10 Years Later," American Library Association, Policy Brief No. 5 (June 2014), http://www.ala.org/offices/sites/ala.org.offices/files/content/oitp/publications/issuebriefs/cipa_report.pdf.
41. "Code of Ethics of the ALA," art. 1.
42. Ibid., preamble.

31

Copyright and Creative Commons

Mary Minow and Liz Hamilton

The Code of Ethics of the American Library Association (ALA) states, "We respect intellectual property rights and advocate balance between the interests of information users and rights holders."[1]

To support this balance, the information professional must first know what rights are reserved to copyright owners and what exceptions to those rights exist for users. This chapter provides a basic introduction to copyright, outlining its origins, what works are legally protected, the exclusive rights of copyright owners, and important exceptions that pertain to information organizations: the first sale doctrine, Section 108 (the library exception), and fair use. It discusses the Digital Millennium Copyright Act, Creative Commons licenses, and click-through and negotiated licenses and their relationship to copyright. It also looks ahead to current developments concerning mass digitization, orphan works, and the Next Great Copyright Act. After reading this chapter, the reader will have a better understanding of the information professional's role as it relates to copyright today, from preserving copyrighted materials to teaching communities about the basics of copyright law in the United States, current developments in copyright law, and the importance of copyright law to the information professional.

Copyright

To explain why copyright matters to information professionals, it is important to first look at what copyright is. American copyright law is drawn from the U.S. Constitution, which grants Congress the power to "promote the Progress of Science and useful Arts, by securing for limited Times to Authors and Inventors the exclusive Right to their respective Writings and Discoveries."[2]

> "Constitutional copyright is intended as a social good. By allowing owners to profit from their works for a limited period of time, Congress hoped to encourage creativity and expand the quantity of published works that would benefit society."

Congress, thus empowered, enacted U.S. copyright law, now in Title 17 of the U.S. Code.[3] The U.S. Copyright Office promulgates and implements regulations in Title 37 of the Code of Federal Regulations. Constitutional copyright is intended as a social good. By allowing owners to profit from their works for a limited period of time, Congress hoped to encourage creativity and expand the quantity of published works that would benefit society. By limiting those times, or the length of copyright protections, Congress intended to expand the public domain, which refers to works that can be used freely by everyone.

Copyright and the Exclusive Rights of Owners

Copyright protection extends to "original works of authorship fixed in any tangible medium of expression," according to Section 102 of the 1976 Copyright Act. It is worth noting that, although originality is necessary for copyright protection, ideas cannot be copyrighted. Poems, songs, stories, and so forth are protected by copyright only when the expression is fixed in a tangible medium, and even then, only the expression itself (not the underlying idea) is protected. Works that qualify for copyright protection include literary, musical, dramatic, artistic, choreographic, pictorial, graphic, sculptural, audiovisual, sound-recording, and architectural works.[4] Both published and unpublished works may be protected by copyright law.[5]

Section 106 of the 1976 Copyright Act grants several exclusive rights to copyright owners (see textbox 31.1).[6] Copyright owners may either exercise these rights on their own or authorize others to do so. While these rights are exclusive, they are balanced with a series of limitations and exceptions, detailed in 17 U.S. Code, Sections 107–122.

TEXTBOX 31.1

The Exclusive Rights of Copyright Owners

1. To reproduce the copyrighted work in copies or phonorecords
2. To prepare derivative works based upon the copyrighted work
3. To distribute copies or phonorecords of the copyrighted work to the public by sale or other transfer of ownership, or by rental, lease, or lending
4. In the case of literary, musical, dramatic, and choreographic works, pantomimes, and motion pictures and other audiovisual works, to perform the copyrighted work publicly
5. In the case of literary, musical, dramatic, and choreographic works, pantomimes, and pictorial, graphic, or sculptural works, including the individual images of a motion picture or other audiovisual work, to display the copyrighted work publicly
6. In the case of sound recordings, to perform the copyrighted work publicly by means of digital audio transmission

U.S. Copyright Act, 17 U.S.C. § 106 (1976).

For example, if a local high school wants to stage a play written by playwright Anita Page, they would have to ask her for permission to publicly perform it (the fourth enumerated exclusive right enjoyed by copyright owners, unless there is a limitation or exception that would allow them to do so without permission. Likewise, a publisher who wants to print copies of the play and sell it as a book would, absent an exception, need the copyright owner's permission, as both the (1) reproduction and (3) distribution rights are implicated. If Professor Smith wanted the library to post a copy of Page's play on his public website for a class to read, the library would also need her permission beforehand, unless an exception applies.

The copyright owner's permission is not necessary if the work has entered the public domain, if a specific exception in the law allows someone other than the copyright owner to undertake a specific use, or if a broad license has already been granted, such as through the Creative Commons.[7] For information professionals, the most important exceptions to the protections of copyright law include Section 109 (the first sale doctrine), Section 108 (the library exception), and Section 107 (fair use). Each is discussed in turn.

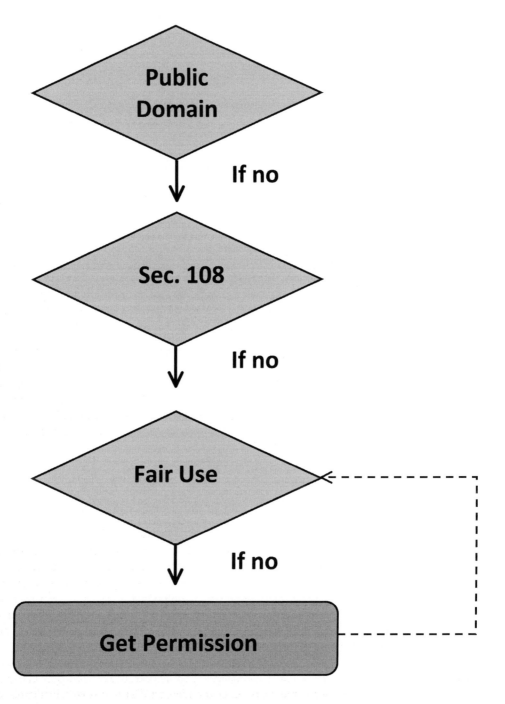

Figure 31.1 Copyright Analysis Flow Chart

Mary Minow and Liz Hamilton

The Public Domain

One of the most common cases where permission is not needed occurs when a work is in the public domain. A work typically enters the public domain after its copyright protection expires. Unpublished works have a copyright term of the author's lifetime plus seventy years. The duration of a published work's copyright protection will vary depending on the circumstances of its publication. For works created on or after January 1, 1978, copyright endures for the life of the author plus 70 years following the author's death. This protection occurs automatically. For anonymous and pseudonymous works and works made for hire (either works created by employees as a part of their employment or created under contract and specified as work for hire), the duration of copyright is 95 years from publication or 120 years from creation, whichever is shorter.[9] Historically, other factors that have dictated the length of copyright protection have included the date the work was originally published, whether the work was published with copyright notice (for example, "Copyright © 1985 by Ryan Anderson"), and whether the work was registered after publication.[9]

Check This Out

Peter Hirtle's "Copyright Term and the Public Domain in the United States" chart
is highly recommended as a resource for determining whether a given
work has passed into the public domain.

Available at:
https://copyright.cornell.edu/resources/publicdomain.cfm

A copyrighted work can also enter the public domain in other ways. U.S. government works are in the public domain by statute 17 U.S.C. § 105. A copyright owner may also dedicate a work to the public domain by adding a statement to that effect. An example of a public domain dedication is the Creative Commons CC0 license, which allows a creator to waive the rights to a work that would otherwise be protected by copyright.[10] This allows others to use that work as freely as possible. Other Creative Commons licenses allow creators to permit some uses of their works but not all of them, as discussed later. Creative Commons also offers a Public Domain Mark, placed on works that have been identified as having safely entered the public domain.[11]

Specific Limitations and Exceptions

THE FIRST SALE DOCTRINE

The first sale doctrine is codified in Section 109 of the copyright law. It allows the owner of a particular copy of a copyrighted work to sell or otherwise dispose of that copy, so long as that owner does not infringe on the other exclusive rights of the copyright owner.[12] For example, if someone buys an authorized copy of *The Bluest Eye*, he can give his copy to a friend when he is done reading it. However, he cannot photocopy the book to give away, as that would infringe on the author's right of reproduction. The first sale doctrine is a limitation only on the right of distribution. The first sale doctrine is what allows Amazon to sell CDs, Netflix to rent DVDs by mail, and—what is most important for information professionals—allows information organizations to lend books and other copyrighted materials.

The doctrine of first sale does not neatly apply in the digital realm because (1) the nature of digital media means reproductions are made in the course of distribution, and (2) in the digital marketplace, licenses rather than sales are the norm. In 2013, a federal district court in New York ruled against

ReDigi, an online used MP3 marketplace, in a lawsuit brought by Capitol Records. Even though ReDigi's customers were required to delete the MP3 from their own computers when selling it to another customer, the court ruled that the initial act of reproduction infringed the copyright owners' rights.[13] Look at the current state of flux in the Next Great Copyright Act.[14]

SECTION 108

Section 108 of Title 17, sometimes called the library exception, allows information organizations to use copyrighted works without permission. Though complex, Section 108 is immensely important to information professionals in library and archival settings, as it allows these information organizations to create up to three preservation and replacement copies for themselves, in addition to a single distribution copy for their patrons. In both cases, the law requires certain conditions to be met: (1) To qualify for this exception, the information organizations must be either open to the public or open to researchers unaffiliated with the information organization or its host institution who are doing research in a specialized field; (2) the reproduction or distribution must be made without the purpose of commercial advantage; and (3) the reproduction must contain a notice of copyright, either the notice printed on the original or, if none, a generic notice that the work may be protected by copyright. In addition, (4) incidents of reproduction and distribution must be isolated and unrelated; that is, information organizations cannot systematically copy and distribute copyrighted materials. And, finally, (5) the types of work to which Section 108 applies are sometimes limited, as outlined below.

Check This Out

The Columbia Copyright Advisory Office is a great resource for model forms and for help in navigating the permissions process.

Visit:
http://copyright.columbia.edu/copyright/permissions

PRESERVATION AND REPLACEMENT

Information organizations are allowed to make up to three copies of works for purposes of preservation or replacement. The specific rules differ slightly for published and unpublished works. Replacement copies of a published work may be made if it is damaged or missing, or if its format has become obsolete and an unused replacement copy cannot be found at a fair price. Preservation copies of an unpublished work may be made solely for purposes of preservation and security, or for deposit for research use in another information organization, and only if the original is currently in the copying organizations' collection. Digital preservation or replacement copies can be made regardless of a work's publication status, but the copies may not be distributed in that format beyond the premises of the information organization.

COPIES FOR PATRONS

Information organizations may also make single copies of materials for distribution to individual patrons. They may make a copy of an article or other small portion of a copyrighted work; or, if a copy of the complete work cannot be obtained at a fair price, the entire work may be copied. In both cases, the copy must become the property of the user, and the institution cannot have had notice that the copy would be used for any reason besides private study or research. The information organization must also display a standard warning of copyright, regulated by the register of copyrights, both where orders for copies are taken and on the order form.[15]

Unlike preservation and replacement copies, these study copies are limited by the type of work. Information organizations may not use this provision to make copies of musical works (i.e. the musical composition and score); pictorial, graphic, or sculptural works; or motion pictures or other audiovisual works that do not deal with news. They may, however, use the provision to share materials with patrons at other institutions through interlibrary loan, provided these copies do not substitute for a subscription to or purchase of such work. The receiving library is responsible for keeping track of these copies.[16]

LAST TWENTY YEARS OF COPYRIGHT—AN UNUSUAL EXCEPTION

During the last twenty years of any published work's copyright term, information organizations and nonprofit educational institutions gain additional privileges under Section 108(h). If the work is not subject to normal commercial exploitation, it cannot be obtained at a reasonable price, and the copyright owner has not provided notice that either of these conditions are false, the institution can reproduce, distribute, display, or perform copies of that work for preservation, scholarship, or research. This exemption does not extend to users beyond the information organization or educational institution.

OTHER PROVISIONS OF SECTION 108

Section 108(f) includes some notable provisions for information organizations. First, it protects these institutions from patron-induced liability for unsupervised use of reproduction equipment on its premises, so long as that equipment displays a notice that the reproduction may be subject to copyright law. No specific language is mandated by law. Second, it notes that Section 108 does not negate fair use. This is important for information organizations, because some actions not permitted under Section 108 may be allowed under the fair use provisions in Section 107. For example, copying a stand-alone photograph from a collection for a researcher is not allowed under Section 108 but might be acceptable as fair use. Finally, any contract the information organization signs may trump its abilities under Section 108. Information organizations should read contracts with vendors carefully so as not to give away any of their privileges under this exception.[17]

Section 108 is a vital protection for information organizations in preserving their materials and connecting their patrons with information. All information professionals should familiarize themselves with its provisions. As of this writing, there have been discussions to revise Section 108 in the Section 108 Study Group[18] and the 2013 Symposium on Section 108 held at Columbia Law School,[19] but as yet no legislation has been proposed.

SECTION 107: FAIR USE

Fair use is a critical exception to copyright law that allows information professionals and others to use copyrighted materials without permission. Fair use is outlined in Section 107 of the copyright law, and its exceptions are available to information organizations in addition to the provisions in Section 108. Section 107 states that the fair use of a copyrighted work "for purposes such as criticism, comment, news reporting, teaching (including multiple copies for classroom use), scholarship, or research, is not an infringement of copyright."[20] See textbox 31.3. (See also chapter 31, "Section 107: Fair Use" in the online supplement).

Recent Developments

The Digital Millennium Copyright Act

The Digital Millennium Copyright Act (DMCA) was signed into law on October 28, 1998. The first title of the DMCA implements two World Intellectual Property Organization (WIPO) treaties of 1996, the WIPO Copyright Treaty and the first title of the WIPO Performances and Phonograms Treaty. It also addresses a variety of other copyright issues.[21]

The DMCA has two parts that are particularly relevant to information organizations and information professionals. The first is a prohibition on circumventing technological protection measures (such as encryption), and the second is a safe harbor for potentially infringing user-generated content.

CIRCUMVENTING TECHNOLOGICAL PROTECTION MEASURES: CHALLENGING FOR LIBRARIES

The DMCA's major significance to information professionals is its prohibition against circumventing technological protection measures that protect DVDs, online works, and the like, essentially prohibiting format transfers such as ripping a DVD to an MP4 format. The one exception written into the law for nonprofit libraries, archives, and educational institutions is not terribly useful. It allows circumventing access controls solely to make a good-faith determination about whether to obtain authorized access to the work.[22] Vendors are likely to offer samples or other evaluative information to make circumvention unnecessary. More important is the DMCA's prohibition that essentially forbids the format shifting that is often needed as media formats evolve.

In 2013, a We the People White House petition garnered over 114,000 signatures complaining that "consumers will no longer be able [to] unlock their phones for use on a different network without carrier permission, even after their contract has expired." This uproar led to legislation to specifically allow telephone unlocking.[23] The cell phone unlocking prohibition was a direct result of the DMCA that, by default, prohibits circumvention of the technological protection measures that safeguard copyrighted material. Every three years, the Library of Congress holds public hearings to examine exceptions to the DMCA. The national debate on cell phone unlocking sparked discussion as to whether the DMCA provisions that govern *all* technological protection measures guarding copyrighted content (including e-books, digital journals, DVDs, etc.) should undergo narrow legislative fixes or a major overhaul. Legislative reforms were initiated, with details available in Jonathan Band's *The Cell Phone Unlocking Saga,*[24] but as of this writing, it appears more likely that a narrow retooling is in store rather than broad changes.[25]

One positive result for information organizations to come out of the triennial public hearings mentioned above is the exemption from the prohibition against circumvention of technological protections outlined by Section 1201 for assistive technologies. Blind people and other people with disabilities can circumvent this protection in order to use screen readers or other assistive technologies, as long as the copy of the work has been lawfully obtained and the rights owner is remunerated for the price of a mainstream copy of the work, or when the work is a lawfully obtained nondramatic literary work.[26] This is a key gain for accessibility and will help many information professionals connect their users to works they could not use previously.

SAFE HARBOR: HELPFUL TO INFORMATION ORGANIZATIONS

The DMCA also created a protection for information organizations and other service providers in Section 512 of the Copyright Act, which offers them safe harbor from liability for infringing materials that users might store on their systems. To qualify for this protection, a service provider must (1) accommodate standard technical measures for identifying and protecting copyright, (2) designate an agent to receive notices of claimed infringement (and file this designation with the U.S. copyright office), (3) take down or block infringing material expeditiously upon receiving proper notice, and (4) adopt and implement a policy of ending the accounts of users who are repeat copyright infringers. In addition, the information provider must not have prior knowledge of the infringing activity and must not receive financial benefit directly from the infringing activity if they have the right and ability to control it. This system also creates a procedure for the copyright owner to give notice of infringement and for the user who originally posted the material to respond with a counternotification.[27]

Check This Out

For a more readable take on the takedown process,
see "Responding to a DMCA Takedown Notice."

Visit:
http://www.nolo.com/legal-encyclopedia/responding-dmca-takedown-notice.html

---

In 2013, the U.S. Department of Commerce's Internet Policy Task Force (IPTF) released a green paper on *Copyright Policy, Creativity, and Innovation in the Digital Economy* in an effort to examine the notice and takedown system established under the DMCA.[28] On March 20, 2014, IPTF held a first public meeting to discuss the practical operation of the existing notice and takedown system. This roundtable emphasized a multistakeholder approach based on consensus, in which the group would select substantive topics to work on for the future, as well as establish the process by which to proceed. The leaders of the discussion proposed three major topics for the group to consider: improving the efficiency of the notice and takedown system, minimizing inaccurate notices and abuse, and focusing on the particular difficulties faced by individuals and small and medium-sized enterprises (SMEs). The group also discussed standardization of the notice and takedown procedure, the unique needs of different types of creators (such as visual artists and filmmakers), the impact of the current system on free expression, the overall effectiveness of the system, the intimidation factor in sending a counternotification in response to a DMCA takedown notice, and the codification of best practices for notice and takedown. Ultimately, the group decided to begin the larger conversation with the topic of standard notices and templates for takedowns.[29] These were discussed at the second public meeting on May 8, 2014, with input from SMEs and presentations on technical issues, moving from there to a smaller working group to continue the process.[30] The working group met twice between then and the third meeting on June 20, 2014, where they reported their initial findings on standardization procedures.

The working group had collected and analyzed model DMCA takedown forms. This led them to decide that their initial project should be the creation of standardized forms that work for both batch and individual sending of takedown notices, as well as a specification for an application programming interface (API) to aid notice sending. As of this writing, the working group planned to have working drafts of standardized notices by September 2014.[31]

Mass Digitization

Mass digitization especially affects information organizations and information professionals. In the context of books, mass digitization usually means large-scale scanning projects conducted systematically.[32] These range from smaller initiatives organized by libraries and other cultural heritage institutions, to scan images and short documents, to collaborative projects scanning full books on a massive scale.[33]

Check This Out

Some examples of mass digitization are Google Books, which has scanned
fifteen million volumes since 2004; Project Gutenberg, which began digitizing books
in 1971 and now offers over thirty-six thousand volumes online;
and the Internet Archive, which began digitizing public domain books in 1999.

Visit:
http://www.copyright.gov/docs/massdigitization/USCOMassDigitization_October2011.pdf

---

Mass digitization projects have many stakeholders: copyright owners (such as authors and artists), libraries, archives, museums, technology companies, educators, users of copyrighted works, and the general public.[34] Different groups take different approaches to copyright issues. The Internet Archive, an online library, initially digitized only public domain materials, thereby keeping themselves safely within the bounds of copyright law. Later it began to add twentieth-century books still in copyright to its library lending program.[35] The Internet Archive uses a "one book, one user" model, with the original print book stored safely in an inaccessible location. In contrast, Google Books has scanned all books regardless of their copyright status and returned the print copies to library shelves. Google has argued that their book-scanning project falls under fair use, since they only display snippet excerpts of books still under copyright.[36] Not all stakeholders agreed with this assessment. In 2005, authors and publishers brought a class-action lawsuit against Google, claiming that the Google Books project constituted willful copyright infringement.[37] The publishers settled the case with Google, but the authors continued the fight. After eight years of litigation, the U.S. District Court for the Southern District of New York dismissed the case, finding that Google had engaged in fair use.[38]

In 2011, the Authors Guild sued five university libraries and the HathiTrust Digital Library over the six libraries' intention to offer access to book scans provided by Google.[39] In June 2014, the U.S. Court of Appeals for the Second Circuit released its opinion in the *Authors Guild v. HathiTrust* case, which addressed the HathiTrust Digital Library's use of copyrighted material and whether it was protected under the doctrine of fair use. The court was particularly concerned with the following issues: the full-text search of HathiTrust's collection, access to the collection for print-disabled users, and the digital preservation of materials already owned by participating libraries. The court concluded that digitization for both full-text search and access for print-disabled patrons constituted fair use, while it vacated the district court's judgment on preservation and remanded to the district court the question of whether the plaintiffs had grounds to challenge the preservation use.[40]

In 2011, the Copyright Office published an analysis and discussion document of legal issues in mass digitization, addressing many of the issues at play in these projects.[41] The current copyright and licensing legal framework looks at the balance between the exclusive rights of the copyright owner, which aspects of digitization are (or should be) covered by fair use and library exceptions, the problem of orphan works (which will be discussed in depth shortly), and what licensing options are now, or could soon be, available. While reliance on fair use supports many digitization projects, it is not a solution for all circumstances. Licensing is proposed by some to help fill the gap between the current exceptions and the resolution of copyright law and mass digitization. Information professionals should pay close attention to developments in this area.

Orphan Works

An orphan work is a work for which the copyright owner cannot be located or identified by an individual who wishes to use that work in a way that would require the copyright owner's permission. Because they are unable to locate the copyright owner, users of these works may face liability for infringement if the owner should later surface. Even though it is in the public interest to make many of these works available, many information organizations will not digitize them because of the risk.

In January 2006, the Copyright Office issued a report on orphan works, which discusses the problem in detail and offers recommendations to Congress for how to proceed with orphan works legislation. The Copyright Office recommended that such legislation incorporate two requirements: that a potential user must conduct a reasonably diligent search for the copyright owner before using the work, and that the user must provide attribution of the original author and copyright owner throughout the work in use. The Copyright Office also recommended limitations on monetary and injunctive relief that the original copyright owner can take in the event they discover the use, a clause making clear that the new legislation does not affect other rights and limitations to copyright elsewhere in the act, and a sunset for the provision after ten years so that Congress can evaluate its effects.[42] Despite legislative efforts in 2008, none of these recommendations were implemented.

In 2012 and 2014, the Copyright Office solicited public comment and held roundtables to give orphan works legislation another chance.[43] The roundtables were held on March 10–11, 2014, and combined discussions on both orphan works and mass digitization. The views presented by the various stakeholders revealed wildly divergent opinions on how to proceed; the only real consensus was caution toward extended collective licensing, though even that was mitigated by previously submitted comments favoring such licenses. After the roundtables, it seems unlikely that all groups will be able to find a mutually acceptable solution to the orphan works question.[44]

The Next Great Copyright Act

Copyright law in the United States saw its last major revision in 1976, before any of the copyright issues of the digital age came into play. The 1976 revision codified the fair use doctrine, affirmed the first sale doctrine, and created exceptions especially for information organizations.[45] However, even at the time of its creation, the 1976 act had not thoroughly considered the needs of emerging technologies.[46] The Next Great Copyright Act is a useful way of referring to the next major revision of U.S. copyright law. The phrase was coined by the current register of copyrights and director of the U.S. Copyright Office, Maria Pallante, in a lecture at Columbia Law School, during which she outlined the many reasons the existing act needs revision and asserted that now is the time for those revisions to be made.[47] In the lecture, Pallante stressed again and again that any revision to the act must be forward thinking but flexible, and must also serve the public interest.[48] As discussed earlier in this chapter, constitutional copyright is intended as a social good, and this idea should inform future revisions of the law.

Now is the time for revision for a number of reasons, according to Pallante. She points out that Congress has always had a valuable role in reviewing the larger policies involved in copyright law. In the age of the Internet, these overarching reviews should happen more frequently.[49] Since the turn of the century, the Copyright Office has prepared many background documents to guide Congress through relevant issues impacting the Next Great Copyright Act. These include completed research on digital first sale, orphan works, statutory licenses for cable and satellite retransmission, pre-1978 contract termination provisions, mass digitization, and pre-1972 sound recordings, as well as pending research on resale royalties for visual artists and small copyright claims.[50] These background reports shed light on many of the issues that would be addressed in a large-scale revision of the Copyright Act. Recent court decisions also call on Congress to legislatively address these issues as they are presented in case law. For example, in *Kirtsaeng v. John Wiley & Sons*, the court pointed out that Congress should decide whether copyright owners should have more than ordinary commercial power to divide international markets when it comes to first sale. Similarly, in *Capitol Records, LLC v. ReDigi, Inc.*, the court stated that it was up to Congress to determine whether the limitation of first sale exceptions to physical copies, rather than digital, is outmoded.[51] As copyright issues affect more people in the digital age, the act needs to be clarified for a wider audience.

The Next Great Copyright Act will need to address many issues that have emerged or expanded since the 1976 act. These include the disadvantages faced by owners of sound recordings, the creation of incidental copies over the course of digital commerce, the enforcement of copyright in the digital marketplace, a review of the DMCA, the application of first sale to digital materials, exceptions and limitations (such as Section 108, exceptions for print disabilities, higher education, and personal use), licensing issues (especially for music), mandatory deposit in the Library of Congress, copyright term, and the need for the new act to be as clear to the layperson as possible. In addition, the Copyright Office must fully become a twenty-first-century agency in order to support a revised Copyright Act.[52] Information professionals should take particular note of revisions to digital first sale, the DMCA, licensing of copyright materials, and the exceptions currently granted to information organizations. To ensure the best results for information organizations and their patrons, it is important to pay close attention to any progress made in copyright law, and voice support for the revisions that support positive results for information users and organizations.

In the conclusion of her lecture, the register of copyrights encouraged Congress and other players to think big when considering revisions to the copyright law and urged that "the Next Great Copyright Act is as possible as it is exciting."[53] Now more than ever, information professionals must act in favor of a copyright act that supports the work of information organizations and their users.

TEXTBOX 31.4

Topic for Discussion

Maria Pallante has argued for copyright reform in the Next Great Copyright Act. What do you think is the most important area in need of reform? Why?

Licenses

Click-Wrap and Negotiated Licenses

Today, virtually all electronic content is regulated by private licenses, a layer of control that trumps copyright law. That is, if a term in a license agreement differs from the rights laid out in copyright law, the license will prevail in nearly every instance. If the license is silent on an issue, then copyright law still regulates who owns what and when (see also chapter 32, "Information Licensing").

Mary Minow and Liz Hamilton

Creative Commons

The Creative Commons organization, founded in 2001, provides licensing that works alongside copyright law and that can be advantageous to libraries. Creative Commons is a nonprofit organization that promotes the sharing of creative works and knowledge. In addition to the public domain dedication (CC0) and Public Domain Mark described (above), Creative Commons offers a free suite of standardized licenses that allow copyright owners to keep their copyrights yet give the public permission to use their works under set conditions. CC licenses benefit information organizations both as copyright creators who wish to more freely share their work, and as users who wish to find sources they can use or adapt freely for their own purposes.

Creative Commons licenses have three layers: a layer written in traditional legal terms, a layer written in more readily understandable language, and a machine-readable code that makes it easier to search for CC content online. The current suite of licenses, version 4.0, identifies four possible conditions for use: Attribution, ShareAlike, NoDerivs, and NonCommercial. These characteristics are combined into six licenses, including CC BY, Attribution; CC BY-SA, Attribution-ShareAlike; CC BY-ND, Attribution-NoDerivs; CC BY-NC, Attribution-NonCommercial; CC BY-NC-SA, Attribution-NonCommercial-ShareAlike; and CC BY-NC-ND, Attribution-NonCommercial-NoDeriv. (See also chapter 31, "Creation Commons and Licenses" in the online supplement to read more about these licenses.)

Information organizations can use works with CC licenses without the need to negotiate further or pay money in cases where the use is nonprofit. One example of this is academic libraries that collect works in an institutional repository. These libraries can freely acquire works issued under CC licenses. Libraries can also create works and use CC licenses to share the works in a seamless manner, so long as the library does not need to get remuneration for nonprofit use of the works. For example, the UCLA Library added a Creative Commons Attribution-NonCommercial-ShareAlike 3.0 U.S. License to its website, granting free permission for noncommercial, attributed use of its content, such as research guides and tutorials.[54]

Copyright and the Information Professional

The changing nature of information requires knowledge of copyright. Information professionals need to keep current on copyright issues so they can help their users with their copyright needs, use material to the greatest extent possible, and protect themselves from liability. As copyright issues become more widespread and more complex, particularly as social media sharing of material flourishes, there is a greater need for information professionals to answer users' copyright questions. Users need to know what they can do with materials created by others, as well as what rights they hold in work they have created themselves.

Assisting users with copyright issues both remotely and on-site has become easier than ever. Many resources are now freely available online to use, and many of those also have Creative Commons licenses, making it possible to copy and reuse the resources in trainings or for other nonprofit purposes. If users approach the information organization remotely—for example, by e-mail or chat reference—the information professional can connect them with a wealth of resources available for free online wherever they are. The Stanford Copyright and Fair Use page includes many current cases as well as background information provided by Nolo.com, a reliable source to send patrons to.

In addition to educating users, information professionals need to be aware of the protections available to them under copyright law. If libraries follow the procedures for safe harbor with DMCA agent registration, they can get protection from liability for user-generated content on their sites.[55] Information organizations also receive protection for designated uses of material under Section 108. It is also important to remember that information professionals are not copyright cops. Placing copyright warning signs near photocopiers insulates the information organization and information professional from liability for user copying. The same warning should be placed near all reproducing equipment, from scanners to computers to 3-D printers. Users can be educated about copyright law, but it is up to them to follow the rules.

Conclusion

Copyright, as formulated in the U.S. Constitution, is a social good. By providing a limited period of time in which creators can profit from their work, Congress hoped to encourage creativity and expand the quantity of works available to the public. Copyright owners have the exclusive right to reproduce and distribute their works, publicly perform and display their works, prepare derivative works, and perform their works publicly by digital audio transmission. These rights are balanced by exceptions such as the first sale doctrine, Section 108, and fair use. At the end of a work's copyright term, it enters the public domain, where it may be freely used by anyone, with no exceptions necessary. Before that time, if no exception fits a particular use, one can always ask the copyright owner for permission to use their work.

Recent developments in copyright law have been numerous. The Digital Millennium Copyright Act created two new elements of copyright law relevant to information organizations: a prohibition on the circumvention of technological protections, and a safe harbor for user-generated infringing content. Mass digitization and orphan works are two other areas that have received much attention by information organizations and others, as technology continues to make the digitization of materials easier. Given the advances in technology, copyright reform is needed now more than ever. Current register of copyrights Maria Pallante is promoting the Next Great Copyright Act in an effort to achieve this necessary update.

As more copyrighted materials become available digitally, information professionals need to be aware of licensing agreements and negotiate for licenses that do not inhibit their traditional rights under copyright law. Information professionals should become familiar with Creative Commons licenses, which allow them to both use more material and create material that others can freely use in turn.

Information professionals need to know about developments in copyright law. The law offers them protection and valuable exceptions that they can use to connect users to the information they seek. It is important for information professionals to be familiar with the law, both so they can use materials to the fullest extent possible and educate their users about copyright.

Acknowledgments

Special thanks to Henry Cohen and Simon Crowley.

Notes

1. "Code of Ethics of the American Library Association," American Library Association, last modified October 21, 2014.
2. U.S. Const. art. I, § 8, cl. 8, http://www.archives.gov/exhibits/charters/constitution_transcript.html.
3. U.S. Copyright Act, 17 U.S.C., http://www.copyright.gov/title17/circ92.pdf.
4. U.S. Copyright Act, 17 U.S.C. § 102.
5. U.S. Copyright Office, "Copyright Basics," *Copyright*, circular 1, (May 2012): 3, http://www.copyright .gov/circs/circ01.pdf.
6. U.S. Copyright Act, 17 U.S.C. § 106.
7. U.S. Copyright Act, 17 U.S.C. § 107–122.
8. USCO, "Copyright Basics" (2012), 2, 5.
9. Ibid., pp. 3–6.
10. "About CC0—'No Rights Reserved,'" Creative Commons, last modified October 28, 2014, http://creative commons.org/about/cc0.
11. "About the Public Domain Mark—'No Known Copyright,'" Creative Commons, last modified October 26, 2014, http://creativecommons.org/about/pdm.
12. U.S. Copyright Act, 17 U.S.C. § 109.
13. Capitol Records, LLC v. ReDigi Inc., 934 F. Suppl., 2d 640 (SD New York Dist. Court, 2013), http://digital commons.law.scu.edu/cgi/viewcontent.cgi?article=1334&context=historical.
14. Marian Pallente, "The Great Copyright Act," *Columbia Journal of Law and the Arts* 36 (2012): 315, http:// www.copyright.gov/docs/next_great_copyright_act.pdf.
15. Code of Federal Regulations, title 37, § 201.14, http://www.copyright.gov/title37/201/37cfr201-14.html.
16. For guidelines, see the "Commission on New Technological Uses of Copyrighted Works (CONTU) Guidelines for Interlibrary Loan Photocopying," http://www.ala.org/advocacy/sites/ala.org.advocacy/ files/content/copyright/GLsInterlibLoan.pdf.
17. U.S. Copyright Act, 17 U.S.C. § 108.
18. "Home," The Section 108 Study Group, last modified February 7, 2014, http://www.section108.gov.
19. "Section 108 Reform," Columbia Law School, last modified December 11, 2013, http://web.law.columbia .edu/kernochan/symposia/section-108-reform.
20. U.S. Copyright Act, 17 U.S.C. § 107.
21. U.S. Copyright Office, *The Digital Millennium Copyright Act of 1998—Summary* (Washington, DC: USCO, December 1998), http://www.copyright.gov/legislation/dmca.pdf.
22. U.S. Copyright Act, 17 U.S.C. § 1201(d).
23. Ezra Mechaber, "Here's How Cell Phone Unlocking Become Legal," *White House Blog*, last modified August 15, 2014, http://www.whitehouse.gov/blog/2014/08/15heres-how-to-cell-phone-unlocking -became-legal.
24. Jonathan Band, "The Cell Phone Unlocking Saga," Infojustice.org, March 13, 2014, http://infojustice.org/ wp-content/uploads/2014/03/band04132014.pdf.
25. Brett Snider, "Is It Legal to 'Unlock' Your Cell Phone?'" *Law and Daily Life* (blog), last modified May 18, 2014, http://blogs.findlaw.com/law_and_life/2014/05/is-it-legal-to-unlock-your-cell-phone.html.
26. U.S. Copyright Office—Library of Congress, "Exemption to Prohibition on Circumvention of Copyright Protection Systems for Access Control Technologies," *Federal Register* 71, no. 227 (November 27, 2006): 68472–68480, http://www.copyright.gov/fedreg/2006/71fr68472.html.
27. USCO, *The Digital Millennium Copyright Act of 1998—Summary* (Washington, DC: U.S. Copyright Office, 1998), 8–13.
28. U.S. Department of Commerce Internet Policy Task Force, *Copyright Policy, Creativity, and Innovation in the Digital Economy* (Washington, DC: U.S. Patent and Trademark Office, July 2013), http://www.uspto.gov/ news/publications/copyrightgreenpaper.pdf.
29. Department of Commerce, "Multistakeholder Forum: Improving the Operation of the DMCA Notice and Takedown Policy First Public Meeting" (Alexandria, VA: U.S. Patent and Trademark Office, March 20, 2014), http://www.uspto.gov/ip/global/copyrights/First_Public_Meeting-Improving_Operation_ of_DMCA_Notice_and_Takedown_Policy.pdf.

30. "Office of Policy and International Affairs—Copyrights," USPTO.gov, last modified July 5, 2014, http://www.uspto.gov/ip/global/copyrights/index.jsp; "May 2014 USPTO Multistakeholder Forum on the DMCA Notice and Takedown System," Berkeley Law University of California, last modified August 4, 2014, http://www.law.berkeley.edu/170804.htm.

31. Department of Commerce, "Multistakeholder Forum on Improving the Operation of the DMCA Notice and Takedown System Third Public Meeting" (Alexandria, VA: U.S. Patent and Trademark Office, June 20, 2014), http://www.uspto.gov/ip/global/copyrights/3rd_plenary_meeting_transcript.pdf.

32. Office of the Register of Copyrights, *Legal Issues in Mass Digitization: A Preliminary Analysis and Discussion Document* (Washington, DC: US Copyright Office, October 2011), 8–9, http://www.copyright.gov/docs/massdigitization/USCOMassDigitization_October2011.pdf.

33. Ibid., 4–5.

34. Ibid., 9.

35. "Borrow eBooks," Open Library, last modified July 2, 2014, https://openlibrary.org/borrow/about.

36. Office of the Register of Copyrights, *Legal Issues in Mass Digitization*, 2011, 22.

37. Ibid., 6.

38. Authors Guild, Inc. v. Google, Inc., 954 F. Suppl., 2d 282 (SD New York Dist. Court, 2013), http://scholar.google.com/scholar_case?case=6510192672912362556&hl=en&as_sdt=6&as_vis=1&oi=scholarr.

39. Office of the Register of Copyrights, *Legal Issues in Mass Digitization*, 2011, i.

40. "Second Circuit Decision on Authors Guild v. HathiTrust," Copyright Alliance, last modified August 4, 2014, http://www.copyrightalliance.org/2014/06/second_circuit_decision_authors_guild_v_hathitrust#; Authors Guild, Inc. v. HathiTrust (Court of Appeals, 2nd Circuit, 2014).

41. Office of the Register of Copyright, *Legal Issues in Mass Digitization*, 2011.

42. Marybeth Peters, *Report on Orphan Works: A Report of the Register of Copyrights* (Washington, DC: U.S. Copyright Office, January 2006), 92–127, http://www.copyright.gov/orphan/orphan-report-full.pdf.

43. "Orphan Works and Mass Digitization," Copyright.gov, last modified May 30, 2014, http://copyright.gov/orphan.

44. "Recap of the Copyright Office's Roundtables on Orphan Works and Mass Digitization," ARL Policy Notes, last modified September 9, 2014, http://policynotes.arl.org/post/79876737815/recap-of-the-copyright-offices-roundtables-on-orphan.

45. Maria A. Pallante, "The Next Great Copyright Act," *Columbia Journal of Law and the Arts* 36 (2012): 315–344, http://www.copyright.gov/docs/next_great_copyright_act.pdf.

46. Ibid., 344.

47. Ibid., 315.

48. Ibid., 323.

49. Ibid., 320.

50. Ibid., 320–322.

51. Ibid., 322–323.

52. Ibid., 324–329.

53. Ibid., 344.

54. "Creative Commons License," last modified July 19, 2014, *UCLA Library*, http://www.library.ucla.edu/creative-commons-license.

55. "Online Service Providers," Copyright.gov, last modified May 12, 2014, http://copyright.gov/onlinesp.

32

Information Licensing

Celeste Feather, Maura Hadaway, and Tom Sanville

Information licensing is a relatively new phenomenon in information organizations. For hundreds of years, information professionals purchased primarily printed books and journals in a straightforward purchase model from publishers and distributors. Even for images, video, and audio materials, the initial means of delivery were physical copies (e.g., print, cassette, CD-ROM, and DVD)[1] that also could be put on the shelf and used, one user at a time.

> "Use of digital content is not inherently limited by a user's physical access to the library."

The acquisition of digital content, now mostly delivered to desktops and devices via the Internet, is a transaction with different dimensions between the information organization and the publisher. No longer are organizations buying physical copies of information with physical limitations. A key difference between the two formats of acquisition is that use of content by one user at a time is no longer an inherent restriction. Use of digital content is also not inherently limited by a user's physical access to an information organization. In addition, the explosion of information via the Internet and the ease of information access have dramatically raised user expectations. In response to these new dimensions and demands, information organizations increasingly license digital content rather than purchase it in traditional physical formats. As information technology continues to change rapidly, so do the dynamics and techniques of licensing.

After completing this chapter, the reader should have an understanding of the origins and rationales for licensing, the underlying business models and important license attributes, and the critical evolving drivers of this field of work. With this introduction, the new information professional can better participate in this relatively new, but now critical, activity of information organizations.

The Origins of Licensing

Acquiring information in physical formats is most often a straightforward one-time sale. But acquiring information in digital formats is fundamentally different. It can be an outright purchase, a sale with perpetual rights, or an annual subscription. Each of these comes with a set of defined authorized users, terms of use, and a time frame for use. The license document is the means by which these terms

> "Digital formats are a threat to the long-standing economic equilibrium of the print-based information marketplace. The specialized field of digital content licensing emerged to address these new dimensions."

are communicated and accepted. Publishers and information organizations established a well-worn and relatively static economic approach for the acquisition of physical items based on the first sale doctrine.[2] Guidelines and practices for resource sharing among information organizations[3] complicated the economic equation, but overall the relationship was stable. The availability of digital content presents dynamic changes and challenges for portability, accessibility, and deliverability through continually evolving technology. Digital formats are a threat to the long-standing economic equilibrium of the print-based information marketplace. The specialized field of digital content licensing emerged to address these new dimensions.

A number of factors came together for the first time in the late 1980s and early 1990s to drive information licensing forward rapidly. Many of these are often taken for granted:

- the widespread adoption by information organizations of integrated management systems[4] to support the breadth of core operations;
- the development in the quality, quantity, and near ubiquity of Internet access;
- the development of user-friendly interfaces, personal computers, and more recently handheld devices to access the Internet;
- the corresponding explosion of information creation and websites on the web to serve all facets of our lives;[5] and
- the corresponding rise in users' expectations.

Increasingly, if information is not found on the Internet in an easily accessible form, it is not used. Information organizations and publishers, after hundreds of years of a very static set of business models, had to make major, rapid, and frequent adaptations to meet the demands of a world where electronic delivery has come to trump, if not totally replace, physical formats.

Publishers' production systems were based on creating print or other physical copies for distribution and sale. These systems had to be retooled to support current, around-the-clock, fast and flexible web access. Publishers and information organizations had to recognize that an advantage of electronic information delivery is that the information can be updated continuously. The concept of the sale of periodic and discreet editions or volumes, such as encyclopedias, gave way to annual subscriptions that ensured continued access to the latest updates. Even for journals that have retained, for the most part, their traditional annual volume and issue structure, information organizations now have both one-time purchase and short-term subscription options.

TEXTBOX 32.1

New Issues in Licensing

- Without the inherent constraints of physical formats limiting use to an organization's traditional constituency, how is access defined and limited to the appropriate clientele for appropriate uses?
- How is the quality of electronic delivery ensured?
- If there is no physical copy and the information organization has continuing rights to access the content even if the latest information from the publisher is not purchased, how will that access be defined and delivered?
- In general, how is electronic information archived and preserved?

Celeste Feather, Maura Hadaway, and Tom Sanville

In most cases, entire copies of the digital content, purchased or subscribed to, are not received physically (e.g., transferred to a local computer) by the information organization. Access is usually via an online system operated by the publisher or a third party aggregating content across publishers. This reality creates a number of new issues that must be addressed.

Other issues to be addressed have developed as a consequence of the evolution of the web, such as compliance with the Americans with Disabilities Act (ADA) and the provision of usage statistics. The full array of terms that must be considered is discussed later in this chapter.

In transitioning from print to electronic, there has been a major change in who is making, administering, and negotiating the purchases. The long-held model of each information organization purchasing its own print collection has given way to a more multidimensional approach involving the addition of a myriad of group-based approaches. While many factors have contributed to this change, two stand out. First, for information organizations to succeed in a world of rapidly expanding information and user expectations, they must find ways to expand the information they provide their clientele. Group-based purchase or subscription programs, which have the objective of expanding access by leveraging the larger buying power of the group to obtain better prices and terms over those possible by individual libraries, have become widespread. Second, in the transition to a mostly, if not entirely, digital world, publisher production processes and costs have evolved, providing new flexibility in the pricing of digital information. While publishers must still invest in the creation of content, they no longer have the sunk costs associated with large print or hard-copy production runs. Once they have invested in creating and making content available electronically on their websites, they have lower marginal production costs as their sales expand. There are more options to offer digital products at prices deemed affordable by more information organizations—either through individual or group licensing. The spectrum of multidimensional purchasing and business models are discussed in the next section of this chapter.

> **TEXTBOX 32.2**
>
> **Topic for Discussion**
>
> What challenges will the continued migration from physical to digital content and delivery present to information professionals as they transform their internal operations to support their user community?

Business Models

Establishing what resource(s) will be accessed, for what period of time, by which organization(s) and users, the terms of use, and the price to be paid are key elements of a license. The combination of these elements is a licensed-content business model. As digital resources, organizational needs, and budgets evolve, license models must as well. Currently, there are many business models for digital-resource licenses based on combinations of all these elements and depending on the nature of the digital content and the needs and preferences of information organizations and publishers.

> "Establishing what resource(s) will be accessed, for what period of time, by which organization(s) and users, the terms of use, and the price to be paid are key elements of a license."

While an annual license for one database is the most common approach for content covered under a single license, there are other variations (see table 32.1, "Content Variations in Licensing"). These variations can apply to content licensed either by annual subscription or by onetime purchase with perpetual access rights. They also apply whether the license is one year or multiyear in duration or for single-institution or group licenses.

Table 32.1. Content Variations in Licensing

Title Level	Access to one title; typically a single e-book or e-journal title. These types of licenses are typically negotiated directly with the publisher at the single institution level.
Database	Access to one electronic database. May be established directly with the publisher, or via a third party. A relationship with a single publisher may include multiple databases covered by the same license. A publisher may bundle multiple databases together and offer more attractive pricing.
Aggregation	Database(s) of content from multiple publishers selected based on subject matter or to cover a spectrum of interests. Content access may vary widely depending upon embargoes from publishers and will typically not provide perpetual access nor the complete range of a publisher's content.
Collection	Multiple e-books, e-journals, or other digital content from a single publisher typically selected based on subject, interest, year, or any other criteria and sold as a single collection or database. This includes both current and archive content.

Pricing Structures

Agreement as to how the price for a resource will be determined is a vital part of licensing digital resources. Some digital content may be priced at a flat rate regardless of the organization's size, type, or other attributes, but many resources are priced based on one or more attributes of the licensing entity. The most common of these is full-time enrollment (FTE) for academic/school/special libraries, and population served (pop. served) for public libraries. The price may be calculated based on the exact value of the attribute (e.g., FTE is exactly 1,534) or arranged in tiers (e.g., all libraries with FTE from 1,000 to 1,999 pay the same price).

Frequently used attributes, often in combinations, are included in table 32.2, "Pricing Structure Attributes," along with the types of information organization or licensing institution for which they are typically relevant.

Single-Institution versus Group Licensing

As noted earlier, the growth of group-based approaches has been a hallmark of the licensing evolution. Information organization groups (most commonly known as consortia but also networks or systems) are plentiful and diverse. Most institutions are members of more than one group through which licensing options are available. All of these groups' licensing activities are intended to help organizations extend their purchasing power over individual approaches. When making a purchase, it is important to consider not only the price, but also all of the license terms negotiated via each group before entering into any agreement. The lowest cost might come with license terms that do not meet the needs of an individual organization in other ways.

A consortium can be based on geography, areas of focus, member attributes, or any other criteria that might help to create a beneficial relationship for the members of the consortium. Types of consortia range from loosely affiliated small groups with one or two common goals and no centralized staff or resources to large groups with highly centralized and well-funded resources; county and regional systems, state libraries, and state-based education and higher education systems are prominent

Celeste Feather, Maura Hadaway, and Tom Sanville

Table 32.2. Pricing Structure Attributes

Attribute	Description	Organization Type
Full-Time Enrollment (FTE)	Number of students enrolled at a given point in time, typically measured annually. Can also be applied to a specific school or program(s) of study for more specialized resources.	• Academic • Community/technical colleges • K–12
Population Served	Number of eligible users of the library or institution's resources.	• Public
Cardholders	Number of registered patrons with a library card.	• Public
Carnegie Classification[1]	Carnegie Foundation assigned level based on established methodology; only for accredited, degree-granting institutions.	• Academic
Simultaneous User	Number of users able to access the resource at the same time. Most suitable for specialized databases and user groups.	• All
Specific User/Seat	Assigned to specific users. While this is a potential model in all types of libraries/institutions, it is largely applied to corporate libraries.	• Corporate
Budget(s)	Typically annual materials or operating budgets.	• All
Buildings/Sites	Number of physical buildings or locations (branch libraries or campuses) where the resource will be accessed.	• All
Hospital Beds	Number of beds in a hospital.	• Medical
Faculty	Number of full-time faculty.	• Academic • Community/technical college
Historical Spending	The current level of spending for publisher content is used as a basis for establishing the price to be paid. This attribute was the widespread basis for many group licenses to publisher electronic journal collections. Often referred to as the "Big Deals."	• All

1. "About Carnegie Classification," *Carnegie Foundation for the Advancement of Teaching—The Carnegie Classification of Institutions of Higher Education*, last modified June 25, 2014, http://classifications.carnegie foundation.org.

examples. Groups that engage in licensing are diverse, and so are the ways in which they fashion their business models. Through a consortium, each information organization may, regardless of what other members of the group decide, choose to license a resource at a reduced price. Commonly, this approach is called an opt-in group license. An opt-in group license may include terms that encourage higher participation among members via even more favorable prices and terms. Another type of group license is known as an all-in license, where common decision making may be required across group members and may offer the widest access and greatest price efficiency across the group if all the members participate. Consortia vary in their use of the opt-in, all-in, or other licensing techniques.

They also vary in whether administration and payment of the license will be direct between each organization and the publisher or coordinated through the consortium.

Group licenses may also be paid by a group centrally, on behalf of constituent members. State libraries are a prime example, as they may provide statewide access to some resources. Such access may include public, K–12, and academic libraries in some combination. Other consortia may also fund group licenses all or in part, especially if they are affiliated with publicly supported education or higher education systems. See table 32.3, "Usage Concepts in Licensing."

Elements of a License

License documents range from short and simple to lengthy and complex. Four major types of license terms are commonly negotiated: usage, legal, business, and technical. Fortunately, through years of experience, the information organization and information professional community have established best practices that address major license issues.[6] Information professionals should also be aware of local requirements related to licenses and negotiate appropriate language as needed.

Elements of a License
- Usage terms
- Legal terms
- Business terms
- Technical terms

Usage Terms

Who is permitted to use the content and what are they allowed to do with it? The terms of a license or contract override national copyright law in the United States. License negotiators should be careful not to sign away existing rights under copyright law and thereby narrow the ways that users are permitted to use the digital content (see also chapter 31, "Copyright and Creative Commons").

Licenses always include a definition of authorized users; these are the persons who are permitted to use the content. Employees, cardholders, faculty, staff, and students are generally in the core group of users. Other authorized users can include the extended community such as on-site guest users or "walk-ins," alumni, and temporary contract research staff.

Lists of authorized and restricted uses in the license establish what can and cannot be done with the content. If there is a statement that a use is not permitted unless explicitly listed, information organizations may be giving up rights normally permitted under copyright law. Key usage concepts and reasons why they are important appear in table 32.3, "Usage Concepts in Licensing."

Legal Terms

Other terms in a license relate to legal matters such as liability, warranty, which jurisdiction's law governs the contract, and how any disputes will be resolved. Sometimes these terms need to be customized to meet the requirements of local or state laws. When no agreement can be reached on the precise language to address these matters, one negotiation strategy can be to omit some of the clauses, also known as "being silent." If a dispute ever arises, the parties will address the conflict at that time. Legal terms that are common points of negotiation and the reasons they deserve special attention appear in table 32.4, "Legal Terms in Licensing."

Celeste Feather, Maura Hadaway, and Tom Sanville

Table 32.3. Usage Concepts in Licensing

Usage Concept	Reasoning
Commercial vs. Noncommercial Use	Limits the purposes for which the content can be used. Generally users at educational organizations are restricted to noncommercial uses.
E-Reserves and Course Management Systems	Permits content to be linked or temporarily stored (cached) in educational courseware for assignment to students in classes.
Printing and Downloading	Allows a user to obtain a printed or digital copy in addition to reading in a browser. There may be issues with how much can be printed and the ease of printing usable portions.
Remote Access	Allows authorized and authenticated users to access content when they are not physically at the organization.
Resource Sharing and Interlibrary Loan	Allows libraries to share resources in compliance with Section 108 of the U.S. Copyright Act[1] and CONTU Guidelines.[2]
Scholarly Sharing	Permits users to share limited content occasionally with scholarly colleagues who are not authorized users.
Text and Data Mining	Permits researchers to use computer-based services to search, index, and extract information from the licensed content and load the results onto their own servers. The purpose is to discover new knowledge from existing information.

1. Copyright Law of the United States of America, U.S. Copyright Office, last modified July 15, 2014, http://www.copyright.gov/title17/92chap1.html#108.
2. "Information Policies: A Compilation of Position Statements, Principles, Statutes, and Other Pertinent Statements," Coalition for Networked Information: National Commission on New Technological Uses of Copyright Works, last modified July 12, 2014, http://old.cni.org/docs/infopols/CONTU.html.

Table 32.4. Legal Terms in Licensing

Breach	Violation of the license terms by either party or an end user; license specifies what happens to stop and repair the damage.
Confidentiality	License terms may be subject to open records laws and Freedom of Information Act requests in a state organization; license may need to acknowledge an organization's need to disclose. User confidentiality is often stated explicitly.
Dispute Resolution	Procedure to follow if parties to license cannot resolve a conflict.
Force Majeure	French for "Act of God," acknowledging that certain events are out of the control of human beings, such as catastrophic weather-related system downtime.
Governing Law and Jurisdiction	Designates the law and court system that will be used to govern the license and address any related legal matter.
Indemnification	Protection by paying for the cost of damage or loss. Vendors generally indemnify licensees in the event that a third party sues the licensee for violating copyright in their use of the content. Many state laws prevent public organizations from indemnifying vendors for misuse of the content by users.
Warranty	Guarantees that specific facts are true. Vendors will warrant that they have the right to license all content and that use of the content as specified will not violate any copyright.

Business Terms

Practical aspects of business relationships are established in licenses. What fees are required and when will they be paid? Does the license cover a onetime purchase of content or an annual subscription? When can an organization cancel a subscription? Under what arrangements will the organization be able to access content in the future after it makes a onetime purchase?

The purpose of carefully negotiated business terms in a license is to ensure that both parties know the conditions that will govern their relationship in the present and future. Some contracts have a definite termination date, some renew annually unless one party decides to cancel, and others establish conditions for content licensed with perpetual access rights such as annual hosting fees that extend indefinitely. See table 32.5, "Business Terms in Licensing."

Table 32.5. Business Terms in Licensing

Cancellation	In a multiyear agreement, specifies the conditions under which an information organization can cancel the contract, including budget reductions, and the date by which the vendor must be notified.
Fees and Payment	Specifies amount of fees to be paid, payment deadlines, and offsetting credits due, such as those for an increasing amount of open-access content in licensed collections.
KBART	For journal content, vendor will supply a title holdings list with metadata in compliance with the KBART[1] initiative.
License Grant	States type of acquisition: annual lease, onetime purchase with perpetual access, etc.
Post-license Access	Methods through which content acquired with perpetual rights will be accessible if license is canceled, including third-party archiving and rights to create/obtain local backup copy.
Preservation	Provides for the long-term accessibility of content on a known preservation hosting platform, including data format migration as technology continues to evolve. Also provides assurance that content will remain accessible if the current publisher or host ceases to exist. Portico[2] and LOCKSS[3] are two established preservation organizations.
Transfer	When journal content moves from one vendor to another, the original vendor is obligated to make certain that the access and perpetual rights transfer to the new site. The Transfer Code of Practice[4] provides guidance.
Withdrawal of Content	If content is removed that renders the product significantly less useful, specifies how licensee will be compensated.

1. "KBART: Knowledge Bases and Related Tools Working Group," UKSG, last modified July 15, 2014, http://www.uksg.org/KBART.
2. "Portico," Ithaka, last modified July 14, 2014, http://www.portico.org/digital-preservation.
3. "LOCKSS," *Stanford University*, last modified July 11, 2014, http://www.lockss.org.
4. "The Transfer Code of Practice," UKSG, last modified December 12, 2013, http://www.uksg.org/transfer/code.

Technical Terms

Licenses also include clauses that address the technical aspects of how the online content will be provided. What are the responsibilities of the actual hosting site and the content provider to make the content available? How will users receive support and technical troubleshooting? Will the content be available in a way that is accessible to all users? How is usage data gathered and shared? Can the content be linked to other services that will help users discover information of interest?

Users now have high expectations about online availability, linking, and accessibility of digital content. Table 32.6, "Technical Terms in Licensing," lists key technical issues that merit careful attention by license negotiators so that acquired online content meets users' needs.

Table 32.6. Technical Terms in Licensing

Authentication Procedures Supported	The technical means by which users will be permitted to have access, usually either by password and/or IP address recognition.
Disabilities Compliance	Vendor may state compliance with the Americans with Disabilities Act[1] and provide a VPAT[2] form to show compliance with federal standards.
Hosting Platform, Access Requirements, and Compatibilities	Establishes the technical requirements for accessing the content at the host site.
Persistent Links	Vendor will comply with the OpenURL[3] standard and provide durable links to licensed content.
Providing Metadata to Discovery Systems	Vendor is obligated to make licensed material accessible for indexing and retrieval by the discovery service used by the licensee.
Required Performance and Remedies	Establishes the acceptable level of downtime in a year and what remedies are appropriate if a vendor does not meet this requirement.
Usage Data	Vendor will provide information about available usage reports. COUNTER[4] and SUSHI[5] are the current usage data collection and reporting standards.
User Support	Hours during which vendor will provide user support and the expected response time.

1. Americans with Disabilities Act of 1990, as Amended, United States Department of Justice, Civil Rights Division, last modified July 13, 2014, http://www.ada.gov/pubs/ada.htm.
2. "Voluntary Product Accessibility Template (VPAT)," United States Department of State, last updated July 28, 2013, http://www.state.gov/m/irm/impact/126343.htm.
3. "NISO Project Overview: ANSI/NISO Z39.88-2004 (R2010), the OpenURL Framework for Context-Sensitive Services," National Information Standards Organization, last modified January 2, 2014, http://www.niso.org/apps/group_public/project/details.php?project_id=82 (accessed June 6, 2014).
4. "About COUNTER," Counting Online Usage of NeTworked Electronic Resources (COUNTER), last modified June 25, 2014, http://www.projectcounter.org.
5. "Standardized Usage Statistics Harvesting Initiative (SUSHI)," National Information Standards Organization (NISO), last modified July 20, 2014, http://www.niso.org/workrooms/sushi (accessed June 6, 2014).

Conclusion

How will licensing evolve? What is its future? Technological changes will continue to drive licensing changes. For example, in 1995, no one contemplated the explosive development of wireless technology and mobile devices. These developments create new licensing issues, as will each successive technological evolution.

With time, many initial publisher fears about the economic threats related to the sale of digital content have been overcome or never materialized. Thus, there is a movement to simplify the transactions for electronic information through techniques such as SERU,[7] which establishes a set of usage terms to which organizations and publishers can agree without signing a legal document. So far, such techniques are not affecting mainstream licensing, but they may in the future.

Pricing models will continue to change to meet evolving user expectations, organizational needs and budgets, and publisher needs and product offerings. This arena will likely be very active as organizations work to meet rising user expectations with limited resources. New and evolving collaborations among groups of information organizations will continue to form for this purpose. Publishers will continue to package their content as effectively as possible to maximize purchases and subscriptions.

The basics of licensing have fallen into place since the 1990s, and evolution of core terms will continue based on changing needs (e.g., text mining) and technology changes (e.g., mobile technologies). With this maturity and widespread prevalence of licensing as the primary avenue through which organizations acquire access to information, there is a movement to use the license as a vehicle to advocate for, and obtain new, organizational and user rights that may not be in current licenses. Author publishing rights, beyond those offered directly by publishers to authors, are one example. Consortia have become the strongest voices in advancing best licensing practices through their consolidated representation of many information organizations.

And of course, with all these simultaneous and uncertain changes, the skills needed by information professionals will evolve as well. The complicated nature of licensing and the delivery of digital content will place an increasing premium on information professionals who understand not only basic organizational operations, but also the business and technology of operating information organizations successfully.

Notes

1. "History of the Compact Disc," Voices.com, last modified July 2, 2014, https://www.voices.com/resources/articles/audio-recording-technology/cd-history-timeline.
2. U.S. Department of Justice, "1854 Copyright Infringement—First Sale Doctrine," last modified September 10, 2014, http://www.justice.gov/usao/eousa/foia_reading_room/usam/title9/crm01854.htm.
3. "Interlibrary Loan Code for the United States," RUSA: Reference and User Services Association: A Division of the American Library Association, last modified October 29, 2013, http://www.ala.org/rusa/resources/guidelines/interlibrary.
4. Marshall Breeding, "A Cloudy Forecast for Libraries," *Computers in Libraries* 31, no. 7 (September 2011): 33–24.
5. "Total Number of Websites," InternetLiveStats.com, last modified July 1, 2014, http://www.internetlivestats.com/total-number-of-websites (accessed July 23, 2014).
6. "Liblicense: Licensing Digital Content—a Resource for Librarians," Center for Research Libraries, last modified July 28, 2014, http://liblicense.crl.edu.
7. "Shared Electronic Resource Understanding (SERU): Recommended Practice," National Information Standards Organization (NISO), last modified July 2, 2014, http://www.niso.org/workrooms/seru (accessed July 24. 2014).

33

Open Access

Heather Joseph

The advent of the Internet brought to light both significant opportunities and new challenges for information organizations. This has become especially evident in the evolution, theory, and practice of how the results of research are communicated and shared. The movement toward open access—the free, unrestricted accessibility and utility of scholarly articles online—has been underway for more than a decade and has made significant strides in improving how scholars and researchers share their work. From the proliferation of open access journal outlets to the burgeoning number of open access digital repositories in U.S. higher education institutions and research facilities, scholars have promising new options for maximizing the impact of their work. While awareness of the potential benefits of increasing the digital reach of scholarly articles continues to grow, significant misconceptions and cultural barriers remain. These barriers must be addressed before open access can be widely accepted and become the norm in the communication of scholarly research.

After completing this chapter, the reader should have an understanding of the potential benefits and challenges that open access presents to the traditional system of scholarly communication, as well as how information professionals can play a key role in addressing today's challenges and fostering a continued transition to a truly open system of sharing scholarly work.

Why Open Access?

The Internet has significantly changed the way people communicate with one another, from how people get their news, to how they shop; from how they stay in touch with their families, to how they work. As information organizations are keenly aware, it has also had a tremendous impact on how scholars and researchers conduct and share scholarly and scientific research. Scholarly work, in all fields, is increasingly digital and now requires new, online solutions to optimize both individual and collective efforts. For researchers, the digital environment offers the very real opportunity to increase the global reach of the results of their work.

This appealing and very immediate possibility of expanding the circulation of knowledge has directly led to the "open access" movement. This movement envisions a new way for scholars and researchers to share their own works—specifically peer-reviewed journal articles—and to access the works of their colleagues freely and immediately online, anytime, anywhere. Authors, researchers, funders, academic institutions, and publishers are actively engaged in exploring new ways of using the Internet to make more of their research available in this way.

TEXTBOX 33.1

Why Scholars and Scientists Conduct Research

Scholars and scientists conduct research so that new ideas can be generated, new discoveries can be uncovered, and the collective understanding of the world and the interactions with it can be enhanced. Scientists—and the organizations who fund their research—rightly consider the communication of the results of their research to be an essential, inextricable component of the research itself.

Scholarly and scientific research is a cumulative process. It can only advance when research is made readily available for others to see, read, use, and, most importantly, build on. And scholarly research has another unique attribute; unlike consumable commodities, the results of scholarly research only gain in value when they are used. The impact of a scholarly work is measured by how it is used by others to stimulate further research, spark discoveries, fuel community engagement, and improve the lives and welfare of fellow citizens. There is a common misconception that research results are just another commodity in a traditional marketplace where scarcity adds value, when actually exactly the opposite is true.

> "The impact of a scholarly work is measured by how it is used by others to stimulate further research, spark discoveries, fuel community engagement, and improve the lives and welfare of fellow citizens."

There is a wonderful quote by the playwright and essayist George Bernard Shaw that illustrates this concept:

> If you have an apple and I have an apple, and we exchange these apples, then you and I will still each have only one apple. But if you have an idea and I have an idea, and we exchange these ideas, then each of us will have two ideas.[1]

Scholarly research is conducted with the express purpose of sharing ideas and new knowledge as rapidly and as broadly as possible for just this reason. And so, given the development of the Internet and its ability to deliver digital information rapidly to a global audience at very little marginal cost, one would think that this information—in particular, scientific research results—should be easily and broadly available. However, the current reality looks very different.

Financial Barriers in the Traditional System of Scholarly Communication

There are very real barriers to gaining access to information regarding much of the research that scholars and scientists conduct. For decades, the primary mechanism for communicating the results of research has been through the publication of articles in peer-reviewed journals. Researchers have traditionally written articles for publication in journals, sharing their research findings. They have also contributed their expertise and time to peer review (and often editing) their colleagues' work for journals—all without the expectation of payment. And yet, when the time comes to access and read articles (their own, as well as their colleagues' articles), they are nearly always required to pay a subscription fee or pay-per-view fee.

The cost to access journal content presents significant barriers to making scholarly communication widely available. Over the past several decades, the journal-publishing market has undergone significant consolidation, with a handful of large, multinational publishing firms dominating the landscape. Journal publishing has become big business, with annual revenues from science, technology, and medical journals of nearly ten billion dollars.[2] As commercialization has increased, so have journal subscription prices, with many costing thousands to tens of thousands of dollars each year and prices escalating at an astounding pace. Research has shown that journal subscription prices have outstripped the pace of inflation by more than 250 percent over a thirty-year period.[3] Information organizations—which are the primary subscribers to journals on behalf of scholars and researchers—cannot keep pace with rising costs.

This has become a global problem, affecting nearly all information organizations. Perhaps one of the most striking illustrations of this occurred in 2012, when Harvard University, arguably one of the most well-funded research universities in the world, issued a memo to its faculty that jolted the academic world. It read (in part),

> We write to communicate an untenable situation facing the Harvard Library. Many large journal publishers have made the scholarly communication environment fiscally unsustainable and academically restrictive. Harvard's annual cost for journals now approaches $3.75M [U.S. dollars]. . . . Prices for online content from two providers have increased by about 145% over the past six years, which far exceeds not only the consumer price index, but also the higher education and the library price indices. These journals claim an ever-increasing share of our overall collection budget. . . . The Faculty Advisory Council to the Library, representing university faculty in all schools and in consultation with the Harvard Library leadership, reached this conclusion: major periodical subscriptions, especially to electronic journals published by historically key providers, cannot be sustained: continuing these subscriptions on their current footing is financially untenable.[4]

This begs the question: if the situation is this dire for Harvard, what is it like for the tens of thousands of other academic and research institutions with budgets that do not come close to that of Harvard? What is it like for scientists and scholars on those campuses who are trying to conduct research? Researchers readily acknowledge that when they are conducting literature searches to further their research, they routinely run into abstracts of papers that they think might be of interest to them. While there is no cost to them to read the abstracts, they often do not read the full articles because their organization does not cover the cost to provide them with access to the full text. It is common practice for them to simply skip to the next paper where full text is available. Rather than reading all relevant articles, they only read the articles where there are no barriers to access. This has become the status quo in research, but it should be unacceptable to scholars, educators, and information professionals.

The status quo means that there are scientists conducting research based only on the previous studies they have access to, rather than all prior studies relevant to their research. They are missing information they might need to inform their current research. Perhaps even more damaging, the instruction they provide to students is based on the information they have access to, not on what the students might truly need to know.[5]

The Phenomenon of the Digital Information Explosion

While the financial pressure alone might be enough to spur information organizations to search for a better solution, the world has also been simultaneously experiencing another phenomenon that further fuels the fire for change: an information explosion.

The move to digital has been happening just about everywhere, and in just about every discipline. From the biological sciences to physics, from anthropology to the humanities, work is increasingly conducted online, and the amount of data generated from research is increasing exponentially.

Similarly, the number of articles reporting on research is skyrocketing, with nearly two million new articles generated annually.[6] The only way to truly make sense of this welcomed, if overwhelming, glut of information is to find new ways for these digital articles (and the underlying data) to not only be accessed, but to also be used.

In today's information environment, simply removing the financial barrier to access and enabling researchers to read an article is not enough. With so many articles being generated annually, the ability of individuals to deal with this explosion of information by sitting down and reading through researchers' papers one by one is untenable. Scholars and researchers want to be able to find that one article in a million that might be of interest in a totally unrelated discipline—the paper that uses a technique or methodology that otherwise would not have been considered. They want to be able to mine the text of digital articles to quickly find the information they seek, without needing to read an entire article. Better yet, they want to access the whole corpus of digital articles to find semantic connections and relationships among research papers that cannot be readily seen by reading a single paper at a time. They want to be able to analyze digital articles, using new cutting-edge computational techniques (and techniques not yet imagined), in order to find the most relevant articles without having to read each one of them. They need to be able to apply the power of networks to this information search, to enable computers as a new category of "user," to help scholars fully unlock the value contained within this explosion of scholarly content.[7] See textbox 33.2.

TEXTBOX 33.2

Computers as "Users"?

The concept of enabling the computer as a new category of "user" correlates to the concept of "machine-readable" scholarly outputs. One nice illustration of this comes from John Wilbanks and Jamie Boyle. In their "Introduction to Science Commons" paper, they talk about a researcher working on one aspect of malaria research (a specific protein called glycophorin A). A literature search turns up nearly two thousand papers that might be relevant; trying to read each one herself would take her, quite literally, years to complete. She needs to be able to use computer-enabled tools to do the kind of semantic and relational text mining that will help her identify key papers—she simply cannot do it alone.[1]

1. John Wilbanks and Jamie Boyle, "Introduction to Science Commons," Science Commons, August 3, 2006, 1, http://sciencecommons.org/wp-content/uploads/ScienceCommons_Concept_Paper.pdf.

Open Access: The New Paradigm

With every crisis comes opportunity. These pressures have sparked conversations about new ways to revolutionize how scholarly research is shared, remove access barriers (i.e., financial, technical, and legal barriers), take advantage of the power of the Internet, and come up with a vision for a new system that better serves scholarship and research. In short, the question that needs to be asked is, if an ideal system could be created from the ground floor up for sharing scientific and scholarly information, what would it look like?

That question was the impetus behind the meeting that ultimately gave rise to the concept of open access. In 2001, the Open Society Foundations convened a small meeting in Budapest. The participants represented diverse points of view, academic disciplines, and geographical and geopolitical areas. A main outcome of the meeting was the expression of a vision to develop such an optimal system—a system that the participants termed "open access."

The participants eloquently prefaced the definition of open access by succinctly framing the broad issues, saying, in part,

> An old tradition and a new technology have converged to make possible an unprecedented public good. The old tradition is the willingness of scientists and scholars to publish the fruits of their research in scholarly journals without payment, for the sake of inquiry and knowledge. The new technology is the Internet. The public good they make possible is the worldwide electronic distribution of the peer-reviewed journal literature and completely free and unrestricted access to it by all. Removing access barriers to this literature will accelerate research, enrich education, share the learning of the rich with the poor and the poor with the rich, make this literature as useful as it can be, and lay the foundation for uniting humanity in a common intellectual conversation and quest for knowledge.[8]

This new "open access" paradigm involves the immediate, free availability of scholarly articles on the public Internet, coupled with the rights to use articles fully in the digital environment, without financial, legal, or technical barriers. The drafters of this Budapest Open Access Initiative were also careful to clearly articulate that the only role for copyright in this domain should be to give authors control over the integrity of their work and the right to be properly acknowledged and cited when others refer to the author's work in their own publications.

First Steps to Achieving Open Access: Building the Infrastructure

Open access is a simple and powerful concept, but can it become a reality? The framers of the Budapest Open Access Initiative initially envisioned two concrete strategies that the scientific and scholarly research community could immediately pursue. These two strategies have been crucial in building the global infrastructure over the last decade needed to support an open access system of scholarly communication.

The first strategy is the establishment of *open digital repositories*, where authors can deposit journal articles to make them freely available to the world—a practice commonly called "self-archiving." When these open digital repositories conform to specific, uniform interoperability standards, search engines and other tools can treat separate archives as one, creating a global networked system of archives, where articles can be readily located and accessed. These types of interoperability standards, known as OAI protocols, have already been developed and are used by many institutions, facilitating efficient content sharing and dissemination. Academic and research libraries, along with other institutions, have embraced this strategy of open digital repositories, and more than 2,600 such open repositories are currently in operation around the world.[9]

The second strategy involves another key piece of infrastructure—the establishment of *open access journals*. In order for scholars and scientists to truly embrace the concept of open access, they need viable, sustainable, high-quality open access journal options where they can publish their articles.

Open access journals function in the same manner as traditional subscription access journals from an editorial and peer review standpoint. However, they differ in two key ways that serve to remove the barriers identified earlier. First, open access journals do not use copyright to restrict access to and use of the material they publish. Instead, they use open licenses (such as Creative Commons licenses) to ensure permanent access to and full use of the articles they publish. Second, open access journals do not charge subscription or access fees of any kind. Instead, they use a variety of other methods—such as article process charges—to cover their publishing costs up front. Since the definition of open access was first articulated, more than nine thousand open access journals have been established.[10]

New business models continue to emerge to support these journals, along with new sources of support. On college and university campuses, libraries are using new strategies, such as redirecting library funds from paying for journal subscriptions to supporting open access publication costs.

Academic libraries are also establishing separate pools of money, often called campus open access funds, setting aside financial resources expressly to support open access publication models. Outside of higher education institutions, foundations and government agencies that fund research are establishing policies that allow researchers to include open access publishing charges in their research budgets, paying for those publishing charges with grant funds. And publishers are experimenting with new ways to support open access journal publishing, including profits from the sale of add-ons to basic texts, membership fees, and other sources of revenue.

TEXTBOX 33.3

Topic for Discussion

Since the introduction of the concept of open access in 2002, awareness and adoption of policies and practices has grown fairly steadily. Are there signs that this will continue, or are there emerging trends that might cause progress to slow down or stop?

Additional Challenges to Achieving Open Access

While these initial strategies to provide open access form a strong foundation to encourage the transition to a new way of sharing scientific research, they are not enough. Over the past decade, it has become evident that simply building infrastructure is not sufficient to encourage the kind of widespread cultural change that is needed for researchers—and institutions—to fully move toward embracing open access. More is needed.

Author Rights

One remaining challenge that must be addressed in order to achieve open access relates to authors understanding their rights. Authors, who control the rights to their research articles unless and until they choose to sign them over to a third party using copyright transfer, are, by and large, unaware of their own rights. They are leery of open access, not fully understanding what it means to forgo signing a traditional copyright transfer form in favor of publishing an article under an open license. They worry that they are being asked to "give up" something that may have value for them in the future. They also do not understand that they are actually strengthening their ability to reach new audiences, who may not only read, but cite, their articles. Many are nervous about treading into what they perceive to be complex legal territory.

Additionally, while standardized open licenses have been established and are widely adopted—specifically the Creative Commons set of open licenses—their adoption is not yet universal. Indeed, one of the major points of contention in the open access community is the ongoing debate about the establishment of the Creative Commons Attribution Only (or CC BY) license as the gold standard for open access journals (see also chapter 31, "Copyright and Creative Commons").

For open access strategies to succeed, authors need to understand their intellectual property rights and the implications of each publishing option available to them. While authors want to ensure that their articles are available to audiences that would benefit from the content, many authors do not fully understand the value of their work, all the ways their content can be used by various audiences, and which approach to publishing is the best option for enabling each type of use.

In the open access environment, new measures are emerging (broadly termed "alternative metrics") that can provide information regarding how often an article is read and cited, as well as the types of individuals who are reading and using articles. Alternative metrics can also provide insight regarding how an article is being used. These article-level alternative metrics have the potential to offer a rich suite of tools to better understand the full story of the utility and value of research articles. These tools can be applied to articles wherever they are located—either in open access journals or in collections in open access repositories.

Information organizations are well positioned to play an active role in helping to change this dynamic and help authors better understand their publishing options. For example, information professionals who work in academic libraries can work closely with faculty to help them understand their options regarding how to publish their articles, including how their choices impact their intellectual property rights, as well as the option to publish content in an open repository hosted by the institution (see also chapter 7, "The Learning and Research Institution: Academic Libraries"). Research funders are also interested in ensuring that findings are broadly shared and typically expect researchers to share findings via articles published in scholarly journals. However, these funders must also be educated about opportunities to offer broader access to findings through open access publishing options so they do not place undue restrictions on access and reuse. Institutions that have explored the idea of supporting the distribution of articles created by their faculty and researchers via an open repository supported by an institutional copyright policy have found that it raises the visibility of their institution's intellectual output and enhances their institution's brand as well.[11]

Incentives to Publish in Open Access Journals

A second remaining challenge to achieving open access is in the area of incentives to publish. For the status quo to truly change, scientists and scholars employed by higher education institutions must be incentivized to make their articles available under open access terms in journals or in digital repositories. As long as they fear that they will not be adequately rewarded—either in the tenure and promotion process, or in the evaluation of research grant funding—by making their work openly accessible, they will choose to continue to follow traditional routines and publish their articles solely in subscription access journals with high impact factors.

Collectively, higher education institutions must review their priorities and decide to actively pursue new measures for judging the impact of a researcher's contribution to their discipline. Initiatives to measure the impact of a researcher's publications should explicitly take into account the value that is added when researchers pursue open access avenues for sharing their work (see also chapter 28, "Demonstrating Value: Assessment").

New Policy Frameworks

A third challenge relates to the need to create a new policy framework to support the transition to open access. Specifically, there is strong evidence that establishing a robust policy framework—on an institutional, national, and international level—to support the transition to open access is a crucial requirement for ensuring a successful transition. While a growing number of open access policies have been proposed and mandated, challenges remain to see that they are successfully implemented.

Over time, widespread understanding regarding how open access can play a key role in stimulating economic development, innovation, and competitiveness has grown markedly, leading to national and global efforts to establish new policies regarding open access. In 2005, the international Organization for Economic Co-operation and Development considered the issue of open access and concluded that it was a strategic necessity, stating,

> Governments would boost innovation and get a better return on their investment in publicly funded research by making research findings more widely available. . . . And by doing so, they would maximize social returns on public investments.[12]

This conclusion has been taken seriously by policy makers and research funders around the world. They realize that these returns include the ability to accelerate the pace of new ideas and discoveries, improve education, empower entrepreneurs to translate research into commercial ventures and jobs, and help revolutionize the research process.

In the United States, the National Institutes of Health (NIH) established its landmark open access policy in 2008, requiring all grant recipients to make articles reporting on the results of their funded research freely available through NIH's digital repository, PubMed Central.[13] And in 2013, the White House Office of Science and Technology Policy issued an executive directive requiring two dozen other federal agencies to create plans for implementing policies similar to that of the NIH.[14]

Policy adoption has been global, with new policies emerging from the UK to the European Union, and from Argentina to South Africa. Perhaps no one has articulated the drivers behind this policy adoption more succinctly than Neelie Kroes, EU commissioner for Europe's Digital Agenda, who successfully led the call—and required—that all research funded by the European Commission be made available under open access conditions. In 2012, she noted,

> Open access to research results—both publications and research data—is not just a luxury—it is a must for Europe if we are to be able to compete internationally. Access to knowledge, information, and data is essential in higher education and research, and using it provides the basis for knowledge transfer and knowledge generation.[15]

"Many institutions are becoming aware of the advantages that can be accrued by retaining digital assets resulting from research and are establishing policies ensuring that locally generated research articles, data, and educational resources are housed in campus repositories."

As a result of this growing understanding, national policies that ensure open access to research articles are proliferating, with more than one hundred research funders and government policies now on the books worldwide.[16]

These national policies are crucial, but the development of institutional (or campus-wide) open access policies also plays an important role. Many institutions are becoming aware of the advantages that can be accrued by retaining digital assets resulting from research and are establishing policies ensuring that locally generated research articles, data, and educational resources are housed in campus repositories. Information organizations have played a key role in championing these policies and in providing ongoing expertise and support to ensure their successful implementation. However, for open access to become the norm, more widespread adoption and cohesive implementation of such policies are needed.

TEXTBOX 33.4

Topic for Discussion

Information organizations and information professionals were among the first communities to recognize the value of open access and to play a central role in promoting it to faculty and administrators. Are there new roles that information organization and professionals can take on that would continue to enhance the understanding of the benefits of open access?

Conclusion

The collective understanding of the benefits to be gained by enabling open access as the default mode for sharing research articles is growing worldwide, and a robust infrastructure of journals and repositories to support this vision has been established. Information organizations have played a key role in educating faculty, researchers, students, and administrators on the advantages of fast, barrier-free communication of research results, and in advocating for the successful adoption of open access policies and practices. Significant challenges remain, particularly around understanding how adoption of open licenses impacts intellectual property rights, the establishment of incentives encouraging open access publication, and the development and implementation of cohesive open access policies on the institutional and national levels. These challenges provide information organizations with the opportunity to take on new roles, developing solutions to today's open access challenges and encouraging the continued evolution toward the vision of a truly "open access" system of sharing research findings and other scholarly activity.

Notes

1. Lewis Hyde, *Common as Air: Revolution, Art and Ownership* (New York: Farrar, Strauss and Giroux, 2010).
2. Mark Ware and Michael Mabe, *The STM Report* (The Hague, NL: International Association of Scientific, Technical and Medical Publishers, 2012), http://www.stm-assoc.org/2012_12_11_STM_Report_2012 .pdf.
3. "Research Library Expenditure Trends," in *ARL Statistics, 2006–2007* (Washington, DC: Association of Research Libraries), https://comminfo.rutgers.edu/~tefko/Courses/e553/Readings/ARL%20statis tics%202006-07.pdf.
4. "Harvard Faculty Advisory Council Memorandum on Journal Pricing," Harvard University, last modified April 17, 2012, http://isites.harvard.edu/icb/icb.do?keyword=k77982&tabgroupid=icb .tabgroup143448.
5. Gary Ward, "Press Conference: Congressman Doyle to Address New Bill to Unlock U.S. $60 Billion Investment in Research," Alliance for Taxpayer Access, April 21, 2010, http://www.taxpayeraccess.org/ issues/frpaa/frpaa_resources/press-conference-congressman-doyle-to-address-new-.shtml.
6. Ware and Mabe, *The STM Report*, 2012.
7. John Wilbanks and Jamie Boyle, "Introduction to Science Commons," Science Commons, August 3, 2006, 1, http://sciencecommons.org/wp-content/uploads/ScienceCommons_Concept_Paper.pdf.
8. "BOAI 10 Recommendations," Budapest Open Access Initiative, last modified July 1, 2014, http://www .budapestopenaccessinitiative.org/boai-10-recommendations.
9. "Directory of Open Access Repositories," OpenDOAR, last modified August 6, 2014, www.opendoar .org.
10. "Home," Directory of Open Access Journals, last modified August 31, 2014, www.doaj.org.
11. "Open Access Policies," Harvard University Library Office of Scholarly Communication, last modified April 16, 22014, https://osc.hul.harvard.edu/policies.
12. "Governments Should Improve Access to Publicly Funded Research, Finds OECD Report," Organisation for Economic Co-operation and Development (OECD), last modified September 2, 2014, http://www .oecd.org/general/governmentsshouldimproveaccesstopubliclyfundedresearchfindsoecdreport.htm.
13. "NIH Public Access Policy Details," U.S. Department of Health and Human Services, last modified March 27, 2014, http://publicaccess.nih.gov/policy.htm.
14. "Open Data Policy—Managing Information as an Asset," Executive Office of the President, Office of Management and Budget, M-13-13, May 9, 2013, http://www.whitehouse.gov/sites/default/files/omb/ memoranda/2013/m-13-13.pdf.
15. Neelie Kroes, "Dutch Open Access Week Address," YouTube video, uploaded by Neelie Kroes, October 18, 2011, https://www.youtube.com/watch?v=taux1l0Vgek.
16. "Home," Registry of Open Access Repositories Mandatory Open Access Policies (ROARMAP), last modified July 14, 2014, http://roarmap.eprints.org.

34

Analog and Digital Curation and Preservation

Katherine Skinner

This chapter provides a broad overview of historical, theoretical, managerial, analytical, and practical aspects of curation and preservation. The chapter marks some of the most important events and shifts in thought regarding both theory and practice. It also provides a brief forecast of what might come in the near future as curation specialists continue to wrestle with difficult issues around the longevity, security, and authenticity of the content they manage. As with other aspects of the information profession, practitioners working in this subfield are grappling with new challenges as evolving technology continuously transforms the work they do and the issues they must address.

After completing this chapter, the reader should have an understanding of how to

- describe the evolution of preservation theory and practice;
- identify the decision-making process involved in selection;
- summarize the causes of deterioration and loss for various types of information objects;
- identify key concepts and standards in digital preservation, including the OAIS model;
- define the principles of preservation policies;
- identify disaster planning, prevention, response, and recovery strategies; and
- locate and evaluate tools, research, and other resources on preservation.

Defining Terms: Curation and Preservation

Curation. Lifecycle management. Preservation. Conservation. These names and subnames describe actions information managers regularly undertake to ensure the longevity and accessibility of content. But what do these terms mean, and how do they relate to one another?

- *Lifecycle management:* the full spectrum of activities a manager undertakes, from creation to disposal of an item or collection. The "DCC Curation Lifecycle Model" offers one influential diagram to explain the broad range of tasks encompassed by this term.
- *Curation:* the range of tasks involved in managing content—including such important steps as selection, acquisition, cataloging, and transformation. It is often conjoined with the term "digital" to mark the specific activities that are undertaken for digital objects.

- *Preservation:* the steps taken to ensure the long-term accessibility and usability of content—including (but not restricted to) activities that prevent content from deteriorating.
- *Conservation:* the set of preservation practices used to rectify damages done to an object and/or the set of actions taken to slow an object's deterioration.

These terms sit in a hierarchy of sorts, with lifecycle management at the broadest level; curation and preservation embedded within it as two essential, interrelated (and sometimes overlapping) sets of activities; and conservation as one way that preservation is accomplished.

Many practitioners use these terms interchangeably, but there are significant distinctions between them. For example, differentiating successfully between conservation and preservation requires an understanding of the role played by *change* in each. Preservation is about ensuring abiding access to an object or collection through whatever means is necessary. Conservation, as a subset of preservation, is ultimately about preventing or repairing changes to the object or collection.

Conservation practices include

- preventive measures, such as placing a fragile document in a protective enclosure;
- remedial activities, such as paper repair and binding replacement; and
- collection-wide activities meant to hinder decay and damage, such as fumigation and deacidification.

Preservation encompasses these actions, but *also includes practices that intentionally change an object or collection* as is necessary to maintain it. Preservation includes conservation activities of all types (preventive, remedial, and collection-wide).

TEXTBOX 34.1

Preservation Activities

- *Refreshing:* transferring content from one container to another container in the same format and media (e.g., copying a cassette tape to another cassette tape).
- *Reformatting:* transferring the intellectual content of an object or collection from one medium to another (e.g., photocopying, microfilming, or digitizing content).
- *Replicating:* making and distributing copies of content.
- *Emulation:* creating an environment that enables digital content to be rendered in new software and hardware environments without changing the content file.

Why Do Information Managers Preserve Content?

The term "preservation" often takes on an antiquated quality, evoking a sense of "memory" in a time when innovation is highly valued. In reality, preservation is about much more than memory—it is about access. Information managers of all types—librarians, archivists, technologists, and curators—preserve content so that people living today and in the future can use it.

The familiar adage "those who cannot remember the past are condemned to repeat it"[1] is one piece of

"Preservation is about much more than memory—it is about access. Information managers of all types—librarians, archivists, technologists, and curators—preserve content so that people living today and in the future can use it."

the logic and rationale undergirding the impulse to preserve, but of equal importance is the concept that today's innovations depend on yesterday's discoveries. Limiting or losing access to content erodes the foundation of knowledge that is built iteratively. To say that more plainly, the ability to innovate depends in large part on the ability to remember and build upon what has come before. Accessing knowledge—both current and historical—is essential to this process.

Milestones in the Subfield of Preservation

The impetus for preserving content is far from new. Preservation practices can be traced back to the infamous Library of Alexandria in the third century BCE. Reformatting and repair examples date back to the earliest media forms and were certainly prevalent with efforts to repair the library's collection of papyrus scrolls.

However, today's strong emphasis on preservation as a field of practice is a more recent phenomenon that dates back only to the 1950s and 1960s, when several occurrences prompted information managers to focus funding and attention on preservation in unprecedented ways. Notably, the preservation subfield as understood today has been undergirded by a sense of foreboding, threat, and destruction. Established in response to concerns about a crisis, a danger-driven sensibility continues to infuse much of the language around preservation, even today. The next subsections address several major milestones in the maturation of "preservation" as a subfield of practice in library and information science.

Brittle Books

The longevity of materials inscribed or printed on papyrus and linen/cotton rag-based paper was established over generations of use. In contrast, wood-pulp paper was a relatively unknown medium from a preservation standpoint, and chemists and specialists began to document their concerns about its stability by the early 1900s. Specifically, the highly acidic nature of wood-pulp paper differentiates it from its papyrus and linen/cotton rag predecessors, putting it at risk of deterioration. Pages become brittle and, when handled, in extreme cases will disintegrate into dust. The challenges associated with wood-pulp paper's stability drew early attention to the process of preservation (see appendix 34.1, "The Brittle Books Phenomenon").

The Florence Flood

In 1966, Italy's Arno River flooded Florence, damaging thousands of library and museum collections. The international response to this catastrophe was dramatic. Representatives from hundreds of libraries and museums around the world contributed to the salvage efforts. Conservators experimented with many different techniques to restore a wide variety of objects. The event provided a distressing example of the extensive damage flooding could do to collections. It also created a research environment where practices and protocols that greatly influenced the emerging field of preservation were established.

Professionalism of Preservation

The convergence of the brittle books crisis and the Florence flood helped to speed the professionalism of preservation practices. The 1966 passage of the National Historic Preservation Act[2] in the United States highlighted the emphasis on preservation in the wake of disaster. As a consequence

- key U.S. institutions[3] established preservation divisions by the early 1970s,[4]
- library science programs at U.S. universities developed and offered dozens of preservation courses,
- professional associations established new committees focused on preservation,[5] and
- numerous conservation programs and research labs were founded.[6]

Katherine Skinner

In addition, continued concerns about the instability of acid-based paper drove additional activities throughout the field,[7] which focused on the preservation microfilming of endangered "brittle" papers, and the advocacy campaign to promote acid-free paper adoption in the publishing industry.[8]

Digital Preservation

Although the earliest digital preservation efforts began in national archives and other cultural establishments in the 1960s,[9] concerns about the longevity—or the lack thereof—of digital content formats were raised to the level of national prominence in the United States in 1994 when the Research Libraries Group and the Commission on Preservation and Access cocreated the Task Force on Digital Archiving in 1994. This group was charged with studying how best to provide "continued access indefinitely into the future of records stored in digital electronic form."[10]

The task force, which included representatives from libraries, museums, foundations, archives, societies, government, and industry, published a groundbreaking report in 1996, "Preserving Digital Information." The report described the dire need for coordination of resources and infrastructure across broad communities of stewards to establish the digital preservation standards, certification procedures, and deep infrastructure necessary to preserve digital content.

Funding provided by private foundations and federal agencies established a large number of initiatives around digital preservation methodologies and infrastructures by the late 1990s and early 2000s. Many of these initiatives stressed the need for collaboration, and most of the successful standards and early operations were borne of national or international collaborations.

TEXTBOX 34.3

Examples of International Collaborations

- *1998:* Stanford University Library developed and released the Open Source software "Lots of Copies Keep Stuff Safe" (LOCKSS)—the world's first community-based preservation network.
- *2000:* The Consultative Committee for Space Data Systems (CCSDS) produced the Reference Model for an Open Archival Information Systems (first circulated as the Draft International Standard).
- *2004:* The National Digital Information Infrastructure and Preservation Program (NDIIPP) made multimillion-dollar preservation awards launched by the Library of Congress.
- *2005:* The Preservation Metadata Implementation Strategies (PREMIS) were developed to tie together the varied international efforts around preservation metadata standards development.

Digital Preservation Milestones

Four key digital preservation initiatives bear significant influence in today's digital preservation practices:

- *Open Archival Information System (OAIS):* describes both the organizational and technical aspects of a preservation approach and model. Released by the CCSDS in 2000 and as an ISO standard in 2003, it provides the core human- and system-level components of a preservation archive (analog or digital) and provides a set of standard vocabulary that is now used across many different information management fields to talk about the various roles and operations within a preservation system. Such commonly understood concepts as "submission information packages" (SIPs) and "producers" were first established within this model.
- *Preservation Metadata Implementation Strategies (PREMIS):* provides a data dictionary and resources to assist information managers in the implementation of preservation metadata efforts. Established as a working group by OCLC/RLG, with its report and data dictionary first released in 2005, PREMIS documentation is housed and maintained by the Library of Congress.
- *Audit and Certification of Trustworthy Digital Repositories Standard (ISO 16363):* provides metrics for certifying preservation archives. It is complemented by ISO 16919, Requirements for Bodies Providing Audit and Certification, which documents how to certify auditors to exercise this standard.
- *Digital Preservation Outreach and Education (DPOE):* developed by the Library of Congress in 2010 as a concerted effort to spread the knowledge and practice of digital preservation throughout the United States. A "train-the-trainer" program developed in 2011 has reached thousands of practitioners throughout the United States and has fostered a national network of digital stewardship.

Key concerns addressed by digital preservation have focused on obsolescence (e.g., an eight-inch floppy with its WordPerfect files from the 1980s is still intact, but entirely unrenderable due to a lack of the necessary equipment and software/operating system components to read them), media failure (e.g., computers or servers experience a virus or catastrophic system failure), and physical loss (e.g., a flood or fire takes out a computer or server entirely). Additional issues arise in the form of security threats, such as the theft, alteration, or deletion of historically significant content. Approaches to digital preservation infrastructures vary widely, with some preservation archives adopting centralized infrastructures (one-site solutions) and others adopting distributed infrastructures (intentionally housed in different locations—commonly referred to as "distributed digital preservation"). Debates and issues have raged within the community regarding the value and distinctions between "bit-level preservation" (preserving the strings of zeros and ones that comprise a file) and other preservation components more commonly referred to as "curation," including format migration and metadata creation. Currently, libraries and archives address both of these essential components in their digital preservation planning and implementation efforts.

Audiovisual Content Preservation

Audiovisual (AV) content preservation refers to efforts to stabilize and maintain a wide variety of AV content, or content that stores and/or reproduces sight and/or sound. The means to preserve and conserve audiovisual content vary widely, depending upon the recording format—film, tape, or digital media.

There are significant differences between these formats. Think, for example, of the media used for sound recordings over the last century, which include the tinfoil "phonograph," the wax cylinder, LPs, a range of magnetic tape devices, cassette tapes, CDs, and digital audio files. Within each of these formats are additional, substantive differences in quality that depend upon their manufacturers.

> "The means to preserve and conserve audiovisual content vary widely, depending upon the recording format—film, tape, or digital media."

Concerns in audiovisual preservation range from the rapid obsolescence of media to the deterioration of the media themselves. For example, eight-track recordings became obsolete when devices used to play them stopped being manufactured in the 1980s with the transition to cassette tapes. And cassette tapes themselves are known to deteriorate over time.

Although the mechanics of conservation and preservation in the audiovisual realm tend to be specific to the media type, common principles undergird their preservation efforts. For example, preservation plans must include

- specific steps around care and handling (limiting use; storing in cool, humidity-controlled, clean environments);
- making multiple copies (at least two copies,[11] stored separately); and
- careful monitoring to ensure that deterioration is identified and rectified regularly.

Preservation Theory and Practices

The Digital Preservation Outreach and Education (DPOE) curriculum (funded by the Institute of Museum and Library Services and initially developed by Nancy McGovern in cooperation with the Office of Strategic Initiatives at the Library of Congress), provides a solid introduction to digital preservation theory and practice. The mission of DPOE is to "foster national outreach and education to encourage individuals and organizations to actively preserve their digital content, building on a collaborative network of instructors, contributors, and institutional partners."[12]

DPOE curriculum focuses on six steps in the preservation workflow:

1. *Identify*: What digital content already exists? Focusing on this question, the "Identify" module helps practitioners think about how to create an inventory of digital content.
2. *Select*: What portion of that content will be preserved? The "Select" module helps practitioners determine what selection/appraisal/acquisition principles make most sense for their local collections.

3. *Store:* How should content be stored for the long term? The "Store" module describes optimal content storage, including what content to store (files plus metadata, encoded as one object), describes what well-managed collections look like, and discusses the optimal storage media options and number of copies recommended for long-term archiving.
4. *Protect:* What steps are needed to protect digital content? The "Protect" module covers the major hazards for digital content (including change and loss, obsolescence of media, inappropriate access, and various disaster scenarios) and details best practices for ensuring that content remains safe, authentic, and trustworthy over time.
5. *Manage:* What provisions are needed for long-term management? The "Manage" module describes management roles—including what staff positions should be involved in preservation, how practices should be documented at the organizational level, how funding impacts preservation, and what standards conformance and good practice should include.
6. *Provide:* How should content be made available over time? The final module, "Provide," focuses on good practices for long-term access to preserved content by users. It discusses organizational responsibilities, access policies, how to understand user needs and expectations (current and future), how to handle intellectual property (IP) and other legal issues, and how to effectively sustain both the preservation program and the collections it protects.

Common Media Types and Their Preservation Challenges

Film

Film (negatives, reels, etc.) consists of three core components: (1) a layer of color dye or silver (black-and-white film), (2) gelatin emulsion that acts as a binder for the image dye, and (3) a clear plastic base. A wide variety of chemical substances have been used in film production over time, and many of the preservation challenges inherent in films are caused by the deterioration of these substances.

Common film issues include the following:

- *Nitrate Deterioration:* Perhaps the most dramatic hazard in film preservation is that of nitrate deterioration. Used until the early 1950s, cellulose nitrate film stock deteriorates under relatively low temperatures (e.g., 106 degrees Fahrenheit) and will spontaneously combust and burn. This process can be slowed through the use of cold storage.
- *Acetate Deterioration (Vinegar Syndrome):* This "safety" film was introduced as an alternative to its highly flammable predecessor, nitrate film. Acetate was popularized in 35 mm, 16 mm, and 8 mm sizes and has been used prevalently by professionals and amateurs alike. When stored in nonideal conditions, acetate film quickly disintegrates through "vinegar syndrome." The symptoms of this deterioration are a vinegar scent, followed by shrinkage and buckling of the film. Many conservationists use A-D Strips to identify vinegar syndrome before the smell arises.
- *Fading:* Color dye films in particular will fade due to chemical changes and decomposition, even in normal room-temperature environments. As with nitrate and acetate deterioration, this process can be slowed substantially by the use of cold storage.
- *Physical Damage:* Usage and storage can cause myriad forms of physical damage. Most can be avoided through applying archival standards to the handling of a collection.

Tape

Magnetic tape is composed of several layers of materials: (1) a top coat that is the polymer binder in which the magnetic "pigment" is embedded (the top coat also includes lubricant, a head-cleaning agent, and carbon black, all of which aid in playback), and (2) the tape backing, which provides the substance to hold the binder and magnetic pigment. Sometimes a third layer called the "back coat" is added to cut down on friction and enable the tape to wind properly. The tape is stored on a reel and encased in a tape pack.

Problems that regularly arise in the preservation of tape are as follows:

- *Lubricant Loss:* Lubricants are added to the binder of a tape during the manufacturing process. This helps to ensure that friction does not compromise the tape. Over time, and with many playbacks of a tape, the lubricant wears down. Relubrication can sometimes salvage severely degraded magnetic tapes.
- *Dust Damage:* If magnetic tape becomes dusty, the dust will scratch the oxide layer of the tape during playback.
- *Binder Breakdown (Sticky-Shed Syndrome):* In the mid-seventies, half of the leading tape manufacturers changed the chemical composition of the binder used in their tape-manufacturing processes. The new binder later proved unstable; the coating of the tape becomes sticky and sheds oxide on its playback equipment in humid conditions.

Optical Media

Compact discs (CDs) and digital video discs (DVDs) are digital optical disc data storage formats. The form includes a polycarbonate (usually) plastic component with a center spindle hole, upon which are multiple recording areas. These areas are encoded with data (machine readable) as "pits," or small indentations. This data layer may be metallic or dye based. A layer of aluminum or gold is applied to the top surface and is protected by a coat of lacquer.

CDs in particular were heralded as a preservation medium at their initial release; however, they have proven highly susceptible to multiple forms of damage and loss—including scratches, label-based problems, and corrosion of the metal layer. Even "archival-quality" gold CDs and DVDs are no longer considered preservation media by most experts, though when they are stored in cold, dry conditions, they may survive up to a century. They are used most widely in memory institutions to provide access copies to material (not for storage masters).

Problems that regularly arise in the preservation of CDs and DVDs are as follows:

- *Scratches:* During normal handling, CDs and DVDs often become scratched. When the scratches occur on the clear side of the disc, they can often be repaired through plastic refills or polishing.
- *Dye Fading:* When the data layer is made of dye (rather than metal), the dye sometimes fades over time, rendering the data unreadable.
- *Bonding Failure:* The bonding on the edges of CDs and DVDs is often unstable and fails over time, allowing moisture and gasses to permeate the data area of the disc, causing failure.
- *Lack of Production Standards:* CDs and DVDs are produced in many factories, with highly variable quality control standards. As a result, one "batch" of CDs or DVDs may be compromised. Archivists are encouraged to ensure that they make multiple copies (one master, a working copy, and a safety copy is a good "rule of threes") and use CDs or DVDs from different batches for these three copies whenever possible.

Future of Preservation

The future of preservation always includes great uncertainty regarding what formats will persist, but also great certainty that there will be a need for preservationists of all kinds across all types of information organizations. With our increased reliance on ephemeral digital content comes further emphasis on preservation across all government, commercial, cultural, and scientific sectors.

Some of the emerging concerns, efforts, and practices in today's preservation environment are described below. They provide a glimpse into how rapidly the preservation environment is changing, how quickly preservationists must grapple with new challenges, and new areas where preservationists will be working in the future.

Web Archiving

Many experts argue that web archiving is among the least attended to and most important frontiers of preservation. In the coming years, much attention will be given to curation (selection, acquisition, cataloging, transforming) and preservation (long-term care) for web-based collections. Since 1996, the Internet Archive in the United States has been crawling and archiving snapshots of websites from across the Internet. The Wayback Machine provides open access to this web archive, which is the largest in the world. Other web-archiving initiatives include many national library efforts, and a significant number of academic library efforts, usually focused on particular topical areas. The International Internet Preservation Consortium is the broadest network of practitioners to date.

Digital Forensics

Digital forensic science is concerned with recovering data from digital devices. First prevalent in criminal investigations of computer-based crimes in the 1980s, applications of digital forensics tools now regularly extend to archival institutions. For these memory organizations, forensics tools and methods must address two fundamental issues that are not addressed by the digital forensics industry but are part of the key practices of preservationists: workflows for incorporating forensic practices into the archival/library/museum content life cycle, and mechanisms for providing public access to the recovered data. The BitCurator Open Source software developed by the University of North Carolina at Chapel Hill School of Information and Library Science and the Maryland Institute for Technology in the Humanities is the most prevalent set of forensics documentation, tools, and approaches in the library, archives, and museum fields.

Hypermedia and Digital Art

Documenting and preserving "variable media" such as hypermedia and digital art installations requires collective approaches that blend art, science, and technology. Many of the pathbreaking publications and artworks of the 1960s forward have occurred in digital forms, and they are notoriously difficult to archive due to the constant technological changes that impact their contexts and compromise their renderability. Efforts to address one of the most complex digital preservation challenges of the early twenty-first century thus far have yielded such experiments as the Archive of Digital Art (ADA, formerly known as the Database of Virtual Art).

EXAMPLE OF DIGITAL ART PRESERVATION

In 2004, an important moment in digital art preservation and emulation experimentation took place through the Guggenheim Museum/Daniel Langlois Foundation exhibition "Seeing Double: Emulation in Theory and Practice." The exhibition featured art in its original, endangered media environments and juxtaposed these side-by-side with new versions emulated in new media environments.

EXAMPLES OF GAME PRESERVATION

Game preservation has been a vibrant subfield of preservation activity since the 1980s. Such projects as Preserving Virtual Worlds (University of Illinois, Rochester Institute of Technology, Stanford University, and University of Maryland) work on computer gaming and interactive fiction as blurred genres of content. Other initiatives emulate game environments of the past (e.g., 1980-games.com and DOSGamesArchive.com) and preserve the hardware and software environments in physical form (e.g., the American Classic Arcade Museum).

Social Media

The challenges of preserving social media come in three main forms: IP and legal issues around privacy for material that is produced in such a public arena, technological challenges, and volume/speed of creation. In 2010, one of the major social media sites—Twitter—donated all of its public tweets to the Library of Congress for preservation and research.

TEXTBOX 34.5

Topic for Discussion

How does selection work as a principle of preservation? What effects (intentional or not) might selection have on historical perspectives of a particular moment in time?

Conclusion

Curation and preservation are information management "must knows" for caretakers of both analog and digital content types. This chapter has introduced these related concepts, highlighted key milestones in preservation development, and provided an overview of current preservation practices across a range of media types. It has also described various "real-world" scenarios in which curation and preservation take place on a routine basis, and the significant work ahead for libraries, archives, and all other curation and preservation realms.

Appendix 34.1: The Brittle Books Phenomenon

William James Barrow was one of the early researchers on acid deterioration, and his name has become synonymous with the "brittle books" phenomenon and early responses to this anticipated crisis. Barrow was a researcher in the paper chemistry field who grew concerned about the acid deterioration of wood-pulp paper and invented several methods to slow this deterioration (including lamination and deacidification). Beginning in the 1930s, he advocated strongly for the adoption of paper preservation, and by the 1950s, his work gained the attention and strong backing of the Council on Library Resources (CLR) and the American Library Association (ALA). Barrow conducted tests that used temperature elevation as a means of speeding the deterioration of wood-pulp paper, and his findings raised alarms throughout the library community. Many libraries (including the Library of Congress) adopted deacidification processes to counter Barrow's predicted demise of up to 97 percent of wood-pulp books, newspapers, maps, and other publications over a fifty-year period.[13] Barrow's most extreme findings were eventually discredited, but the very real acid-based problems inherent in wood-pulp paper continued to provoke a sense of urgency regarding the preservation of the written record throughout the library community.

Notes

1. George Santayana, "The Santayana Edition," last modified August 20, 2014, http://iat.iupui.edu/santayana/content/santayana-quotations.
2. National Historic Preservation Act of 1966, Pub. L. 89-665 80, Stat. 89-665, http://www.achp.gov/docs/nhpa%202008-final.pdf.
3. The Library of Congress, Yale University, and the New York Public Library.
4. George Bobinski. *Libraries and Librarianship: Sixty Years of Challenge and Change, 1945–2005.* New York, NY: Scarecrow Press, 2007, 105–110.
5. ALA's "Committee on Preservation of Library Materials," 1970; AIC's "Book and Paper Group," 1980; CLR's "Commission on Preservation and Access," 1986.
6. Bobinski, *Libraries and Librarianship*, 2007; NEDCC "History of the Northeast Document Conservation Center," last modified August 13, 2014, http://www.nedcc.org/about/history/overview; Preservation 101, "Introduction to Preservation," last modified June 30, 2013, http://unfacilitated.preservation101.org/session1/expl_whatis-libraries.asp.
7. National Endowment for the Humanities (NEH) U.S. Newspaper Program in 1982.
8. Bobinski, *Libraries and Librarianship*, 2007.
9. Anne R. Kenney and Nancy Y. McGovern, "The Five Organizational Stages of Digital Preservation," in *Digital Libraries: A Vision for the Twenty-First Century, a Festschrift to Honor Wendy Lougee* (Ann Arbor: Michigan Publishing, 2003), http://quod.lib.umich.edu/cgi/t/text/text-idx?c=spobooks;idno=bbv9812.0001.001;rgn=div1;view=text;cc=spobooks;node=bbv9812.0001.001%3A11.
10. From the Commission on Preservation and Access and Research Libraries Group's charge to the Task Force, 1994. John R. Garrett, "Task Force on Archiving of Digital Information," *D-lib Magazine*, last modified September 1995, http://dlib.org/dlib/september95/09garrett.html.
11. U.S. Copyright law allows up to three copies of a work to be made by cultural institutions for works that are endangered or damaged, so long as a replacement is not easily available. U.S. Copyright Act, 14 U.S.C. § Circ. 2, http://copyright.gov/title17/circ92.pdf.
12. Digital Preservation Outreach and Education (DPOE), "About DPOE," last modified June 25, 2014, http://www.digitalpreservation.gov/education.
13. Library of Congress, "Mass Deacidification," last modified July 1, 2014, http://www.loc.gov/preservation/about/deacid/index.html.

Katherine Skinner

35

Information Privacy and Cybersecurity

Cherie L. Givens

Information privacy and cybersecurity threats have become regular news topics. Changes in technology and threats to personal data from online activities have increased concerns about privacy and the need for security, particularly in online environments. Reports of data breaches[1] at major retailers such as Target and Neiman Marcus,[2] the likely theft of personal information from a major contractor of the U.S. Department of Homeland Security,[3] and the reported data breaches that have affected millions of patient health records[4] have increased concerns about the security of personal data and the need for increased cybersecurity. Changing privacy protections for social networking sites such as Facebook[5] and the large-scale data collection by the National Security Agency (NSA)[6] have left many wondering what has happened to our information privacy rights.

> Growing privacy concerns signal a need for changes in privacy and security policies, practices, and laws. They also offer the opportunity for information professionals to help shape the direction of future practices regarding information privacy and security.

Americans' concerns about online privacy and security are evidenced by a September 2013 Pew report[7] that examined adults' attitudes about anonymity, privacy, and security in the online environment. The results of the study of 792 Internet and smart-phone users indicate a desire for online privacy and concern about the adequacy of privacy protections currently available. For example, researchers found that "86% of Internet users have tried to use the Internet in ways to minimize the visibility of their digital footprints," and "55% of Internet users have taken steps to avoid observation by specific people, organizations, or the government."[8] According to the study, confidence in current legal privacy protections is low, with 68 percent of Internet users reporting that they find current privacy laws inadequate to protect privacy online. Participants cited a variety of privacy concerns, including compromises to e-mails or social networking accounts, theft of personally identifiable information, and damage to reputations.[9]

After completing this chapter, the reader should have an understanding of

- key information privacy concepts, as well as an awareness of laws that protect privacy and may limit privacy;

- Fair Information Practice Principles (FIPPs) and how these principles influence international agreements and guidelines to safeguard information privacy;
- threats to personal data, the role of government in improving cybersecurity, and basic measures information professionals can take to help ensure information privacy and security; and
- how and why information professionals should be involved in ensuring information privacy and assisting in cybersecurity efforts.

Definitions

Before discussing information privacy and cybersecurity further, it is important to define key terms.

- *Information Privacy:* Information privacy focuses on "the right of individuals and organizations to control the collection and sharing of their personal information without consent."[10] Failing to protect information privacy can impact the daily lives of individuals whose information is stolen or compromised, damage professional reputations, and inhibit the free exercise of our civil liberties.[11] Protecting information privacy requires implementing physical and virtual security measures.
- *Information Security:* Information security refers to the protection of data, in any form, from unauthorized access, disclosure, alteration, or destruction. This protection involves assessing and monitoring threats and risks to data, as well as establishing policies, procedures, and controls to preserve the confidentiality, integrity, and availability of data. It is easy to see how information privacy and information security work together.
- *Cybersecurity:* Cybersecurity is a form of information security. The U.S. Department of Homeland Security defines cybersecurity as the "activity or process, ability or capability, or state whereby information and communications systems and the information contained therein are protected from and/or defended against damage, unauthorized use or modification, or exploitation."[12] Cybersecurity can be thought of as information security in the online environment. The practice of cybersecurity is necessary to ensure information privacy in online environments.

The Right to Information Privacy

"Privacy issues exist in a wide range of information environments, including libraries, government agencies, hospitals, businesses, institutes of higher education, and any environment where personal data is collected."

Privacy issues exist in a wide range of information environments, including libraries, government agencies, hospitals, businesses, institutes of higher education, and any environment where personal data is collected. Individuals in most parts of the world, including the United States, Canada, and the European Union, enjoy privacy rights and expect that those rights will be protected when they provide or seek information in information environments and when they use websites that purport to have privacy policies and security. Every individual needs to feel free to seek and share information and ideas without scrutiny or other negative effects.[13] Thus, because information professionals are tasked with managing information, they benefit from an understanding of the laws affecting the collection, use, and storage of personal data.

Although the word "privacy" does not appear in the U.S. Constitution, language in the Bill of Rights reflects a focus on protecting privacy. Amendments I,[14] IV,[15] V,[16] and XIV[17] address aspects of privacy. The right to privacy was addressed in 1890 by attorneys Samuel Warren and Louis Brandeis in their seminal essay "The Right to Privacy" where they defined privacy as "the right to be let alone."[18] Brandeis, who later became a U.S. Supreme Court justice, affirmed this definition of privacy in the context of government action in his dissent in *Olmstead v. United States.*[19]

TEXTBOX 35.1

Information Privacy Terms

Certain terms are used to identify personal data in the context of U.S. privacy laws. It is helpful to have an understanding of the meanings of these terms and their relationship to one another.

- *Personal Data:* "information relating to an identified or identifiable person. What constitutes personal data varies by country."[1]
- *Personally Identifiable Information (PII):* a term "used in U.S. privacy law to refer to personal data. Countries differ on their identification of the types of personal data that are considered PII."[2]
- *Sensitive Personal Data:* is a "subset of PII that includes data that is specifically protected. In the U.S. this includes social security numbers, identifiable health records and identifiable financial records."[3]

---

1. Cherie Givens, *Information Privacy Fundamentals for Librarians and Information Professionals* (Lanham, MD: Rowman & Littlefield, 2014), glossary.
2. Ibid.
3. Ibid.

Information Privacy Protections in the United States

In the United States, information privacy rights are protected through a combination of legislation, regulation, and self-regulation known as the sectoral approach.[20] Several federal laws provide protections for different sectors of privacy, including the activity of children online, as well as education records, financial records, health information, and records containing personally identifiable information (PII) kept by the federal government.

A number of federal agencies also assist in preserving privacy rights by exercising regulating functions related to privacy, including the Federal Trade Commission (FTC) and the Federal Communications Commission (FCC). Some agencies are involved in federal privacy policy making, including the U.S. Department of Commerce, the U.S. Office of Management and Budget, and the U.S. Department of Justice. Others, such as the Office of Civil Rights of the U.S. Department of Health and Human Services, are empowered to enforce actions. Private-sector industries also engage in self-regulation, providing guidance on privacy practices to members of associations or groups.[21]

Federal Laws that Protect Information Privacy

Information professionals work in a variety of settings and manage a range of types of information. Thus, the information they manage, the clients they serve, and the activities they are involved with to collect and share data may be governed by federal laws that protect information privacy.

CHILDREN'S ONLINE PRIVACY PROTECTION ACT OF 1998 (COPPA)

COPPA[22] is a federal law created to protect the online information privacy of children under the age of thirteen. It regulates the collection and use of information that children under the age of thirteen provide to commercial website operators. The act applies to operators of commercial websites and online services such as mobile apps. The act is applicable to websites that do not specifically target children but have "actual knowledge" that information they are collecting is from children under the age of thirteen and from "websites or online services that have actual knowledge that they are collecting personal information directly from users of another website or online service directed to children."[23] Website operators for whom COPPA is applicable must adhere to rules for collecting and notifying users about the collection of personal data.

FAMILY EDUCATIONAL RIGHTS AND PRIVACY ACT (FERPA) AND THE PROTECTION OF PUPIL RIGHTS AMENDMENT (PPRA)

Information professionals working in education settings or with access to education records should be aware of the privacy protections provided by the Family Educational Rights and Privacy Act (FERPA). Education records are provided special privacy protections in the United States. FERPA limits the allowed disclosure of education records without the student's consent. Disclosure without written consent is generally allowed only for legitimate educational uses, health and safety emergencies, and release to state and local authorities to whom such disclosure is allowed pursuant to state statutes.[24] Directory information may be released without consent if students or the parents of students under the age of eighteen are notified ahead of time and given a reasonable time to request that the information not be disclosed.[25]

The Protection of Pupil Rights Amendment (PPRA) amended FERPA in 1978. PPRA is applicable to educational programs receiving funding from the U.S. Department of Education. Under PPRA, written consent must be obtained from parents of minor children before those children can participate in surveys, analyses, or evaluations seeking information about sensitive subjects.[26] The No Child Left Behind Act of 2001 expanded PPRA's protections that limit the collection and disclosure of sensitive information to federally funded elementary and secondary schools. These schools must enact policies regarding collection and disclosure, allow parents access to inspect surveys, provide notice of survey activities, and make available to parents the right to opt out of sharing student information for commercial purposes.[27]

GRAMM-LEACH-BLILEY ACT AND THE FAIR CREDIT REPORTING ACT

The Gramm-Leach-Bliley Act of 1999 applies to private financial records. It requires that financial institutions protect the consumer information they collect. Financial institutions are also required to inform customers about their information-sharing practices.[28]

The Fair Credit Reporting Act (FCRA) is another consumer protection act. Enacted in 1970, it was created to ensure that consumer reporting agencies adopt reasonable procedures in credit reporting and provide consumers with the ability to access and correct the information about them that is contained in credit reports. Under FCRA, the use of consumer credit reports is limited to certain "permissible purposes."[29]

The FCRA was amended by the Fair and Accurate Credit Transaction Act (FACT Act) of 2003. "The FACT Act requires that the three major credit reporting agencies provide consumers with free copies of their credit reports every 12 months" and allows individuals who may have been the victim of credit fraud to place alerts in these files.[30]

THE HEALTH INSURANCE PORTABILITY ACT OF 1996 (HIPAA)

The Health Insurance Portability Act of 1996 (HIPAA) was established to protect health information. HIPAA's "privacy rule" addresses how health information may be used and disclosed. It functions to balance privacy with the need to transmit health information.[31] HIPAA applies to health-care providers of all sizes, providers of health-care plans, and health-care clearinghouses.

Under HIPAA, all individually identifiable health information is considered "protected health information" (PHI).[32] "HIPAA includes a security rule that mandates how PHI must be secured and contains a notice-of-breach requirement requiring notice to those whose PHI has been breached. Information professionals seeking positions in health-related environments will benefit from reviewing HIPAA's privacy and security requirements."[33]

THE PRIVACY ACT OF 1974

The Privacy Act of 1974 regulates the government's collection, use, and disclosure of personal information about individuals contained in systems of records that allow data to be searched and retrieved through the use of personal identifiers, such as individuals' names or Social Security numbers. It provides individuals with a right to review information about themselves and amend or correct incorrect information.[34]

Federal Laws that May Limit Privacy

In addition to the laws that protect information privacy, there are a few to be aware of that may limit information privacy. These include the Foreign Intelligence Surveillance Act (FISA)[35] and the USA PATRIOT Act,[36] which pertain to terrorism investigation.

"Under FISA the government may conduct electronic surveillance to collect foreign intelligence in the United States. FISA establishes standards for the use of electronic surveillance and government requests."[37] The USA PATRIOT Act expands the ability of the U.S. government to seek information under administrative subpoenas and "expands the powers of law enforcement for surveillance and investigation to deter terrorism. Its enforcement accordingly places limits on information privacy protection."[38]

State-Level Protection of Information Privacy

States have also enacted privacy protections. In some instances, these protections may be more comprehensive than existing federal laws. Privacy protections may be found in a number of state constitutions and statutes. The following states address privacy specifically in their state constitutions: Alaska, Arizona, California, Florida, Hawaii, Illinois, Louisiana, Montana, South Carolina, and Washington.[39]

TEXTBOX 35.2

Topic for Discussion

How do information privacy and cybersecurity impact the work done by information professionals?

Information Privacy Protections in Canada

Like the United States, Canada works with businesses toward the goal of privacy compliance. Its approach to privacy is more comprehensive than that of the United States. Sections 7 and 8 of Canada's Charter of Rights and Freedoms have been interpreted to offer privacy protections. They provide that "Everyone has the right to life, liberty and security of the person and the right not to be deprived thereof except in accordance with the principles of fundamental justice. Everyone has the right to be secure against unreasonable search or seizure."[40]

Canada has two main federal laws that govern the handling of personal data: the Privacy Act of 1983 and the Personal Information Protection and Electronic Documents Act of 2000 (PIPEDA). The Privacy Act governs the handling of personal data by federal agencies and departments. It provides individuals with a right to access personal information about themselves in the government's possession and request correction of incorrect information. PIPEDA governs the private sector's collection, use, and disclosure of personal data. PIPEDA allows individuals to request access to information collected about them and correct inaccuracies.[41] Information professionals working in Canada should consult the Office of the Privacy Commissioner[42] of Canada and provincial privacy offices' websites, which offer a wealth of privacy information, tutorials, and teaching materials on the topic of information privacy.

Fair Information Practice Principles

Fair Information Practice Principles (FIPPs) "are a widely accepted framework of principles used to evaluate systems, processes, or programs that affect individual privacy."[43] The FIPPs provide guidance concerning the handling of personal data. "Understanding and being able to apply recognized fair information privacy practices is necessary for responsible handling of personal information."[44]

The FIPPs have their origins in a 1973 report by the U.S. Department of Health, Education & Welfare's advisory committee on Automated Personal Data, which indicated that an individual's privacy was "poorly protected" under the law and existing record-keeping practices. The 1973 report recommended that a federal code of information practice be enacted.[45]

> "Fair Information Practice Principles provide guidance concerning the handling of personal data."

A 2011 White House report, *National Strategy for Trusted Identities in Cyberspace: Enhancing Online Choice, Efficiency, Security, and Privacy*, identified the universal application of FIPPs as "the basis for confidence and trust in online transactions."[46] The report includes a description of the principles, along with guidance on how organizations can comply with the principles. Both are reproduced below.

- *Transparency:* Organizations should be transparent and notify individuals regarding collection, use, dissemination, and maintenance of personally identifiable information (PII).
- *Individual Participation:* Organizations should involve the individual in the process of using PII and, to the extent practicable, seek individual consent for the collection, use, dissemination, and maintenance of PII. Organizations should also provide mechanisms for appropriate access, correction, and redress regarding use of PII.
- *Purpose Specification:* Organizations should specifically articulate the authority that permits the collection of PII and specifically articulate the purpose or purposes for which the PII is intended to be used.
- *Data Minimization:* Organizations should only collect PII that is directly relevant and necessary to accomplish the specified purpose(s) and only retain PII for as long as is necessary to fulfill the specified purpose(s).
- *Use Limitation:* Organizations should use PII solely for the purpose(s) specified in the notice. Sharing PII should be for a purpose compatible with the purpose for which the PII was collected.
- *Data Quality and Integrity:* Organizations should, to the extent practicable, ensure that PII is accurate, relevant, timely, and complete.
- *Security:* Organizations should protect PII (in all media) through appropriate security safeguards against risks such as loss, unauthorized access or use, destruction, modification, or unintended or inappropriate disclosure.
- *Accountability and Auditing:* Organizations should be accountable for complying with these principles, providing training to all employees and contractors who use PII, and auditing the actual use of PII to demonstrate compliance with these principles and all applicable privacy protection requirements.[47]

Global Information Privacy and Security Practices

Fair Information Practice Principles have influenced the development of international guidelines such as the Organization for Economic Co-operation and Development's *Guidelines Governing the Protection of Privacy and Transborder Data Flows of Personal Data* (OECD Guidelines).[1] They are widely recognized and applied by the OECD's thirty-four member countries, including the United States and Canada. Fair information practice principles have been implemented by other international associations and countries to ensure the privacy and security of personal data and to assist in the free flow of data across borders. Examples include the European Union's Data Directive[2] and the Asia-Pacific Economic Cooperation (APEC) Privacy Framework.[3]

1. "Organisation for Economic Co-Operation and Development, Recommendation of the Council Concerning Guidelines Governing the Protection of Privacy and Transborder Flows of Personal Data (2013)," OECD Privacy Framework, www.oecd.org/sti/ieconomy/2013-oecd-privacy-guidelines.pdf.
2. "Directive 95/46/EC of the European Parliament and of the Council of 24 October 1995 on the Protection of Individuals with Regard to the Processing of Personal Data and on the Free Movement of Such Data," http://eur-lex.europa.eu/LexUriServ/LexUriServ.do?uri=CELEX:31995L0046:en:HTML.
3. "Privacy Framework," Asia-Pacific Economic Cooperation (APEC) (Singapore: APEC Secretariat, 2005), http://www.apec.org/Groups/Committee-on-Trade-and-Investment/~/media/Files/Groups/ECSG/05_ecsg_privacyframewk.ashx.

Cybersecurity and Threats to Data Protection

The importance of cybersecurity continues to grow in response to society's expanding reliance on the Internet. Growing numbers of individuals now perform daily activities online, including shopping, banking, teleworking, scheduling appointments, and completing online forms that request personal data. Increased use of the Internet has brought increasing dangers from hackers, phishing scams, viruses, and more. Rising numbers of successful cyberattacks are reported in the media.

Given these online dangers, the need to practice cybersecurity and educate others about threats to personal data and safe online practices is imperative. Individuals need training to understand the dangers of clicking on unknown links in e-mails and unknown attachments, as well as downloading programs and suspicious content from the web. They need to be made aware of the dangers of providing too much information on social media sites and the security threats posed by malware and hackers that can compromise an entire organization and place proprietary/trade secret information and personal data at risk. Information professionals can play important roles supporting cybersecurity efforts and educating others about information security.

Government Cybersecurity Initiatives

Recognizing the importance of information security to economic and national security interests, the U.S. government enacted the Federal Information Security Management Act (FISMA) in 2002. FISMA, Title III of the E-Government Act (Public Law 107-347), requiring that federal agencies develop and implement agency-wide information security programs to

"Information professionals can play important roles supporting cybersecurity efforts and educating others about information security."

safeguard information and information systems that support "the operations and assets" of agencies. FISMA applies to the operations and assets of the agencies themselves and of those provided by another agency, contractor, or another source.[48] FISMA represents one of the earliest cybersecurity initiatives of the federal government.

A Framework for Improving Cybersecurity

In February 2013, President Obama issued Executive Order 13636, Improving Critical Infrastructure Cybersecurity.[49] This order directed the National Institute of Standards and Technology (NIST) to work with stakeholders, including those from private industry, to create a voluntary framework to reduce cyber-risks to critical U.S. infrastructure. In February 2014, NIST released the initial version of the *Framework for Improving Critical Infrastructure Cybersecurity*. The framework represents a collaboration between government and industry. It is based on existing standards, guidelines, and practices, as well as input from professionals in the security and privacy communities.[50]

The framework includes a methodology to address the privacy implications of cybersecurity activities. While not mandatory, it includes advice for organizations to "consider how . . . their cybersecurity program[s] might incorporate privacy principles."[51] These include measures that are in keeping with the Fair Information Practice Principles (FIPPs) discussed earlier. Information privacy and security professionals have already begun using the framework to assess and improve their cybersecurity programs.[52]

Big Data Concerns

In May 2014, the Executive Office of the President released a report describing their findings based on a ninety-day review of big data and privacy. The study focused on how big data is being used by private industry, academia, and the government.[53] As part of the study, the administration solicited public opinion about these issues through a survey. The findings indicated that most of the 24,092 respondents felt strongly about data use and collection practices. They were very concerned about data storage and use; the need for transparency about data use; legal standards and oversight; and the collection of video, audio, and telecommunication data. Based on their analysis of survey results, the administration concluded that "respondents were most wary of how intelligence and law enforcement agencies are collecting and using data about them, particularly when they have little insight into these practices."[54]

This report highlighted potential benefits of big data analytics while acknowledging concerns about data protection in online environments. The report's discussion of data brokers points out that these brokers are unregulated and that their profiles of consumers can include information that is both factual and inferred. This information may be collected without the knowledge or consent of the individual and can be used in ways that are discriminatory.[55] There is also no consensus on "do not track" policies, leaving online users in limbo about what to expect when they ask not to be tracked. The report's findings indicate the need to address these issues related to big data and privacy (see also chapter 28, "Demonstrating Value: Assessment," for more information about big data).

Basic Measures to Help Ensure Information Privacy and Security

Organizations can take basic measures to help ensure information privacy and security by tracking and evaluating how the organization collects, uses, stores, shares, secures, and disposes of data; performing privacy audits; and providing training to employees. Documenting these data practices through policies made available to customers demonstrates transparency and emphasizes the organization's commitment to information privacy and security (see also chapter 29, "Information Policy").

Privacy and Security Policies

Every organization that collects personal information should provide its privacy policy to customers and users. This policy should document the organization's data practices, including security measures, and provide assurance to users that the organization takes privacy seriously. A well-written privacy policy explains what information is being collected, how the information is used, and with whom it may be shared. It should be easy to understand and readily accessible. Documenting and following a privacy policy assists in good customer relations and sends a message to regulators that information privacy is a priority for the organization.

Businesses often have multiple privacy and security policies for a variety of reasons, including multiple locations, websites, and differing services. Some privacy policies are internal and serve to guide those working in a company, while others are designed to inform both internal and external audiences. All policies directed to and shared with customers and other outside individuals must be understood and supported by employees. External-facing policies and internal procedures must align. Privacy programs should encompass all of an organization's privacy practices and actions necessary to ensure privacy.

Track and Evaluate Data Collection, Use, Risk, and Security

Tracking and evaluating how an organization collects, uses, stores, shares, secures, and disposes of data is a necessary initial step in planning a privacy policy. Employees from all divisions must be involved to help determine where data is housed and how it is used. Information assets should also be clearly identified and inventoried, and their sensitivity levels need to be determined. Security measures should be implemented in accordance with the level of risk and the sensitivity of the information.

Privacy Audit

Performing a privacy audit,[56] or assessment of how an organization manages privacy risks, is a necessary task to get a baseline assessment of how well an organization is protecting data. Privacy audits involve reviewing all documentation addressing privacy, including privacy policies, procedures, and checklists. The flow of data through an organization and data-handling practices are assessed. Audits may also focus on compliance and examine whether privacy policies and procedures are being followed. Privacy audits can determine areas for improvement and identify gaps in security or compliance.

Training

Privacy training for all employees should be a priority. Everyone working in an organization needs to have access to a copy of the privacy policy. In addition to ongoing privacy training, employees must be accountable for implementing the organization's privacy policies and procedures. Periodic specialized training sessions focused on the work of individual units and the implementation of accountability measures can help ensure that privacy remains a high priority.

The Role of Information Professionals

Information professionals are in an opportune position to take the lead in information privacy education and management and to assist in cybersecurity efforts to ensure privacy rights. They are on the front lines addressing information privacy and security issues. They

> "Information professionals are in an opportune position to take the lead in information privacy education and management and to assist in cybersecurity efforts to ensure privacy rights."

can apply their expertise in managing information to identify and understand information privacy issues, apply Fair Information Practice Principles, create privacy policies, manage privacy programs, and instruct others in privacy literacy. Information professionals can prepare clients and coworkers for the online threats they will encounter by providing a basic understanding of vulnerabilities and measures that can be taken to protect users while online. The role of information professionals is to set policy, ensure information privacy, and educate others. They should also seek ways to be involved in decision making and implementation of information privacy and cybersecurity efforts.

Conclusion

The fields of information privacy and cybersecurity continue to grow and change in response to changes in technology, threats to personal data, laws, and industry practices. Information professionals can take a leading role in shaping policy, advocating for privacy rights, and instructing others in the safeguarding of their personal data. It is time to become involved in discussions aimed at shaping information privacy and security policies, best practices, and laws.

Notes

1. "The unauthorized access or acquisition of computerized data that compromises or has likely compromised the security, confidentiality, or integrity of information that relates to an identified or identifiable person or persons. Breaches may be intentional or unintentional." Cherie Givens, *Information Privacy Fundamentals for Librarians and Information Professionals* (Lanham, MD: Rowman & Littlefield, 2014), glossary.
2. Craig A. Newman and Daniel L. Stein, "Who Should Pay for Data Theft?" *Bloomberg Businessweek*, last modified February 20, 2014, http://www.businessweek.com/articles/2014-02-20/who-should-pay-for-data-theft.
3. Zack Whittaker, "US Contractor Firm That Vetted Snowden Suffers Major Breach; Data Likely Snatched," ZDNet, last modified August 6, 2014, http://www.zdnet.com/us-contractor-firm-that-vetted-snowden-suffers-major-breach-data-likely-snatched-7000032397.
4. Erin McCann, "HIPAA Data Breaches Climb 138 Percent," *Healthcare IT News*, last modified February 6, 2014, http://www.healthcareitnews.com/news/hipaa-data-breaches-climb-138-percent.
5. Brian Fung, "Your Facebook Privacy Settings Are about to Change. Again," *Washington Post*, last modified April 4, 2014, http://www.washingtonpost.com/blogs/the-switch/wp/2014/04/08/your-facebook-privacy-settings-are-about-to-change-again.
6. Barton Gellman, Julie Tate, and Ashkan Soltani, "In NSA-Intercepted Data, Those Not Targeted Far Outnumber the Foreigners Who Are," *Washington Post*, last modified July 5, 2014, http://www.washingtonpost.com/world/national-security/in-nsa-intercepted-data-those-not-targeted-far-outnumber-the-foreigners-who-are/2014/07/05/8139adf8-045a-11e4-8572-4b1b969b6322_story.html.
7. Lee Rainie, Sara Kiesler, Ruogu Kang, and Mary Madden, "Anonymity, Privacy, and Security Online," PewResearch Internet Project, last modified September 5, 2013, http://www.pewinternet.org/2013/09/05/anonymity-privacy-and-security-online.
8. Ibid., 2.
9. Ibid., 2.
10. Givens, *Information Privacy Fundamentals*, 2014, glossary.
11. Ibid., chap. 1.
12. National Initiative for Cybersecurity Careers and Studies, "Cyber Glossary," Department of Homeland Security, last modified June 26, 2014, http://niccs.us-cert.gov/glossary#cybersecurity.

Cherie L. Givens

13. Givens, *Information Privacy Fundamentals*, 2014, chap. 2.
14. U.S. Const. amend. I: "Congress shall make no law respecting an establishment of religion, or prohibiting the free exercise thereof; or abridging the freedom of speech, or of the press; or the right of the people peaceably to assemble, and to petition the government for a redress of grievances." http://www.uscon stitution.net/const.pdf.
15. U.S. Const. amend. IV: "The right of the people to be secure in their persons, houses, papers, and effects, against unreasonable searches and seizures, shall not be violated, and no warrants shall issue, but upon probable cause, supported by oath or affirmation, and particularly describing the place to be searched, and the persons or things to be seized." http://www.usconstitution.net/const.pdf.
16. U.S. Const. amend. V: "No person shall be held to answer for a capital, or otherwise infamous crime, unless on a presentment or indictment of a grand jury, except in cases arising in the land or naval forces, or in the militia, when in actual service in time of war or public danger; nor shall any person be subject for the same offense to be twice put in jeopardy of life or limb; nor shall be compelled in any criminal case to be a witness against himself, nor be deprived of life, liberty, or property, without due process of law; nor shall private property be taken for public use, without just compensation." http://www.usconstitution.net/const.pdf.
17. U.S. Const. amend. XIV, § 1: "All persons born or naturalized in the United States, and subject to the jurisdiction thereof, are citizens of the U.S. and of the state wherein they reside. No state shall make or enforce any law which shall abridge the privileges or immunities of citizens of the United States; nor shall any state deprive any person of life, liberty, or property, without due process of law; nor deny to any person within its jurisdiction the equal protection of the laws." http://www.usconstitution.net/const.pdf.
18. Samuel Warren and Louis Brandeis, "The Right to Privacy," *Harvard Law Review* 4, no. 5 (December 15, 1890): 193, http://groups.csail.mit.edu/mac/classes/6.805/articles/privacy/Privacy_brand_warr2.html.
19. Olmstead v. United States, 277 U.S. 438, 478-79 (1928), *Justia*, last modified February 21, 2014, https://supreme.justia.com/cases/federal/us/277/438/case.html.
20. Givens, *Information Privacy Fundamentals*, 2014, chap. 3.
21. Ibid.
22. Bureau of Consumer Protection Center, "The Children's Online Privacy Protection Act of 1998 (COPPA)," 5 U.S.C. 6501-6505, Federal Trade Commission, http://www.ftc.gov/ogc/coppa1.htm.
23. Bureau of Consumer Protection Center, "Complying with COPPA: Frequently Asked Questions; A Guide for Business and Parents and Small Entity Compliance Guide," Federal Trade Commission, last modified August 29, 2014, http://www.business.ftc.gov/documents/Complying-with-COPPA-Frequently-Asked-Questions.
24. Family Educational Rights and Privacy Act (FERPA), 20 U.S.C. § 1232g, http://www.gpo.gov/fdsys/pkg/USCODE-2012-title20/pdf/USCODE-2012-title20-chap31-subchaplll-part4-sec1232g.pdf.
25. "Family Educational Rights and Privacy Act (FERPA)," U.S. Department of Education, last modified March 26, 2013, http://www.ed.gov/policy/gen/guid/fpco/ferpa/index.html.
26. Protection of Pupil Rights, 20 U.S. Code § 1232H, GPO, http://www.gpo.gov/fdsys/granule/USCODE-2010-title20/USCODE-2010-title20-chap31-subchaplll-part4-sec1232h/content-detail.html.
27. No Child Left Behind (NCLB) Act of 2001, Pub. L. No. 107-110, § 115, Stat. 1425 (2002), http://www2.ed.gov/policy/elsec/leg/esea02/107-110.pdf.
28. Gramm-Leach-Bliley Act, Pub. L. 106-102, 113 Stat. 1338. The Bureau of Consumer Protection provides information for institutions on how to comply with the Gramm-Leach-Bliley Act as well as helpful information for consumers at http://business.ftc.gov/privacy-and-security/gramm-leach-bliley-act.
29. The complete text of the Fair Credit Reporting Act (FCRA), 15 U.S.C. § 1681 et seq., is available at http://www.ftc.gov/os/statutes/031224fcra.pdf.
30. Givens, *Information Privacy Fundamentals*, chap. 3.
31. "OCR Privacy Brief: Summary of the HIPAA Privacy Rule," United States Department of Health and Human Services, May 2003, 1, http://www.hhs.gov/ocr/privacy/hipaa/understanding/summary/privacy summary.pdf.
32. Ibid., 3-4.
33. Givens, *Information Privacy Fundamentals*, chap. 3.
34. Office of Privacy and Civil Liberties, Privacy Act of 1974 5 U.S.C. § 5529, United States Department of Justice, http://www.gpo.gov/fdsys/pkg/USCODE-2012-title5/pdf/USCODE-2012-title5-partl-chap5-subchapll-sec552a.pdf.

35. Foreign Intelligence Surveillance Act (FISA), 50 U.S.C. §§ 1801–1811 (1978), http://www.gpo.gov/fdsys/pkg/STATUTE-92/pdf/STATUTE-92-Pg1783.pdf.
36. The full text of the USA PATRIOT Act, Pub. L. 107-56 (Oct. 26, 2001), is available through the U.S. Government Printing Office at http://www.gpo.gov/fdsys/pkg/PLAW-107publ56/pdf/PLAW-107publ56.pdf.
37. Givens, *Information Privacy Fundamental*, chap. 3.
38. Ibid.
39. National Conference of State Legislatures, "Privacy Protections in State Constitutions," n.d., http://www.ncsl.org/research/telecommunications-and-information-technology/privacy-protections-in-state-constitutions.aspx (accessed October 28, 2013).
40. Canadian Charter of Rights and Freedoms, §§ 7–8, Part I of the Constitution Act, 1982, http://laws-lois.justice.gc.ca/eng/const/page-15.html.
41. "Legal Information Related to the Privacy Act," Office of the Privacy Commissioner of Canada, last modified July 22, 2014, http://www.priv.gc.ca/leg_c/leg_c_a_e.asp; "Legal Information Related to the PIPEDA," Office of the Privacy Commissioner of Canada, last modified August 31, 2014, http://www.priv.gc.ca/leg_c/leg_c_p_e.asp.
42. Office of the Privacy Commission of Canada, last modified October 28, 2014, https://www.priv.gc.ca/index_e.asp.
43. White House, *National Strategy for Trusted Identities in Cyberspace: Enhancing Online Choice, Efficiency, Security, and Privacy*, April 2011, http://www.whitehouse.gov/sites/default/files/rss_viewer/NSTICstrategy_041511.pdf.
44. Givens, *Information Privacy Fundamentals*, chap. 7.
45. Secretary's Advisory Committee on Automated Personal Data Systems, "Records, Computers, and the Rights of Citizens," No. (OS) 73-94, U.S. Department of Health, Education & Welfare, 1973, http://www.justice.gov/opcl/docs/rec-com-rights.pdf.
46. White House, *National Strategy for Trusted Identities in Cyberspace*, April 2011.
47. Ibid., appendix A.
48. National Institute of Standards and Technology, "FISMA Detailed Overview," last modified April 1, 2014, http://csrc.nist.gov/groups/SMA/fisma/overview.html.
49. Critical infrastructure has been defined by the Executive Office to include the systems and assets that are critical to national security, economic security, and health and safety. Jaikumar Vijayan, "Obama Executive Order Redefines Critical Infrastructure," *Computerworld*, last modified February 14, 2013 http://www.computerworld.com/article/2494979/security0/obama-executive-order-redefines-critical-infrastructure.html.
50. National Institute of Standards and Technology, *Framework for Improving Critical Cybersecurity Infrastructure*, version 1.0, last modified February 12, 2014, http://www.nist.gov/cyberframework/upload/cybersecurity-framework-021214.pdf.
51. Ibid., 16.
52. The framework and assessments were addressed in several sessions of the IAPP Global Privacy Summit in Washington, DC, March 4–6, 2014. Discussion included how some organizations have begun using the assessments and guidance. https://privacyassociation.org/conference/global-privacy-summit-2014.
53. "Big Data: Seizing Opportunities, Preserving Values," Executive Office of the President, last modified September 15, 2014, http://www.whitehouse.gov/issues/technology/big-data-review.
54. Ibid., 79.
55. Ibid., 44–45.
56. "An assessment that focuses on privacy risk which includes evaluation of all privacy documentation and examines how data flows through an organization as well as data handling practices." Givens, *Information Privacy Fundamentals*, glossary.

36

Intellectual Freedom

Barbara M. Jones

"Intellectual freedom" is a term used by information professionals to describe the individual's freedom to read, view, discuss, or interact with information in any format. With the expanding availability of online information and opportunities to create content online, user privacy has become an increasingly important element of intellectual freedom in the twenty-first century. Information consumers must be able to engage with or create content with their personal privacy intact, free from government or corporate intrusion.

In addition to raising new issues regarding user privacy, digital information technology has expanded the definition of intellectual freedom to include interaction. Digital technology enables more robust content creation by users, as well as new ways to engage with online content. For example, today's information consumer can write, watch, or participate in a performance. Consumers can play a video game or create an online game. Individuals can discuss legislation in an online community or read about it privately in a magazine or on the Internet. The term "intellectual freedom" covers all of these types of activities, formats, and content. And so the digital delivery of content in the twenty-first century has only made intellectual freedom more important and complex for information professionals, who are charged with providing users with access to a broad range of resources, in a variety of evolving formats, along with opportunities for users to engage with that content.

After completing this chapter, the reader should have an understanding of how issues related to intellectual freedom impact the practice of information professionals, especially those who work in libraries. This chapter also spotlights emerging areas of concern regarding intellectual freedom research, policy, and action, including

- academic freedom and other issues in higher education,
- privacy and surveillance,
- filters and other electronic barriers to information, and
- interactive and user-created content.

Intellectual Freedom Supports Democratic Values

Intellectual freedom has been framed in a number of compelling ways, including discourse analysis, new historical frameworks, and interdisciplinary cultural studies. As an ethical problem, it is viewed most often as the conflict of equally important values. But it is best known within its legal framework, based on the First Amendment of the Bill of Rights of the United States Constitution. Therefore, in the field of information studies, it fits comfortably in the area of the law and ethics of information. And, in reality, when all is said and done, most intellectual freedom issues must eventually be tested within the legal framework. At the same time, the study and practice of intellectual freedom is undoubtedly enriched by other academic fields and contexts.

Intellectual freedom is, above all, a practice based on democratic values. Social reformer Jane Addams emphasized that "action indeed is the sole medium of expression for ethics." Today, Rutgers University/Newark University chancellor Nancy Cantor adds, "Don't always look from the field into your world, look from the world into your field."[1] So, too, intellectual freedom is embedded in expressing values by providing information services and content to the community.

Information Organizations and Intellectual Freedom

Employees of information organizations practice intellectual freedom daily. For example, an exhibit of young adult (YA) vampire novels expresses the information organization's support for content much beloved by teens but sometimes controversial in the larger community. An information organization's decision to maintain unfiltered Internet access demonstrates a commitment to keeping information as unfettered and diverse as possible, and also demonstrates recognition that First Amendment–protected information should be available to those who seek it—whether on the Internet or in a print book. When developing the policy framework for the profession and for information organizations, intellectual freedom and privacy principles should be included—not only for legal reasons, but also to provide excellent and open access to a diverse world of information (see also chapter 33, "Open Access," and chapter 35, "Information Privacy and Cybersecurity").

Practicing intellectual freedom requires constant advocacy. Community members and politicians sometimes view the restriction of information as a "quick fix" for enormously expensive and complex social problems like teen suicide or gun violence. Intellectual freedom can be viewed as an inconvenient obstacle for creating what is perceived as a "safe" environment for youth. When a local high school student commits suicide, well-meaning parents may want to remove all young adult (YA) books about suicide from the curriculum and library. That is why education, advocacy, and civic engagement are often included in the assigned duties of information professionals. Intellectual freedom principles focus on reading and engaging with new and sometimes uncomfortable ideas, in an environment where the information seeker can consult with parents, teachers, information professionals, and other trusted community members. This is viewed as the strategy most likely to prepare people for college, family life, and the world of work.

The increasing importance of advocacy has led intellectual freedom practitioners to embrace the emerging field of action research and scholarship. Effective lines of communication, deep ties between information organizations and their communities, and civic engagement projects can reduce conflict and misunderstandings about an organization's collections and services. Intellectual freedom practitioners are increasingly testing these new approaches in order to prevent the expensive legal conflicts that can tear a community apart.

Best practices in information services rest on a foundation of well-developed, regularly updated policies (see also chapter 29, "Information Policy"). The most prominent policy formulation for intellectual freedom for information organizations currently lies in the *Intellectual Freedom Manual* published by the American Library Association (ALA). The Library

TEXTBOX 36.1

Topic for Discussion

How can information professionals handle sensitive issues such as abortion or anarchy without compromising intellectual freedom?

Barbara M. Jones

Bill of Rights (LBOR) is ALA's major policy document on intellectual freedom. While it has no legal force, the LBOR is based on the U.S. Bill of Rights and similar human rights–based documents. The Interpretations of the Library Bill of Rights allow ALA to retain core intellectual freedom principles and still address emerging issues such as the impact of technology, growing concerns over user privacy, and the impact of economic barriers and poverty on access to information. The Code of Ethics of the American Library Association is another core document affirming intellectual freedom and privacy.

Censorship and Library Collections

Censorship in the United States has a particular meaning. Unlike some countries, the United States does not have a national censorship board exercising "prior restraint" to publish a book or website. Thus, it sometimes appears that there is more information censorship in the United States than in other parts of the world, when in fact controversial information is more likely to be published and thus be vulnerable to the censors. For example, school libraries' collections are not based on a list of books mandated by the federal government. Instead, information professionals have the freedom to develop a collection that meets their users' information needs, although those decisions are sometimes challenged by those who wish to censor certain content.

> The first association many people make between libraries and intellectual freedom is Banned Books Week, which has become a national tradition since its inception in 1982 and receives more press coverage than any other library-related advocacy event related to censorship.
>
> Visit: www.bannedbooksweek.org

However, it is important to remember that employees of a public institution—be it a school, public, or academic library—are government officials. And so, if information is censored by a public school administrator or librarian, for example, that information has been removed by a government official. While in the United States this is more likely to be a locally contained incident, it is still government action against free speech, which can be a violation of the First Amendment.

Finally, U.S. information professionals or whistle-blowers tend to publicize censorship of information rather than hide it. For example, the American Library Association's annual Top Ten Banned Books List tallies the results of a challenge report database that collects information from information professionals and the general public. While information professionals in other countries may be more likely to hide these incidents for fear of retribution, the U.S. information profession has a long tradition of publicizing censorship attempts and advocating for the freedom to read.

In light of these issues regarding censorship, written collection development policies remain an important tool for guiding information professionals as they decide what to include in their collections, as well as what to exclude (see also chapter 25, "Managing Collections"). However, in the digital environment, open content cannot be refereed as easily. In addition to the open web, bundled journal collections are curated by vendors, not by local information professionals, and therefore some of the content may conflict with local collection development policies.

The Public Forum and Barriers to Open Information

The public forum analysis is a useful framework to help information professionals understand traditional and evolving areas of intellectual freedom. Sandra Braman[2] described this policy framework as "constitutional principles and the information spaces they create." This analysis depends upon the legal definition of the public forum and also the ideas promoted by the civic engagement community.

The public forum analysis considers the many barriers that limit total openness. Many of these barriers are ironically enabled by the same technology that erases barriers to open information. For example, the Internet has revolutionized health-care information. Searchers can discover the very latest information on the Ebola virus and act accordingly to protect themselves. But health-care information can also be filtered by software mounted on library computer terminals, so that students and faculty in Advanced Placement Biology cannot access this information because it may have sexually explicit words that are blocked. It is a two-edged sword that information professionals must be aware of.

The public forum was described in ancient times as agora—although women and lower classes were not included. German scholar Jürgen Habermas imagines a more inclusive public sphere to discuss and test ideas which then are used to formulate action plans for reforming civil society.

Source: Jürgen Habermas, *The Structural Transformation of the Public Sphere: An Inquiry into a Category of Bourgeois Society* (Cambridge, MA: MIT Press, 1989).

In the United States, the legal public forum doctrine defines three types of public forums where citizens can discuss and test ideas. Many information and cultural institutions are considered "limited public forums"—"limited" by time, place, and manner restrictions. (Libraries can set public hours, for example.) In the United States, library accessibility policy tends to be very inclusive. Based on ethics, policies, and civil rights laws and regulations, the limited public forum of a public library space is open to everyone regardless of citizenship status, race or ethnic identity, gender, age, disability, or economic status. The First Amendment also establishes limits on openness, including defining unprotected speech to include obscenity and child pornography, and determining content harmful to minors by state statute. The word "pornography" used alone is not a term of law. A court must determine whether or not content is protected. Such legal distinctions must be understood so that information professionals can make decisions and communicate with others about their decisions using accurate definitions, not emotional assumptions.

Intellectual Freedom in Higher Education

The twenty-first century has ushered in many complex intellectual freedom challenges in higher education—a surprise for those who assumed that the tradition of academic freedom would prevail when barriers to free speech arose. But the threats to information access in higher education are arguably among the most politicized and far reaching. In an economic downturn, intellectual freedom is often the victim of influential donors who try to influence how contributed funds are allocated, and state and federal governments as they seek ways to reduce spending.

One example among many is the recent South Carolina state budget discussions in early 2014 threatening to reduce spending by two state universities on LGBT materials. After a national outcry that included the information and civil liberties communities, the budget signed by the governor did not specifically mention or prohibit the purchase of LGBT materials. However, the approved budget included the caveat that the schools need to spend funds on the purchase of U.S. founding documents, thus providing specific direction regarding what should be included in campus collections. This kind of legislation typically results in action by information professionals and others interested in intellectual freedom. In this case, the South Carolina Library Association, the South Carolina chapter of the American Civil Liberties Union, and others worked hourly during the legislative session to get the best result possible for the information community and its consumers.[3]

Barbara M. Jones

Another example of recent challenges to intellectual freedom involves "trigger warnings," or alerts that particular course content might cause posttraumatic stress disorder (PTSD) arousal in some students who have been victims of violence. Some campuses are placing these warnings on course syllabi—that *To Kill a Mockingbird*, for example, might upset students who have been raped. At the time of writing this chapter, this controversy is still very much alive on many campuses. Currently the discourse regarding these "trigger warnings" in course syllabi centers on the civil rights of victims versus academic freedom.

Other more traditional barriers to information remain. Technology has rendered moot certain aspects of collection development policies, as bundled information and open web content make it impossible to control what is available on the campus. However, many questions remain regarding what information should be available on college campuses. For example, the question of whether information regarding creationism, which some consider to be a pseudoscience, should be available on campus is still debated, as is the possession of work by controversial faculty like Ward Churchill, whose controversial remarks about 9/11 caused the University of Colorado to rescind his tenure and professorship.

Privacy and Surveillance

The focus on privacy and surveillance issues is arguably the most significant shift in twenty-first-century information policy activity. After the Edward Snowden revelations and the confirmation that cellular phone data of "ordinary citizens" was being collected by the U.S. federal government, the general public began to pay more attention to the numerous intrusions into their lives by governments and corporations alike.

There is no question that privacy and surveillance issues have come to the forefront because technology enables massive data collection by governments and corporations. While this big data can be used for such purposes as determining the best location for a new health clinic, it can also be used to prevent an employee from getting health insurance due to a prior medical condition.

Information professionals work at the core of privacy and surveillance activism and policy making—partly because of expertise in this area and partly because of public trust in the profession's ethical commitment. As early as 2005, the Open Society Foundations (OSF) granted the ALA Office for Intellectual Freedom the funding to establish a model program regarding user privacy for libraries. The OSF saw early on that libraries were an ideal place to establish a user privacy program because their professional ethics promoted best practices regarding privacy, and because libraries are trusted community spaces where the general public could be informed about this important issue. Because all fifty states have some legal form of a library confidentiality mandate, information professionals all over the country are accustomed to protecting user privacy. Finally, libraries offer programming regarding topics with significant privacy implications, such as financial literacy and health care.

The acknowledgment that the information profession cares about privacy and surveillance issues has served as an important impetus for library commitment to privacy. The information profession links intellectual freedom to privacy by pointing out the chilling effect on reading with the government looking over one's shoulder. Information professionals have also framed privacy as a process of informed choice. Most argue that one would have to live as a hermit in order to remain totally private. But there are many smaller choices one can make to protect personal privacy—in the use of credit cards or consumer coupons, and the filling out of nonessential forms at stores or even at hospitals.

Much privacy research is now focused on how and whether young people care about or are even aware of privacy issues. As prospective employers and colleges use social media to research candidates, youth in particular need to be careful about what they post. Youth privacy scholar Danah Boyd's new book, *It's Complicated*, is an excellent source for data to show how young people use social media and develop strategies for protecting their privacy.[4]

The daily operations of information organizations reveal how many "choice points" exist that compromise or protect privacy and confidentiality. Some involve the capabilities of software to invade user privacy as confidential information is gathered. Examples include course software, where students post personal information; online public access catalogs that enable readers to insert notes; and reader information collected from borrowed e-readers. Many information organizations are conducting privacy audits to determine where such privacy breaches exist. And some professional associations—in California and Missouri, for example—are working with their state legislatures to draft new confidentiality statutes that incorporate privacy principles regarding patron use of e-resources.

Software Filters

Technology gives, and it takes away. The same technology that promises more access to information has also provided new ways to create barriers. Software filters on the Internet are arguably one of the most insidious forms of censorship because in many cases the information user is unaware of what is being blocked.

One serious and influential barrier is overfiltering of Internet access. Libraries that accept government E-rate funds to help cover their expenses associated with offering Internet access to patrons must agree to install filters to block Internet visual images that are "obscene," "harmful to minors," or "child pornography." And yet research shows that in many cases, libraries are filtering out content that is actually protected by the First Amendment and should be made available. Research on filters indicates that subjects that tend to be overfiltered include anti-LGBT content and health information. No filtering product currently on the market is synchronized with legal definitions regarding obscenity or child pornography, although vendors are not always straightforward about this lack of alignment in their material describing their products. Because vendor software algorithms are proprietary, it is difficult to determine the extent of the filtering.

TEXTBOX 36.3

The Concern of Overfiltering

A two-day meeting of experts in 2013 revealed the extent of overfiltering, as well as the limitations of filtering software. Research shows that the federal filtering mandate libraries must follow when they accept E-rate funds is being misinterpreted and overapplied, many filters are ideological, and access permitted by filters is unbalanced (for example, gay-hostile content is not filtered as much as gay-friendly content). Research is currently being conducted to examine whether filters discriminate against poor people. Because filters are installed more frequently in economically deprived areas, filters perpetuate the status of "information have-nots" in those areas. Students who have no home Internet access and who must resort to filtered access offered via school computers are less likely to get the full range of content for any given topic. This puts them at a disadvantage as they move to college and the workplace. The results of this conference are in a white paper, "Fencing Out Knowledge."[1]

1. Kristin R. Batch, *Fencing Out Knowledge: Impacts of the Children's Internet Protection Act 10 Years Later*, ALA OIF/OITP Policy Brief No. 5, June 2014, http://connect.ala.org/files/cipa_report.pdf.

Intellectual Freedom and User-Created Content

Information consumption has always included interaction between the consumer and the content. This type of interaction can be found when reading a paperback book, using Facebook, or playing a video game. But in today's digital environment, an electronic interaction can even *alter* the content, raising new types of concerns regarding intellectual freedom.

Video games offer one illustration of the special intellectual freedom challenges associated with today's types of interactive content. Video games have been the target of many censorship challenges because of their sometimes violent content. Such content has often been perceived to cause sensory overload and violent behavior in young people, and thus concerns have escalated among elected officials and the general public. Also, with the rash of gun violence in the United States in recent years, efforts to censor or ban violent video games have intensified. Psychologists and social scientists have weighed in on both sides of this intellectual freedom battle, and the U.S. Supreme Court issued an important 2011 decision in *Brown v. Entertainment Merchants Association*.[5] The court ruled that video games are protected speech under the First Amendment. The justices did not create another category of unprotected speech. Further, the case included submission of scholarly research regarding the impact of video games on players. The research linking violence to video game play did not convince the court to limit access to video game content. The *Brown v. EMA* decision supports efforts by information professionals to use video games for youth programming and to encourage game creation in their organization's makerspaces.

Makerspaces create interesting questions about information technology, policy, and intellectual freedom (see also chapter 19, "Creation Culture and Makerspaces," and chapter 24, "Managing Facilities"). These spaces are dedicated to "do-it-yourself" pursuits, often involving technology. Libraries, cities, and community organizations often offer makerspaces. The makerspace at the Chicago Public Library, for example, is part of the organization's strategy to promote collaborative learning environments and to promote job creation in communities with high unemployment.

But, like many innovative information programs, makerspaces often lack intellectual freedom policies. Many intellectual freedom issues arise in makerspace environments, such as questions about making sex toys or guns, or the liability of creating an object that causes a child to choke. Because makerspace equipment is expensive and the creation process is time consuming, many organizations require that all projects be approved prior to creation. This requirement could easily limit options for patrons who want to use makerspace equipment to create content.

Some users of makerspaces may think that it is better to take the risk and move forward without what they perceive to be bureaucratic policy restrictions, rather than limiting the scope of content creation allowed in makerspaces. In fact, some makerspaces deliberately post their policies on whiteboards. These concerns about limiting creativity are understandable. But good policy, along with training requirements, can enable makers to create more freely and safely, learn about the myriad options for content creation, and often eliminate the need for approval prior to starting a project. More research on this topic is needed, as well as further efforts to establish policies for this exciting new library-based content creation activity.

Conclusion

In the high-tech environment of the twenty-first century, consumers of information need intellectual freedom and privacy more than ever. Information professionals will continue to be challenged by this increasingly complex environment, which extends far beyond the traditional types of censorship of the printed word. And the general public, nonprofit organizations, and politicians will depend on solid research from trusted information organizations to make public policy. Information professionals should view this "messy" environment as a challenge and opportunity to reframe the issues and play a major role in shaping how technology will enable society to enhance creative expression and entrepreneurship—not chill it.

Notes

1. Walter Mischel, "Nancy Cantor: A View from the Chancellor's Office," *Observer* 22, no. 3 (March 2009), http://www.psychologicalscience.org/index.php/publications/observer/2009/march-09/nancy-cantor-a-view-from-the-chancellors-office.html.
2. Sandra Braman, "Constitutional Principles and the Information Spaces They Create," in *Change of State: Information, Policy, and Power* (Cambridge, MA: MIT Press, 2006).
3. ACLU, "This Compromise Is Not Acceptable: Constitutionally Suspect South Carolina Budget Measure Is an Assault on Academic Freedom," last modified June 13, 2014, http://www.aclusouthcarolina.org/news/2014/06/13/compromise-not-acceptable-constitutionally-suspect-south-car.
4. Danah Boyd, *It's Complicated: The Social Lives of Networked Teens* (New Haven, CT: Yale University Press, 2014).
5. *Brown v. Entertainment Merchants Association*, No. 564 U.S. 08-1448, 132 S. Ct. 81 (Supreme Ct. Oct. 3, 2011).

Barbara M. Jones

Part VII

Information Horizons
Career Management and Leadership Strategies

I am personally convinced that one person can be a change catalyst, a "transformer" in any situation, any organization. Such an individual is yeast that can leaven an entire loaf. It requires vision, initiative, patience, respect, persistence, courage, and faith to be a transforming leader.

—Stephen Covey (2013)

It is an exciting time to be an information professional. With a plethora of career opportunities and a vast global information landscape that offers expanded opportunities in professional networking and development, information professionals today have the opportunity to become dynamic catalysts of change: for themselves, for their organization, and for the profession as a whole. Successful information professionals take great measures in planning effective and forward-moving career strategies, engaging in professional development and networking activities, and becoming effective leaders in their communities and the profession.

Part VII focuses on the essential ingredient of the information profession—the information professional. It provides guidance, resources, tools, and examples about various career trajectories available to the information professional. It also highlights the essential value of developing a personal learning network and providing information professionals with resources for engaging—and leading—in the global information environment. Whether starting out as a brand new information professional, changing careers, or identifying new opportunities, this section offers the guidance, tools, and inspiration to achieve professional success.

Welcome to *Part VII: Information Horizons: Career Management and Leadership Strategies!*

37

Career Management Strategies for Lifelong Success

Naomi House

The landscape of library and information science (LIS) is evolving. Information professionals need to be aware of these changes and work on transforming their skills and knowledge to meet the evolving needs of the organizations where they work and the communities they serve. In a field experiencing so much rapid change, effective career strategies can help information professionals achieve job satisfaction and find a fulfilling career trajectory.

Today, information professionals work in libraries and other types of information organizations, often in roles that many define as "traditional." These traditional roles—such as cataloging, providing reference services, conducting research, or managing collection development/acquisitions—are still needed. Beyond these roles, which are often based in school, public, academic, and special libraries, today's information professionals are also actively involved in scientific research, competitive intelligence for businesses, and more. As long as organizations need skilled researchers, information analysts, user experience professionals, and knowledge managers, there will be a need for information professionals.

After completing this chapter, readers should have an understanding of how to discover their skill sets and assess the types of career fields where they can use those skills. The reader will also better understand the wide variety of jobs held by information professionals. The chapter also explores today's career strategies for information professionals, including creating a professional brand, taking an active role in professional associations, and identifying the best career trajectory to pursue.

The Value of LIS Skill Sets

Check This Out

Although "traditional" roles for information professionals in libraries are still vital, job seekers are not limited to these roles or employment environments. Information professionals offer an extremely valuable set of skills, valued in a wide range of employment settings. To learn more about alternate LIS careers, check out chapter 11, "Expanding the Horizon of the MLIS."

Skill sets are what individuals know how to do, including their knowledge regarding how to use specific tools. A skill set is what makes someone a valuable employee. For the information professional, skill sets can include having strong emotional intelligence and negotiation skills, the ability to prioritize time and tasks, analytical and technical skills, the ability to manage databases, knowledge of programming languages—and the list goes on. While earning an LIS master's degree does help information professionals grow their skill sets, those skill sets are not limited to just what students learn in their LIS program. Information professional, consultant, and LIS instructor Kim Dority said it best when she stated that LIS graduates are fortunate because they "work with the two most important resources of the twenty-first century—information and knowledge. [Information professionals] have a skill set whose applicability across all types of organizations, industries, and communities is limited only by your imagination."[1]

Developing a Skill Set List

One strategy that can help support career development is creating a list of all the skills the professional has. Creating the skill set list allows individuals to better assess the types of jobs they might pursue. Steps for creating a skill set list include the following:

1. Consider one's strengths and weaknesses in order to create a skill set list that emphasizes strengths.
2. Consider transferrable skills gained in jobs that one can leverage in a new job environment. Examples include customer service, training, and supervising.
3. List past experiences that demonstrate one's effective use of skills on the job.
4. Ask others to provide their perspectives on one's strengths and skills.
5. Review the endorsements posted by others on one's LinkedIn profile to identify the skills that are most prevalent—then add them to the skill set list.

Listing or grouping skill sets together can help connect skills that may at first seem different but are in fact complementary (see also chapter 37, "Librarian Skill Sets" in the online supplement for an example of a skill set "grouping").

Matching the Skill Set List to Career Opportunities

Key Words in Job Postings
Using skill sets as keywords can help job seekers match their skills to real jobs. Examples:

- Big data
- Cataloging
- Competitive intelligence
- Data curation
- Data visualization
- Information architect
- Knowledge management

- Program analyst
- Research
- Social marketer
- Technology trainer
- User experience design
- Websites

For a complete list, check out chapter 37, "Key Words for Searching" in the online supplement.

The next step is for information professionals to use their skill set list to research the types of jobs LIS professionals pursue using those skills. By matching real jobs to their skill set list, information professionals may discover potential jobs that interest them—LIS jobs they were not aware existed but that might be an excellent fit for their experience and education (see also chapter 37, "Linguistics Skill Set Based Job Families" in the online supplement for an example of how linguistic students matched their skill sets to real jobs). Information professionals may also identify skill sets they lack but employers value; this gives information professionals an opportunity to find ways to develop those missing skills (e.g., through course selection, MOOCs, workshops, etc.). By continuously learning new skills, information professionals can be ready to respond to changing job demands in this evolving information field.

Using Job Families and Job Clusters to Facilitate a Career Strategy

Many new information professionals are not aware of the broad range of jobs available to them today, and they have a hard time envisioning the jobs of tomorrow. When searching job aggregators and websites, it is important to expand the search beyond keywords such as "librarian" or "library." One useful strategy for expanding a search of job listings and identifying exciting new career trajectories is by using job families. MIT's human resources department defines jobs families as "a group of jobs involving similar types of work and requiring similar training, skills, knowledge, and expertise."[2] Using the framework of job families is an excellent way to search for LIS jobs, whether the goal is to make a job change in the near future or to identify career options to explore as part of an overall career development strategy.

In order to find related jobs in the same job family, use Boolean operators and limiters. Searching using multiple fields and using the Boolean operator "or" expands search results beyond jobs an information professional may typically expect to find.

> With so many research results, it can be difficult to narrow down choices or even become familiar with exactly what certain jobs entail and what experience and knowledge employers desire. Information interviews are one tool that job seekers have to learn about an employer's expectations. Check out the online supplement under chapter 37 for a list of resources regarding information interviews.

Job Clusters

Another way to make sense of a large number of search results and identify jobs that are of interest is to group the information into job clusters. Four examples are provided here: The "in" cluster, business and profit cluster, academic and nonprofit cluster, and "bling" cluster.

"IN" CLUSTER

One type of job cluster is known as the "in" cluster because each job title starts with the letters "in." Examples include

- *Informationist:* a job typically found in a government agency or business
- *Intelligence or Information Analysts:* government agency positions with a research focus
- *Informatician:* positions involving systems and human interaction, which may appeal to professionals with knowledge of user experience design
- *Indexer:* a position that deals with taxonomies and may appeal to metadata and cataloging specialists

- *Information Architects:* professionals who organize content and flow of online information for their employers
- *Information Resource Officers:* professionals who create information initiatives, such as information shared via social media, for government agencies or businesses

BUSINESS AND PROFIT CLUSTER

Business and profit cluster positions are often found in businesses and are housed either in information organizations or more commonly now as solo positions embedded in a range of departments. Examples include

- *Competitive Intelligence Analysts:* professionals who specialize in data gathering and using that data to analyze competitors
- *Market Analysts:* professionals who analyze the attractiveness of markets, using research skills that make the jobs interesting to many in the LIS field

ACADEMIC AND NONPROFIT CLUSTER

If the business world does not appear to be a good fit, another option is to use research and analysis skills in the third job cluster, the academic and nonprofit cluster. Examples include

- *Prospect Researchers and Development:* professionals who work for universities and nonprofit organizations, performing research regarding individuals known as prospects, or potential donors to institutions
- *Technology Trainers:* professionals who are skilled at using and understanding technology and can train others to use technology

There is one position that is found in both the business and profit cluster and the academic and nonprofit cluster—knowledge managers (see also chapter 9, "Information Centers: Special Libraries"). These professionals help document, and often create, repositories of institutional knowledge and memory. In fact, working as a knowledge manager can be seen as a bridge career between any of these clusters, as all organizations need this type of professional if they are to function efficiently.

"BLING" JOBS CLUSTER

Finally, a job cluster known as "bling" jobs includes positions that few in the LIS field are qualified to do, unless they also bring some additional skill sets. Examples include

- *Data Visualization Specialists:* professionals who often work in journalism and statistics and who are skilled at communicating and storytelling and presenting data in visual terms
- *Social Media Manager or Online Community Manager:* professionals who use skill sets that often involve intense understanding of user experience (UX) and a high level of engagement on social media
- *Library and Technology Futurists:* professionals who focus on analyzing published trends

TEXTBOX 37.1

Topic for Discussion

What are your top five skills? How do they work together to make a skill set? Do they complement each other and give you any ideas on potential job families?

Naomi House

- *User Experience Design (UXD):* professionals who are trained in user experience on various platforms and are perceptive of user needs regarding how to find information online or using software tools (see also chapter 17, "User Experience")

Building a Professional Brand

One of the best ways to establish a professional presence and be more competitive in most job fields is through branding. Although many organizations engage in branding in an effort to ensure that the public easily recognizes their core attributes, through professional branding, individuals can be more readily recognized for their accomplishments.

Professional Organizations

To build a professional brand, it is important to network with other professionals and be highly visible in the professional community. One of the best ways to do this is by joining a professional association, attending online and on-site conferences, making presentations, planning programs, and serving on committees. Joining associations adds value, not only through volunteer work and networking opportunities, but also through opportunities to build new skills and knowledge and learn about emerging trends in the field (see also "Key Resources—LIS Professional Associations" in the online supplement).

Information professionals should be strategic regarding the associations selected, finding those that are the best fit for future career goals, rather than joining a lot of associations but not getting deeply involved in any of them. Getting involved in a local association that is a good fit for future career goals can also help when job seeking, allowing the professional to meet colleagues from local institutions that may be hiring. Many associations also offer reduced fees for students, as well as unemployed or underemployed professionals. Some national associations offer memberships that include membership in a state or local group. Many of these professional associations offer opportunities for online events, discussion boards, and workshops; this can reduce the investment of time and money that is often associated with participating in these associations.

Online Networking and Forums

Another way to gain recognition and establish a brand is through social media, online networking, and online forums. There are many free social media platforms and LIS online networking groups available that provide opportunities to build a professional reputation online and can also be used to educate those outside the LIS field about important topics (see appendix 37.1, "Tips for Effective Online Communication").

Career Trajectories: Thinking Strategically

Not everyone has a straightforward career trajectory (i.e., moving without interruption from earning an undergraduate degree to going to graduate school and then starting a job as an information professional). Although many people do follow this type of career path, many others transition to careers as information professionals after working first in other fields, or working in a staff position at an information organization before deciding to earn an MLIS degree later in their careers. There is no one strategy for career success.

Although information professionals arrive at their first positions after taking a range of paths, it is important to be strategic. Several types of career strategies can be followed, and each has its own advantages and disadvantages. This section focuses on three strategies for career transitions: lateral moves, moving up the career ladder, and the corkscrew path.

Lateral Job Changes

Lateral job changes involve moving from one position to another similar position, either within the same organization or with a new organization.

- *Pros:* It is easy to make these types of job transitions because existing knowledge and skills are a good fit for the position, and the professional can easily hit the ground running. Also, job seekers using this type of career transition strategy are strong job candidates, able to clearly articulate why they are right for the job during interviews.
- *Cons:* Although lateral job changes made to positions in new types of information organizations offer opportunities to gain expanded knowledge, many lateral job changes are to fairly similar positions. These types of lateral job changes may offer limited opportunity for professional growth.
- *Addressing Hiring Manager Concerns:* When hiring managers review applications from individuals making a lateral transition, they may have some concerns. The job candidate can address these concerns by sharing some reasons for making the change, such as seeking a similar position after relocating a long distance, or seeking a job after a previous employer downsized the organization and eliminated the position.

Moving Up the Ladder

Moving up the ladder is a common phrase describing someone who is promoted or takes positions of increasing responsibility. Some of these individuals move up the ladder within the same organization, while others move from workplace to workplace, but always at a higher level. Moving up the ladder does not always mean a position involving managing staff. It does usually mean an increase in responsibility.

- *Pros:* This is a great strategy to gain managerial experience and demonstrate the professional's ability to handle increased responsibility. It is often a great strategy for receiving a salary increase as well.
- *Cons:* This strategy is not a good fit for those who are comfortable with the work they are currently doing and do not seek further responsibility. Also, this strategy, when used without transitioning to a new workplace, might result in managing former coworkers or friends.
- *Addressing Hiring Manager Concerns:* Some hiring managers are required to consider attributes and aspects of both internal and external candidates equally, so internal candidates may have to sell themselves as the best fit, emphasizing their knowledge of the organization and their readiness to take on new responsibilities. When seeking to move into a senior position at another workplace, candidates need to convince hiring managers that not only will they be a great fit for the position, but also that they understand the organization's culture.

The Corkscrew Path

The corkscrew path involves leveraging past work in other fields to transition into positions in the information profession.

- *Pros:* This strategy provides opportunities to tackle new challenges and expand knowledge by applying existing skills in new ways. The corkscrew path is also useful for current information professionals who are interested in transitioning to positions in job settings quite different from those where they have worked in the past.
- *Cons:* It can be difficult to assess whether the new work environment will be one the professional will enjoy. Even though similar types of tasks will be done, organizational cultures can vary extensively, and new ways of applying existing skills may not be satisfying.

- *Addressing Hiring Manager Concerns:* Hiring managers may be concerned about candidates who have no experience working in the job environment or applying skills in the type of position that is open. In these situations, job candidates will need to mitigate hiring manager concerns by emphasizing transferable skills as well as other skills that can be valuable in the new work environment and can be shared with other employees. In addition, candidates need to do research before applying for the position, identifying how existing skills transfer to the new environment, and then demonstrate to hiring managers that they understand how existing skills are valuable in the new work environment. The key to success is demonstrating an understanding of the field the candidate is moving into.

TEXTBOX 37.2

Topic for Discussion

Which career trajectory have you followed so far? Has it worked well? Do you think following a different type of career trajectory in the future would work better? Why or why not?

Conclusion

Information professionals have a wide range of career options to choose from, making it important to have a well-defined career development strategy. The LIS degree and the skill sets that accompany it can be beneficial to many different fields and types of work environments. Understanding how skill sets can be applied in various jobs is not only key to finding a job that provides satisfaction but also helps information professionals better determine which career trajectories fit their needs and wants. One unifying aspect of the work that information professionals do is their emphasis on service to individuals, organizations, and entire communities. The LIS degree opens doors to new job families, fields, and specific jobs that either require the accredited degree or appreciate its value. It is fundamentally important that LIS job hunters recognize that the decisions they make will have a ripple effect on their career, but through analysis and a commitment to lifelong learning, they can throw a new stone in and create a new ripple and head down a new path.

No LIS career is the result of a single decision, and no two careers will be the same. Each choice builds on previous decisions. Although a career may not be stitched as originally planned, it can still be an exciting adventure.

Appendix 37.1: Tips for Effective Online Communication

- *Listening:* Participation is not just a chance to communicate ideas, but a chance to hear others' opinions both inside and outside the LIS field. Not every conversation is one that will best be served by commenting. Take the time to actively listen to others and learn about their perspectives.
- *Sharing:* This type of participation is about starting a conversation that others can participate in. It can be RTing (retweeting) something someone else shares on Twitter, for example, or new content. The purpose is to share with your community and potentially to engage in communication.
- *Respecting and Setting Boundaries:* When interacting with others online, respect the boundaries that they set for themselves. If asked to stop communicating with someone, respect their wishes. Likewise, it is perfectly OK to state expectations and enforce them with others. This turns potentially negative situations into ones where information professionals can gain respect for themselves and those they interact with or choose not to.

Notes

1. Kim G. Dority, *Rethinking Information Work: A Career Guide for Librarians and Other Information Professionals* (Santa Barbara, CA: Libraries Unlimited, 2006).
2. MIT Human Resources, "Compensation: Job Families," last modified August 29, 2014, http://hrweb.mit .edu/compensation/job-evaluations/job-families.

38

Global Learning Networks

Jan Holmquist

The world keeps getting smaller. Technology has challenged the need for physical presence regarding how, when, and where learning, collaboration, and sharing information takes place. The world's best universities offer global learning for free, online communities attract worldwide participation, and an ever-increasing amount of information is instantly available for free. The wealth of information now available for this worldwide audience is massive, and technology has paved the way to unlimited access to information.

What does it mean to be an information professional in a global community? It means embracing the value of ideas, knowledge, and projects in the information world outside one's own community. Many of the challenges information organizations face locally are the same worldwide. While the profession's core functions (e.g., managing information resources, advocating intellectual freedom, providing access) are still important, many new opportunities and functions have emerged due to the global nature of information today. Information professionals connect with a global network, use inspiration (e.g., ideas, projects, learning experiences) from the worldwide information community, and translate and adapt those ideas—thereby bringing value into their own local community.

This chapter elaborates on this philosophy and offers some starting points and practical examples for what it means to be an information professional today in a global community. After completing this chapter, the reader should have an understanding of how to

- bring value to local information communities through global inspiration,
- collaborate internationally to improve information services worldwide, and
- build one's own global personal learning network (PLN).

Global Learning and Collaboration

Global communities of information professionals are not limited to international organizations like IFLA.[1] There are many other global opportunities for information professionals to exchange ideas, experiences, and customs and to learn from each other. Professional networks can be quickly assembled and thrive via the bits and bytes sent across the globe every second. These networks connect ideas, perspectives, and experiences and have the potential to directly impact the innovation of new ideas and programs for information organizations at the local level. Global learning communities and global collaboration are two ways that global communities can connect and benefit from this engagement.

Global Learning Communities

One way to connect with these global networks is through an approach called connected learning. Connected learning is when learning is powered by an individual's interests and passions and supported by peers, and when it exists in spaces where an individual feels valued and safe. Libraries in New York, Chattanooga, Chicago, the Netherlands, and Sweden, for example, have all taken decisive steps to become community hubs for connected learning.[2] Opportunities for connected learning take on a digital form through the web and also expand cooperation between information organizations around the world. For example, connecting to the HIVE network, which uses connected learning to focus on digital skills and web literacy in global communities,[3] or choosing another way to work strategically with the global information community is a good option for local information organizations. These opportunities connect citizens of different countries with each other for the purpose of learning together and sharing knowledge, with the information organization as facilitator.

Check This Out

The HIVE network uses connected learning to focus on digital skills and web literacy in global communities.

Visit:
http://hivelearningnetworks.org

In today's world, there are no limits to learning with people from other continents (see also chapter 20, "Infinite Learning"). Learning communities now engage in a global environment through collaborative learning experiences such as massive open online courses (MOOCs). MOOCs provide learners with several benefits: the ability to get educated by some of the best universities in the world, study with people from all over the globe, develop new networks, learn from wherever they reside, and apply the new global knowledge they gained from these experiences to their own communities.[4] See textbox 38.1.

TEXTBOX 38.1

Hyperlinked Library MOOC

In the Hyperlinked Library MOOC, participants were prompted to play, work with problems encountered in their own information environments via reflection and the creation of course artifacts, innovate, and experiment in self-directed yet social learning challenges. Weekly modules, covering concepts such as community engagement, transparency, privacy, and user experience, provided MOOC participants with the opportunity to explore, experiment, and reflect on the ideas and challenges associated with them. Participants shared with the larger Hyperlinked Library community, learned from each other's experiences, and reflected on their own learning and growth. The Hyperlinked Library MOOC was offered by the San José State University School of Information and taught by Dr. Michael Stephens and Kyle Jones in 2013. Check out the online supplement for more information.

A less structured global learning platform is the 23 Things model, which was originally launched by Helene Blowers as a Learning 2.0 program. Early versions of this 23 Things program utilized online learning environments for staff working in organizations like libraries and museums; the program's goal was to encourage information organization staff to learn about and experiment with new and emerging technologies. This model spread worldwide, impacting the learning and professional development activities in information organizations everywhere. More recent versions, such as 23 Mobile Things,[5] have engaged participants from different countries. While less structured than a MOOC, this program offers online learning opportunities via online tools like Twitter and extends participants' PLNs through hashtags, webinars, Twitter chats, and more.

Global Collaboration

"Connectedness" relates both to learning and also to people who help to manage, organize, and disseminate resources. This connectedness has fostered global collaborations that directly impact both local and global communities.

A practical example of global collaboration and the impact it can have on communities is the Buy India a Library[6] project, which aimed to crowd-fund money for building a library in India. The global team encompassed members from Denmark, the United Kingdom, and the United States. When the project began, the team had never met face to face. The idea was developed through Twitter and e-mails. A blog that all members of the team could edit was set up and, by making a lot of #buyalib noise on social media, Buy India a Library collected 2,420 British pounds; the equivalent of approximately four thousand U.S. dollars, this money was raised in two weeks from one hundred contributors from all over the world. This was more than what was needed to fund a library in Mysore, India, resulting in a bigger library, bigger collection, and staff salaries for two years. Excess funds from the program paid for four donkey-driven mobile libraries in Africa.

Another example of global collaboration is the international Internet-based TV show, *This Week in Libraries*,[7] which was also crowd-funded by information professionals and information lovers who wanted the show to remain online. The global team encompassed members from the United States, Denmark, and Australia. Part of the show's success was based on the availability of team members who could answer questions and market the show 24/7/365, since each team member lived in a different time zone.

In Denmark, information professionals launched a web app with a mobile game by bringing together a global team, which worked together to impact local communities. This app brought the library out of the building in a gamified way, showing people the city's cultural and literary histories and pointing it all back to the library. This idea was inspired by gamification projects within a library context in Canada, the United States, and the United Kingdom, as well as by a Swedish project from the Malmö festival where a crime story took place with the city as a location.

As these examples show, many opportunities exist for information professionals to connect—through learning and collaboration—across global boundaries to make a difference in their own knowledge and expertise, as well as in information organizations and communities around the world. The next section of this chapter explores the idea of what it means to be a global information professional.

The Global Information Professional: Think Globally—Act Locally

What does it mean to be a global information professional? There is no specific exam to pass, job to attain, or status to achieve that instantly qualifies someone for this role. A global information professional is someone who thinks about the information field on a global scale—as a global environment to share and learn collaboratively, gain inspiration, and facilitate new knowledge that can generate new ideas. Global information professionals result in information organizations that are more connected and stronger both globally and locally.

Jan Holmquist

The benefits of thinking globally and acting locally are not unique to the field of library and information science. Here are some examples of other industries that have adopted a global approach to benefit local initiatives:

- Starbucks made the My Starbucks idea where people worldwide can share, discuss, and vote for new ideas to improve Starbucks.
- In a sense, one could say that the whole development of the European Union is an example of countries working closely together—demonstrating a global collaboration that started long before the technology revolution had its influence.

Exciting things can happen when people collaborate on a global level—contributing a diversity of ideas, experiences, and cultural knowledge to solve problems and come up with new ideas. But how can information professionals engage in the global information environment?

There are various ways an information professional can begin participating in the global information environment. Information professionals can

> **TEXTBOX 38.2**
>
> **Topic for Discussion**
>
> How can information professionals maintain their local presence while finding the time to locate and participate in a global community?

- engage in global learning communities, as discussed earlier;
- read articles about libraries and information organizations worldwide;
- attend conferences (state, national, and international); and
- "follow," "pin," or "search" information professionals and information organizations online.

However, to truly develop themselves as global information professionals and discover their potential (personally, socially, and professionally) within the global environment, information professionals must not only develop a dynamic personal learning network but also become active contributors in the global conversation about libraries, information services, information users, communities, and more. The next section of this chapter expands upon this concept and offers strategies for the global information professional.

Personal Learning Networks

In order to adapt to the ever-changing technological landscape, information professionals today must strategically guide their careers through professional development and engagement. "Strategies which resist or even adapt to a constantly changing world are insufficient to keep up. Information professionals need ways to embrace change and even enjoy making sense out of a constantly changing world. Denying change has become a losing strategy."[8] Strategies provide a "headlight" to guide the way, illuminating the opportunities, threats, and challenges that lie ahead.

One of the most important strategies for learning and building a global community is to cultivate a personal learning network (PLN). Throughout this book, authors have referred to the value and adoption of a PLN. A PLN is defined as a group of people with whom one connects with to

- interact and exchange information and resources;
- share knowledge, experiences, and ideas; and
- collect and create an informed guide to professional development opportunities and lifelong learning.[9]

> "While building a PLN may take time, it is well worth the investment so that one day information professionals will have access to a 24/7/365 global network that is always available."

"Establishing a personal learning network is an approach to meet constantly evolving professional goals, learning needs, and objectives."[10] While building a PLN may take time, it is well worth the investment so that one day information professionals will have access to a 24/7/365 global network that is always available.[11] Through the strategic selection of social media networks and online tools and a purposeful connection with information organizations outside their own community, state, and country, information professionals can easily develop their own professional network.

Social Media

There are many social media sites (e.g., Facebook, Twitter, Google+, and Tumblr) that can be part of a PLN. The goal is to shape the "following" and "friending" in a professional way where the "feeds" become a tool or resource for collaborating, sharing knowledge, developing ideas, and learning from other information professionals worldwide. Indeed, social media can become a very powerful tool.

Twitter (www.twitter.com) is a good network to begin with because of the asymmetrical follow principle where Twitter users can follow anyone they want to with no obligation to be followed back or be accepted as a friend. Part of the culture on Twitter is also that people answer the @mentions. This makes it easy to connect and talk professionally on a global level. Twitter is a great, easy, and cheap way to begin expanding a global PLN.

TEXTBOX 38.3

Topic for Discussion

What will be your first three steps in building your own PLN? What LIS associations will you add? What international groups will you engage with? What blogs will you follow? And how will you maintain your PLN?

The International Librarians Network

The International Librarians Network (ILN) is a "facilitated peer mentoring program aimed at helping librarians develop international networks. It is built on the belief that innovation and inspiration can cross borders, and that expanding networks beyond participants' home countries can make library professionals better at what they do."[12]

International Professional Organizations

Another tremendous resource for the global PLN is engagement with internationally based professional organizations. Two primary ones worth considering are the International Federation of Library Associations and Institutions (IFLA) and the Special Libraries Association (SLA). IFLA is an international organization that provides information, services, and networking opportunities for information organizations and information professionals. "It is the global voice of the library and information profession."[13] SLA is a "nonprofit global organization for innovative information professionals that promotes and strengthens its members through learning, advocacy, and networking initiatives."[14] These organizations offer a network for information professionals interested in engaging with the global information environment. See table 38.1, "Resources for Engaging in the Global Information Environment."

Jan Holmquist

Table 38.1. Resources for Engaging in the Global Information Environment

Organization	Website
Association for Information and Image Management (AIIM)	http://www.aiim.org
Association of Information Science & Technology (ASIS&T), special interest group on international information issues	http://www.asis.org/SIG/iii.html
Global Voices	http://globalvoicesonline.org
Global Knowledge Partnership Foundation (GKPF)	http://gkpfoundation.org
International Association for Development of the Information Society (IADIS)	http://www.iadisportal.org
International Federation of Library Associations and Institutions (IFLA)	http://www.ifla.org
International Society for Information Studies (ISIS)	http://www.is4is.org
National Information Standards Organization (NISO)	http://www.niso.org
Special Libraries Association (SLA)	http://www.sla.org
World Intellectual Property Organization (WIPO)	http://www.wipo.int/portal/en
World Wide Web Consortium (W3C)	http://www.w3.org

Conclusion

The chapter has looked at how the world has become smaller because of technology, how areas like learning and finding inspiration to impact local initiatives have been affected, and how information professionals can use this in a strategic way to become connected learners on a global level by sharing knowledge with information professionals worldwide via technology, social media, and the Internet. When information professionals engage in the global information environment and expand their networks and experiences globally, they gain new knowledge and competencies, opportunities, and even access to new information for their communities. When information professionals develop programs that attract and engage their communities as a result of ideas gained from a global network, the efforts begin to pay off. This is where the strategy moves into the next phase of making a difference in the local community.

> "When information professionals engage in the global information environment and expand their networks and experiences globally, they gain new knowledge and competencies, opportunities, and even access to new information for their communities."

Notes

1. International Federation of Libraries Association (IFLA), last modified September 8, 2014, www.ifla.org.
2. Åke Nygren, *The Public Library as a Community Hub for Connected Learning* (paper submitted at the IFLA Conference, August 4, 2014), http://library.ifla.org/1014/1/167-nygren-en.pdf.

3. Hive Learning Networks, last modified September 3, 2014, http://hivelearningnetworks.org.
4. San José State University School of Information, "Hyperlinked Library MOOC," n.d., http://ischool.sjsu .edu/hyperlinked-library-mooc-1.
5. "23 Mobile Things," last modified September 3, 2014, http://23mobilethings.net/wpress.
6. "Buy India a Library," blog post by jamholdquist, May 28, 2012, http://buyindiaalibrary.wordpress.com.
7. "Home," This Week in Libraries, last modified October 2, 2014, http://www.thisweekinlibraries.com.
8. John Seely Brown, "A New Culture of Learning: Cultivating the Imagination for a World of Constant Change" (Colorado Springs, CO: Createspace, 2011).
9. A. Howlett, "Connecting to the LIS Online Community: A New Information Professional Developing a Personal Learning Network" (ALIA 5th New Librarians Symposium 2011, Metamorphosis: What Will You Become Today?, Perth, Australia, 2011), 2.
10. Ibid., 1.
11. D. Wagner, "Personal Education Networks for Educators," Getting Smart, http://gettingsmart.com/2012/ 01/personal-learning-networks-for-educators-10-tips.
12. International Librarians Network, blog, last modified October 3, 2014, http://ilnetwork.wordpress.com.
13. IFLA, 2014.
14. Special Libraries Association (SLA), "About SLA," last modified August 26, 2014, https://www.sla.org/ about-sla.

Jan Holmquist

39

Leadership for Today and Tomorrow

Carol H. Sawyer

Leadership matters: in families, in communities, in organizations, in society, and in the global land-scape. Great leaders are essential to the information profession as well, bringing vision in a time when the profession is experiencing rapid change, and offering inspiration to seek solutions in an environment where there are a multitude of new problems to address. After completing this chapter, the reader should have an understanding of what the word "leadership" means and what the characteristics of excellent leaders are in the twenty-first century. The chapter explores who leaders are and what they do. The chapter also examines why effective leadership is important for information professionals and information organizations. Anyone can learn to be a leader, yet leadership development is a life-long process. The chapter provides a starting point for the learning journey.

Defining Leadership

Frequently, the terms "manager" and "leader" are used interchangeably (see also chapter 21, "Management Skills"). Joseph Rost, in his book *Leadership for the 21st Century*, devoted almost half of that pub-lication to a well-researched discussion regarding how frequently twentieth-century scholars used the term "leadership" to describe what management actually was. After discussing how frequently the term "leadership" is used to describe management, he then crafted his definition of leadership: "Leadership is an influence relationship among leaders and collaborators who intend real changes that reflect their mutual purposes."[1]

Scholars now distinguish between leadership and management and recognize the complementary roles that each plays in organizational life. Scholar Warren Bennis sought to capture the distinction with a comparative checklist that wrapped up with his often-quoted phrase: "The manager does things right; the leader does the right thing."[2] Harvard professor emeritus John Kotter wrote, "Management is about coping with complexity. . . . Leadership, by contrast, is about coping with change."[3]

In the past twenty years, more attention has been given to the role of followers when seeking to define leadership. Authors Jim Kouzes and Barry Posner define leadership as "a relationship between those who aspire to lead and those who choose to follow."[4] James MacGregor Burns, political sci-entist and authority on leadership studies, described the leader/follower relationship dynamic with these words: "I define leadership as leaders inducing followers to act for certain goals that represent the values and the motivations—the wants and needs, the aspirations and expectations—of both leaders and followers."[5] That values-grounded approach is echoed in this definition of leadership from Knowles: "the highest function of leadership is releasing the energy of the people in the system and managing the processes for giving that energy direction toward mutually beneficial goals."[6]

Leadership is always attentive, directly or indirectly, to power because "leadership inevitably requires using power to influence the thoughts and actions of other people."[7] Leaders have the power to inspire others and shape some part of the world.[8]

> "It is not necessary to hold an important title to be an effective organizational leader. Having the courage to ask the right questions, with the right words, asked in the right way, in the right time and place, may be the essence of effective and significant leadership."

Leadership studies have shifted from a focus on theories of "the great man" to a more inclusive definition of a leader. Today, scholars recognize that one can lead without a formal position, from anywhere within an organization. Perhaps one of the most important things to do in work, and in life, is to recognize where, when, and how to step forward to lead. It is not necessary to hold an important title to be an effective organizational leader. Having the courage to ask the right questions, with the right words, asked in the right way, in the right time and place may be the essence of effective and significant leadership.[9] [10] [11]

TEXTBOX 39.1

Other Definitions of Leadership[1]

- "A leader is anyone willing to help, anyone who sees something that needs to change and takes the first steps to influence that situation."
- "Leadership has nothing to do with title. It is a way of life, a way of being in the world."
- "Leadership is a matter of how to be, not how to do."

---

1. Joseph Rost, *Leadership for the 21st Century* (Westport, CT: Praeger, 1991).

Characteristics of Effective Leaders

Most individuals, at one time or another, have been part of organizations that were not led well. Through those experiences, employees learn that good leadership can foster a positive, effective work environment. Quality leadership makes a difference in an employees' sense of belonging, commitment, engagement, happiness, and productivity. A good leader draws from many disciplines—psychology, sociology, philosophy, organizational development, and communication—just to name a few.

The complexities of organizational life, the tumult Peter Vaill has called our time of "permanent white water,"[12] include sweeping changes in the very nature of information and information organizations. These sweeping changes demand that attention be paid to the practice of leadership. In fact, information organizations can expect many more massive changes in the years to come. These times of sweeping change call for bold action on the part of leaders and the

TEXTBOX 39.2

Topic for Discussion

How can information professionals become leaders in inspiring positive change in their communities?

willingness to take risks in situations where there may not be predictable outcomes.[13] Kouzes and Posner identified four characteristics people seek out in leaders they will follow willingly. These characteristics are the same for all leaders, regardless of the leader's age, gender, ethnicity, discipline, or level in the organization. The types of leaders people want to follow are forward looking, inspiring, competent, and honest.[14]

Leadership Competencies

The classic book *On Becoming a Leader* describes the characteristics and competencies of leaders. The book highlights four competencies that its author calls "essential."[15]

One of the leadership competencies highlighted in the book is especially relevant to information organizations, where leaders need to establish a vision for the future in a profession experiencing ongoing transformation. This competency involves the ability to engage others in the creation of shared meaning. Exceptional leadership embodies compelling vision and the ability to cultivate that focus in others, resulting in their commitment to move toward the future. "Leaders are expected to have a sense of direction and a concern for the future of the organization. Leaders must know where they are going. They must have a destination in mind when asking others to join them on a journey into the unknown."[16] This quality imbues a discipleship based on mutually agreed-upon values and goals.

> **Leadership: Four Essential Competencies**
> - Creation of shared meaning
> - Distinctive voice
> - Emotional intelligence
> - Integrity
>
> Warren Bennis, *On Becoming a Leader*, 20th anniversary edition (Philadelphia, PA: Basic Books, 2009).

Another "essential" competency is a distinctive voice, a cluster of related qualities, including a sense of purpose, self-confidence, and a sense of self. During times of change, confident leaders with a clear sense of purpose are needed.

Often this "distinctive voice" is identified as emotional intelligence[17] (see also chapter 23, "Managing Personnel"). For example, emotional intelligence includes the ability to authentically listen to colleagues and stakeholders and facilitate dialogue. Leaders with emotional intelligence have empathy and are attuned to the needs and motivations of their followers. Leaders know how to express themselves fully. They know who they are, what their strengths and weaknesses are, and how to fully deploy their strengths and compensate for their weaknesses. They also know what they want, why they want it, and how to communicate what they want to others in order to gain their cooperation and support. This emphasis on a leader's emotional intelligence is closely linked with the third essential competency of integrity.

The key competency that is absolutely essential and perhaps the one that information professionals cannot do without is adaptive capacity. Adaptive capacity is what allows leaders to respond quickly and intelligently to relentless change. Adaptive capacity allows today's leaders to act, and then to evaluate the results of their actions, instead of relying on the traditional decision-making model, which calls for collecting and analyzing the data, then acting. Today's leaders know that time is of the essence and that they must often act before all the data are available. They must assess the result of their actions, correct their course, and quickly act again.

Adaptive capacity is made up of many things, including resilience and creativity. It encompasses the

> "Today's leaders know that time is of the essence, and that they must often act before all the data are available. They must assess the result of their actions, correct their course, and quickly act again."

ability to identify and seize opportunities.[18] Adaptability is focused on the creative, right-brain tasks of preparing for tomorrow, which include developing capabilities needed to survive in an uncertain future. Leaders of highly adaptive organizations must be mentally ambidextrous, keeping the present system functioning while creating an environment where followers positively respond to change and embrace innovation.[19]

Leaders as Change Agents

Leaders can do a range of things to foster an environment where organizational change is possible. Strategic leaders provide a vision, recruit disciples, and communicate the need for change. They can create the need for change and provide the context for change by focusing on what needs to change and why it needs to change. They also create the environment for change by providing resources and removing obstacles, and by energizing, enabling, and rewarding followers.[20] Leaders make it possible to get extraordinary things done by inspiring a shared vision and enabling others to act.

Effective leaders possess what has been called the "do-something" mind-set. They are confident leaders rather than passive observers. They "write the scripts of their own lives,"[21] and in doing so, they have a much greater impact on the world around them. Because they believe their actions can make a positive difference, they take action. They recognize that waiting for a perfect plan would take too long or may never happen, so they move forward. They know they will not always be right, but they are optimistic about their ability to take risks and, if necessary, make midcourse corrections when seeking to implement their ideas.

Leaders love to learn. Even being wrong provides an opportunity to learn. Anything a person does will be "more wrong until one learns how to do it more right."[22]

Effective leaders are interested in developing the capacities of others, investing in the individuals they lead. They are focused on mobilizing the creativity and energy of the people they lead to address the problems the organization faces.[23] Great leaders bring forth the best in people, inspire hope, and encourage a commitment to addressing challenges.

The information profession is facing sweeping changes, and professionals should pay attention to those changes. But efforts to address too many changes at once can lead to confusion. Leaders can bring clarity in times of confusion, identifying where to focus efforts.[24] In a profession that continues to evolve rapidly, it is important for leaders to prepare for these major transformations. Leaders who understand and prepare for change thrive, and those who do not are left behind.[25]

> ### TEXTBOX 39.3
>
> **Topic for Discussion**
>
> How can information professionals become leaders in inspiring positive change in their communities?

Learning to Lead

Learning to lead is possible for everyone. Each person has the capacity for leadership. In fact, effective leaders are committed to an ongoing learning process, where they continue to build their knowledge.[26]

More than 2,500 years ago, Confucius admonished leaders to seek perspective and wisdom through reflection, rather than simply attempting to learn through experience and imitation. Confirming Confucius's understanding, Harvard professor Howard Gardner's contemporary research identified daily reflection as one of only three core competencies that distinguish leaders who make an extraordinary difference in the world from those who do not.[27] Management guru Peter Drucker similarly advocated daily reflection, as have many other prominent leadership experts.[28] Reflection allows leaders to:

Carol H. Sawyer

- envision initiatives that matter;
- gain perspective, seeing reality as it actually is rather than continuing to rely on illusions perpetuated by colleagues, the media, and the broader culture;
- aspire to achieve exciting possibilities by drawing on the depths of their own and others' hopes, aspirations, and creativity; and
- inspire others to move beyond the current reality and embrace what can be possible in the future.[29]

In addition to reflection, leaders can learn through

- experience (learning by doing);
- example (learning from other successful organizations);
- mentoring (learning from senior, successful people);
- discussion (both in person and online); and
- method (reading and reflection).[30]

Information professionals need to seek varied ways of learning about leadership, including engaging with other professionals in a mutual learning journey. For example, professional associations provide resources and opportunities to share knowledge regarding effective leadership practices (see also "Key Resources—Professional LIS Professional Associations" in the online supplement for a list of LIS-related professional associations). Leaders should tap into the expertise of colleagues and position themselves in situations that will provide access to new learning.[31]

Learning as a way of being[32] is essential for thought leaders in the field of information science. The organizational cultures they craft and nourish are cultures of lifelong learning as well. Effective leaders inspire their colleagues to confront challenges, change perspectives, and learn new habits.[33] The cultures they create are places where people can be comfortable asking questions, such as, What happened? Why did it happen? and What can we learn from it? Great leaders also help people answer these questions.[34]

Conclusion

Information professionals are leaders who are working "out there on the frontier where tomorrow is taking shape."[35] Leadership in the twenty-first century is based on hope, aspiration, and innovation. It is an exciting time to lead an information organization because "the gap between what people can imagine and what they can accomplish has never been smaller."[36]

In the rapidly evolving information profession, there is a need for leaders who will challenge others to face problems for which there are no simple, painless solutions—problems that require professionals to learn new ways to find solutions.[37] Rather than leaders who influence people to follow the leader's vision, the profession needs leaders who influence the community to engage in collaborative problem solving.[38]

Perhaps one of the most positive and enduring gifts leaders can give to the people they lead is creating a sense of greater purpose. A clearly articulated purpose provides the foundation upon which to build an information organization that is compassionate and resilient during uncertain times. A sense of purpose instills a sense of connectedness with other information professionals who are working to achieve similar goals.[39]

Notes

1. Joseph Rost, *Leadership for the 21st Century* (Westport, CT: Praeger, 1991).
2. Warren Bennis, *On Becoming a Leader*, 20th anniversary ed. (Philadelphia, PA: Basic Books, 2009).
3. John Kotter, "What Leaders Really Do," in *HBR's 10 Must Reads: On Leadership*, 37–56 (Cambridge, MA: Harvard Business School Publishing, 2011).

4. J. M. Kouzes and B. Z. Posner, *Credibility: How Leaders Gain and Lose It; Why People Demand It* (San Francisco, CA: Jossey-Bass, 2011), 2.
5. James MacGregor Burns, *Leadership* (New York: Harper Perennial Modern Classics, 2010), 19.
6. Malcolm S. Knowles, "Making Things Happen by Releasing the Energy of Others," *Journal of Management Development*, September 1983, 182–190.
7. Abraham Zaleznik, "Managers and Leaders: Are They Different?" Reprint. *The Best of HBR 1977* (2004): 1–10.
8. Peter Parker, "Introduction," in *Leading from Within: Poetry That Sustains the Courage to Lead*, ed. Sam Intrater and Megan Scribner (New York: Wiley & Sons, 2007).
9. Margaret J. Wheatley, *Turning to One Another: Simple Conversations to Restore Hope to the Future* (San Francisco, CA: Berrett-Koehler, 2009), 144.
10. Judy Brown, *A Leader's Guide to Reflective Practice* (Victoria, BC: Trafford Publishing, 2007), 9.
11. Frances Hesselbein, "Definition of Leadership," YouTube video, uploaded by mentorsgallery, January 26, 2010, https://www.youtube.com/watch?v=chLuLUqy9OM.
12. Peter B. Vaill, *Learning as a Way of Being: Strategies for Survival in a World of Permanent White Water* (San Francisco, CA: Jossey-Bass, 1996), 4.
13. Kouzes and Posner, *Credibility*, 2011, xxxxi.
14. Ibid., 7.
15. Bennis, *On Becoming a Leader*, 2009.
16. Kouzes and Posner, *Credibility*, 2011, 10.
17. D. Goleman, R. Boyatzis, and A. McKee, *Primal Leadership: Learning to Lead with Emotional Intelligence* (Boston, MA: Harvard Business School, 2004).
18. Bennis, *On Being a Leader*, 2009, xii.
19. Ibid., 33–34.
20. James O'Toole, *Leadership A to Z; A Guide for the Appropriately Ambitious* (San Francisco, CA: Jossey-Bass, 1999), 128.
21. T. Kelley and D. Kelley, *Creative Confidence: Unleashing the Creative Potential within Us All* (New York: Crown Business, 2013), 115–116.
22. John Maeda, *Redesigning Leadership* (Cambridge, MA: MIT Press, 2011), 22.
23. Tom Richman, "Leadership Expert Ronald Heifetz," Inc.com, last updated October 1, 1988, http://www.inc.com/magazine/19881001/5990.html.
24. Ibid.
25. Stephen Apkon, *The Age of the Image: Redefining Literacy in a World of Screens* (New York: Farrar, Straus & Giroux, 2013), 14.
26. N. M Tichy and W. G. Bennis, *Judgment: How Winning Leaders Make Great Calls* (New York: Penguin, 2007), 238.
27. Veronica Boix Mansilla and Howard Gardner, "From Teaching Globalization to Nurturing Global Consciousness," in *Learning in the Global Era: International Perspectives on Globalization and Education*, ed. Marcelo Suarez-Orozo (Berkeley and Los Angeles: University of California Press, 2007), 58.
28. Peter Drucker, *Management Challenges for the 21st Century* (New York: Harper Business, 2001).
29. Nancy J. Adler, *Leadership Insight* (New York: Routledge, 2010).
30. Carol Sawyer, citing Dr. Warren Bennis, "Linking People, Process and Technology in Leadership Development," in *Turning the Prism: Three Explorations of Knowledge Management Through Network and Communities of Practice* (paper presented at the 3rd European Conference on Organizational Knowledge, Learning and Capabilities, Athens, April 5–6, 2002), 7, http://www2.warwick.ac.uk/fac/soc/wbs/conf/olkc/archive/oklc3/papers/id287.pdf.
31. M. W. McCall Jr., M. M. Lombardo, and A. M. Morrison, *The Lessons of Experiences: How Successful Executives Develop on the Job* (Lexington, MA: Lexington Books, 1988).
32. Vaill, *Learning as a Way of Being*, 1996.
33. R. A. Heifetz and D. L. Laurie, "The Work of Leadership," *The Best of HBR* (Boston, MA: Harvard Business School Press, 2001), http://dmcodyssey.org/wp-content/uploads/2013/09/EQ-Daniel-Goleman-in-HBR_10_Must_Reads_on_Leadership.pdf#page=38.

34. Bo Burlingham, "Jim Collins: Be Great Now," Inc.com, last modified May 29, 2012, http://www.inc.com/magazine/201206/bo-burlingham/jim-collins-exclusive-interview-be-great-now.html#ixzz3EU8YGsBg.

35. Bennis, *On Being a Leader*, 2009, xxxiii.

36. Adler, *Leadership Insight*, 2010.

37. Ronald A. Heifetz, *Leadership without Easy Answers* (Boston, MA: Harvard University Press, 1998), 2.

38. Ibid., 14.

39. Brandon Mikel Smith and Mary Ann Glynn, "Leading with Purpose: Fueling the Human Spirit in Times of Uncertainty," Center for Positive Organizations (Ann Arbor, MI: Ross School of Business, University of Michigan, n.d.), http://positiveorgs.bus.umich.edu/essays/leading-with-purpose-fueling-the-human-spirit-in-times-of-uncertainty.

Glossary of Terms

3-D printer: a computer-driven digital tool that melts spools of plastic or resin and extrudes it to create, layer by layer, a three-dimensional object.

Access: the ability of an information seeker to acquire information either in physical or digital form. It is also the availability of materials or tools, such as computers and the Internet, to find information and expert assistance from information professionals.

Access services: administrative umbrella under which circulation, reserves, interlibrary loan, stacks maintenance, and related functions reside.

Active learning: teaching method built on the premise that students are active participants in the learning process and construct their own meaning by engaging with a topic or concept, often by working with peers.

Adaptive capacity: components that allow leaders to respond quickly and intelligently to relentless change.

Advocacy: the process of increasing awareness and support for information organizations through public/stakeholder increased visibility.

Advocacy campaign: often conducted to persuade stakeholders or constituents to a specific policy direction or resource distribution.

Affective states: the emotional responses people have when interacting with information and information resources; this may range from positive emotions, such as satisfaction, to negative emotions, such as frustration.

Aggregation: database(s) of content from multiple publishers—selected based on subject matter or to cover a spectrum of interests.

All-in group license: a license wherein all members of a consortium gain access to the digital content being licensed.

Allocation: a budgeting term used for the distribution of money to a particular department or sections of a department. In determining allocations, information organizations have to take into consideration many factors, such as users' needs, trends, and personnel development.

Alternative metrics: an emerging set of metrics that provide an alternative to established citation counts and usage statistics for assessing the impact of a scholarly work; also called altmetrics.

Archival quality: a nonscientific term referring to storage media that meet the standards prevalently used by curators and librarians in preservation work.

Arduino: an open source microcontroller (a small computer that can run only one program at a time) cocreated by Massimo Banzi that connects computer code to sensors, lights, and mechanical actions.

Assessment: the set of practices used both to evaluate a program, service, collection, or other offering and to show how it creates value by meeting the needs of stakeholders.

Asynchronous learning: a type of online learning that does not require real-time interaction and communication, such as through e-mail, discussion boards, and recorded lectures.

Audiovisual: types of recorded content that involve image and sound capture.

Audit: a systematic examination of financial or accounting records by an auditor to verify their accuracy and truthfulness.

Authority: the role of managers who are given and assume responsibility for running their organizations. Power and control are necessary components of an authoritarian role.

Authority controlled headings: headings used in a library catalog or bibliographic records that are based on an authoritative list (or authority file) to provide consistency of form.

Authority file (or authoritative list): a list of authoritative forms of the headings used in a library catalog or a file of bibliographic records, maintained to ensure that the headings are applied consistently as new items are added to a collection.

Authorized user: those users of an information organization defined in a license as being eligible to access the licensed digital content.

Automated storage and retrieval system: a computer-controlled system found within the information organization's physical building to facilitate storing and retrieving information resources.

Basic literacy: the ability to read and write words.

BIBFRAME: an initiative of the Library of Congress to replace MARC as a means of expressing bibliographic data for the future. The project is still under development.

Bibliographic instruction: teaching users how an information organization functions, how materials are organized, and how to take advantage of information services.

Bibliographic records: an entry representing a specific item in a library catalog or bibliographic database containing all the data elements necessary for a full description, presented in a specific bibliographic format.

Big6: a six-stage model to help anyone solve problems or make decisions by using information. The six stages are (1) task definition, (2) information-seeking strategies, (3) location and access, (4) use of information, (5) synthesis, and (6) evaluation.

Big data: data sets derived from millions of transactions taking place on the Internet, through cell phones, via GPS, and by other electronic devices; analysis of these anonymous transactions can reveal broad patterns in human behavior and information use.

Big deals: agreements or subscriptions with the large, expensive journal publishers in the STEM fields, such as Elsevier and Wiley.

Blended learning: a combination of in-classroom and asynchronous online instruction.

Bookmobile: a large motorized vehicle, such as a bus or van, that is furnished with a small library collection and is usually operated by a librarian or library staff and serves as a traveling branch of the neighborhood public library system. It serves community members living in remote areas or those who have no access to transportation.

Boolean operators: logical command (and, or, not) that allows users to combine words or phrases when searching online resources, such as an online catalog or bibliographic database.

Brand: a symbol that is often signified by a logo, which can be a name, term, design, or symbol designed to memorably communicate the organization and its products and services.

Branding: the systematic process of maintaining and developing quality products and services that create goodwill and loyalty among customer groups.

Budget: a plan that allocates monetary amounts to specific elements of income.

Bundled information: refers to information content being selected and prepackaged before it is sold to an information organization. For example, sets of books may be "bundled" and sold as a set.

Care-based ethics: an approach to ethics with caring for other people at the heart of all decisions.

Cataloger: an information professional who specializes in or supervises the cataloging process in an information organization, including preparing bibliographic records, subject analysis, and classification.

Cataloging: the process of creating bibliographic entries and metadata for a library catalog.

CC BY: the Creative Commons Attribution Only license, which is the most permissive of the suite of Creative Commons licenses, allowing users the freedom to use and reuse content in any way they wish, provided that proper credit (attribution) is given to the author.

Censorship: prohibition of the production, distribution, circulation, or display of any work deemed objectionable by a governing authority because of language, content, or other ideas it views as dangerous and detrimental to its readers; examples include a software filter on the Internet or a book removed permanently from library shelves.

Circulating library: a library whose collections reflect popular reading materials with an emphasis on fiction (as distinguished from literature).

Circulation: the dual role of facilitating the access of physical items between the information organization and the user and of being able to identify the location of any item in the physical collection at all times.

Classification scheme: a list of classes arranged according to a set of preestablished principles for the purpose of organizing items in a collection, or entries in an index, bibliography, or catalog, into groups based on their similarities and differences to facilitate access and retrieval. In the United States, most library collections are classified by subject.

Cloud: a descriptor for computing services and resources stored on off-site servers and accessible from anywhere. "My files are stored in the cloud."

Cloud computing: a model of technology deployment based on hardware and software accessed via the Internet without the need for software installed on local servers or on the devices of those that use the service.

Cloud storage: digital file storage, which may be outsourced or freely available, that is distributed across multiple and sometimes dispersed locations.

cMOOC: also called a connectivist MOOC, a MOOC that is learner centered, collaborative, and based on learning through relationships and connections; cMOOCs are associated with George Siemens's (2005) connectivism theory. cMOOCs can be contrasted with xMOOCs.

Code of ethics: a collection of values and principles by which a profession governs itself.

Cognitive processes: cognitive activities such as perceiving, interpreting, and evaluating information, solving a problem, making a decision, reasoning, and so forth that people engage in when interacting with information.

Collection building: the process of creating a collection or adding to an existing collection based on a specific purpose, group of people, location, or time to make the collection relevant to its users.

Collection development: the process of identifying the strengths or weaknesses of a collection in terms of patron needs and community resources and using the information gathered to strengthen all or parts of a collection to better serve its users.

Common Core: a set of standards that promotes student-driven learning in which evidence in the form of texts is used to build knowledge and understanding.

Community analysis: the gathering of information (e.g., demographic, economic, political, geographic, sociological information) about a community or organization that will be served by an information organization to aid in activities such as collection development and advocacy. Community analysis tools may include census data, surveys, statistical analysis, and personal observations.

Community hub: a physical or online environment that is accessible to all groups in the community or area it serves—providing a focal point for the community, fostering greater local community interaction, and bringing residents together to improve their quality of life, see or make friends, and get information and support.

Compact shelving: compressed shelving units that provide information organizations with the ability to store more physical materials in their collections.

Competency: ability, knowledge, or skill set needed to meet performance objectives for a specific task.

Competitive intelligence: data gathering and analysis to research competitors.

Connected learning: an educational model that uses the power of today's technology (e.g., mobile devices, open networks) to engage the learner's interest, support collaborative learning, keep learning relevant, and enable access to learning experiences on demand.

Conservation: the set of preservation practices used to rectify damage done to an object and/or the set of actions taken to slow an object's deterioration.

Consortia: groups of information organizations based on geography, areas of focus, member attributes, or any other criteria that might help to create a beneficial relationship for the members around one or more cooperative activities.

Consortial lending partnerships: groups of libraries, often based on geographic region, that agree to share their materials with one another at low cost or no cost by entering into a consortium.

Control: knowing what is occurring in an organization in comparison to preset standards or objectives and then making any necessary corrections. Also indicates the authority or ability to manage or direct funds use and allocation.

Cooperative collection development: a model of collection development in which partner libraries agree to divide up collecting areas between them in order to build complementary rather than duplicative collections and share their acquisitions freely with each other.

Copy cataloging: a model of describing collection materials where a bibliographic record from an external service is identified and downloaded into the database of the local system. Copy cataloging also includes enhancing substandard or incomplete records found on a bibliographic service to a higher level.

Copyright: a legal term of protection for original works fixed in a tangible medium, subject to a variety of limitations. Copyright gives a work's creator the exclusive rights of reproduction, distribution, preparing derivative works, public display, public performance, and public performance by digital audio transmission.

Creation culture: a contemporary subculture of people who are dedicated to craftsmanship and creation, particularly encouraging the use of new technologies and unique applications. Also known as maker culture.

Creative Commons (CC): a nonprofit organization that promotes the sharing of creative works and knowledge via a free suite of standardized licenses which allow copyright owners to give the public permission to use their work under set conditions. CC licenses benefit both creators who wish to share their works more freely, and users who wish to use or adapt works for their own projects. Creative Commons licenses do not replace copyright but are based upon it.

Critical information literacy: the idea that the information environment is politically and socially constructed. Therefore, users need to know more than how to survive within the existing environment; they also need to learn how to critically evaluate the environment and devise ways to change it.

Critical thinking: the ability to use higher-order thinking skills, such as analysis, synthesis, and evaluation, in order to accomplish a specific goal.

Cross section: views that illustrate heights and vertical relationships (as in blueprints).

Cultural competence: skill and proficiency developed through and exemplified by interaction, experience, behavior, and respect with individuals from diverse cultural backgrounds and the use of these skills in services, work, and organizational development.

Cultural pluralism: minority groups, or perceived minority groups, are encouraged to maintain their unique identities while at the same time being respected within the dominant culture.

Culture of assessment: a consistent awareness of the need to continuously review and evaluate programs, services, collections, and other offerings provided through information centers, and to ensure that each is aligned with the organization's mission, values, and goals.

Curation: denotes the range of tasks involved in managing content—including such important steps as selection, acquisition, cataloging, and transformation. It is often conjoined with the term "digital" to mark the specific activities that are undertaken for digital objects.

Customer markets: are people who express an interest in what (e.g., products, services) the organization offers.

Cybersecurity: a form of information security that is focused on the protection of information, communications, and systems in the online environment.

Dark archive: a storage location that is intentionally restricted for access and which is intended to see little regular activity.

Dashboard: a customized, updateable set of widgets designed to meet the needs of a specific employee, executive(s), work team, or group in an organization. A digital dashboard might include stock prices, competitor profiles, weather data, a calendar management function, e-mail access, news feeds, and various types of company-specific information.

Data breach: the unauthorized access or acquisition of computerized data that compromises or has likely compromised the security, confidentiality, or integrity of information that relates to an identified or identifiable person or persons. Breaches may be intentional or unintentional.

Data broker: a business or entity that collects, analyzes, and packages information about consumers with the intention of selling the data to individuals, advertisers, or the government without the consumers' knowledge or permission.

Data curation: the management of research data to enable discovery and retrieval, maintain its quality, add value, and ensure its preservation.

Data curator (or manager or steward): someone who plans and manages a digital object throughout its entire life cycle, from creation to ongoing preservation or scheduled destruction.

Data grid: a method of storing extremely large quantities of data across multiple locations and multiple types of storage media, which also provides software and services to enable consistent access.

Data integrity: accuracy and consistency of stored data that is characterized by the lack of alteration in data between updates or migration of the data record.

Data literacy: the notion that as the importance of and access to raw data for analysis grows, the more critical users and data consumers must be able to assess both the quality of the data being analyzed as well as the rigor applied to its analysis.

Data visualization: uses visuals to tell a story or communicate data and its significance.

Deaccessioning: removal of an item or items from a library collection, usually undertaken in order to weed out unused material and make room for new acquisitions.

Deacidification: treatment used to stabilize paper that is deteriorating due to its acid content.

Deontology: a rule-based approach to ethics popularized by Immanuel Kant.

Digital asset: an item that has been formatted into a binary source; it may be defined as textual content (digital assets), images (media assets), and multimedia (media assets).

Digital asset management system: a system designed to organize and display digital content produced in a variety of media types. The content is usually locally owned and controlled, rather than licensed from a third party.

Digital connectivity: utilizing cellular and Wi-Fi networks to connect to information and participatory social networks.

Digital content: a common term used for information that is accessed in a digital format through a medium that requires a device to either retrieve, use, or store the information in order to be used by a user. Computer files, e-books, databases, streaming media, audio files, and websites are all considered digital content and are also sometimes referred to as e-content, e-resources, or virtual content.

Digital curation: the process of maintaining, preserving, and adding value to digital research data throughout its life cycle.

Digital divide: the chasm between people who have access to the Internet, the hardware, and the ability to use it and those who do not. Often correlated with low socioeconomic status or rural locations.

Digital librarian: an information professional who employs the traditional tenets of library science (e.g., collection development, resource description and organization, guided access to information) to digital objects and collections.

Digital library: involves information products and services that are organized, described, and delivered through technology.

Digital literacy: a set of skills and abilities to use technology tools and resources effectively.

Digital Millennium Copyright Act (DMCA): an addition to U.S. copyright law signed on October 28, 1998, that addresses a variety of copyright issues. Most important for information professionals, it prohibits the circumvention of technological protection measures (such as encryption) and offers online service providers a safe harbor for potentially infringing user-generated content.

Digital native: someone who has been exposed to and freely used digital technology throughout their entire lives.

Digital preservation: a series of managed activities necessary to ensure continued access to digital materials for as long as they are needed.

Digital repository: an online archive for collecting, preserving, and disseminating the intellectual outputs of an institution, collection of institutions, or discipline.

Digital surrogates: electronic reproductions of typically printed library materials.

Digitization: the process of capturing a digital version of a physical object. Also called digital reformatting.

Direct value: a tangible and clear worth of a product or service (e.g., the financial savings one realizes by borrowing a book through a library rather than purchasing it; or the improvement in grades achieved by a student after receiving research instruction).

Diversity: acknowledgment of different cultural groups within a society and the resulting exclusion, prejudice, discrimination, and isolation experienced by those groups; diversity assumes a commitment to upending or righting the wrongs experienced by different cultural groups.

Dublin Core: a metadata standard comprised of fifteen elements, commonly used to describe digital objects.

e-Book: digital version of a published book or, more recently, an original written work whose first conception is already in digital format.

Ecological systems theory: an approach to human behavior and development that focuses on interactions among people (individuals, relationships with others) and their environments (community, culture). Sometimes referred to as the ecological systems perspective or the social ecological model.

Economic impact: the compounded financial effect of a service, organization, or event on a specified population; in the case of information organizations, this is most often its immediate community.

Embedded e-brarian: a virtual embedded librarian.

Embedded librarian: a librarian who proactively goes to where library users are rather than waiting for users to approach him or her. The embedded librarian is not bound to a physical library but works collaboratively with faculty as part of a team or participates in an online learning management system to support student information needs.

Embedded librarianship: a service model in which the information professional is integrated fully into the community being served.

Emotional intelligence: being aware of and sensitive to one's own and others' emotions. This includes having the ability to authentically listen to colleagues and stakeholders and to facilitate dialogue.

Emotional style: how a person manages the complexity of emotions with other people.

Emulation: creating an environment that enables digital content to be rendered in new software and hardware environments without changing the content file.

Encumbrance: a commitment to pay a particular amount of money in the future. In a budget, it can be done with a purchase order or a standing order or any type of commitment to ensure the money promised is available to be spent.

Environmental scanning: proactively identifies external opportunities and threats that affect the organization as well as internal organizational strengths and weaknesses.

Equity of access: the creation and sustaining of quality services for all users through active and regular consideration of their multiple perspectives and experiences. Also called equitable access.

E-rate funds: federal funds established by the Federal Communications Commission (FCC) to give libraries a discount on telecommunications services such as Internet access; requires the adoption of Internet filters as part of accepting the discount.

Ethics: a set of principles that guide decision making in a specified setting.

Ethnographic methods: a qualitative research approach that involves collecting data through field-work so as to understand the user and culture in context.

Evaluation: a process that measures inputs (number of staff and holdings), outputs (percentage of customers served), and outcomes (customer satisfaction).

Evidence-based practice: the notion that practitioners in a given profession seek out and apply research to a topic as part of the decision-making process.

Expenditures: the amounts of money that purchase goods, services, and all costs for human resources.

Explicit knowledge: knowledge that has been articulated, codified, and stored in certain media, making it easily shared and accessible to others. The information contained in encyclopedias and textbooks are good examples of explicit knowledge.

Fabrication: production or manufacture.

Fair use: a limitation within U.S. copyright law (Section 107) that allows the use of copyrighted materials without permission in certain situations, such as those that often involve teaching, classroom use, or other educational purposes.

First sale doctrine: a part of U.S. copyright law (Section 109) that allows the owner of a particular copy of a copyrighted work to sell, give away, or otherwise dispose of that copy, as long as other exclusive rights of the copyright owner are not infringed.

Flipped classroom: a pedagogical model where students review lectures and course materials outside of class time and engage in discussion and other active learning activities in class.

Formal learning: a type of learning that is structured and organized by an institution. Learning is intentional and guided by a curriculum, usually based on a formal program.

Formalized question: an articulated information need which an individual has transformed into a query that can be posed to an information system (e.g., librarian, search engine).

Formative assessment: evaluating learning, during an instructional experience, in order to determine users' current understanding and progress so instruction can be modified to better meet the learning needs of the students (rather than at the end of an instructional experience).

Freedom of Information Act (FOIA): the Freedom of Information Act was enacted in 1966, when it provided for significant expansion of public access to government information.

Friends of the Library: a support organization that provides funding (e.g., for operational items like books and programming) to the library, often through used book sales and book stores run by volunteers.

Fumigation: method of pest control in which gas-based pesticides are dispersed in a closed location to suffocate insects and other living pests.

Gamification: applying game structure to learning and other environments that can be enriched with gamelike elements.

General fund: the resources used to sustain the daily activities of organizations and pay for operation and administrative expenses.

General ledger account: an account used to sort and store balance sheet and income statement transactions.

Geolocation: utilizing the geographic location identified by a networked device, such as a smart phone or tablet, to display information about that location; comments, reviews, and "check ins" might be recorded as well.

Geopolitical: a combination of geographic and political factors relating to or influencing a nation or region.

Globalization: a process of interaction and integration among the peoples, companies, and governments of different countries.

Guerilla user testing: low-cost user/usability testing (such as for a website) that takes place "in the wild" by approaching members of the intended audience with a request for quick feedback.

HathiTrust: a large-scale partnership of academic and research libraries offering millions of titles including content digitized via the Google Books project and the Internet Archive.

Human–computer interaction: a broad field that studies how computer technology influences human work and activities.

Hyperlinked library: an open, participatory institution that welcomes user input and creativity. It is built on human connections and conversations via networked tools and in-person interactions.

Hypermedia: linked content of diverse types (e.g., data, text, image, audio, video) stored in a database format.

Inclusion: the act or practice of recognizing and valuing the unique skills, perspectives, and experiences of different people.

Incognizance: a state of not knowing what one does not know; not having the awareness or familiarity with a topic to acknowledge or assess one's related information needs.

Indexer: creates complex indexes and taxonomies.

Indirect value: may be expressed through tangible worth (e.g., the profit realized by the respending of dollars invested in salaries) or intangible benefit (e.g., the greater sense of community created by the presence of publicly accessible spaces).

Infinite learning: the ability to learn anytime and anywhere, and the role that information professionals play in supporting learners in communities using a range of technologies.

Informal learning: a type of learning that is not organized and not guided by a rigid curriculum; it is often thought of as experimental and spontaneous.

Informatician: someone who works with creating and modifying systems based on human interaction and needs.

Informatics: a broad academic field comprising information processing and the creation of information systems and technology tools using computer programming.

Information architect: someone who organizes content and flow of information, often online, for their employers.

Information architecture: the structural design of shared information environments, which increases the findability and usability of the information.

Information behavior: an umbrella term that encompasses people's interactions with information, from seeking, to finding and evaluating, to use.

Information cycle: the term refers to the creation, dissemination, evaluation, and use of information in its various media formats (e.g., print, audio, video) and access mechanisms (e.g., Internet, intranets, web, and physical).

Information ethics: a set of principles that guide decision making as it relates to the use—and abuse—of information, information technology, and information systems.

Information intermediator: a person who searches for information on behalf of or who facilitates access to information for another person; librarians and other information professionals may be considered "intermediaries."

Information licensing: the transaction between information organization and publisher by which information in digital formats is purchased or leased.

Information literacy: the ability to engage in practices related to accessing, evaluating, and using information to build knowledge.

Information Literacy Competency Standards for Higher Education: a set of four standards and related performance indicators developed by ACRL.

Information literacy instruction: the teaching of strategies, methods, and processes by an information professional for finding and using information effectively and efficiently.

Information need: information that people need to facilitate the performance of a work, academic, or everyday-life task; pursue something pleasurable; satisfy curiosity; or solve a problem. Needs may or may not be articulated by a user community.

Information packaging: also known as data packaging, a process of collecting data and other assets in a "package" to provide convenient delivery, installation, and managing of data sets.

Information policies: all rules, laws, and restrictions, both explicit and tacit, including international, national, regional, local, and organizational, that affect the creation, access, use, and dissemination of information.

Information privacy: the right of individuals and organizations to control the collection and sharing of their personal information without consent.

Information professional: a person who uses specialized knowledge to advance the mission of an organization and empowers clients to understand and know the provided information.

Information repositories: online archives for collecting, preserving, and providing access to electronic versions of the intellectual productions of an institution; for a university, this might include monographs, journal articles, theses, and dissertations.

Information resource officer: typically an information professional with a degree in library and information science who works for the U.S. Department of State and is responsible for information policy development, program planning, and budgeting; works with officials and foreign national staff to design, implement, evaluate, and promote Information Resource Center programs in a cross-cultural environment.

Innovation labs: spaces in information organizations that provide new technology to personnel and clients. These facilities support experimental and creative projects using technologies early in their deployment cycles. These technologies may not be widely available or may be at a level of expense that limits their availability to the general public.

Inquiry-based learning: engaging in learning by asking questions rather than having information provided.

Institutional repository: an online collection of the output of staff members at an institution, intended to serve as both a place of preservation and access; frequently used in higher education.

Instructional design: a systematic process for designing instructional experiences based on the population being taught and the outcomes desired.

Integrated library system (ILS): originally developed to manage print collections, ILS is a business application to support the operation of libraries and related organizations; it is based on databases with multiple functional modules (e.g., cataloging for the description of resources, circulation to manage lending and returns of physical collection items, acquisitions for the procurement of materials, serials control, and an online catalog to provide customer-oriented services).

Intellectual freedom: the right to explore information and ideas without interference or fear of retribution based on the content of that information.

Intellectual property: content and ideas protected by one or more legal options, including copyright, trademarks, service marks, and/or patents.

Intelligence analyst: a researcher who supports an agency's information and research needs.

Interlibrary loan: the process of securing materials from another information organization.

Internal controls: processes that control risk for an organization to conduct business in an orderly manner; to safeguard assets and resources; to deter and detect errors, fraud, and theft; and to ensure accuracy and completeness of accounting information and produce reliable and timely financial information.

Internet filtering: automated software that restricts access to certain websites or types of content based on lists of unauthorized sites, keyword triggers, or other methods for detecting unacceptable content.

Intranet: a private computer network that uses Internet protocol technology to share information, content, policies, operational systems, or computing services within an organization; often restricted to employees of the organization.

iSearch: a European Union project that aims to provide a unified framework for multimodal content indexing, sharing, search, and retrieval.

Issues tracking: the process of tracking issues that have a material effect on the success of an enterprise. Examples could include tracking competitors, customer comments, etc.

JavaScript: a computer programming language frequently used on the web.

KBART Initiative: a project by the National Information Standards Organization (NISO) and the United Kingdom Serials Group (UKSG) that established a set of best practices for the exchange of electronic resource holdings metadata between content providers and knowledge base developers. It relieves information professionals of the time-consuming process of reconciling e-journal title lists and other inadequacies common in title holding lists.

Knowledge management: the process of using an integrated approach to identifying, capturing, sorting, evaluating, and storing an entity's information that makes knowledge easily searchable. The types of information managed by an enterprise depend on the nature of the organization and may include documents, policies, procedures and databases, to name a few.

Knowledge manager: someone who is responsible for organizing, harvesting, and creating a sharing structure or platform for institutional knowledge.

Leadership: the act of leading people, staff, or organizations to ensure growth and success of initiatives and actions.

Learning 2.0: an online professional development program focused on emerging technology for library staff originating at the Charlotte Mecklenburg Library in 2006 and replicated throughout the world. Also known as "23 Things."

Learning commons: a full-service learning, research, and project space typically combining library resources, such as expert help, with a computer lab and moveable furniture in a repurposed space designed to facilitate both individual and group work.

Learning management system (LMS): an integrated set of online applications used to provide access to course materials, particularly in college and universities to support online programs.

Learning outcomes: statements that describe the end goal of a learning activity, identifying what users should be able to do, know, or value as a result of that activity.

LibGuide: research or subject guides to library resources that support academic courses, topics, or disciplines taught in colleges and universities, named after a content management system developed by Springshare.

Library Bill of Rights (LBOR): the key intellectual freedom policy document for the American Library Association. Based on the First Amendment, LBOR and its Interpretations outline how library workers should address various situations in libraries, such as services to children, privacy protection for library users, services to disabled people, and best practices for collection development.

Library district: one of the geographical areas into which a state is divided for the purpose of administering libraries in accordance with a comprehensive statewide tax plan.

Library foundation: a support organization that provides funding to the library. Often resources come from fund-raisers, cultivated donors, estates, and capital campaigns. A foundation often supports larger capital needs, like buildings and furnishings.

Library services platforms: a new genre of business applications for libraries designed to address a wide range of library materials and based on current technology platforms and computer architectures. Library services platforms support multiple metadata formats, allow flexible workflows surrounding the procurement and management of different types of materials, make use of shared knowledge bases, and are deployed through multitenant Software-as-a-Service platforms.

License: a type of contract; a private, legally binding agreement between parties who may negotiate their terms and conditions; the document between the information organization(s) and publisher that defines the digital content, users, terms, and prices under which access will be provided to the information organization(s).

Licensed content business model: the combination of what resource(s) will be accessed, for what period of time, by which organization(s) and authorized users, terms of use, and the price to be paid for that digital content.

Lifecycle management: refers to the full spectrum of activities a manager undertakes, from creation to disposal of an item or collection.

Lifelong learning: the recognition that learning is an ongoing process that occurs in different contexts.

Limited faceted searching: the use of a faceted search interface, which uses structured metadata that provides an overview of results with clickable categories. The interface allows searchers a fluid transition between narrowing their results without reformulating their queries.

Line-item budgets: lists items in the expense category item by item by the type of expense.

Linked data: data that is structured consistently across multiple sources so that they can be programmatically associated with each other, enabling both stability and interoperability.

Long-range planning: the development of a plan of action by an organization in order to create a long-term direction.

Machine readable: content that is designed to be read by a computer.

Machine-readable cataloging (MARC): a standard digital format for describing bibliographic items, developed by the Library of Congress in the 1960s to enable computerized cataloging.

Macro-level: high level or cultural.

Maker: an amateur or professional creator who engages in the process of transforming materials from one form to another.

Makerspace: a place with equipment, supplies, and instruction for exploring technology and creating, sharing, and collaborating on new things; can involve high-tech items like 3-D printers or low-tech like sewing machines.

Management: the process of coordinating, planning, and assessing the workflow of an organization.

Manager: a person in a position of authority in an organization having the responsibility for employing human and material resources to accomplish the organization's purpose.

Market analyst: works at assessing the attractiveness of markets for the employer.

Marketing: a systematic set of planning tools that are mission driven and optimize product/service delivery to targeted customer groups through customer research, segmentation, mix strategy, and evaluation.

Marketing mix strategy: the cooperation between the aspects of price (customer costs), place of delivery, and promotion of any product/service/offer to optimize customer satisfaction.

Marketing research: the process of finding out all that is possible about factors affecting the organization's environments and actual and potential customer groups, ultimately refining and defining problems, solutions, and opportunities.

Mash-up: describes merging two tools or resource sets into one; for example, merging a census data set onto a Google map.

Meso-level: mid-level or relational.

Metadata: data used to describe objects or other data; structured information describing information resources/objects for a variety of purposes. There are two types of metadata: structural metadata are about the design and specification of data structures and are more properly called "data about the containers of data"; descriptive metadata, on the other hand, are about individual instances of application data, the data content.

Metadata crosswalk: a table or mapping of bibliographic data elements used to convert metadata terms from one schema to another. Also known as a schema crosswalk.

Metaliteracy: overarching term that recognizes the contributions of a wide range of literacies to a user's ability to not just find, evaluate, and use information effectively, but to perform these activities in a collaborative, online environment.

Microaggression: an act of discrimination by those who think they are not intending to be prejudiced.

Microcontroller: a small computer mounted on a circuit board that can only run one program at a time.

Micro-level: small level or individual.

Mobile technologies: the technologies employed by portable devices that allow users to perform a wide variety of tasks, such as web browsing, instant messaging, video gaming, and social networking on cellular phones, tablets, laptops, GPS navigation devices, etc.

MOOC: also known as a massive open online course, an online course aimed at teaching large numbers of participants and often offered by renowned schools. Courses are free, but students do not always get university credit or graded work (e.g., assignments, exams); sometimes participants can pay to get proof of attendance, such as a certificate. See also cMOOC and xMOOC.

Multiculturalism: the promotion, celebration, or recognition of different cultural groups within a society.

Multitype library system: a multitype library system embraces two or more types of libraries in the same system or consortia.

Needs assessment: evaluating the gap between the current situation of an organization and the future desired state based on understanding user and institutional needs.

Negotiation skills: a skill set that includes strategies and techniques that facilitate the resolution of a common problem, make deals, and manage conflicts.

Nitrite deterioration: decomposition of nitrate film in which the film spontaneously combusts and burns when stored at moderately hot temperatures (greater than 106 degrees Fahrenheit).

Offer: the product or service that the organization offers to meet customer needs.

Online learning: delivers courses over the Internet either synchronously or asynchronously. Also called e-learning.

Ontology: a formal, explicit specification of a shared conceptualization; provides a common vocabulary to denote the types, properties, and interrelationships of concepts in a specific domain of knowledge.

Open access: the free, immediate availability of scholarly articles on the open Internet, coupled with the rights to use these articles fully in the digital environment, free of most copyright and licensing restrictions.

Open access funds: financial resources set aside by an institution to support publication models that enable free, immediate, online distribution of, and access to, scholarly research.

Open access journals: scholarly journals that are available online to the reader without financial, legal, or technical barriers other than those inseparable from gaining access to the Internet itself.

Open Archives Initiative: an initiative that develops and promotes interoperability standards that aim to facilitate the efficient dissemination of content.

Open digital repositories: digital repositories that house open access articles and manuscripts.

Open source: code, blueprints, patterns, or designs that are openly shared with anyone and can be reused, changed, updated, or adapted by others, with the understanding that others will then share their versions with the larger community as well.

Open source software: applications and source codes that are developed and distributed for free and allow modification and redistribution of new versions.

Optical media: storage media designed for digital content to be written/read by lasers. Compact discs are a form of optical media.

Opt-in group license: a license wherein each library decides to participate to gain access to the digital content being licensed.

Organization development: a management concept applied to planned efforts to increase organizational performance focusing on the human side of an organization.

Original cataloging: involves creating an entirely new record for an item when no other record is available from an external bibliographic service.

Orphan work: a work for which the copyright owner cannot be located or identified by an individual who wishes to use that work after making diligent efforts.

Page view: one instance of a user viewing a web page.

Paraprofessionals: a member of the library support staff who usually performs technical support duties or performs specific procedures and tasks that do not involve professional judgment.

Peer review: the evaluation of work by one or more people of similar competence to the producers of the work (peers). Peer review methods are employed to maintain standards of quality, improve performance, and provide credibility for a scholarly work.

Performance budgets: budgets where the funds are attached to performance objectives; connects the input of resources with the output of services.

Performance evaluation: the analysis of how closely a person, program, service, or organization has met previously stated goals.

Performance objectives: descriptions of the types of activities a learner can accomplish at the end of a specific time period that demonstrates the understanding of a skill or concept.

Personal data: information relating to an identified or identifiable person; varies by country. See also personally identifiable information.

Personal learning networks (PLN): a series of online and in-person connections used to enhance learning; includes professional groups, social networks, blogs and microblogging sites, and any other platform where ideas are exchanged.

Personally identifiable information (PII): used in U.S. privacy law to refer to personal data. Countries differ on their identification of the types of personal data that are considered PII. See also personal data.

Planning: determining meaningful, achievable, and quantifiable objectives that an organization needs to pursue and what is needed to implement them.

Policy paradox: a situation where a policy attempts to satisfy priorities from conflicting sets of values.

Power: the capacity or ability to direct or influence the behavior of others or the course of events.

Preservation: designates the steps taken to ensure the long-term accessibility and usability of content—including (but not restricted to) activities that prevent content from deteriorating; may include printed and digital materials.

Principle: fundamental idea that serves as the basis for something; in an ethical context, may also be referred to as morals, values, or beliefs.

Prior restraint: a legal term referring to "precensorship," usually through government action, to prevent the publication or distribution of content to information seekers or to information organizations.

Privacy: the right to control or block the collection and dissemination of information; can be personal or institutional.

Privacy audit: an assessment that focuses on privacy risk which includes evaluation of all privacy documentation and examines how data flows through an organization as well as data-handling practices.

Privacy literacy: a concept that assesses and explains consumers' attitudes regarding the collection, processing, and employment of their personal data.

Problem situation: a situation that arises from factors within the individual (e.g., curiosity, uncertainty) or the environment (e.g., work task) whereby the individual realizes that they need information in order to move forward.

Program budgets: budgets where all the expenses are grouped by program.

Promotion: an aspect of marketing that embodies marketing communication tools, such as advertising, direct mail, personal selling, sales promotion, or publicity, delivered by media ranging from print to online to targeted customer groups.

Proprietary software: applications whose creator retains full control and exclusive ownership.

Prospect research and development: works with an organization researching those who donate and potential donors.

Protective enclosure: mechanism (e.g., box, case) intended to physically support and buffer a fragile item so that its pieces remain together, intact, and undisturbed over time.

Public domain: a way of referring to works not protected by copyright ("in the public domain"). This is usually because copyright protection has expired, although sometimes authors intentionally give up their copyright to make the work publicly usable.

Public forum analysis: a legal term referring to government property (local, state, or federal) that is open to First Amendment expression. Some limits can be placed on access to the forum.

Public good: a service or institution that has a primary purpose of improving the community and is open to all.

Public relations: activities designed to promote and boost the organization's image and present its customer offers as unique and competitive.

Publicity: a promotional tool that relies on free media or special events in lieu of paid advertising.

Purpose specification: the principle that exemplifies that a citizen be informed of the specific purpose of the collection of personal data for which it is processed and stored.

Python: a programming language known for its readability and brevity.

Reading promotion: the support for personal and academic reading of print through programs that model and encourage reading.

Ready reference questions: reference questions that have a brief, factual answer.

Records management (RM): the professional practice or discipline of controlling and governing the most important records of an organization throughout the record's life cycles; includes identifying, classifying, prioritizing, storing, securing, archiving, preserving, retrieving, tracking, and destroying records.

Reference interview: the conversation between an information seeker and information professional, whereby the professional asks strategic questions to understand the information need presented and determine the best course of action.

Reflective ceiling plans: plans that indicate tile patterns and, more importantly, where lighting fixtures will be positioned (as in blueprints).

Reformatting: transferring the intellectual content of an object or collection from one medium to another (e.g., photocopying, microfilming, or digitizing content).

Refreshing: transferring content from one container to another container in the same format and media (e.g., copying a cassette tape to another cassette tape).

Relevancy ranking: an attempt to measure how closely a web page or entry fits possible search terms. Results are ranked with the "best match" having the highest relevance ranking, and they are usually best for searches that are not either/or types of searches.

Remote storage: the storage of collections off-site.

Replicating: making and distributing copies of content.

Repository: the physical space, usually a library or museum, that is used as a place of storage of archival materials, such as manuscripts, rare books, documents, photographs, or born-digital items. Depending on policy, a repository may or may not be accessible to the public.

Reserves: potentially high-use course-related items used for short periods, often kept behind the circulation desk; increasingly being made available online through e-reserves.

Resource sharing: the borrowing and lending of content from information organization collections between information organizations.

Responsibility: an obligation one assumes or is appointed, resulting in being answerable or accountable for something within one's power, control, or management.

Responsive web design: web design that allows a website or web-based software application to adapt to the varying capabilities of devices (especially mobile devices) used to access them.

Revenue: the resources that are allocated (raised or brought in) as income to be used by the organization to fulfill its mission.

Roving reference: a reference service model in which the information professional physically approaches users throughout the library or information organization to solicit questions and provide assistance.

Scaffolding: creating learning experiences that support learners in acquiring new skills while providing enough challenge to the learners so that, with practice and experience, the support can gradually be removed and they can eventually become autonomous.

Scholarly communication: the system by which research and other scholarly output is created, vetted, transmitted to the scholarly community, and preserved for the future.

Scholarly communication program: a library-based initiative to explore and raise awareness of new tools, models, projects, forums, and services designed to help faculty, students, and staff communicate the results of their research and scholarship.

Scholarly publishing: publishing that incorporates peer review.

Scholarly work: a publication that has been peer-reviewed, written by an authority on the subject at hand, and/or is produced by a reputable association.

Second screen sharing: a participatory process in which users might tweet, post to social sites, or interact while watching broadcast programs and events or consuming other types of media.

Section 108: the section of U.S. copyright law that allows libraries and archives to make certain uses of copyrighted works if they meet certain criteria. Sometimes called the library exception.

Sectoral approach: a strategy that consists of policies and measures adopted by a government as a plan of action for a particular area of the economy or society.

Selection: an aspect of collection development that involves the evaluation of materials and making decisions on what to purchase, retain, or remove from the collection. Selection is usually based on established collection development policies, which vary from one type of organization to the other.

Selection tools: materials used by collection developers to make informed decisions before purchasing items for the collection. These could include journals or websites with current book reviews from library professionals who understand the needs and demands of their libraries and users.

Self-check terminal: a kiosk where users can check out library materials on their own without the aid of library staff members.

Sensitive personal data: a subset of personally identifiable information that includes data that is specifically protected. In the United States, this includes social security numbers, identifiable health records, and identifiable financial records.

Serials: publications that are recurring and distributed in successive parts, such as periodicals, newspapers, electronic magazines and journals, and annuals (reports, yearbooks).

Service model: the method of providing information services (e.g., service points, hours, delivery methods, levels of service) that determines how staff members interact with the users who need information, physically or virtually.

SharePoint: a Microsoft computer program that is the dominant intranet software for enterprise applications.

Shelf-reading: the periodic checking of the collection's spine labels to ensure items are in call number order.

Shifting: the process of moving parts of the collection to accommodate growth.

Short-term planning: a type of planning that is task oriented and specific; is used to cover time periods of less than one year in order to help the organization move along within the confines of its long-term plan.

Social capital: the perceived sets of benefits that occur when organizations, groups, or individuals work together (e.g., for the public good).

Social impact: the effect of a service, organization, or event on the welfare and well-being of a specified population; in the case of libraries, this is most often described as the effect on literacy levels, achievement, generalized trust, community cohesion, and the like.

Social library: a library whose collections emphasize literature, history, science, and theology.

Social media manager/online community manager: someone who manages the branding for an organization online and in social media.

Social responsibility: an institution or profession's obligation to make decisions or take actions that will have a positive impact on society.

Software as a Service (SaaS): provides a fully web-based application, usually through commercial subscription fees (in cloud computing).

Spine label: a label on a book's spine that states its location (call number).

Stacks management: the collected processes of maintaining the physical collections of the information organization.

Standards: the established criteria against which subsequent performance can be compared and evaluations can be made. Also descriptions of what a learner should know at the end of a specific time span, course, or grade level.

Sticky-shed syndrome: deterioration of the binder used in tape manufacturing in which the coating of the tape becomes sticky and sheds oxide.

Strategic planning: the process that an organization uses to envision its future, identify what is needed to get there, and define the procedures that are necessary to achieve that future; identifying outcomes and the means to achieve them.

Summative assessment: evaluating learning after an instructional experience in order to determine the efficacy of instruction or if users have met specific learning outcomes or performance objectives.

Surrogate records: a substitute used in place of the original object; in a library catalog, it is a record that contains the description of the actual physical object, in bibliographic form.

Surveillance: in information theory, the government monitoring of actions and behaviors through direct observation of a person, or in the twenty-first century, by collecting data such as telephone records.

Synchronous learning: a type of online learning that is commonly achieved through videoconferencing and chat and is done in real time.

Tablet computing: the use of a portable PC that is equipped with a touch screen interface and usually has a virtual keyboard, built-in web-browsing capabilities, multiple connectivity options, and high-definition support.

Tacit knowledge: a kind of knowledge that is difficult to transfer to another person by means of writing it down or verbalizing it.

Taxonomy: the science of categorization or classification of things based on a predetermined system.

Technical services: an aspect of library operations that includes acquisition, bibliographic control, physical processing, and maintaining library collections.

Technological literacy: the ability to use available hardware, software, and web applications to solve problems and communicate effectively in order to accomplish a specific goal.

Technology futurist: a person who studies and analyzes trends in technology in order to help people understand, anticipate, and prepare for coming changes.

Tenure track: a job classification in North American institutions of higher education used to indicate that an academic (e.g., professor or librarian) is eligible for a permanent, or tenured, position.

Third place: a space for learning practices beyond the home and work/school sphere.

Threshold concepts: key concepts in a discipline or field of study. Once learners understand the concept, their perception of the topic is completely transformed and they are unable to go back to their previous way of thinking.

Tiered reference: a reference service model in which a library assistant screens questions and refers a user to an information professional only when an information need requires the knowledge and skills of an information professional, while answering the questions that do not require an information professional.

Tinkering: the act of puttering or exploring the creation of something that keeps the focus on the process of making, not the product.

Transliteracy: the ability to read, write, and communicate using a variety of media and platforms.

Transparency: the open two-way flow of communication and sharing between governing bodies, frontline workers, and the public.

Union catalog: a listing of the holdings of all the libraries in a library system.

USA PATRIOT Act: a 2001 federal law passed by Congress shortly after the September 11, 2001, terrorist attacks, which provided for a broad expansion of the government's surveillance and data-gathering authority. Of particular concern to libraries and information professionals were the provisions that allowed for government's ability to receive access to patron records without a court order, and the concurrent gag order that prohibited the library from informing the patron that his or her record had been requested by the government. The act has undergone revisions and reauthorizations since 2001.

User-created content: content in libraries created by users, such as comments on social media pages, user reviews in catalogs, or materials created in a makerspace.

User experience: a broad term for several disciplines that study the effect of design on the ease of use and level of satisfaction and quality of user interaction with and perceptions of a product, site, or system.

User experience design (UXD): actively works with programmers and others to create the best online or software experience for users.

User satisfaction: the continuum measuring the feeling of having one's needs met as a client, customer, patron, or other person taking advantage of a service, program, or organizational offering.

Utilitarianism: an approach to ethics emphasizing the maximizing of benefits when making decisions, sometimes with a cost to a minority of people impacted by a decision.

Value: the demonstration of the worth of a product, service, or offering to stakeholders, variously expressed through monetary or social terms.

Values: the principles or sense of worth held by an individual or by a collective, such as within a family, an organization, a society, or a government.

Vinegar syndrome: disintegration of acetate film marked by symptoms including a vinegar scent, followed by shrinkage and buckling of the film.

Virtual reference: a method of providing service in which the reference interview is conducted online using communication technologies such as instant messaging, videoconferencing, chat, or e-mail.

Visceral: the internal state whereby people recognize they have an information need but are not able to formally articulate it.

VRA Core: a metadata element scheme developed by the Visual Resources Association for describing works of visual culture and images that document them to facilitate the sharing of information among visual resources collections.

Web analytics: statistics that measure the use of content delivered via the web.

Web scripting: adding interactivity to web pages through automation.

xMOOCs: often aligned with a behaviorist approach to learning, where instruction is divided into small manageable chunks of information, frequently delivered in video lecture style formats and supported by multiple-choice assessment used to provide feedback on performance. Well-known xMOOC providers include EdX, Coursera, and Udacity. xMOOCs can be contrasted with cMOOCs.

Zero-based budget: budgets where all the budget numbers are rebuilt from zero. This means justification is needed for each and every line item or category.

Bibliography

23 Mobile Things. Last modified September 3, 2014. http://23mobilethings.net/wpress.

Aabø, Svanhild. "The Role and Value of Public Libraries in the Age of Digital Technologies." *Journal of Librarianship and Information Science* 37, no. 4 (2005): 205–210. doi:10.1177/0961000605057855.

Abram, Stephen. "Post-Information Age Positioning for Special Librarians." In *Out Front with Stephen Abram: A Guide for Information Leaders*. Chicago, IL: American Library Association, 2007.

————. *Stephen's Lighthouse* (blog). Last modified October 22, 2014. http://stephenslighthouse.com.

Acronymfinder. "IRO." http://www.acronymfinder.com/information-resource-office-(US-Department -of-State).(IRO).html.

Adeyoyin, Samue, Imam Abayomi, and Taofik Olatunde Bello. "Management of Change in the 21st Century Libraries and Information Centres." *Library Philosophy & Practice*, paper 695 (2012). http:// digitalcommons.unl.edu/libphilprac/695.

Adler, Melissa A. "The ALA Task Force on Gay Liberation: Effecting Change in Naming and Classification of GLBTQ Subjects." *Advances in Classification Research Online* 23, no. 1 (2013). https://journals.lib .washington.edu/index.php/acro/article/viewFile/14226/12086.

Adler, Nancy J. *Leadership Insight*. New York: Routledge, 2010.

Agosto, Denise E., and Sandra Hughes-Hassell. "Toward a Model of the Everyday Life Information Needs of Urban Teenagers, Part 1: Theoretical Model." *Journal of the American Society for Information Science and Technology* 57, no. 10 (2006): 1394–1403.

Aguiar, Mark, and Erik Hunt. "Measuring Trends in Libraries: The Allocation of Time Over Five Decades." *Quarterly Journal of Economics* 122, no. 3 (August 2007): 969–1006.

Alexander, F. King. "The Changing Face of Accountability: Monitoring and Assessing Institutional Performance in Higher Education." *The Journal of Higher Education* 71, no. 4 (July–August 2000): 411–431. http://www.jstor.org/stable/2649146.

Amazon.com. "Amazon.com Now Selling More Kindle Books Than Print Books." Last modified May 19, 2011. http://phx.corporate-ir.net/phoenix.zhtml?c=176060&p=irol-newsArticle&ID=1565581&highlight.

American Association of Colleges and Universities. "Information Literacy Value Rubric." Last modified July 20, 2014. http://www.aacu.org/value/rubrics/InformationLiteracy.cfm.

American Association of School Librarians (AASL). *Implementing the Common Core State Standards: The Role of the School Librarian*. American Library Association. Last modified November 11, 2013. http:// www.ala.org/aasl/sites/ala.org.aasl/files/content/externalrelations/CCSSLibrariansBrief_FINAL. pdf.

————. "Information Power: Guidelines for School Library Media Programs." Last modified May 2, 2014. http://www.d91.net/LRC/LRCPDF/Attachment%201-A.pdf.

———. *Standards for the 21st Century Learner*. Chicago, IL: American Association of School Librarians, 2007. http://www.ala.org/aasl/sites/ala.org.aasl/files/content/guidelinesandstandards/learning standards/AASL_Learning_Standards_2007.pdf.

American Association of School Librarians (AASL) and Association for Educational Communications and Technology (AECT). *Information Literacy Standards for Student Learning*. Chicago, IL: American Library Association, 1998. http://umanitoba.ca/libraries/units/education/media/InformationLiteracy Standards_final.pdf.

———. *Information Power: Building Partnerships for Learning*. Chicago, IL: American Library Association, 1998.

American Association of School Libraries National Research Forum. "Causality: School Libraries and Student Success." Last modified June 25, 2014. http://www.ala.org/aasl/sites/ala.org.aasl/files/content/researchandstatistics/CLASSWhitePaper_6-24-14_DRAFT.pdf.

American Civil Liberties Union (ACLU). "This Compromise Is Not Acceptable: Constitutionally Suspect South Carolina Budget Measure Is An Assault on Academic Freedom." Last modified June 13, 2014. http://www.aclusouthcarolina.org/news/2014/06/13/compromise-not-acceptable -constitutionally-suspect-south-car.

American Institute for Conservation (AIC). "Book and Paper Group." Last modified April 18, 2014. http://cool.conservation-us.org/coolaic/sg/bpg.

American Library Association (ALA). "2007 Paul Howard Award for Courage Recipient Named." Last modified May 15, 2007. http://www.ala.org/Template.cfm?Section=archive&template=/content management/contentdisplay.cfm&ContentID=157765.

———. *Anglo-American Cataloging Rules*. 2nd ed. Chicago, IL: American Library Association, 2009.

———. "Code of Ethics of the American Library Association." 2008. Last modified October 21, 2014. http://www.ala.org/advocacy/proethics/codeofethics/codeethics.

———. "Commission on New Technological Uses of Copyrighted Works (CONTU) Guidelines for Interlibrary Loan Photocopying." http://www.ala.org/advocacy/sites/ala.org.advocacy/files/content/copyright/GLsInterlibLoan.pdf.

———. "Core Competencies—Section 8, Administration and Management." Last modified August 12, 2014. http://www.ala.org/educationcareers/careers/corecomp/corecompetences.

———. "Core Values of Librarianship." Last modified June 29, 2004. http://www.ala.org/advocacy/intfreedom/statementspols/corevalues.

———. "Diversity Counts." Accessed July 24, 2014. http://www.ala.org/offices/diversity/diversitycounts/divcounts.

———. "Frontline Advocacy Toolkit." Last modified July 8, 2014. http://www.ala.org/advocacy/advleg/advocacyuniversity/frontline_advocacy.

———. "Intellectual Freedom." Last modified September 17, 2014. http://www.ala.org/advocacy/intfreedom.

———. *Intellectual Freedom Manual*. 8th ed. Chicago, IL: American Library Association, 2010. https://canvas.uw.edu/courses/883067/files/25513452/download?wrap=1.

———. "Office of Government Relations." Last modified October 10, 2014. http://www.ala.org/offices/ogr.

———. "Presidential Committee on Information Literacy: Final Report. January 10, 1989." Last modified July 20, 2014. http://www.ala.org/acrl/publications/whitepapers/presidential.

———. "Public Library Use." In ALA Annual Report, 2014. http://www.ala.org/tools/libfactsheets/alalibraryfactsheet06.

———. RDA: Resource Description and Access. Chicago, IL: American Library Association, 2013.

———. Strategic Plan 2011–2015. Chicago, IL: American Library Association, 2010. http://www.ala.org/aboutala/sites/ala.org.aboutala/files/content/missionhistory/plan/strategic%20plan%202015%20documents/strategic_plan_2.pdf.

———. "Workforce Investment Act (WIA)." Last modified July 20, 2014. http://www.ala.org/advocacy/workforce-investment-act-wia.

American Library Association (ALA) and Association of Educational Communications and Technology (AECT). "Chapter 1—The Vision." In Information Power: Building Partnerships for Learning. Chicago, IL: American Library Association, 1998. http://www.d91.net/LRC/LRCPDF/Attachment%201-A.pdf.

American Library Association Archives. http://archives.library.illinois.edu/alaarchon/?p=creators/creator&id=3476.

American Library Association Council. "Policy B.2.1.11 Diversity in Collection Development." American Library Association Policy Manual. Chicago, IL: American Library Association, 2013. http://www.ala.org/aboutala/governance/policymanual.

———. "Policy B.2.1.12 Universal Right to Free Expression." American Library Association Policy Manual. Chicago, IL: American Library Association, 2013. http://www.ala.org/aboutala/governance/policymanual.

———. "Policy B.2.1.15 Access to Library Resources and Services Regardless of Sex, Gender Identity, Gender Expression, or Sexual Orientation." American Library Association Policy Manual. Chicago, IL: American Library Association, 2013. http://www.ala.org/aboutala/governance/policymanual.

———. "Policy B.2.1.20 Services to Persons with Disabilities." American Library Association Policy Manual. Chicago, IL: American Library Association, 2013. http://www.ala.org/aboutala/governance/policymanual.

———. "Policy B.2.3.1 Linguistic Pluralism." American Library Association Policy Manual. Chicago, IL: American Library Association, 2013. http://www.ala.org/aboutala/governance/policymanual.

American Marketing Association—Dictionary. "Brand." https://www.ama.org/resources/Pages/Dictionary.aspx?dLetter=B&dLetter=B.

Anderson, Mark. Personal communication, September 23, 2013.

Andreasen, Alan R., and Philip Kotler. Strategic Marketing for Nonprofit Organizations. 6th ed. Upper Saddle River, NJ: Prentice Hall, 2003.

Angelo, Thomas A., and K. Patricia Cross. Classroom Assessment Techniques: A Handbook for College Teachers. San Francisco: Jossey-Bass, 1993.

AOL. "Joint Study from AOL and BBDO Turns Traditional View of Mobile Space on Its Head." AOL Press Release. Last modified October 3, 2012. http://corp.aol.com/2012/10/03/joint-study-from-aol-and-bbdo-turns-traditional-view-of-mobile-s.

Apkon, Stephen. The Age of the Image: Redefining Literacy in a World of Screens. New York: Farrar, Straus & Giroux, 2013.

Arma International. *Glossary of Records and Information Management*. Overland Park, KS: Arma International, 2012.

Asher, Andrew, and Susan Miller. "So You Want to Do Anthropology in Your Library? or A Practical Guide to Ethnographic Research in Academic Libraries." ERIAL Project. Last modified September 4, 2014. http://www.erialproject.org/publications/toolkit.

Asia-Pacific Economic Cooperation (APEC). "Privacy Framework." Singapore, APEC Secretariat, 2005. http://www.apec.org/Groups/Committee-on-Trade-and-Investment/~/media/Files/Groups/ECSG/05_ecsg_privacyframewk.ashx.

ASLIB: The Association of Information Management. "About Us." Last modified July 17, 2014. http://aslib.com/about/about_us.htm.

Aspen Institute. "Dialogue on Public Libraries: Aspen Ideas Festival—'The Public Library Reimagined.'" Last modified August 28, 2014. http://www.aspeninstitute.org/policy-work/communications-society/our-work/dialogue-public-libraries.

Association of College and Research Libraries (ACRL). "Academic Library Statistics." Last modified August 3, 2014. http://www.ala.org/acrl/publications/trends.

———. "Framework for Information Literacy for Higher Education." Last modified July 20, 2014. http://acrl.ala.org/ilstandards/?page_id=133.

———. "Information Literacy Competency Standards for Higher Education." Last modified July 12, 2014. http://www.ala.org/acrl/standards/informationliteracycompetency.

Association of Independent Information Professionals. "Code of Ethical Business Practice." Last modified April 20, 2002. http://aiip.org/content/code-ethical-business-practices.

Association for Information and Image Professionals. "What Is Collaboration?" Last modified January 15, 2014. http://www.aiim.org/What-is-Collaboration#sthash.1hDyl26v.dpuf.

Association for Library Services to Children (ALSC). "Competencies for Librarians Serving Children in Public Libraries." (2009). http://www.ala.org/alsc/edcareeers/alsccorecomps.

Association of Research Libraries (ARL). "21st-Century Collections: Calibration of Investment and Collaborative Action." ARL Issue Brief. Washington, DC: Association of Research Libraries, March 10, 2012. http://www.arl.org/storage/documents/publications/issue-brief-21st-century-collections-2012.pdf.

———. "Research Library Expenditure Trends." In *ARL Statistics, 2006–2007*. Washington, DC: Association of Research Libraries, 2007.

———. "Statistics and Assessment Surveys (Canada & US)." Last modified July 13, 2014. http://www.arl.org/focus-areas/statistics-assessment#.U8kbAPlznTo.

Association of Research Libraries Policy Notes. "Recap of the Copyright Office's Roundtables on Orphan Works and Mass Digitization." Last modified September 9, 2014. http://policynotes.arl.org/post/79876737815/recap-of-the-copyright-offices-roundtables-on-orphan.

Association of Specialized and Cooperative Library Agencies (ASCLA). Last modified July 8, 2014. http://www.ala.org/ascla/asclaourassoc/asclainterest/list.

Arbogast, Brian, and Eliza Dresang. "Information Organizations: About the Concept." Unpublished course materials. LIS 5408 Management of Information Organizations, n.d. Florida State University, School of Information.

Atherton, P., D. King, and R. R. Freeman. *Evaluation of the Retrieval of Nuclear Science Document References Using the Universal Decimal Classification in a Computer-Based System*. AIP-UDC-8. New York: American Institute of Physics, 1968.

Authors Guild, Inc. v. Google Inc. 954 F. Supp. 2d 282 (S.D.N.Y. 2013).

Authors Guild, Inc. v. HathiTrust. No. 12-4547-cv (2nd Cir. June 10, 2014).

Baker, Betsy. "Bibliographic Instruction: Building the Librarian/Faculty Partnership." *Reference Librarian* 10, no. 24 (1989): 311–328. http://www.tandfonline.com/doi/abs/10.1300/J120v10n24_25#preview.

Baker, Meredith Attwell. "Why Consumers Care about Spectrum." YouTube video. Posted by CTIA The Wireless Association, July 8, 2014. https://www.youtube.com/watch?v=XA16b_H-ah0.

Baker & Taylor: The Future Delivered. "Home." Last modified September 19, 2014. http://www.baker-taylor.com.

Band, Jonathan. "The Cell Phone Unlocking Saga." Infojustice.org. Last modified March 13, 2014. http://infojustice.org/wp-content/uploads/2014/03/band04132014.pdf.

Banzi, Massimo. "Making Is Best When It's Done Together." *Make* (blog). Last modified February 7, 2014. http://makezine.com/magazine/making-is-best-when-its-done-together.

Batch, Kristin R. *Fencing Out Knowledge: Impacts of the Children's Internet Protection Act 10 Years Later*. ALA OIF/OITP Policy Brief No. 5, June 2014. http://connect.ala.org/files/cipa_report.pdf.

Bates, Marcia. "An Operational Definition of the Information Disciplines." *iConference 2010 Proceedings*, University of Illinois, Champaign, Illinois, 2010, 19–25.

Bates, Mary Ellen. *The True Value of Information: Making the Case for Value-Added Aggregators*. Factiva Institute, 2011. http://www.dowjones.com/factiva/institutefiles/14-The%20True%20Value%20of%20Information%20e-Book.pdf.

Battles, David. M. *The History of Public Library Access for African Americans in the South or Leaving Behind the Plow*. Lanham, MD: Scarecrow Press, 2009.

Bay Area Cancer Connections. "Medical Information Services." Last modified August 17, 2014. http://bcconnections.org/our-services/understanding-cancer.

Bedwell, Linda, and Caitlin Banks. "Seeing through the Eyes of Students: Participant Observation in an Academic Library." *Partnership: The Canadian Journal of Library & Information Practice & Research*, 8, no. 1 (January 2013): 1–17.

Belkin, Nicholas J., and Alina Vickery. *Interaction in Information Systems: A Review of Research from Document Retrieval to Knowledge-Based Systems*. London: British Library, 1985.

Bell, Steven J., and Michael J. Krasulski. "Electronic Reserves, Library Databases and Courseware: A Complementary Relationship." *Journal of Interlibrary Loan, Document Delivery, & Electronic Reserves* 15, no. 1 (2004): 75–85.

Bell, Steven J., and John D. Shank. *Academic Librarianship by Design: A Blended Librarian's Guide to the Tools and Techniques*. Chicago, IL: American Library Association, 2007.

Bennis, Warren. *On Becoming a Leader*. 20th anniversary edition. Philadelphia, PA: Basic Books, 2009.

BerkeleyLaw UCLA. "May 2014 USPTO Multistakeholder Forum on the DMCA Notice and Takedown System." Last modified August 4, 2014. http://www.law.berkeley.edu/17084.htm.

Berman, S. *Prejudices and Antipathies: A Tract on the LC Subject Heads Concerning People*. Reprint ed. Jefferson, NC: McFarland, 2013.

Bernier, Anthony, and Mike Malel. "YA Spaces and the End of Postural Tyranny." *Public Libraries* 53, no. 4 (July/August 2004).

Berry, John N., III. "Library Freedom Fighter Zoia Horn Remembered." *Library Journal*.

Last modified August 19, 2014. http://lj.libraryjournal.com/2014/08/people/library-freedom-fighter -zoia-horn-remembered.

Berry, Patrick W., Alexandra Cavallaro, Elaine Vázquez, Carlos R. DeJesús, and Naomi García. "(Re) voicing Teaching, Learning, and Possibility in Paseo Boricua." In *Youth Community Inquiry: New Media for Community and Personal Growth*, edited by B. C. Bruce, A. Bishop, and N. R. Budhathok. New York: Lang, 2014.

Bertot, John Carlo, Charles R. McClure, and Joe Ryan. "Impact of External Technology Funding Programs for Public Libraries: A Study of LSTA, E-rate, Gates, and Others." *Public Libraries* 41, no. 3 (May/June 2002): 166–171.

Big6.com. "What Is Big6?" Last modified September 3, 2014. http://big6.com.

Blue Ribbon Task Force on Sustainable Digital Preservation and Access. *Sustainable Economics for a Digital Planet: Ensuring Long-Term Access to Digital Information*. Final report. February 2010. http:// brtf.sdsc.edu/biblio/BRTF_Final_Report.pdf.

Bobinski, George S. *Carnegie Libraries: Their History and Impact on American Library Development*. Chicago, IL: American Library Association, 1969.

———. *Libraries and Librarianship*. Lanham, MD: Scarecrow Press, 2007.

———. *Libraries and Librarianship: Sixty Years of Challenge and Change, 1945–2005*. New York: Scarecrow Press, 2007.

Bolorizadeh, A., M. Brannen, R. Gibbs, and T. Mack. "Making Instruction Mobile." *Reference Librarian* 53, no. 4 (2012): 373–383. doi:10.1080/02763877.2012.707488.

Bolt, Nancy. "Libraries from Now On: Imagining the Future of Libraries; ALA Summit on the Future of Libraries—Report to ALA Membership." *ALA Connect*, May 19, 2014. http://connect.ala.org/ node/223667.

Booth, Andrew. "Clear and Present Questions: Formulating Questions for Evidence Based Practice." *Library Hi Tech* 24, no. 3 (2006): 355.

Booth, Char. *Reflective Teaching, Effective Learning: Instructional Literacy for Library Educators*. Chicago, IL: American Library Association, 2011.

Booth, Char, and Dani Brecher. "OK, Library: Implications and Opportunities for Google Glass." *College & Research Libraries News* 75, no. 5 (2014): 234–239. http://crln.acrl.org/content/75/5/234.full.

Borrow Direct. Last modified September 3, 2014. http://www.borrowdirect.org.

Boston Public Library. *Report of the Trustees of the Public Library to the City of Boston* (1852). http:// www.bpl.org/govinfo/online-collections/regional-boston-and-massachusetts/boston-public -library-documents-1852-1998.

Bottorff, David W., Katherine Furlong, and David McCaslin. "Building Management Responsibilities for Access Services." In *Twenty-First Century Access Services*, edited by Michael Krasulski and Trevor Dawes. Chicago, IL: American Library Association, 2013.

Bourne, Jill. "Finding the Sweet Spot for Libraries in the Digital Age." Last modified September 11, 2014. http://www.knightfoundation.org/blogs/knightblog/2014/9/11/finding-sweet-spot-libraries -digital-age.

Bowker, George C., and Susan L. Star. *Sorting Things Out*. Cambridge, MA: MIT Press, 2000.

Boyd, Danah. *It's Complicated: The Social Lives of Networked Teens*. New Haven, CT: Yale University Press, 2014.

Boyd, Danah, and Kate Crawford. "Six Provocations for Big Data." Presentation. In *Oxford Internet Institute's A Decade in Internet Time: Symposium on the Dynamics of the Internet and Society*. Oxford, UK: September 21, 2011. http://papers.ssrn.com/sol3/papers.cfm?abstract_id=1926431.

Boyd, Donald C. "The Book Women of Kentucky: The WPA Pack Horse Library Project, 1935–1943." *Libraries and the Cultural Record* 42, no. 2 (2007): 111–128.

Braman, Sandra. *Change of State: Information, Policy and Power*. Cambridge, MA: MIT Press, 2009.

———. "Constitutional Principles and the Information Spaces They Create." In *Change of State: Information, Policy, and Power*. Cambridge, MA: MIT Press, 2006.

Breeding, Marshall. "A Cloudy Forecast for Libraries." *Computers in Libraries* 31, no. 7 (September 2011): 33–24.

———. "Forging Ahead through Times of Major Transitions." *Computers in Libraries* 31, no. 10 (December 2011): 26–29.

———. "The Many Facets of Managing Electronic Resources." *Computers in Libraries* 24, no. 1 (2004): 25.

———. "Technology to Empower Library Control of e-Book Lending." *Smart Libraries Newsletter* 33, no. 8 (2013): 3–6.

———. "The Year of ERM." *Smart Libraries Newsletter* 25, no. 3 (2005): 2.

Brendle-Moczuk, Daniel. "Encouraging Students' Lifelong Learning through Graded Information Literacy Assignments." *Reference Services Review* 34, no. 4 (2006): 498–508. doi:10.1108/ 00907320610716404.

Briden, Judi. "Photo Surveys: Eliciting More Than You Knew to Ask For." In *Studying Students: The Undergraduate Research Project at the University of Rochester*, edited by Nancy Fried Foster and Susan Gibbons. Washington, DC: Association of College and Research Libraries, 2007.

Bronfenbrenner, Urie. *The Ecology of Human Development: Experiments by Nature and Design*. Cambridge, MA: Harvard University Press, 1979.

Brown, Jeanne M. "Informal Assessment for Library Middle Managers." *Library Leadership and Management* 24, no. 1 (Winter 2010): 18–22.

Brown, John Seely "A New Culture of Learning: Cultivating the Imagination for a World of Constant Change." Colorado Springs, CO: Createspace, 2011.

Brown, Judy. *A Leader's Guide to Reflective Practice*. Victoria, BC: Trafford Publishing, 2007.

Brown, Richard D. "William Bentley and the Ideal of Universal Information in the Enlightened Republic." In *Knowledge Is Power: The Diffusion of Information in Early America, 1700–1865*, 197–217. New York: Oxford University Press, 1989.

Brown v. Entertainment Merchants Association. No. 564 U.S. 08-1448. 132 S. Ct. 81 (Supreme Ct. Oct. 3, 2011).

Bryson, John M. *Strategic Planning for Public and Nonprofit Organizations: A Guide to Strengthening and Sustaining Organizational Achievement.* San Francisco, CA: Jossey-Bass, 1995.

Budapest Open Access Initiative. "BOAI 10 Recommendations." Last modified July 1, 2014. http://www.budapestopenaccessinitiative.org/boai-10-recommendations.

Burchell, Noel, and Darl Kolb. "Stability and Change for Sustainability." *Business Review* (University of Auckland Business School) 8, no. 2 (2006): 3.

Bureau of Consumer Protection Center. "The Children's Online Privacy Protection Act of 1998 (COPPA)." 5 U.S.C. 6501–6505. Federal Trade Commission. http://www.ftc.gov/ogc/coppa1.htm.

———. "Complying with COPPA: Frequently Asked Questions; A Guide for Business and Parents and Small Entity Compliance Guide." Federal Trade Commission. Last modified August 29, 2014. http://www.business.ftc.gov/documents/Complying-with-COPPA-Frequently-Asked-Questions.

Burek Pierce, Jennifer. "Young Adult Sexual and Reproductive Health Information Needs." *Youth Information-Seeking Behavior II: Context, Theories, Models, and Issues*, edited by Mary K. Chelton and Colleen Cool, 63–91. Lanham, MD: Scarecrow Press, 2007.

Burgess, Richard. "South Regional Library to Give 3-D Printing, Electronic Kits Trial Run over Summer." *The Advocate.* Last modified July 20, 2014. http://theadvocate.com/news/9184745-123/south-regional-library-to-give.

Burhanna, Kenneth J., Tammy J. Eschedor Voelker, and Julie A. Gedeon. "Virtually the Same: Comparing the Effectiveness of Online versus in-Person Library Tours." *Public Services Quarterly* 4, no. 4 (2008): 317–338. doi:10.1080/15228950802461616.

Burkhardt, Joanna M., Jim Kinnie, and Carina M. Cournoyer. "Information Literacy Successes Compared: Online vs. Face to Face." *Journal of Library Administration* 48, nos. 3/4 (2008): 379–389. http://www.tandfonline.com/doi/full/10.1080/01930820802289425#.VB5PTOcgbDQ.

Burlingham, Bo. "Jim Collins: Be Great Now." Inc.com. Last modified May 29, 2012. http://www.inc.com/magazine/201206/bo-burlingham/jim-collins-exclusive-interview-be-great-now.html#ixzz3EU8YGsBg.

Burnes, Bernard. "Kurt Lewin and the Planned Approach to Change: A Re-appraisal." *Journal of Management Studies* 41, no. 6 (September 2004): 977–1002.

Burns, James MacGregor. *Leadership.* New York: Harper Perennial Modern Classics, 2010.

Burt, Ronald S. "Social Origins of Good Ideas." *American Journal of Sociology* 110, no. 2 (September 2004). http://web.upcomillas.es/personal/rgimeno/doctorado/SOGI.pdf.

Bush, Vannevar. "As We May Think." *The Atlantic*, July 1, 1945. http://www.theatlantic.com/magazine/archive/1945/07/as-we-may-think/303881/?single_page=true.

Business Dictionary. "Data Integrity." Last modified July 31, 2014. http://www.businessdictionary.com/definition/data-integrity.html.

Buy India a Library Blog. "Update: The Library You Helped Build for the Buy India a Library Project." Blog post by jamholdquist, May 28, 2012. http://buyindiaalibrary.wordpress.com.

Canadian Charter of Rights and Freedoms, §§ 7–8, Part I of the Constitution Act, 1982, http://laws-lois.justice.gc.ca/eng/const/page-15.html.

Capitol Records, LLC v. ReDigi Inc. 934 F. Supp. 2d 640 (SD New York District Court, 2013).

Caplan, Priscilla. *Understanding PREMIS*. Washington, DC: Library of Congress, 2009. http://www.loc .gov/standards/premis/understanding-premis.pdf.

Carnegie Foundation for the Advancement of Teaching—The Carnegie Classification of Institutions of Higher Education. "About Carnegie Classification." Last modified June 25, 2014. http://classifications .carnegiefoundation.org.

Carpenter, Kenneth E. "Libraries." In *An Extensive Republic: Print, Culture, and Society in the New Nation*, edited by Robert A. Gross and Mary Kelley, 278-279. Chapel Hill: University of North Carolina Press, 2010.

Case, Donald O. *Looking for Information: A Survey of Research on Information Seeking, Needs and Behavior*. 3rd ed. Bingley, UK: Emerald Group, 2012.

Casey, Genevieve M., ed. "Federal Aid to Libraries: Its History, Impact, Future." *Library Trends* 24 (July 1975).

Cecil, Henry L., and Willard A. Heaps. *School Library Service in the United States: An Interpretive Survey*. New York: H. W. Wilson, 1940. Reprinted in Melvin M. Bowie, *Historic Documents of School Libraries*, 175-191. Fayetteville, AR: Hi Willow Research & Publishing, 1986.

Center for Democracy and Technology. Last modified July 15, 2014. https://cdt.org.

Center for Research Libraries. "Liblicense: Licensing Digital Content—A Resource for Librarians." Last modified July 28, 2014. http://liblicense.crl.edu.

Chatman, E. A. "Framing Social Life in Theory and Research." *New Review of Information Behaviour Research* 1 (2000): 3-18.

Chicago Public Library. *38th Annual Report*, 1909-1910, 17.

———. *42nd Annual Report*, 1913-1914, 23, 27-28.

Chief Officers of State Library Agencies (COSLA). http://www.cosla.org/profiles.

Childers, T. *The Information-Poor in America*. Metuchen, NJ: Rowman & Littlefield, 1975.

Christensen, K., and D. Levinson, eds. "Introduction & Reader's Guide." In *Encyclopedia of Community: From the Village to the Virtual World*, xxxi–xlii. Thousand Oaks, CA: Sage Reference, 2003.

Code of Federal Regulations, title 37, sec. 201.14. http://www.copyright.gov/title37/201/37cfr201-14 .html.

Cohen, Alex. "Outcomes Survey for Public Libraries." Aaron Cohen Associates, 2014. https://docs .google.com/forms/d/1OQbGDkH9mKiJQLvZcoLfEZjhIgwT99x2QEhfdYqk2OU/viewform.

Cole, Charles. *Information Need: A Theory Connecting Information Search to Knowledge Formation*. Medford, NJ: Information Today, 2012.

Columbia Law School. "Section 108 Reform." Last modified December 11, 2013. http://web.law.columbia .edu/kernochan/symposia/section-108-reform.

Commission on Preservation and Access and Research Libraries Group. "Charge to the Task Force." 1994.

Common Core State Standards Initiative. "About the Standards." Last modified September 12, 2014. http://www.corestandards.org.

———. "English Language Arts Standards." Last modified September 12, 2014. http://www.core standards.org/ELA-Literacy.

Connaway, Lynn S., and Timothy J. Dickey. *Digital Information Seeker: Report of Findings from Selected OCLC, RIN and JISC User Behaviour Projects.* Document No. 706 Version 1.1, March, 2010.

Connected Learning. "Connected Learning FAQ." Last modified August 27, 2014. http://connected learning.tv/what-is-connected-learning.

Cook, Jean Marie. "A Library Credit Course and Student Success Rates: A Longitudinal Study." *College & Research Libraries* 75, no. 3 (May 2014): 272–283. http://crl.acrl.org/content/early/2012/12/19/ crl12-424.full.pdf+html.

Copyright Alliance. "Second Circuit Decision on Authors Guild v. HathiTrust." Last modified August 4, 2014.

Council on Library and Information Resources (CLIR). "Commission on Preservation and Access." 1986.

———. "Participatory Design in Academic Libraries Methods, Findings, and Implementations." Counting Opinions. Last modified July 15, 2014. http://www.countingopinions.com.

Courtois, Martin P., and Maira Liriano. "Tips for Roving Reference: How to Best Serve Library Users." *College & Research Libraries News* 61, no. 4 (2000): 289–315.

Covey, Stephen. *The Seven Habits of Highly Effective People.* Anniversary edition. New York: Simon & Schuster: 2013.

Creative Commons. "About CC0—'No Rights Reserved.'" Last modified October 28, 2014. http://creative commons.org/about/cc0.

———. "About the Public Domain Mark—'No Known Copyright.'" Last modified October 26, 2014. http://creativecommons.org/about/pdm.

Cresente, May Louise, and Doris Lee. "Critical Issues in M-Learning: Design Models, Adoption Processes & Future Trends." *Journal of the Chinese Institute of Industrial Engineers* 28, no. 2 (March 2011): 111–123. doi:10.1080/10170669.2010.548856.

Crompton, Helen. "A Historical Overview of M-Learning: Toward Learner-Centered Education." In *Handbook of Mobile Learning,* edited by Zane Berge and Lin Muilenburg. New York: Routledge, 2013.

Croneis, Karen S., and Pat Henderson. "Electronic and Digital Librarian Positions: A Content Analysis of Announcements from 1990 through 2000." *Journal of Academic Librarianship* 28, no. 4 (2002): 232–237.

Cross, T., B. Bazron, K. Dennis, and M. Isaacs. *Toward a Culturally Competent System of Care.* Vol. 1. Washington, DC: Georgetown University, 1989.

Crozier, Michel, and Erhard Friedberg. *Actors and Systems: The Politics of Collective Action.* Translated by Arthur Goldhammer. Chicago, IL: University of Chicago Press, 1980.

Csikszentmihalyi, Mihaly, and Kim Hermanson. "Intrinsic Motivation in Museums: What Makes Visitors Want to Learn?" *Museum News* 74, no. 3 (1995): 34–37, 59–62.

Curti, Merle, and Vernon Carstensen. *The University of Wisconsin: A History.* Vol. 1. Madison, WI: University of Wisconsin Press, 1949. http://digicoll.library.wisc.edu/cgi-bin/UW/UW -idx?type=header&id=UW.UWHist18481925v1.

Dain, Phyllis P. *The New York Public Library: A History of Its Founding and Early Years*. New York: New York Public Library, 1972.

Dardano, Michael. "Grand Opening of the Edge at the White Plains Public Library." *White Plains Patch*. Last modified December 11, 2013. http://whiteplains.patch.com/groups/announcements/p/grand-opening-of-the-edge-at-the-white-plains-public-library_613afe1e.

Dataprotocols. "Data Packages." Last modified July 9, 2014. http://dataprotocols.org/data-packages.

Daugherty, Alice L., and Michael F. Russo, eds. *Embedded Librarianship: What Every Academic Librarian Should Know*. Santa Barbara, CA: Libraries Unlimited, 2013.

Davenport, Thomas H. "Saving IT's Soul: Human Centered Information Management." *Harvard Business Review* 72, no. 2 (1994): 119–131.

Dawes, Trevor A., and Michael J. Krasulski. "Conclusion." In *Twenty-First Century Access Services*, 243–246. Chicago, IL: American Library Association, 2013.

Dawson, Alma. "Celebrating African-American Librarians and Librarianship." *Library Trends* 49 (Summer 2000): 49–87.

Dee, Cheryl. "MEDLARS: Development of MEDLARS (Medical Literature Analysis and Retrieval System)." *Journal of the Medical Library Association* 95, no. 4 (October 2007): 416–425. doi:10.3163/1536-5050.95.4.416. http://www.pubmedcentral.nih.gov/tocrender.fcgi?iid=150885.

Dee, Cheryl R., and R. Blazek. "Information Needs of Rural Physicians: A Descriptive Study." *Bulletin of the Medical Library Association* 81, no. 3 (1993): 259–264. http://www.pubmedcentral.nih.gov/picrender.fcgi?artid=225785andblobtype=pdf.

Dee, Cheryl, and Joselyn Rankin. "Health Science Professional Literatures and Their Users." In *Encyclopedia of Library and Information Sciences*, edited by Marcia Bates and Mary Niles Maack, 3rd ed. Boca Raton, FL: CRC Press, 2009. http://www.tandfonline.com/doi/full/10.1081/.VA9uvfldWSo.

————. "Medical and Allied Health Sciences Literatures and Their Users." In *Encyclopedia of Library and Information Sciences*, edited by Marcia Bates and Mary Niles Maack, 3rd ed. Boca Raton, FL: CRC Press, 2009.

Dee, Cheryl R., and K. A. Smith. "Martin M. Cummings MD, 1920–2011." Obituary. *Journal of the Medical Library Association* 100, no. 3 (July 2012): 157–160. http://www.ncbi.nlm.nih.gov/pmc/articles/PMC3411258.

Dempsey, Lorcan. "Thirteen Ways of Looking at Libraries, Discovery, and the Catalog: Scale, Workflow, Attention." Last modified December 10, 2012. http://www.educause.edu/ero/article/thirteen-ways-looking-libraries-discovery-and-catalog-scale-workflow-attention.

Department of Commerce Internet Policy Task Force. "Copyright Policy, Creativity and Innovation in the Digital Economy." Green paper. 2012. http://www.uspto.gov/news/publications/copyright greenpaper.pdf.

DeRosa, Cathy, Joanne Cantrell, Diane Callentani, Janet Hawk, Lillie Jenkins, and Alane Wilson. *Perceptions of Libraries and Information Resources*. Report to membership. Dublin, OH: OCLC Online Computer Library Center, 2005. http://www.oclc.org/content/dam/oclc/reports/pdfs/Percept_all .pdf.

Dervin, B., L. Foreman-Wernet, and E. Lauterbach, eds. *Sense-Making Methodology Reader: Selected Writings of Brenda Dervin*. Cresskill, NJ: Hampton Press, 2003.

Dervin, Brenda. "What Methodology Does to Theory: Sense-Making Methodology as Exemplar." In *Theories of Information Behavior*, edited by Karen E. Fisher, Sandra Erdelez, and Lynne E. F. McKechnie, 25–30. Medford, NJ: Information Today, 2005.

Dervin, Brenda, and Patricia Dewdney. "Neutral Questioning: A New Approach to the Reference Interview." *RQ* (1986): 506–513.

Deskins, Liz. "Inquiry Studies: Needed Skills." *School Library Monthly* 28, no. 5 (2012): 20–23.

Dethloff, Nora, and Paul Sharpe. "Access Services and the Success of the Academic Library." In *Twenty-First Century Access Services*, edited by Michael Krasulski and Trevor Dawes, 69–89. Chicago, IL: American Library Association, 2013.

Dewdney, P., and R. M. Harris. *Barriers to Information: How Formal Help Systems Fail Battered Women*. Santa Barbara, CA: Praeger, 1994.

Dewey, Barbara I. "The Embedded Librarian: Strategic Campus Collaborations." *Resource Sharing & Information Networks* 17, nos. 1–2 (2005): 5–17. doi:10.1300/J121v17n01_02.

Dewey, John. "The School and the Life of the Child." *School and Society: Being Three Lectures*. Chicago, IL: University of Chicago Press, 1900. http://books.google.com/books?id=QWYWAAAAIAAJ.

Dewey, Melvil. *A Classification and Subject Index for Cataloging and Arranging the Books and Pamphlets in the Library [Dewey Decimal Classification]*. Facsimile. Project Gutenberg. http://www.gutenberg.org/files/12513/12513-h/12513-h.htm.

———. "Why a Library Does or Does Not Succeed." In *Library Notes: Improved Methods and Labor-Savers for Librarians, Readers and Writers*. Boston, MA: Library Bureau, 1887.

Digital Commons. "College and University Institutional Repositories." Last modified September 13, 2014. http://digitalcommons.bepress.com/institutional-repository-colleges.

Digital Curation Centre. "What Is Digital Curation?" Last modified October 9, 2014. http://www.dcc.ac.uk/digital-curation/what-digital-curation.

Digital Preservation Network (DPN). "The Digital Preservation Network." Last modified July 7, 2014. http://www.dpn.org.

Digital Preservation Outreach and Education (DPOE). "About DPOE." Last modified June 25, 2014. http://www.digitalpreservation.gov/education.

The Digital Shift. "2012 Survey of Ebook Usage in U.S. Academic Libraries." *Library Journal*. 2012. http://www.thedigitalshift.com/research/ebook-usage-reports/academic.

———. "2012 Survey of Ebook Usage in U.S. Public Libraries." *Library Journal*. 2012. http://www.thedigitalshift.com/research/ebook-usage-reports/public.

Directory of Open Access Journals. Last modified August 31, 2014. www.doaj.org.

Ditzion, Sidney. *Arsenals of a Democratic Culture: A Social History of the Public Library Movement in New England and the Middle States from 1850 to 1900* (Chicago, IL: American Library Association, 1947), 30.

The dSchool Institute of Design at Stanford. *Bootcamp Bootleg* 2 (2010). http://dschool.stanford.edu/wp-content/uploads/2011/03/BootcampBootleg2010v2SLIM.pdf.

Dix, Alan. "Human-Computer Interaction." In *Encyclopedia for Library and Information Science*, edited by Marcia Bates and Mary Niles Maack, 3rd ed. Boca Raton, FL: 2009.

Doe v. Gonzales. 546 U.S. 1301 (2005). http://www.supremecourt.gov/opinions/05pdf/05a295.pdf.

Dority, G. Kim. *Rethinking Information Work: A Career Guide for Librarians and Other Information Professionals*. Westport, CT: Libraries Unlimited, 2006.

Dougherty, Dale. "We Are Makers." TED Talks video, 11:47 min. January 2011. http://www.ted.com/talks/dale_dougherty_we_are_makers.

Drucker, Peter. *Management Challenges for the 21st Century*. New York: Harper Business, 2001.

———. *Management: Tasks, Responsibilities, Practices* (New York: HarperCollins, 1973).

———. *Managing for Results: Economic Tasks and Risk-Taking Decisions*. New York: Harper & Row, 1964.

Dubie, Denise. "Time Spent Searching Cuts into Company Productivity." *Networkworld*. Last modified October 20, 2006. http://www.networkworld.com/article/2300548/infrastructure-management/time-spent-searching-cuts-into-company-productivity.html.

Dudley, Michael. *Public Libraries and Resilient Cities*. Chicago, IL: American Library Association, 2013.

Duggan, Maeve, and Aaron Smith. "Cell Internet Use 2013." Pew Research Center. http://www.pewinternet.org/2013/09/16/cell-internet-use-2013.

Düren, Petra. "Leadership in Libraries in Times of Change." *IFLA Journal* 39, no. 2 (2013): 134–139.

Durrance, Joanne. C. "The Vital Role of Librarians in Creating Information Communities: Strategies for Success." *Library Administration and Management* 15, no. 3 (2001): 161–168.

EBSCOhost Support. "What Is KBART? Does EBSCO Endorse the KBART Initiative?" http://support.epnet/com/knowledge-base/detail.php?id=6563.

Eddy, Jacalyn. *Bookwomen: Creating an Empire in Children's Book Publishing, 1919–1939*. Madison: University of Wisconsin Press, 2006.

Edwards, Julie Biando, Melissa Rauseo, and Kelley Rae Unger. *Transforming Libraries, Building Communities: The Community Centered Library*. Lanham, MD: Scarecrow Press, 2013.

Elmborg, James. "Critical Information Literacy: Implications for Instructional Practice." *Journal of Academic Librarianship* 32, no. 2 (2006): 192–199. doi:10.1016/j.calib.2005.12.004.

———. "Teaching at the Desk: Toward a Reference Pedagogy." *portal: Libraries and the Academy* 2, no. 3 (2002): 455–464.

Elmborg, Jim. "Literacies, Narratives, and Adult Learning and Libraries." *New Directions for Adult and Continuing Education*, no. 127 (2010): 67–76. doi:10.1002/ace.382.

Elrod, Edwin M., and Martha M. Smith. "Information Ethics." In *Encyclopedia of Science, Technology, and Ethics*. Detroit, MI: Macmillan Reference USA, 2005.

Elsweiler, David, Max L. Wilson, and Brian K. Lund. "Understanding Casual-Leisure Information Behavior." *New Directions in Information Behavior*, edited by Amanda Spink and Jannica Heinström, 211–241. Bingley, UK: Emerald Group, 2011.

Enis, Matt. "CPL, NYPL WiFi Hotspot Lending Programs Funded by Knight Foundation Grants." *The Digital Shift*. Last modified June 25, 2014. http://www.thedigitalshift.com/2014/06/digital-divide/cpl-nypl-wifi-hotspot-lending-programs-funded-knight-foundation-grants.

Enoch Pratt Free Library. "Baltimarket: The Virtual Supermarket Project." http://www.prattlibrary.org/home/index.aspx?id=61972.

Etches, Amanda. "Know Thy Users." *Reference & User Services Quarterly* 53, no. 1 (2013): 13–17.

European Parliament and of the Council of 24 October 1995 on the Protection of Individuals with Regard to the Processing of Personal Data and on the Free Movement of Such Data. "Directive 95/46/EC." http://eur-lex.europa.eu/LexUriServ/LexUriServ.do?uri=CELEX:31995L0046:en:HTML.

Every Child Ready to Read at Your Library. http://www.everychildreadytoread.org.

Every Library. Last modified September 17, 2014. http://everylibrary.org.

Executive Office of the President. "Big Data: Seizing Opportunities, Preserving Values." Last modified September 15, 2014. http://www.whitehouse.gov/issues/technology/big-data-review.

Executive Office of the President, Office of Management and Budget. "Open Data Policy—Managing Information as an Asset." M-13-13 (May 9, 2013).

Exemption to Prohibition on Circumvention of Copyright Protection Systems for Access Control Technologies. 77 Fed. Reg. 65260 (Oct. 26, 2012).

Facebook. https://www.facebook.com.

Fain, Elaine. "The Library and American Education: Education through Secondary School." *Library Trends* 27 (Winter 1979): 327–352.

Fair Credit Reporting Act (FCRA). 15 U.S.C. § 1681 et seq. http://www.ftc.gov/os/statutes/031224fcra.pdf.

Family Educational Rights and Privacy Act (FERPA). 20 U.S.C. § 1232g. http://www.gpo.gov/fdsys/pkg/USCODE-2012-title20/pdf/USCODE-2012-title20-chap31-subchapIII-part4-sec1232g.pdf.

Federal Communications Commission. "Universal Service." Last modified September 30, 2014. http://www.fcc.gov/encyclopedia/universal-service.

FemTechNet Commons. Last modified August 17, 2014. http://femtechnet.org.

Ferguson, E. "Association Highlights." In *Special Library Association: Its First 50 Years, 1909–1959*. New York: Special Libraries Association, 1959.

FIRE (Foundation for Individual Rights in Education). http://www.thefire.org.

Fisher, Erin. "Makerspaces Move into Academic Libraries." *ACRL TechConnect Blog*, November 28, 2012. http://acrl.ala.org/techconnect/?p=2340.

Fisher, K. E., J. C. Durrance, and M. B. Hinton. "Information Grounds and the Use of Need-Based Services by Immigrants in Queens, NY: A Context-Based, Outcome Evaluation Approach." *Journal of the American Society for Information Science & Technology* 55, no. 8 (2004): 754–766.

Fisher, K. E., C. F. Landry, and C. M. Naumer. "Social Spaces, Casual Interactions, Meaningful Exchanges: An Information Ground Typology Based on the College Student Experience." *Information Research* 12, no. 2 (2007). http://informationr.net/ir/12-2/paper291.html.

Fisher, K. E., K. T. Unruh, and J. C. Durrance. "Information Communities: Characteristics Gleaned from Studies of Three Online Networks." In *Proceedings of the 66th Annual Meeting of the American Society for Information Science & Technology*, edited by R. J. Todd, 299–305. Medford, NJ: Information Today, 2003.

Fister, Barbara. "Critical Assets: Academic Libraries, a View from the Administration Building." *Library Journal*, May 29, 2010. http://lj.libraryjournal.com/2010/05/academic-libraries/critical-assets-academic-libraries-a-view-from-the-administration-building/#.

———. "Smoke and Mirrors: Finding Order in a Chaotic World." *Research Strategies* 20, no. 3 (2005): 99–107. doi:10.1016./j.resstr.2005.10.005.

Flickr. "Chicago Public Library Makerspace." n.d. https://www.flickr.com/photos/cpl_makerspace/sets.

———. "Westport Library Maker Space." n.d. https://www.flickr.com/photos/mauimakers/sets/72157644802128769.

Florida Department of State, Division of Library & Information Services. "Return on Investment in Florida Public Libraries—2013 Study." Last modified June 29, 2014. http://dlis.dos.state.fl.us/bld/roi.

Flowers, Sarah. *Young Adults Deserve the Best: YALSA's Competencies in Action.* Chicago, IL: American Library Association, 2011.

Fontichiaro, Kristin. "A Charter for Your School Makerspace?" *Active Learning* (blog). Last modified September 4, 2014. http://www.fontichiaro.com/activelearning/2014/09/04/a-charter-for-your-school-makerspace.

———. "Reflections on North Quad MakerFest." *Active Learning* (blog). Last modified December 18, 2013. http://www.fontichiaro.com/activelearning/2013/12/18/reflections-on-north-quad-makerfest.

———. "What Is the Spine of Your Makerspace? A Day with Plano ISD Librarians." *Active Learning* (blog). Last modified August 23, 2014. http://www.fontichiaro.com/activelearning/2014/08/23/what-is-the-spine-of-your-makerspace-a-day-with-plano-isd-librarians.

Foreign Intelligence Surveillance Act (FISA). 50 U.S.C. §§ 1801–1811 (1978). http://www.gpo.gov/fdsys/pkg/STATUTE-92/pdf/STATUTE-92-Pg1783.pdf.

Foreman, Joel. "Distance Learning & Synchronous Interaction." Technology Source Archives at the University of North Carolina. Last modified June 30, 2012. http://technologysource.org/article/distance_learning_and_synchronous_interaction.

Fortenberry, John, Jr. *Nonprofit Marketing: Tools and Techniques.* Burlington, MA: Jones & Bartlett Learning, 2013.

Fox, Susannah, and Lee Rainie. "The Web at 25 in the U.S." Pew Research Internet Project. Last modified February 27, 2014. http://www.pewinternet.org/2014/02/27/the-web-at-25-in-the-u-s.

Francis, Mary. "Weeding the Reference Collection: A Case Study of Collection Management." *Reference Librarian* 53, no. 2 (2012): 219–234.

Franklin, Benjamin. *The Autobiography of Benjamin Franklin.* Charlottesville, VA: University of Virginia Library, 1995.

Fraser-Arnott, M. "Library and Information Science (LIS) Transferable Competencies." *Partnership: The Canadian Journal of Library and Information Practice and Research* 8, no. 2 (2013). https://journal.lib.uoguelph.ca/index.php/perj/article/view/2595#.U_qXBmPHTpw.

Frederiksen, Linda. "Access Services Librarians: A Content Analysis of Job Advertisements, 1977–2004." *Journal of Access Services* 3, no. 2 (2005): 15–27.

Freedom of Information Act of 1967. Pub. L. 89–487, 80 Stat. 250 (1967). http://www.foia.gov.

French, John R. P., Jr., and Bertram H. Raven. "The Bases of Social Power." In *Studies in Social Power*, edited by Dorwin Cartwright, 150–167. Ann Arbor, MI: Institute for Social Research, 1959.

Fung, Brian. "Your Facebook Privacy Settings Are About to Change. Again." *Washington Post*. Last modified April 4, 2014. http://www.washingtonpost.com/blogs/the-switch/wp/2014/04/08/your-facebook-privacy-settings-are-about-to-change-again.

Gadsby, Joanna, and Shu Qian. "Using an iPad to Redefine Roving Reference Service in an Academic Library." *Library Hi Tech News* 29, no. 4 (2012): 1–5. doi:10.1108/07419051211249446.

Galston, Colbe, Elizabeth Kelsen Huber, Katherine Johnson, and Amy Long. "Community Reference: Making Libraries Indispensable in a New Way." *American Libraries*. Last modified June 13, 2012. http://www.americanlibrariesmagazine.org/article/community-reference-making-libraries-indispensable-new-way.

Garceau, Oliver. *The Public Library in the Political Process: A Report of the Public Library Inquiry*. New York: Columbia University Press, 1949.

Garcia, June, and Sandra Nelson. *2007 Public Library Service Responses*. Chicago, IL: Public Library Association, 2007. http://ryepubliclibrary.org/wp-content/uploads/2012/05/ALAserviceresponses.pdf.

Gardiner, John Jacob Z., and E. L. Walker. "Transcendent Leadership: Theory and Practice of an Emergent Metaphor." *International Journal of Servant-Leadership*, no. 5 (2009).

Gardner, David P., and the United States National Commission on Excellence in Education. *A Nation at Risk: The Imperative for Educational Reform; A Report to the Nation and the Secretary of Education*. Washington, DC: Government Printing Office, 1983. http://www.eric.ed.gov/contentdelivery/servlet/ERICServlet?accno=ED226006.

Garmer, Amy. *Rising to the Challenge: Re-Envisioning Public Libraries*. Washington, DC: Aspen Institute, October 2014.

Garrett, John R. "Task Force on Archiving of Digital Information." *D-lib Magazine*. Last modified September 1995. http://dlib.org/dlib/september95/09garrett.html.

Garrison, Dee. *Apostles of Culture: The Public Librarian and American Society, 1876–1920*. Madison: University of Wisconsin Press, 2003.

Gathegi, John N. *The Digital Librarian's Legal Handbook*. Chicago, IL: Neal-Schuman, 2011. http://www.jisc.ac.uk/media/documents/publications/reports/2010/digitalinformationseekerreport.pdf.

Gehner, John. "Libraries, Low-Income People, and Social Exclusion." *Public Library Quarterly* 29, no. 1 (2010): 39–47.

Gellman, Barton, Julie Tate, and Ashkan Soltani. "In NSA-Intercepted Data, Those Not Targeted Far Outnumber the Foreigners Who Are." *Washington Post*. Last modified July 5, 2014. http://www.washingtonpost.com/world/national-security/in-nsa-intercepted-data-those-not-targeted-far-outnumber-the-foreigners-who-are/2014/07/05/8139adf8-045a-11e4-8572-4b1b969b6322_story.html.

Giles, David. *Branches of Opportunity*. Center for an Urban Future, January 2013. http://nycfuture.org/pdf/Branches_of_Opportunity.pdf.

Gilman, Todd, and Thea Lindquist. "Academic/Research Librarians with Subject Doctorates: Experiences and Perceptions, 1965–2006." *portal: Libraries and the Academy* 10, no. 4 (2010): 399–412.

Gisolfi, Peter. "Melding Minds to Make a Library: Successful Libraries Are Designed Collaboratively." *American Libraries*, September/October 2013, 40–41.

Givens, Cherie. *Information Privacy Fundamentals for Librarians and Information Professionals*. Lanham, MD: Rowman & Littlefield, 2014.

Gleason, Eliza Atkins. *The Southern Negro and the Public Library: A Study of the Government and Administration of Public Library Service to Negroes in the South*. Chicago, IL: University of Chicago Press, 1941.

Glenn, Jerome C. "Futures Research Methodology Version 2.0." In *The Futures Research Methods Series*, edited by Jerome C. Glenn and Theodore J. Gordon. The Millennium Project. American Council for the United Nations University. Last modified August 21, 2009. http://www.millennium-project.org/millennium/FRM-v2.html.

Globalization101. "What Is Globalization?" Last modified July 3, 2014. http://www.globalization101.org/what-is-globalization.

Goleman, Daniel. *Emotional Intelligence: Why It Can Matter More than IQ*. New York: Bantam, 2005.

———. "Leadership That Gets Results." *Harvard Business Review*, March-April 2000, 78–90.

Goleman, Daniel, Richard Boyatzis, and Annie McKee. *Primal Leadership: Learning to Lead with Emotional Intelligence*. Boston, MA: Harvard Business School, 2004.

———. "Primal Leadership: The Hidden Driver of Great Performance." *Harvard Business Review* 79, no. 11 (2001): 42–53. http://www.researchgate.net/publication/40964875_Primal_leadership__the_hidden_driver_of_great_performance/file/3deec52a72500dff3f.pdf.

Gramm-Leach-Bliley Act. Pub. L. 106–102, 113 Stat. 1338. The Bureau of Consumer Protection provides information for institutions on how to comply with the Gramm-Leach-Bliley Act as well as helpful information for consumers at http://business.ftc.gov/privacy-and-security/gramm-leach-bliley-act.

Greater Western Library Alliance. Last modified July 9, 2014. http://www.gwla.org.

Green, Samuel S. "Personal Relations between Librarians and Readers." *Library Journal* 1, no. 2 (1876): 74–81. http://pacificreference.pbworks.com/f/Personal%20Relations%20Between%20Librarians%20and%20Readers.pdf.

Greyson, Devon, Soleil Surette, Liz Dennett, and Trish Chatterley. "'You're Just One of the Group When You're Embedded': Report from a Mixed-Method Investigation of the Research-Embedded Health Librarian Experience." *Journal of the Medical Library Association* 101, no. 4 (2013): 287–297.

Griswold v. Connecticut. 381 U.S. 479 (1965). http://web.stanford.edu/~mrosenfe/Griswold_v_CT_US_1965.pdf.

Groszins, Dean, and Leon Jackson. "Colleges and Print Culture." In *An Extensive Republic: Print, Culture, and Society in the New Nation*, edited by Robert A. Gross and Mary Kelley. Chapel Hill: University of North Carolina Press, 2010.

Gruber, Thomas. "A Translation Approach to Portable Ontology Specifications." Knowledge Systems Laboratory Revised Technical Report KSL 92-71, April 1993. http://tomgruber.org/writing/ontolingua-kaj-1993.pdf.

Guenter, Rebecca, and Jaqueline Radebaugh. *Understanding Metadata*. Bethesda, MD: NISO Press. http://www.niso.org/publications/press/UnderstandingMetadata.pdf.

Hall-Ellis, Sylvia D. "Metadata Competencies for Entry-Level Positions: What Employers Expect as Reflected in Position Descriptions 2000–2013." *Journal of Library Metadata* (in press).

Halsted, Deborah D., Shari Clifton, and Daniel T. Wilson. *Library as Safe Haven: Disaster Planning, Response, and Recovery*. Chicago, IL: American Library Association, 2014.

Halvorson, Kristina. *Content Strategy for the Web*. Berkeley, CA: New Riders, 2010.

Hansen, Mary Anne, Jakob Harnest, Virginia Steel,   Joan Ellen Stein, and Pat Weaver-Myers. "A Question and Answer Forum on the Origin, Evolution and Future of Access Services." *Journal of Access Services* 1, no. 1 (2002): 5–24.

Hargittai, Eszter. "Second-Level Digital Divide: Differences in People's Online Skills." *First Monday*, 7 no. 4 (2002). doi:10.5210/fm.v7i4.942.

Hart Research Associates. "Attitudes toward Re-Envisioning the UC Berkeley Library: An Online Survey of the UC Campus Community." Washington, DC: Hart Research Associates, July 2012. http://www.lib.berkeley.edu/AboutLibrary/Hart_Survey_Report_Re-Envisioning_UC_Berkeley_Library.pdf.

———. *It Takes More than a Major: Employer Priorities for College Learning and Student Success; A National Survey of Business and Non Profit Leaders*. Washington, DC: Hart Research Associates, 2013. http://www.aacu.org/leap/documents/2013_EmployerSurvey.pdf.

Harvard University. "Harvard Faculty Advisory Council Memorandum on Journal Pricing." Last modified April 17, 2012. http://isites.harvard.edu/icb/icb.do?keyword=k77982&tabgroupid=icb.tabgroup143448.

Harvard University Library Office of Scholarly Communication. "Open Access Policies." Last modified April 16, 2014. https://osc.hul.harvard.edu/policies.

HathiTrust. "Our Digital Library." Last modified September 24, 2014. http://www.hathitrust.org/digital_library.

Haycock, K., and C. Garner. "The Bunheads Are Dead: Discovering High-Tech, High-Touch Opportunities in Library and Information Science." *American Libraries Digital Supplement Winter 2009* (2009): 6–10. http://www.eslarp.uiuc.edu/news/AmericanLibraries2009.pdf.

Head, Alison J., Michele Van Hoeck, Jordan Eschler, and Sean Fullerton. "What Information Competencies Matter in Today's Workplace?" *Library and Information Research* 37, no. 114 (May 2013): 75–104. http://www.lirgjournal.org.uk/lir/ojs/index.php/lir/article/view/557/593.

Healey, Paul D. "Go and Tell the World: Charles R. McCarthy and the Evolution of the Legislative Reference Movement, 1901–1917." *Law Library Journal* 99, no. 1 (2007): 36. http://www.aallnet.org/main-menu/Publications/llj/LLJ-Archives/Vol-99/pub_llj_v99n01/2007-02.pdf.

Heifetz, R. A., and D. L. Laurie. "The Work of Leadership." *The Best of HBR*. Boston, MA: Harvard Business School Press, 2001. http://dmcodyssey.org/wp-content/uploads/2013/09/EQ-Daniel-Goleman-in-HBR_10_Must_Reads_on_Leadership.pdf#page=38.

Heifetz, Ronald A. *Leadership without Easy Answers*. Boston, MA: Harvard University Press, 1998.

Held, Ray E. *The Rise of the Public Library in California*. Chicago, IL: American Library Association, 1973.

Held, Virginia. "The Ethics of Care." In *The Oxford Handbook of Ethical Theory*, edited by David Copp. New York: Oxford University Press, 2009. doi:10.1093/oxfordhb/9780195325911.003.0020 (accessed July 22, 2014).

Hernon, Peter, and Ellen Altman. *Assessing Service Quality: Satisfying the Expectations of Library Customers*. Chicago, IL: American Library Association, 1998.

Herring, Cedric. "Does Diversity Pay? Race, Gender and the Business Case for Diversity." *American Sociological Review* 74, no. 2 (April 2009).

Herring, James E. "Year 7 Students, Information Literacy, and Transfer: A Grounded Theory." *School Library Media Research* 14 (2011). http://www.ala.org/aasl/sites/ala.org.aasl/files/content/aasl pubsandjournals/slr/vol14/SLR_Year7Students_V14.pdf.

Herzog, Brian. "Update on Eliminating Our Reference Collection." *Swiss Army Librarian Blog*. Last modified April 7, 2011. http://www.swissarmylibrarian.net/2011/04/07/update-on-eliminating -our-reference-collection.

Hesselbein, Frances. "Definition of Leadership." YouTube video. Posted by mentorsgailery, January 26, 2010. https://www.youtube.com/watch?v=chLuLUqy9OM.

Hillary, G. A. "Definitions of Community: Areas of Agreement." *Rural Sociology* 20 (1955).

Himmel, Ethel, and William James Wilson. *Planning for Results: A Public Library Transformation Process*. Chicago, IL: American Library Association, 1998.

Hirsh, S. "Preparing Future Professionals through Broad Competency Planning." *Information Outlook* 16, no. 1 (2012): 9–11. https://slisweb.sjsu.edu/downloads/future_professionals.pdf.

Hirsh, S., Metz, R., Brown, S., Serrano, L., and Gurtu, S. "Developing a Technology Integration Residency Model: The Catalyst Project Report." Paper 1. *Faculty Publications*, 2012. http://scholarworks.sjsu .edu/slis_pub/1.

Hive Learning Networks. Last modified September 3, 2014. http://hivelearningnetworks.org.

Hofer, Amy R., and Karen Munro. "Embedding in the LMS: Faculty Evaluations of a Low-Touch Widget." In *Virtually Embedded: The Librarian in an Online Environment*. Chicago, IL: American Library Association, 2014. Kindle edition.

Hoffman, Debra, and Amy Wallace. "Intentional Informationists: Re-Envisioning Information Literacy and Re-Designing Instructional Programs around Faculty Librarians' Strength as Campus Connectors, Information Professionals, and Course Designers." *Journal of Academic Librarianship* 39, no. 6 (2013): 546–551. doi:10.1016/j.acalib.2013.06.004.

Hoffman, Judy, John Carlo Bertot, and Denise M. Davis. "Libraries Connect Communities: Public Library Funding & Technology Access Study 2011–2012." Digital supplement, *American Libraries*, Summer 2012. http://viewer.zmags.com/publication/4673a369.

Holt, Glen. "Exploring Public Library Contributions to Urban Resiliency." In *Public Libraries and Resilient Cities*, 37–56. Chicago, IL: American Library Association, 2013.

Horowitz, Lisa R. "Assessing Library Services: A Practical Guide for the Non-expert." *Library Leadership and Management* 25, no. 4 (2009): 193–203.

Horton, Forest Woody, Jr. *Understanding Information Literacy: A Primer*. Paris: UNESCO, 2007. http:// unesdoc.unesco.org/images/0015/001570/157020e.pdf.

Housewright, Ross, Roger C. Schonfeld, and Kate Wulfson. *Ithaka S+R US Faculty Survey*. (April 8, 2013): 69. http://www.sr.ithaka.org/sites/default/files/reports/Ithaka_SR_US_Faculty_Survey_2012_ FINAL.pdf.

Hovendick, B. "What I Learned about the Value of an MLIS Degree: An LIS Student's Perspective." *Fast Facts—Recent Statistics from the Library Research Service*. Colorado State Library. no. 110.10.271 (2009). http://www.lrs.org/documents/fastfacts/271_Student_Perspective.pdf.

Howlett, A. "Connecting to the LIS Online Community: A New Information Professional Developing a Personal Learning Network." ALIA 5th New Librarians Symposium 2011, Metamorphosis: What Will You Become Today?, Perth, Australia, 2011.

Hrastiki, Stefan. "Asynchronous & Synchronous E-Learning." *Educause Quarterly* 3, no. 4 (2008). http://net.educause.edu/ir/library/pdf/EQM0848.pdf.

Hunt, Deborah, and David Grossman. *The Librarian's Skillbook: 51 Essential Skills for Information Professionals*. San Leandro, CA: Information Edge, 2013.

Hyde, Lewis. *Common as Air: Revolution, Art and Ownership*. New York: Farrar, Strauss and Giroux, 2010.

International Federation of Library Associations and Institutions (IFLA). "11th IFLA International Marketing Award." http://www.ifla.org/node/6922.

———. Last modified September 8, 2014. www.ifla.org.

———. "IFLA Code of Ethics for Librarians and Other Information Workers." Last modified August 12, 2012. http://www.ifla.org/news/ifla-code-of-ethics-for-librarians-and-other-information -workers-full-version.

———. *Riding the Waves or Caught in the Tide? Navigating the Evolving Information Environment—Insights from the IFLA Trend Report*. The Hague, NL: IFLA, 2013. http://trends.ifla.org/insights-document.

Imholz, Susan, and Jennifer Weil Arns. "Worth Their Weight: An Assessment of the Evolving Field of Library Evaluation." *Public Library Quarterly* 26, nos. 3/4 (July 2007): 31.

Ingram. Last modified September 22, 2014. http://www.ingramcontent.com/pages/home.aspx.

InfoMe Program. Last modified October 3, 2013. http://infome.uw.edu.

The Information Architecture Institute. "What Is Information Architecture." Information Architecture Institute, 2013. http://www.iainstitute.org/documents/learn/What_is_IA.pdf.

International Federation of Library Associations and Institutions. "IFLA Code of Ethics for Librarians and Other Information Workers." Last modified August 12, 2012. http://www.ifla.org/news/ifla-code-of-ethics-for-librarians-and-other-information-workers-full-version.

International Librarians Network Blog. Last modified October 3, 2014. http://ilnetwork.wordpress.com.

International Standards for Technology in Education (ISTE). "Standards." Last modified September 3, 2014. http://www.iste.org/standards.

Institute of Museum and Library Services (IMLS). Last modified August 28, 2014. http://www.imls.gov.

———. "Digital Storytime Means Serious Fun—and Vital Learning—for Arizona Toddlers." http://www.imls.gov/digital_storytime_means_serious_fun_and_vital_learning_for_arizona_toddlers.aspx?CategoryId=2&pg=5 (accessed July 12, 2014).

———. "Grants to State Library Administrative Agencies." Last modified October 28, 2014. http://www.imls.gov/programs.

———. "IMLS 2010 Public Library Survey Results Announced." Last modified April 10, 2014. http://www.imls.gov/imls_2010_public_library_survey_results_announced.aspx.

———. "Legislation and Budget." Last modified October 28, 2014. http://www.imls.gov/about/legislation _and_budget.aspx.

————. *National Medal for Museum and Library Service.* 2014. http://www.imls.gov/assets/1/AssetManager/Medals2014Brochure.pdf.

————. "Number and Percentage of Libraries by Select Characteristics." In *Public Libraries in the United States Survey: Fiscal Year 2011.* Washington, DC: Institute of Museum and Library Services, 2014. http://www.imls.gov/research/public_libraries_in_the_us_fy_2011_tables.aspx.

————. *Public Libraries in the United States Survey: Fiscal Year 2011.* Washington, DC: Institute of Museum and Library Services, 2014.

————. "Research Data Collection." Last modified June 30, 2014. http://www.imls.gov/research/data_collection.aspx.

————. "Table 5: Percentage Distribution of Public Libraries, by Type of Legal Basis and State: Fiscal Year 2011." In *Public Libraries in the United States Survey: Fiscal Year 2011.* Washington, DC: Institute of Museum and Library Services, 2014. http://www.imls.gov/research/public_libraries_in_the_us_fy_2011_tables.aspx.

————. "Table 8. Number of Public Library Services, by Type of Service and State: Fiscal Year 2011." In *Public Libraries in the United States Survey: Fiscal Year 2011.* Washington, DC: Institute of Museum and Library Services, 2014. http://www.imls.gov/assets/1/AssetManager/FY2011_PLS_Tables_8-17A.pdf.

InternetLiveStats. "Total Number of Websites." Last modified July 1, 2014. http://www.internetlivestats.com/total-number-of-websites.

iSearch. "About the Project." Last modified January 8, 2014. http://www.isearch-project.eu/isearch.

Ito, Mimi, Kris Gutierrez, Sonia Livingstone, et al. *Connected Learning: An Agenda for Research and Design.* Irvine. CA: Digital Media and Learning Research Hub. http://dmlhub.net/sites/default/files/ConnectedLearning_report.pdf.

Jacobs, Heidi L. M. "Information Literacy and Reflective Pedagogical Praxis." *Journal of Academic Librarianship* 34, no. 3 (2008): 256–262. doi:10.1016/j.acalib.2008.03.009.

Jacobs, Warren N. "Embedded Librarianship Is a Winning Proposition." *Education Libraries* 33, no. 2 (2010): 3–10.

Jaeger, P. T., N. G. Taylor, and U. Gorham. *Libraries, Human Rights, and Social Justice: Enabling Access and Promoting Inclusion.* Lanham, MD: Rowman & Littlefield, in press.

Jaeger, P. T., et. al. "The Public Library in the Local Political Process." In *Public Libraries, Public Policies, and Political Processes: Serving and Transforming Communities in Times of Economic and Political Constraint.* Lanham, MD: Rowman & Littlefield, 2014.

Jaeger, Paul T., John Carlo Bertot, Kim M. Thompson, Sarah M. Katz, and Elizabeth J. DeCoster. "The Intersection of Public Policy and Public Access: Digital Divides, Digital Literacy, Digital Inclusion, and Public Libraries." *Public Library Quarterly* 31, no. 1 (2012): 1–20. doi:10.1080/01616846.2012.654728.

James, Russell D. and Peter J. Wosh, eds., *Public Relations and Marketing for Archives: A How To Do It Manual.* Chicago, IL: Society of American Archivists, and New York: Neal-Schuman, 2011.

JISC Digital Media. "Guide: Putting Things in Order; A Directory of Metadata Schemas and Related Standards." Last modified July 14, 2014. http://www.jiscdigitalmedia.ac.uk/guide/putting-things-in-order-links-to-metadata-schemas-and-related-standards.

Joeckel, Carleton. *Post-War Standards for Public Libraries*. Chicago, IL: American Library Association, 1943.

Joeckel Carleton B., and Amy Winslow. *A National Plan for Public Library Service*. Chicago, IL: American Library Association, 1948.

Joeckel, Carleton Bruns, and Leon Carnovsky. *A Metropolitan Library in Action: A Survey of the Chicago Public Library*. Chicago, IL: University of Chicago Press, 1940.

Johnson, L., S. Adams Becker, M. Cummins, V. Estrada, A. Freeman, and H. Austin Ludgate. *NMC Horizon Report: 2013 Higher Education Edition*. Austin, TX: New Media Consortium, 2013. http://net .educause.edu/ir/library/pdf/HR2013.pdf.

Johnson, Larry, Samantha Adams, and M. Cummins. *The NMC Horizon Report: 2012 Higher Education Edition*. Austin, TX: New Media Consortium, 2012. http://www.nmc.org/pdf/2012-horizon-report -HE.pdf.

Johnson, Larry, Samantha Adams Becker, Victoria Estrada, and Alex Freeman. *NMC Horizon Report: 2014 Higher Education Edition*. Austin, TX: New Media Consortium, 2014.

Josey, E. J. *The Black Librarian in America*. Metuchen, NJ: Scarecrow Press, 1970.

Kahneman, D., and A. Tversky. "Prospect Theory: An Analysis of Decision under Risk." *Econometrica* 47, no. 2 (1979): 263–292.

Kammerlocher, Lisa, Juliann Couture, Olivia Sparks, Matthew Harp, Tammy Allgood. "Information Literacy in Learning Landscapes: Flexible, Adaptable, Low-Cost Solutions." *Reference Services Review* 39, no. 3 (2011): 390–400. http://www.emeraldinsight.com/doi/pdfplus/10.1108/00907321111161395.

Kaplowitz, Joan R. *Transforming Information Literacy Instruction Using Learner-Centered Teaching*. New York: Neal-Schuman, 2012.

Keleman, Aubri, Tara Robertson, "Diane," and Samantha Sinanan. Telephone interviews by Diane O'Brien and Devon Greyson. June 2014.

Kelley, Michael. "The New Normal." *Library Journal*. Last modified January 16, 2012. http:// lj.libraryjournal.com/2012/01/funding/the-new-normal-annual-library-budgets-survey-2012.

Kelley, T., and D. Kelley. *Creative Confidence. Unleashing the Creative Potential within Us All*. New York: Crown Business, 2013.

Kelly, Betsy, Claire Hamasu, and Barbara Jones. "Applying Return on Investment (ROI) in Libraries." *Journal of Library Administration* 52, no. 8 (November 2012): 656–671. doi:10.1080/01930826.201 2.747383.

Kende, Michael. *Internet Society Global Internet Report 2014*. 2014. http://www.internetsociety.org/ sites/default/files/Global_Internet_Report_2014_0.pdf.

Kenefick, Colleen. "The Case for Embedded Hospital Librarianship." *Journal of Hospital Librarianship* 11, no. 2 (2011): 195–199. doi:10.1080/15323269.2011.558407.

Kenney, Anne R., and Nancy Y. McGovern. "The Five Organizational Stages of Digital Preservation." In *Digital Libraries: A Vision for the Twenty-First Century, a Festschrift to Honor Wendy Lougee*. Ann Arbor, MI: Michigan Publishing, 2003. http://quod.lib.umich.edu/cgi/t/text/text-idx?c=spobooks;idno=b bv9812.0001.001;rgn=div1;view=text;cc=spobooks;node=bbv9812.0001.001%3A11.

Keralis, Spencer D. C., Shannon Stark, Martin Halbert, and William E. Moen. "Research Data Management in Policy and Practice: The DataRes Project." In *Research Data Management: Principles, Practices, and Prospects*. Washington, DC: Council on Library and Information Resources, 2013.

Kern, M. "Continuity and Change or Will I Ever Be Prepared for What Comes Next?" *Reference and User Services Quarterly* 53, no. 4 (2014): 282–285.

Kernohan, David John Gray, and John Daish. *User Participation in Building Design and Management: A Generic Approach to Building Evaluation*. Oxford, UK: Butterworth Architecture, 1992.

Khoo, C. "Competencies for New Era Librarians and Information Professionals." In *International Conference on Libraries*, 2005, 14–16.

Killeen, Erlene Bishop. "Yesterday, Today, and Tomorrow: Transitions of the Work but not the Mission." *Teacher Librarian* 36, no. 5 (2009): 8–13.

Kim, Bohyun. "Harnessing the Power of Game Dynamics." *College & Research Libraries News* 73, no. 8 (2012): 465–469.

Kim, Mun-Cho, and Jong-Kil Kim. "Digital Divide: Conceptual Discussions and Prospect." In *The Human Society and the Internet: Internet-Related Socio-Economic Issues*, edited by Won Kim, Tok-Wang Ling, Yoon-Joon Lee, and Seung-Soo Park. Berlin, DE: Springer, 2001.

King, Nathaniel. "Nice vs. Necessary: Reference Collections in ARL Member Libraries." *Reference Librarian* 53, no. 2 (2012): 138–155. doi:10.1080/02763877.2011.607415.

Knowles, M. "Making Things Happen by Releasing the Energy of Others." *Journal of Management Development*, September 1983, 182–190.

Knowles, Malcolm, Elwood F. Holton III, and Richard A. Swanson. *The Adult Learner: The Definitive Classic in Adult Education and Human Resource Development*. 6th ed. Burlington, MA: Elsevier, 2005.

Knox, Emily. "The Challengers of West Bend: The Library as a Community Institution." In *Libraries and the Reading Public in Twentieth Century America*, edited by Christine Pawley and Louise S. Robbins. Madison: University of Wisconsin Press, 2013.

Komita, L. "Electronic Communities in an Information Society: Paradise, Mirage, or Malaise?" *Journal of Documentation* 57, no. 1 (January 2001): 115–129.

Kong, Luis. "Failing to Read Well: The Role of Public Libraries in Adult Literacy, Immigrant Community Building, and Free Access to Learning." *Public Libraries Online* 52, no. 1 (January/February 2013). http://publiclibrariesonline.org/2013/03/failing-to-read-well-the-role-of-public-libraries-in-adult-literacy-immigrant-community-building-and-free-access-to-learning.

Koontz, Christie, ed. "Marketing Glossary." IFLA.org, 2001. Extracted with permission from *Dictionary of Marketing Terms*, edited by Peter D. Bennett, 2nd ed. Chicago, IL: American Marketing Association; Lincolnwood, IL: NTC Publishing Group, 1995, http://archive.ifla.org/VII/s34/pubs/glossary.htm.

Koontz, Christie, and Lorri Mon. *Marketing and Social Media: A Guide for Libraries, Archives and Museums*. Lanham, MD: Rowman & Littlefield, 2014.

Kotler, Neil G., Philip Kotler, and Wendy Kotler. *Museum Marketing & Strategy: Designing Missions, Building Audiences, Generating Revenues and Resources*. 2nd ed. San Francisco, CA: Jossey-Bass, 2008.

Kotler, Philip. "Strategies for Introducing Marketing to Nonprofit Organizations." *Journal of Marketing* 43, no. 1 (1979): 40. http://www.jstor.org/stable/1250756.

Kotter, John. "What Leaders Really Do." In *HBR's 10 Must Reads: On Leadership*, 37–56. Cambridge, MA: Harvard Business School Publishing, 2011.

Kouzes, J. M., and Posner, B. Z. *Credibility: How Leaders Gain and Lose It; Why People Demand It*. San Francisco, CA: Jossey-Bass, 2011.

Krasulski, Michael J. "'Where Do They Come From, and How Are They Trained?' Professional Education and Training of Access Services Librarians in Academic Libraries." *Journal of Access Services* 11, no. 1 (2014): 14–29.

Kroes, Neelie. "Dutch Open Access Week Address." YouTube video. Posted October 18, 2011. https://www.youtube.com/watch?v=taux1l0Vgek.

Kruse, Kevin M. "What Is Leadership?" Forbes.com. Last modified April 9, 2013. http://www.forbes.com/sites/kevinkruse/2013/04/09.

———. *White Flight: Atlanta and the Making of Modern Conservatism*. Princeton, NJ: Princeton University Press, 2007.

Kuhlmann, L. Meghann, Denise Agosto, Jonathan P. Bell, and Anthony Bernier. "Learning from Librarians and Teens about YA Library Spaces." *Public Libraries* 53, no. 3 (2014): 24–28.

Kuhlthau, Carol C. "Inside the Search Process: Information Seeking from the User's Perspective." *Journal of the American Society for Information Science* 42 (1991): 361–371.

Kvenlid, Cassandra, and Kaijsa Calkins. *Embedded Librarians: Moving beyond One-Shot Instruction*. Chicago, IL: Association of College and Research Libraries, 2011.

Lamont, Bridget L. "The Legacy of the Library Services & Construction Act in Illinois." *Illinois Libraries* 80 (Summer 1998): 93–184.

Lankes, R. David. *The Atlas of New Librarianship*. Cambridge, MA: MIT Press, 2011.

Larsen, David K. "Assessing and Benchmarking Access Services." In *Twenty-First Century Access Services*, edited by Michael Krasulski and Trevor Dawes. Chicago, IL: American Library Association, 2013.

LaRue, James. "Why Build Libraries?" *Public Libraries* 53 (July/August 2014): 12–17.

Learned, William S. *The American Public Library and the Diffusion of Knowledge*. New York: Harcourt, 1924.

Lee, Robert Ellis. *Continuing Education for Adults through the American Public Library, 1833–1864*. Chicago, IL: American Library Association, 1966.

Leonard, Elizabeth, and Erin McCaffrey. "MOOCs: Getting Involved." In *Virtually Embedded: The Librarian in an Online Environment*, edited by Elizabeth Leonard and Erin McCaffrey. Chicago, IL: American Library Association, 2014. Kindle edition.

———. *Virtually Embedded: The Librarian in an Online Environment*. Chicago, IL: American Library Association.

Levien, Roger. "Policy Brief No. 4: Confronting the Future." Office for Information Technology Policy. Chicago, IL: American Library Association, June 2011. http://en.www.mcu.es/bibliotecas/docs/MC/2012/CongresoBP/leviening.pdf.

LIBLICENSE. "Licensing Information." Last modified July 5, 2014. http://liblicense.crl.edu/licensing-information.

Libraries and Maker Culture: A Resource Guide. "Makerspaces: What Are They?" Last modified August 7, 2013. http://library-maker-culture.weebly.com/what-are-they.html.

Library Game. "Engaging Libraries with Library Game." Last modified July 6, 2014. http://librarygame.co.uk.

Library Juice. "The Library as Social Centre." Last modified July 17, 2012. http://libr.org/juice/issues/vol3/LJ_3.12.html#13.

Library of Congress. "Dublin Core to MARC Crosswalk." Last modified April 23, 2008. http://www.loc.gov/marc/dccross.html.

———. "Library of Congress Classification." Last modified July 24, 2014. http://www.loc.gov/catdir/cpso/lcc.html.

———. "Library of Congress Subject Headings PDF Files." Last modified August 20, 2014. http://www.loc.gov/aba/publications/FreeLCSH/freelcsh.html.

———. "MARC Documentation." Last modified July 17, 2014. http://www.loc.gov/marc/marcdocz.html.

———. "Mass Deacidification." Last modified July 1, 2014. http://www.loc.gov/preservation/about/deacid/index.html.

Library Services and Technology Act (LSTA). Last modified August 14, 2014. http://www.ala.org/advocacy/advleg/federallegislation/lsta.

Lin, Pei-chun, Kuan-nien Chen, and Sung-Shan Chang. "Before There Was a Place Called Library—Library Space as an Invisible Factor Affecting Students' Learning." *Libri: International Journal of Libraries and Information Services* 60, no. 4 (2010): 339–351.

Lindquist, Thea, and Todd Gilman. "Academic/Research Librarians with Subject Doctorates: Data and Trends 1965–2006." *portal: Libraries and the Academy* 8, no. 1 (2008): 31–52.

LinkedIn. https://www.linkedin.com.

Literary Lots. Last modified July 28, 2014. http://literarylots.org.

LittleBits Electronics. "Home." Last modified September 12, 2014. http://littlebits.cc.

LLAMA Competency Task Force. *LLAMA Competencies Committee Report 2013–2014.* Report to LLAMA Board. ALA conference, Las Vegas, Nevada, 2014.

Lotts, Megan, and Stephanie Graves. "Using the iPad for Reference Services: Librarians Go Mobile." *College & Research Libraries News* 72, no. 4 (2011): 217–220.

Lumina Foundation. *The Degree Qualifications Profile 2.0: Defining U.S. Degrees through Demonstration and Documentation of College Learning.* Last modified February 6, 2014. http://www.luminafoundation.org/publications/DQP/DQP2.0-draft.pdf.

Lundin, Anne. "Anne Carroll Moore: 'I Have Spun out a Long Thread.'" In *Reclaiming the American Library Past: Writing the Women In*, edited by Suzanne Hildenbrand. Norwood, NJ: Ablex, 1996.

Luo, Lili, and Emily Weak. "Texting 4 Answers: What Questions Do People Ask?" *Reference & User Services Quarterly* 51, no. 2 (Winter 2011): 133–142.

The "M" Word—Marketing Libraries: Marketing Tips and Trends for Libraries and Non-Profits. Last modified August 30, 2013. http://themwordblog.blogspot.com.

Maack, Mary Niles. "Public Libraries in Transition: Ideals, Strategies and Research." *Libraries and Culture* 29 (Winter 1994): 79.

MacWhinnie, Laurie A. "The Information Commons: The Academic Library of the Future." *portal: Libraries and the Academy* 3, no. 2 (2003): 241–257. https://muse.jhu.edu/journals/portal_libraries_ and_the_academy/v003/3.2macwhinnie.html.

Maeda, John. *Redesigning Leadership*. Cambridge, MA: MIT Press, 2011.

Maker Faire. "How to Make a Maker Faire." Last modified July 2, 2014. http://makerfaire.com/mini.

Manyika, James et al. (2013). "Disruptive technologies: Advances that will transform life, business, and the global economy," McKinsey & Company, http://www.mckinsey.com/insights/ business_technology/disruptive_technologies?cid=disruptive_tech-eml-alt-mip-mck-oth-1305.

Manzilla, Veronica Boix, and Howard Gardner. "From Teaching Globalization to Nurturing Global Consciousness." In *Learning in the Global Era: International Perspectives on Globalization and Education*, edited by Marcelo Suarez-Orozo. Berkeley and Los Angeles: University of California Press, 2007.

MarketingCharts. "American Households Are Getting Smaller—And Headed by Older Adults." Last modified November 27, 2012. http://www.marketingcharts.com/traditional/american-households -are-getting-smaller-and-headed-by-older-adults-24981.

Maslow, Abraham H. "A Theory of Human Motivation." *Psychological Review* 50, no. 4 (1943): 370–396. doi:10.1037/h0054346.

Mason, Richard A. "What Is an Information Professional?" *Journal of Education for Library and Information Science* 31, no. 2 (1990): 133–138.

Mathews, Anne. "Use of Marketing Principles in Library Planning." In *Marketing for Libraries and Information Agencies*, edited by Darlene E. Weingand. Norwood, NJ: Ablex Publishing, 1984.

Matthews, Joseph R. *The Evaluation and Measurement of Library Services*. Westport, CT: Libraries Unlimited, 2007.

————. *Research-Based Planning for Public Libraries: Increasing Relevance in the Digital Age*. Santa Barbara, CA: Libraries Unlimited, 2013.

Matthews, Stephen A., and Kimberly D. Matthews. *Crash Course in Strategic Planning*. Santa Barbara, CA: Libraries Unlimited, 2013.

Matthias, Cynthia, and Christy Mulligan. "Hennepin County Library's Teen Tech Squad: Youth Leadership and Technology Free-for-All." *Young Adult Library Services* 8, no. 2 (2010): 13–16.

McCall, M. W., Jr., M. M. Lombardo, and A. M. Morrison. *The Lessons of Experiences: How Successful Executives Develop on the Job*. Lexington, MA: Lexington Books, 1988.

McCann, Erin. "HIPAA Data Breaches Climb 138 Percent." *Healthcare IT News*. Last modified February 6, 2014. http://www.healthcareitnews.com/news/hipaa-data-breaches-climb-138-percent.

McCaslin, David. "Access Services Education in Library and Information Science Programs." *Journal of Access Services* 6, no. 4 (2009): 485–496.

McClure, Charles R. *A Planning Process for Public Libraries*. Chicago, IL: American Library Association, 1987.

McClure, Charles R., and Paul T. Jaeger. *Public Libraries and Internet Service Roles: Measuring and Maximizing Internet Services*. Chicago, IL: American Library Association, 2009.

McCook, Kathleen de la Peña. "Administration and Staffing." In *Introduction to Public Librarianship*, 2nd ed., 137–140. New York: Neal-Schuman, 2011.

———. "Brahmins, Bequests, and Determined Women: The Beginnings to 1918." In *Introduction to Public Librarianship*, 2nd ed., 17–34. New York: Neal-Schuman, 2011.

———. "Organization, Law, Advocacy, Funding and Politics." In *Introduction to Public Librarianship*, 2nd ed., 101–130. New York: Neal-Schuman, 2011.

———. "Statistics, Standards, Planning, Results, and Quality of Life." In *Introduction to Public Librarianship*, 2nd ed., 76–82. New York: Neal-Schuman, 2011.

———. "Structure and Infrastructure." In *Introduction to Public Librarianship*, 2nd ed., 159–198. New York: Neal-Schuman, 2011.

McCook, Kathleen de la Peña, and Peggy Barber. "Public Policy as a Factor Influencing Adult Lifelong Learning, Adult Literacy and Public Libraries." *Reference & User Services Quarterly* 42, no. 1 (2002): 66–75.

McCook, Kathleen de la Peña, and Katharine J. Phenix. "The Future of Public Libraries in the Twenty-First Century: Human Rights and Human Capabilities." In *Introduction to Public Librarianship*, 339–360. New York: Neal-Schuman, 2011.

———. "Public Librarianship." In *Encyclopedia of Library and Information Sciences*, 3rd ed. London: Taylor and Routledge, 2010.

McHenry, Elizabeth. "'An Association of Kindred Spirits': Black Readers and Their Reading Rooms." In *Institutions of Reading: The Social Life of Libraries in the United States*, edited by Thomas Augst and Kenneth Carpenter. Amherst: University of Massachusetts Press, 2007.

McKendrick, J. *Libraries: At the Epicenter of the Digital Disruption; The Library Guide Benchmark Study on 2013/14 Library Spending Plans*. Medford, NJ: Information Today, 2013.

McKendrick, Joseph. *Funding and Priorities: The Library Resource Guide Benchmark Study on 2011 Library Spending Plans*. Chatham, NJ: Unisphere Research, 2011. http://lgdata.s3-website-us-east-1.amazonaws.com/docs/231/215960/Funding-and-PrioritiesThe-Library-Resource-Guide-Benchmark-Study-on-2011-Library-Spending-Plans.pdf.

McLeish, Kenneth, ed. "Profession." In *Bloomsbury Guide to Human Thought*. New York: Oxford University Press, 2009. doi:10.1093/oxfordhb/9780195325911.003.0020.

McMullen, Haynes. *American Libraries before 1876*. Westport, CT: Greenwood, 2000.

The Measurement Standard. "Katie Delahaye Paine's New Social Media Measurement Checklist." Last modified January 23, 2010. http://kdpaine.blogs.com/themeasurementstandard/2010/01/katie-paines-social-media-measurement-checklist.html.

Mechaber, Ezra. "Here's How Cell Phone Unlocking Became Legal." *White House Blog*. Last modified August 15, 2014. http://www.whitehouse.gov/blog/2014/08/15/heres-how-cell-phone-unlocking-became-legal.

Medical Library Association. "MLA Top Health Websites." Last modified July 8, 2014. https://www.mlanet.org/resources/medspeak/topten.html.

Meehan, T. P. "Bibframe." *Catalogue and Index* 174 (2014): 43–52.

Mehra, B., K. Black, V. Singh, and J. Nolt. "What Is the Value of LIS Education? A Qualitative Study of the Perspectives of Tennessee's Rural Librarians." *Journal of Education for Library and Information Science* 52, no. 4 (2011): 265–278.

Menchaca, Frank. "Start a New Fire: Measuring the Value of Academic Libraries in Undergraduate Learning." *portal: Libraries and the Academy* 14, no. 3 (2014): 353–367. doi:10.135/pla.2014.0020.

Merriam-Webster. "Librarian." http://www.merriam-webster.com/dictionary/librarian.

———. "Library." http://www.merriam-webster.com/dictionary/library?show=0&t=1410888178.

Mery, Yvonne, Jill Newby, and Ke Peng. "Why One-Shot Information Literacy Sessions Are Not the Future of Instruction: A Case for Online Credit Courses." *College & Research Libraries* 73, no. 4 (2012): 366–377. http://crl.acrl.org/content/73/4/366.full.pdf+html.

Meulemans, Yvonne Nalani, and Allison Carr. "Not at Your Service: Building Genuine Faculty-Librarian Partnerships." *Reference Services Review* 41, no. 1 (2013): 80–90, doi:10.1108/00907321311300893.

Micka, Tracy. "Demonstrating the Value of the Public Library: Economic Valuation and the Advocacy Imperative." *Student Research Journal* 3, no. 1 (2013): 6. http://scholarworks.sjsu.edu/cgi/viewcontent.cgi?article=1127&context=slissrj.

The Microaggressions Project. "Microaggressions." Last modified July 20, 2014. http://microaggressions.tumblr.com.

Middle States Commission on Higher Education. *Characteristics of Excellence in Higher Education: Requirements of Affiliation and Standards for Accreditation*. Philadelphia, PA: Middle States Commission on Higher Education, 2011. http://planning.umbc.edu/files/2013/11/Middle-States-14-Characteristics-of-Excellence-Summary.pdf.

Mill, John Stuart. *Utilitarianism*. London: Parker, Son & Bourne, 1863.

Millem, Jeffrey F., Mitchell J. Chang, and Anthony Lising Antonio. "Making Diversity Work on Campus: A Research-Based Perspective." Making Excellence Inclusive Initiative. Washington, DC: Association of American Colleges and Universities, 2005. http://www.aacu.org/inclusive_excellence/documents/Milem_et_al.pdf.

Miller, Kelly E. "Imagine! On the Future of Teaching and Learning and the Academic Research Library." *portal: Libraries and the Academy* 14, no. 3 (2014): 329–351. doi:10.1353/pla.2014.0018.

Mischel, Walter. "Nancy Cantor: A View from the Chancellor's Office." *Observer* 22, no. 3 (March 2009). http://www.psychologicalscience.org/index.php/publications/observer/2009/march-09/nancy-cantor-a-view-from-the-chancellors-office.html.

MIT Human Resources. "Compensation: Job Families." Last modified August 29, 2014. http://hrweb.mit.edu/compensation/job-evaluations/job-families.

Mitchell, A. C. *Special Libraries Association: Its First Fifty Years, 1909–1959*. New York: Special Libraries Association, 1959.

Mitchell, Erik T. "The Role of Information Organization and Metadata in Digital Documents." PhD. diss., University of North Carolina–Chapel Hill, 2009.

Morris, Jacquelyn M. *Bibliographic Instruction in Academic Libraries: A Review of the Literature and Selected Bibliography*. Facsimile. Champaign, IL: ERIC (1979): 1–48. http://files.eric.ed.gov/fulltext/ED180505.pdf.

Morrison, J. L. "Environmental Scanning." In *A Primer for New Institutional Researchers*, edited by M. A. Whitely, J. D. Porter, and R. H. Fenske. Tallahassee, FL: Association for Institutional Research, 1991.

Mosley, Pixey A. "Assessing User Interactions at the Desk Nearest the Front Door." *Reference & User Services Quarterly* 47, no. 2 (2007): 159–167.

Mount, E., and Massoud, R. *Special Libraries and Information Centers: An Introductory Text* New York: Special Libraries Association, 1999.

Mueller, Barbar. *Communicating with the Multicultural Consumer: Theoretical and Practical Perspectives*. Washington, DC: Peter Lang, 2008.

Multnomah County Library. "My Librarian." Last modified July 3, 2014. https://multcolib.org/my-librarian.

Myburgh, Sue. *The New Information Professional: How to Thrive in the Information Age Doing What You Love*. Oxford, UK: Chandos Publishing, 2011.

MyInfoQuest. "Welcome to My Info Quest—Txt 4 Answers!" Last modified September 3, 2014. http://www.myinfoquest.info.

Nahl, D., and D. Bilal. "The Centrality of Affect in Information Behavior." In *Information and Emotion: The Emergent Affective Paradigm in Information Behavior Research and Theory*. Medford, NJ: Information Today, 2007.

Naismith, Rachael. "Library Service to Migrant Farm Workers." *Library Journal* 114, no. 4 (1989): 54.

Nardi, B. A., and V. O'Day. *Information Ecologies: Using Technology with Heart*. Cambridge, MA: MIT Press, 2000.

National Cancer Institute. "Cancer.gov." http://cancer.gov.

National Center of Education Statistics (NCES). "Chapter 3: Budgeting." In *Financial Accounting for Local and State School Systems*, 2003 ed. Last modified July 2, 2013. http://nces.ed.gov/pubs2004/h2r2/ch_3.asp.

———. "Surveys and Programs." Last modified September 8, 2014. http://nces.ed.gov.

National Conference of State Legislatures. "Privacy Protections in State Constitutions." n.d. http://www.ncsl.org/research/telecommunications-and-information-technology/privacy-protections-in-state-constitutions.aspx.

National Council of Teachers of English. "The NCTE Definition of 21st Century Literacies." Last modified February 2013. http://www.ncte.org/positions/statements/21stcentdefinition.

National Endowment for the Humanities (NEH). "U.S. Newspaper Program." 1982.

National Historic Preservation Act of 1966. Pub. L. 89–665, 80 Stat. 89–665. http://www.achp.gov/docs/nhpa%202008-final.pdf.

National Information Standards Organization (NISO). "Shared Electronic Resource Understanding (SERU): Recommended Practice." Last modified July 2, 2014. http://www.niso.org/workrooms/seru.

National Initiative for Cybersecurity Careers and Studies. "Cyber Glossary." Department of Homeland Security. Last modified June 26, 2014. http://niccs.us-cert.gov/glossary#cybersecurity.

National Institute of Standards and Technology. "FISMA Detailed Overview." Last modified April 1, 2014. http://csrc.nist.gov/groups/SMA/fisma/overview.html.

National Institute of Standards and Technology. *Framework for Improving Critical Cybersecurity Infrastructure*, version 1.0. Last modified February 12, 2014. http://www.nist.gov/cyberframework/upload/cybersecurity-framework-021214.pdf.

Naumer, Charles M., and Karen E. Fisher. "Information Needs." In *Encyclopedia of Library and Information Sciences*, edited by Marcia J. Bates and Mary N. Maack, 3rd ed., 2452–2458. Abingdon, UK: Taylor & Francis, 2009.

Neal, James. "Foreword." In *Twenty-First Century Access Services*, edited by Michael Krasulski and Trevor Dawes, v–vii. Chicago, IL: American Library Association, 2013.

Nelson, Sandra. *The New Planning for Results: A Streamlined Approach*. Chicago, IL: American Library, 2001.

———. *Strategic Planning for Results*. Chicago, IL: American Library Association, 2008.

New Media Consortium. "About the NMC." *New Media Consortium*. Last modified July 1, 2014. http://www.nmc.org/about.

———. "NMC Horizon Project." 2014 Higher Education Edition. http://www.nmc.org/pdf/2014-nmc-horizon-report-he-EN.pdf.

Newman, Craig A., and Daniel L. Stein. "Who Should Pay for Data Theft?" *Bloomberg Businessweek*. Last modified February 20, 2014. http://www.businessweek.com/articles/2014-02-20/who-should-pay-for-data-theft.

Next Generation Science Standards. "About the Standards." Last modified June 25, 2014. http://www.nextgenscience.org/about-standards-development-process.

Nicholas, David. *Assessing Information Needs: Tools, Techniques and Concepts for the Internet Age*. 2nd ed. London: ASLIB, 2000.

NIH U.S. National Library of Medicine. "DOCLINE." Last modified December 19, 2013. http://www.nlm.nih.gov/pubs/factsheets/docline.html.

———. "Fact Sheet: Medical Subject Headings (MeSH®)." Last modified July 5, 2014. http://www.nlm.nih.gov/pubs/factsheets/mesh.html.

———. "Fact Sheet: NLM Classification." Last modified July 5, 2014. http://www.nlm.nih.gov/pubs/factsheets/nlmclassif.html.

———. "Fact Sheet: Unified Medical Language System® (UMLS®) Metathesaurus®." Last modified July 5, 2014. http://www.nlm.nih.gov/pubs/factsheets/umlsmeta.html.

———. "In His Own Words: Martin Cummings and the NLM." *History of Medicine*. Last modified July 5, 2014. http://www.nlm.nih.gov/hmd/digicolls/cummings/index.html.

———. "MedlinePlus." Last modified July 26, 2014. http://www.nlm.nih.gov/medlineplus.

———. "NLM Classification 2014." Last modified July 7, 2014. http://www.nlm.nih.gov/class.

———. "PubMed." Last modified July 27, 2014. http://www.ncbi.nlm.nih.gov/pubmed.

———. "PubMed Central." Last modified July 27, 2014. http://www.ncbi.nlm.nih.gov/pmc.

———. "TOXNET: Toxicology Data Network." http://toxnet.nlm.nih.gov/cgi-bin/sis/htmlgen?TOXLINE.

No Child Left Behind (NCLB) Act of 2001. Pub. L. No. 107–110 § 115, Stat. 1425 (2002). http://www2.ed.gov/policy/elsec/leg/esea02/107-110.pdf.

Northeast Document Conservation Center. "dPlan: The Online Disaster-Planning Tool for Cultural and Civic Institutions." 2006. https://www.dplan.org.

————. "History of the Northeast Document Conservation Center." Last modified August 13, 2014. http://www.nedcc.org/about/history/overview.

Northern Onodaga Public Library. "LibraryFarm." Last modified September 11, 2014. http://www.nopl .org/library-farm.

Nygren, Åke "The Public Library as a Community Hub for Connected Learning." Paper submitted at IFLA Conference, August 4, 2014. http://library.ifla.org/1014/1/167-nygren-en.pdf.

Oakleaf, Megan. *Value of Academic Libraries: A Comprehensive Research Review and Report.* Chicago, IL: Association of College and Research Libraries, 2010. http://www.ala.org/acrl/sites/ala.org.acrl/ files/content/issues/value/val_report.pdf.

Octopus Communities. "What Is a Community Hub?" Last modified June 22, 2013. http://www.octopus communities.org.uk/our-projects/community-hubs/what-is-a-community-hub.

OECD. *Organisation for Economic Co-Operation and Development, Recommendation of the Council Concerning Guidelines Governing the Protection of Privacy and Transborder Flows of Personal Data, 2013.* www.oecd.org/sti/ieconomy/2013-oecd-privacy-guidelines.pdf.

————. "Recognition of Non-formal & Informal Learning-Home." Last modified February 9, 2014. http:// www.oecd.org/education/skills-beyond-school/recognitionofnon-formalandinformallearning -home.htm.

OECD Glossary of Statistical Terms. "Sectoral Strategy." Last modified July 23, 2007. http://stats.oecd .org/glossary/detail.asp?ID=7241.

Office for Literacy and Outreach Services. "Mission." Last modified October 9, 2014. http://www.ala .org/offices/olos.

Office of the Privacy Commissioner of Canada. "Legal Information Related to the Privacy Act." Last modified July 22, 2014. http://www.priv.gc.ca/leg_c/leg_c_a_e.asp.

Office of the Register of Copyright. "Legal Issues in Mass Digitization: A Preliminary Analysis and Discussion Document." Washington, DC: U.S. Copyright Office, October 2011. http://www.copyright .gov/docs/massdigitization/USCOMassDigitization_October2011.pdf.

Ogburn, Joyce L. "The Imperative for Data Curation." *portal: Libraries and the Academy* 10, no. 2 (April 2010): 241–246.

O'Kelly, Mary, and Colleen Lyon. "Google Like a Librarian: Sharing Skills for Search Success." *College and Research Libraries News.* Last modified June 13, 2013. http://crln.acrl.org/content/72/6/330.full.

Okobi, Elise A. Rogers Halliday. "History and Development of Adult Services." In *Library Services for Adults in the 21st Century*, 19–28. Santa Barbara, CA: Libraries Unlimited, 2014.

Olmstead v. United States. 277 U.S. 438, 478–479 (1928). *Justia.* Last modified February 21, 2014. https://supreme.justia.com/cases/federal/us/277/438/case.html.

Online Computer Library Center (OCLC). "OCLC Research." Last modified August 14, 2014. http:// oclc.org/research.html.

————. "QuestionPoint." Last modified August 22, 2014. http://oclc.org/questionpoint.en.html.

Online Dictionary for Library and Information Science. http://www.abc-clio.com/ODLIS/odlis_s.aspx.

OpenDOAR. "Directory of Open Access Repositories." Last modified August 6, 2014. www.opendoar .org.

Open Library. "Borrow eBooks." Last modified July 2, 2014. https://openlibrary.org/borrow/about.

Orange, Satia Marshall, and Robin Osborne. "Introduction." *From Outreach to Equity: Innovative Models of Library Policy and Practice.* Chicago, IL: American Library Association, 2004.

O'Toole, James. *Leadership A to Z: A Guide for the Appropriately Ambitious.* San Francisco, CA: Jossey-Bass, 1999.

Overman, E. Sam, and Anthony G. Cahill. "Information Policy: A Study of Values in the Policy Process." *Policy Studies Review* 9, no. 4 (1990): 803–818. https://courses.ischool.utexas.edu/lynnwest/2008/fall/INF180J/overman_informationpolicy.pdf.

Oxford Dictionaries. "Advocacy." http://www.oxforddictionaries.com (accessed August 1, 2014).

Oxford Dictionaries. "Power." http://www.oxforddictionaries.com (accessed August 1, 2014).

P21 Framework Definitions. *Partnership for 21st Century Skills.* December 2009. http://www.p21.org/storage/documents/P21_Framework_Definitions.pdf.

Paine, Katie D. "Social Media Measurement Manifesto: Yes We CAN, and Already ARE Measuring Social Media." White paper, Berlin, New Hampshire, 2009. http://dmabenchmarkshub.wikispaces.com/file/view/Yes+we+Can+measure+social+media+white+paper+r.pdf.

Pallante, Maria A. "The Next Great Copyright Act." *Columbia Journal of Law & the Arts* 36 (2012): 315. http://www.copyright.gov/docs/next_great_copyright_act.pdf.

Palmour, Vernon, Marcia C. Bellassai, and Nancy V. DeWath. *A Planning Process for Public Libraries.* Chicago, IL: American Library Association, 1980.

Pardavila, John. "Librarians with a Latte." University Libraries: University at Albany State University of New York. Last modified April 1, 2013. http://liblogs.albany.edu/librarynews/2013/04/got_questions_got_research_anx.html.

Parker, Peter. "Introduction." In *Leading from Within: Poetry That Sustains the Courage to Lead*, edited by Sam Intrater and Megan Scribner. New York: Wiley, 2007.

Passet, Joanne E. *Cultural Crusaders: Women Librarians in the American West, 1900–1917.* Albuquerque: University of New Mexico Press, 1994.

Pateman, John, and Ken Williment. *Developing Community-Led Public Libraries.* Surrey, UK: Ashgate, 2013.

Patrick, Harold Andrew, and Vincent Raj Kumar. "Managing Workplace Diversity: Issues and Challenges." *SAGE Open* 2, no. 2 (June 2012). doi:10.1177/2158244012444615. http://classic.sgo.sagepub.com/content/2/2/2158244012444615.full.pdf+html.

Patterson, Toby Graham. *A Right to Read: Segregation and Civil Rights in Alabama's Public Libraries, 1900–1965.* Tuscaloosa: University of Alabama Press, 2002.

Pawley, Christine. "Advocate of Access: Lutie Stearns and the Traveling Libraries of the Wisconsin Free Library Commission, 1895–1914." *Libraries and Culture* 35 (Summer 2000): 434–458.

———. *Reading on the Middle Border: The Culture of Print in Late Nineteenth Century Osage, Iowa.* Amherst: University of Massachusetts Press, 2001.

———. *Reading Places: Literacy, Democracy, and the Public Library in Cold War America.* Amherst: University of Massachusetts Press, 2010.

Parry, Marc. "A High-Tech Library Keeps Books at Faculty Fingertips—with Robot Help." *Chronicle of Higher Education* 57, no. 42 (July 24, 2011): A12–A13.

Pendell, Kimberly, Elizabeth Withers, Jill Castek, and Stephen Reder. "Tutor-Facilitated Adult Digital Literacy Learning: Insights from a Case Study." *Internet Reference Services Quarterly* 18, no. 2 (2013): 105–125. doi:10.1080/10875301.2013.800013.

Penna, Robert, and William Phillips. "Promising Practices: Eight Outcome Models." *Evaluation Exchange* 11, no. 2 (Summer 2005). http://www.hfrp.org/evaluation/the-evaluation-exchange/issue-archive/evaluation-methodology/eight-outcome-models.

Peter, J. Paul, and James H. Donnelly Jr. *A Preface to Marketing Management*, 13th ed. New York: McGraw-Hill Irwin, 2013.

Peters, Marybeth. "Report on Orphan Works—A Report of the Register of Copyrights." Washington, DC: U.S. Copyright Office, January 2006. http://www.copyright.gov/orphan/orphan-report-full.pdf.

Pettigrew, K. E. "Waiting for Chiropody: Contextual Results from an Ethnographic Study of the Information Behavior among Attendees at Community Clinics." *Information Processing & Management* 35, no. 6 (1999): 801–817.

Pew Research American Life Project. "Libraries." Last modified July 13, 2014. http://libraries.pewinternet.org.

Pew Research Internet Project. "Mobile Technology Fact Sheet." Last modified June 25, 2014. http://www.pewinternet.or/fact-sheets/mobile-technology-fact-sheet.

Pink, Daniel. *Drive*. New York: Riverhead Publishing, 2011.

Plaks, Andrew H. "Golden Rule." In *Encyclopedia of Religion*. Detroit, MI: Macmillan Reference USA, 2005.

Poole, William F. "Progress of Library Architecture." *Library Journal* 7, no. 134 (1882): 1908–1909.

PREMIS Editorial Committee. "Data Dictionary Section from PREMIS Data Dictionary for Preservation Metadata Version 2.0." Washington, DC: Library of Congress, 2008. http://www.loc.gov/standards/premis/v2/premis-dd-2-0.pdf.

Preservation 101. "Introduction to Preservation." Last modified June 30, 2013. http://unfacilitated.preservation101.org/session1/expl_whatis-libraries.asp.

Price, Jay. "NCSU's Hyper-Modern James B. Hunt Jr. Library Poised to Open." *News Observer*. Last modified December 18, 2012. http://www.newsobserver.com/2012/12/18/2553438/ncsus-hyper-modern-new-james-b.html.

Program on Negotiation Daily Blog. "Negotiation Skills." Harvard Law School. Last modified August 19, 2014. http://www.pon.harvard.edu/category/daily/negotiation-skills-daily.

Progressive Librarian. 1990–present. http://progressivelibrariansguild.org/PL_Jnl/jnl_contents.shtml.

Proquest. "AquaBrowser." N.d. http://www.proquest.com/products-services/AquaBrowser.html.

Protection of Pupil Rights. 20 U.S. Code § 1232h, GPO.

Public Library Association (PLA). "PLDS and PLAmetrics." Last modified August 13, 2014. http://www.ala.org/pla/publications/plds.

———. "Strategic Plan." Last modified April 14, 2014. http://www.ala.org/pla/about/strategicplan.

Puerto Rican Cultural Center. Last modified November 17, 2013. http://prcc-chgo.org.

Putnam, Robert D. *Better Together: Restoring the American Community*. New York: Simon & Schuster, 2003.

Quattrochi, Christina. 2013. "MAKE'ing More Diverse Makers." EdSurge. Last modified October 29, 2014. https://www.edsurge.com/n/2013-10-29-make-ing-more-diverse-makers.

Quinney, Kayla L., Sara D. Smith, and Quinn Galbraith. "Bridging the Gap: Self-Directed Staff Technology Training." *Information Technology and Libraries*, December 2010, 205–206. http://ejournals.bc.edu/ojs/index.php/ital/article/viewFile/3131/2746.

Raber, Douglas. *Librarianship and Legitimacy: The Ideology of the Public Library Inquiry*. Westport, CT: Greenwood, 1997.

Radford, Neil. *The Carnegie Corporation and the Development of American Academic Libraries, 1928–1941*. Chicago, IL: American Library Association, 1984.

Ranganathan, S. R, *The Five Laws of Library Science* (Madras, IN: Madras Library Association, 1931).

Rainie, Lee, Sara Kiesler, Ruogu Kang, and Mary Madden. "Anonymity, Privacy, and Security Online." Pew Research Internet Project. Last modified September 5, 2013. http://www.pewinternet.org/2013/09/05/anonymity-privacy-and-security-online.

Raitz, Joan M. *Dictionary for Library and Information Science*. Santa Barbara, CA: Libraries Unlimited, 2004. www.abc-clio/ODLIS/odlis_1.aspx.

Raven, Bertram H. "Social Influence and Power." In *Current Studies in Social Psychology*, edited by Ivan Dale Steiner and Martin Fishbein, 371–382. York, UK: Holt, Rinehart, Winston, 1965.

Raven, James. "Social Libraries and Library Societies in Eighteenth-Century North America." In *Institutions of Reading: The Social Life of Libraries in the United States*, edited by Thomas Augst and Kenneth Carpenter, 24–52. Amherst: University of Massachusetts Press, 2007.

Reath, Andrews. "Kant's Moral Philosophy." In *The Oxford Handbook of Ethical Theory*, edited by Roger Crisp. New York: Oxford University Press, 2013. doi:10.1093/oxfordhb/9780199545971.013.0021.

Reed, Sally Gardner. *Libraries Need Friends United for Libraries: The Association of Library Trustees, Advocates, Friends and Foundations*. 2012. http://www.ala.org/united/sites/ala.org.united/files/content/friendszone/toolkits/libraries-need-friends-1.pdf.

Reed, Sally Gardner, and Jillian Kalonick. *The Complete Library Trustee Handbook*. New York: Neal-Schuman, 2010.

Registry of Open Access Repositories Mandatory Open Access Policies (ROARMAP). Last modified July 14, 2014. http://roarmap.eprints.org.

Reid, Ian. "The Public Library Data Service 2012 Statistical Report." *Public Libraries* 5, no. 6 (2012): 36–46.

Richman, Tom. "Leadership Expert Ronald Heifetz." Inc.com. Last updated October 1, 1988. http://www.inc.com/magazine/19881001/5990.html.

Risdon, Chris. "The Anatomy of an Experience Map." Last modified November 30, 2011. http://www.adaptivepath.com/ideas/the-anatomy-of-an-experience-map.

Robbins, Louise S. *Censorship and the American Library: The American Library Association's Response to Threats to Intellectual Freedom, 1939–1969*. Westport, CT: Greenwood, 1996.

————. *The Dismissal of Miss Ruth Brown: Civil Rights, Censorship, and the American Library*. Norman: University of Oklahoma Press, 2000.

Robert T. Stafford Disaster Relief and Emergency Assistance Act. PL 93–288 (June 2007). https://www.fema.gov/robert-t-stafford-disaster-relief-and-emergency-assistance-act-public-law-93-288-amended.

Robinson, Otis H. "College Library Administration." In *Public Libraries in the United States Public Libraries in the United States: Their Condition and Management*, 520–525. Department of the Interior, Bureau of Education. Washington, DC: Government Printing Office, 1876. Facsimile of the first edition, with an introduction by Francis Keppel. Champaign, IL: University of Illinois, [1967?].

Rodger, Eleanor Jo. "What's a Library Worth." *American Libraries* 38, no. 8 (September 1, 2007). http://www.questia.com/magazine/1G1-168739901/what-s-a-library-worth-piecing-together-the-structure.

Rogers, Carl. *Freedom to Learn: A Vision of What Education Might Become*. Columbus, OH: C. E. Merrill, 1969.

Rollins, Charlemae Hill. *We Build Together: A Reader's Guide to Negro Life and Literature for Elementary and High School Use*. Chicago, IL: National Council for Teachers of English, 1941.

Rost, Joseph. *Leadership for the 21st Century*. Westport, CT: Praeger, 1991.

Rowlands, Ian. "Understanding Information Policies." *Journal of Information Science* 22, no. 1 (1996): 13–25. http://infocuib.laborales.unam.mx/~mt09s02a/archivos/data/u2rowlands.pdf.

Reference and User Services Association (RUSA). "Guidelines for Behavioral Performance of Reference and Information Service Providers." Last modified August 30, 2014. http://www.ala.org/rusa/resources/guidelines/guidelinesbehavioral.

Reference and User Services Association (RUSA). "Interlibrary Loan Code for the United States." Last modified October 29, 2013. http://www.ala.org/rusa/resources/guidelines/interlibrary.

SalesForce. https://www.salesforce.com.

Samek, Toni. *Librarianship and Human Rights*. Oxford: Chandos, 2007.

San Diego Public Library Foundation. "San Diego Public Library's Award-Winning Literacy Services." Support My Library San Diego. Last modified February 22, 2011. https://supportmylibrary.org/?attachment_id=516.

San José State University School of Information. "Emerging Career Trends for Information Professionals: A Snapshot of Job Titles in Summer 2013." San José, CA: San José State University, 2013. http://slisweb.sjsu.edu/downloads/emerging_trends_2012.pdf.

San José State University School of Information. "Hyperlinked Library MOOC." N.d. http://ischool.sjsu.edu/hyperlinked-library-mooc-1.

Santayana, George. "The Santayana Edition." Last modified August 20, 2014. http://iat.iupui.edu/santayana/content/santayana-quotations.

Sawyer, Carol. "Linking People, Process and Technology in Leadership Development." In *Turning the Prism: Three Explorations of Knowledge Management through Network and Communities of Practice*. Paper presented at the 3rd European Conference on Organizational Knowledge, Learning and Capabilities, Athens, April 5–6, 2002. http://www2.warwick.ac.uk/fac/soc/wbs/conf/olkc/archive/oklc3/papers/id287.pdf.

Schement, Jorge Reina, and Terry Curtis. *Tendencies and Tensions of the Information Age: The Production and Distribution of Information in the United States*. New Brunswick, NJ: Transaction Publishers, 1995.

Scheppke, Jim. "Public Library Buildings in Oregon: A Historical Sketch." *OPL Quarterly* 15, no. 3 (2014): 8–11.

Schmidt, Aaron, and Amana Etches. *User Experience (UX) Design for Libraries*. Tech Set Series 18. Chicago, IL: ALA TechSource, 2012.

Scroggs, Wanita, JD, MLS. Personal communication, June 8, 2014.

The Secretary's Commission on Achieving Necessary Skills. *What Work Requires of Schools: A SCANS Report for America 2000*. Washington, DC: U.S. Department of Labor, 1991. http://wdr.doleta.gov/SCANS/whatwork.

The Section 108 Study Group. Last modified February 7, 2014. http://www.section108.gov.

Shank, Patti. "eLearning Guild Research: How Important Is Informal Learning?" *Learning Solutions Magazine*. Last modified September 13, 2012. http://www.learningsolutionsmag.com/articles/1009/elearning-guild-research-how-important-is-informal-learning.

Sharpe, Stephanie Atkins. "Access Services within Campus and Library Organizations." In *Twenty-First Century Access Services*, edited by Michael Krasulski and Trevor Dawes, 119–134. Chicago, IL: American Library Association, 2013.

Sheldon, Brooke E. "Another Look at Leadership." In *The Portable MLIS: Insights from the Experts*, edited by Ken Haycock and Brooke E. Sheldon. Santa Barbara, CA: Libraries Unlimited, 2008.

Shera, Jesse. *Foundations of the Public Library: The Origins of the Public Library Movement in New England, 1629–1855*. Chicago, IL: University of Chicago Press, 1949.

———. "The Social Library I: Origins, Form, and Economic Backgrounds." In *Foundations of the Public Library*, 68–85. Chicago, IL: University of Chicago Press, 1949.

Shields, David S. "Eighteenth-Century Literary Culture." In *The Colonial Book in the Atlantic World*, edited by Hugh Amory and David D. Hall, 474–475. Chapel Hill, NC: University of North Carolina Press, 2007.

Shongwe, M., and D. N. Ocholla. "A Tracer Study of LIS Graduates at the University of Zululand, 2000–2009." *Mousaison* 29, no. 2 (2011): 227–248.

Shumaker, D. *Models of Embedded Librarianship: Final Report*. Washington, DC: SLA, 2009. http://hq.sla.org/pdfs/EmbeddedLibrarianshipFinalRptRev.pdf.

Shumaker, David. *The Embedded Librarian: Innovative Strategies for Taking Knowledge Where It's Needed*. Medford, NJ: Information Today, 2012.

———. "Who Let the Librarians Out? Embedded Librarianship and the Library Manager." *Reference & User Services Quarterly* (2009): 239–257.

Simon, H. A. "A Behavioral Model of Rational Choice." *Quarterly Journal of Economics* 69, no. 1 (1955): 99–188.

Simon, Herbert A. *Administrative Behavior*. New York: Free Press, 1997.

Sittler, Ryan, and Douglas Cook. *The Library Instruction Cookbook*. Chicago, IL: Association of College and Research Libraries, 2009.

Smith, Brandon Mikel, and Mary Ann Glynn. "Leading with Purpose: Fueling the Human Spirit in Times of Uncertainty." Center for Positive Organizations. Ann Arbor, MI: Ross School of Business, University of Michigan, n.d. http://positiveorgs.bus.umich.edu/wp-content/uploads/Leading-With-Purpose-SmithGlynn.pdf.

Smith, Michael M., and Barbara A. Pietraszewski. "Enabling the Roving Reference Librarian: Wireless Access with Tablet PCs." *Reference Services Review* 32, no. 3 (2004): 249-255. doi:10.1108/00907320410553650.

Snapcircuits. "Home." Last modified August 19, 2014. http://www.snapcircuits.net.

Snider, Brett. "Is it Legal to 'Unlock' Your Cell Phone?" *Law and Daily Life* (blog). Last modified May 18, 2014. http://blogs.findlaw.com/law_and_life/2014/05/is-it-legal-to-unlock-your-cell-phone.html. doi:10.1093/oxfordhb/9780199545971.013.0021.

Socialbrite—Social Solutions for Nonprofits. "How to Measure Your Nonprofit's Social Media Success." Last modified July 3, 2014. http://www.socialbrite.org/2010/12/15/how-to-measure-your-nonprofits-social-media-success.

Society of American Archivists. "Code of Ethics for Archivists." Last modified January 2012. http://www2.archivists.org/statements/saa-core-values-statement-and-code-of-ethics.

———. "Core Values of Archivists." Last modified May 2011. http://www2.archivists.org/statements/saa-core-values-statement-and-code-of-ethics.

Special Libraries Association (SLA). "About Information Professionals." Last modified August 26, 2014. https://www.sla.org/career-center/about-information-professionals.

———. "About SLA." Last modified August 26, 2014. https://www.sla.org/about-sla.

———. *Alignment Project, 2008–2009.* http://dbiosla.org/Alignment%20Project%20Article.pdf.

———. "Chapters." Last modified November 25, 2013. http://www.sla.org/get-involved/chapters.

———. "Constitution of Special Libraries Association." *Special Libraries* 1, no. 1 (January 1910): 1, 8.

———. "Vision, Mission, and Core Values Statements." Last modified August 2, 2014. http://www.sla.org/about-sla/vision-mission-core-value.

Squishy Circuits. "Squishy Circuits Project Page." Last modified July 26, 2014. http://courseweb.stthomas.edu/apthomas/SquishyCircuits.

St. Clair, Guy, Andrew Berner, and Rebecca Vargha. "Special Libraries (SLA)." In *Encyclopedia of Library and Information Science*, 3rd ed. Boca Raton, FL: CRC Press, 2009.

St. Jean, Beth. "'I Just Don't Know What I Don't Know!' A Longitudinal Investigation of the Perceived Usefulness of Information to People with Type 2 Diabetes." *Proceedings of the American Society for Information Science and Technology* 49, no. 1 (2012): 1–10.

Staker, Heather, and Michael B. Horn. "Classifying K–12 Blended Learning." Innosight Institute. May 2012. http://www.innosightinstitute.org/innosight/wp-content/uploads/2012/05/Classifying-K-12-blended-learning2.pdf.

Stenstrom, Cheryl, and Ken Haycock. "Influence and Increased Funding in Canadian Public Libraries." *Library Quarterly* 84, no. 1 (2014): 49–68.

Stephens, Julia. "English Spoken Here." *American Libraries* 38, no. 10 (November 2007): 41, 43–44.

Stephens, Michael. "Exemplary Practice for Learning 2.0." *Reference & User Services Quarterly* 53, no. 2 (2013): 129–139.

———. "The Hyperlinked Library." White paper. *Tame the Web (TTW)* (blog), 2011. http://mooc .hyperlib.sjsu.edu/wp-content/uploads/2013/07/StephensHyperlinkedLinked2011.pdf.

———. "Infinite Learning: Office Hours." *Library Journal.* Last modified October 23, 2013. http:// lj.libraryjournal.com/2013/10/opinion/michael-stephens/infinite-learning-office-hours/#_.

———. "Learning Everywhere." *ACCESS* 26, no. 4 (2012): 4–6. http://www.asla.org.au/publications/ access/access-commentaries/learning-everywhere.aspx.

Stephens, Michael, and Michael Collins. "Web 2.0, Library 2.0, and the Hyperlinked Library." *Serials Review* 33, no. 4 (2007): 253–256.

Stieg, Margaret F. *Change and Challenge in Library and Information Science Education.* Chicago, IL: American Library Association, 1991.

Stiglitz, J., and A. Weiss. "Credit Rationing in Markets with Imperfect Information." *American Economic Review* 71, no. 3 (1981): 393–410.

Stolarick, Kevin, and Kimberly Silk. "So Much More: The Economic Impact of the Toronto Public Library on the City of Toronto." Report. Martin Prosperity Institute, 2013. http://martinprosperity.org/ media/TPL%20Economic%20Impact_Dec2013_LR_FINAL.pdf.

Stone, Elizabeth. *Policy Paradox: The Art of Political Decision Making.* Rev. ed. New York: Norton, 2002.

Strategic Growth Concepts. "What Is Mobile Technology?" Last modified December 26, 2013. http:// www.strategicgrowthconcepts.com/growth/increase-productivity-profitability/mobile-tech nology-facts.html.

Strieb, Karla L., and Julia C. Blixrud. "Unwrapping the Bundle: An Examination of Research Libraries and the 'Big Deal.'" *portal: Libraries and the Academy* 14, no. 4 (2014, in press). http://kb.osu.edu/ dspace/bitstream/handle/1811/59293/StriebKL_BlixrudJC_Portal_2014_authors-final-version .pdf?sequence=1.

Stronski, L. M. "Thinking Outside the Library: Employment Trends of Special Libraries Association Members." Master's paper, University of North Carolina–Chapel Hill, 2004. https://cdr.lib.unc.edu/ indexablecontent/uuid:c6ba86cf-f78c-4329-8aa1-710e893c5da1?dl=true.

Stueart, Robert D., and Barbara B. Moran. *Library and Information Center Management.* Westport, CT: Libraries Unlimited, 2002.

Surowiecki, James. *The Wisdom of Crowds: Why the Many Are Smarter than the Few and How Collective Wisdom Shapes Business, Economics, Societies and Nations.* New York: Doubleday Press, 2004.

Swain, Martha H. "A New Deal in Libraries: Federal Relief Work and Library Service, 1933–43." *Libraries & Culture* 30, no. 3 (Summer 1995): 268–270.

Taylor, Jenny. "Studying Your Users to Improve Services." *Information Outlook* 18, no. 2 (2014): 10–12.

Taylor, N. G., U. Gorham, P. T. Jaeger, and J. C. Bertot. "IT and Collaborative Community Services: The Roles of the Public Library, Local Government, and Nonprofit Entity Partnerships." *International Journal of Public Administration in the Digital Age* 1, no. 1 (2014): 91–107.

Taylor, Robert S. "Question-Negotiation and Information Seeking in Libraries." *College & Research Libraries* 29, no. 3 (1968): 178–194. http://crl.acrl.org/content/29/3/178.full.pdf.

Taylor, S. D., R. A. Perry, J. L. Barton, and B. Spender. "A Follow-Up Study of the Factors Shaping the Career Choices of Library School Students at the University of Alabama." *Reference & User Services Quarterly* 50, no. 1 (2010): 35–47.

Technopedia. "Tablet PC." Last modified October 3, 2014. http://www.technopedia.com/definition/2662/tablet.pc.

Texas Library Association College and University Libraries Division Blog (TLACULD). "Faculty-in-Residence: Taking Embedded Librarianship to a New Level." Blog entry by tlaculd, August 13, 2013. http://culd.wordpress.com/2013/08/23/faculty-in-residence-taking-embedded-librarianship-to-a-new-level.

This Week in Libraries. Last modified October 2, 2014. http://www.thisweekinlibraries.com/Titlewave.

Tichy, N. M., and W. G. Bennis. *Judgment: How Winning Leaders Make Great Calls.* New York: Penguin, 2007.

Tinkerlab. "Challenges." Last modified June 25, 2014. http://tinkerlab.com/challenges.

Tolppanen, Bradley. "A Survey of Current Tasks and Future Trends in Access Services." *Journal of Access Services* 2, no. 3 (2004): 1–14.

Tucker, John M. *Untold Stories: Civil Rights, Libraries and Black Librarianship.* Champaign: University of Illinois, 1998.

———. "User Education in Academic Libraries: A Century in Retrospect." *Library Trends* 29, no. 1 (1980): 9–27.

Tyckoson, David A. "Issues and Trends in the Management of Reference Services: A Historical Perspective." *Journal of Library Administration* 51, no. 3 (2011): 259–278. doi:10.1080/01930826.2012.707953.

Tzoc, Elías, and John Millard. "Technical Skills for New Digital Librarians." *Library Hi Tech News* 28, no. 8 (2011): 11–15.

UCLA Library. "Creative Commons License." Last modified July 19, 2014. http://www.library.ucla.edu/creative-commons-license.

UNESCO. *Paris Declaration on Media and Information Literacy in the Digital Era.* UNESCO, 2014. http://www.unesco.org/new/fileadmin/MULTIMEDIA/HQ/CI/CI/pdf/news/paris_mil_declaration.pdf.

United Kingdom Serials Group (UKSG). "KBART." http://www.uksg.org.

United Nations Development Programme. "The Global Learning Network." N.d. http://www.undp.org/content/undp/en/home/ourwork/capacitybuilding/focus_areas/focus_area_details4/pppsd/global-learning-network.html.

United States History. "The New Deal." Last modified August 9, 2014. http://www.u-s-history.com/pages/h1851.html.

University of Alberta Student Success Centre Specialized Support and Disability Services. "Embedded Librarian at SSDS for Winter 2014 Term." Last modified November 13, 2013. http://www.ssds.ualberta.ca/en/News/2013/November/EmbeddedLibrarianatSSDS.aspx.

University of Iowa Libraries. "Learning Commons." Last modified August 22, 2014. http://www.lib.uiowa.edu/commons.

U.S. Const. amend. I: http://www.usconstitution.net/const.pdf.

———. amend. IV:

———. amend. V:

———. amend. XIV, § 1:

———. art. 1. sec. 8. cl. 8. http://www.archives.gov/exhibits/charters/constitution_transcript.html.

U.S. Copyright Act 14 U.S.C. § *Circ. 2 (December 2011). http://www.copyright.gov/title17/circ92.pdf.*

U.S. Copyright Act, 17 U.S.C. http://www.copyright.gov/title17/circ92.pdf.

U.S. Copyright Office (USCO). "Copyright Basics." *Copyright*, circular 1 (May 2012). Washington, DC: U.S. Copyright Office, 2012. http://www.copyright.gov/circs/circ01.pdf.

———. *The Digital Millennium Copyright Act of 1998*. Washington, DC: U.S. Copyright Office, December 1998. http://www.copyright.gov/legislation/dmca.pdf.

———. "Online Service Providers." Last modified August 16, 2014. http://copyright.gov/onlinesp.

———. "Orphan Works and Mass Digitization." Last modified September 7, 2014. http://copyright .gov/orphan.

U.S. Copyright Office—Library of Congress. "Exemption to Prohibition on Circumvention of Copyright Protection Systems for Access Control Technologies." *Federal Register* 71, no. 227 (November 27, 2006): 68472–68480. http://www.copyright.gov/fedreg/2006/71fr68472.html.

U.S. Department of Commerce. "Falling through the Net: A Survey of the 'Have Nots' in Rural and Urban America." *National Telecommunications & Information Administration*, July 1995. http://www .ntia.doc.gov/ntiahome/fallingthru.html.

U.S. Department of Commerce Internet Policy Task Force. *Copyright Policy, Creativity, and Innovation in the Digital Economy*. Washington, DC: U.S. Patent and Trademark Office, July 2013. http://www .uspto.gov/news/publications/copyrightgreenpaper.pdf.

U.S. Department of Education. "Family Educational Rights and Privacy Act (FERPA)." Last modified March 26, 2013. http://www.ed.gov/policy/gen/guid/fpco/ferpa/index.html.

U.S. Department of Health and Human Services. "NIH Public Access Policy Details." Last modified March 27, 2014. http://publicaccess.nih.gov/policy.htm.

———. "OCR Privacy Brief: Summary of the HIPAA Privacy Rule." May 2003. http://www.hhs.gov/ ocr/privacy/hipaa/understanding/summary/privacysummary.pdf.

U.S. Department of Health, Education & Welfare. "Records, Computers, and the Rights of Citizens." Secretary's Advisory Committee on Automated Personal Data Systems, No. (OS) 73-94, 1973. http://www.justice.gov/opcl/docs/rec-com-rights.pdf.

U.S. Department of Justice. "1854 Copyright Infringement—First Sale Doctrine." Last modified September 10, 2014. http://www.justice.gov/usao/eousa/foia_reading_room/usam/title9/crm 01854.htm.

———. "Privacy Act of 1974 5 U.S.C. § 5529." Office of Privacy and Civil Liberties. http://www.gpo .gov/fdsys/pkg/USCODE-2012-title5/pdf/USCODE-2012-title5-partI-chap5-subchapII-sec552a .pdf.

U.S. Department of Justice Civil Rights Division. "Introduction to the ADA." Information and Technical Assistance on the Americans with Disabilities Act. Last modified August 10, 2014. http://www.ada .gov/ada_intro.htm.

U.S. Department of Labor. "Libraries and Workforce Development." Last modified July 7, 2014. http://www.doleta.gov/usworkforce/uswf_nav.cfm.

U.S. Department of State Careers Site. "Information Resource Officer." http://host.careers.state.gov/specialist/self_evals/iro.qual.html.

U.S. Government Printing Office. "Federal Digital System." Last modified July 15, 2014. http://www.gpo.gov/fdsys.

U.S. Office of Personnel Management. "Developing Performance Standards." Last modified August 3, 2014. http://www.opm.gov/policy-data-oversight/performance-management/performance-management-cycle/pianning/developing-performance-standards.

U.S. Patent and Trademark Office. "Office of Policy and International Affairs—Copyrights." Last modified July 5, 2014. http://www.uspto.gov/ip/global/copyrights/index.jsp.

———. "Department of Commerce Multistakeholder Forum—Improving the Operation of the DMCA Notice and Takedown Policy First Public Meeting." Washington, DC: U.S. Patent and Trademark Office, March 20, 2014. http://www.uspto.gov/ip/global/copyrights/First_Public_Meeting-Improving_Operation_of_DMCA_Notice_and_Takedown_Policy.pdf.

———. "Department of Commerce Multistakeholder Forum on Improving the Operation of the DMCA Notice and Takedown System Third Public Meeting." Washington, DC: U.S. Patent and Trademark Office, June 20, 2014. http://www.uspto.gov/ip/global/copyrights/3rd_plenary_meeting_transcript.pdf.

U.S.A. Patriot Act of 2001. Pub. L. No. 107–56, 115 Stat. 272 (2001). http://www.ala.org/advocacy/advleg/federallegislation/theusapatriotact.

Usability.gov. "Glossary." N.d. http://www.usability.gov/what-and-why/glossary/u/index.html.

Vaidhyanathan, Siva. *The Googlization of Everything (and Why We Should Worry)*. Berkeley, CA: University of California Press, 2012.

Vaill, Peter B. *Learning as a Way of Being; Strategies for Survival in a World of Permanent White Water*. San Francisco, CA: Jossey-Bass, 1996.

Van Epps, Amy, and Megan Sapp Nelson. "One-Shot or Embedded? Assessing Different Delivery Timing for Information Resources Relevant to Assignments." *Evidence Based Library and Information Practice* 8, no. 1 (2013): 4–18.

Van Slyck, Abigail. *Free to All: Carnegie Libraries and American Culture, 1890–1920*. Chicago, IL: University of Chicago Press, 1995.

Vancouver Public Library. "FAQ: VPL Branch and YWCA Housing." Last modified October 15, 2012. http://www.vpl.ca/news/details/faq_vpl_branch_and_ywca_housing.

Varheim, Andreas. "Social Capital and Public Libraries: The Need for Research." *Library & Information Science Research* 29, no. 3 (2007): 416.

Vetruba, Brian. "Embedded Librarian: Meeting Users on Their Turf." Slideshare presentation, posted by Brian Vetruba, February 20, 2011. http://www.slideshare.net/bvetruba/embedded-librarian-meeting-users-on-their-turf.

Vijayan, Jaikumar. "Obama Executive Order Redefines Critical Infrastructure." *Computerworld*. Last modified February 14, 2013. http://www.computerworld.com/article/2494979/security0/obama-executive-order-redefines-critical-infrastructure.html.

Voices.com. "History of the Compact Disc." Last modified July 2, 2014. https://www.voices.com/resources/articles/audio-recording-technology/cd-history-timeline.

Wagner, D. "Personal Education Networks for Educators." Getting Smart. Last modified January 31, 2012. http://gettingsmart.com/2012/01/personal-learning-networks-for-educators-10-tips.

Ward, Gary. "Press Conference: Congressman Doyle to Address New Bill to Unlock U.S. $60 Billion Investment in Research." Alliance for Taxpayer Access. Last modified April 21, 2010. http://www.taxpayeraccess.org/issues/frpaa/frpaa_resources/press-conference-congressman-doyle-to-address-new-.shtml.

Ware, Mark, and Michael Mabe. *The STM Report*. The Hague, Netherlands: International Association of Scientific, Technical and Medical Publishers, 2012. http://www.stm-assoc.org/2012_12_11_STM_Report_2012.pdf.

Warren, Samuel, and Louis Brandeis. "The Right to Privacy." *Harvard Law Review* 4, no. 5 (December 15, 1890): 193–220. http://groups.csail.mit.edu/mac/classes/6.805/articles/privacy/Privacy_brand_warr2.html.

Watson, Paula D. "Founding Mothers: The Contribution of Women's Organizations to Public Library Development in the United States." *Library Quarterly* 64, no. 3 (1994): 233–269. http://www.jstor.org/stable/4308944.

————. "Valleys without Sunsets: Women's Clubs and Traveling Libraries." In *Libraries to the People: Histories of Outreach*, edited by Robert S. Freeman and David M. Hovde, 73–95. Jefferson, NC: McFarland, 2003.

WBDG. "Engage the Integrated Design Process." Last modified August 31, 2014. http://www.wbdg.org/design/engage_process.php.

Webopedia. "Taxonomy." Last modified January 22, 2014. http://www.webopedia.com/TERM/T/taxonomy.html.

Weech, T. L., and A. M. Konieczny. "Alternative Careers for Graduates of LIS Schools: The North American Perspective—An Analysis of the Literature." *Journal of Librarianship and Information Science* 39, no. 2 (2007): 67–78.

Weinberger, David. *Too Big to Know: Rethinking Knowledge Now That the Facts Aren't the Facts, Experts Are Everywhere, and the Smartest Person in the Room Is the Room*. New York: Basic Books, 2012.

Wells, Mark. "A Growing World of Connected Devices—May WOW Insider Interview." YouTube video. Posted by CTIA The Wireless Association, May 5, 2014. https://www.youtube.com/watch?v=HxK46CFsJeM&list=PLE53CB584A01349B5.

West, Henry R. "J. S. Mill." In *The Oxford Handbook of the History of Ethics*, edited by Roger Crisp. New York: Oxford University Press, 2013. doi:10.1093/oxfordhb/9780199545971.013.0025.

Western Association of Schools and Colleges, Senior College and University Commission. "Core Competency FAQs." Last modified June 2014. http://www.wascsenior.org/content/core-competency-faqs.

WhatIs.com. "Data Broker." Last modified December 25, 2013. http://whatis.techtarget.com.

Wheatley, Margaret J. *Turning to One Another: Simple Conversations to Restore Hope to the Future*. San Francisco, CA: Berrett-Koehler, 2009.

White House. *National Strategy for Trusted Identities in Cyberspace: Enhancing Online Choice, Efficiency, Security, and Privacy*. April 2011. http://www.whitehouse.gov/sites/default/files/rss_viewer/NSTICstrategy_041511.pdf.

Whitehill, Walter Muir. *Boston Public Library: A Centennial History*. Cambridge, MA: Harvard University Press, 1956. https://archive.org/details/bostonpubliclibr010132mbp.

Whittaker, Zack. "US Contractor Firm That Vetted Snowden Suffers Major Breach; Data Likely Snatched." ZDNet. Last modified August 6, 2014. http://www.zdnet.com/us-contractor-firm-that-vetted-snowden-suffers-major-breach-data-likely-snatched-7000032397.

Wiegand, Wayne A. *An Active Instrument for Propaganda: The American Public Library during World War I*. New York: Greenwood, 1989.

———. *Main Street Public Library: Community Places and Reading Spaces in the Rural Heartland, 1876–1956*. Iowa City: University of Iowa Press, 2011.

Wiggins, Grant, and Jay McTighe. *Understanding by Design*. Upper Saddle River, NJ: Merrill Prentice Hall, 1998.

Wilbanks, John, and Jamie Boyle. *Introduction to Science Commons*. Science Commons, August 3, 2006. http://sciencecommons.org/wp-content/uploads/ScienceCommons_Concept_Paper.pdf.

Wilson, Duane. "Reenvisioning Access Services: A Survey of Access Services Departments in ARL Libraries." *Journal of Access Services* 10, no. 3 (2013): 153–171.

Wilson, Thomas D. "Models in Information Behavior Research." *Journal of Documentation* 55, no. 3 (1999): 249.

———. "On User Studies and Information Needs." *Journal of Documentation* 37 (1981): 3–15.

Woolls, Blanche, Ann C. Weeks, and Sharon Coatney. *The School Library Manager*. 5th ed. Santa Barbara, CA: Libraries Unlimited, 2013.

Xie, Jenny. "Two Major Public Library Systems Are about to Start Lending Wi-Fi Hotspots." CityLab. Last modified June 23, 2014. http://www.citylab.com/cityfixer/2014/06/two-major-public-library-systems-are-about-to-start-lending-wi-fi-hotspots/373233.

Yammer. https://www.yammer.com.

Yarrow, Alexandra, Barbara Clubb, and Jennifer-Lynn Draper. "Public Libraries, Archives and Museums: Trends in Collaboration and Cooperation." *IFLA Professional Reports* 5 (2008). http://archive.ifla.org/VII/s8/pub/Profrep108.pdf.

YBP Library Services. Last modified July 4, 2014. http://www.ybp.com.

Youngok, Choi, and Edie Henderson. "What Is Needed to Educate Future Digital Librarians." *D-Lib Magazine* 12, no. 6 (2006). http://www.dlib.org/dlib/september06/choi/09choi.html.

Zaleznik, Abraham. "Managers and Leaders: Are They Different?" Reprint. *The Best of HBR 1977*, 2004, 1–10. http://books.google.com/books?hl=en&lr=&id=N1A4rnVMRuAC&oi=fnd&pg=PA64&dq=Managers+and+Leaders:+Are+They+Different&ots=2E04IATyA1&sig=Ak9sDZmGutNhckYfAj_slb87Ntw#v=onepage&q=Managers%20and%20Leaders%3A%20Are%20They%20Different&f=false.

Zickuhr, Kathryn, Lee Rainie, Kristine Purcell, and Maeve Dugan. *How Americans Value Libraries in Their Communities*. Pew Internet Research Project. Last modified December 11, 2013. http://libraries.pewinternet.org/2013/12/11/libraries-in-communities.

———. "Section 2." In *How Americans Value Public Libraries in Their Communities*. Pew Research Center, December 2013. http://libraries.pewinternet.org/files/legacy-pdf/PIP_Libraries%20in%20communities.pdf.

Zweizig, Douglas L. "Predicting Amount of Library Use: An Empirical Study of the Public Library in the Life of the Adult Public." PhD diss., Syracuse University, 1973.

Index

brand, 262, 268, 331, 391; awareness, 268; book, 243; marketing's role, 268; professional branding, 367, 371

British Library, 187

Brittle Books, 336, 343–44

Brown, Ruth, 286. *See also* Bartlesville Oklahoma Public Library

Budapest Open Access Initiative. *See* Open Society Foundations

budget, 220–27, 390; allocations and policies, 222, 227; analysts, *108*; and revenue, 220–21; audits, 226; budgeting activities, 221; cycle, *223*; evaluating, 224; expenditures, *221–22, 224–22*, 227; general fund, 221, 225, 228; performance based, 224; policy formulation, 285; process, *222–24, 226*, 247; special purpose fund, *221*; tax revenue, 220, 225, 227–28; types, 222. *See also* financial management principles; funding; management skills

building management, 150, 154, *157*, 221. *See also* management skills

bundled information, 361, 391

California Digital Library, *246*

Canada's Charter of Rights and Freedoms, 349

care-based ethics, 290, 390. *See also* ethical theories

career: development, *77*, 368–69, 373; management strategies, 367–73; trajectory, 367, 371, 373

Carnegie: Classification, 319; Corporation, 13; Foundation, 319

catalogers, 95, 97–98, 103, 107, 141, 143, 145, 391

cataloging, 97, 101, 139, 141–44, 148, 150, 180, 255, 334, 368, 391; modules, 255; specialists, 369; three step process, 142–44

CC BY. *See* Creative Commons

censorship, 15, *283*, 296, 359, 362–63, 391

change management, 209, 211–12, 242. *See also* management

chat reference, 95, 132, 135, 312

Chatman, Elfreda, 22

Chicago Public Library, 12, 182, 363; Hotspots, 182; Maker Labs, 194; YouMedia, 193

Chief Officer of State Library Agencies (COSLA), 74

Childers, Thomas, 21. *See also* community approach

Children's Online Privacy Protection Act (COPPA), 347–48

Chinese American Librarians Association (CALA), 33

Choose Privacy Week, 295

Circulating: collection, 132; library, 71, 391

circulation, 66, 97, 147–48, 149–51, 153, 155–56, *157*, 325, 390; desk, 132, 150–52, 156, 181; modules, 150, 255; policies, 253; records 151; staff, 144; successful, *151*; unrestricted, 17

civic engagement, 228n2, 358–59

classification, 88, 142–43, 146; schemes, 139–42, 391; systems, 21, 176. *See also* Dewey Decimal Classification; Library of Congress classification; National Library of Medicine

click-through licenses. *See* licenses

client/server architecture, 252. *See also* local computing

cloud, 392; based services, 187; computing, *44*, 50, 185, 252, 254–56, 260–61, 392; content curation and management, 188; landscapes, 188; storage, 100, 392

cMOOC, 392. *See also* massive open online course; xMOOC

coaching, 231–32. *See also* management

Cochrane, Pauline Atherton, 21. *See also* community approach

coding standards, 258. *See also* CSS; HTML

cognitive process, 121, 392

collaboration, 22, 27, 30–31, *44*, 49, 54, 97, 99, 132, 193, 204, 215–16; collaborative learning, 53, 202, 375; collaboratives, 209; effective, 216; in learning, 204; interlibrary, 17; space, 194, 234. *See also* consortia; diverse communities; global communication; makerspace; partnerships

collection, 66, 98, 242–44, 250–51, 254–55, 271, 273–75, 318; building, 246–49, 392; data, 237, 283; digitized, 225; everywhere, 187; partnerships, 246; preservation, 66; print, 242, 317; special, 147–48, 238; web-based, 342. *See also* cloud computing; digital collections; hyperlinked library integrated library system; licensing; physical collections; strategic planning

collection development, 62, 66–67, 144, 194, 244, 248, 274, 392; cooperative, 246; developers, 242, 248; policies, 249, 359. *See also* models; patron-driven acquisitions

collection management, 127, 146, 242–47, 249, 255–56, 259; challenges and opportunities, 246; managers, 242–43, 245

Columbia University, 13, 67, 149

Commission on Preservation and Access, 337

Common Core, 54, 56–58, 165, 392; English Language Arts (ELA), 56

Communication, 110; analyst, 112; technologies, 135

community, 20; analysis, 248, 392; anchor, 75–78; approach, 21–22; engagement, *44*, 51, 77, 326; four angles of, 20–21; hub, 375, 392; learning, 51; networks, 23. *See also* diverse communities; information communities

compact shelving, 152, 392
competency, 7–8, 42, 77–78, 87, 109–11, 392; core, 161, 209, 217–18, 384; cultural, 27, 33–34; for librarians serving children, 77; for success, 162; leadership, 383; most commonly requested, *109*; transferable, 106
competitive intelligence, *83–86*, 109, *367–68*, 392. *See also* knowledge management; analyst, 370; research specialist, 114
computer: architecture, 260; as users, *328*; crime, 283, 342; systems administrator, *108*; systems analysts, *108*; training space, *44*, 50
confidentiality, *283*, 346, 362; mandate, 361; shared principle, *292*
connected learning, 53, 57–60, 202, 375–76, 393
conservation, 62, 71, 334–35, 339, 393
consortia, 43, 46, 51, 67, 144, 146, 148–49, 246, 248, 252, 318–20, 393
consortial lending partnerships, 393
content: audits, 177–78, 180, 251; management system, 102. *See also* Drupal; user experience techniques
contextual inquiries, 177–79. *See also* user experience techniques
control, 210–11, 393; organizational, *210*. *See also* authority control; management; power
controlled vocabularies. *See* vocabularies
cooperative collection development, 67, 246, 393
copies for patrons, 304–5
copy cataloging, 143, 148, 392. *See also* cataloging
copyright, 67, 154, 187, 283, 295–97, 300–311, 320–21, 329–31, 393; institutional policy, 331; limitations or exceptions, 301; notice, 303; protection, 301, 303; term, 303, 310; transfer, 330. *See also* copyright law
Copyright Analysis Flow Chart, *302*
copyright law, 96–97, 99, 300–312; Section 102, 301; Section 106, 301; Section 107 (fair use), 302, 305, 309; Section 108 (library exception), 300, 302, 304–5, 309–10, 312; Section 109, 300, 302–3; Section 512 (safe harbor), 307; Section 1201 (assistive technology), 307; Title 17, U.S. Code, 300; Title 37, Code of Federal Regulations, 300
the Copyright Office, 309
copyright owners, 300–301, 303–5, 307–12; exclusive rights, 301
core curriculum, 53. *See also* Common Core
core values, 43, 82, 104, 211, 286, 291–94
corporate knowledge center, 84
course: management systems, 23, 149, 321; reserves, 96; software, 362
creation culture, 173, 192–93, 197, 393

Creative Commons, 97, 99, 194, 300–303, 311–12, 329–30, 393; Attribution Only (CC BY), 330. *See also* license; licensing; standardized license
Critical information literacy, 160, 393. *See also* information literacy
critical thinking, 55–56, 58, 64, *160*, 393
cross section, 216, 235, 393
CSS, 258, 260. *See also* web standards and protocols
cultural competency, 31–35, 394; essential elements for, *32*; language, 31; talent management plan, 34. *See also* diversity
cultural heritage, 47, 103, 145, 147, 297, 308. *See also* digital assets; media assets
cultural norms. *See* diverse communities
culture of assessment, 237, 272, 394. *See also* assessment
cultural pluralism, 232–33, 394. *See also* management
cultural preservation, 76
curation, 188, 334–35, 339, 342–43, 394. *See also* data curation
curator, 108
curriculum, 53–54, 60–61, 156, 161, 166; generalists, 56, 59; planning and instruction, 56; specialists, 57
customer, 82, 84–89, 113, 215, 253, 257, 263–69; centered approach, 214; facing discovery services, 260; facing interfaces, 258; first focus, 44, 51; groups, 262, 265–67; information needs, 91; inquiries, 112; journey map, 179; market, 263, 394; market segmentation, 262–64; needs, 262; oriented working environment, 112; service, 109, 110, 113, 156–57, 178, 368
cybersecurity, 6, 345–46, 351–54, 394

dark archive, 98, 394
dashboards, 86, 89, 91, 394
data: analysis, 6, 112; breach, 345, 394; broker, 352, 394; curation, 64, 97, 368, 394; curator, 97, 100, 104, 394; grid, 98, 100, 394; integrity, 394; literacy, 274, 395; minimization, 350; mining, 89, 110, 112, 321; repositories, 64; security, 253; sharing protocols, 102. *See also* cybersecurity; Fair Information Practice Principles
data visualization, 368, 395; specialists, 370
database: administration, *108*, 253; design, 130; engines, 253; framework, 140; maintenance, 142; management, 7, 253, 283. *See also* BIBFRAME; MARC; metadata schema
DDC Curation Lifecyle Model, 334
deaccessioning, 66, 395
deacidification, 335, 343

information needs, 8, 21, 56, 60, 78, 82, 85–87, 117–28, 131, 142, 244–47, 359, 400; factors, 122–24; instructional design principle, 166; target audience, 263. *See also* diversity; macro-level; Maslow's Theory of Human Motivation; meso-level; micro-level

information organization, 4; desired attribute, 110; facility and service trends, 51; skills, 87. *See also* trends

information policies, 279, 281–87, 361, 400; development, 281; evaluation, 283; issues, 283; responsibilities and opportunities, 286–87

information privacy, 6, 282, 345–54, 400; basic measures, 352–54; Canada, 349–50; Global, 351; professionals, 352; rights, 347; value, 287. *See also* personal data; personally identifiable information; privacy; sensitive personal data

information professional (definition), 4, 400; competencies, 7–8, 42, 65, 87, 109–11, 141, 209, 217–18, 379, 383; roles, 7, 20, 39, 53, 63, 91, 97–103, 156, 168, 201, 286, 340, 353, 367. *See also* skill sets

information security, 346, 351. *See also* cybersecurity; information privacy

information service, 14, 21–25, 50–51, 106, 130–36, 201, 209, 262, 269, 287, 291, 294, 358, 374, 377–78; best practices, 358; competencies for, 7, 20, 274; delivery, 48, 87; development, 30; digital, 73; evaluation, 217–18; fee-based, *283*; in hyperlinked libraries, 185–89; key trends, 4–5; platforms, 256; promoting, 88; specialized, 84–85; user-defined, 3

information systems, *83*, 121, 125, 260, 289, 352; manager, *108*, 210; medical and health, 283. *See also* geographic information systems

information technology (IT), 83, 106, 110, 162, 164, 211, 289, 315, 363; department, 252; designing, 24; digital, 357; early adopters, 16–17; emerging, 108; professionals, 110; trends, 50, 250. *See also* digital technology; technology trends

information users, 3, 30, 48, 50, 119, 136, 175–77, 180, 189, 235, 245, 248, 279, 310, 377; community of, 245; engagement, 5–6; interests of, 300; learning needs, 199–205; rights of, 294; teaching, 159–69; web-savvy, *44*, 49

informationist, 369

InfoMe, 23–25. *See also* community network

informed citizen, 10–11, *77*, 279; Code of Ethics, 279, 292; Information Literacy Competency Standards for Higher Education goal, 17. *See also* American Library Association; Association of College and Research Libraries; William Bentley

innovation, 27, 42–43, 82, 86, 88, 136, 149, 218, 235, 242, 246–47, 331, 335, 374, 378; centers for technology and, 51, 56; in stacks management, 152; labs, 259, 400; technological, 68; user-centered, 10, 136, 195, 202. *See also* makerspace; user experience; Workforce Innovation and Opportunity Act

inquiry-based learning, 57–60, 400

Instagram, 24, 188, 197

Institute of Museum and Library Services (IMLS), 73–74, 216, 226, 237, 339; examples of collaboration, 216; Library Services and Technology Act (LSTA), 14, 73–74, 226

institutional library, 11–12

institutional repository (IR), 64, 273, 311, 400

institutional review board (IRB), 237

instruction, 53–57, 61, 125–27, 136, 163, 165–67, 327; assessment, 166, 273; benchmarks, 55; bibliographic, 99, *160*, 390; competency, *109*; computer-use, 161; design, 166, 136, 400; hands-on, 50; librarians, 163, 166; models, 57; online, 135, 167–68, 200; practices, 55; research, 165–66; standards, 160; technology, 63, 65, 117; tools, 127. *See also* assessment; LigGuides; technology literacy

integrated library system (ILS), 125, 139, 147, 150, 252–53, 255–58, 400; competency with, 7–8

intellectual freedom, 15, 30, *279*, 281–*83*; 286–87, 300, 357–63, 374, 401; Code of Ethics, 279; Code of the Colorado Association of Libraries, *297*; Office for Intellectual Freedom, 297; policies, 30; principle, *292*, 293, 358–59; value, 43. *See also* American Library Association

intellectual property (IP), 97, 279, 281–*83*, 294, 340, 401; rights, 330–31, 333. *See also* copyright, World Intellectual Property Organization

Intelligence analyst, 370, 401. *See also* information analyst

interaction design, 175–76. *See also* user experience

intercultural communication. *See* diversity

interlibrary loan (ILL), 62, 65, 67, 147, 149–50, 153–54, *157*, 321, 401; and copyright law, 154

internal: control, 226; data, 274

International Association for Development of the Information Society (IADIS), 379

international communication policy, *283*

International Federation of Library Associations (IFLA): Access to Information, 291, 378–*79*; Codes of Ethics for Libraries and Other Information Workers, 291; Division of Special Libraries, 83; International Marketing Award, 268; shared principles, 291–94; Trends Report, 5

International Internet Preservation Consortium, 342

International Librarians Network (ILN), 378

International Society for Information Studies (ISIS), 379

International Society of Technology in Education (ISTE), 55; National Educational Technology Standards (NETS), 56; Performance Indicators for Students, 56

Internet Archive, 67, 308, 342

internet filtering, 295, 401. *See also* filters

Internet Policy Task Force. *See* United States Department of Commerce

internships, *107*

interoperability technologies, 139

intranets, 88-89, 91, 401

inventory control, 244

iSearch, 165, 401. *See also* Common Core

issues tracking, 85, 401

Ivy League's Borrow Direct, 67. *See also* consortia

Javascript, 102, 254, 401

job clusters, 369-71; academic and nonprofit, 370; business and profit, 370; "IN" Cluster, 369

job families, 369, 373

job opportunities, 111-12

jobber, 142, 145

journal subscription, 327, 329. *See also* e-journals; subscriptions

Kant, Immanuel, 290. *See also* deontology; ethical code

KBART Initiative, 322, 401. *See also* licensing

knowledge: actual 347-48; based society, 283; collective, 59; competencies/skills, 109, 210, 217, 369; creation, 4, 159, 177, 192; cultural, 32, 242, 377; develop knowledge base, *31*; explicit, 397; global, 375; management, 83, 85-87, 109-10, 368, 401; manager, 86, 367, 370, 401; networking, *186*, 190, 195, 377-78; portals, 89, 256; tacit, 410. *See also* digital knowledge center; Global Knowledge Partnership Foundation

language. *See* cultural competency

layered discovery tools, 139

leader, 34, 46, 209, 227, 233; change agents, 383; characteristics of, 382; cultural competency, 32; emotional style, 230, 396; learning to lead, 384-85; organizational, 232, 382, 462; transcendent, 229-30, 233

leadership, 34, 82, 130, 168, 197, 212, 220, 365, 381-85, 401; competencies/skills, 42, 109, 209;

four essential competencies, 383; mentorship and, 197; Special Libraries Association Division. *See also* Special Library Association

Learning 2.0, 188, 376, 401; 23 Mobile Things, 188, 376; 23 Things, 376

learning approach, 59, 202; learner-centric, 202; teacher-centric, 202

learning commons, 59-61, 66, 132, 402

learning management systems (LMS), 200, 402

learning outcomes, 7, 117, 402

leases, 145. *See also* databases

legacy print collection, 145

Legislative Reference Service, 14

LibGuide, 63, 127, 136, 402

LIBQUAL+, 67, 155. *See also* user satisfaction studies

librarian, 4. *See also* academic librarian; public librarian; school librarian; systems librarian; virtual librarian

Libraries Change Lives initiative. *See* American Library Association; Barbara Stripling

library: accessibility policy, 360; as place, 75; commission, 13, 72; district, 402; foundation, 221, 225, 402; futurist, 370; legislation, 72; services platform, 255-56, 260, 402; without walls, 16. *See also* academic library; institutional library; public library; school library; virtual library

Library Bill of Rights. *See* American Library Association

library exception. *See* copyright law

Library Journal, 13, 107, 199, 249, 268

Library of Alexandria, 242, 336-37

Library of Congress, 98, 104, 144, 287, 306, 310, 338, 343; BIBFRAME, 390; classification, 98, 140, 143; Digital Preservation Outreach and Education (DPOE), 338-39; Farm Security Administration/Office of War Information, 63; Office of Strategic Initiatives, 339; Subject Headings, 98, 143, 287. *See also* machine-readable cataloging (MARC)

library portals, 257

Library Services and Construction Act (LSCA), 14, 73

Library Services and Technology Act (LSTA). *See* Institute of Museum and Library Services

LibSat, 155. *See also* user satisfaction studies

license, 303, 309-11, 315-23, 402; cancellation, 322; click-wrap, 310; commercial, 251; elements of, 317, 320; negotiated, 246, 300, 310-12, 320; opt-in license, 319, 405; origins, 315; post-license access, 322; pricing structures, 318-23; transfer, 322; withdrawal of content, 322. *See also* Creative Commons; e-book; e-journal

management, 47, 101; record, 140–41, 145; schema, 109, 139–40, 143; shared, 103, 256; standards, 97, 98, 102; three step process, 142–44; transcription, 139. *See also* cataloging; controlled vocabularies; Digital Public Library; Dublin Core; KBART Initiative; Preservation Implementation Strategies

metadata object descript schema (MODS), 102, 143

metaliteracy, 160, 404. *See also* information literacy

Michigan Makers project, 196. *See also* makerspace

micro-level, 119–20, 124, 404; factors, 127. *See also* information needs; macro-level; meso-level

microaggression, 233, 403

microcontroller, 192–93, 404. *See also* Arduino microcontroller

Middle States Commission on Higher Education, 155

Mill, John Stuart, 290. *See also* utilitarianism; ethical theories

mobile: access, 187; device, 4–5, 42, *44*, 50, 86, 95, 133, 176, 184–89, 199–200, 269; learning via, 187–89, 199–201; resources, 6; revolution, 91; services, 89; strategies, 91; trends, 188–89; user, 17, 49, 268

mobile applications, 5, 65, 126, 185–88, 347; development, 190

mobile technology, 5, 8, 186–88, 254, 248, 404; influence, 186. *See also* hyperlinked library; Learning 2.0; online learning

multicounty library systems, 15

multiculturalism, 27–28, 404

multitenant platform, 252, 254, 256. *See also* Software as a Service (SaaS)

multitype library system, 404

museum workers, 108

MyInfoQuest, 135

Nardi, Bonnie, 22. *See also* community approach

National Association of State Libraries, *83*

National Association to Promote Library and Information Science to Latinos and the Spanish Speaking (REFORMA), 33

National Commission on Excellence in Education, 161

National Council of Teachers of English, 159

National Digital Information Infrastructure and Preservation Program (NDIIPP), 338

National Historic Preservation Act, 336–37

National Information Standards Organization (NISO), 260. *See also* KBART Initiative

National Institute of Standards and Technology (NIST), 352; Framework for Improving Critical Infrastructure Cybersecurity, 352

National Institutes of Health (NIH), 64, 332

National Library Legislative Day. *See* advocacy; American Library Association

National Library of Medicine (NLM), 84–85, 90, 140, 143; Classification Scheme, 143

National Medal for Museum and Library Service, 76

National Science Foundation (NSF), 64

national security, 281, 283–84, 287, 351

National Security Agency, 296, 345

National Telecommunications and Information Administration, 161

near-field communications, 42, 259; iBeacons, 42. *See also* mobile applications

needs assessment, 236, 404

negotiated licenses. *See* licenses

negotiation skills, 368, 404

network, 88, 103, 147, 216–18, 253, 275, 328, 371, 374–78; computer and hardware, 248, 252; connectivity, 253, 260; global/international, 329, 338, 374–75, 378; local, 252–53; network and computer systems administrators, 108; open, 59–60; organizational, 7, 50; security, 253; social, 48, 88, 185–86, 265, 345, 371, 374, 378; systems administrator, *108*. *See also* advocacy; Digital Preservation Network; HIVE network; local area networks; personal learning networks

New Deal, 14

New Media Consortium (NMC), 204; Horizon Report, 5, 47, 187, 204; Horizon Report, Higher Education Edition, 189; Horizon Report, Library Edition, 5, 204

New York Public Library, 14, 132, 187

Newark Public Library, 82

next-generation catalog, 147

Next Generation Science Standards, 57

Next Great Copyright Act, 300, 304, 309–10, 312

nitrate deterioration, 340, 404

No Child Left Behind Act, 57, 348

North Carolina Digital Heritage Center, 100

Northeast Document Conservation Center (NEDCC), 238; Online Disaster-Planning Tool, 238

Northeast Regional Libraries Consortium, 246. *See also* consortia

O'Day, Vicki, 22. *See also* community approach

offer, 404

Office for Intellectual Freedom. *See* American Library Association

Office of the Privacy Commissioner of Canada, 350

political: action committee (PAC), 217; scientists, *108. See also advocacy; management*

power. *See* management

preservation, 97, 334–44; activities, 335; and replacement, 304; audiovisual (AV), 339; digital; future of, 342; game, 343; practices, 337; shared principle, *292*, 296; standards, 337; theory and practice, 339; workflow, 339–40. *See also* Brittle Books; conservation; curation; digital forensic science; digital preservation; lifecyle management; Preserving Virtual Worlds

The Preservation Metadata Implementation Strategies (PREMIS), 338

Preserving Virtual Worlds, 343

principles, 289, 112; competing, 291; core/ foundational, 10, 130, 134, 297–98; design, *59*; education and instruction design, 59, 166; ethical, 289–91; Fair Information Practice Principles (FIPPs), 346, 350, 352, 354; financial management, 226–27; operating, 17–18, 217; privacy; shared, 291–92; user experience, 176. *See also* American Library Association Code of Ethics; budget; equity of access; ethics; information ethics; information privacy, privacy; intellectual freedom; user experience

print reserves. *See* reserves

prior restraint, 391, 406

privacy, 45, 96, 189, 281, 286–87, 343, 345–54, 358–59, 406; audit, 353, 406; citizens right to, 287; laws, 347–49; literacy, 406; patron, 282–84; personal, 282–83, 296; policy, 282–83, 353; professional value, 297; rights and protections, 346–47; shared principle, *292*; training, 353; user, 54. *See also* assessment; big data; Choose Privacy Week; cybersecurity; fair information practice principles; information privacy; personal data; personally identifiable information; sensitive personal data; Zoia Horn

Privacy Act: of 1974, 349; of 1983, 349

private good, 272, 283

problem-based learning. *See* inquiry-based learning

problem situation, 120–22, 406

processing, 62, 142, 144. *See also* serials

production studies. *See* makerspace

professional brand, 367, 371

professional development, 8, 45, 57, 63, 167–68, 201, 230–31, 294, 365, 376–77; institutional, 126; on demand, 185, 188. *See also* Learning 2.0; lifelong learning; massive open online courses; personal learning networks

professional organizations, 85, 371, 378

professional values, 289, 297. *See also* values

professionalism, 293; of preservation, 336; shared principle, *292*

program budgets. *See* budget

programming languages, 258, 260, 368. *See also* JavaScript; Python

project-based learning. *See* inquiry-based learning

Project Gutenberg, 308

promotional strategies, 265–66. *See also* marketing strategies

proprietary software, *251*, 406, 406. *See also* open source software

prospect research and development, 370, 407

The Protection of Pupil Rights Amendment (PPRA), 348

protective enclosure 335, 407

Pub Med Central, 332

public catalog module, 255. *See also* cataloging

public domain, 99, 281, *283*, 301, 303, *308*, 311–12, 407; Public Domain Mark, 303, 311. *See also* copyright; Creative Commons

public forum analysis, 359–60, 407

public good, 283–84, 292–94, 329, 407

public learning environment, 234–35

public librarians, 17, 21, 27, 72–75, 78, 134, 161, 164–65. *See also* competencies

public library, 11–12, 70–78, 193; history, 71–72; information literacy and research training, 165; management and staffing, 74–75; promoting early literacy, 163; service roles, 77. *See also* management

Public Library Association, 73, 76, 159

Public Library Data Service (PLDS), 75

Public Library Inquiry, 73

public relations, 106, 262, 267–68, 277, 407; specialists, 108. *See also* marketing

public services staff, 139–41, 146–47

publicity, 224, 265, 267, 407

purchasing, 34, 96, 101, 142, 144, 222, 317–18

purpose specification, 350, 407. *See also* Fair Information Practice Principles

Python, 101, 407

QR codes, 42, 268

race and ethnicity. *See* diversity

Race to the Top, 57

Ranganathan's Laws of Library Science, 180, *245*

Read at Your Library, 77

ready reference questions, *77*, 84, 135, 407. *See also* reference

records management, *83*–85; 88–89; 114–15; 125–26; 407. *See also* archives; repository

tenure track, 62, 65, 411

third place, 59–60, 234, 411

threshold concepts, 159, 411

tiered reference. *See* reference

tinkering, 192, 411

touch points, 176–82. *See also* experience safaris; pain points; user experience

transactional management. *See* management

transcendent leader. *See* leader

transferable competencies. *See* competencies

transliteracy, 411

transparency, 185, 350, 352, 375, 411

traveling libraries, 14, 72. *See also* bookmobiles

trends, 42, 47, 90, 263; emerging, *5–8, 45, 50, 188, 197, 371*; facility and service, *44*, 51–52; global, *5*; labor, *44*, 49; lifestyle and society, *44*, 48–50; technology, *5, 44*, 50–51, 250. *See also* Horizon Report; Pew Report; statistics

trigger warning, 361. *See also* intellectual freedom

Tumblr, 378. *See also* blog; online communication; social media

Twitter, 21, 91, 133, 147, 151, 203–4, 343, 373, 376–78. *See also* online communication; social media

UNESCO, 159, 167

union catalog, 14,

unique identifiers, 98

United States Constitution, 300, 312, 346, 358; Bill of Rights, 15, 346, 358; First Amendment, 346, 358, 362

United States Department of Commerce Internet Policy Task Force, 307

United States Department of Health, Education, and Welfare, 347, 350; Automated Personal Data advisory committee, 350

United States Department of Homeland Security, 345–46

United States Department of Justice, 347

United States National Library of Medicine, 84–85, 90; Classification, 84; Medical Subject Headings (MeSH), 84; Unified Medical Language System (UMLS), 84

United States Office of Management and Budget (OMB), 36, 347

United States Office of Personnel Management, 215

universal access. *See* access

USA PATRIOT Act, 282, 287, 349, 411

usability, 101, 110, 176–77, 335; testing, 67, 177–80. *See also* Guerilla user testing; user experience

usage statistics. *See* statistics

use limitation, 350. *See also* Fair Information Practice Principles

user: and public service professionals, 141; behavior, 8, 47, 101, 177, 236, 243, 265; centered design concept, 180; created content, *44, 50, 296, 363, 411*; education, 130–31, 160; goals, 177; interface, 147, 151; interviews, 177, 180; participation, 234–35; satisfaction, 155, 265, 272–73, 277, 411. *See also* makerspace; user-generated content

user experience (UX), 175–82, 254, 370, 411; attending a library event, 176; audits, 177–78; design, 371, 411; examples, 182; partnerships, 177–78; professional, 367; techniques, 177–80; two-step process, 176. *See also* design thinking process; contextual inquiries; experience mapping; experience safaris; usability testing; content audits

user needs, 6, 27, 125–26, 175–77, 236–38, 248; analysis, 10; assessment, 30, 124, 155, 235–37; diverse, 128; expressing, 236, 238; satisfaction studies, 155. *See also* assessments; ethnographic method; LibQUAL+; LibSat

utilitarianism, 290, 412. *See also* ethical theories

value, 272, 289–98, 412; as drivers of government action, 285; conveying, 275–76; definition, 271–72, 285; democratic, 357–58; demonstrating, 221, 271–77; direct, 273–74, 396; indirect, 273–74; multicultural, 15–17, 31, 124; of the information professional, 43, 169; professional, 279, 289, 293; scholarly, 326–31. *See also* advocacy; assessment; core values; economic impact; information communities; information ethics; information professional; marketing; preservation; social impact; user satisfaction

Veinot, Tiffany, 22. *See also* community approach

vendor, 202, 238, 248, 251–52, 255, 305–6, 322–23; based discovery interfaces, 257; hosted model, 252–53. *See also* collection management; E-rate funds; information licensing

vinegar syndrome, 340, 412

virtual: browsing, 152; learning, 60, 126; librarian, 126–27; library, 51; reference, 134–35, 411. *See also* online learning; embedded information professional; Virtual Library Service

Virtual Librarian Service (VLS), 126

visceral, 122, 412

vocabularies, 98, 102; controlled, 98, 257. *See also* cataloging; metadata

VRA Core, 102, 412

Wayback Machine, 342

Web 2.0 technologies, 151, 160. *See also* social media

About the Editor and Contributors

Sandra Hirsh has an extensive and varied background as a library and information science educator, leader, researcher, and professional—both in library and other information environments. She is currently professor and director of the School of Information at San José State University, directing the school's 100 percent online programs, with students and faculty from around the world. She taught previously at the University of Arizona and University of Washington.

As a second-generation librarian, she recognized early on the value of the library and information science degree. After getting a PhD from UCLA and an MILS from the University of Michigan, she applied her own library and information science skill set to work for more than a decade in leading Silicon Valley companies in user experience, developing and managing web, mobile, and TV consumer products, resulting in five U.S. patents/applications as well as in research and development. She has also worked in academic, public, and special libraries.

Dr. Hirsh's research and professional activities span the globe. Her research interests focus on information-seeking behavior, online and global learning, and the changing role of the information professional; this work has been published in peer-reviewed journals and has appeared in international conference proceedings. She is the cochair and cocreator of the global virtual Library 2.0 conference series, the 2015 president of the Association for Information Science and Technology, and a 2013 Salzburg Fellow. She has also held leadership and committee roles in other associations, including the American Library Association (ALA), the Special Libraries Association (SLA), and the International Federation of Library Associations and Institutions (IFLA).

In addition to these roles, she has worked in her own local community, serving for many years on Palo Alto's Library Advisory Commission and the Palo Alto Library Bond Oversight Committee to realize the long-term vision of exciting new library facilities for the city.

* * *

Stephen Abram, MLS, is a strategy and direction planning consultant for libraries and the information industry as principal of Lighthouse Consulting Inc. and executive director of the Federation of Ontario Public Libraries. He is a library trend watcher, keynote speaker, innovator, and author of *Stephen's Lighthouse* blog. He has held leadership positions in special libraries, associations, and as an executive at Cengage Learning (Gale), SirsiDynix, Thomson, Micromedia ProQuest, and IHS, in addition to managing several libraries.

Ann P. Bishop, PhD, is an associate professor emerita from the Graduate School of Library and Information Science at the University of Illinois. Her work explores information theory and practice in marginalized communities. She has taught Community Engagement, Community Inquiry, Participatory Action Research, and Community Informatics. Her primary community partners include Sisternet and Spanish-speaking immigrant families in Champaign-Urbana, and the Puerto Rican Cultural Center in Chicago. Her research has been sponsored by the U.S. Institute of Museum and Library Services, the U.S. Department of Commerce, the W. K. Kellogg Foundation, and the National Science Foundation. She earned her BA from Cornell University and her MLS and PhD in Information Transfer from Syracuse University.

Marshall Breeding works as an independent consultant providing services related to the strategic use of technology to libraries and related organizations. He created and maintains Library Technology Guides and has authored or edited seven books and hundreds of articles and essays. He is the editor of *Smart Libraries Newsletter*, published by ALA TechSource; a columnist for *Computers in Libraries*; and the author of the annual Library Systems Report published by *American Libraries*. From 1985 to 2012 he held a variety of positions in the Vanderbilt University Libraries.

April Cunningham is the instruction and information literacy librarian at Palomar College in California. Since 2003, she has worked on local, state, and national initiatives to promote instructional improvement and learning outcomes assessments in academic libraries.

Cheryl R. Dee, MLS, PhD, teaches management at San José State University, medical and consumer health information sources at Florida State University, and special libraries at other universities. Her research and publications focuses on digital publication, the information-seeking behavior of health-care professionals. She serves as a faculty advisor for the San José State University Special Libraries Student Group and has held numerous leadership positions in the Medical Library Association and its sections and chapters as well as the board of directors of altruistic community-based organizations.

Wayne Disher is an instructor at San José State University and previous director of library services at Hemet Public Library in Hemet, California. Mr. Disher served as president of the California Library Association and has published several textbooks. He holds a master's degree in library and information science from San José State University.

Celeste Feather has been at LYRASIS since 2010, and previously held positions at OhioLINK (2008–2010) and several university libraries (1989–2008). Oberlin College, BA; George Washington University, MA; University of Maryland, MLS.

Miguel Figuero has previously held positions at the American Theological Library Association (ATLA), the American Library Association (as director of the Office for Diversity and Spectrum Scholarship Program and the Office for Literacy and Outreach Services), New York University's Langone Medical Center Ehrman Medical Library, and Neal-Schuman Publishers. He is a graduate of the University of Arizona's Knowledge River Program.

Karen E. Fisher, PhD, professor at the University of Washington Information School and adjunct professor of communication, focuses on how people experience information as part of everyday life, particularly in informal social settings (aka *information grounds*). Her current work (InfoMe.uw.edu) asks how ethnic minority youth help other people through information, and how they can be supported through codesigning technology, services, and policy at Teen Design Days. Coauthor of the ASIST top monograph, *Theories of Information Behavior*, Karen was twice awarded the ALA Jesse H. Shera Award for her research with youth and libraries, and supporters of her work include the U.S. Institute of Museum and Library Services, Microsoft, the Bill and Melinda Gates Foundation, the LEGO Foundation, and the National Science Foundation.

Kristin Fontichiaro teaches at the University of Michigan School of Information, where she coordinates the Michigan Makers mobile makerspace project, which partners university students with K–12 makers in underserved communities. She is the series editor and contributing author to Cherry Lake Publishing's Makers as Innovators series for middle-grade readers, which was identified by *Booklist* as one of 2014's Top Ten Series Nonfiction.

Melissa Fraser-Arnott is a PhD candidate in the Queensland University of Technology–San José State University (QUT-SJSU) Gateway PhD Program. Her research interest is the professional identities and professional experiences of LIS graduates in nonlibrary roles. Melissa is the knowledge management librarian for the Office of the Privacy Commissioner of Canada in Ottawa, Ontario.

Martin L. Garnar is the reference services librarian and a professor of library science at the Dayton Memorial Library of Regis University in Denver, Colorado. Martin also teaches professional ethics, library instruction, and foundations of library and information science for the University of Denver's library and information science program, where he was recognized with the university's 2014 Ruth Murray Underhill Award for teaching excellence by an adjunct. He has served as chair of the ALA Intellectual Freedom Committee and the Committee on Professional Ethics, is a past president of the Colorado Association of Libraries, and speaks frequently on ethics and intellectual freedom at national and local conferences.

Todd Gilman recently published a major scholarly biography, *The Theatre Career of Thomas Arne* (2013). In addition to numerous articles on seventeenth- and eighteenth-century London theatre and music, he has written journalistic essays as a frequent contributor to the *Chronicle of Higher Education*. Since 2001 he has served as librarian for literature in English at Yale, and since 2004 as a member of the teaching faculty of the School of Information, San José State University.

Cherie L. Givens, JD, PhD, CIPP, is a privacy consultant, attorney, and lecturer. Her consulting focuses on the privacy matters of businesses, libraries, and other information environments. Cherie teaches information privacy courses and is the author of *Information Privacy Fundamentals for Librarians and Information Professionals* (Rowman & Littlefield, 2014). She is certified as an information privacy professional (CIPP/US) by the International Association of Privacy Professionals. You can contact Cherie at linkedin.com/in/cheriegivens.

Paul Glassman is the dean of the David and Lorraine Cheng Library at William Paterson University and the former director of library services and associate professor at Felician College, the Franciscan college of New Jersey, where he contributed the architectural program to the renovation of twenty thousand square feet of space into an education commons. In addition to library and master of business administration degrees, he holds a master of architecture degree. He teaches architectural history and design at Yeshiva University and offers a course in library design at Rutgers, the State University of New Jersey, during the summer session.

Janine Golden is an associate clinical professor in the MMLIS program at the USC Marshall School of Business. Dr. Golden earned her PhD from the University of Pittsburgh School of Information Sciences; an MLS from the School of Library and Information Science, Indiana University, Bloomington; and an MEd in educational administration from The Pennsylvania State University. Dr. Golden is a past president of the American Library Association's division Library Leadership and Management Association (LLAMA) and is currently coeditor of the Emerald series Advances in Library Administration and Organization.

Lisa Gregory is the digital projects librarian at the North Carolina Digital Heritage Center, where she oversees the digitization and online publishing of materials for a diverse group of partners throughout North Carolina. Previously she developed preservation workflows and digital collections as the digital collections manager at the State Library of North Carolina. Gregory was a Digital Curation Fellow at the School of Information and Library Science at the University of North Carolina at Chapel Hill.

Devon Greyson (MLIS) is a PhD candidate in the Interdisciplinary Studies Graduate Program at the University of British Columbia in Vancouver. She researches and teaches about gender, youth, health, information, and public policy. She is particularly interested in the relationships between information practices and social equity.

Maura Hadaway has worked for LYRASIS since 2011 in several capacities, and in licensing since 2013. Prior experience includes technical services in a community college library and project management in library networks and the telecommunications industries. University of Wyoming, BS; University of Washington, MLIS.

Sylvia Hall-Ellis has unique expertise in the areas of database building and maintenance, cataloging, Internet searching techniques, information systems, instructional design, copyright, research, and grant writing. She has more than forty years of experience working in libraries as an administrator, development officer, and project manager. She is a member of a variety of professional organizations and has published numerous technical reports, articles, and five monographs and has conducted major field-based research studies.

Liz Hamilton is permissions manager and assistant to the director at Northwestern University Press. She is an MLIS candidate at Dominican University and has a BA from Oberlin College.

Mary Ann Harlan, PhD, is the program coordinator of the Teacher Librarian Program at San José State University School of Information. She has worked in public education for twenty years, fourteen years in middle and high schools, and ten years as a teacher librarian.

Jan Holmquist is an assistant library director of Guldborgsund Public Library, Denmark, and a *Library Journal* Mover & Shaker 2014. Jan has made international library projects like the professional development program 23mobilethings.net and the crowd-funding projects Buy India a Library and Help This Week in Libraries in the global online library community. Jan blogs at janholmquist.net and is on Twitter @janholmquist.

Naomi House is the founder, editor, and publisher of the popular LIS and libraries jobs website, INALJ. com. She is a former reference, marketing, and acquisitions librarian at a federal library and now devotes her time to advocacy, consulting, and new business ventures. She is the CMO (chief marketing officer) for T160K.org, a social purpose corporation dedicated to funding African patrimony projects.

Deb Hunt, MLS, is the coauthor of *The Librarian's Skillbook: 51 Essential Skills for Information Professionals* and believes that learning never stops. Deb is the immediate past president of SLA. She has authored numerous articles, presented at many conferences, and has received several professional awards.

Barbara Jones holds an MLS from Columbia University, an MA in history with a Certificate in Archival Studies from New York University, and a PhD in U.S. history from the University of Minnesota. For thirty-five years she has written and spoken extensively on the subject of intellectual freedom. She is currently a consultant to the Free Access to Information and Free Expression (FAIFE) Committee of the International Federation of Library Associations (IFLA) and has conducted workshops in North and South America, Asia, Western and Eastern Europe, and Africa.

Sara Jones joined the Marin County Free Library as director of library services in 2013. Marin County Free Library has ten branches and is headquartered in San Rafael, California, in the Marin County Civic Center, a National Historic Landmark designed by Frank Lloyd Wright. Sara has twenty-five years of experience in a variety of libraries and served as Nevada's state librarian and administrator of the Nevada State Library and Archives from 2001 to 2007.

Heather Joseph is the executive director of SPARC (The Scholarly Publishing and Academic Resources Coalition), an international coalition of libraries that promotes the open sharing of scholarship. As SPARC's director, she has supported the creation and implementation of open access infrastructure, policies, and practices and is the architect of SPARC's advocacy agenda. Prior to joining SPARC, she spent fifteen years as a journal publisher in both commercial and not-for-profit publishing organizations.

Christie Koontz, PhD, has been on the faculty of Florida State University's School of Information since 1990, and part-time faculty of San José State University's School of Information for a decade. Koontz serves as director of GeoLib (www.geolib.org), focusing on spatial customer markets of individual libraries. She teaches marketing, management, and an online interactive storytelling course; serves on committees of state, national, and international library and information organizations; and has won numerous awards for her research and teaching.

Michael J. Krasulski is assistant professor of information science and coordinator of access services at University of the Sciences, Philadelphia. He coedited *Twenty-First-Century Access Services: On the Front Line of Academic Librarianship*, which was published by the Association of College and Research Libraries in 2013. Michael serves on the editorial board of the *Journal of Access Services* and earned his MSLIS from Drexel University and an additional master's degree from Temple University.

Cass Mabbott has been a public librarian/manager for over fifteen years, a part-time lecturer at the iSchool at the University of Washington for over five years, and is currently pursuing her doctorate in library and information science at the University of Illinois, Urbana-Champaign.

Kate Marek, MLIS, PhD, is dean and professor at the Graduate School of Library and Information Science at Dominican University. Marek's interests and expertise focus on information policy, technology developments, and rapid changes in society as they affect libraries and the information professions and LIS curriculum. Her recent publications include *Using Web Analytics in the Library* (2011) and *Organizational Storytelling for Librarians: Using Stories for Effective Leadership* (2010).

Kathleen de la Peña McCook is distinguished university professor at the School of Information, University of South Florida. In 2014 she wrote "Librarians as Wikipedians" for the *Progressive Librarian Journal*. Kathleen spoke on Librarians and Human Rights as the 2010 Jean E. Coleman Lecturer for the ALA Office for Literacy and Outreach Services. She is the author of *Introduction to Public Librarianship* (2011).

Mary Minow is counsel to the Califa Library Group in California. She edits the Stanford Copyright and Fair Use site at http://fairuse.stanford.edu. She has a JD from Stanford University, an AMLS from the University of Michigan, and a BA from Brown University.

Heather O'Brien, MLIS, PhD, is a faculty member at the School of Library, Archival and Information Studies, University of British Columbia in Vancouver, British Columbia, Canada. Her research and teaching interests are in the areas of information-seeking behavior and use and user experience with information media, specifically the nature and measurement of user engagement with information systems.

Christine Pawley retired in 2012 as professor and director at the School of Library and Information Studies and director of the Center for the History of Print and Digital Culture at the University of Wisconsin–Madison, where she now teaches part time. She is author of two award-winning books— *Reading on the Middle Border: The Culture of Print in Late Nineteenth Century Osage, Iowa* (2001) and *Reading Places: Literacy, Democracy, and the Public Library in Cold War America* (2010)—and is coeditor with Louise S. Robbins of *Libraries and the Reading Public in Twentieth Century America* (2013).

Stephanie Rosenblatt is an instruction librarian and the electronic resources/serials coordinator at Cerritos College in Southern California. She's been involved in information literacy instruction at public, school, and academic libraries and has worked with library users of all ages.

Amy Rudersdorf is the assistant director for content at the Digital Public Library of America (DPLA), where she is responsible for digitization partnerships and related workflows, metadata normalization and shareability, and community engagement to promote the DPLA as a community resource. She has served as the director of the Digital Information Management Program at the State Library of North Carolina, coordinated digital collections at North Carolina State University and the University of Wisconsin–Madison, and worked with public libraries throughout Wisconsin to aid in the development and coordination of digitization grants. Rudersdorf was a Library of Congress National Digital Stewardship Alliance coordinating committee member and has taught master's courses as part of library and information science programs on digital libraries and preservation (San José State University) and metadata (North Carolina Central University).

Tom Sanville has been senior director of licensing and strategic partnerships since 2010, having previously been OhioLINK executive director (1992–2010) and worked at OCLC serving in various positions (1981–1991). Georgia Institute of Technology, BS; University of Michigan, MBA.

Carol H. Sawyer, PhD, is a distinguished professor of organizational leadership in the College of Business and Public Management, University of La Verne, recognized by that university with the Excellence in Teaching Award. She is a frequent presenter at national and international conferences on leadership, organizational change, and organizational development. Her interests are in the use of design thinking for strengthening graduate management education, and in the application of the arts and learning theory in both managerial and educational settings.

Aaron Schmidt has been a circulation clerk, reference librarian, and library director for over ten years. Currently he is the principal of Influx Library User Experience Consulting. Recent projects include user-focused strategic planning for a public library and organizing and facilitating a library innovation exchange with library organizations in Mexico City. Schmidt serves on the editorial board for *Weave: the Journal of Library User Experience*.

Paul Signorelli, former director of volunteer services and staff training for the San Francisco Public Library system, pursues a variety of interests as a San Francisco–based writer, trainer, instructional designer, social media strategist, presenter, and consultant. He is active at several levels in the American Library Association, the New Media Consortium, and the Association for Talent Development (formerly the American Society for Training & Development). He earned his MLIS through the University of North Texas, and he blogs at http://buildingcreativebridges.wordpress.com.

Michelle Holschuh Simmons currently teaches reference and information literacy classes in the School of Information at San José State University. She was formerly an academic librarian and a high school English teacher. She holds a BA in English from the College of St. Benedict, an MAT in English from Minnesota State University, an MA in library and information science from the University of Iowa, and a PhD in language, literacy, and culture from the University of Iowa.

Katherine Skinner, PhD, is the executive director of the Educopia Institute (http://www.educopia.org), a not-for-profit organization that hosts interinstitutional, collaborative communities and projects through which it advances the state of the art in the production, dissemination, and preservation of digital scholarship. She is a cofounder of the MetaArchive Cooperative, the Library Publishing Coalition, and the BitCurator Consortium, thriving communities that promote collaborative practices and the building of infrastructure and expertise within memory organizations. Skinner received her PhD from Emory University. She has served as PI on many federal grants and contracts. She has coedited three books and has authored and coauthored numerous reports and articles. She regularly teaches graduate courses and workshops on digital library and digital scholarship topics and provides consultation services to groups that are planning or implementing digital scholarship and digital preservation programs or communities. She has also hosted national and international events on digital preservation and digital scholarship topics, including the "Aligning National Approaches to Digital Preservation" series.

Cheryl Stenström is a full-time lecturer at San José State University's School of Information and the assistant coordinator of the San José Gateway PhD program. She teaches courses on management, advocacy, and research methods and is interested in the intersection of social influence and decision making in the political arena, particularly as it affects funding for libraries. She is a graduate of the San José Gateway PhD program.

Michael Stephens is assistant professor in the School of Information at San José State University and presents to both national and international audiences about emerging technologies, learning, innovation, and libraries. Since 2010, Dr. Stephens has written the monthly column "Office Hours" for *Library Journal*, exploring the issues, ideas, and emerging trends in library and information science education. To review Dr. Stephen's archive of work, visit his Tame the Web website and blog: http://tametheweb.com.

Patty Wong has held positions at Stockton–San Joaquin County Public Library, Oakland Public Library, and Berkeley Public Library (CA) in children's and young adult services and management. She has worked as a consultant in youth development, grant writing, and leadership and has publications on diversity, serving underserved communities, and partnerships. She is part-time faculty for San José State University's School of Information and graduated from the University of California, Berkeley, School of Library and Information Science.